An

English-Punjabi Dictionary

An

English-Punjabi Dictionary

Rev. W.P. Hares

ASIAN EDUCATIONAL SERVICES
NEW DELHI ★ MADRAS ★ 1998

ASIAN EDUCATIONAL SERVICES

* 31, HAUZ KHAS VILLAGE, NEW DELHI - 110016.
  CABLE : ASIA BOOKS, PH. : 660187, 668594, FAX : 011-6852805
* 5, SRIPURAM FIRST STREET, MADRAS - 600014. PH. / FAX. : 8265040

Price : Rs. 395
First Published : London, 1929
First AES Reprint : New Delhi, 1988
Fourth AES Reprint : New Delhi, 1998
ISBN : 81-206-0414-8

Published by J. Jetley
for ASIAN EDUCATIONAL SERVICES
C-2/15, SDA New Delhi - 110016
Printed at Subham Offset, Delhi - 110032

AN
ENGLISH-PANJABI
DICTIONARY.

During twenty-five years' residence in the Panjab, living in close contact with the people in their villages, I have constantly felt the need of an English-Panjabi Dictionary. There are two very good Panjabi-English Dictionaries in existence, but the only English-Panjabi one available up to 1919 was a small vocabulary published by Munshi Jawahir Singh for the use of army officers. This was of very little use to those who wished to understand the people by talking with them in their own beloved Panjabi. In 1919 the Rev. T. Grahame Bailey, of the Scotch Mission, Wazirabad, published a somewhat larger English-Panjabi Dictionary, which has proved most useful to those who live and work amongst Panjabis, but the vocabulary is still only a small one, and its many cross references are very annoying to one in a hurry. In 1923 another English-Panjabi-Hindi Dictionary was published by Lala Salig Ram Bajaj, but as no differentiating marks were used to enable the reader to distinguish between Panjabi and Hindi words, and the translations were printed in the Gurmukhi character, the book was not of much use to the English student. So with some diffidence the present larger work, which has occupied my leisure time for the last twenty years, has been published in the hope that it may supply a long felt need.

The number of English words in the vocabulary is about 15,000, and of these some 55,000 meanings have been given in Roman Panjabi. It must be pointed out, however, that with the remarkable spread of primary education in the Central Panjab in recent years a very large number of Urdu, Hindi, Sanskrit, Persian and Arabic words have been incorporated into the Panjabi language, and even a quite illiterate villager will use such words freely, and when asked about them will assert that they are pure Panjabi words. In the popular Panjabi songs sung at weddings, &c., this tendency to incorporate Urdu, Persian and Arabic words in a Panjabi form is very common. The reader must be prepared then to find in this work many words which are Urdu, Hindi, Sanskrit, Arabic and Persian, and they have been freely included as they are in common daily use amongst the villagers. There are also many English words for which there is no equivalent whatever in Panjabi, and in these cases simple Urdu or Hindi words, well understood by even the illiterate villager, have been used to express their meanings.

In looking through the Dictionary a casual reader may discover a large number of words with which he may be unacquainted, and may be tempted to express the opinion that many words have been included which are not generally known, but it must be remembered that the Panjabi language varies in every district, and certain words which are in common use, for example, in the Ludhiana district are almost unknown in the Sialkot district, and *vice versa*. As I have spent the last twelve years in the Chenab Colony, where settlers have come from almost every district of the Panjab, I have had exceptional opportunities of hearing the various dialects of the whole

Province, and can assure the reader that every word in the Dictionary has been tested in several ways, and passed by the people as being used by Panjabis. Every word has been found in some Gurmukhi or Persian Panjabi book, or has been heard in personal conversation; it has then been checked with a Gurmukhi dictionary or tested in conversation, and only then included in this Dictionary.

An effort has been made to include only those words which are in ordinary daily use by the people, and those words have been discarded which—although they may be found even in the Granth Sahib—are not understood by ordinary people. Where a number of Panjabi words are found to express an English word the most commonly used will be generally found standing first. This is not always the case, but I have tried as far as possible to work according to that rule.

In many cases where Sanskrit, Arabic and Persian words have found a place in Panjabi their form has often been corrupted and their pronunciation altered. For example, 'j' often takes the place of 'z' *e.g.*, 'jarúr' for 'zarúr', 'jabardastí' for 'zabardastí,' 'jabán' for 'zabán'; the position of a consonant may be altered as 'hanerí' or 'anherí' for 'andherí', 'matbal' for 'matlab', 'armán' for 'árám.' An educated man will usually prefer the correct form, but the illiterate villager will more often than not use the debased form of the word. In many cases I have included both forms of the word, the pure and the debased.

The spelling of many words in Roman varies very considerably in books by different authors. For example the most common word 'vichch' may be found spelt as 'vich', 'vichch', 'vichh', 'wich' and 'wichch'; again the doubling of letters, *e.g.*, 'rakhna' and 'rakkhna,' 'manukh' and 'manukkh' is very common. Throughout the Dictionary I have tried to regularize the spelling and used throughout that which is in more common use.

There is an astonishing lack of true Adverbs in the Panjabi language, but this lack is frequently made up by using a Noun with the Preposition 'nál,' *e.g.*, 'bravely' is translated 'dilerí nál'; by the addition of a Present Participle to an Adjective, 'diler hoke'; or by the use of a Noun with Present Participle, 'sher banke'.

The vocabularies of religious terms used by Hindus and Muhammadans vary greatly, and the letter M after a word signifies that it is a Muhammadan term and the letter H means that the word is used by Hindus.

A sparing use has been made of cross references in order to reduce the size and cost of the book, and it will be found advisable to make use of them where they occur. A number of useful lists of words will be found under the words 'hair, birds, land, sugar, trees, charms, payments, clothes, cotton, sugarcane, ornaments, colour, worship, camel, buffalo, &c., &c.' It is hoped that the many idiomatic phrases and sentences scattered throughout the book will be found useful. They are all in common use among the people and will be understood by everyone.

The work has been revised many times, and yet I am conscious that there are still some mistakes and mistranslations to be corrected. In a work of this size and nature, in spite of the greatest care in proof reading, some misprints are to be expected, and I can only express my regret that such errors have been overlooked, and ask that the reader will regard with indulgence such errors or defects, whether of printing or of translating.

My most grateful thanks are due to the very many Panjabi friends who have given me their willing help and advice in bringing this work to completion. They are too many to mention individually by name, but I am grateful to them all for their assistance, criticism and advice.

W. P. HARES,

C. M. S.,

GOJRA,

District Lyallpur.

LIST OF ABBREVIATIONS.

The abbreviations used in the book are the following :—N. for noun; A. for adjective; Adv. for adverb; V. T. for transitive verb; V. I. for intransitive verb; Prep. for preposition; P. for pronoun; Conj. for conjunction; Art. for Article; M. for Muhammadan; H. for Hindu.

AN
ENGLISH PANJABI
DICTIONARY.

A

A OR AN, *Art.*
 ikk ; hikk ; koí ;
ABACK, *Adv.*
 acháṇak ; acháṇchak ;
ABAFT, *Prep.*
 pichche ;
ABANDON, TO, *V. T.*
 chhaḍḍná ; chhaḍḍ dená ; ján
 dená ; tark karná ; tajná ; tiágná ;
ABANDONED, *A.*
 1. deserted, desolate. virán ; ujáṛ ;
 chhaḍḍí hoí jagáh ; ujjaṛ pujjaṛ ;
 sunn masunn ;
 2. profligate. luchchá ; luṇḍá ;
 pápí ; guṇḍá ; badmásh ; kharáb ;
 3. shameless. belajjá ; behayá ;
ABANDONMENT, *N.*
 1. a state of being forsaken. tark. *f ;*
 chhaḍḍává. *m ;*
 2. abandonment of grief. ḍáḍḍhá
 gam. *m ;* baṛá sakht gam. *m ;*
 3. freedom of manner. besharmí. *f ;*
 beháyáí. *f ;* khullhí majáj. *f ;*
 4. forsaking the world. sanyás. *f ;*
ABASE, TO, *V. T.*
 níweáṇ karná ; baqadr karná ;
 adhín karná ; ḍigáuná ; bepat te
 níwáṇ karná ; sharmindiá karná ;
 thiṭṭh karná.
ABASEMENT, *N.*
 bijjatí. *f ;* bepatí. *f ;* namoshí. *f ;*
 beqadri. *f ;*
ABASH, TO, *V. T.*
 sharmáuná ; thiṭṭh karná : lajáuná ;
 jháṛ suṭṭná ; jháṛ páuná ;
ABASHED, TO BE, *V. I.*
 saṇgná ; múṇh lukáuná ;
ABASHED, *A.*
 1. bashful. lájwant ; lajjí ;
 2. ashamed. sharmindá ; lajílá ;
ABATE, TO, *V. T.*
 ghaṭáuná ; thoṛá karná ; halká
 karná ; ghaṭṭ karná ;

ABATE, TO, *V. I.*
 ghaṭṭ jáná ; thuṛ jáná ; ghaṭṭ
 honá ; khuṭṭ jáná ;
ABATEMENT, *N.*
 gháṭṭá. *m ;* kasar. *m ;* kamí. *f ;*
 ghaṭṭáo. *m ;* hín. *f ;* hínat. *f ;* hín-
 táí. *f ;*
ABBEY, *N.*
 waḍḍá girjá. *m :*
ABBOT, *N.*
 mahant. *m ;*
ABBREVIATE, TO, *V. T.*
 nichoṛ kaḍḍhná ; sár kaḍḍhná
 chhoṭá karná ;
ABBREVIATION, *N.*
 nichoṛ. *m ;* sár. *m ;* arq. *m ;* chho-
 ṭáí. *f ;*
A. B. C., *N.*
 alaf be pe ;
ABDICATE, TO, *V. T.*
 tiág dená ; chhaḍḍ dená ;
ABDICATION, *N.*
 tiág. *m ;*
ABDOMEN, *N.*
 peṭ. *m ;* ḍhiḍḍ. *m ;* ḍhiḍḍh. *m ;*
ABDOMINAL, *A.*
 peṭ dá ; ḍhiḍḍh dá ;
ABDUCT, TO, *V. T.*
 badobadí laí jáná ; kaḍḍh laí jáná ;
 udhálná ;
ABDUCTION, *N.*
 udhál. *f ;* udhláí. *f ;*
ABDUCTOR, *N.*
 udhálú. *m ;*
ABERRANCE, *N.*
 1. mistake. bhulekhá. *m ;* bhull.
 f ; wissar bholá. *m ;* bholá. *m ;*
 2. wandering from the right path.
 kuráhí. *f ;* badráhí. *f ;*
ABERRANT, *A.*
 gumráh ; bhulliá hoyá ;

ABERRATION, *N.*
gumráhí. *f* ; badráhí. *f* ; kuráh. *m* ; mental aberration. sudá. *m* ; págalpuṇá. *m* ; matt márí. *f* ;
ABET, TO, *V. T.*
1. to help. madat dení ; dilerí dení ; sahaitá dení ; sáth dená ;
2. to assist in wrong doing. uskáuná ; qusúr karan vichch madat dení ;
ABETMENT, *N.*
madat. *f* ; sahaitá. *m* ; saháí. *f* ;
ABETTOR, *N.*
madatgár. *m* ; sahaití. *m* ; madádí. *m* ; himaití. *m* ; saháí. *m* ;
ABHOR, TO, *V. T.*
ghiṇ áuní ; ghiṇáuná ; karaiyat áuní ; nafrat áuní ;
ABHORRENCE, *N.*
ghiṇ. *f* ; karaiyat. *f* ; súg. *f* ;
ABHORRENT, *A.*
bahut búrá ; bharist ; palít ; nápasiṇd ;
ABHORRENTLY, *Adv.*
baṛí nafrat nál ; baṛí karaiyat de nál ;
ABIDE, TO, *V. I.*
1. to stay. ṭikkná ; rahná ; ṭhahrná ; khalo jáná ;
2. to dwell. wassná ; rahná ;
3. to endure. sahná ; sah lainá ; jhallná ;
4. to abide by one's promise. qaul nabáhuná ; apná wádá purá karná ;
ABIDING, *A.*
qaim ; pakká ; sábit ; tagaṛá ;
ABIDINGLY, *Adv.*
sadá ; har vele ; hameshá ; oṛak ;
ABILITY, *N.*
liyáqat. *f* ; jor. *m* ; guṇ. *m* ; hujdá. *m* ; wass. *m* ; vall. *m* ; bal. *m* ; jách. *f* ; himmat. *f* ; táqat. *f* ; shakhtí. *f* ; chárá. *m* ; majál. *f* ; wáh. *m* ;
ABJECT, *A.*
máṛá ; nakárá ; nikammá ; nachíj ; ních ; chaṇḍál ; kamíná ;
ABJECTION, *N.*
kamínpuṇá. *m* ; ájizí. *f* ;
ABJECTLY, *Adv.*
ájizí nál ; baṛe kamínpuṇe de nál ;
ABJECTNESS, *N.*
kamínpuṇá. *m* ;
ABJURATION, *N.*
sauṇh khá ke inkár. *m* ;
ABJURE, TO, *V. T.*
1. to deny. inkár karná ; mukkar painá OR jáná ;
2. to give up. chhaḍḍná ; jáṇ dená ;
ABLAZE, *A.*
saṛdá baldá ; baldá hoyá ;
ABLE, *A.*
laiq ; jog ; jogá ; tagṛá ; guṇí ;
ABLE, TO BE, *V. I.*
laiq honá ; kar sakkná ;
if you are able. je wass lage ;
ABLE BODIED, *A.*
takṛá ; tagṛá ; balwán ;
ABLOOM, *A.*
phul khere hoye ; phuliá phaliá ;
ABLUTION, *N.*
ashnán. *m* ;
ceremonial ablution. wazú. *m*, M ; ashnán. *m*, H ;
ABLY, *Adv.*
chaṇgí taráh nál ; achchhí taráh nál ; ṭhík taráh ; banáke ; saṇwárke ;
ABNEGATE, TO, *V. T.*
1. to renounce. chhaḍḍ dená ; tark karná ; muṛná ;
2. to deny. inkár karná ; mukkarná ; náṇh karná ;
ABNEGATION, *N.*
inkár. *m* ; tark. *f* ;
ABNEGATOR, *N.*
inkárí. *m* ; namukkar. *m* ;
ABNORMAL, *A.*
ajíb ; acharaj ; kurúp ; beḍhabá ; aṇokhá ;
ABNORMALITY, *N.*
kuḍhab. *m* ; aṇokh. *m* ;
ABOARD, *A.*
jaháj OR beṛe te chaṛhiá hoya ; jaháj te sawár hoke ;
ABODE, *N.*
ghar. *m* ; makán. *m* ; thán. *m* ; ḍerá. m ; jagáh. *f* ; ṭhikáná. *m* ;
ABOLISH, TO, *V. T.*
band karná ; mauqúf karná ; haṭa dená ; haṭauná ;
ABOLITION, *N.*
mauqúfí. *f* ; ṭál. *f* ; haṭau. *f* ;
ABOMINABLE, *A.*
bahut búrá ; ghináuná ; bharist ; napák ; palít ; gaṇdá ;

ABOMINABLENESS, *N.*
ghin. *f;* karaiyat. *f;*
ABOMINABLY, *Adv.*
búrí taráh nál; búre salúk nál;
ABOMINATE, TO, *V. T.*
nafrat karní; ghinauná; karaiyat áuní; kirak áuní; see HATE.
ABOMINATION, *N.*
ghin. *f;* napákí. *f;* karaiyat. *f;*
ABORIGINAL, *A.*
jangalí;
ABORIGINEES, *N.*
aslí wiskín. *m;* jángalí. *m;*
ABORT, TO, *V. T.*
1. human. garbh pát karná; garbh chhan jáná;
2. animal. tú jáná; tarú jáná;
ABORTION, *N.*
garbh pát. *m;*
ABORTIVE, *A.*
befaidá; akárath;
ABOUND. TO, *V. I.*
bharpúr honá; bhar jáná; waddhná; bahut honá;
ABOUT, *Prep.* and *Adv.*
bábat;
1. concerning. bábat; de báre vichch;
2. near to. pás; kol; neṛe; neṛe teṛe;
3. round about. ále duále; ás pás; ídar gidar; chauphere;
4. on the point of. taiyár;
5. more or less. thoṛá bahut;
6. about me. mere haqq vichch; merí bábat;
7. more or less. ghaṭṭ waddh;
ABOVE, *Prep.*
1. more than. wadhík; ziyádáh; wadh ke;
2. on the top of. upar; utte; te;
3. before. agge;
4. from above. uparoṇ;
5. beyond. agge; pare;
ABOVE, *Adv.*
1. overhead. upar; utáhán; uchchá; utlá;
2. beyond. wadh ke; agge;
3. above mentioned. jih dá zikr pahlá hoyá;
ABOVE BOARD, *A.*
khullhá; khullam khullhá; khullhá khullhí; khullhá mukhullhá; sabhnáṇ de sámhne;
ABOVE MEASURE, *A.*
aṇgiṇt; behadd; behisáb;
ABRASION, *N.*
ragaṛ. *f;* jharít. *f;* ghássá. *m;* chhiliá hoyá tháṇ. *m;*
ABRADGE, TO, *V. T.*
ragaṛná; chhillná;
ABREAST, *A.*
nálonál; sáth sáth;
ABRIDGE, TO, *V. T.*
1. to epitomise. khulásá karná; nichoṛná; arq kaḍḍhná;
2. to diminish. chhoṭá karná; ghaṭṭ karná; ghaṭṭáuná; kamtí karní; sár karná;
ABRIDGEMENT, *N.*
nichoṛ. *m;* sár. *m;* ghaṭaú. *m;*
ABROAD, *A.*
1. out of the house. báhar;
2. in another country. pardes vichch;
3. gone visiting. wáṇḍhe gáyá;
ABROGATE, TO, *V. T.*
radd kar dená; miṭa dená; mauqúf karná; band karná;
ABROGATION, *N.*
khaṇḍan. *m;*
ABRUPT, *A.*
1. sudden. acháṇak; acháṇchet; achán chakk;
2. unceremonious. beḍhaṇgá;
ABRUPTLY, *Adv.*
1. suddenly. acháṇchet; jhaṭṭ paṭṭ;
2. unceremoniously. awallá; kuwallá;
ABRUPTNESS, *N.*
káhlí. *f;* chhetí. *f;*
ABSCESS, *N.*
phoṛá. *m;* páká. *m;* gaṛ. *m;*
to lance an abscess. phoṛe núṇ chirá dená; chír phár karná;
ABSCIND, TO, *V. T.*
1. to reject. radd karná;
2. to cut off. kaṭṭná; waḍḍhná;
3. to expel. chhekná; wakkh karná;
ABSCOND, TO, *V. I.*
1. to run away. bhajj jáná; naṭṭhná; nassná; nass jáná;
2. to hide. chhip jáná;
ABSCONDER, *N.*
chor, *m;*

ABSENCE, *N*.
gairhájarí. *f*;
absence of mind. gáfalí. *f*;
ḍhill maṭṭh. *m*; ḍhill. *f*;
in my absence. mere pichhche; mere magaroṇ;

ABSENT, TO BE, *V. I.*
pachhaṛ jáná; pachhaṛná;

ABSENT, *A*.
1. not present. gairhájar; itthe hai nahíṇ;
2. not attentive. gáfal; láparwáh; ḍhillá; dochitt; dochittá; bechittá; ḍhillá maṭṭhá;

ABSENTLY, *Adv.*
gáfalí nál; dhián nál nahíṇ; biná soche samjhe;

ABSENT MINDEDNESS, *N*.
ḍhill. *f*; gáfalí. *f*; dochittí. *f*; bechittí. *f*;

ABSINTHE, *N*.
ikk qism dá sharáb. *m*;

ABSOLUTE, *A*.
1. without limitation. haddoṇ muḍḍhoṇ; muloṇ muḍḍhoṇ;
2. perfect. purá;
3. certain. pakká;
4. despotic. purá ikhtiyárwálá;

ABSOLUTELY, *Adv.*
ukká mukká; haddoṇ muḍḍhoṇ muloṇ;

ABSOLUTION, *N*.
muáfí. *f*; chhuṭkárá. *m*; riháí. *f*; ḳhalásí. *f*;

ABSOLVE, TO, *V. T.*
muáf karná; muáfí dení; chhuṭkárá dená; rihá karná; ḳhalásí karní;

ABSORB, TO, *V. T.*
chupná; chup lainá; píná; chusaná;

ABSORBED, TO BE, *V. I.*
rachná; rach jáná; dhass jáná; jiurná;

ABSORPTION, *N*.
1. process of absorbing. suk. *f*;
2. mental preoccupation. dhián. *m*; soch wichár. *m*;

ABSTAIN, TO, *V. T.*
parej karná; chhaḍḍ dená; muṇh moṛná; lámbhe ho jáná; báj rahná; hatte rahná; bachiá rahná;
1. to abstain from defiled food. gaṇde kháneoṇ thú thú karná; ghiṇ karní;
2. to abstain from fleshly lusts. nafs díáṇ buríáṇ ḳháshisháṇ thoṇ parej karná;
3. to abstain from all evil. chhilá karná; 'chhilá' means literally the forty days when a man sits in seclusion for worship and meditation.

bhorhe bahiná OR painá. Bhorhá is a pit in which a faqir or devotee sits fasting for a number of days.

ABSTAINER, *N*.
parejí. *m*; parejgár. *m*;

ABSTEMIOUSLY, *Adv.*
parejgárí nál; parejí nál; jat sat nál;

ABSTEMIOUSNESS, *N*.
parejgárí. *f*; rakkh shakkh. *f*;

ABSTENTION, *N*.
1. abstinence. parejgárí. *f*;
2. absence. gairhájarí. *f*;

ABSTINENCE, *N*.
parejgárí. *f*; ḳháhisháṇ núṇ qábu vichch rakkhná; *m*; rakkh shakkh. *f*;

ABSTINENT, *A*.
parejgár; bhagat; jatí satí;

ABSTRACT, *N*.
arq. *m*; nichoṛ. *m*; sár. *m*;

ABSTRACT, TO, *V. T.*
1. to take from. nikálná; kaḍḍhná;
2. to purloin. chorí karní; churáke le jáná;
3. to summarize. arq kaḍḍhna; chhoṭá karná; nichoṛná;

ABSTRACT, *A*.
1. fine. barík; mahín;
2. difficult. kaṭṭhan; aukhí gal; guṛhí gal; mushkil;
3. beyond understanding. samajhoṇ pare;

ABSTRACTED, *A*.
beḳhud; gáfal; bemukh;

ABSTRACTION, *N*.
beḳhabarí. *f*;

ABSTRUSE, *A*.
1. difficult. kaṭṭhan; mushkil; aukhí gal;

2. not clear. sáf nahíṇ; samajh nahíṇ áundí;
ABSURD, *A.*
wáhiyát; behudá; befaidá;
ABSURDITY, *N.*
wáhiyátí. *f*; behudagí. *f*;
ABSURDLY, *Adv.*
bewaqúfí nál;
ABUNDANCE, *N.*
ḍher. *m*; bahtáit. *f*; batáit. *f*; relpel. *f*;
ABUNDANT, *A.*
bahut; bahterá; bahut sárá; bahutá; chokkhá; wáfar; ḍher;
ABUNDANTLY, *Adv.*
wadhík; bahtáit nál;
ABUSE, *N.*
1. scurrilous language. gál. *f*; gálí. *f*; gálí galuch. *f*; gaṇd jabání. *f*; mehná. *m*; bhaṇḍí. *f*; phakkaṛí. *f*;
2. corrupt practice. búrí rít. *f*; bhaiṛí rasm. *f*; búrá dastúr. *m*; búrá wartárá. *m*; búrá wartává. *m*; kharábíáṇ. *f*;
ABUSE, TO, *V. T.*
1. to vilify. gál kaḍḍhní; gálí déní; badnám karná; phakkaṛ tolná; ijjat láhuní; bijjtí karní; mehná dená; búrá bhalá kahná; gaṇd bakná; niṇdiá karná; jháṛ dená; punná;
2. to misuse. mandí OR búrí taráh wartná;
3. to spoil. wigárṇa; kharáb karná;
4. to defile one's person. badfelí karní; múṭṭh mární;
ABUSED, TO BE, *V. I.*
gál khání; phiṭkár khání OR lainí;
ABUSER, *N.*
gálí denwálá. *m*; baṛa gaṇd jabán. *m*; gaṇdí jabánwálá. *m*; niṇdak. *m*;
ABUSES, *N.*
kharábíáṇ. *f*; buríáíáṇ. *f*; bhaiṛíáṇ gallán. *f*;
ABUSIVE, *A.*
badjabán; gaṇdá;
ABYSS, *N.*
atháh gaṛhá. *m*; ḍunghái. *f*; duṇghíai. *f*; ḍuṇghá ṭoá. *m*;
ACACIA GUM, *N.*
kikkar dí gúnd. *f*;
ACACIA TREE, *N.*
kikkar. *m*;
ACCEDE, TO, *V. T.*
manzúr karná; háṇ karní; manná; man lainá;
ACCELERATE, TO, *V. T.*
1. to hasten. tez karná; jaldí karní;
2. to cause to walk quickly. chhetí ṭuráuná;
ACCELERATION, *N.*
tezí. *f*; shatábí. *f*; káhli. *f*;
ACCENT, *N.*
chaj. *m*; laihjá. *m*; kise lafz utte zor. *m*;
ACCENTUATE, TO, *V. T.*
ṭhík bolná; chaj nál bolná; ḍhaṇg nál bolná; kise lafz utte zor dená;
ACCEPT, TO, *V. T.*
manjúr karná; qabul karná; manná; qabulná;
ACCEPTABLE, *A.*
manjúr; manan jog; man pasiṇd;
ACCEPTANCE, *N.*
manjúrí. *f*; pasiṇd. *m*;
ACCESS, *N.*
1. liberty to approach. guzar. *f*; dakhal. *f*; pahuṇch. *f*;
2. increase. wáddhá. *f*; waddh. *f*;
ACCESSIBLE, *A.*
1. that may be approached. pahuṇchaṇ jog;
2. affable. milauṛá; komal; muhabbatí; saṇgatí;
ACCESSION, *N.*
rájtilak. *m*; gaddí nasíní. *f*; takht nashíní. *f*;
ACCESSORY, *N.*
madatgár. *m*; sahaí. *m*; sahaití.; *m*; bhetí. *m*; saṇgí. *m*; sánjhí. *m*; sangatí. *m*;
ACCESSORY, *A.*
bahutá; ziyádá; wadherá; wadhìk
ACCIDENT, *N.*
1. mishap. hádsá. *m*; honí. *f*; musíbat. *f*; ḍho. *m*;
2. quality. guṇ. *m*; sift. *f*;
ACCIDENTAL, *A.*
itifáqí; takdírí; aiweṇ; sabab nál;
ACCIDENTALLY, *Adv.*
sabab nál; aiweṇ; acháṇak; achaṇchet; eweṇ; itifáq nál;

ACCLAIM, TO, *V.T.*
shábá shábá karní ; wáh wáh karná ; dhann dhann ákhná ;
ACCLAMATION, *N.*
dhann. *m* ; wáh wáh. *f* ;
ACCLIVITY, *N.*
chaṛháí. *f* ; chaṛháú. *m* ; ḍháyá. *m* ;
a slope. dhál. *f* ; ḍháyá. *m* ;
ACCOMMODATE, TO, *V. T.*
1. to make suitable. muwáfiq karná ; jog kar dená ; laiq banáuná ; sáurná ; ṭhík ṭhák karná ; sudhárná ;
2. to supply. dená ;
3. to conform to. banjáná ; sáurná ;
ACCOMMODATING, *A.*
mihrbán ; kirpál ;
ACCOMMODATION, *N.*
1. room. kamrá. *m* ;
2. capacity. samáí. *f* ; gunjaish. *f* ;
3. loan. udhár. *m* ; qarz. *m* ;
4. adaptation. guzárá. *m* ;
5. a place. jagáh. *f* ; thán, *f* ;
ACCOMPANY, TO, *V. I.*
nál nál jáná ; nál nál chalná ; nál nál turná ;
ACCOMPLICE, *N.*
bhetí. *m* ; sánjhí. *m* ; madatgár. *m* : saháí. *m* ; saṇgatí. *m* ; sáthí. *m* ;
ACCOMPLISH, TO, *V. T.*
púrá karná ; síddh karná ; nabáhuná ; kar lainá ; kar chhaḍḍná ; muká dená ; mukáuná ; naberná ;
ACCOMPLISHED, *A.*
guṇi ; álam ; fájal ;
ACCOMPLISHMENT, *N.*
1. completion. nabáh. *m* ; naberá. *m* ;
2. attainment. jách. *f* ; guṇ. *m* ; vall. *m* ;
3. elegance. guṇ. *m* ; hundar. *m* ;
ACCORD, *N.*
1. impulse. marjí. *f* ; ḳhushí. *f* ; cháh. *f* ; tángh. *f* ;
2. unison. ikk dilí. *f* ; ekká. *m* ; mel miláp. *m* ; mel jol. *f* ;
ACCORD, TO, *V. T.*
1. to concede. háṇ karní ; manzúr karná ; manná ;
2. to give. dená ;
3. to make to agree. manáuná ;
ACCORD, TO, *V. I.*
milná ; sajná ; ralná ;
ACCORDANCE, *N.*
mel. *m* ; mel jol. *f* ; ekká. *m* ; in accordance with. de mujib ;
ACCORDING, *A.*
according to. de mujib ; de mutábiq ; de wángún ; use jehá ;
according as. jis taráh ;
ACCORDINGLY, *Adv.*
is laí ; is wáste ; so ;
ACCOST, TO, *V. T.*
1. to salute. salám karná ;
2. to speak to. ákhná ; bolná ; kahná ;
ACCOUCHEUSE, *N.*
daí. *f* ;
pay of daí ; jaṇwáí. *f* ;
ACCOUNT, *N.*
1. bill. hisáb. *m* ; lekhá. *m* ; gintí. *f* ; lekhá jokhá. *m* ; lekhá pattá. *m* ; hisáb kitáb. *f* ;
2. narration. bayán. *m* ; gal. *f* ; kathá. *m* ; wártá. *f* ;
3. sake. káran ; ḳhátir ; laí ; wáste ; sabab ;
4. account book. behí. *f* ; wehí. *f* ; hisáb dí kitáb. *f* ; rokaṛ. *f* ; see BOOK
5. of no account. nikammá ; máṛá ;
6. on no account. kadí nahíṇ ; kisí taráh nahíṇ ;
7. on this very account. ise karke ;
ACCOUNT, TO, *V. T.*
1. to regard. liház karná ; pasiṇd karná ; ḳhátirdárí karní.
2. to explain. samjháuná ; vervá kaḍḍhná ; bayán karná ; nawair kaḍḍhná ;
3. to keep an account. hisáb rakkhná ;
4. to render an account. hisáb dená OR dassná ; lekhá dená.
5. to account righteous. dharmí ṭhahráuná ; sachchá ṭhahráuná ;
ACCOUNTABILITY, *N.*
zimmewárí. *f* ; zimmá. *m* ; jummá. *m* ; jummewárí. *f* ;
ACCOUNTABLE, *A.*
zimmewár ; jummewár ;
to make oneself accountable. zimmá chukkná ; jámin banná ;
ACCOUNTANT, *N.*
muním. *m* ; hisábí. *m* ; ḳhajánchí. *m* ; munshí. *m* ; musaddí. *m* ;

1. village accountant. patwárí. *m ;* dharwáí. *m ;*
2. head accountant. gardaur. *m ;* kánúngo. *m ;*

ACCOUNTANTSHIP, *N.*
gardaurí. *f ;*

ACCOUNT BOOK, *N.*
1. day book. chaupattrá. *m ;* hisáb dí kitáb. *f ;* surh. *m ;* rokaṛ wehí. *f ;*
2. ledger. wehí. *f ;* behí. *f ;* khatá wehí. *f ;*

ACCOUTRE, TO, *V. T.*
hathiyár páuná ; shastar OR sastar bannhná ;

ACCOUTREMENTS, *N.*
hathiyár. *m ;* jangí asbáb. *m ;* kíl káṇṭá. *m ;* sáj samán. *m ;*

ACCREDIT. TO, *V. T.*
iḳhtiyár dená ; muḳhtiár karná ;

ACCRUE, TO, *V. I.*
paidá honá ; hásil honá ; labbhná ; milná ;

ACCUMULATE, TO, *V. T.*
kaṭṭhá karná ; joṛna ; jamá karná ; ḍher láuná ;

ACCUMULATE, TO, *V. I.*
kaṭṭhá honá ; jamá honá ;

ACCUMULATION, *N.*
ḍher. *m ;*

ACCURACY, *N.*
durústí. *f ;* sahí. *f ;* suddhái. *f ;*

ACCURATE, *A.*
ṭhík ; durust ; sahí ; ṭhík ṭhák ; suddh ;

ACCURATELY, *Adv.*
durustí nál ; banáke ; saṇwárke ; ṭhík ṭhík ; ṭhíkam ṭhík ;

ACCURATENESS, *N.*
durustí. *f ;* sahí. *f ;*

ACCURSE, TO, *V. T.*
lánat karná ; saráp dená ; bad asís dená ;

ACCURSED, *A.*
lánatí ; sarápiá hoyá ; sarápí ; sarápat ;

ACCUSATION, *N.*
ilzám. *m ;* ujj. *f ;* dosh. m ; dos. *m ;* shikáyat. *f ;*

ACCUSE, TO, *V. T.*
ilzám láuná ; dosh OR dos láuná ; aib láuná ; butáṇ láuná ; kise de sir utte agg bálná ; shikáyat karní ; bhaṇḍná ; nálish karná ; gilá karná ; bhagí karní ;

ACCUSED, *A.*
mulzam ; doshí ; muddá alaí ;

ACCUSER, *N.*
ilzám láunwálá. *m ;* ilzámí. *m ;* faryádí. *m ;* tohmatí. *m ;*
legal ; muddáí. *m ;* nálish karnwálá. *m ;*

ACCUSTOM, TO, *V. T.*
gijjháuná ; ádat páuní ; wáddí páuní ; bán páuní ;

ACCUSTOMED, TO BE, *V. I.*
ádat paí jáná ; gijjhná ; gijjh jáná ;

ACCUSTOMED, *A.*
mámúlí ; rawájí ;

ACE, *N.*
yakká. *m ;*

ACERB, *A.*
1. bitter. kauṛá ;
2. sharp. khaṭṭá ;

ACERBITY, *N.*
1. sharpness. khaṭṭá. *m ;* khaṭṭíáí. *f ;*
2. bitterness or severity. saḳhtí. *f ;* talḳhí. *f ;* talḳháí. *f ;* jástí, *f ;* jálmí. *f ;* julm. *m ;*

ACERVATE, TO, *V. T.*
ḍher karná OR láuná ; kusak láuná ; kunnu láuná ;

ACHE, *N.*
píṛ. *f ;* dard. *f ;* dukh. *m ;* chís. *f ;*

ACHE, TO, *V. T.*
dukhná ; karáhná ; chís mární ; dukh bhogná ; dukh kaṭṭná OR jhallná ;
to make one's head ache with talking. sir khapáuná ; sir kháná ;

ACHIEVANCE, *N.*
kamm. *m ;* nabáh. *m ;* nibbaṛ tibbaṛ. *m ;*

ACHIEVE, TO, *V. T.*
purá karná ; nabáhuná ; muká dená ; naberná ; mukáuná ;

ACHIEVEMENT, *N.*
1. brave act. bahádurí dá kamm. *m;*
2. settlement. naberá. *m;* faisalá. *m;*

ACHING *N.*
pír. *f*; dukh. *m*;
ACID, *N.*
tejáb. *m*;
sulphuric acid. gandhak tejáb. *m*;
hydro chloric acid. nimak dá tejáb. *m*;
nitric acid. shore dá tejáb. *m*;
ACID, *A.*
khaṭṭá; very acid. khaṭṭá tít;
ACIDIFY, TO, *V. T.*
khaṭṭá banáuná OR kar dená;
ACIDITY, *N.*
khaṭṭá. *m*; khaṭṭíái. *f*; khaṭás. *m*;
ACIDULATE, TO, *V. T.*
khaṭṭá banáuná; turas karná; tursáuná;
ACIDULENT, *A.*
khaṭṭá;
ACKNOWLEDGE, TO, *V. T.*
1. to admit. iqrár karná; manná; mann lainá; dam bharná;
2. to acknowledge a letter. tarjawáb dená; uttar patá dená; jawáb dená;
3. to acknowledge money. rasíd likhná; patá dená;
ACKNOWLEDGMENT, *N.*
1. confession. iqrár. *m*; man manáutí. *f*;
2. receipt. rasíd. *f*;
3. answer. jawáb. *m*;
ACME, *N.*
sir. *m*; choṭṭí. *f*;
ACONITE, *N.*
mitthá teliá. *m*;
ACONIUM FEROX, *N.*
teliá. *m*;
ACORN, *N.*
bilút dá phal. *m*;
ACOUSTICS, *N.*
awáz dá ilm. *m*;
ACQUAINT, TO, *V. T.*
1. to inform. ḳhabar dení; saneha ghallná; dassná; jatáuná; patá dená; akhwá ghallná,
2. to introduce. wáqabí karáuní; mel gel karáuná; miláuná;
ACQUAINTANCE, *N.*
1. a friend. wáqab. *m*; ján pachán. *m*; jánú. *m*; dost. *m*; jánú pachhánú. *m*; melí. *m*; yár. *m*; wáqabí. *m*;
2. knowledge, wáqabí. *f*; ilm. *m*;
ACQUAINTANCESHIP, *N.*
wáqabi. *f*; dostí. *f*; shakal shabá. *f*;
ACQUAINTED, *A.*
wáqab; wáqif;
ACQUEDUCT, *N.*
khál. *m*; kassí. *f*; nálí. *f*;
ACQUIESCE, TO, *V. T.*
háṇ karná; man lainá; manzúr karná; pasiṇd karná; huṇgúrá karná;
ACQUIESCENCE, *N.*
manzúrí. *f*; huṇgúrá. *m*; razámandí. *f*;
ACQUIESCENT, *A.*
rází; ḳhush;
ACQUIRE, TO, *V. T.*
hásil karná; pá lainá; labbhná; khaṭṭná; milná; kamáuná; hatth áuná; parápat karná;
without labour. gapphá lag jáná;
ACQUIREMENT, *N.*
hundar. *m*;
ACQUISITION, *N.*
1. something acquired. hásal. *m*; gapphá. *m*;
2. gain. lábh. *m*; faidá. *m*; nafá. *m*; parápat. *f*; labhat. *f*; láh. *m*;
ACQUIT, TO, *V. T.*
1. to forgive. muáf karná; baḳhshná; chhaḍḍ dená; riháí dení;
2. to free from accusation. begunáh ṭhahráuná; ilzám thoṇ barí karná; rihá kar dená; mukat karná;
3. to conduct oneself. chaṇgí taráh karná; chaṇgí taráh pesh áuná;
ACQUITTED, TO BE, *V. I.*
riháí páuní; chhuṭṭ jáná; sáf nikal jáná; chhuṭṭná; rihá ho jáná; bequsúr nikal jáná; ḳhalási ho jání;
ACQUITTAL, *N.*
chhuṭkárá. *m*; nistárá. *m*;
ACQUITTANCE, *N.*
1. release. ḳhalási. *f*; chhuṭkárá. *m*;
2. a written discharge. rasíd. *m*;
3. a divorce paper. párkhatí. *f*; taláqnámá. *m*; tiág pattrí. *f*; likhat. *f*;
ACRE, *N.*
kilá. *m*; ekar. *m*; ghamá. *m*; pailí. *f*;

ACRID, *A*.
kaṛá ; khaṭṭá ; tez ;
ACRIDITY, *N*.
khaṭṭíái. *f* ; talḳhí. *f* ;
ACRIMONIOUS, *A*.
kauṛá ; khaṭṭá ; tez ; talḳh ; karṛá ; rukkhá ;
ACRIMONIOUSLY, *Adv*.
jhagṛá karke ; talḳhí nál ;
ACRIMONY, *N*.
talḳhí. *f* ; saḳhtí. *f* ; tezí. *f* ; chiṛ chiṛát. *m* ;
ACROBAT, *N*.
naṭ. *m* ; naṭní. *f* ; bájígar. *m* ; tamáshá karnwálá. *m* ; pherní. *f* ;
ACROSS, *Prep.* & *Adv*.
pár ; parle páse ;
ACT, *N*.
1. a deed. kamm. *m* ; karm. *m* ; amal. *m* ; kartabb. *m* ; kamm káj. *m* ;
2. a decree. qánún. *m* ; hukm. *m* ;
3. division of a play. nátak. *m* ;
ACT, TO, *V. T*.
1. to do. kamm karná ; karná ; amal karná ;
2. to perform on the stage. nakal utární ; sáṇg wikháuná ;
ACTING, *N*.
sáṇg. *m* ;
ACTING, *A*.
iwají, uh de tháṇ ; uh de wáste ; uh de badle ;
ACTION, *N*.
1. a deed. kamm. *m* ; kartab. *m* ; kár. *f* ; karm. *m* ; kár 'rawái. *f* ; karní. *f* ;
2. a battle. laṛái. *f* ; jaṇg. *m* ; juddh. *m* ;
3. a gesture. sainat. *f* ;
4. conduct. lachchhan. *m* ; chál ḍhál. *f* ; chál chalan. *m* ; chál. *m* ; bol chál. *m* ; ḍhaṇg. *m* ;
5. legal action. nálish. *f* ; arzí. *f* ; dáwá. *m* ;
A. criminal action. faujdárí dá dáwá. *m* ;
B. civil action. diwání dá dáwá OR arzí. *f* ;
ACTIONABLE, *A*.
nálish de laiq. ;

ACTIVE, *A*.
chalák ; tagṛá ; tarikkhá ; tej ; chust ; uddamí ; uḍḍná ; phurtílá ; achpal ; tikkhá ; tarrár ;
ACTIVELY, *Adv*.
chhetí nál ; uddam nál ; baṛí shitábí nál ; jaldí ; dabádab ;
ACTIVITY, *N*.
tezí. *f* ; uddam. *m* ; shitábí. *f* ; chalákí. *f* ; chustí. *f* ; phurtí. *f* ;
ACTOR, *N*.
1. a stage player. bhaṇḍ. *m* ; naṭ. *m* ; nakliá. *m* ; sáṇgí. *m* ;
2. a doer. karanwálá. *m* ;
3. a Divine Worker. kartá. *m* ; kartár. *m* ;
ACTRESS, *N*.
bhaṇḍí. *f* ; naṭní. *f* ; kaṇjarí. *f* ; bhaṇḍní. *f* ;
ACTUAL, *A*.
aslí ; sachchí gal ; ṭhík ṭhák ;
actual state of affairs. aslí hál ; asl hál ; haqqí gal ;
ACTUALITY, *N*.
asl. m ; muḍḍh. *m* ; sachchíái. *f* ;
ACTUALLY, *Adv*.
asl vichch ; sachchí muchchí ; sachch muchch ; ṭhík ;
ACTUARY, *N*.
muním. *m* ; munshí. *m* ; kánungo. *m* ;
ACTUATE, TO, *V. T*.
chukkná ; jagáuná ; khará karná ; uksáuná ;
ACUMEN, *N*.
hoshiyárí. *f* ; fahm. *m* ; dánái. *f* ; buddh. *f* ;
ACUTE, *A*.
hoshíyár ; buddhwán ; siáná ; aqlwálá ; chaldá púrzá ; phurtílá ;
ACUTELY, *Adv*.
baṛí hoshíyárí nál; baṛí chalákí nál ;
ACUTENESS, *N*.
tezí. *f* ; hoshíyárí. *f* ; chalákí. *f* ;
ADAGE, *N*.
misál. *f* ; kahaut. *f* ; ákhiá. *m* ; ákhan. *m* ; ákhaná. *m* ;
ADAMANTINE, *A*.
bahut saḳht ; ḍáḍḍhí ;
ADAM'S APPLE, *N*.
ghaṇḍí. *f* ; ghaṇḍ. *m* ;

ADAPT, TO, *V. T.*
muwáfiq karná ; uh de jehá banáuná ; ṭhík karná ; laiq OR jog banáuná ; uh de wargá banáuná ;

ADAPTABILITY, *N.*
laiqí. *f ;*

ADAPTABLE, *A.*
laiq ; joggá ; wargá ;

ADAPTATION, *N.*
laiqí. *f ;* jog. *f ;*

ADAYS, *Adv.*
ajj kal ; ajj bhalak ;

ADD, TO, *V. T.*
1. to augment. hor dená ; wadháuná ; wadh dená ;
2. to join. joṛná ; miláuná ; mel dená ; raláuná ;
3. to say further. ih ví kahná ;
4. to add up a sum. joṛná ; jamá karná ;

ADDENDUM, *N.*
wáddhá, *m ;* zamímá. *m ;*

ADDER, *N.*
sapp. *m ;*

ADDICT, TO, *V. T.*
gajjhná ; ádat páuní ; wáddí pá lainí ;

ADDICTED, TO BECOME, *V. I.*
ádat paí jáná ; gijjhná ; gijjh jáná ;

ADDITION, *N.*
1. increase. wáddhá. *m ;* ziyásatí. *f ;*
2. arithmetic. jamá. *f ;* joṛ. *m ;*
3. in addition. ih de aláva hor ví wadhke ;

ADDITIONAL, *A.*
wadhík ; wadherá ; ziyáda ; wádhú ;

ADDLED, *A.*
gaṇdá ;
an addled egg. gaṇdá áṇḍḍá. *m ;*
addled headed. bewaqúf ; beaql ; kamlá ;

ADDRESS, *N.*
1. a speech. wáz. *m ;* nasíhat. *f ;* bachan. *m ;*
2. direction of a letter. sarnámá, *m ;* patá. *m ;*

ADDRESS, TO, *V. T.*
1. to speak or preach. wáz karná ; nasíhat denì ; bolná ; updesh karná OR dená ; sikkhiá dená ;
2. to address a letter. patá nishání likhná ; sarnámá likhná ;
3. to apply oneself. dil lagáuná ; jí lagáuná ;

ADDUCE, TO, *V. T.*
pesh karná ; dalíl dená ; raí dení ;

ADEPT, *A.*
guṇí ; hoshíyár ; chalák ; pakká ; guṇwáṇ ; kárígar ;

ADEQUATE, *A.*
bahut ; bas ; joggá ; káfí ; ṭhík ; laiq ; ṭhík ṭhák ; batherá ;

ADEQUATELY, *Adv.*
púrí taráṇ ; púrá púrá ;

ADHERE, TO, *V. I.*
1. to stick. lag jáná ; chambaṛná ; chipakná ; chipaṭná ; lipaṭná ;
2. to remain firm. pakká rahná ; qaim te mazbut rahná ; apní gal ná chhaḍḍní ; apní zidd ná chhaḍḍní ;
3. to remain with a party. nál rahná ; laggiá rahná ;

ADHERENCE, *N.*
sábatí. *f ;* wafádárí. *f ;*

ADHERENT, *N.*
lágú. *m ;* muríd. *m ;* shágird. *m ;* mannanwálá. *m ;* chelá. *m ;* bálká. *m ;*

ADHESION, *N.*
1. assent. manzúrí. *f ;* huṇgúrá. *m ;*
2. adhesiveness. lagáú. *m ;* chíp. *f ;* chipak. *m ;*

ADHESIVE, *A.*
leslá ; lesdár ; chíplá ;

ADIEU, *Interj.*
1. Christian. salám ;
2. Muhammadan. salám ; Alláh terá nigáhbán ; Alláh de hawále.
3. Hindu. Rám Rám ; Ishar bhalá kare ; Parmeshwar rákkhiá kare ;
4. Sikh. Wáhgurú jí kí fateh ; Sat sirí akál ;
5. Arya. namúste.

ADJACENT, *A.*
kol ; pás ; neṛe ; nál dá ; nikaṭ ; nikṭe ;

ADJECTIVE, N.
  sift. f ; ism sift. f ;
ADJOIN, TO, V. T.
  joṛná ; miláuná ; lagá dená ;
  chamaṛá dená ; raláuná ;
ADJOIN, TO, V. I.
  juṛná ; juṛídá ; pás honá ; lagá
  hoyá honá ;
ADJOINING, A.
  miliá hoyá ; nál dá ; kol ; neṛe ;
  pás dá ;
ADJOURN, TO, V. T.
  addh varítá chhaḍḍná ; agge de
  wáste rahn dená ; mulṭaví karní ;
  chhaḍḍná ;
ADJOURN, TO, V. I.
  rah jáná ;
ADJUDGE, TO, V. T.
  faisalá karná ; rái dení ; nabeṛná ;
  to give a decree. digrí dení ;
ADJUDICATION, N.
  faisalá. m ;
  legal decree. digṛí. f ;
ADJUNCT, N.
  joṛ. m ; milí hoí chíz. f ;
ADJURATION, N.
  sauṇh. f ; qasm. f ; saugaṇd. f ;
ADJURE, TO, V. T.
  sauṇh dení ; qasm páuní OR
  dení ; kalimá paṛháuná ;
ADJUST, TO, V. T.
  1. to put in order.   suárná ;
  ṭhík karná ; ṭhík ṭhák karná ;
  sudhárná ; sajáuná ; sar karná ;
  2. to settle. faisalá karná ;
  rází karní ; nabeṛná ;
ADJUST, TO V. I.
  saurná ; saur jáná ;
ADJUSTABLE, A.
  ṭhík karn jog ;
ADJUSTMENT, N.
  bandobast. m ; durústí. f ; safáí. f ;
  tartíb. m ;
  decision. faisalá. m ;
ADJUTANT, N.
  ajíṭan. m ;
ADMINISTER, TO, V. T.
  1. to manage. intizám karná ;
  guzárá karná ; oṛtoṛ karná ;
  2. to administer justice. adálat
  karní ; níáṇ karná ; insáf karná ;
  munsifí karní ;

3. to administer the Sacrament.
  Pák Baptismá dená ; Ashá-i-
  Rabbáṇí dení ;
4. to act as an agent. mukhtiárí
  karní ; sarbaráhí karní ;
ADMINISTRATION, N.
  1. management. bandobast. m ;
  intizám. m ;
  2. government. ráj káj. m ; ráj
  pát. f ; hukúmat. f ;
  3. of an estate.   intizám. m ;
  mukhtiárí. f ;
ADMINISTRATIVE, A.
  intizámí ;
ADMINISTRATOR, N.
  intizám karanwálá. m ; sarbaráh.
  m ; mukhtiár. m ;
ADMINISTRATORSHIP, N.
  sarbaráhí. f ;
ADMIRABLE, A.
  sohná ; chaṇgá ; baṛá chaṇgá ;
  uttam ; suthrá ; táríf de laiq ;
ADMIRABLY, Adv.
  chaṇgí taráh nál ;
ADMIRAL, N.
  jangí jaházáṇ dá sardár OR waḍḍa
  áfisar. m ;
ADMIRATION, N.
  táríf. f ; waḍíáí. f ; saláhat. f ;
  saráhat. f ;
ADMIRE, TO. V. T.
  táríf karní ; waḍíáí karní ; wekh
  ke khush honá ;   saláhná ;
  saráhná ; guṇ gáuná ;
ADMIRER, N.
  1. one who admires. táríf karanwálá. m ; sift karanwálá. m ;
  2. a lover. premí. m ; áshak. m ;
ADMISSIBLE, A.
  rawá, jáiz ; wájib ;
ADMISSION, N.
  1. entrance. dakhal. f ; ḍhoí. f ;
  andar jáná. m ;
  2. acknowledgment. iqrár. m ;
  manautí. f ;
ADMISSION FEE, N.
  1. for a show. ṭikat. m ;
  2. for an examination. dákhalá.
  m ;
ADMIT, TO, V. T.
  1. to allow in. andar áun dená ;
  dákhal hon dená ; laṇgh áun dená ;

2. to accept as true. mann lainá; yaqín ján lená;
3. to confess. manná; iqrár karná; háṇ karná;

ADMITTANCE, *N.*
dákhal. *f*; ḍhoí. *f*; andar ján dí ijázat. *f*;

ADMITTEDLY, *Adv.*
beshakk;

ADMIXTURE, *N.*
milautí. *f*; miláú. *m*;

ADMONISH, TO, *V. T.*
1. to reprove. jhiṛakná; jháṛ páíná; ḍhíṭṭh karná; ghurakná; dutkárná; samjháuná; dáṇṭná;
2. to exhort. samjháuná; nasíhat dení; sikkhiá dená; updesh dená;
3. to warn. samjháuná; sikhláuná; nasíhat karní;
4. having well admonished. samjhá samjhúke;

ADMONITION, *N.*
1. reproof. malámat. *f*; jhiṛak. *f*; [illegible] *f*; diṇṭ. *f*;
2. exhortation. nasíhat. *f*; updesh. *m*; sikkhiá. *f*;
3. advice. saláh. *f*; hidayat. *f*; ráí. *f*;

ADO, *N.*
shor. *m*; raulá. *m*; dauṛ dhúp. *f*; dhúm. *m*; daṇdh. *m*; wrangling. bakheṛá. *m*;

ADOLESCENCE, *N.*
juání. *f*; jawáni. *f*; joban. *m*;

ADOLESCENT, *A.*
juán;

ADOPT, TO, *V. T.*
1. to take as one's own. manzúr karná; man lainá; iḳhtiyár karná; qabúlná;
2. to adopt a child. a girl; dhí karke rakkhní; a boy. putrelá banáuná; puttar banáuná; apná puttar karke pálná;
3. an adopted son. putrelá. *m*;

ADORABLE, *A.*
táríf de laiq; mán jog;

ADORATION, *N.*
bandagí. *f*; ibádat. *f*; ustút. *f*; waḍiái. *f*; mán. *m*; pújá. *f*; bhagtí. *f*; pújá páṭ. *f*; pújá partishtá. *f*;

ADORE, TO, *V. T.*
1. to pay divine honour to. Ḳhudá dí bandagí karní;
A. Christian. bandagí OR ibádat karní;
B. Muhammadan. namáz paṛhní; ibádat karní;
C. Hindu. pújná; pújá páṭ karní; tapassiá karná; bandagí karní;
D. Sikh. kaṇ̣h páth karná; shabad báṇí paṛhná; bhagtí karní; jap karná;
E. Chuhṛa. matthá tekná; pújná;
2. to love greatly. dil nál pyár karná; muhabbat karní; prem pyár karná;

ADORER, *N.*
1. a worshipper.
A. Christian. bandagí karnwálá. *m*; sachchá bhagat. *m*;
B. Muhammadan. namájí. *m*; namází. *m*;
C. Hindu. pújárí. *m*; pújak. *m*; pújá karnwála. *m*; bhagtí karnwálá. *m*;
D. Sikh. giání. *m*; sewak. *m*; bhagat lok. *m*; tapassí. *m*;
2. an admirer. áshak. *m*; premí. *m*;

ADORINGLY, *Adv.*
baṛí adab nál; baṛí ájizí nál; ádar nál;

ADORN, TO, *V. T.*
suárná; sajáuná; shaṇgárná; ṭíp ṭáp karná; sajáwat karní; sudhárná; hár saṇgár karná;

ADORNED, *A.*
sajjiá hoyá;

ADORNMENT, *N.*
shaṇgár. *m*; sajáut. *f*; sajáú. *f*;

ADRIFT, *A.*
ruṛhiá hoyá;

ADROIT, *A.*
hoshiyár; chúst; chalák; phurtílá; kárígar; huṇḍarí;

ADROITNESS, *N.*
hoshiyárí. *f*; chustí. *f*; jách. *f*; withiá. *f*; guṇ. *m*; chaláki. *f*;

ADULATE, TO, *V. T.*
gaddoṇ khurkí karní; purmáuná; phuláuná; lallo patto karná;

ADULATION, *N*.
lallo patto. *f*; leṭí peṭí *f*; choj. *m*;

ADULATOR, *N*.
cháplús. *m*; jholí chukk. *m*;

ADULT, *N*.
ádmí. *m*; baṇdá. *m*; gabbhru. *m*; juán. *m*;

ADULT, *A*.
bálig; juán; gabbhru; siáná;

ADULTERATE, TO, *V. T*.
khoṭ páuná; ralá páuná; khoṭṭá banáuná; wigáṛná;

ADULTERATED, *A*.
khoṭṭá; ralá milá;
adulterated ghi, dasaurí gheu. *m*; galle dá gheu *m*; dare dá gheu. *m*; ralle dá gheu. *m*;

ADULTERATION, *N*.
khoṭ. *f*; ralá. *m*; miláú. *m*;

ADULTERER, *N*.
zinákár. *m*; zání. *m*; harámkár. *m*; badkár. *m*; járná. *m*; jaṇáhí. *m*;

ADULTERESS, *N*.
zinákár. *f*; badkár aurat. *f*; yární. *f*; jární. *f*; kanjarí. *f*; badchalan aurat. *f*; janáhaṇ. f;

ADULTEROUS, *A*.
badkár; harámkár; uchakká;

ADULTERY, *N*.
zinákárí. *f*; ziná. *m*; badkárí. *f*; dostí. *f*; harámkárí. *f*; yárí *f*; janáh. *m*;
to commit adultery. ziná OR yárí OR badkárí karná;

ADVANCE, *N*.
1. a going forward. agge jáná; agge waddhná;
2. improvement. taraqqí. *f*;
3. increase. wáddhá. *m*; wadháu. *m*;
4. of money. agáúṇ. *m*; peshgí. *f*;
5. of salary. taraqqí. *f*; wáddhá. *m*;
6. a deposit. amánat. *f*;
7. part of the price to be paid. sái. *f*;

ADVANCE, TO, *V. T*.
1. to improve. taraqqí karní;
2. to bring forward. wadháuná; pesh karná;
3. to pay a deposit. agáúṇ dená; peshgí dení; sái dení;
4. to deposit with the idea of receiving back. amánat rakkhná.
5. to advance an opinion. gal karní; saláh dení; dalíl láuní; rái pesh karní;
6. to promote. taraqqí dení;

ADVANCE, TO, *V. I*.
1. to go forward. agge waddhná; waddh jáná;
2. to rise in position. taraqqí milní;

ADVANCEMENT, *N*.
taraqqí. *f*; wáddhá. *m*;

ADVANTAGE, *N*.
1. gain. faidá. *m*; nafá. *m*; lachchu. *m*; lábh. *m*; láh. *m*; bhadraká. *m*;
2. opportunity. mauqá. *m*; dá. *f*; ḍho. *m*; gáshá. *m*;
3. advantage and disadvantage. nafá nuqsán. *m*; ghátṭá wáddhá. *m*;
4. to take advantage of. mauqá páke; velá wekh ke;
5 to reap an advantage. nafá uṭháuná;

ADVANTAGEOUS. *A*.
faidá deṇwála, faidedár; nafewálá; nafewaṇd, chaṇgá;

ADVANTAGEOUSLY. *Adv*.
faidá pá ke;

ADVENT, *N*.
ámad. *f*; áuná. *m*;
the advent of Christ. Masíh dí dujjí ámad. *f*;

ADVENTURE, *N*.
hádsá. *m*;

ADVENTURE, TO, *V. T*.
nasíbáṇ wal wekh ke aukhá kamm karná; koshish karní; himmat karní; jurat karní; dilerí karní;

ADVENTURER, *N*.
dhokkhebáj. *m*; farebí. *m*, ṭhagg. *m*;

ADVENTUROUS, A.
   waḍḍá dilwálá; bahádur; diler;
   diláwar; dilaur; himmatwálá;
   súrmá; ján báj; hauṇsilewálá;
ADVENTUROUSLY, Adv.
   dilerí nál.
ADVERSARY, N.
   dushman. m; vairí. m; virodhí. m;
   muḳhálif. m; ján dá márú. m;
ADVERSE, A.
   ulṭá; ḳhiláf; virodh;
ADVERSITY, N.
   musíbat. f; taklíf. f; dukh. m;
   balá. f; biptá. f; kales. m;
   waḳht. m; benasíbí. f;
ADVERTISE, TO, V. T.
   ḍhanḍhorá dená; ḍauṇḍí pherní;
   manádí karní; ḳhabar dení;
   ḍhanḍhorá pherná; hoká dená;
ADVERTISEMENT, N.
   1. in newspaper. aḳhbár vichch
      kisí chíz dá ishtehár. m;
   2. notice by proclamation.
      ḍhanḍhorá. m; manádí. f;
      ḍauṇḍí. f; hoká. m;
ADVICE, N.
   saláh. f; nasíhat. f; matt. f;
   math. f; matte. f; hidayat. f;
   ráí. f; gurmatá. m; gurmat. m;
   saláh mashwará. m;
   religious advice. updes. m;
   updesh. m;
ADVISABLE, A.
   munásib; laiq; cháhidá; jarúrí;
ADVISE, TO, V. T.
   nasíhat dení; saláh dení; matt
   dení; matá karná; matá pakáuná;
   updesh dená; dassná;
ADVISEDLY, Adv.
   soch wichár ke; soch samajhke;
ADVISER, N.
   saláhkár. m; saláhí. m; saláh
   denwálá. m;
   religious adviser. updeshak. m;
ADVOCACY, N.
   sifárish. f;
ADVOCATE, N.
   1. legal. wakíl. m;
   2. helper. hámí. m; madadgár,
      m; belí. m;

ADZE, N.
   tesá. m; tesí. f;
AEROPLANE, N.
   hawáí jaháj. m;
AFAR, A.
   dur; pare; duráḍḍá; dureḍe;
   afar off. dúroṇ; dur sáre;
AFFABILITY, N.
   milansárí. f; komaltáí. f; bhal-
   mánsáú. m; muláhjá. m; bháú. m;
AFFABLE, A.
   milauṛá; komal; milansár;
   milápaṛá; milanwálá;
AFFAIR, N.
   wáqíá. m; muámalá. m; kamm.
   m; gal bát. f;
AFFAIRS, N.
   kamm dhaṇdá. m; káŕ bár. m;
   hál. m;
   pecuniary. leṇ deṇ. f;
AFFECTATION, N.
   báṇkpuṇá. m; maṭak. f;
AFFECTED, A.
   báṇká; mizájí;
AFFECTION, N.
   pyár. m; muhabbat. f; prem. m;
   prít. f; láḍ. m; moh. m; dostí. f;
   cháh. f; sandeh. m; hit. m;
AFFECTIONATE, A.
   mihrbán; hitwálá; premí;
   muhabbatí;
AFFECTIONATELY, Adv.
   pyár nál; prem nál; prem pyár
   nál;
AFFINITY, N.
   mel. m; sarbaṇdhí. f;
AFFIRM, TO, V. T.
   bayán karná; bolná; dassná;
   ímán nál iqrár karná; tágíd nál
   bolná;
AFFIRMATION, N.
   bayán. m, iqrár. m; dalíl. f;
   qarár. m;
AFFIX, TO, V. T.
   láuná; lagáuná; joṛná; miláuná;
AFFLICT, TO, V. T.
   satáuná, dukh dená; dukháuná;
   aukhíáṇ karná; aukhá karná;
   taklíf dení; taṇg karná; tarsáuná;
   chheṛná; kasálá karná;

AFFLICTED, *A*.
dukhiá; dukhiárá; aukhá; taṇg; ḳhastá hál wálá;
AFFLICTION, *N*.
musíbat. *f*; dukh. *m*; biptá. *f*; balá. *f*; aukhí. *f*; vaḳht. *m*; dukhṛa. *m*; taṇgí. *f*; kasálá. *m*;
AFFLUENCE, *N*.
mál. *m*; dhan. *m*; daulat. *f*; máyá. *f*; amírí. *f*; máldárí. *f*;
AFFLUENT, *A*.
máldár; amír; baḳhtáwar; dhaṇí;
AFFORD, TO, *V. T.*
de sakkná; núṇ sarná;
AFFRAY, *N*.
fasád. *m*; jhagṛá. *m*; laṛáí. *f*; daṇggá fasád. *m*; már kuṭái. *f*; raṭṭá. *m*; hal chal. *f*; hullar. *m*; bakheṛá. *m*;
AFFRIGHT, TO, *V. T.*
ḍaráuná; ḍar páuná; ḳhauf vichch páuná;
AFFRONT, TO, *V. T.*
beizzatí karní; bijjtí karní; bepatí karní; ijjat láhuní; mukálá karná; namoshí karní;
AFFRONT, *N*.
bepatí. *f*; beizzatí. *f*; bijjtí. *f*; beadabí. *f*; beqadrí. *f*; namoshí. *f*;
AFFUSE, TO, *V. T.*
traukná; dálná; páuná; chhiṛkaná; chhinkáuná;
AFOOT, *A*.
paidal; pairíṇ ṭurke; paidal ṭurdá;
AFOREHAND, *Adv.*
agetare; aggoṇ; pahloṇ hí;
AFORESAID, *A*.
jih dá zikr hoyá;
AFORETIME, *Adv.*
pahláṇ; paihloṇ; chirokná; puráne same vichch;
AFRAID, TO BE, *V. I.*
ḍarná; ḍar á painá; ḍar laggná; haul karná; bhau áuná;
AFRAID, *A*.
bháímán;
AFRESH, *A*.
nawe siroṇ;
AFTER, *Prep.* and *Adv.*
pichchoṇ; magaroṇ; de magar; de pichche;
after these things. aidoṇ pichchoṇ;

AFTERNOON, *N*.
about 1 p.m. kachchí peshí; *f*;
about 2 p.m. peshí. *f*;
3 p. m. nikkí ḍígar;
4-5 p.m. din dhale; ḍígar velá. *m*;
about 5 p.m. lauḍhe velá. *m*;
AFTERWARDS, *Adv.*
magaroṇ; pichchoṇ; pichche; chhekaṛ;
AGAIN, *Adv.*
pher; muṛke; dujjí wár; muṛ; watt;
again and again. ghaṛí muṛí; muṛ muṛ ke; bár bár karke;
a second time. dujjí wárí; dujje phere;
AGAINST, *Prep.*
de ḳhiláf; de barḳhiláf; virodh;
AGE, *N*.
1. oldness. umr. *f*;
2. period. zamáná. *m*; samá. *m*; jugg. *m*;
3. generation. píṛhí. *f*;
AGED, *A*.
buḍḍhá; buḍḍhí; umrwálá; jahíf; baṛí umrwálí;
very aged. buḍḍhrá; fachch;
AGENCY, *N*.
1. business. áhrat. *f*; dalálí. *f*;
2. instrumentality. wasílá. *m*; duáre; ráhíṇ;
AGENT, *N*.
dalál. *m*; árhatí. *m*; muḳhtár; gumáshtá. *m*; ḍharwái. *m*; sarbaráh. *m*;
AGGRANDIZEMENT, *N*.
taraqqí. *f*;
AGGRAVATION, *N*.
1. provocation. chheṛ. *f*; ziyádatí. *f*; jichái. *f*;
2. irritation. narázagí. *f*; kar odh. *m*;
AGGRAVATE, TO, *V. T.*
1. to provoke. chheṛná, bhaṛkáuná; gussá chaṛháuná agg láuná; chiṛáuná; bhab káuná; luhná;
2. to make worse. bahutá ḳharáb kar dená; jaṛ már dená;
AGGREGATE, *N*.
sab dá sab; sáre dá sárá; kaṭṭhá. *m*;

AGGRESSION, *N.*
jástí. *f*; chaṛhái. *f*; dabáu. *m*; zabardastí. *f*; ziyádatí. *f*;
a criminal assault. faujdárí. *f*;
AGGRESSIVE, *A.*
zabardast; virodhí; rukkhá; laṛáká; jhagṛálú;
AGGRIEVE, TO, *V. T.*
dukh dená; satáuná; aukhíáṇ karná; taklíf dení;
AGGRIEVED, *A.*
dukhí; dukhiá;
AGHAST, *A.*
hairán; hakká bakká; dangg;
AGILE, *A.*
chalák; tez; chust; phurtílá; káhlá;
AGILITY, *N.*
uddam. *m*; phurtí. *f*; chalákí. *f*, chustí. *f*;
AGITATE, TO, *V. T.*
1. to disturb. daṛáuná; ghabrá-dená; bhaṛkáuná; taṛpháuná;
2. to shake. hiláuná; ḍolná;
3. to stir up. chukkná; josh duáuná;
AGITATED, TO BE, *V. I.*
ghábar jáná; ṭharakná; biákal honá;
AGITATED, *A.*
bechain; bearám; aukhá; dukhí; achpal; betáb; gháúṇ máúṇ;
AGITATION, *N.*
1. perturbation, bechainí. *f*; bearám. *f*; beqarárí. *f*;
2. confusion. halchal. *f*; josh. *m*;
AGITATOR, *N.*
fasádí. *m*; lokáṇ núṇ bhaṛkán-wálá. *m*;
AGO, *Adv.*
pahloṇ pahal; bitá hoyá;
AGONY, *N.*
ḍáḍḍhí píṛ. *f*; sakht píṛ. *f*; ján kaṇḍaní. *f*; ján kaṇaní. *f*; tarchh. *f*; kasṭaní. *f*;
AGREE, TO, *V. T.*
man lainá; háṇ karná; manzúr karná; ekká karná; itifáq karná; manná; huṇgurá OR huṇgárá bharná;
to promise. chuká lainá; wádá dená;

AGREE, TO, *V. I.*
ikko jehá honá; ekká karná;
AGREEABLE, *A.*
manzúr; man pasiṇd; parwán; rází; man bhauná;
AGREEABLY, *Adv.*
muwáfiq; mujib;
AGREEMENT, *N.*
1. stipulation. qarár. *m*; wádá. *m*; bachan. *m*;
2. a written agreement. astám. *m*; rajastrí. *f*; iqrár námá. *m*;
3. concord. ekká. *m*; mel. *m*; mel jol. *f*; ikk dilí. *f*;
AGRICULTURE, *N.*
zamíndárí. *f*; khetí. *f*; wáhí. *f*; khetí bárí. *f*; jimíndárí. *f*; khetí pati. *f*;
legal term. káshtkárí. *f*;
AGRICULTURIST, *N.*
jaṭṭ. *m*; zamíndár. *m*; káshtkár. *m*; wáhí karnwálá. *m*;
AGROUND, *A.*
ṭik jáná;
AGUE, *N.*
kámbú táp. *m*; kánbe dá táp. *m*; kámbú. *m*; ṭhaṇḍá táp. *m*;
AH, *Interj.*
of regret. hai hai; afsos; ham-sos;
Interj. of joy. wáh wáh; this is also used satirically.
Interj. of wonder. bhale bhale; hekháṇ;
AHEAD, *Adv.*
agge; pahloṇ; muhre; agháṇ; agere; agárá; sáhmne;
AID, *N.*
madat. *f*; sahárá. *m*; sahaitá. *m*; sahái. *f*; chárá. *m*; kumak *f*;
AID, TO, *V. T.*
madat ḍení; sahaitá karní; sahárá dená;
AIL, TO, *V. I.*
bímár honá; máṇḍá honá; tagṛeáṇ ná rahná; dukhí rahná;
AILING, *A.*
bímár; máṇḍá; rogí; dukhiá; tagṛá nahíṇ;
AILMENT, *N.*
bímárí. *f*; máṇdagí. *f*; rog. *m*;

AIM, *N.*
1. purpose. manshá. *m;* matlab. *m;* matabal. *m;* marzí. *f;* níat. *f;* irádá. *m;* dalíl. *f;* manorath. *m;*
2. mark. nisháná. *m;*
AIM, TO, *V. T.*
1. to purpose. irádá karná; jí karná; saláh karní;
2. to sight a gun. nisháná márná; sist bannhní;
AIMING, *N.*
sist. *f;*
AIMLESS, *A.*
aiweṇ; eweṇ;
AIR, *N.*
wá. *f;* paun. *f;* wáo. *f;*
AIR, TO, *V. T.*
1. to take the air. wá bhakkhná; sail karná;
2. to air clothes. kapṛe sukháuná;
3. to give oneself airs. sheḳhí mární; ákaṛná;
4. to bring to notice. mashhúr karná; dassná; ḳhabar dení;
AIRY, *A.*
hawádár; kullhá;
AIRILY, *Adv.*
aiweṇ; láparwáhí nál;
AKIN, *A.*
raldá mildá; ral mil; wargá;
ALACRITY, *N.*
phurtí. *f;* chustí. *f;* uddam. *m;* chohlí. *f;*
ALARM, *N.*
1. fear. ḍar. *f;* ḳhauf. *m;* haul. *m;* handeshá. *m;* ghabrát. *f;* dhaṛkí. *f;* dhaṛká. *m;* harbarí. *f;*
2. warning. hál pukár. *f;* duhái páhriá. *f;* ḳhabar. *f;*
ALARM, TO, *V. T.*
1. to rouse. hál pukár karná; duhái páhriá karní;
2. to frighten. ḍaráuná; ḍar páuná; dhamkáuná;
ALARMED, TO BE, *V. I.*
labhakná;
ALARMED, *A.*
ghábar gayá;
ALARMING, *A.*
ḍaráunwálá; ḍaráuná;

ALAS, *Interj.*
hai hai; hoe hoe; hamsos;
ALBEIT, *Conj.*
tad bhí;
ALBINO, *A.*
baggá; kakká; kakká búrá;
ALCOHOL, *N.*
sharáb. *f;* dárú. *m;*
ALCOVE, *N.*
ták. *m;* álá. *m;*
ALE, *N.*
sharáb. *f;* dárú, *m;*
ALERT, *A.*
chalák; hoshiyár; takṛá; lakk bannh ke; phurtílá; taiyar ho ke;
ALIEN, *A.*
begáná; paráyá; oprá;
ALIEN, *N.*
oprá bandá. *m;* pardesí. *m;*
ALIENATE, TO, *V. T.*
apne walloṇ dil khaṭṭá karná;
ALIGHT, TO, *V. I.*
uttarná; láhiná;
ALIKE, *A.*
ikko jehá; raldá mildá; wargá; wáṇgar; ikk raṇg;
ALIMENT, *N.*
gijá. *f;* see FOOD.
ALIVE, *A.*
jíuṇdá; jíuṇdíáṇ jí; jíuṇdá jágdá;
ALIVE, TO MAKE, *V. T.*
jiwauná; juauná; jilauná; jiwálná; juálná;
ALL, *A.*
sáre; sabh; sabho; sabbhe; sarbatt; sáre de sáre; sárá; sarab;
nothing at all. kujh ví nahíṇ;
all at once. jhaṭṭ paṭṭ; eká ekí; pal vichch;
all the time. har vele; aṭhe paihar;
ALLAY, TO, *V. T.*
dhímá karná; hausilá dená; tasallá dená; dilásá dená;
ALLEGATION, *N.*
ilzám. *m;* dosh. *m;* shikayat. *f;*
ALLEGE, TO, *V. T.*
újj láuná; bayán karná; see AFFIRM.

ALLEGIANCE, *N.*
tábegírí. *f*; tábedári. *f*; misal. *f*; nimak halálí. *f*; ágiákárí *f*;
ALLEGORICAL, *A.*
misálí;
ALLEGORY, *N.*
misál. *f*;
ALLEVIATE. TO, *V. T.*
1. to relieve. arám OR armán dená;
2. to lessen. ghaṭáuná; dhímá karná; maṭṭhá karná;
ALLEVIATION, *N.*
arám. *m*; ramán. *m*; armán. *m*;
ALLEY, *N.*
galí. *f*; kúchá. *m*;
ALLIANCE, *N.*
1. treaty. nem. *m*; ahad. *m*;
2. relationship. rishtá. *m*; sák. *m*; náttá. *m*; sákádárí, *f*; bháíchárá. *m*;
3. friendship. dostí. *f*; mittartáí. *f*; millat. *f*;
4. confederation. ekká. *m*; bannat. *f*; junglá. *m*; kaṭṭh. *m*;
ALLIGATOR, *N.*
magar machh. *m*;
ALLOCATE, TO, *V. T.*
waṇḍná; waṇḍ dená; waṇḍí páuní; ṭhahráuná;
ALLOCATION, *N.*
waṇḍá. *m*; hissá. *m*;
ALLOT. TO, *V. T.*
dená; hissá dená; waṇḍ dená; for two only. adho adh karná;
ALLOTMENT, *N.*
hissá. *m*;
ALLOW, TO, *V. T.*
dená; ijan dená; manná; ijázat dení; see CONCEDE;
ALLOWANCE, *N.*
1. travelling allowance. bhattá. *m*; safar ḳharach. *m*;
2. food. rásan. *m*; rasad. *m*;
ALLOY, *N.*
khoṭ. *f*; raláu. *m*;
ALLOY, TO, *V. T.*
khoṭ miláuná;
ALLUDE, TO, *V. T.*
ishárá karná; hawálá dená;
ALLURE, TO, *V. T.*
lálach dená; lalcháuná; lubháuná; tama dená; lab karná;

ALLUSION, *N.*
ishárá. *m*; patá. *m*;
ALLY, *N.*
madatgár. *m*; sáṇjhí. *m*; dost. *m*; hamaití. *m*;
ALLY, TO, *V. T.*
joṛná; miláuná; raláuná;
ALMANAC, *N.*
jantarí. *f*; patarí. *f*;
ALMIGHTY GOD, *N.*
1. Muhammadans and Christians. Qádir-i-Mutlaq Ḳhudá. *m*; Allah. *m*; Rabb. *m*;
2. Sikhs and Hindus. Parmeshur. *m*; Ishwar. *m*; Kartár. *m*; Sarbshaktímán. *m*;
ALMOND, *N.*
badám. *m*;
ALMOND COLOURED, *A.*
badámí;
ALMOST, *Adv.*
qaríb qaríb; lag bhag; neṛe teṛe;
ALMS, *N.*
1. Muhammadans and Christians. chandá. *m*; ḳhairát. *f*; ḳhair. *f*;
2. Sikhs and Hindus. dán. *m*; punn. *m*; dán punn. *m*; punn dán. *m*; sadká. *m*; bhíkh. *f*; bhichhiá. *m*;
3. alms given in the name of a dead person. sarádh. *m. H.*; karm kiriá. *m. H.*; darúd dená. *M.*;
4. to give alms. dán karná. *H.*;
ALMS, TO GIVE, *V. T.*
chandá dená; ḳhairát dení; dán karná; mans dená; sadká dená; to distribute food as alms. langar waṇḍná OR kholná;
ALMS HOUSE, *N.*
garíb ḳhána. *m*; dharmsálá. *m*;
ALOES. *N.*
keoṛá. *m*; musabbar. *m*; elúá. *m*; kuár ganḍal. *f*;
ALONE, *A.*
akallá; kallá; ikláppá; kall mukallá; ikánt; chaṛá muṛá; chaṛ mushṛá; chaṛá cháṇḍ;
ALONG, *Adv.*
nál nál; nálo nál; nál; along a road. saṛake saṛake; along a bank. kaṇḍhe kaṇḍhe; alongside. saṇg;

ALOOF, *A*.
alag ; wakhre ; wakkh ; judá ;
ALOUD, *Adv*.
uchchí uchchí karke bolná ;
uchchí bolná ;
ALPHABET, *N*.
paintí. *f* ; alaf be. *f* ;
ALREADY, *Adv*.
pahláṇ ; aggoṇ ; huṇ hí ;
ALRIGHT, *A*.
ṭhík ; chaṇgá ; bhalá ;
Interj. ḳhair sallá ;
ALSO, *Conj*.
nále ; ví ; bhí ;
ALTAR, *N*.
qurbángáh. *f*, *M* ; jagvedí. *f*, *H* ;
ALTER, TO, *V*. *T*.
waṭáuná ; badalná ; márchá karná OR márná ; badalí karní ; waṭá dená ; waṭáṇḍrá karná ;
ALTERATION, *N*.
badal. *m* ; adal badal. *m* ; tabdílí. *f* ;
ALTERCATION, *N*.
jhagṛá. *m* ; laṛái. *f* ; takrár. *m* ; fasád. *f* ; ṭaṇṭá. *m* ; jhagṛá-jháṇjhá. *m*;
ALTERNATE, TO, *V*. *T*.
wárí wárí karní ;
ALTERNATELY, *Adv*.
wárowárí ; ikk ikk karke ; wáro wárí ; wáro waṭṭí ;
ALTERNATIVE, *N*.
chárá. *m* ; koí hor tajwíz. *f* ;
ALTHOUGH, *Conj*.
bháṇweṇ ; háláṇ ;
ALTITUDE, *N*.
uchchíáí. *f* ;
ALTOGETHER, *Adv*.
1. unitedly. sáre milke ; milkar; ikk dil hoke ; kaṭṭhe hoke ;
2. all. kull ; sáre dá sárá ;
3. entirely. muloṇ muḍḍhoṇ ; ukká mukká ;
ALUM, *N*.
phaṭkárí. *f* ;
ALWAYS, *Adv*.
nitt ; hameshá ; har ghaṛí ; sadá ; har dam ;
AM, *V*. *I*.
háṇ ;

AMALGAMATE, TO, *V*. *T*.
miláuná ; raláuná ;
AMALGAMATION, *N*.
mel. *m* ; mel jol. *f* ;
AMASS, TO, *V*. *T*.
joṛná ; kaṭṭhá karná ; jamá karná ;
AMAZE, TO, *V*. *T*.
ghabrá dená ; hairán karná ; acharaj karná ; achambá karná ; hakká bakká karná ; ghabrá rakkhná;
AMAZED, TO BE, *V*. *I*.
hairán honá ; ghábar jáná ; hakká bakká ho jáná OR ráhná ;
AMAZED, *A*.
hakkṛá pakkṛá ; daṇgg ; hakká-bakká ;
AMAZEMENT, *N*.
haráni. *f* ; haránagí. *f* ; tajjab. *m* ; see PERPLEXITY.
AMAZING, *A*.
acharaj ; ajíb ; aṇokhá ;
AMBASSADOR, *N*.
elchí. *m* ; dút. *m* ;
a messenger. lággí. *m* ;
AMBASSAGE, *N*.
wakíl. *m* ;
AMBIGUITY, *N*.
dubdhá. *f* ; shakk. *m* ;
AMBIGUOUS, *A*.
gol mol ; gumm sud ; shakkí ; jih dá matlab sáf nahíṇ ;
AMBITION, *N*.
ichchhiá. *f* ; táṇgh. *f* ; ríjh. *f* ; cháh. *f*;
AMBITIOUS, *A*.
lobhí ; hirsí ;
AMBLE, *N*.
of a horse. rawhál. *m* ; chalná. *m* ;
AMBROSIA, *N*.
amritt. *m* ;
AMBUSH, *N*.
ghát. *m* ; dá ghát. *m* ; dá. *f* ; chhahí. *f*;
AMELIORATE, TO, *V*. *T*.
sudhárná ; suárná ; madad karní ;
AMEND, TO, *V*. *T*.
ṭhík karná ; sudhárná ; suárná ; chál chalan durúst karná ; ṭhík ṭhák karná ; sahí karná ; sodhná;
AMEND, TO, *V*. *I*.
saurná ; saur jáná ; ṭhík ho jáná ;

AMENDMENT, *N.*
sudháí. *f* ; durustí. *f* ; sudhár. *m* ; siddhíáí. *f* ;
AMENDS, *N.*
badlá. *m* ;
AMENITY, *N.*
ḳhubí. *f* ;
AMIABILITY, *N.*
ḳhushmizájí. *f* ; komaltáí. *f* ; síl. *f* ;
AMIABLE, A.
hass mukhá ; ḳhush dil ; sílwant ; he is an amiable man. oh ádmí hassu hassu kardá rahndá ;
AMICABLE, *A.*
yár básh ; mittar ; muhabbatí ; mihrbán ;
AMIDST, *Adv.*
vichkár ; vichch ; vichghár ;
AMISS, TO TAKE, *V. I.*
búrá manná ; búrá laggná ;
AMITY, *N.*
dostí. *f* ; mel miláp. *m* ; mel jol. *f* ; melí gelí. *f* ; millat. *f* ;
AMMONIA CHLORIDE, *N.*
nasádar. *m* ;
AMMUNITION, *N.*
golí chikká. *f* ; barúd. *m* ; dárú chikká. *f* ;
AMNESTY, *N.*
muáfí, *f* ; khimá. *f* ;
AMONG, *Prep.*
vichch ; vichkár ; vikhe ;
AMOUNT, *N.*
rakam. *f* ; náwán. *f* ;
AMPHITHEATRE, *N.*
akháṛá. *m* ; ghol. *m* ;
AMPLE, *A.*
bahut ; bahterá ; bahutá ; waḍḍá ; ghanerá ; ḍher ;
AMPLIFY, TO, *V. T.*
wadháuná ; bahutá karná; wadherá karná ; jádá karná ;
AMPLY, *Adv.*
jádá ; bahut sárá ; ḍher sáre ;
AMPUTATE, TO, *V. T.*
waḍḍhná ; tukkná ;
AMULET, *N.*
tawít. *m* ; tawít dhággá. *m* ; jádú tawít. *m* ; jádú guddá. *m* ; see CHARM.

AMUSE, TO, *V. T.*
parcháuná ; ḳhush karná ; dil ḳhush karná ; anaṇd karná ; mauj karní ; parsinn karná ; baláuná ; warcháuná ;
to amuse a child. khaḍáuná ; lorí dení ; tháparná ;
AMUSED, TO BE, *V. I.*
parcháyá jáná ;
AMUSEMENT, *N.*
parcháú. *m* ; parcháwá. *m* ; tamáshá. *m* ;
AMUSING, *A.*
hassanwálí gal ; man bhauní gal ;
ANALYSIS, *N.*
wichár. *m* ; arth. *m* ;
ANARCHY, *N.*
fasád. *f* ; gaṛbarí. *f* ; hallá gullá. *m* ; anher. *m* ; hal chal. *f* ; balwá. *m* ;
ANATHEMA, *N.*
lánat. *f* ; lakkh lánat. *f*; hardúlánat. *f* ; see CURSE.
ANATHEMATIZE, TO, *V. T.*
bad duá dení ; lánat dení ; phiṭak dení ;
ANCESTORS, *N.*
waḍḍ waḍere. *m* ; dádde padádde. *m* ; pio dáde. *m* ;
ANCESTRAL, *A.*
jaddí ; ádí ; muḍḍh qadímí ;
ANCESTRY, *N.*
ḳhándán. *m* ; jadd. *f* ; jadd pusht. *m* ;
ANCIENT, *A.*
puráne jamáne dá ; puráne same dá ; sanátan ;
AND, *Conj.*
te ; ate ; ar ; nále ;
ANECDOTE, *N.*
kathá; *f* ; kathiá. *f*; bát páuní. *f*;
ANEW, *A.*
nawe sireoṇ ;
ANGEL, *N.*
firishtá. *m* ; dút. *m* ;
angel of death. jamdút. *m* ;
ANGER, *N.*
gussá. *m* ; karodh. *m* ; roh. *m* ; waṭṭ. *m* ; hirkh. *m* ; gajab. *m* ; gachch. *m* ; tamak. *f* ; ḳauṛ. *m* ; kop. *m* ; rossá. *m* ;

ANGER, TO, *V. T.*
rassáuná ; gussá karná ; naráj karná ; karodh karná ; rerrná ;

ANGRILY, *Adv.*
russke ; gusse nál ;

ANGRY, TO BE, *V. I.*
gusse honá ; lál honá ; lusná ; saṛná ; gussá chaṛhná ; gussá áuná ; taṛiṇgg ho jáná ; gusse nál bhar jáná ; russ jáná ; rat o rat ho jáná ; tapná ; tamakná ;
don't be so angry. aiḍá waṭṭ ná kariá kar ;

ANGRY, *A.*
bhuhe ; naráj ; ruṭṭhiá hoyá ; ruṭṭhá hoyá ; russiá hoyá ; taṛiṇgg ; jaliá baliá ; lohá lákkhá ;

ANGLE, *N.*
nukkar, *f* ; guṭṭh. *f* ; nok. *f* ; khúnj. *f* ; khúṇjá. *m* ;

ANGUISH, *N.*
1. pain. sakht píṛ. *f* ; ḍáḍḍhí píṛ. *f* ; ján kaṇḍal. *f* ;
2. sorrow. gam. *m* ; hamsos. *f* ; birláp. *m* ; santáp. *m* ; ranj. *m.*
3. to be in anguish or pain. taṛaphná ;

ANIMAL, *N.*
jánwar. *m* ; chupáyá. *m* ; passú. *m* ; pashú. *m* ; hawán. *m* ;

ANIMALS, *N.*
chaupáye. *m* ;

ANIMATE, *A.*
sajív ;

ANIMATE, TO, *V. T.*
jor te tázagí dení ; uddam dená ; josh diláuná ; tagṛeáṇ karná ;

ANIMATION, *N.*
josh. *m* ;

ANIMOSITY, *N.*
vair. *m* ; dushmaní. *f* ; adávat. *f* ; kíná. *m* ; dushmanaigí. *f* ; khár. *f* ; virodh. *m* ; karodh. *m* ;
mutual ill feeling. aṇ baṇ. *f* ;

ANISEED, *N.*
sauf. *f* ; soíaṇ. *f* ;

ANKLE, N.
giṭṭá. *m* ;

ANKLET, *N.*
kaṛí. *f* ; toṛá, *m* ; báṇk. *f* ; see ORNAMENT.

ANNA, *N.*
anná. *m* ;
two annas. duanní. *f* ;
four annas. paulí. *f* ; chauanní. *f* ;
eight annas. dhellí. *f* ; aṭhíanní. *f* ;

ANNEX, TO, *V. T.*
mál lainá ; mál márná ; qábú kar lainá ; kho lainá ;

ANNIHILATE, TO, *V. T.*
sattiá nás karná ; jaṛ puṭṭná ; miṭáuná ; dá nás karná ; taraṭṭí chauṛ karní.
to be totally annihilated. taraṭṭí chauṛ honí ;

ANNIVERSARY, *N.*
din diháṛá. *m* ; yádgírí dá din. *m* ;
birthday. janam din. *m* ;

ANNOUNCE, TO, *V. T.*
khabar dení ; ishtihár dená ; saneḥá dená ; patá dená ; taláh dení ; dassná ; kah dená ;
by proclamation. hoká dená ; ḍhanḍhorá dená ;

ANNOUNCEMENT, *N.*
khabar. *f* ; saneḥá. *m* ; itiláh. *f* ; patá. *m* ; suh. *f* ; ḍáh. *m* ;

ANNOY, TO, *V. T.*
jich karná ; chheṛná ; taṇg karná ; satáuná ; dikk karná ; rassáuná ; aukkhiáṇ karná ; sir khapáuná ; akáuná ; khijáuná ; kechal karná ; rerrná ;

ANNOYED, TO BE, *V. I.*
russ jáná OR painá ; naráj honá ; akkná ; wiṭṭarná ;

ANNOYANCE, *N.*
kast *m* ; taklíf. *f* ; dikk. *f* ; jich. *m* ;

ANNUAL, *A.*
sáláná ; waṛhe de waṛhe ;

ANNUL, TO, *V. T.*
radd kar dená ; mansukh karná ; meṭná ;

ANNULMENT, *N.*
khanḍaṇ. *m* ;

ANOINT, TO, *V. T.*
1. to rub with oil. tel malná ; tel láuná ; chopaṛná ; lep karná ; málish karná ;
2. to anoint with oil. itr lá dená ;
3. to consecrate. masah karná ; ghumáuná ; jhassná ;

ANOINTING, *N.*
jhasáí. *f* ;
ANONYMOUS, *A.*
gumnám ;
ANOTHER, *A.*
ikk hor ; dujjá ; duá ; dígar
ANSWER, *N.*
jawáb. *m* ; uttar. *m* ;
a refusal. sukká jawáb. *m*; inkár. *m*;
ANSWER, TO, *V. T.*
jawáb dená ; uttar dená ;
to know the answer. jawáb áuná ;
ANSWERABLE, *A.*
jummewár ; zimmewár ;
ANT, *N.*
kíṛí. *f*;
white ant. siok. *f* ; dímak. *f* ;
ant hill. bhauṇ. *m*
ANTAGONIST, *N.*
dushman. *m* ; vairí. *m* ; virodhí. *m* ;
a man of the other side. dujjí dhir dá ; dujje pásse dá ;
ANTAGONISM, *N.*
dushmaní. *f*, vair. *m* ; barḳhiláfí. *f* ;
jiraṛ *f* ; bháṇjí. *f* ;
ANTECEDENTS, *N.*
pahlá hál. *m* ; pahlá chál chalan. *m* ;
ANTELOPE, *N.*
hiran. *m* ; hirní. *f* ;
ANTERIOR, *A.*
pahláṇ ; aglá ;
ANTICIPATE, TO, *V. T.*
uḍíkná ; intizárí karní ;
ANTICIPATION, *N.*
ummed. *f* ; uḍík. *f* ;
ANTICS, *N.*
kheḍ. *f* ; ṭhaṭṭhá. *m* ;
ANTIDOTE, *N.*
iláj. *m* ; jáhir mauhrá. *m* ;
ANTIMONY, *N.*
kajjal. *m* ; surman. *m* ;
ANTIPATHY, *N.*
1. enmity. dushmaní. *f* ; adávat. *f* ; vair. *f* ;
2. detestation. karáhat. *f* ; ghin. *f* ;
ANTIQUATED, *A.*
puráná ;
ANTITHESIS, *N.*
muqábalá. *m* ;
ANTLER, *N.*
siṇgg. *m* ;

ANUS, *N.*
gáṇḍ. *f* ; chittar. *m* ; ḍhúá. *m* ;
of a horse. liddáhṇá. *m* ;
ANVIL, *N.*
áiran. *f* ; ahiran. *f* ;
ANXIETY, *N.*
fikr. *m* ; chiṇtá. *m* ; haul. *m* ; andeshá. *m* ; saiṇsá. *m* ; firák. *m* ; dhuk dhuká. *m* ; wiswás. *m* ; chitt chetá. *f* ; vahimá. *m* ;
free from anxiety. achiṇt ;
ANXIOUS, *A.*
bechain ; chiṇtáwálá ; chiṇtáwáṇ ;
biákul ; sasdil ;
to be anxious. chiṇtá karná ;
I became anxious. mainúṇ táṇ huṇ chiṇtá ḥo gayí hai ; mere dil núṇ chiṇtá lag gayí ;
I am not anxious. mainúṇ koí saiṇsá nahíṇ ; mainúṇ koí fikr nahíṇ ; mainúṇ chiṇtá nahíṇ ;
Don't be anxious. túṇ chiṇtá ná kar ;
ANXIOUSLY, *Adv.*
baṛe fikr nál ;
ANY, *A.*
koí ; kujh ;
ANYHOW, *Adv.*
aiweṇ ; kise taráh ;
ANYONE ELSE, *Pro.*
hor koí ;
ANYTHING, *N.*
kujh ;
ANYWHERE ; *Adv.*
kite ; kidhre ; kitale ;
APACE, *Adv.*
jaldí ;
APART, *Adv.*
vakkhrá; alag ; aḍḍ ; niárá ; ikk pásse ; ikk wall ; pasittá ; vakkh o vakkh ; nirále vichch ;
to go apart. ikalwanje jáná ;
sown far apart, thinly. wirle ;
APARTMENTS, *N.*
1. men's. koṭhṛí. *f* ;
2. women's. janáná makáṇ. *m* ;
APATHETIC, *A.*
sust ; ḍhillá ; maṭṭhá ; postí ;
APATHY, *N.*
sustí. *f*; láparwáhí. *f* ; ḍhill maṭṭh. *f* ;

APE, *N*.
bándar. *m* ;
APE, TO, *V. T.*
sáṇg láuná ; naql karná ;
APERIENT, *N*.
juláb. *m* ;
APERTURE, *N*.
morí. *f* ; pár. *f* ; chhek. *m* ; khuḍḍ. *f* ; muṇh. *m* ;
APEX, *N*.
nok. *f* ;
APIECE, *A*.
ikk ikk karke ;
APOLOGISE, TO, *V. T.*
muá'í maṇgní ; ṭhuná dená ; afsos záhir karná ;
APOLOGUE, *N*.
misál. *f* ;
APOLOGY, *N*.
1. regret. pachhtává. *m* ; pachchotái. *f* ; pastává. *m* ;
2. plea. bentí. *f* ; arz. *f* ; arzú. *f* ; minnat. *f* ; sawál. *m* ;
3. excuse. uzr. *f* ; ṭhuṇá. *m* ; pajj. *m* ; huṭṭar. *m* ;
APOSTACY, *N*.
dharm thoṇ inkár. *m* ; murtadpúṇá. *m* ;
APOSTATE, *N*.
bemajhab. *m* ; inkárí. *m* ; munkir. *m* ;
APOSTATISE, TO, *V. T.*
mazhab thoṇ inkár karná ; dharm thoṇ phirná OR haṭná ;
APOSTLE, *N*.
rasúl. *m* ;
APOSTLESHIP, *N*.
rasálat. *f* ;
APPAL, TO, *V. T.*
ḍaráuná ; ḍar páuná ; kachráuná ; akkh wikháuná ;
APPARATUS, *N*.
samián. *m* ; dum dawál. *m* ;
APPAREL, *N*.
kapṛe. *m* ; bhes. *m* ; líṛá laṭṭá. *m* ; see CLOTHES.
APPARENT, *A*
záhir ; jáppdá;
to be apparent. dissná ; jápná ;
APPARENTLY, *Adv.*
vekhan vichch ;

APPARITION, *N*.
bhút. *m* ; bhutṇá. *m* ;
APPEAL, *N*.
duhái. *f* ; fariyád. *f* ; durohí. *f* ; sawál. *m* ;
a legal appeal. apíl. *f* ;
APPEAL, TO, *V. T.*
1. legal. apíl karní ;
2. to implore. giṛgaṛáuná ; duhái dení ; minnat karní ; bentí karní ;
APPEAR, TO, *V. I.*
dissná ; jápná ; malúm ho jáná ; pargaṭ honá ; wikhálí dení ; wikhái dení ; sujhná ;
APPEARANCE, *N*.
1. form. rúp. *m* ; shakal. *f* ; ákár. *m* ; raṇg rúp. *m* ;
2. act of appearing. ḍídár. *m* ; dikhlái. *f* ;
APPEASE, TO, *V. T.*
rází karní ; manáuná ; ṭhaṇḍá karná ; dhímá karná ; thamá dená ; suláh karáuní ;
I was appeased. mere dil vichchoṇ sáṛ uṭṭhiá ;
APPETITE, *N*.
bhukkh. *f* ; khuddhiá. *f* ;
desire or liking. shauq. *m* ; ichchhiá. *f* ; táṇgh. *f* ; cháu. *m* ; cháh. *f* ; loch. *f* ;
APPLAUD, TO, *V. T.*
1. to shout applause. shábá shábá karná ; wáh wáh karná ; bale bale karná ;
2. to clap hands, girls. mághá márná ; giṛdhá márná ;
3 to clap hands, boys, men. tauṛí bajáuní ; táṛí mární ;
4. to praise. táríf karní ; gún gáuná ; waḍiái karní ; saráuhná ; saláuhná ; waḍiáuná ;
APPLAUSE, *N*.
wáh wáh. *m* ; táríf. *f* ; saráhat. *f* ;
APPLE, *N*.
seu. *m* ;
APPLIANCES, *N*.
samán. *m* ; asbáb. *m* ; samián. *m* ; daṇg dawál. *m* ;
APPLICABLE, *A*.
ṭhík ; durust ; joggá ;

APPLICANT, *N.*
ummedwár. *m* ; darkhást karnwálá. *m* ; sawálí. *m* ; cháhwáṇ. *m* ; ásháwáṇd. *m* ; arzí denwálá. *m* ;

APPLICATION, *N.*
arz. *f* ; darkhást. *f* ; sawál. *m* ;

APPLY, TO, *V. T.*
1. to request. arz karní ; maṇgná ; darkhást karní ;
2. a written request. arzí dení ;
3. to stick. láuná ; lagáuná ; rakkhná ;
4. to hang. ṭaṇgná ; laṭkáuná ; see ANOINT.

APPOINT, TO, *V. T.*
muqarrar karná ; ṭhahráuná ; tháp-ná ;
1. to appoint a servant. naukar rakkhná;
2. to appoint a day. din mitthná ; tárikh páuní OR mitthní ;

APPOINTED, TO BE, *V. I.*
muqarrar honá ;

APPOINTMENT, *N.*
naukarí. *f* ; kamm. *m* ; chákarí. *f* ;

APPORTION, TO, *V. T.*
waṇḍná ; waṇḍ dená ;
amongst two only. adho addh karná ;

APPOSITE, *A.*
joggá ; laiq ; ṭhík ;

APPRAISE, TO, *V. T.*
mull chukáuná ; háṛá lainá ;

APPRAISING, *N.*
háṛá. *m* ;

APPRECIATE, TO, *V. T.*
qadr karná ; pasiṇd karná ; liház karná ; chaṇgá laggná ;

APPREHEND, TO, *V. T.*
1. to seize. phaṛná ; pakaṛ lainá ; phagarṇá ; napp lainá ;
2. to understand. samajh lainá ; bujjhná ; samajh áuní ;
3. to fear. ḍarná ; ḍar laggná ; haul karná ; ghábar jáná ;

APPREHENSION, *N.*
1. seizure. pagaṛ. *f* ; pagaṛái. *f* ; phaṛá phaṛí. *f* ;
2. understanding. samajh. *f* ; aql. *f* ; buddh. *f* ;
3. fear. ḍar. *m* ; khauf. *m* ; khauf jhakk. *m* ; dhuṛká. *m* ; dhuk dhuká. *m* ; dhaṛká. *m* ; dhaṛkí. *f* ; sainsá. *m* ; khaṭká. *m* ;

APPREHENSIVE, *A.*
ḍaranwálá ; ḍarákal ;

APPRENTICE, *N.*
shágird. *m* ; chelá. *m* ;

APPRISE, TO, *V. T.*
khabar dení ; chitárná ; dassná ; jatáuná ; sanehá ghallná ;

APPROACH, TO, *V. T.*
appaṛná ; pahuṇchná ; ḍhukkná ; agge áuná ; neṛe áuná ;

APPROACH, *N.*
ráh. *m* ; rastá. *m* ; ḍhoí. *f* ;

APPROBATION, *N.*
1. approval. manzúrí. *f* ;
2. commendation. táríf. *f* ; waḍiái ; *f* ;

APPROPRIATE, TO, *V. T.*
apne hí wáste rakkhná ; apne hí wal khichná ; khoh lená ;

APPROVAL, *N.*
manzúrí. *f* ; pasiṇd. *m* ;

APPROVE, TO, *V. T.*
1. to sanction. manzúr karná ; pasiṇd karná ;
2. to commend. táríf karni ; saráhná ; saláhná ; waḍiáuná ;

APPROXIMATELY, *Adv.*
lag bhag ; neṛe ; kú ; láge cháge ; qaríb qaríb ;

APPURTENANCES, *N.*
samián. *m* ; parwán. *m* ; daṇg dawál. *m* ; wast waleveán. *f* ;

APRICOT, *N.*
khurmánní. *f* ; saftálu. *m* ;

APRIL, *N.*
aprail. *m* ; wasákh. *m* ;

APT, *A.*
laiq ; hoshiyár ; siáná ; samajhdár ; siánaf ;

APTITUDE, *N.*
liyáqat. *f* ; jách. *f* ; laiqí. *f* ;

APTLY, *Adv.*
laiq taur nál ; chaṇgí taráh nál ; banáke ;

AQUEDUCT, *N.*
rájbáh. *m* ; nálí. *f* ; kassí. *f* ; súá. *m* ; khál. *m* ;

ARAB, *N.*
Arab. *m ;*

ARBITER, *N.*
sálas. *m ;* tarfain. *m ;*
mediator. wicholá. *m ;*

ARBITRARY, *A.*
1. despotic. jabardast ; jálim ; karṛá ;
2. capricious. dodilá ;

ARBITRATE, TO, *V. T.*
sálasí karní ; pancháyat karná ; faisalá karná ; mithná ;

ARBITRATION, *N.*
sálasí. *f ;* faisalá. *m ;*

ARCH, *N.*
ḍáṭ. *f ;*

ARCHANGEL, *N.*
álá firishtá. *m ;*

ARCHBISHOP, *N.*
wáḍḍá lát bishap sáhib. *m ;*

ARCHER, *N.*
tírandáj. *m ;* nishánebáj. *m ;* nishánchí. *m ;*

ARCHERY, *N.*
tírandájí. *f ;*

ARCHITECTURE, *N.*
bánikárí. *f ;*

ARDENT, *A.*
joshwálá ; sargarm ; tez ; jataní ; himmatí ; shukín ;

ARDOUR, *N.*
josh. *m ;* shauq. *m ;* tezí. *f ;* sargarmí. *f ;*

ARDUOUS, *A.*
sauṛá ; bikhṛá ; aukhá ;

AREA, *N.*
1. compound. hátá. *m ;* wehṛá. *m ;*
2. arena. akháṛá. *m ;* ghol. *m ;*
3. open space. maidán. *m ;* raṛá. *m ;*

ARECA NUT, *N.*
supárí. *f ;*

ARENA, *N.*
akháṛá. *m ;* píṛ. *m ;*
especially for wrestling. daṇggal. *m ;*
ghol. *m ;*

ARGUE, TO, *V. T.*
baihs karní ; dalíláṇ dená ; jhagaṛná ; qánún chháṇṭná ;

ARGUMENT, *N.*
1. controversy. baihs. *f ;* takrár. *m ;*
2. proof. dalíl. *f ;* pramán. *m ;* sabút. *f ;*
3. quibble. hujjat. *f ;*

ARGUMENTATIVE. *A.*
baihs karnwálá ; hujjatí ;

ARID, *A.*
sukká ; raṛá ; khallar ; jitthe pání hai nahíṇ ;

ARISE, TO, *V. I.*
uṭṭhná ; chaṛhná ; khalo jáná ;

ARITHMETIC, *N.*
hisáb. *m ;* lekkhá pattá. *m ;*

ARK, *N.*
1. Noah's ark. kishtí. *f ;* beṛá. *m ;*
2. ark of the Jews. sandúq. *m ;*

ARM, *N.*
báṇh. *f ;* bájú. *m ;*
1. forearm. víní. *f ;*
2. upper arm. ḍaulá. *m ;*
3. armpit. kachch. *f ;* bagal. *m ;*
4. armful. thabbá. *m ;* thabbí. *f ;* kaláwá. *m ;*
5. in the arms. kuchchhar vichch ;
6. to take in the arms. kuchchhar chukkná ;
7. arm of a river. shákh. *f ;* báhá. *m ;*
8. arm of a chair. báṇh. *f ;*
9. an armful of grass, straw, etc. satthrí. *f ;*

ARM, TO, *V. T.*
hathiyár bannhná OR láuná ; shastar OR sastar bannhná ;

ARMED, *A.*
hathiyár laggiá hoyá ; shastar dhárí ;

ARMLET, *N.*
táḍáṇ. *f,* plur ;

ARMS, *N.*
hathiyár. *m ;* shastar bastar. *m ;*

ARMOUR, *N.*
laṛáí de vichch bacháun laí hathiyár. *m ;*

ARMY, *N.*
fauj. *f ;* lashkar. *m ;* sainá. *f ;*

AROMA, *N.*
ḳhushbú. *f ;* dhúp. *f ;* see PERFUME.

AROUND, Adv.

  ále duálc; ás pás; ássá pássá;
  girde; lámbh chámbh; ird gird;
  irde girde;

AROUSE, TO, V. T.

  1. to awaken. jagáuná; uṭháuná;
  2. to animate. chukkná; tagṛeáṇ
  karná;

ARRAIGN, TO, V. T.

  ilzám láuná; nálish karná; see
  ACCUSE.

ARRAIGNMENT, N.

  ilzám. m; dáwá. f; see ACCUSA-
  TION.

ARRANGE, TO, V. T.

  1. to make an arrangement.
  intizám karná;
  2. to place in order. ṭhík ṭhák
  karná; sajáuná; suárná;

ARRANGEMENT, N.

  rahit bahit. f; intizám. m;
  bandobast. m;

ARRAY, TO, V. T.

  kapṛe OR líṛe páuná;

ARREARS, N.

  bakáyá. m; báqí hisáb. m;
  pichchhí talab. f;

ARREST, TO, V. T.

  1. to seize. phaṛná; pakaṛná;
  phagaṛná; qábú karná; giriftár
  karná;
  2. to stop. rokná; rukáuná;
  aṭkáuná; ḍakkná;

ARREST, N.

  1. seizure. pakaṛ. f; phaṛáí. f;
  phaṛwáí. f;
  2. hindrance. rok tok. f; rukáí. f;
  rukáwat. f;

ARRIVAL, N.

  appaṛáí. f; pahuṇch. f; áuná. m;
  1. arrival of wedding party.
  ḍhuká. m; áuná. m;
  2. news of arrival. awáí. f;
  3. on arrival. aundeáṇ sár;

ARRIVE, TO, V. I.

  appaṛná; á ḍhukkná; pujná; áuná;
  pahuṇchná;
  to arrive suddenly. chupaṭṭá nikalná;

ARROGANCE, N.

  gamrúrí. f; magrúrí. f; ghamaṇḍ.
  m; gustáḵhí. f; hekaṛ. f; mikk. f;
  ákaṛ. f; heṇh. f; garab. m; see
  PRIDE.

ARROGANT, A.

  gustáḵh; magrúr; gamrúr; ghamaṇḍí; garban garbí; ḍhíṭh; magrá;
  hekaṛí; majájí; nak chaṛhiá;
  ákaṛ báj;

ARROGANTLY, Adv.

  gustáḵhí nál; baṛí magrúrí nál;
  ákaṛ nál; majáj nál;

ARROW, N.

  tír. m; kání. f; báṇ. m;

ARSENAL, N.

  top ḵháná. m;

ARSENIC, N.

  1. white arsenic. saṇkhiá. m; du-
  dhyá. m;
  2. vitreous arsenic. pílá saṇkhiá.
  m;
  3. bisulphide of arsenic. lál saṇkhiá. m;

ART, N.

  1. ability. guṇ. m; hundar. f;
  hujdá. m; jách. f;
  2. handiwork. dastkárí. f;

ARTERY, N.

  náṛ. f; rag. f;

ARTFUL, A.

  chalák; hílebáj;

ARTFULLY, Adv.

  chaláki nál; fareb nál;

ARTFULNESS, N.

  chaláki. f; makkárí. f; see
  DECEIT.

ARTICLE, N.

  chíz. f; chíj wast. f; shai. f;

ARTICULATE, TO, V. T.

  sáf sáf bolná; sahíh bolná; ṭhík
  bolná; safáí nál bolná;

ARTIFICE, N.

  chaláki. f; fareb. m; dhokhá. m;
  dá f; bal chhal. m;

ARTIFICER, N.

  kárígar. m; mistrí. m;

ARTIFICIAL, A.

  banautí; jáhli; naklí;

ARTILLERY, *N.*
top kháná. *m ;*
ARTISAN, *N.*
kárígar. *m ;* mistrí. *m ;*
ARTLESS, *A.*
siddhá sádá ; sádá ; sidháraṇ ; bholá bhálá ;
ARTESSLY, *Adv.*
safái nál ; sachchíáí nál ;
AS, *Adv.*
jihá ; jíkar ; jíweṇ ; jis taráh ; jihákú ;
as if. jíweṇ ; goyá ; jáno ;
as for example. jihákú ;
as long as. jihdá ; jihdí ;
ASAFŒTIDA, *N.*
hiṇg. *f ;*
ASCEND, TO, *V. T.*
chaṛhná ; utáṇ chaṛhná ;
to cause to ascend. chaṛháuná ;
ASCENDANCY, *N.*
iḳhtiyár. *m ;*
ASCENSION, *N.*
chaṛháí. *f ;*
Christ's ascension. Masíh dá asmán de utte chaṛh jáná ;
ASCENT, *N.*
chaṛháí. *f ;*
ASCERTAIN, TO, *V. T.*
malúm karná ; daryáft karná ;
patá lainá OR karná ; puchchná ;
ASCETIC, *N.*
faqír. *m ;* saniásí. *m ;* tiágí. *m ;* sádhú. *m ;* darvesh. *m ;*
ASCETICISM, *N.*
faqírí. *f ;*
ASHAMED, *A.*
sharmindá ; lajílá ; beháyá ; sharmílá ; lajjiáwáṇ ;
are not you ashamed ? tainúṇ kujh laj nahíṇ áundí ?
ASHES, *N.*
sawáh. *f ;* sáh. *f ;* chhái. *f ;* bhassam. *f ;* wibhút. *f ;*
1. hot ashes. bhubbal. *f ;* dhuddal *f ;*
2. ashes on a faqir. bhabút. *f ;*
3. ashes of the dead. masán. *m ;* saṛí. *f ;* marí. *f ;* phúl. *m ;*

ASIDE, *Adv.*
alag ; wakkh ; ikkalwaṇjá ; see APART.
ASK, TO, *V. T.*
1. to ask a question. sawál karná ; puchchná ;
2. to ask a riddle. pahelí páuní ; bujhárat bujjhná ;
3. to make a request. maṇgná ; darḳhást karní ; arz karní ; sawál karná ;
4. to ask after health. dí surt lainá ; dá patá karná ;
ASLANT, *A.*
kuásá ;
crooked. diṇgá ; wiṇgá ;
ASLEEP, *A.*
suttiá hoyá ; níṇd vichch ;
ASP, *N.*
sapp. *m ;*
ASPECT, *N.*
1. state. hálat. *f ;*
2. shape. shakal. *f ;* rup. *f ;*
ASPERITY, *N.*
gussá. *m ;* talḳhí. *f ;* tezí. *f ;* narázagí. *f ;*
severity. saḳhtí. *f ;*
ASPERSE, TO, *V. T.*
badnám karná ; aib láuná ; niṇdiá karná ;
ASPERSION, *N.*
badnámí. *f ;* tohmat. *f ;* niṇdiá. *f ;*
ASPIRANT, *N.*
ummedwár. *m ;* áswaṇd. *m ;*
ASPIRATION, *N.*
cháh. *f ;* táṇgh. *f ;* ichchhiá. *f ;*
ASPIRE, TO, *V. T.*
cháhná ; dil karná ; jí baṛá karná ;
ASPIRING, *A.*
uddamí ; hirsí ; lohbí ;
ASS, *N.*
khottá. *m ;* gaddhá. *m ;* gaddoṇ. *m ;*
any beast of burden. waihatar. *m ;*
ASSAIL, TO, *V. T.*
márná ; chaṛháí karná ; faujdárí karní ; see ATTACK.
ASSAILANT, *N.*
hamlá karnwálá. *m ;* hallá karnwálá. *m ;*
ASSASSIN, N.
ḳhuní. *m ;* ádam már. *m ;*

ASSASSINATE, TO, *V. T.*
már dálná ; jánoṇ waḍḍhná ; ḳhun karná ; thánoṇ már suṭṭná ;
ASSASSINATION, *N.*
qatal. *m* ; ḳhun. *m* ;
ASSAULT, *N.*
már kuṭṭ. *f* ; már piṭṭ. *f* ; már kuṭái. *f* ; hallá. *m* ; dháwá. *m* ;
ASSAULT, TO, *V. T.*
márná ; dháunná ; hallá karná ; dháwá karná ;
ASSAY, TO, *V. T.*
1. to test. táuná ; parakhná ; táná ;
2. to endeavour. koshish karní ; uddam karná ; himmat karní ;
ASSEMBLAGE, *N.*
jamát. *f* ; maṇḍlí. *f* ; majlis. *f* ; jalsá. *m* ; kaṭṭh. *m* ; ḍhání. *f* ; sabhá. *f* ; saṇgat. *f* ; samáj. *f* ; mahain. *m* ; ṭollí. *f* ;
ASSEMBLE, TO, *V. T.*
kaṭṭhá karná ; jamá karná ;
ASSEMBLED, TO BE, *V. I.*
kaṭṭhá honá ; ḍhání bannhní ;
a very great mela assembles here. itthe ekk waḍḍá bhárí melá laggdá hai ;
many people assembled together. lok bahut joṛ páye ;
ASSEMBLY, *N.*
kaṭṭh. *m* ; díwán. *m* ; jhunḍḍí. *f* ; see ASSEMBLAGE.
ASSENT, *N.*
manzúrí. *f* ; huṇgárá. *m* ; hámí. *f* ; huṇgúrá. *m* ;
ASSENT, TO, *V. T.*
háṇ karní ; manná ; huṇgárá OR huṇgúrá bharná ; hámí bharní ;
ASSERT, TO, *V. T.*
jor nál ákhná ; tágíd nál bolná ; see AFFIRM.
ASSERTION, *N.*
bát. *f* ; bachan. *f* ; qarár. *m* ;
ASSESS, TO, *V. T.*
1. to tax. muámalá láuná ; taks láuná ;
2. to guess at. háṛá lainá ; jáchná ; jokhná ;
ASSESSMENT, *N.*
1. for land revenue. muámalá. *m* ;
2. octroi duty. máhsúl. *m* ;
3. tax. taks. *m* ;

ASSETS, *N.*
jáedád. *f* ;
ASSERVATE, TO, *V. T.*
kah dená ; iqrár karná ; ákhná ; dassná ;
ASSIDUITY, *N.*
jatan. *m* ; uddam. *m* ; ríjh. *f* ;
ASSIDUOUS, *A.*
árí ; mihnatí ; jataní ;
ASSIDUOUSLY, *Adv.*
jatan nál; uddam nál ; chaṇgí taráh nál ; dabádab ; ár nál ; dil nál ; dil lagáke ; ríjh nál ;
ASSIGN, TO, *V. T.*
dená ; waṇḍná ; waṇḍ dená ; waṇḍí páuṇí ;
ASSIST, TO, *V. T.*
madat karní ; sahárná ; sahaitá dení ; sahárá dená ; uprálá karná ;
ASSISTANCE, *N.*
madat. *f* ; sahaitá. *f* ; see AID.
ASSISTANT, *N.*
madatgár. *m* ; belí. *m* ; sahaik. *m* ; sáṇjhí. *m* ; sáthí. *m* ;
ASSOCIATE, *N.*
saṇgatí. *m* ; sáthí. *m* ; melí. *m* ; sáwan. *m* ; belí. *m* ; gelí. *m* ; yár. *m* ; milápí. *m* ;
ASSOCIATE, TO, *V. T.*
milná ; milná julná ; wartná ; mel rakkhná ;
ASSOCIATION, *N.*
1. a society. samáj. *f* ; sabhá. *f* ; saṇg. *m* ; saṇgat. *f* ;
2. union. mel miláp. *m* ; mel joṛ. *m* ; ekká. *m* ;
ASSORTMENT, *N.*
dheṛ. *m* ;
ASSUME, TO, *V. T.*
dhárná ; ḳhayál karná ;
ASSUMPTION, *N.*
ḳhayál. *m* ;
ASSURANCE, *N.*
1. promise. wádá. *m* ; qaul qarár. *m* ; sukhan. *m* ; bachan. *m* ;
2. belief. bharosá. *m* ; yaqín. *m* ; ásrá. *m* ; ímán. *m* ; partít. *m* ;
ASSURE, TO, *V. T.*
1. to promise. wádá dená ; qaul qarár karná ; sukhan karná ; bachan karná OR dená ;
2. to give confidence. tasallí dení ; yaqín duáná ;

ASSUREDLY, *Adv.*
sach much ; sache muche ; beshakk ;
ASTHMA, *N.*
dame dá rog. *m* ; damá. *m* ;
ASTONISH, TO, *V. T.*
hairán karná ; hakká bakká karná ; achanbá karná ;
ASTONISHED, TO BE, *V. I.*
hairán honá ; acharaj honá ; daṇgg ho jáná ; hakká bakká rahná ;
ASTONISHED, *A.*
daṇgg ; hakká bakká ; hakkṛá bakkṛá ;
ASTONISHING, *A.*
acharaj ;
ASTONISHMENT, *N.*
haránagi. *f* ; haráni. *f* ; tajjab. *m* ;
ASTOUND, TO, *V. T.*
hairán karná ;
ASTRAY, TO GO, *V. T.*
bhullná ; awárá phirná ; ghussná ; khuṇjhná ; awárá ho jáná ;
ASTRAY, *A.*
awárá ; guwáchan ;
to lead astray bhuláuná ; badráh kar dená ;
ASTRIDE, *A.*
sawár ;
ASTRINGENT, *A.*
kauṛá kasailá ;
ASTROLOGER, *N.*
najúmí. *m* ; jotsí. *m* ; ramlí. *m* ;
ASTROLOGY, *N.*
najúmián dá ilm. *m* ; najúm. *m* ; jotas. *m* ; jotash. *m* ;
ASTUTE, *A.*
hoshiyár ; siyáná ; chalák ; dáná ;
ASTUTENESS, *N.*
hoshiyárí. *f* ; chalákí. *f* ;
ASUNDER, *Adv.*
alag ; aḍḍ ; vakkho vakkhí ; vakkh ; vakkhrá ;
ASYLUM, *N.*
1. place of safety. saran. *f* ; charní. *f* ;
2. mad house. págal ḳháná. *m* ;
AT, *Prep.*
te ; vichch ; pásse ; wall ;
1. at first. pahláṇ ; pahle ;
2. at once. huṇe ; turt ;
3. at last. oṛak núṇ ; chekaṛ núṇ ; aṇt núṇ

ATHEIST, *N.*
daihríá. *m* ; Ḳhudá dá munkir. *m* ; nástík. *m* ;
ATHLETE, *N.*
pahlwán. *m* ;
ATMOSPHERE, *N.*
1. The air. wá. *f* ;
2. The sky. ákas. *m* ; akás, *m* ;
ATOMS, *N.*
chaknáchúr. *m* ; chúr chúr. *m* ;
ATONE, TO, *V. T.*
badlá dená ; kafárá dená ; balídán karná ;
ATONEMENT, *N.*
badlá. *m* ; kafárá. *m* ; chaṛháwá. *m* ; balídán. *m* ; see SACRIFICE.
ATROCIOUS, *A.*
bahut búrá ; máṛá ; bhaiṛá ;
ATTACH, TO, *V. T.*
joṛná ; láuná ; miláuná ; lagáuná ; to tie together. gaṇḍhná ; raláuná ;
ATTACHMENT, *N.*
1. affection. cháh. *f* ; pyár. *m* ; moh. *m* ; muhabbat. *f* ; prem. *m* ;
2. legal attachment. kurkí. *f* ;
ATTACK, TO, *V. T.*
chaṛháí karní ; sáhmná karná ; hallá karná ; dháwá márná ;
ATTACK, *N.*
chaṛháí. *f* ; hallá. *m* ; már kuṭṭ. *f* ; dháwá. *m* ;
ATTAIN, TO, *V. T.*
labbhná ; parápat karná ;
ATTAINMENT, *N.*
1. success. kámyábí. *f* ;
2. completion. nabeṛa. *m* ; nabáh. *m* ; nibbaṛ tibbaṛ. *m* ;
3. accomplishment. guṇ. *m* ; hundar. *m* ;
ATTEMPT, TO, *V. T.*
koshish karní ; mihnat karní ; jatan karná ; uddam karná ;
ATTEMPT, *N.*
uddam. *m* ;
ATTEND, TO, *V. T.*
1. to pay attention. dhián karná ; soch lená ; ḳhayál karná ; man dená ; gaur nál sunná ; kann dharná ;
2. to serve. ṭahl karní ; ḳhidmat karní ; ṭahl sewá karná ; ṭahl tawajjá karná ; mijmání karní ;

ATTENDANCE, *N.*
hájarí. *f ;* házari. *f ;*
to mark attendance. hájarí láuní ;

ATTENDANT, *N.*
naukar. *m ;* chákar. *m ;* ṭahliá. *m ;*
sewak. *m ;* ṭahlaṇ. *f ;* laggá
baddhá. *m ;*
attendants. jaḷeb. *m ;*

ATTENTION, *N.*
dhián. *m ;* gaur. *m ;* gauh. *m ;* surt.
f ; birtí. *f ;*

ATTENTION, TO PAY, *V. T.*
jí lagáuná ; birtí rakkhní ; gauh
karná ; kann láuná ;

ATTENTIVE, *A.*
suchet ; chatann ; chaukas ; chátar ;

ATTENTIVELY, *Adv.*
diloṇ wajhoṇ hoke ; kann láke ;
dhián nál ; dil nál ; gauh karke ;
listen attentively. ohitt láke suno ;
kann dharke suno ;

ATTENUATED, *A.*
lissá ; dublá ; máṛá ; kamjor ;

ATTEST, TO, *V. T.*
gawáhí dení ; bayán karná ; sákhí
dení ;

ATTESTATION, *N.*
shahádat. *f ;* gawáhí. *f ;* guáhí. *f ;*

ATTESTATION PAPER, *N.*
qarár náma dá kágat. *m ;*

ATTIRE, *N.*
bhes. *n ;* kapṛe. *m ;* líṛe. *m ;*

ATTIRE, TO, *V. T.*
kapṛe páʾuná ; líṛe páuná ;

ATTORNEY, *N.*
1. lawyer. wakíl. *m ;*
2. agent. muḳhtiár. *m ;*

ATTRACT, TO, *V. T.*
lubháuná ; tamá dená ; lalcháuná ;
lab karná ;

ATTRACTION, *N.*
moh. *m ;* hirs. *f ;*

ATTRACTIVE, *A.*
manmohan ;

ATTRIBUTE, *N.*
gúṇ. *m ;* sift. *f ;*

ATTRITION, *N.*
ragaṛ. *f ;* ghasar. *m ;* ghássá. *m ;*
a cut. jhariṭ. *f ;*

AUCTION, *N.*
nilám. *m ;* lalám. *m ;*

AUCTION, TO, *V. T.*
lalám karná ;

AUCTIONEER, *N.*
lalám karnwálá. *m ;*

AUDACIOUS, *A.*
diler ; gustáḳh ; see IMPUDENT ;

AUDACITY, *N.*
dilerí. *f ;* gustáḳhí. *f ;* beadabí. *f:*

AUDIBLY, *Adv.*
uchchí áwáz nál ; uchchí karke ;

AUDIENCE, *N.*
jamát. *f ;* pareh. *f ;*
the people present. házarín. *m ;*

AUDIT, TO, *V. T.*
paṛtál karná ;

AUGMENT, TO, *V. T.*
wadháuná ;

AUGMENTATION, *N.*
wadháo. *m ;*

AUGURY, *N.*
fál. *m ;* sagan. *m ;* warmá. *m ;*

AUGUST, *N.*
Bhádaron. 13 August to 12 Sep-
tember.

AUNT, *N.*
1. father's sister. bhúá. *f ;* phup-
phí. *f ;*
2. mother's sister. mássí. *f ;*
3. father's younger brother's wife.
cháchchí. *f ;*
4. mother's brother's wife. mámmí.
f ;
5. father's elder brother's wife.
táí. *f ;*

AUSPICIOUS, *A.*
chaṇgá ; mubárik ; subh ; shubh ;
mahúrat chaṇgá ;

AUSTERE, *A.*
saḳht ; tuṇd mizáj ; karṛá ;

AUSTERITY, *N.*
saḳhtí. *f ;*
religious austerities. tap. *m ;*

AUTHENTIC, *A.*
aslí ; ṭhík ; sáhí ;

AUTHOR, *N.*
1. an agent. kartár. *m ;*
2. of a book. likhanwálá. *m ;* kitáb
banáunwálá. *m ;*

AUTHORITY, *N.*
ikhtiyár. *m* ; wass. *m* ; jor. *m* ; haqq. *m* ; hukúmat. f ; hukm hásal. *m* ;
to have under my authority. mere ákhe vichch ;
AUTHORISE, TO, *V. T.*
1. to order. hukm dená ;
2. to permit. ijázat dení ;
3. to give power to another. ikhtiyár dená ; mukhtiár banáuná ;
AUTOCRAT, *N.*
hákim. *m* ;
AUTOGRAPH, *N.*
dastkhat. *m* ;
thumb mark. angguthá. *m* ;
AVAIL, TO, *V. I.*
chalná ; kamm vichch áuná ;
AVARICE, *N.*
lálach. *m* ; lobh. *m* ; hirs. *f* ; laulá. *m* ;
AVARICIOUS, *A.*
lobhí ; lálachí ; hirsí ;
AVARICIOUSLY, *Adv.*
lálach karke ;
AVENGE, TO, *V. T.*
badlá lainá ; sijjhná ; milná ;
AVENGER, *N.*
badlá lainwálá. *m* ; wattá lainwálá. *m* ;
AVER, TO, *V. T.*
bayán karná ; dassná ; see ASSERT.
AVERAGE, *N.*
aust. *f* ; ausat. *f* ;
AVERAGE, TO STRIKE AN, *V. T.*
ausat kaddhní ;
AVERAGE, *A.*
khásá ; mamúlí ;
AVERSE, *A.*
virodh ; khiláf ;
AVERSION, *N.*
karáhat, *f* ; ghin. *f* ;
AVERT, TO, *V. T.*
rokná ; tálná ; dur karná ;
AVIDITY, *N.*
cháh. *f*; hirs. *f*; kháhish. *f* ; ríjh. *f* ;
AVOCATION, *N.*
kamm. *m* ; dhandá. *m* ;
AVOID, TO, *V. T.*
múnh lukáuná ; nere ná jáná ; kanárá karná ; katráuná ; matthe ná laggná ; khikhiáuná ;

AVOIDANCE, *N.*
parhez. *f* ;
AVOW, TO, *V. T.*
manná ; dam bharná ;
AVOWAL, *N.*
qarár. *m* ; qaul. *m* ; qaul qarár. *m* ;
AVOWEDLY, *Adv.*
khullá khullí ;
AWAIT, TO, *V. T.*
ráh takkná ; udíkná ;
AWAKE, *A.*
jágdá ;
one who keeps awake. jággú, *m* ;
AWAKEN, TO, *V. T.*
jagáuná ;
AWAKENING, *N.*
jág. *m* ; hosh. *m* ;
AWARD, *N*
ínám. *m* ; inám shinám, *m* ; ajr. *m* ;
AWARD, TO, *V. T.*
dená ;
AWARE, TO BE, *V. I.*
patá honá ; málum honá ; khabar honí ;
AWAY, *Adv.*
dur ;
AWAY, *A.*
absent, wáhndá ;
AWE. *N.*
dar. *f* ; bháú. *m* ; khauf, *m* ; dabká. *m* ;
a person's influence. rohb. *m* ;
AWE, TO, *V. T.*
daráuná ;
AWFUL, *A.*
dáddhá daráuná ;
AWHILE, *Adv.*
thorí der ;
AWKWARD, *A.*
kuwallá ; bathawá ; bhaddá ; kudhabbá ;
AWKWARDLY, *Adv.*
búrí taráh nál ;
AWL, *N.*
ár. *f* ;
AWNING, *N.*
1. for shops, &c. chappar. *m* ; tarappar. *m* ; tirpál. *f* ; chhajjá. *m* ;
2. as a tent. chánaní. *f* ; shámiáná. *m* ;

AXE, *N*.
kuháṛá. *m*; kuháṛí. *f*; gandásá, *m*;
AXIS, *N*.
dhurí. *f*;
AXLE, *N*.
dhurá. *m*; dhurí. *f*; dhur. *m*; laṭṭh. *f*;
AZURE, *A*.
asmání rang.

B.

BAA, *N*.
bhaiṇ. *f*; máṇ. *f*;
BAA, TO, *V. T*.
miánkná; bhaiṇ bhaiṇ karná;
BABBLE, *N*.
bakbak. *m*; bak jhak. *f*; wáhiyát galláṇ. *f*; gapp. *f*; bahutíáṇ galláṇ. *f*; wádhíáṇ gallán. *f*; fijul gallán. *f*;
BABBLE, TO, *V. T*.
bakná; láuná; bak bak karná; ṭarkná; aiweṇ bolná; ṭaiṇ ṭaiṇ karná; bataule márná; ṭarṭar karná;
BABBLER, *N*.
palálí. *m*; jatallí. *m*; lutrá. *m*; butuní. *m*; baturá. *m*; bataulá. *m*; bakwádhí. *m*; bakwádhaṇ. *f*; baṛbolá, *m*; baṛbaṛiyá. *m*;
BABBLING, *N*.
baṛbaṛát. *m*; fijul gallán. *f*;
BABE, *N*.
ayáná. *m*; bachchá. *m*; bál. *m*; bálak. *m*; káká. *m*;
BABEL, *N*.
raulá. *m*; ghaṛbaṛí. *f*; harolí, *f*;
BABOON, *N*.
bándar. *m*; bujjo. *m*;
BABY, *N*.
ayáná. *m*; bál. *m*; káká. *m*; bachchá. *m*; bachchṛí. *f*;
English baby. báwá. *m*;
BABYISH, *A*.
nadán jehá; bholá bhálá; bhálá bholá;
BABYHOOD, *N*.
ayánpuṇá. *m*; bachchpan. *m*; bálpan. *m*;
BACHELOR, *N*.
kuárá. *m*;
an unmarried man over 30, or a widower. chhaṛá. *m*;

BACK, *N*.
piṭṭh. *f*; ḍhúí. *f*; ḍhúa. *m*;
1. lower part of back. lakk. *m*;
2. upper part of back. maur. *m*; kaṇḍ. *f*;
3. back of the house. pachhwáṛá. *m*;
BACK, *Adv*.
pichchoṇ.
behind one's back. piṭṭh pichche;
BACK, TO, *V. I*.
of a horse. aṛí karní;
to back out. haṭná; phirná; thaṛná; pasarná;
to turn the back. piṭṭh de dení;
BACKBITE, TO, *V. T*.
burá kahná; kann bharná; badnám karná; lutíáṇ láuná; niṇdiá karná: piṭṭh pichche kahná; aib láuní; jaṛ phuṭṭná; bakhílí karní; bhagí karní;
BACKBITER, *N*.
búrá ákhanwálá. *m*; chugal. *m*; chuglí ḳhor. *m*; niṇdak. *m*;
BACKBITING, *N*.
chuglí. *f*; chugalḳhorí. *f*; niṇdiá. *f*; lútí. *f*; bakhílí. *f*; ujj. *f*; bhagí. *f*;
BACKBONE, *N*.
piṭṭh dí haḍḍí. *f*; kamar dí haḍḍí. *f*;
BACKSLIDE, TO, *V. T*.
phir jáná; haṭná; gumráh honá; ḍhilliáṇ paí jáná;
BACKSLIDER, *N*.
munkir. *m*; inkárí. *m*;
BACKWARD, *Adv*.
pishán; pichchhe;
BACKWARD, *A*.
1. behind. pichchhe;
2. slow. sust; ḍhillá; ḍhillá maṭṭhá;
BACKWARDNESS, *N*.
sustí. *f*; ḍhill. *m*;
BACON, *N*.
suar dá más. *m*;
BAD, *A*.
1. evil. burá; bhairá; ḳharáb; dusht; sharírí; khoṭṭá; lúṇḍá; kupattá; uchakká; chauṛ chaupaṭṭ; kuchál;
2. useless. nakárá, nikammá; raddí;
3. bad-tempered. saṛú; saṛúká; karodhí; majáj dá máriá hoyá;

BADGE, *N*.
nishán. *m*; billá. *m*; chaprás. *f*; nishání. *f*; patá. *m*;

BADGER, *N*.
ud. *m*;

BADGER, TO, *V. T.*
aukhiáṇ karná; dikk karná; jich karná; chheṛná; satáuná; sir khá jáná; dukháuná; akáuná;

BADINAGE, *N*.
hássá. *m*; makhaul. *m*; ṭhaṭṭhá; *m*;

BADLY, *Adv*.
búrí taráṇ; kharábí nál;
how badly you do that. tainúṇ kí búrí wáddí paí gayí hai?

BADNESS, *N*.
buriáí. *f*; badí. *f*; sharárat. *f*; maṇdíáí. *f*; máṛá kamm. *m*; kharábí. *f*; bhaiṛ. *f*;

BAFFLE, TO, *V. T.*
1. to amaze. ghabráuná; ghábbarná; hairán karná; aql már dení; sudáí karní;
2. to stop. rokná; ḍakkná; aṭkáuná; khaliárná;

BAG, *N*.
1. small. thailí. *f*; jholí. *f*; guthlí. *f*;
2. large. thailá. *m*; guthlá. *m*; jholá. *m*;
3. for school books. bastá. *m*;
4. beggar's bag. baglí. *f*;
5. barber's leather bag. rashání. *f*; guchchhí. *f*;
6. sack. borí. *f*; borá. *m*;

BAGGAGE, *N*.
nikk sukk. *m*; wast walevá. *m*; chíjwast. *f*; wast. *f*; bugchá. *m*; bag and baggage. gaṇḍh gaṭṭhṛí. *f*; bistrá boríá. *m*;

BAGPIPES, *N*.
bín bájá. *m*;

BAIL, *N*.
1. security. zamánat. *f*; jamánat. *f*; zámní. *f*; jámní. *f*; hájar jámaní. *f*;
2. cricket bails. gullíyáṇ. *f*; bel. *f*;

BAIL, TO GIVE, *V. T.*
jamánat dení; jámní dení; vichchho khaloná;

BAILIFF, *N*.
sarbaráh. *m*; piádá. *m*;

BAIT, *N*.
1. for fish. chárá. *m*;
2. enticement. lálach. *m*; lobh. *m*; lábh. *m*;

BAIT, TO, *V. T.*
chárá lagáuná;

BAKE, TO, *V. T.*
pakáuná; rihnanná; rasoí karní; bhunná;

BAKED, *A*.
pakká; pakká hoyá; rihnniá hoyá; riddhá hoyá; rijjhá hoyá; rijjhiá hoyá;

BAKEHOUSE, *N*.
bawárchí khána. *m*: jhulání. *f*, *M*; rasoí. *f*, *H*; sabát. *f*, *M*;

BAKER, *N*.
bawárchí. *m*; babárchí. *m*; khánsámáṇ. *m*; roṭíwálá. *m*; nánbáí. *m*; nánwáí. *m*; rasoyá. *m*; láṇgarí. *m*; láṇgariá. *m*;

BAKING, *N*.
pakáí. *f*;

BAKING PAN, *N*.
degchá. *m*; degchí. *f*; háṇḍí. *f*; iron plate for baking. tawá. *m*;

BALANCE, *N*.
1. small scales. takkṛí. *f*;
2. large scales. takkaṛ. *m*; kaṇḍḍá. *m*; tarájú. *m*;
3. one side of the scales. chhabbá. *m*;
4. scales for weighing silver, &c., kaṇḍḍí. *f*; kaṇḍḍá. *m*;
5. balance of an account. baqáyá. *m*; báqí. *f*; bachchat. *f*;

BALANCE, TO, *V. T.*
1. to weigh. tolná; jokhná;
2. to balance an account. baqáyá kaḍḍhná;

BALCONY, *N*.
barándá. *m*;

BALD, *A*.
gaṇjá; roḍḍá bhoḍḍá; ghonná monná;

BALDERDASH, *N*.
wáhiyát galláṇ. *f*;

BALDNESS, *N*.
gaṇj. *m*; ghon. *m*; sir dá chánd. *m*; sir dí chándí. *f*;

BALE, *N*.
1. bundle. gaṭhṛí. *f* ; gaṭṭhaṛ. *m* ;
2. bale of grass. paṇḍ. *f* ; gaṭṭhá. *m* ; bíṇḍá. *m* ;
3. load. bhár. *m* ; bojh. *m* ; bojhá. *m* ;

BALE, TO, *V. T.*
gaṭhṛí bannhní ; gaṇḍh bannhná ; bíṇḍá walná ; paṇḍ bannhní ;

BALK, TO, *V. T.*
rokná ; ḍakkná ; aṭkáuná ;

BALL, *N*.
khehnúṇ. *m* ; khinnú. *m* ; khenú. *m* ; khiddo. *m* ;
1. cricket ball. bál. *m* ;
2. canon ball. golá. *m* ;
3. ball made of cloth. khiddo. *m* ;
4. ball of gur. guṛ di roṛí *f* ; guṛ dí bhellí. *f* ; guṛ dá bhellá. *m* ; guṛ dí mikkar. *f* ;
5. a dance. nách. *m* ;
6. bat and ball. geṇd ballá. *m* ; geṇd baiṭ. *m* ;
7. ball of carded cotton. gohuṛa. *m* ;
8. ball of twine ; pinná. *m*;

BALLAD, *N*.
gít. *m* ; bhajan. *m* ; rág. *m* ;

BALLAST, *N*.
roṛe. *m* ;

BALLET, *N*.
nách. *m* ; náṭak. *m* ;

BALLOON, *N*.
gubárá. *m* ; burj. *m* ;

BALLOT, TO, *V. T.*
raí dení ; voṭ dení ;

BALLROOM, *N*.
nách ghar. *m* ;

BALM, *N*.
malham. *f* ;

BALUSTRADE, *N*.
jaṇgalá. *m* ;

BAMBOO, *N*.
báṇs. *m* ; wáṇs. *m* ; waṇjh. *m* ;

BAMBOOZLE, TO, *V. T.*
buttá márná ; dhokhá dená ; ṭhaggí mární OR karní ; ṭhaggná ;

BAN, TO, *V. T.*
1. to interdict. maná karná ; band karná ; warjná ;
2. to curse. lánat dení ; saráp dená ; bad duá dení ;

BAN, *N*.
1. a curse. **lánat**. *f* ; saráp. *m* ; duṛú, *m* ;
2. excommunication. ḳhárij. *m* ; chhek. *m* ;

BANANA, *N*.
kelá. *m* ; phalí. *f* ; kele dí chhallí *f* ;

BAND, *N*.
1. a company. bhíṛ. *f* ; akaṭṭh. *m* ; jatthá. *m* ; ṭollá. *m* ; ṭollí. *f* ;
2. of musicians. wájewále. *m* ; báje wajáuṇwále. *m* ;
3. of robbers. dháṛví jatthá. *m* ; ḍákuáṇ dá jatthá. *m* ;
4. a tie. bannhan. *m* ;
5. band round a sheaf. subb. *m* ; beṛ. *m* ;

BANDAGE, *N*.
paṭṭí. *f* ; lammí tákí. *f* ; lír. *f* ;

BANDAGE, TO, *V. T.*
paṭṭí bannhná ; paṭṭí karní ;

BANDBOX, *N*.
peṭí. *f* ; sandúq. *m* ;

BANDIT, *N*.
ḍákú. *m* ; dháṛví. *m* ; luṭerá. *m* ;

BANDY, TO, *V. T.*
takrár karná ; jhagaṛná ;

BANDYLEGGED, *A*.
ḍuḍḍá ; ḍuḍḍíáṇ laṭṭáṇwálá ; wiṇgíáṇ pairáṇwálá ;

BANE, *N*.
nuqsán. *m* ; halákí. *f* ; barbádí. *f* ;

BANEFUL, *A*.
ḳhatre dá ; nuqsánwálá ;

BANEFULLY, *Adv*.
búrí taráh nál ;

BANG, *N*.
1. a blow. mukká. *m* ; mukkí. *f* ; ghusunn. *m* ; húrá. *m* ;
2. a noise. kaṛak. *m* ;

BANG, TO, *V. T.*
1. to hit. mukká márná ; ghusunn márná.
2. to bang the door. zor nál buhá band karná.

BANG, TO, *V. I.*
ṭhín ṭhiṇ karná ;

BANGLE, *N*.
ghokhrú. *m* ; kaṛá. *m* ; kaṛíáṇ. *f* ; chuṛá. *m* ; see ORNAMENT.

BANISH, TO, *V. T.*
mulkoṇ báhar kaḍḍhná ; des nikálá dená ; dúr karná ; nikálná ;
BANISHMENT, *N.*
des nikálá. *m* ;
BANK, *N.*
1. for money. baṇk. *m* ; ḳhajánná. *m* ;
2. of a river. kanḍhá. *m* ; kinárá. *m* ; banná, *m* ;
3. of a canal. paṭṛí. *f* ;
4. of clouds. baddalán dá joṛ. *m* ; baṛá baddal. *m* ;
BANK, TO, *V. T.*
ḳhajánne vichch rupae rakkhná ;
BANKER, *N.*
1. bankers. bankwálá. *m* ; bank dá manajar. *m* ; ḳhajánchí. *m* ;
2. moneylenders. sháhukár. *m* ; sháh. *m* ; karáṛ. *m* ; saráf. *m* ; maháján. *m* ; seṭh. *m* ;
BANKING, *N.*
sháhukárí. *f* ; saráfí. *f* ;
BANKNOTE, *N.*
. noṭ. *m* ; huṇḍí. *f* ,
BANKRUPT. *N.*
dawáliá. *m* ;
to become bankrupt. dawálá kaḍdhná ; dawálá nikalná ;
BANKRUPTCY, *N.*
dawálá. *m* ;
BANNER, *N.*
jhanḍá. *m* ; jhanḍí. *f* ;
flag used by beggars. ḍhal. *f* ;
BANNS, *N.*
shádí dí pukár. *f* ;
BANQUET, *N.*
kháná. *m* ; ziáfat. *f* ;
BANQUET, TO GIVE A, *V. T.*
ziáfat karní ; baṛá kháná karná ; dáwat karní ;
to give a feast after the death of an aged person. roṭí karní ; kaṭṭh karná ;
BANTER, *N.*
maḳhaul. *m* ; ṭhaṭṭhá. *m* ; hássá. *m* ; háṇsí. *f* ;
in a bad sense. maskarí. *f* ;
BANTER, TO, *V. T.*
maḳhaul karná ; ṭhaṭṭhá karná ; háṇsí karní ; hássá karná ;
in a bad sense. maskarí karní ;
BANTLING, *N.*
bachchá. *m* ; ayáná. *m* ; káká. *m* ;
BANYAN TREE, *N.*
boṛh. *m* ; bohṛ. *m* ; baṛh. *m* ;
BAPTISM, *N.*
1. Christian. báptismá. *m* ;
2. Sikh. páhul. *f* ;
BAPTISE, TO, *B. T.*
1. Christian. báptismá dená ;
2. Sikh. páhul dení.
BAPTISED, TO BE, *V. I.*
1. Christian. báptismá milná OR lainá OR honá ;
2. Sikh. páhul lainá ; amrit chhakná ;
BAR, *N.*
1. of metal. moṭí síkh. *f* ;
2. thin metal rod. salákh. *f* ;
3. of wood. ḍanḍá. *m* ;
4. of a door. arl. *f* ;
5. a barrier. wáṛ. *f* ; rok. *f* ; rukáwat. *f* ; aṭkáú. *f* ;
BAR, TO, *V. T.*
1. to stop. rokná ; ṭokná ; hatkáná; ḍakkná ;
2. to prohibit. warajná ; band karná ;
3. to exclude. chhekná ; alag karná; ḳhárij karná ;
4. to shut the door. buhá márná ; buhá dhoná ; buhá bheṛ dená ; buhá band karná ;
BARB, *N.*
nok. *f* ; chuṇj. *f* ; ár. *f*
a thorn. kaṇḍḍá. *m* ;
BARBARIAN, *N.*
jangalí. *m* ; waihshí. *m* ; malechch. *m* ;
BARBARIC, *A.*
jangalí ; waihshí ;
BARBARISM, *N.*
1. condition. jangalí hál. *m* ; guṇwárpúṇá. *m* ;
2. cruelty. baṛí beráhmí. *f* ; baṛí saḳhtí. *f* ; loṛhá. *m* ;
BARBARITY, *N.*
saḳhtí. *f* ; zulm. *m* ; jabardastí. *f* ; rákhaspuṇá. *m* ;
BARBAROUS, *A.*
1. brutal. beráhm ; saḳht ; kabbá ; patthardil ;
2. uncivilised. janglí ;

BARBED, *A*.
kaṇḍḍedár ;
BARBER, *N*.
naí. *m* ; rájá. *m* ;
BARD, *N*.
mirásí. *m* ; dúm. *m* ; bhaṇḍ. *m* ; bhaṭṭ. *m* ; These are names of different castes, all of whom sing and play musical instruments, &c.
BARE, *A*.
naṇgá ; naṇgá paṇgá ; naṇg panaṇgá ; náṇgaṇ ;
BARE, TO, *V. T*.
naṇgá karná ; kholná ; ughár karná ; ughárná ;
BAREFACED, *A*.
besharm ; beháyá ; belajjá ; belajjí ;
BAREFACEDNESS, *N*.
beháyáí. *f* ; besharmí. *f* ;
BAREFOOTED, *A*.
naṇgíṇ pairíṇ ; jutíáṇ biná ; naṇge pair ;
BAREHEADED, *A*.
naṇge sir ;
BARELY, *Adv*.
nirá ; kewal ; kassá ;
with difficulty. masáṇ ; masáṇ kiweṇ ;
BARENESS, *N*.
1. poverty. garíbí. *f* ; kangálí. *f* ; taṇgí. *f* ; taṇgsí. *f* ;
taṇgí turshí. *f* ;
2. nakedness. naṇg. *m* ;
BARGAIN, N.
1. something cheap. chaṇgá saudá, *m* ; saudá sút. *m* ;
2. a contract. bachan. *m* ; qaul qarár. *m* ; sukhan. *m* ; bol. *m* ;
BARGAIN, TO, *V. T*.
saudá karná ; mull karná OR chukáuná ; leṇ deṇ karná ;
1. to sell. vechná ; mull dená ;
2. to exchange. waṭáuná ; waṭṭo saṭṭá karná ;
BARGE, *N*.
ḍoṇgá. *m* ; beṛá. *m* ; beṛí. *f* ;
BARK, *N*.
1. of a tree. sakk. *m* ; chhillaṛ. *f* ; chhil. *f* ; sakkaṛ. *m* ; sakṛá. *m* ;
2. of a dog. kutte dí awáz. *f* ; bhauṇk. *m* ;
3. a ship. jaház. *f* ; beṛá. *m* ;

BARK, TO, *V. T*.
bhauṇkná ;
to growl. ghuṛná ;
BARLEY, *N*.
jauṇ. *m* ; jau. *m* ;
BARLEY MEAL, *N*.
jauṇ dá áṭá. *m* ; sattú. *m* ;
BARM, *N*.
khamír. *m* ;
BARN, *N*.
koṭṭhí. *f* ; koṭṭhá. *m* ;
BAROUCHE, *N*.
ṭiṭan gárí. *f* ;
BARRACK, *N*.
bárak. *f* ; faují goreáṇ dá ghar. *m* ;
BARREL, *N*.
1. a cask. pípá. *m* ; biám. *m* ;
2. of a gun. banduq dí nálí. *f* ;
BARREN, *A*.
1. sterile land. banjar jamín ; kallar jamín ; kauṛi jamín ; kalraṭṭhí jamín ; bhassar jamín karlaṭṭhí jamín ;
2. childless. báṇjh ; dhí puttar nahíṇ ; sanḍh ;
3. barren cow. phaṇḍar ;
4. barren goat or sheep. bekanní ;
5. barren tree. apphal ; nisphal ;
BARRENNESS, *N*.
banjarpaṇ. *m* ;
BARRICADE, *N*.
náká bandí. *f* ; rok. *f* ;
trench. morchá. *m* ;
BARRICADE, TO, *V. T*.
náká bandí karní ; rokná ;
to make a trench. morchá bandí karní ;
BARRIER, *N*.
jaṇgalá. *m* ; wáṛ. *f* ; rok. *f* ;
BARRISTER, *N*.
barristar. *m* ; wakíl. *m* ;
BARROW, *N*.
hatth gaddí. *f* ; reṛhí. *f* ;
BARTER, *N*.
wanj bipár. *m* ; bupár. *m* ; leṇ deṇ. *f* ; waṭṭá-saṭṭá. *m* ;
BARTER, TO, *V. T*.
leṇ deṇ karná ; mull karná ; see BARGAIN.

BASE, *A*.
1. vile. nikammá; nakárá; badját; kaminá; máṛá; chaṇḍál;
2. base coin. khoṭṭá;
3. baseborn. harám dá;

BASELESS, *A*.
khashufá; jhuṭhí kḥabar; uḍḍí uḍḍí kḥabar; uḍḍí puḍḍí kḥabar;

BASELY, *Adv*.
burí taráh nál; baṛe kamínpuṇe de nál;

BASENESS, *N*.
ních kamm. *m*; kamínpuṇá. *m*; chaṇḍálpuṇá. *m*; beimáni. *f*; kabáhat. *f*;

BASHFUL, *A*.
háyáwálá; háyáwálí; lajwálí; lajjí;

BASHFUL, TO BE, *V. I.*
saṇgná; muṇh lukáuná; jhakná; laj rakkhní; jhijakná;

BASHFULNESS, *N*.
háyá. *m*; sharm. *f*; saṇg. *f*; laj. *f*;

BASIN, *N*.
bháṇḍá. *m*;
of baked clay. daurá. *m*; baṭhal. *m*;

BASIS, *N*.
níṇh. *f*;

BASK, TO, *V. I.*
dhupp sekná; dhuppe bahná; síe bahná;

BASKET, *N*.
1. small. ṭokrí. *f*;
2. small. with lid. paṭárí. *f*;
3. large. ṭokrá. *m*; paṭár. *m*; paṭárá. *m*;
4. for fruit and vegetables. chhábṛí. *f*;
5. for winnowing. chhajj. *m*;
6. for food. chhábbá. *m*; chhábbí. *f*;
7. for sweetmeats. chaṇgger. *f*; chhikṛí. *f*; chhiku. *m*;

BASTARD, *N*.
harám dá. *m*; harámí. *f*;
an abusive term. kumút. *m*;

BASTE, TO, *V. T.*
chopaṛná;

BASTION, *N*.
burj. *m*; gummaṭ. *m*;
a trench. morchá. *m*;

BAT, *N*.
1. animal.
large, chamgiddaṛ. *m*; chámchaṛikí. *f*;
small, chámchiṭh. *f*;
2. cricket bat. paṭṭí. *f*; baiṭ. *m*; ballá. *m*;
3. bat and ball. khiddo paṭṭí, *f*; khehnúṇ ṭullá. *m*; khiddokhúndí. *f*;

BATCH, *N*.
khep. *f*;

BATH, *N*.
tapp. *m*; tab. *m*;

BATHE, TO, *V. T.*
náháuná; ashnán karná; náuná;
1. to bathe a corpse. loth OR maiyat núṇ náháuná OR nalwháná OR nuháíná OR nuláuná;
2. to bathe the bride before the marriage ceremony. kháre chaṛháuná;
3. ceremonial bathing. wazú karná, *M*; ashnán karná, *H*;

BATHING, *N*.
gusl. *m*; ashnán. *m*;
religious bathing. wazú. *m*, *M*; ashnán. *m*, *H*;

BATHING PLACE, *N*.
1. by a river, &c., gháṭ. *m*;
2. in a house. gusl kḥáná. *m*;

BATH ROOM, *N*.
gusl kḥáná. *m*;

BATON, *N*.
chob. *f*;

BATTALION, *N*.
baṭályan. *f*; paltan. *f*; parṭal. *f*; fauj. *f*;

BATTEN, *N*.
1. planed. ballá. *m*;
2. rough. kaṛí. *f*;

BATTEN, TO, *V. I.*
moṭṭá tázá ho jáná;

BATTEN, TO, *V. T.*
bhasar bhasar kháná; nákoṇ nák bharná; gulkná;

BATTER, TO, *V. T.*
mukke márná; már kuṭṭ karná; see BEAT.

BATTERY, *N*.
top. *f*; top kḥáná. *m*;

BATTLE, *N.*
  laṛáí. *f;* jaṇg. *m;* raṇ. *m;* juddh. *m ;*
  1. battle array. laṛáíáṇ díáṇ
    sattaráṇ. *f;*
  2. battlefield. laṛáí dá maidán. *m ;*
    raṇ bhúm. *f;*
BATTLE, TO, *V. T.*
  laṛáí karní; laṛná; jaṇg karná;
  juddh karná;
BATTLESHIP, *N.*
  jaṇgí jaház. *m;*
BAWL, *N.*
  kúk. *f;* awáz. *f;* chíkh. *f;*
BAWL, TO, *V. T.*
  kúk márni, chíkh márni; awáz dení;
  chichláuná; shor macháuná; chís-
  láuná; ḍaṇḍ páuná; chaṇghárná;
BAY, *A.*
  1. chestnut bay. suraṇg;
  2. dark bay. kamait; kamaid;
    telíyá;
BAY, *N.*
  1. of the sea. khalíj. *m ;* kháṛí. *f;*
  2. of a dog. bhauṇkáṇ dí awáz. *f;*
BAY, TO, *V. T.*
  bhauṇkná;
BAYONET, *N.*
  saṇgín. *f;*
BAYONET, TO, *V. T.*
  saṇgín márni;
BAYRUM, *N.*
  tel. *m;*
BAZAR, *N.*
  bazár. *m ;* bajár. *m ;*
BE, TO, *V. I.*
  honá; ho jáná;
BEACH, *N.*
  samundar dá kaṇdhá OR kanárá
  OR banná. *m ;*
BEACON, *N.*
  nishán. *m ;*
BEAD, *N.*
  málá dá dáná. *m ;* maṇká. *m ;*
  1. glass bead. pot. *f;*
  2. of a rosary. maṇká. *m ;*
BEAGLE, *N.*
  shikárí kuttá. *m ;*
BEAK, *N.*
  chuṇjh. *f;* chiṇjh. *f;*

BEAM, *N.*
  1. of wood, small. kaṛi, *f ;* ballá.
    m ; shatíri. *f;* chhatan. *m ;*
  2. of wood, large. shatír. *m ;*
    toṛá. *m ;* laṭṭh. *m ;*
  3. of wood, very large. kánjaṇ. *f;*
  4. of steel. gárdar. *m ;*
  5. of a loom. tur. *f;*
  6. of light. kiraṇ. *f;* chamak. *f;*
    lát. *f;*
  7. for Persian well. kánjaṇ. *f;*

BEAMING, *A.*
  chamakdár;
BEAN, *N.*
  phalí. *f;* sem. *m ;* frás bín. *f;*
BEAR, *N.*
  bhálú. *m ;* báhlú. *m ;* richch. *m ;*
  ríchchní. *f;*
BEAR, TO, *V. T.*
  1. to endure. saihná; sahárná;
    jhallná; saháuná; jarná; sabr
    karná; dhímá karná;
  2. to carry. chukkná; bhár
    chukkná; bojh uṭháuná;
  3. to bear down. dubáuná;
  4. to bear children. jammná;
    bachchá dená; ghar bachchá
    honá;
  5. to bear fruit. phalná; phal dená;
    phal leggná;
  6. to bear in mind. yád rakkhná;
    chete rakkhná;
  7. to bear witness. gawáhí dení;
    guwáh bhugtaná; shákhí dení;
  8. to bear up, support. sámbhaná;
    samáh lená;
  9. cattle to bear young. súná;
    bachchá dená;
BEARABLE, *A.*
  sahn jogg;
BEARD, *N.*
  dáṛlú. *f;* dáhṛí. *f;*
  the first growth of a young man's
  beard. mass. *f;*
BEARDED, *A.*
  dáṛhíwálá;
BEARER, *N.*
  baihrá. *m ;*
BEARING, *N.*
  1. appearance. rup. *m ;*
  2. demeanour. rohb. *m ;*

BEAST, *N.*
pasú. *m*; jánwar. *m*;
a beast of burden or for riding. wahitar. *m*;
BEASTLINESS, *N.*
gandagí. *f*; palítí. *f*; ayáshí. *f*; luchchpuṇá. *m*;
BEASTLY, *A.*
luchchá; gúṇḍá;
BEAT, *N.*
1. in music. tál. *m*;
2. a blow. már. *f*; hurá. *m*; ghusann *m*; mukkí. *f*;
BEAT, TO, *V. T.*
már kuṭṭná; már kuṭṭ karná; márná; dhappá márná; kuṭṭná; phaṇḍná; már kuṭṭái karní;
1. to beat with fists. húre mukkíáṇ márná;
2. to beat with a shoe. jutíáuná;
3. to beat with a whip. sáṛ sáṛ márná; sará sat márná;
4. to beat severely. sakhtí nál márná; ghiss cháhaṛná; kise dí múnj swárná; dhaṛo dhaṛí már suṭṭná; dhauṛí udheṛní; ghiss karní;
5. to beat a drum. wajáná;
6. to beat time. tál dená;
7. to beat clothes on a stone; chhaṭṭná;
8. to beat a tree. jhambná;
BEATEN, TO BE, *V. I.*
már kháṇí; máriá jáná; kuṭṭiá jáná; with a shoe. juttí kháṇí;
BEATER, *N.*
márú. *m*;
BEATING, *N.*
1. chastisement. már. *f*; már kuṭṭ. *f*; kuṭṭ. *f*; sazá. *f*;
2. defeat. hár. *f*; bháṇj. *f*;
BEATITUDE, *N.*
mubárakbádí. *f*; wadhái. *f*;
BEAU, *N.*
báṇká. *m*;
BEAUTEOUS, *A.*
khubsurat; sohná; sundar;
BEAUTIFUL, *A.*
sohná; darshaní; chhel; soháwará; shaklwálá;
very beautiful. ḍáḍḍhá sohná;
BEAUTIFULLY, *Adv.*
khubsuratí nál;
BEAUTIFULNESS, *N.*
sohnápaṇ. *f*; jobaṇ. *m*;
BEAUTIFY, TO, *V. T.*
sajáuná; sawárná; shangárná; sudhárná; típ táp karná; sáf súf karná;
for a woman only. hár sangár karná;
BEAUTY, *N.*
sohappan. *m*; sohj. *m*; ḍuss. *f*; joban. *m*; jamál. *m*; husaṇ. *m*; suthrái. *f*; suṇdartái. *f*; suṇdartá. *f*;
BEAVER, *N.*
uddh. *m*; uddh biláo. *m*; (really means an otter.)
BECALM, TO, *V. T.*
ṭhandá karná; rází karní; dhímá karná, thamá dená;
BECAME, *V. I.*
ho jáná; sajná;
BECAUSE, *Conj.*
kyuṇ jo; kyuṇkí; is laí; is wáste; is karke; is káran;
because of fear. ḍar de máríáṇ;
BECK, *N.*
sainat. *f*;
BECKON, TO, *V. T.*
sainat mární; hatth nál saddná;
BECOME, TO, *V. I.*
honá; ho jáná; sajná;
BECOMING, *A.*
1. suitable. laiq; munásib; durust; ṭhík; jogg;
2. graceful. sohná;
BECOMINGLY, *Adv.*
changí taráh nál; laiq taur nál;
BED, *N.*
1. bedstead. manjí. *f*; manjá. *m*;
2. of a river. daryá dá thallá. *m*; daryá dí tháh. *f*;
3. of flowers. kiárá. *m*; kiárí. *f*;
4. of roses. phulláṇ dí sej. *f*;
5. bed and board. roṭí kapṛá. *m*; an páni te kapṛá lattá. *m*;
BEDCHAMBER, *N.*
sauná kamrá. *m*;

BEDDING, *N.*
wichháuná. *m*; wichhái. *f*; bichháuná. *m*; sot. *f*; lef tulái. *f*; julí jappí. *f*;
1. a light mattress. gadelá. *m*; nihálí. *f*; tulái. *f*; julí. *f*;
2. other bedding. rasái. *f*; lef. *m*; julá. *m*;

BEDECK, TO, *V. T.*
sajáuná; shangárná; see BEAUTIFY.

BEDEW, TO, *V. T.*
bheuná;

BEDIM, TO, *V. T.*
dhuṇḍlá karná;

BEDIZEN, TO, *V. T.*
banáuná tanáuná; hár sangár karná;

BEDPOST, *N.*
1. end. serú. *m*; serúá. *m*;
2. head. sarháṇḍí. *f*; sarháná. *m*;
3. sides. híáṇ. *f*; báiáṇ. *f*;
4. legs. páwe. *m*;
5. bottom. pawáṇḍí. *f*;

BEDRAGGLE, TO, *V. T.*
mailá karná; gaṇḍá karná OR banáuná; palít karná;

BEDRENCH, TO, *V. T.*
bheuná;

BEDROOM, *N.*
sauná kamrá. *m*;

BEDSPREAD, *N.*
palaṅgposh. *m*;

BEDSTEAD, *N.*
manjí. *f*;
1. child's bedstead hanging from ceiling. pangghúṛá. *m*; jhulá. *m*;
2. child's bedstead standing on ground. palaṇghírí. *f*;

BEE, *N.*
makkhí. *f*; shahd dí makkhí. *f*; swarm of bees. makhír. *m*;

BEEF, *N.*
gao dá gosht. *m*;

BEEF TEA, *N.*
shurúá. *m*; lás. *m*;

BEE HIVE, *N.*
álá. *m*; (really a hole or recess in the wall or roof.)
1. a full honeycomb, chhatá. *m*;
2. an empty honeycomb. khaggá. *m*;

BEER, *N.*
bír sharáb. *m*; nashá pání. *m*;

BEER HOUSE, *N.*
sharáb ḳháná. *m*; kalál ḳháná. *m*; sharáb dí dukán. *f*;

BEERSELLER, *N.*
kalál. *m*;

BEESWAX, *N.*
mom. *m*;

BEET, *N.*
chukandar. *m*;

BEETLE, *N.*
1. insect. kíṛá. *m*; gabrílá. *m*;
2. for levelling the ground. dámúsá. *m*;

BEFALL, TO, *V. I.*
á painá; ho jáná;

BEFITTING, *A.*
laiq; jogg; ṭhík; munásib;

BEFOG, TO, *V. T.*
ghabrá dená;

BEFOOL, TO, *V. T.*
dhokhá dená; dam vichch láuná; see DECEIVE.

BEFORE, *Prep.*
de agge; muhre; sámhne;
Adv. agge; agge núṇ; agetare; paihlá; agáháṇ; áhmo sámhno; agere;

BEFOREHAND, *Adv.*
pahloṇ hí; aggoṇ hi; agetare hí; to tell beforehand. pahloṇ hí dass chhaḍḍná;

BEFORE MENTIONED,
us gal dí babat jih dá zikr hoyá OR kítá gáyá;

BEFOUL, TO, *V. T.*
gaṇḍá karná; mailá karná; palít karná;

BEFRIEND, TO, *V. T.*
dostí karní; dáyá karná; mihrbání karní; madad dení; sahárá karná;

BEG, TO, *V. T.*
1. to ask alms, maṇgná; ḳhair maṇgná; bhíkh maṇgní; pinná maṇgná; gadá karná; maṇgná pinná; bhichhiá maṇgná; tukkaṛ ḳhair maṇgná;
2. I live by begging. asiṇ bhichhiá maṇg maṇg kháṇde háṇ;
3. to ask earnestly. minnat karní; suwál karná; bentí karní; duá karní; arz karní; tarlá minnat karní; giṛgaṛáuná;

BEGET, TO, *V. T.*
jamná ; see BEAR.
BEGGAR, *N.*
bhíkh maṇgaṇwálá. *m* ; maṇgtá. *m* ; faqír. *m* ; suálí. *m* ; bikhárí. *m* ; bhichhak, *m* ;
1. beggar's bag. ; baglí, *f* ; jamíl, *f* ;
2. beggar's blanket, jullí, *f* ; godrí, *f* ; godrá, *m* ;
3. begger's patched coat. kafní ; *f* ;
4. beggar's bowl. chíppí, *f* ; kapprí. *f* ; kishtá, *m* ;
5. brahmin beggar. bháṭṛá. *m* ;
BEGGARLY, *A.*
kamíná ;
BEGGARY, *N.*
kaṇgáli, *f* ; garíbí. *f* ; maskíní. *f* ; taṇgí. *f*, taṇgsí. *f* ; faqírí. *f* ;
BEGGING, *N.*
bhíkkh, *f* ; galá. *m* ; gajá. *m* ; maṇgan. *m* ;
BEGIN, TO, *V. T.*
chherná ; laggná ; shurú karná ; chho dená ; ád karná ; áraṇbh karná ; árambhná ; tumná ;
I will begin this work tomorrow. bhalke hí maíṇ is kamm núṇ karan lagg páwáṇgá ;
BEGIN, TO, *V. I.*
shurú honá ; wiḍḍiá jáná ;
BEGINNER, *B.*
aje hune sikkhaṇwálá. *m* ;
BEGINNING, *N.*
muḍḍh. *m* ; ád. *m* ; áraṇbh. *m* ; chhiṛt. *f* ; pahil. *m* ;
from the beginning, shurú thoṇ nawen sire ; nawen siríoṇ ; muḍḍhoṇ ; dhuráke,
BEGONE, *Interj.*
pare ho já ; dur ho já ; chaliá já ;
BEGRIME, TO, *V. T.*
mailá karná ; gaṇdá karná ; palít karná ;
BEGRUDGE, TO, *V. T.*
saṛná ; hasad karná ; kuṛkuṛáná ; khár kháná ;
BEGUILE, TO, *V. T.*
dhokhá dená ; fareb dená ; ṭhaggná ; see DECEIVE.
BEGUILED, *A.*
dhokhá khádá ;
BEGUILEMENT, *N.*
makar. *m* ; fareb. *m* ; lárá. *m* ; see DECEIT.
BEGUILER, *N.*
dhokhebáj. *m* ; see DECEIVER ;
BEHALF, *N.*
káran. *m* ; khátir. *f* ; wáste. *m* ; sabab. *m* ; laí. *f* ;
BEHAVE, TO, *V. T.*
salúk karná ; pesh áuná ; adab karná ; wartná ;
BEHAVIOUR, *N.*
lachchhan, *m* ; chál chalan. *m* ; salúk. *m* ; buhár. *m* ; kamm. *m* ; ḍaul. *f* ; wartáo *m* ; bol chál. *f* ; ḍhaṇg. *m* ; chál ḍhál. *f* ;
BEHEAD, TO, *V. T.*
sir láh dená ; sir waḍḍhná ; sir uḍá dená ;
BEHEST, *N.*
hukm. *m* ; ágiá. *m* ;
BEHIND, *Prep.*
de pichchhe ; de magar ;
Adv. pichchhe ; pichere ; piṭṭh pichchhe ; pishán ; pishere ;
1. from behind. pichchhoṇ ; pichcháṛí ; pishereoṇ ;
2. to pass behind. pichchhoṇ dí langhná, pichcháṛíoṇ langhná ;
BEHINDHAND, *A.*
pichchhe ;
BEHOLD, TO, *V. T.*
wekhná ; takkná ;
BEHOLDER, *N.*
wekhanwálá. *m* ; takkanwálá. *m* ;
BEING, *N.*
1. hastí. *f* ; honá. *m* ;
2. a creature. jándár. *m* ; (paráṇí. *m* ; of human beings only)
BELABOUR, TO, *V. T.*
már kuṭṭná ; khub márná ; mukke márná ; see BEAT.
BELCH, *N.*
ḍakár. *f* ;
BELCH, TO, *V. T.*
ḍakár márná ; ḍakár lená ; ḍakárná ; ḍakráuná ;
BELDAM, *N.*
buḍḍharí, *f* ; jihf. zanání. *f* ; birdani. *f* ;

BELEAGUER, TO, *V. T.*
gherná; gherá páuná; gherá ghatná; walná;
BELFRY, *N.*
burji. *f;*
BELIE, TO, *V. T.*
1. to lie. jhuṭh márná; jhuṭh bolná; kalank láuná;
2. to prove false. jhuṭhá karná; jhuṭhá banáuná; jhuṭhiáuná;
BELIEF, *N.*
imán. *m;* yaqín. *m;* partít. *f;* ásrá. *m;* sardhá. *f;* nischá. *m;* nihchá. *f;* patíj. *f;* biswás. *m;* mán. *m;* dharm. *m;*
BELIEVABLE, *A.*
yaqín de laiq; mannaṇ jog;
BELIEVE, TO, *V. T.*
manná; ímán le áuná; yaqín karná; atbár karná; partít áuní; nihchá karná; patíjná; satt jánná; partít karní; mán rakkhná;
BELIEVER, *N.*
ímándár. *m;* dharmí. *m;*
BELIEVINGLY, *Adv.*
yaqín de nál; yaqín karke;
BELIKE, *Adv.*
shayad; ho sakdá;
BELITTLE, TO, *V. T.*
1. to make smaller. chhoṭá banáuná; ghaṭṭáuná;
2. to speak disparagingly. badnám karná; niṇdiá karná;
BELL, *N.*
ghaṇṭá. *m;* ṭall. *m;*
1. gong. ghaṛeál. *m;* ghattiál. *m;*
2. bell on necks of cattle, small. tallí. *f;* ghuṇggarú. *m;* large. jang. *m;* ṭall. *m;*
3. bells for the feet. ghuṇggarú. *m;*
4. iron bar used as a bell. ghaiṇṭí. *f;*
BELLADONNA, *N.*
makú. *m;*
BELLICOSE, *A.*
fasádí; daṇggái; laṛáká; jhagṛálú; khappí;
BELLMAN, *N.*
ḍhanḍoriá. *m;*
BELLOW, *V. T.*
1 to bawl. kúk mární; hák mární;
2. to low, cow, aringná;
3. to low, buffalo. aṛáuná;
BELLOWS, *N.*
dhauṇkní. *f;*
BELLY, *N.*
ḍhiḍḍ. *m;*
a big belly, goguṛ. *f;*
BELLYACHE, *N.*
ḍhiḍḍ vichch píṛ. *f;* maroṛ. *m;* maroṛá. *m;*
BELLYBAND, *N.*
faráki. *f;* patká. *m;*
BELONGINGS, *N.*
asbáb. *m;* samán. *m;* wast walevá. *m;*
BELONGING, TO, *Prep.*
dá; de; dí;
BELOVED, *A.*
pyárá; pyárí; azíz; láḍlá; jání;
BELOW, *Prep.*
heṭh; heṭháṇ;
BELOW, *Adv.*
heṭh; thalle; heṭhon heṭh; heṭhle páse; heṭháṇ;
BELT, *N.*
bilṭ. *m;* petí. *f;*
sword belt. partalá. *m;*
BEMIRE, TO, *V. T.*
mailá karná; gaṇdá karná;
BEMOAN, TO, *V. T.*
phus phus karná; kurláuná; roná;
BENCH, *N.*
baiṇch. *m;* takhtposh. *m;*
BEND, TO, *V. T.*
lafáuná;
to bend the head. sir jhukáuná; neuṇná;
BEND, TO, *V. I.*
to bend down. niwáṇ karná; lifná; jhukkná;
BEND, *N.*
moṛ. *m;* wall. *m;* wiṇgg. *m;* ḍiṇgg. *m;*
BENDABLE, *A.*
lifanwálá; lifáú;
BENEATH, *Adv.*
heṭh; heṭhoṇ heṭh;
BENEDICT, *A.*
wiahyá hoyá;
BENEDICTION, *N.*
barakat. *f;* asís. *f;* dúá. *f;* barakat dá kalimá. *m;* asírbád. *m;*
BENEFACTION, *N.*
chandá. *m;* ḳhairát. *f;* dán punn. *m;*

BENEFACTOR, *N.*
dátá. *m;* kirpálu. *m;* dayálu. *m;* upkárí. *m;* murabbí. *m;*
BENEFACTRESS, *N.*
dáyáwantí. *f;* upkáraṇ. *f;*
BENEFICIENCE, *N.*
dáyá. *f;* kirpá. *f;* mihrbání. *f;* ahsán. *m;*
BENEFICIENT, *A.*
mihrbán; sukhdáik;
BENEFICIENTLY, *Adv.*
kirpá nál; mihrbání nál;
BENEFICIAL, *A.*
faidemand; faidedár; mufíd;
BENEFIT, *N.*
1. a favour. mihrbání. *f;* dáyá. *f;* ahsán. *m;* kirpá *f;*
2. profit. faidá. *m;* lábh. *m;* parápat.
BENEFIT, TO, *V. T.*
bhalá karná; lábh páuná; kirpá karná; dáyá karná; ahsán karná; madad karní; kam sárná; kam sawárná;
BENEFIT, TO, *V. I.*
faidá honá;
BENEVOLENCE, *N.*
dáyá. *f;* kirpá. *f;* hit. *m;* mihrbání. *f;* mihrbánagí. *f;* síl. *f;* sumatt. *f;*
BENEVOLENT, *A.*
mihrbán; dáyáwán; kirpálu; parupkár; sílwaṇt;
BENEVOLENTLY, *Adv.*
mihrbání nál; dáyá nál; kirpá nál;
BENIGHTED, *A.*
khajjal kharáb; bhambal bhuse;
BENIGN, *A.*
mihrbán; dayál;
BENIGNANT, *A.*
ráhmdil; mihrbán;
BENIGNITY, *N.*
mihrbání. *f;* dáyá. *f;* kirpá. *f;*
BENIGNLY. *Adv.*
mihrbání nál;
BENISON, *N.*
barakat. *f;* asís. *f;*
BENT, *A.*
wiṇgá; ḍiṇgá; ḍiṇg phaṛiṇgá;
BEQUEATH, TO, *V. T.*
wasíat karke dená; wasíat kar jáná;
BEQUEST, *N.*
sankalap. *m;*
BEREAVE, TO, *V. T.*
khoh lená; luṭṭná;
BEREAVEMENT, *N.*
ranj. *m;*
BEREFT, *A.*
khutthá putthá; chaur chapaṭṭ;
BERRY, *N.*
dáná. *m;*
BERTH, *N.*
naukarí. *f;* asámí. *f;*
BESEECH, TO, *V. T.*
tarle minnat karní; hatth bannhke arz karní; bentí karní; giṛgaṛáuná; minnat karní; ardás karní;
BESEECHER, *N.*
sawálí. *m;*
BESEECHING, *N.*
tarlá. *m;* minnat. *f;* arz. *f;* ardás. *f;* beṇtí. *f;*
BESEECHINGLY, *Adv.*
minnat nál; tarle nál; hatth bannhke;
BESIEGE, TO, *V. T.*
gherná; gherá páuná;
BESET, TO, *V. T.*
ṭuṭṭke painá; chaṛhái karní;
BESIDE, *Prep.*
kol; pás; neṛe;
BESIDES, *Adv.*
eh de siwá; eh núṇ chhaḍḍke; nále: is te biná; bájhoṇ;
BESMEAR, TO,
chopaṛná; malná; pochná;
BESOM, *N.*
jháṛú. *m;* bauhkar. *f;* buhárí. *f;* máṇjá. *m;*
BESOT, TO, *V. T.*
behosh karná;
BESOTTED, *A.*
nashe vichch; khumárí vichch;
BESPANGLE, TO, *V. T.*
sitáre láuná;
BESPATTER, TO, *V. T.*
chikkaṛ de chhiṭṭe páuná;
to get clothes spattered with mud. kapṛe bharná;

BEST, *A.*
sáreáṇ náloṇ chaṇgá; sabh te chaṇgá; achchhe thoṇ achchhá; bhale thoṇ bhalá; waḍḍá chaṇgá;
BESTIAL, *A.*
luchchá;
BESTIALITY, *N.*
luchchpuṇá. *m;* beparejí, *f;*
BESTIALIZE, TO. *V. T.*
bigáṛná; palít karná; ḳharábkarná;
BESTIR, TO, *V. T.*
jagáuná; uṭháuná;
BESTOW, TO, *V. T.*
dená; baḳhshná;
to bestow, alms. pun karná; dáṇ karná;
BESTOWAL, *N.*
dán. *m;* dát. *f;*
BESTOWER, *N.*
dátá. *m;* denwálá. *m;*
BESTREW, TO, *V. T.*
khilárná;
BESTRIDE, TO, *V. I.*
chaṛhná; sawár honá;
BET, TO, *V. T.*
bájí lagáuná; sharat láuná;
BET, *N.*
bájí. *f;* sharat. *f;*
BETEL LEAF, *N.*
pán. *m;*
BETEL NUT, *N.*
sipárí. *f;*
BETHINK, TO, *V. T.*
yád karná; sochná; wichárná; chettá karná; thauh karná;
BETIMES, *Adv.*
vele sir;
BETRAY, TO, *V. T.*
phaṛwáná; pakṛá dená; phaṛáuná;
to betray a secret. bhed dass dená OR kholná;
BETRAYAL, *N.*
phaṛái. *f;*
BETRAYER, *N.*
phaṛáunwálá. *m;*
BETROTH, TO, *V. T.*
maṇgní karní; maṇgá dená; kurmái karní;
BETROTHAL, *N.*
maṇgní. *f;* kurmái. *f;*
BETTER, *A.*
changerá; bhalá;
BETTERMENT, *N.*
ḅihtarí. *f;*
BETTERMOST, *A.*
sabh thoṇ chaṇgá; see BEST;
BETTOR, *N.*
juáriá; juebáz. *m;* juárí. *m;* khiḍárí. *m;*
BETWEEN, *Prep.*
vichkár; viche vichch;
BEVEL, *N.*
guṇiá. *m;*
BEVERAGE, *N.*
No word in use; use the name of the thing to be drunk.
BEWAIL, TO, *V. T.*
roná; hamsos karní; hatth malná; mátam karná; kurláuná;
BEWARE, TO, *V. T.*
ḳhabardárí karní; hoshiyárí karní; hosh karná;
BEWILDER, TO, *V. T.*
ghabrá dená; raulá páuná;
BEWILDERED, TO BE, *V. I.*
ghábar jáná; biákal honá; ghábarná;
BEWILDERMENT, *N.*
ghabrát. *f;* ghabrá. *m;* hairáni. *f;* see PERPLEXITY.
BEWITCH, TO, *V. T.*
1. to charm. ḳhush karná; dil ḳhush karná; parcháuná;
2. to affect by witchcraft. jádú karná; ṭúná karná; maṇtar márná OR chaláuná OR paṛhná; guḍḍe páuná; najráuná;
BEWITCHERY, *N.*
1. fascination. moh, *m;*
2. sorcery. maṇtar jaṇtar. *m;* jádú. *m;* jádúgarí. *f;* ṭúná. *m;*
BEWITCHING, *A.*
dilpasand; mohní;
BEWRAY, TO, *V. T.*
phaṛáuná;
BEYOND, *Prep.*
de pare; de parle páse; de pár;
BEYOND, *Adv.*
pare; parle páse; pár; parlá pár; pare pareḍe; parere; paṛháṇ;

BHANG, *N.*
1. taken as a liquid. bhaṇg. *f;*
2. smoked in a pipe. charas. *f;*
3. a bhang eater. bhaṇggí. *m;*

BIAS, *N.*
tarafdárí. *f;* liház. *m;* pachchh-dárí. *f;* pachchh. *m;*

BIASSED, *A.*
uh de wal;
he is biassed in their favour. uh unháṇ dá pachhwár hai; uhunháṇ de wal hai; uh uhnáṇ wal dá;

BIBBER, *N.*
sharábí. *m;* sharábí kabábí. *m;*

BIBLE, *N.*
Baibal Sharíf. *f;* Ḳhudá dá kalám. *m;* Pák Kalám. *m;* Kalám Ulláh. *m;*

BIBULOUS, *A.*
sharábí;

BICKER, TO, *V. T.*
jhagaṛná; khaṭ paṭ karná;

BICKERING, *N.*
ṭanṭá. *m;* khaṭ paṭí. *f;*

BICYCLE, *N.*
baisakal. *m;* pair gaḍḍí. *f;* lohe dá ghoṛá. *m;*

BID, TO, *V. T.*
1. at an auction. bolí dení;
2. to command. hukm dená; ágiá dená;

BID, *N.*
bolí. *f;*

BIDDING, *N.*
hukm. *m;* ágiá. *m;*

BIDE, TO, *V. I.*
rahná; wassná; ṭikkná;

BIENNIAL, *A.*
dosálá;

BIENNIALLY, *Adv.*
dujje sál;

BIER, *N.*
1. Muhammadan. maṇjí. *f;* tabút. *f;*
2. Hindu. chikhá. *f;* siṛhí. *f;* arthí. *f;*
3. Hindu, used for an aged person. babáṇ. *m;*

BIER CLOTH, *N.*
1. Muhammadan. uchhár. *m;* kafan. *f;*
2. Hindu. doshállá. *m;* wehiṛ. *f;*

BIFARIOUS, *A.*
duguṇá; duṇá;

BIG, *A.*
waḍḍá; baṛá;
big and little. nikká shukká; nikká mukká;

BIGAMIST, *N.*
do ṭabbarwálá. *m;* do auratáṇwálá. *m;*

BIGGISH, *A.*
waḍḍá jehá;

BIGOTED, *A.*
gal dá púrá; gal dá pakká; haṭhílá;

BIGOTRY, *N.*
haṭh. *m;*
religious bigotry. haṭh dharmí. *m;*

BILE, *N.*
pitt. *f;* safrá. *f;*

BILIOUSNESS, *N.*
garmí. *f;* garmí khorá. *m;* bádí de ḍakár. *m;* bádí. *f;*

BILL, *N.*
1. beak. chuṇj. *f;* chiṇj. *f;*
2. account. hisáb. *m;*
3. of exchange. huṇḍí. *f;*

BILLET, *N.*
naukarí. *f;* kamm. *m;*

BILLOW, *N.*
ṭháṭh. *f;* chhal. *f;* mauj. *f;* káṇgg. *f;* lahr. *f;*

BIN, *N.*
1. square. koṭhí. *f;*
2. round. bhaṛolá. *m;*

BIND, TO, *V. T.*
bannhná; gaṇḍhná; aráuná; jakaṛná; júṛ dená;
to bind books. jild bannhní;

BINDING, *N.*
jild. *f;*

BINOCULARS, *N.*
dúrbín. *f;*

BIOGRAPHY, *N.*
janamsákhí. *f;* (particularly of Nanak and other Gurus).

BIPED, *N.*
dupáiá. *m;*

BIRD, *N.*
paiṇchí. *f;* paṇkherú. *m;* chiṛí. *f;* janaur. *m;*

List of Panjab birds.

Adjutant. lamḍhiṇg. *m* ;
babbler or seven sisters. sehṛ. *m* ; sehṛí. *f* ;
bee catcher. harí chiṛí. *f* ;
bittern. baglá. *m* ;
bulbul or nightingale. bulbul. *f* ;
bustard. gurain. *m* ;
cock. kukkaṛ. *m* ;
crane. kúnj. *f* ; lamḍhiṇg. *m* ;
crow. káṇ. *m* ; kauṇ. *m* ; kág. *m* ; kuá. *m* ; kauá. *m* ;
cuckoo. bambíhá. *m* ;
dabchick. ḍubkú. *m* ; jalkukkaṛ. *m* ; murgábí. *f* ;
dove, ring. ghuggí. *f* ;
dove, turtle, brown. ṭoṭrú. *m* ;
duck, domesticated. batakh. *f* ; batkhá. *m* ;
duck, wild. murgábí. *f* ; murgráí. *f* ;
duck, Brahmani. maggh. *m* ;
duck, red crested pochard. ratbá. *m* ;
eagle. ukáb. *m* ;
egret. baglá. *m* ;
falcon. lagaṛ. *m* ; jarrá. *m* ;
flamingo. lamḍhiṇg. *m* ;
goose, domesticated. batakh. *f* ; batkhá. *m* ;
goose, wild. maggh. *m* ;
goshawk. báz. *m* ;
grouse. bhatittar. *m* ; bakhtittar. *m* ;
guinea fowl, tittarí. *f* ; sometimes chikor. *m* ;
hawk. turmatí. *f* ; shikrá. *m* ; báj. *m* ; báz. *m* ;
hawk under a year old, that has not been hunted. chuj. *m* ;
hen. kukkṛí. *f* ;
heron, pond. baglá. *m* ;
heron, grey and larger. waḍḍá baglá. *m* ; naṛí. *f* ; ḍhiṇg. *m* ;
hoopoe. chakkí ráh. *m* ;
ibis, black and white. bozá. *m* ; bojá. *m* ;
jay, blue. cháṇ. *m* ; garaṛ. *m* ; laláran. *m* ;
kestrel. chuhe már. *m* ;
king crow. kál kaṛichchí. *f* ; kál kalichchí. *f* ;
king fisher. machchí már. *m* ;
kite. ill. *m* ;
koel. koel. *m* ; kol. *m* ;
lapwing. ṭaṭaulí. *f* ;
lark. chanḍol. *m* ;
merlin. turmatí. *f* ; turmchí. *f* ;
minivet. lál. *m* ; surkh. *m* ;
myna. lállí. *f* ; lálṛí. *f* ; shárká. *m* ; shárak *m* ;
nightjar. chapákhí. *f* ;
nightingale. bulbul. *f* ;
owl. ullú. *m* ;
owlet. bilbataurí. *f* ;
paddy bird. baglá. *m* ;
parrot. tottá, *m* ; ratottá. *m* ;
partridge. tittar. *m* ; bhatittar. *m*,
partridge, black. kálá tittar. *m* ;
peacock. mor. *m* ; morní. *f* ;
pigeon. kabútar. *m* ; kabútrí. *f* ;
pigeon, wild green. haryál. *m* ;
pigeon, fantail. lakká. *m* ;
pigeon, tumbler, lotáṇ. *m* ;
quail. baterá. *m* ;
raven. pahárí káṇ. *m* ; ḍhoḍḍaṛ kán. *m* ; ḍhoḍḍarí. *f* ;
robin, and other small birds. piddí. *f* ;
sandpiper. kakaúá. *m* ;
shrike. sioṇ chiṛí. *f* ; soṇ chiṛí. *f* ;
snipe. chahá. *m* ;
sparrow. chiṛiá. *m* ; chiṛí. *f* ;
sparrow, young. chaṛúnggaṛí. *f* ;
sparrow hawk. laṭorá. *m* ;
starling. tilyár. *m* ;
stork. lamḍhíng. *m* ;
swallow. abábíl. *f* ;
teal. karaṛí. *f* ;
tern. jhiúrí. *f* ;
tomtit. pidrá. *m* ; piddá. *m* ;
treepie. bámbíhá. *m* ;
turkey. perú. *m* ;
vulture. girjh. *m* ; chiṭṭí ill. *f* ; baggí ill. *f* ; dhaulí ill. *f* ; ganjá. *m* ; súṇdá. *m* ;
wagtail. mamolá. *m* ;
woodpecker. tokká. *m* ; tarkhán. *m* ;
weaver bird. bayyá. *m* ; bayyaṛá. *m* ;

BIRDCATCHER. *N.*
chiṛimár. *m* ;

BIRD'S NEST. *N.*
áhlaná. *m* ; waserá. *m* ;

BIRTH, *N.*
janam. *m* ; jaram. *m* ; paidaish. *f* ;

BIRTHDAY, *N.*
janam din. *m* ;
BIRTH PLACE, *N.*
janam bhúmí. *f* ;
BIRTHRIGHT, *N.*
wirsá. *m* ;
BISCUIT, *N.*
biskut. *m* ; kulchá. *m* ;
native biscuit. khatáí. *f* ;
BISECT, TO, *V. T.*
adho adh karná ; do hisse banáuná ;
BISHOP, *N.*
Lát Bishap Sáhib. *m* ;
Bishop in chess. filá. *m* ;
BIT, *N.*
1. a fragment. ṭukṛá. *m* ;
2. a piece of bread. burkí. *f* ; ṭukkar. *m* ;
3. a mouthful. giráhí. *f* ;
4. bit for a horse. dahánú. *m* ; kaṛiálá. *m* ;
5. has iron pieces fixed on mouth pieces, a very cruel bit indeed. kanḍiálá. *m* ;
BITCH, *N.*
kuttí. *f* ;
BITE, TO, *V. T.*
waḍḍhná ; chak márná ; ḍanḍ márná ;
1. of a horse. chak márná ; muṇh márná ;
2. of a dog. waḍḍhná ; laṛná ;
3. of a mosquito. laṛná ;
4. of a snake. laṛná ;
BITE, *N.*
gáchí. *f* ;
of an animal. chak. *m* ;
BITING, *N.*
gáchí. *f* ;
BITTER, *A.*
kauṛá ; kuṛangá ;
not very bitter. kasailá ;
BITTERLY, *Adv.*
saṛke ; ḍhaiṇ márke ;
to weep bitterly. uchchí uchchí roná ; bhabháṇ márke roná ;
BITTERNESS, *N.*
kauṛittaṇ. *f* ;
BITUMEN, *N.*
gáṛá. *m* ;
BIVOUAC, *N.*
fauj dá paṛáo. *m* ;

BLAB, TO, *V. T.*
kann bharná ;
BLABBER, *N.*
chugalkhor. *m* ; kann khor. *m* ;
BLACK, *A.*
kálá ; siáh ;
used of animals only. lákhá ;
BLACKBOARD, *N.*
borḍ. *m* ;
BLACKEN, TO, *V. T.*
1. to make black. kálá karná ;
2. to defame. niṇdiá karná ; badnám karná ; tohmat láuní ;
BLACKGUARD, *N.*
mushtandá. *m* ; badmásh. *m* ; sharír. *m* ; luchchá. *m*
BLACKING, *N.*
siáhí. *f* ;
BLACKMAIL, *N.*
waḍḍhí. *f* ;
BLACKMAIL, TO, *V. T.*
lekhá láuná ;
BLACKNESS, *N.*
siáhí. *f* ;
especially from soot. kálak. *f* ;
BLACKSMITH, *N.*
lohár. *m* ;
BLADDER, *N.*
bhukánná. *m* ;
BLADE, *N.*
1. of a knife. phal. *m* ;
2. of grass. gháh dá paṭṭhá. *m* ;
BLAIN, *N.*
1. soft blister. chhállá. *m* ;
2. hard blister. chandí. *f* ; bhaurí. *f* ;
BLAMEABLE, *A.*
malámat de laiq ;
BLAME, TO, *V. T.*
líkáṇ láuná ; shikayat karní ; ilzám láuná ; aib láuná ; bhaṇḍná ; dosh dená OR láuná ; dokh dená ; ḍhiṭṭh karná ;
BLAME, *N.*
ilzám. *m* ; shikayat. *f* ; dosh. *m* ; gilá. *m* ; lík. *f* ; dokh. *m* ; jhiṛak. *f* ; ḍhíṭṭh. *f* ;
BLAMELESS, *A.*
begunáh ; bequsur ; beilzám ; bedosh ; rihá ;
BLAMELESSNESS, *N.*
bequsurí. *f* ; begunáhí. *f* ; bedoshí. *f* ;

BLAMEWORTHY, *A.*
malámat de laiq ;
BLANCH, TO, *V. T.*
sufed OR chiṭṭá karná ;
BLAND, *A.*
narm ; mulaim ; komal ; milauṛá ; milápaṛá ;
BLANDISHMENT, *N.*
chochlá. *m* ; nakhrá. *m* ; choj. *m* ; leṭ peṭ. *f* ; hej. *m* ;
BLANDNESS, *N.*
narmí. *f* ;
BLANK, *A.*
1. empty ; ḳhálí ;
2. clear. sáf ;
3. blank paper. korá. *m* ;
BLANKET, *N.*
kambal. *m* ;
1. long cotton blanket. khes. *m* ;
2. long light woolen blanket. loí. *f* ;
3. expensive camel's hair blanket. dhussá. *m* ;
4. horse blanket. bhúrá. *m* ; jhull. *m* ;
5. for horse's head and neck. gardaní. *f* ;
BLARNEY, *N.*
chochlá. *m* ; leṭí peṭí. *f* ;
BLARNEY, TO, *V. T.*
phuláuná ; leṭ phaṛná ;
BLASPHEME, TO, *V. T.*
kufr bakná ; kufr dá kalimá muṇh-oṇ kaḍḍhná ;
BLASPHEMER, *N.*
kufr bakaṇwálá. *m* ; káfar. *m* ;
BLASPHEMOUS, *A.*
kufr dí gal ;
BLASPHEMY, *N.*
kufr. *m* ; kufr dá kalmá. *m* ; dur-bachan. *m* ;
BLAST, *N.*
1. storm. hanerí. *f* ; anherí. *f* ;
2. blast of a storm. jhoká. *m* ; bullá. *m* ;
3. sound of a tempest. anherí dí shúkar. *f* ;
BLASTED, TO BE, *V. I.*
kamláuná ; jhuls jáná ;
BLATANT, *A.*
shorí ; khappí ;
BLAZE, TO, *V. I.*
bhakhná ; bhaṛakná ; balná ; bhakh páiná ;
BLAZE, *N.*
1. blaze. bhaṛak. *f* ; bhabháká. *m* ;
2. just burning. láṭ. *f* ;
3. fire spread out. lamb. *m* ;
4. blazing straw, etc. muáṭaṛá. *m* ;
BLAZING FIRE, *N.*
bhámbaṛ. *m* ;
BLAZON, TO, *V. T.*
ḍhanḍhorá dená ;
BLEACH, TO, *V. T.*
chiṭṭá karná ;
BLEAK, *A.*
wirán ; ujáṛ ; sunsán ;
BLEAKNESS, *N.*
wiránagí. *f* ;
BLEARY, *A.*
chuchchá ; chuṇdhá ; chipṛá ; ghutt mutt ; chunhá ;
a bleareyed man. chipṛú. *m* ;
BLEAT, TO, *V. T.*
mamiáuná ; miáṇkná ; bhaiṇ bhaiṇ karná ;
BLEAT, *N.*
mamiáná. *m* ; bhaiṇ. *f* ;
BLEED, TO, *V. I.*
lahú wagná ; ratt wagná ;
to pass blood. lahú áuná ;
BLEED, TO, *V. T.*
lahú kaḍḍhná ;
BLEEDING, *A.*
lahú luhán ; lahú luhák ;
bleeding at the nose. naksír. *f* ;
BLEMISH, *N.*
nuqs. *m* ; dág. *m* ; dos. *m* ; aib. *m* ; dokh. *m* ; káṇ. *f* ; augan. *m* ; kalaṇk. *m* ; augún. *m* ; kasar. *m* ; khoṭ. *f* ;
BLENCH, TO, *V. I.*
jhijakná ; see SHRINK.
BLESS, TO, *V. T.*
barakat dení ; asísáṇ dení ;
BLESSED, *A.*
mubárik ; dhann ; bhágwán ; see HAPPY.
BLESSEDNESS, *N.*
ḳhushhálí. *f* ; anaṇdtái. *f* ; bhág-wání. *f* ; ḳhushí. *f* ;

BLESSING, *N.*
1. benediction. barakat. *f ;* asís. *f ;* dhann. *m ;* dúá. *f ;* barakat dá kalimá. *m ;* púranbhág. *m ;* ashírbád. *m ;*
2. something good. padárath. *m ;*
BLIGHT. *N.*
1. caused by insects. kuṇgí. *f ;*
2. caused by drought. soká. *m ;*
BLIGHTED, TO BE, *V. I.*
kuṇggí laggní ;
BLIND, *A.*
annhá ; manákhá ;
blind in one eye. káná ;
BLIND, TO, *V. T.*
1. to make blind. annhá karná ;
2. to conceal. lukáuná; chhipáuná ;
BLINDLY, *Adv.*
besoche samjhe ; biná soche samjhe ;
BLINKING, *N.*
akkh jhamkaní. *f ;*
BLINKER, *N.*
khopá. *m ;*
BLISS, *N.*
ḳhushí. *f ;* anaṇd. *m ;* sukh. *m ;* ḳhushhálí. *f ;* partáp. *m ;* anaṇdtái. *f ;* bhágwání. *f ;*
BLISSFUL, *A.*
ḳhush ; rázi. *f ;* anaṇdí; magan ; bhágwán ;
BLISSFULLY, *Adv.*
ḳhush hoke ; anaṇd hoke ; ḳhushí nál ;
BLISSFULNESS, *N.*
ḳhushí. *f ;* anaṇd. *m ;* anaṇdtái. *f ;*
BLISTER, *N.*
chhállá. *m ;* gadd. *m ;* see BLAIN.
BLISTER, TO, *V. I.*
chhállá páiná ; gadd páiní ;
to open a blister. chhállá phehná ;
BLITHE, *A.*
ḳhush ; rází ; magan ;
BLITHELY, *Adv.*
ḳhushí nál ; ḳhush hoke ; chá nál ; jam jam ;
BLITHENESS, *N.*
ḳhushí. *f ;* anaṇdtái. *f ;*
BLITHESOME, *A.*
anaṇdí ; ḳhush ; rází ;
BLIZZARD, *N.*
jhakkaṛ. *m ;* tufán. *m ;*

BLOCK, TO, *V. T.*
band karná ; rokná ; dáṭná ;
BLOCK, *N.*
rok. *f ;* rukáwat. *f ;* ḍakká. *m ;*
BLOCKADE, TO, *V. T.*
gherná ; gherá páuná ;
BLOCKADE, *N.*
gherá. *m ;*
BLOCKHEAD, *N.*
ullú. *m ;* aql dá annhá. *m ;* anárí. *m ;* uṭṭ. *m ;* aql dá púrá. *m ;* dhaggá. *m ;* ghaṭṭá. *m ;*
BLOOD, *N.*
lahú, *m ;* ḳhun. *m ;* ratt. *f ;*
BLOOD LETTING, *N.*
fassad. *m ;*
BLOODSHOT, *A.*
lál ;
BLOODSTAIN, *N.*
lahú dá dág. *m ;*
BLOODSUCKER, *N.*
jok. *f ;*
BLOODTHIRSTY, *A.*
lahú dá taháyá ; ḳhun dá piásá ;
BLOODY, *A.*
lahú luhán ;
BLOOM, TO, *V. I.*
khiṛná ; phullná ; ṭahikná ; kalíáṇ nikalná ;
BLOOM, *N.*
phull. *m ;*
BLOOMING, *A.*
phuldár ;
BLOSSOM, *N.*
phul, *m ;* kalí. *f ;*
BLOSSOM, TO, *V. T.*
phul páiná ; khiṛná ; see BLOOM.
BLOT, *N.*
dág. *m ;* dhabbá. *m ;* phuṭkaṛí. *f ;*
BLOT OUT, TO, *V. T.*
meṭná ; miṭáuná ; miṭá dená ; púṇjhaná ;
to cross out. kalam pherní ;
BLOTCH, *N.*
dág. *m ;*
on the body. lassaṇ. *m ;*
BLOTTING PAPER, *N.*
siyáhíchaṭ. *m ;* sháhíchús. *m ;* blátiṇ. *m ;*

BLOUSE, *N*.
1. small. cholí. *f*;
2. longer. jhaggí. *f*;
3. still longer. kuṛtí *f*;
BLOW, *N*.
1. a hitting. hurá. *m*; chaper. *f*; ghusann. *m*; hujj. *f*; dhappá. *m*; dhaul. *m*; mukkí. *f*; már. *f*;
2. a calamity. balá. *f*; honí. *f*; musíbat. *f*;
BLOW, TO, *V. T.*
phúk mární;
1. to blow up. uḍá dená;
2. to blow a musical instrument. wajáná;
3. to blow the bellows. dhaungkná;
4. wind blowing. wá waggní; jhullná;
5. to blow the nose. sunkaná;
BLOWPIPE, *N*.
phúkní. *f*;
BLUBBER, TO, *V. T.*
roná; hanjú waháuná; kurláuná; wilkná;
BLUDGEON, *N*.
ḍaṇḍá. *m*; soṭṭá. *m*;
BLUE, *A*.
1. light blue. halká níllá;
2. sky blue. asmání níllá;
3. dark blue. guṛhá níllá;
BLUEBOTTLE, *N*.
makkh. *m*; billá makkh. *m*;
BLUFF, TO, *V. T.*
dhokhá dená;
BLUNDER, *N*.
bhull chukk. *f*; chukk. *f*; bhulekhá. *m*; bholí. *f*; bholá. *m*;
BLUNDER, TO, *V. T.*
bhull jáná; bhulekhá laggná; khuṇjhná; ghuss jáná; ukk jáná;
BLUNDERBUSS, *N*.
baṇdukṛá. *m*;
BLUNDERER, *N*.
sudáí. *m*; ghutthú; *m*;
BLUNT, *A*.
kuṇḍ; maṭṭhá; khuṇḍhá;
BLUR, *N*.
1. a stain or blot. dág. *m*;
2. haze. gahir. *f*; dhuṇd. *f*; dhuṇḍúkár. *m*;
BLUR, TO, *V. T.*
dhuṇḍhlá karná;
BLUSH, *N*.
lállí. *f*;
BLUSH, TO, *V. I.*
gallháṇ te lállí áuní; múṇh lál honá;
to blush from anger or excitement. lál pílá honá; lohí honá;
BLUSTER, *N*.
shekhí. *f*; ákaṛ. *f*; phauṛ. *m*; see BOAST.
BLUSTER, TO, *V. T.*
shekhí mární; ákaṛná; see TO BOAST.
BLUSTERER, *N*.
laṛáká. *m*; palálí. *m*;
BOAR, *N*.
sur. *m*; úṇdhá. *m*; úṇhdá. *m*; bhaiṛá. *m*;
BOAR'S TUSK, *N*.
sur dá huḍḍ. *m*;
BOARD, *N*.
phaṭṭá. *m*; takhtá. *m*;
BOARD, TO, *V. T.*
berí te charhná;
BOAST, *N*.
shekhí. *f*; gappáṇ. *f*; gapp shapp. *f*; palál, *m*; tár. *f*; phauṛ. *m*; phúṇ phúṇ. *f*;
BOAST, TO, *V. T.*
shekhí mární; dam márná; apná rág gáuná; garbná; gap mární; taṛ taṛ karní; baṛíáṇ galláṇ karní; phúṇ phúṇ karná; waḍḍe bol bolná; phauṛ karná;
BOASTER, *N*.
gappí. *m*; palálí. *m*; ḍhakárí. *m*; gappáṇ. *f*;
BOASTFUL, *A*.
gachchí; shekhí khor;
BOASTING, *N*.
ḍhakár. *m*; ḍhaṇkár. *m*; phauṛ. *m*; gapp. *f*; gaṛapp-chaṛapp. *f*; ghamaṇḍ. *m*; gapp shaṛapp. *f*;
BOAT, *N*.
1. small. machwá. *m*; berí, *f*;
2. large. beṛa. *m*;
BOATMAN, *N*.
malláh. *m*; maihr. *m*; wáṇjhí. *m*; máṇjhí. *m*; háṇjí. *m*;

BODICE, *N.*
jhaggí. *f*; cholí. *f*; beur. *m*; kurtí. *f*; see BLOUSE.
BODY, *N.*
badan. *m*; sarír. *m*; piṇḍá *m*; jism. *m*; tan. *m*; jussá. *m*; deh. *f*; dhaṛ. *f*;
a dead body. loth. *f*; maiyat. *f*;
BOG, *N.*
jillhan. *f*; dhasaṇ. *m*; jhill. *m*; khobha. *m*;
BOGEY, *N.*
bhutṇá. *m*; jin. *m*; hauá. *m*; dáin. *m*;
BOGUS, *A.*
khoṭṭá; jáhlí; banautí; naklí;
BOIL, *N.*
1. small boil. phimhní. *f*;
2. large boil. phoṛá. *m*;
3. abscess. gaṛ. *m*;
BOIL, TO, *V. T.*
ubbálná; káṛhná; ubbál dená; tal suṭṭná;
BOIL, TO, *V. I.*
ubbalná; kaṛhná;
BOILED, *A.*
kaṛhiyá hoyá;
half boiled. addh rijjhá;
BOILER, *N.*
deg. *f*; karáhá. *m*;
BOILING, *A.*
khauldá khauldá; ubbaldá ubbaldá;
1. boiling water. ubbaldá ubbaldá pání. *m*;
2. hot water. tattá pání. *m*;
BOISTEROUS, *A.*
shorí;
BOLD, *A.*
diler; dilwálá; takṛa; bedhaṛak; dilaur; bahádur; variám; hauslewálá;
BOLDFACED, *A.*
belajjá; beháyá; besharm;
BOLDLY, *Adv.*
dilerí nál; sher hoke; bedhaṛak; waḍḍí sakhtí nál; naḍar hoke;
BOLDNESS, *N.*
dilerí. *f*; himmat. *f*; dilaurí. *f*; wariámgí. *f*; dalelí. *f*;
BOLSTER, *N.*
sarháná. *m*;
BOLT, *N.*
billí. *f*; chitkaní. *f*;
BOLT, TO, *V. T.*
1. to lock. billí láuní; band karná;
2. to run away. bhaj jáná; nas jáná;
3. to gulp down. haṛapp karná; haṛapp gaṛapp kháná;
BOMB, *N.*
bamb dá golá. *m*; golá. *m*;
BOMBARD, TO, *V. T.*
golá chaláuná OR márná;
BOND, *N.*
1. agreement. qarár. *m*; likhat. *f*; qarárnámá. *m*; tamassak. *m*; ashṭám. *m*;
2. that which binds. bandhan. *m*;
BONDAGE, *N.*
gulámí. *f*;
BONDMAID, *N.*
gollí. *f*; dássí. *f*; launḍí. *f*;
BONDMAN, *N.*
gulám. *m*; gollá. *m*; dás. *m*; bardá. *m*;
BONE, *N.*
haḍḍí. *f*; haḍḍ. *m*;
BONESPAVIN, *N.*
haḍḍá. *m*;
BONFIRE, *N.*
bhámbaṛ. *m*; bhámṛí,. *f*;
BONUS, *N.*
málí. *f*; inám. *m*;
BOOK, *N.*
kitáb. *f*; pothí. *f*; pustak. *m*;
1. account book for daily sales for cash. rokuṛ. *f*;
2. ledger. behí. *f*; wehí. *f*;
3. account book for cash or credit sales. suhar. *f*;
4. 1st and 2nd Gurmukhi Readers. guṭká. *m*;
BOOKBINDER, *N.*
jildband. *m*;
BOOKBINDING, *N.*
jildbandí. *f*;
BOOKCASE, *N.*
almárí. *f*;
BOOK KEEPER, *N.*
muním. *m*;
BOOK KEEPING, *N.*
hisáb kitáb. *f*;

BOOK SELLER, *N.*
kutub farosh. *m ;*
BOON, *N.*
baḳhshish. *f ;* mihrbání. *f ;* pún dán. *m ;* gún. *m ;*
BOOR, *N.*
gaṇwár. *m ;*
BOORISH, *A.*
jangalí ; hoshá ; see RUDE.
BOORISHNESS, *N.*
gaṇwárpuṇ. *m ;* beadabí. *f ;*
BOOT, *N.*
búṭ. *m ;* juttí. *f ;*
BOOTH, *N.*
chhappar. *m ;* jhugghí. *f ;* chhapprí. *f ;*
BOOTMAKER, *N.*
mochí. *m ;*
BOOTY, *N.*
luṭṭ. *f ;* luṭṭ dá mál. *m ;*
BORAX, *N.*
suhágá. *m ;*
BORDER, *N.*
1. of land. hadd. *f ;* banná. *m ;* kinárá. *m ;*
2. border of cloth tacked to edge of garment. sanjáf. *f ;* kor. *f ;*
3. border of a garment. jhálar. *f ;* pallúṛá. *m ;*
4. margin of a page. kanní. *f ;*
BORE, TO, *V. T.*
1. to annoy. sir khapáuná ; dikk karná ; akáuná ;
2. to pierce. chhek painá, chhedná ; vinnhná ; morí karní ;
BORING, *N.*
vinnhái. *f ;* chhidwái. *f ;*
BORN, TO BE, *V. I.*
paidá honá ; jammná ; janam dhárná ;
BORROW, TO, *V. T.*
udhár lainá ; qarz chukkná ; hudár lainá ;
BORROWED, *A.*
udhárá ;
BORROWER, *N.*
1. of money. hudár lainwálá. *m ;* qarzái. *m ;* sámí. *m ;*
2. of things. maṇgtá. *m ;*
BOSH, *N.*
wáhiyát galláṇ. *f ;* fujúl galláṇ. *f ;* see BABBLE.
BOSOM, *N.*
hikk. *f ;*
bosom friend. laṇgoṭiá. *m ;* laṇgoṭiá yár. *m ;* gur yár. *m ;* parm mittar. *m ;* kháskí yár. *m ;*
BOTH, *A.*
doweṇ ; doháṇ ; dohíṇ ;
both of them. doweṇ de doweṇ ;
BOTHER, *N.*
dikk. *m ;* taklíf. *f ;* aukkh. *f ;*
BOTHER, TO, *V. T.*
dikk karná ; aukkhíáṇ karní ; chheṛná ; satáuná ; kechal karní ; see ANNOY.
BOTHERER, *N.*
taklíf denwálá. *m ;* dokhí. *m ;* dokhaṇ. *f ;* aukkhiáṇ karnwálá. *m ;*
BOTTLE, *N.*
boḍal. *f ;* sísí. *f ;*
BOTTOM, *N.*
thallá. *m ;* tháh. *m ;*
BOTTOMLESS, *A.*
atháh ; ih dá tháh koí nahíṇ ;
BOUGH, *N.*
ṭáhná. *m ;* see BRANCH.
BOULDER, *N.*
patthar. *m ;* waṭṭá. *m ;* patthar waṭṭá. *m ;*
BOUNCE, TO, *V. I.*
kuddná ; bhurkná ; ubbharná ;
BOUND, *N.*
chhál. *f ;* tapp. *m ;* dakk. *m;* tappí. *f ;*
BOUND, *P. P.*
baddhá hoyá ;
BOUND, TO, *V. I.*
kuddná ; tappná ; chhál mární ; dhurlí mární ;
BOUND, TO BE, *V. I.*
bannhiá jána ;
BOUND UP, TO, *V. I.*
uchchhalná ;
BOUNDARY, *N.*
hadd. *m ;* kanárá. *m ;* hadd banná. *m ;*
1. boundary of a field. waṭṭ. *f ;* banná. *m ;* banná channá *m ;*
2. boundary pillar. ṭhaḍḍá. *m ;* munára. *m ;*
BOUNDLESS, *A.*
aṇgint ; beaṇt ; beoṛak ; behadd ; haddon-waddh ;

BOUNTEOUS, *A.*
dilwálá ; kirpál ;
BOUNTIFULNESS, *N.*
dát. *f ;*
BOUQUET, *N.*
phuláṇ dá guchchhá. *m ;*
BOVINE, *A.*
dhagge jehá ;
BOW, *N.*
kamáṇ. *f ;* gulel. *f ;*
1. bow and arrows. tír kamáṇ. *f ;*
2. bowstring. chillá. *m ;*
3. bow for cotton carding. piṇjan. *m ;*
4. bow of a violin. gaj. *m ;*
5. to draw a bow. chillá jharáuná.
6. rain bow. guḍḍe guḍḍe dí píṇgh; *f ;*
BOW, TO, *V.T.*
1. to salute anyone. salám dená ; parnám karná ; sir jhukáuná ; matthá tekná ; hatth bannhke salám dená ; dhanwat karná; sís nimáuná ;
2. to bow in worship. godde nawáuná ; sijdá karná ;
BOWELS, *N.*
ándríáṇ. *f ;*
BOWL, *N.*
chilamchí. *f ;*
1. bowl of a huqqa. ṭoppí. *f ;*
2. a cup. piyálá. *m ;*
3. brass cup or glass. gílás. *m ;*
4. earthenware cup or bowl. ṭhuṭhí. *f ;* ṭhuṭhá. *m ;*
5. bason of baked clay. daurá. *m ;* baṭhal. *m ;*
6. shallow brass drinking vessel. chhanná. *m ;*
BOW LEGGED, *A.*
ḍuḍḍá báṇḍá ; see BANDY LEGGED.
BOWMAN, *N.*
tírandáj *m ;*
BOWSTRING, *N.*
chillá. *m ;* táṇt. *f ;*
BOX, *N.*
sanduq. *m ;* sanduqṛí. *f ;* peṭí. *f ;*
1. very small. ḍabbí. *f ;*
2. steel trunk. ṭarank. *m ;*

BOY, *N.*
muṇḍá. *m ;* laṛká. *m ;* kákká. *m ;* níṇgar. *m ;* játak. *m ;* chhohrá, *m ;* chhokrá. *m ;* niáná. *m ;*
1. boys. muṇḍe khuṇḍe. *m ;*
2. term of endearment. bíbá. *m ;*
BOYHOOD, *N.*
laṛakpan. *m ;* bálakpan. *m ;*
BRACELET, *N.*
chuṛí. *f ;* gokhrú. *m ;* kaṛá. *m ;* baṇggrí. *f ;* baṇgguri. *f ;* kaṇg. *m ;* waṇgg. *m ;* pauṇhchí. *f ;*
BRACES, *N.*
wadhar. *m ;*
BRACKEN, *N.*
jháṛíáṇ. *f ;* jangal. *m ;*
BRACKET, *N.*
dawálgír. *m ;*
BRACKISH, *A.*
khárá ; khárí ; kauṛá ; nimkín ;
BRACKISHNESS, *N.*
khár. *m ;* nimkíní. *f ;*
BRAD, *N.*
brinjí. *f ;*
BRAG, *N.*
phauṛ. *m ;* gappáṇ. *f ;* palál. *m ;* see BOAST.
BRAG, TO, *V. T.*
gapp márná ; garbná ; see TO BOAST.
BRAGGART, *N.*
ḍhakárí. *m ;* gappí. *m ;* gappaurí. *m ;* see BOASTER.
BRAIDING, *N.*
guhaj. *f ;*
gold braiding. tillá. *m ;*
BRAIN, *N.*
bhejjá. *m ;* ḍamák. *m ;*
BRAINLESS, *A.*
beaql ; bewuqúf ; jáhil;
BRAKE VAN, *N.*
brek. *m ;*
BRAMBLE, *N.*
ḍhíṇgar. *m ;* ḍhíṇgarí. *f ;* kaṇḍeáṇwálí jháṛí. *f ;*
BRAN, *N.*
1. of gram. súṛhí. *f ;*
2. of wheat. chháṇ. *f ;* súṛhá. *m ;*
BRANCH, *N.*
1. of a tree. ṭáhní. *f ;* ḍálí. *f ;* chhamak. *f ;* shushak. *f ;* laggar. *f ;*
2. of a river. pháṇṭ. *m ;* shákk. *m ;* chharhá. *m ;*

BRAND, *N.*
ḍambh. *m*; dág. *m*;
small mark on forehead. kalaṇk. *m*; tilak. *m*, H;

BRAND, TO, *V. T.*
dág láná; ḍambh dená; ḍambh láuná;

BRANDY, *N.*
brándí sharáb. *m*;

BRASS, *N.*
pittal. *m*;

BRASS CUP, *N.*
pittal dá kaṭorá. *m*;
brass glass. pittal dá gilás. *m*;

BRASS WORKER, *N.*
ṭhaṭherá. *m*; kaserá. *m*; ṭhaṭhiárá. *m*;

BRAVADO, *N.*
shekhí. *f*; gapp. *f*; see BOASTING.

BRAVE, *A.*
diler; dilaur; diláwar, tagṛá; takkṛá; himmatí; bahádur; variám; surmáṇ;

BRAVELY, *Adv.*
dilerí nál; bahádurí nál;

BRAVERY, *N.*
dilerí. *f*; himmat. *f*; hausilá. *m*; dalelí. *f*; diláwarí. *f*; dilaurí. *f*; surbirtá. *f*; jigará. *m*; wariámgí. *f*;

BRAVO, *Exclam.*
shábásh; achchhá; shábáse; balle balle; shábá; dhann;

BRAWL, *N.*
jhagṛá. *m*; fasád. *f*; daṇgá fasád. *f*; laṛáí. *f*; rattá. *m*;

BRAWL TO, *V. T.*
jhagṛá ragṛá karná;

BRAWNY, *A.*
moṭṭa tázá; tagṛá; takkṛá; jorwálá; ṭhullhá;

BRAY, *N.*
hiṇkáṭ. *m*;

BRAY, TO, *V. T.*
hiṇkaná.

BRAZEN, *A.*
beháyá; belajj; besharm; ḍhíṭh; gustáḳh; belajjá;

BRAZIER, *N.*
ṭhaṭherá. *m*; kaserá. *m*; ṭhaṭhiárá. *m*;

BREACH, *N.*
1. separation. wichhoṛá. *m*;
2. hole. morí. *f*; mogh. *m*; chhek. *m*;

BREAD, *N.*
roṭí. *f*; manní. *f*;
1. stale bread. behí roṭí. *f*
2. new bread. sajjarí roṭí. *f*;
3. English bread. dabal roṭí. *f*;

BREADTH, *N.*
chauṛáí. *f*; pet. *m*;
1. breadth of cloth. paṭṭ. *m*;
2. breadth of a river. pát. *m*;
3. a hand's breadth. giṭh bhar;

BREAK, *N.*
khaṇḍan. *m*;
1. dawn. dhammí velá. *m*;
2. time of morning twilight. muhánjlá. *m*; ghusmusá. *m*; jhusmusrá. *m*;
3. break of day. sohjalá. *m*; sohjará. *m*; sawerá. *m*; taṛká. *m*;
4. early morning. waḍḍá velá. *m*;

BREAK, TO, *V. T.*
ṭorná; bhanná; taroṛná; bhan suṭṭná; khaṇḍná; toṛ táṛ dená; to cause another to break. bhanáuná;
1. to break a promise. qaul thoṛ hárná; qaul qarár bhan dená;
2. to break into a house. sannh mární;
3. to break into pieces. ṭoṭe ṭoṭe karná; chúr karná; chúrná; chakná chúr karná;

BREAK TO, *V. I.*
bhajj jáná; ṭuṭná; ṭuṭ phuṭ jáná; as glass. bhurná;

BREAKAGE, *N.*
ṭuṭ. *f*; khaṇḍan. *m*;

BREAKFAST, *N.*
sawere dí roṭí. *f*; házarí. *f*;
any thing eaten early in the morning. nástá. *m*;

BREAST, *N.*
hikk. *f*;

BREATH, *N.*
sáh. *n*; sáṇs. *m*; dam. *m*; suás. *m*; prán. *m*;
1. to breathe one's last. dam chhaḍḍná;
2. to be out of breath. hafh jáná;

BREATHING, *N.*
sáh. *m* ;
BREECHES, *N.*
kachchh. *f* ;
BREED *N.*
ját. *f* ;
BREED, TO, *V. T.*
bachchá dená ;
for a cow. súṇná ;
BREEDING, *N.*
1. deportment. chál ḍhál. *f* ; bol chál. *m* ; lachchhan. *m* ; wartáo. *m* ;
2. training. tálím. *f* ;
BREEZE, *N.*
wá. *f* ; pauṇ. *m* ; wáu. *f* ;
BRETHREN, *N.*
bhaí. *m* ; bhará. *m* ; bhaíchárá. *m* ; barádarí. *f* ; aṇgsák. *m* ;
BREVITY, *N.*
kamí. *f* ;
BREW, TO, *V. T.*
sharáb kaḍḍhná ;
BRIAR, *N.*
paṇgá. *m* ; kaṇḍḍá. *m* ; malhá. *m* ; khittí. *f* ;
BRIBE, *N.*
waḍḍhí. *f* ; waḍḍí. *f* ;
BRIBE, TO, *V. T.*
waḍḍhí OR waḍḍí deni ; chándí dí juttí mární ;
to take a bribe. waḍḍhí lení OR khání ; hatth rangná ; gapphá milná ;
BRIBERY, *N.*
waḍḍhí. *f* ;
BRICK, *N.*
iṭṭ. *f* ;
1. fire burnt brick. pakkí iṭṭ. *f* ;
2. half burnt brick. pillí iṭṭ. *f* ;
3. sun dried brick. kachchí iṭṭ. *f* ;
4. brickbats, roṛe. *m* ; roṛí. *f* ;
5. brick dust in kiln. kerí. *f* ;
6. pounded brick dust for mortar. surkhí. *f* ;
7. brickkiln, excavated. bhaṭṭhá. *m* ;
8. brick kiln, mound. awá. *m* ;
9. brick maker. patherá. *m* ; baterāh. *m* ;
10. brick mould. sáṇchá. *m* ;
11. bricklayer. ráj. *m* ;
12. brick laying. chinái. *f* ; usárí. *f* ;

BRIDAL PROCESSION. *N.*
janj. *f* ; janet. *m* ;
BRIDE, *N.*
láṛí. *f* ;
BRIDEGROOM, *N.*
láṛá. *m* ; niṇgarchand. *m* ; war. *m* ; dulo. *m* ;
BRIDGE, *N.*
1. large. pul. *m* ;
2. small. pulí. *f* ;
BRIDLE, *N.*
1. headpiece. lagám. *f* ;
2. reins. wág. *f* ; bág. *f* ;
3. camel's bridle. nakel. *f* ;
BRIDLE, TO, *V. T.*
lagám cháṛhní ;
BRIEF, *A.*
duharfí ;
BRIERS. *N.*
jhill. *m* ;
BRIGAND, *N.*
ḍákú. *m* ; luteṛá. *m* ; chor. *m* ; dháṛví. *m* ; ráhmár. *m* ;
BRIGANDAGE, *N.*
chorí. *f* ; ḍáká. *m* ;
BRIGHT, *A.*
chamkílá ; sáf ; ujalá ;
BRIGHTLY, *Adv.*
chamak nál ;
BRIGHTNESS, *N.*
chamak. *f* ; damak. *f* ; chamkáṭ. *f* ; chilak. *f* ; chilkárá. *m* ; chamkárá. *m* ; jhalak. *f* ;
BRILLIANCE, *N.*
jagmag. *f* ; chhab. *f* ; jhalak. *f* ;
BRILLIANT, *A.*
raunaqwálá ; chamkílá ;
to make brilliant. jagmag jagmag karná ;
BRIM, *N.*
kaṇḍhá. *m* ;
up to the brim. dakádak ; múṇhoṇ múṇh ; múṇhá múṇh ;
BRIMFUL, *A.*
múṇhoṇ múṇh ;
BRIMSTONE, *N.*
gaṇdhak. *f* ; gandraf. *f* ;
RBINE, *N.*
khárá pání. *m* ;
BRING, TO, *V. T.*
lai áuná ; le áuná ; dho dená ; dhohṇá ;

1. to bring away. kaḍḍh leáuná;
2. to bring an action against. arzí páuní; nálish karná; dáwá karná;
3. to bring forth, animals. súṇná;
4. to bring a bride home. saheṛná;

BRINJAL, *N*.
batáúṇ. *m*;

BRINK, *N*.
kaṇḍhá. *m*;

BRISK, *A*.
chalák; tagṛá; chust; achpal; uddamí; phurtílá;

BRISKLY, *Adv*.
jaldí; uddam nál; chustí nál; shitábí nál;

BRISKNESS, *N*.
phurtí; chustí. *f*; uddam. *m*; chalákí. *f*;

BRISTLE, *N*.
súr dá bál. *m*;

BRITISH, *N*.
Angrej. *m*;

BRITISH, *A*.
Angrejí;

BRITTLE, *A*.
ṭuṭṭaṇwálá; nájak; bhurbhurá;

BROAD, *A*.
khullhá; chauṛá; moklá; khulá;

BROADISH, *A*.
chureṛá;

BROADCAST TO SOW, *V. T*.
khilárná; bí dená OR suṭṭná; bakherná;

BROADEN, TO, *V. T*.
chauṛá karná; moklá karná; khullhá karná;

BROCADE, *N*.
badlá. *m*;
gold or silver lace. goṭṭá. *m*;

BROCCOLI, *N*.
phulgobí. *f*;

BROIDER, TO, *V. T*.
kasídá kaḍḍhná;

BROIL, *N*.
jhagṛá. *m*; fasád. *f*; takrár. *m*; laṛái. *f*;

BROILED, *P. P*.
bhujjiá hoyá;

BROKEN, *A*.
ṭuṭṭá hoyá; ṭuṭṭá phuṭá;

BROKEN HEARTED, *A*.
udás; dil ṭuṭṭá hoyá; masosiá hoyá;

BROKER, *N*.
dalál. *m*;

BROKERAGE, *N*.
dalálí *f*;

BRONCHITIS, *N*.
purání kaṇgh. *f*;

BRONZE, *N*.
bharat. *m*;

BROOD, *N*.
jholí. *f*;

BROOK, *N*.
nálá. *m*; nadí. *f*;

BROOM, *N*.
jháṛú. *m*; máṇjá. *m*; bauhkar *f*; buhárí. *f*; bahárí. *f*; raṛká. *m*;

BROTH, *N*.
shorá. *m*; shoruá. *m*;

BROTHEL, *N*.
chaklá. *m*;

BROTHER, *N*.
bhará. *m*; bhái. *m*; bharáú. *m*;
1. used only by women and girls. vír. *m*; bír. *m*;
2. stepbrother. matreá bhará. *m*;
3. wife's brother, sálá *m*;
4. sister's husband. bhaníjá. *m*;
5. husband's elder brother. jeṭh. *m*;
6. husband's younger brother. deor. *m*;

BROTHERHOOD, *N*.
barádarí. *f*; bháíchárá. *m*; bhái baṇdí. *f*;

BROW, *N*.
matthá. *m*;
brow of a hill. pahár dí ṭísí. *f*;

BROWBEAT, TO, *V. T*.
ghurakná; akkh wakháuná; akkhíáṇ kaḍḍhní; áne kaḍḍhná; ḍaráuná; ghurákí dení; dhamkáuná;

BROWBEATING, *N*.
ghurákí. *f*; ghurkí. *f*; dhamkí. *f*; dábbá. *m*;

BROWN, *A*.
1. reddish brown. bhurá;
2. dark brown. bhuslá;
3. almond. badámí;

BRUISE, *N.*
satṭ. *f;*
bruise in a metal vessel. chibb. *m;*
BRUISE, TO, *V. T.*
kuṭṭná; phená; dararná; ragarná; miṇdháuná; kuchalná;
BRUISED, TO BE, *V. I.*
saṭṭ laggní; miṇdhá honá;
BRUSH, *N.*
bhuárí. *f;* see BROOM.
for cleaning earthenware vessels. kuchchí. *f;* subbí. *f;*
BRUSH, TO, *V. T.*
jhárná; jhambhná;
BRUSHWOOD, *N.*
ḍhíṇgar. *m;* malhe. *m;* jhárián. *f;* khittí. *f;*
BRUTAL, *A.*
sakht; beráhm; kaṭhor; kabbá;
BRUTALITY, *N.*
sakhtí. *f;* zulm. *m;* beráhmí. *f;*
BRUTE, *N.*
pasú. *m;* ḍaṇggar. *m;*
BRUTISH, *A.*
beráhm; haiṇsiárá; bedard; hatthiárá;
BUBBLE, *N.*
1. large. pání dá bulbulá. *m;*
2. small. burburí. *f;*
BUBO, *N.*
phorá. *m;* waddh. *f;* sunḍá. *m;*
in the armpit. kachhrálí. *f;*
BUCK, *N.*
hiran. *m;*
BUCKET, *N.*
báltí. *f;* ḍol. *m;*
1. leather bucket, drawn up by hand. bokká. *m;*
2. leather bucket, drawn up by bullock. charsá. *m;*
BUCKLE, *N.*
bagsúá. *m;* baksúá. *m;*
BUD, *N.*
kalí. *f;* ḍoḍí. *f;* kúmal. *f;* kúmbal. *f;* kúmali. *f;* kúmbalí. *f;*
BUDGE, TO, *V. I.*
haṭná; ṭalná;
BUFFALO, *N.*
1. male. saṇḍhá. *m;* maiṇháṇ. *m;*
2. female. maj. *f;* majjh. *f;* mahíṇ. *f;* maiṇh. *f;*
3. a wandering bull. málí. *m;*
4. buffaloes generally. maihrú. *m;* mahirú. *m;*
5. young buffalo. jhoṭṭá. *m;* jhoṭṭí. *f;*
6. an old buffalo. kholá. *m;* kholí. *f;*
BUFFET, *N.*
húrá. *m;* chaper. *f;* mukkí. *f;* hujká. *m;*
to be buffeted. bare hujke kháná;
BUFFOON, *N.*
maskará. *m;* mashkará. *m;*
professional. bhaṇḍ. *m;*
BUG, *N.*
máṇgnú. *m;*
BUGBEAR, *N.*
balá. *f;* see BOGEY.
BUGLE, *N.*
túrhí. *f;*
BUILD, TO, *V. T.*
banáuná; usárná; usárí karní;
to build again. murke usárná;
BUILDING, *N.*
makán. *m;*
the act of building. usárá. *m;* usárí. *f;*
BULGE. *N.*
ubhár. *m;*
BULK, *N.*
ḍíl. *m;* ḍíl ḍaul. *m;*
BULKY, *A.*
moṭṭá; waḍḍá; bhárá;
BULL, *N.*
sáṇh. *m;* sáṇdh. *m;*
BULL CALF, *N.*
1. quite young. wachchá. *m;*
2. older. waihrá. *m;* wairká. *m;*
BULLET, *N.*
golí. *f;*
BULLOCK, *N.*
bald. *m;* bauld. *m;* dhaggá. *m;* ḍáṇd. *m;*
a bullock that kicks. chharílá. *m;*
BULRUSH, *N.*
sirkaṇḍá. *m;*
BUMP, *N.*
rorá. *m;* soj. *f;* gilhṭí. *f;*
to get a bump. ror ubharná;
BUNCH, *N.*
guchchhá. *m;*

BUNDLE, *N.*
gathrí. *f;* gaṭṭhá. *m;* bushká. *m;* gaṭṭhaṛ. *m;*
1. of corn. bharí. *f;* pulí. *f;*
2. of grass. pand. *f;*
3. of clothes. buchká. *m;* ganḍhrí. *f;*
4. of books. bastá. *m;*
5. of sugarcane, &c. pulá. *m;* datthá. *m;*
6. of grass slung over shoulder. maṇgará. *m;*
7. of clothes carried by dhobi's bullock. laddá. *m;*
8. of money. gaṭṭh. *m;*

BUNGALOW, *N.*
koṭhí. *f;* banglá. *m;*

BUNGLER, *N.*
beaql ádmí. *m;*

BUNKUM, *N.*
bakwás. *m;* see BABBLE.

BURDEN, *N.*
bhár. *m;* bojh. *m;*

BURDENED, *A.*
bhár heṭh dabbiá hoyá; bhár heṭh nappiá hoyá;

BURDENSOME, *A.*
bhárá; bhárí;

BURGLAR, *N.*
chor. *m;*

BURGLARY, *N.*
sannh. *f;* chorí. *f;*

BURIAL, *N.*
janázá. *m;* M;

BURIAL PROCESSION, *N.*
janázewále. *m;*

BURN, *N.*
sáṛ. *m;* saṛaṇ dá jakham. *m;*

BURN, TO, *V. T.*
sáṛná; bálná; jálná; phuk suṭṭná; jaláuná;

BURN, TO, *V. I.*
saṛ jáná; balná; jalná; lús jáná;

BURNED, *A.*
lúh;

BURNING PLACE, *N.*
marhiáṇ. *f;* masán. *m;* samshán bhúmí. *f;*

BURNISH, TO, *V. T.*
chilkáuná; lishkáuná;

BURNT OFFERING, *N.*
hom. *m;* H;

BURROW, *N.*
1. of a hare. bhohrá. *m;*
2. of other animals. khuḍḍ. *f;* ghurná. *m;*

BURST, TO, *V. I.*
1. of clothes. paṭṭná;
2. of fruit, &c. phutná; phut jáná;
3. of crockery, &c. tuṭṭná; bhaj jáná;
4. to burst into leaf. patthé phutná;
5. for clothes only. chhan jáná;

BURY, TO, *V. T.*
dafn karná; dabb dená; nap dená; gaḍ dená; dafanáuná; dafaná dená;
to cause to be buried. gaḍáuná; dabáuná;

BURIED, TO BE, *V. I.*
dafn honá; dabbná; dabbiá jáná;

BUSH, *N.*
buṭá. *m;* jháṛí. *f;* buṭí. *f;*
1. many bushes. jháṛ. *m;*
2. bushes cut and dried for fuel. ḍhinggar. *m;* khittí. *f;*

BUSINESS, *N.*
kamm. *m;* kamm dhaṇdá. *m;* kár bár. *m;* kár. *m;* kamm káj. *m;* kár gujárí. *f;* láṇjhá. *m;*
business of a wedding. káraj. *m;* káj. *m;*

BUSTARD, *N.*
gurain. *m;*

BUSTLE, *N.*
shor. *m;* raulá. *m;* khap. *m;* dand. *f;* garbharí. *f;* dhumm. *f;* gahimá gahim. *m;* hill jull. *f;*

BUSY, *A.*
lagá hoyá; ruddhiá hoyá; rujjhiá hoyá; kamm vichch laggá hoyá; áhrí;

BUSY, TO BE, *V. I.*
rujjhná; kamm vichch laggá honá;

BUT, *Prep.* & *Conj.*
balak; sagoṇ; par; magar; sagmáṇ;

BUTCHER, *N.*
kasáí. *m;*

BUTLER, *N.*
sardár. *m;*

BUTT, TO, *V. T.*
bhiṛná; matthá bhiṛná; sing márná; dhusná; dhuss márná; ṭakkar láuní OR mární; ḍhuḍh láuná OR márná;
BUTT, OF A GUN, *N.*
hatthá. *m;*
BUTTER, *N.*
makkhan. *m;* makkhani. *f;* clarified butter. gheo. *m;* thaṇḍá. *m;*
BUTTER, TO, *V. T.*
chopaṛná;
BUTTER DISH, *N.*
makkhandán. *m;*
BUTTERFLY, *N.*
bhambírí. *f;* bhaman. *m;*
BUTTER MILK, *N.*
lassí. *f;* lassí lussí. *f;* kangh. *m;*
BUTTING, *N.*
ḍhuḍh. *m;*
BUTTOCK, *N.*
chittaṛ. *m;* chutaṛ. *m;* ḍhúá. *m;* ḍhúhá. *m;* dungá. *m;* dunganí. *f;*
BUTTON, *N.*
bíṛá. *m;*
made of cloth. ghuṇḍí. *f;*
BUTTONHOLE, *N.*
káj. *m;*
BUTTRESS, *N.*
thamm. *m;*
BUY, TO, *V. T.*
mull lainá; kharídná;
BUYER, *N.*
gáhak. *m;* saudá lainwalá. *m;*
BUZZ, TO, *V. I.*
makkhiáṇ bhinkná; bhuṇ bhuṇ karná; bhiṇ bhiṇ karná;
BUZZING, *N.*
gúṇj. *f;*
BY, *Prep.*
duáre; ráhín; wasíle;
BY AND BYE, *Adv.*
ṭhahr ke; thoṛí der de bád; magaroṇ; pichchhe; gharí núṇ; hatt ke; palak núṇ; jará kú núṇ; jhaṭṭ ko núṇ;
BYRE, *N.*
kuṛh. *f;*
BYWAY, *N.*
ráh. *m;* rastá. *m;* dandí. *f;* a village road. páyá. *m;*

C.

CABBAGE, *N.*
gobhí. *f;* band gobhí. *f;* gaṇḍh gobí. *f;*
CABIN, *N.*
koṭhṛí. *f;*
CABLE, *N.*
1. a telegram. tár. *m;*
2. a rope. rassá. *m;* bel. *f;* lajj. *f;*
CABLE, TO, *V. T.*
tár ghallná OR márná OR páuná OR dená;
CACKLE, TO, *V. T.*
kuṛ kuṛ karná; kuṛkuṛáuná;
CACTUS, *N.*
1. flat species. chittar thohar. *f;* nágphalí. *f;*
2. round species. thohar ḍaṇḍá. *m;*
CAGE, *N.*
piṇjrá. *m;* piṇjrí. *f;*
CAGE, TO, *V. T.*
piṇjre vichch wár dená;
CAJOLE, TO, *V. T.*
chukkná; buttá márná OR dená; chálá dená; hatthí cháṛhná; adhe utte láuná; phaláuná;
CAJOLERY, *N.*
buttá. *m;*
CAKE, *N.*
kek. *m;*
1. a rich native cake. málpúrá. *m;* guṇá. *m;*
2. a cake of soap. gáchí. *f;*
CALAMITY, *N.*
balá. *f;* biptá. *f;* garauh *m;* bijj. *f;* ḍobbá sokká. *m;* pheṭṭí. *f;*
CALCULATE, TO, *V. T.*
1. to reckon. hisáb karná OR joṛná; ginná; minná; gin min lená; lekhá lainá;
2. to consider. kíás karní; wichárná; sochná; soch wichár karná; samajh sochná;
3. to calculate time. velá wichárna;

CALCULATION, *N.*
hisáb. *m ;* lekhá. *m ;* gintí. *f ;* see
COMPUTATION.

CALDRON, *N.*
deg. *f ;* degchá. *m ;*
1. somewhat smaller, walṭohá. *m ;*
2. large and shallow; karáhá. *m ;*

CALENDAR, *N.*
jaṇtrí. *f ;* pattrí. *f ;*

CALF, *N.*
1. of a cow. wachchá. *m;* wachchí. *f;*
weṛká. *m ;* waihṛá. *m ;*
2. of four or five months. khírá. *m ;*
3. with two teeth. donddá. *m ;*
4. with four teeth. chaugá. *m ;*
5. with six teeth. chiggá. *m ;*
chhagar. *m ;* chhigar. *m ;*
6. of a buffalo, kaṭṭá. *m ;*
7. of the leg. pinní. *f ;*

CALICO, *N.*
chhíṇt. *f ;*

CALIGRAPHY, *N.*
likháí. *f ;* likhat. *f ;*

CALIPH, *N.*
kalífhá. *m ;*

CALL, *N.*
pukár. *f ;* wáz. *f ;* wáj. *f ;* duháí. *f ;*
lalkárá. *m ;* hák. *f ;* kúk. *f ;*
Muhammadan call to prayers.
báng. *f ;*

CALL, TO, *V. T.*
wáj mární ; duháí dení ; kuáná ;
kúk márná ; hák mární ; lalkárná ;
hákkáṇ mární ;
1. to pay a call. milan jáná ;
2. to call an animal. buchkárná ;
3. to call out. ḍaḍiá uṭṭhná ;
4. to call upon God. nám dhiáuná ;
nám jappná ; nám lená ;
5. to call anyone. saddná ; buláuná;
6. to call anyone, by means of a
message. sadwá bhejná ; sanehá
ghalná ;
7. what is it called ? ih núṇ kí
ákhídá hai ;

CALLIGRAPHY, *N.*
khatt. *m ;* see CALIGRAPHY.

CALLING, *N.*
1. a summons. sadd. *f ;* buláwá. *m ;*
saddá. *f ;*
2. a trade. peshá. *m ;* kamm. *m ;*

3. shouting. hák. *f ;* hák pukár. *f ;*
raulá. *m ;* wázáṇ. *f ;*

CALLOUS, *A.*
sakht ; beráhm ; patthar dil ;

CALM, *A.*
1. of a person. chup cháp ;
2. of climate. hussar hoyá ;
3. of water. khalotá hoyá ;

CALM, TO. *V. T.*
ṭhaṇḍá karná ; maṭṭhá karná ;
pher rází karní ; thamá dená ;
dhímá karná ;
1. to calm a child. lorí dení ;
warcháuná ;
2. to calm an animal. buchkárná ;

CALM, *N.*
hussar. *m ;*

CALMNESS, *N.*
sáṇt. *f ;* sáṇtagí. *f ;* chain. *f ;*

CALMLY, *Adv.*
haule haule ; saijh nál ; hausle
nál ; aman nál ; dhíraj nál ;

CALOMEL, *N.*
raskapúr. *m ;*

CALUMINATE, TO, *V. T.*
badnám karná ; nahaqq bolná ;
mukálá karná ; bhagí karní ;
baḳhílí karní ; újj láuní ; aib
láuní ; niṇdiá karná ;

CALUMINATION, *N.*
badnámí. *f ;* niṇdiá. *f ;* bijjtí. *f ;*
beizzatí. *f ;* baḳhílí. *f ;* bhagí. *f ;*
leṇjh. *f ;*

CALUMINATOR, *N.*
niṇdak. *m ;* tohmat láunwálá. *m ;*
tohmatí. *m ;*

CALUMNY, *N.*
niṇdiá. *f ;* ujj. *f ;* see CALUMINA-
TION.

CALVE, TO, *V. T.*
súṇná ; bachchá dená ;

CAMEL, *N.*
uṭṭ. *m ;* uṭṭh. *m ;* uṭṭhní. *f ;* dáchí.
f ; sánnhaṇí. *f ;*
1. a young camel. bottá. *m ;*
ṭoḍḍá. *m ;*
2. a camel up to five years of age.
ḍoák. *m ;*
3. a camel driver. sarwán. *m ;*
4. a camel's guiding rope. nakel.
f ;
5. a camel's saddle. kacháwá. *m ;*

CAMP, *N.*
1. ground. paṛáú. *m*; paṛá. *m*;
2. tents. kampú. *m*; ḍerá. *m*; tambú ṭapprí. *f*;
CAMP, TO, *V. T.*
tambú khará karná; ḍerá láuná OR utarná;
used of gypsies. ṭapprí láuní;
CAMPAIGN, *N.*
1. all preparations for fighting. lám. *f*;
2. the fighting. laṛáí. *f*; múṭh bheṛ *f*; jang. *m*;
CAMPHOR, *N.*
kápúr. *m*; mushk kápúr. *m*;
CAN, *N.*
ṭín. *m*; pípá. *m*; kanastar. *m*;
CANAL, *N.*
naihr. *m*;
1. a branch canal. rajwáh. *m*;
2. smaller branch canal. súá. *m*; mindar. *m*;
3. small watercourse. khál. *m*; kassí. *f*;
4. water outlet from canal. mohgá. *m*;
5. canal bank. paṭṛí. *f*;
6. a canal dam. jhál. *m*;
CANASTER, *N.*
pípá. *m*; see CAN.
CANCEL, TO, *V. T.*
hukm band karná; meṭná; miṭáuná; moṛná; maná karná;
by writing. kalam pherní;
CANDIDATE, *N.*
ummedwár. *m*; ásháwáṇd. *m*; loṛwand. *m*; cháhwand. *m*;
for an examination. imtihán denwálá. *m*;
CANDIDLY, *Adv.*
dil kholke; safái nál; nitár ke; khullhe dil nál;
CANDLE, *N.*
mombattí. *f*;
CANDLESTICK, *N.*
battídán. *m*;
a tiny shelf in wall for a light. dawákhá. *m*; dawákhaṛí. *f*;
CANDOUR, *N.*
safái. *f*; sáf sáf ákhná. *m*;
to speak with candour. chaṇgí chaṇgí taráh dassná;
CANDY, *N.*
misrí. *f*;
CANE, *N.*
1 stick. baiṇt. *m*; soṭṭí. *f*;
2. sugarcane generally. kamád. *m*; ikh. *m*;
3. each stick of sugarcane. ganná. *m*;
CANE, TO, *V. T.*
baiṇt márná OR ṭhokná OR lagáuná;
CANED, TO BE, *V. I.*
baiṇt kháná;
CANISTER, *N.*
kanastar. *m*; see CAN.
CANNIBAL, *N.*
ḍain. *m*; ádam k̲hor. *m*; bandeáṇ dá más khánwálá. *m*;
CANNON, *N.*
top. *f*;
CANNON BALL, *N.*
golá. *m*;
CANNOT DO, *V. I.*
nahíṇ kar sakkná;
I cannot do this. maithoṇ ih síápá nahíṇ hundá.
CANNY, *A.*
hoshiyár; chalák; síáná; jánúṇ ján;
CANOE, *N.*
beṛí. *f*;
CANOPY, *N.*
chánaní. *f*; shamiáná. *m*; samíáná. *m*;
over shop front. chhajjá. *m*;
CANT, *N.*
gapp. *f*;
CANTANKEROUS, *A.*
ḍhíṭh; ziddí; laṛáká;
CANTEEN, *N.*
kanṭín. *f*;
CANTER, *N.*
poiá. *m*;
CANTER, TO, *V. T.*
poiá páuná;
CANTONMENT, *N.*
chauṇí. *f*;
CANVASS, TO, *V. T.*
kise ádmí núṇ voṭ len wáste bent karní;
CAP, *N.*
ṭopí. *f*;

CAPABILITY, *N.*
liyáqat. *f;* guṇ. *m;* majál. *f;* see ABILITY.
CAPABLE, *A.*
laiq; jog; tagṛá; kárígar; for GOD only. qádir;
CAPACIOUS, *A.*
moklá; khullhá;
CAPACITY, *N.*
gunjaish. *f;* samáí. *f;* pujj. *m;* tháṇ. *m;* see EXTENT.
CAPER, *N.*
luḍí. *f;* chhál. *f;* nách. *m;*
a lamb or kid capering. bhuṛakná; ṭappná;
CAPITAL, *N.*
1. money. rupáye. *m;* dhan. *m;*
2. stock. púṇjí. *f;* rás. *f;* sarmáyá. *m;*
3. town. májhá. *m;* waḍḍá shahr. *m;* ráj dháṇí. *f;*
4. exclamation. achchhá; bhale bhale;
CAPITALIST, *N.*
waḍḍá máldár ádmí. *m;* lakkh patí. *m;* dhaṇwáṇ. *m;*
CAPITULATE, TO, *V. T.*
hár jáná; chhaḍḍ dená; ján dená;
CAPRICE, *N.*
lahir. *f;* manmauj. *f;*
CAPRICIOUSLY, *Adv.*
lahir vichch;
CAPSIZE, TO, *V. T.*
ultá dená OR karná; múdhá karná; palṭáuná;
CAPTAIN, *N.*
kaptán sáhib. *m;*
CAPTIVATE TO, *V. T.*
baṛá ḳhush karná; parcháuná; dil ḳhush karná; maná lainá; dil moh lainá; rájí karná;
CAPTIVATING, *A.*
manmohan; manmohaní;
CAPTIVE, *N.*
qaidí. *m;* bandhúá. *m;*
CAPTIVITY, *N.*
qaid. *f;* najarbandí. *f;*
1. in another country. asírí. *f;*
2. slavery. gulámí. *f;*
CAPTURE, TO.
phaṛná; phaṛ lainá; napp lainá; phagaṛná;
CAR, *N.*
gaḍḍí. *f;*
CARAVAN, *N.*
ṭollá. *m;* ṭollí. *f;* káflá. *m;* káfílá. *m;* saṇg. *f;*
CARBUNCLE, *N.*
roṛá. *m;*
CARCASS, *N.*
murdár. *m;*
of a man. loth. *f;*
CARD, *N.*
1. postcard. káṭ. *m;* ḳhatt. *m;*
2. playing cards. tásh. *m;*
3. to play cards. tásh kheḍṇá;
4. to card cotton. jhambhná; jhambh suṭṭná; piṇjná;
5. cardplayer. kumárbáj. *m;*
6. cardplaying. kumárbájí. *f;*
CARDAMOM, *N.*
láchí. *f;* iláichí. *f;*
CARE, *N.*
1. anxiety. fikr. *m;* chiṇtá. *f;* chitt chetá. *f;* soch. *m;* parwáh. *f;* sár. *f;*
2. caution, ḳhabardárí. *f;* hoshiyárí. *f;* sár. *f;* chaukasí. *f;*
3. charge. hawálá. *m;* sapurdagí. *f;* qábú. *m;*
CARE TO TAKE, *V. T.*
ḳhabardárí karní; parwáh karní; sár lainí; surt lainí; chaukas rahná;
CAREFUL, *A.*
hoshiyár; suchet; jataní;
thrifty. sanjúhṛá; sanjúhṛí;
CAREFULLY, *Adv.*
ḳhabardárí nál; jatan nál; tirke; changí taráh nál; hosh karke; soch sambhal ke; apná karke; gauh nál; soch ke; rás ke; saṇwár ke; bachke; soch samajh ke; hosh nál;
CAREFULNESS, *N.*
ḳhabardárí. *f;* hoshiyárí. *f;* chaukasí. *f;*
CARELESS, *A.*
ḍhillá maṭṭhá; gáfal; láparwáh; beparwáh; sust; ḍhillá; bemukh; dawáná; besurt;
he has become careless. us ne loí láh chhaḍḍí;

CARELESSLY, *Adv.*
láparwáí nál; aiweṇ;
CARELESSNESS, *N.*
láparwáí. *f*; gáfalí. *f*; ḍhill. *f*; befikrí. *f*; sustí. *f*;
CARESS, *N.*
pyár. *m*; láḍ. *m*; puchkárá. *m*; puchkárí. *f*;
CARESS, TO, *V. T.*
pyár dená; hatth pherná; láḍ laḍáuná; puchkárná;
CARETAKER, *N.*
chaukídár. *m*; rakhwálá. *m*;
CARGO, *N.*
jaház dí bhartí. *f*; mál asbáb. *m*;
CARNAL, *A.*
luchchá; mastáná;
CARNIVEROUS, *A.*
másḳhor; más OR gosht khánwálá;
CAROD, *N.*
gít. *m*; rágní bhajan. *m*; raṇg rág. *m*;
CAROL, TO, *V. T.*
gít gáuná; bhajan gáuná;
CARPENTER, *N.*
tarḳhán. *m*; taḳhán. *m*; báḍḍhí. *m*;
wife of carpenter. tarḳháṇí. *f*;
CARPET, *N.*
faras. *m*; farash. *m*; darí. *f*;
mat. galíchá. *m*; ásaṇ. *m*;
CARRIAGE, *N.*
gaḍḍí. *f*;
1. a trap. ṭamṭam. *f*; baggí. *f*; ṭángá. *m*; gaḍḍí. *f*;
2. a railway carriage. rel gaḍḍí. *f*;
3. a bullock cart. gaḍḍá. *m*; gaḍḍí. *f*; gaḍḍ. *m*;
4. a hand cart. rehṛí. *f*; rehṛá. *m*; reṛhí. *f*; gaḍḍí. *f*;
CARRION, *N.*
murdár. *m*;
CARROT, *N.*
gájar. *f*;
CARRY, TO, *V. T.*
chukkná; ḍhoná; laí jáná; chukkke khaṛná;
CARRYING, *N.*
ḍhuláí. *f*; ḍhulwáí. *f*;
CART, *N.*
gaḍḍí. *f*; see CARRIAGE.
CARTAGE, *N.*
ḍhuáí. *f*; ḍhuláí. *f*;
CARTRIDGE, *N.*
kártús. *m*;
a blank cartridge. chhalkí kártús. *m*;
CARTWHEEL, *N.*
pahiá. *m*;
CARVE, TO, *V. T.*
ghaṛná; ukkaṛná;
CASE, *N.*
1. a lawsuit. muqadamá. *m*; nálish. *m*; dává. *f*;
2. a box. sandúq. *m*; peṭí. *f*;
CASE, TO BRING A, *V. T.*
kise te arjí páuní; dává karná; nálish karná;
CASH, *N.*
rokaṛ. *f*; rok. *f*; ṭake. *m*;
CASHIER, *N.*
ḳhazánchí. *m*; rokaṛíá. *m*;
CASH BOOK, *N.*
1. day book. suhaṛ. *m*; rokuṛ. *f*;
2. ledger. behí. *f*; wehí. *f*; khátá. *m*;
CASK, *N.*
pípá. *m*; biám. *m*;
CASKET, *N.*
dabbí. *f*;
CAST, TO, *V. T.*
suṭṭná; páuná; dálná; ghattná; paṭak dená; see THROW.
1. to cast lots. chiṭṭhí kaḍḍhní; guṇe páuná; látrí páuná; haunsí páuná;
2. to cast out. kaḍḍh dená; khaderná; nikál dená; chhekná; dhakkíáuná;
3. to cast away. paráṇ suṭṭ dená;
4. to cast down headlong. sir parne ḍeg dená;
CASTE, *N.*
ját. *f*; zát. *f*; qaum. *f*; got. *f*; ṭollá. *m*;
1. low caste. níwíṇ zát. *f*; níchch játí. *f*;
2. high caste. uchchí zát. *f*; uttam játí. *f*;
CASTLE, *N.*
qilá. *m*; koṭ. *m*; gaṛh. *m*;
CASTOR OIL, *N.*
hariṇḍ dá tel. *m*;

CASTOR OIL PLANT, *N.*
hariṇd, *m* ; hariṇdí. *f* ; harnaulí. *f* ; haṇḍolá. *m* ;
CASTRATE, TO, *V. T.*
khassí karní ; ákhtá karná ;
a castrated animal. khassí. *m* ;
CASUAL, *A.*
láparwáh ;
CASUALLY, *Adv.*
aiweṇ ; sabab nál ; be sababoṇ ;
CAT, *N.*
1. an animal. billí. *f* ; billá. *m* ;
2. tipcat. gullí. *f* ;
3. game of tipcat. gullí ḍanḍḍá. *m* ;
CATECHEU, *N.*
katth. *m* ; katthá. *m* ;
CATAMENIAL DISCHARGE, *N.*
nichaṛe. *f* ;
CATARACT, *N.*
motiá bind. *m* ;
CATARRH, *N.*
najlá. *m* ; jukám. *m* ; jukhám. *m* ;
CATASTROPHE, *N.*
balá. *f* ; biptá. *f* ; haner. *m* ;
CATCH, TO, *V. T.*
phaṛná ; pakaṛná ; phaṛá dená ; see GRASP.
1. to catch a ball. bochná ; juppná : jhopná ;
2. to catch hold firmly. ghuṭṭ ke phaṛná ; jor nál phaṛná ; tagṛeáṇ karke phaṛná ; tagṛái nál phaṛná ;
CATCHING OF THE BREATH, *N.*
hatkorá. *m* ; hiḍkorá. *m* ;
CATECHISE, TO, *V. T.*
sawál karná ; puchchhná ;
CATECHISM, *N.*
katikismas. *m* ; sawál te jawáb. *m* ;
CATECHUMEN, *N.*
iqrárí. *m* ; mutaláshí. *m* ;
CATERPILLAR, *N.*
suṇḍí. *f* ; lúṛí. *f* ; bhaṇgú kuttá. *m* ;
CATGUT, *N.*
taṇḍ. *m* ; táṇt. *f* ;
CATHEDRAL, *N.*
waḍḍá girjá. *m* ;
CATHOLIC, *A.*
kulliá ;
CATTLE, *N.*
danggar. *m* ; mál. *m* ; ḍhaggá. *m* ; bald. *m* ; dhaṇ. *m* ; danggar dhor. *m* ; dáṇḍ. *m* ; pasú. *m* ; goká. *m* ; gokká. *m* ; danggar chaukhur. *m* ; chaukhar. *m* ;
CAULDRON, *N.*
deg. *m* ; see CALDRON.
CAULIFLOWER, *N.*
phul gobí. *f* ;
CAUSE, *N.*
káran. *m* ; sabab. *m* ; wajhá. *f* ;
CAUSELESSLY, *Adv.*
biná wajhe ; besababoṇ ; aiweṇ ;
CAUSTERIZE, TO, *V. T.*
dág dená ;
CAUSTIC, *N.*
tejáb. *m* ;
CAUTION, *N.*
1. carefulness. chaukasí. *f* ; ḳhabardárí. *f* ; hoshiyárí. *f* ; hosh. *m* ; surt. *f* ; ḳhabargírí. *f* ;
2. warning. nasíhat. *f* ;
CAUTION, TO, *V. T.*
jatáuná ; samjháuná ;
CAUTIOUS, *A.*
suchet ; síáná ; hoshiyár ; chaukas ; chalák ; dáná ; see PRUDENT.
CAUTIOUSLY, *Adv.*
hosh nál ; ḳhabardári nál ;
to go cautiously. dekh bhálke jáná. see CAREFULLY ;
CAVALRY, *N.*
1. British. gorá risálá. *m* ;
2. Native. risálá. *m* ;
CAVE. *N.*
khuṇdhar. *m* ; ghuṛhá. *m* ; gufhá. *m* ; khoh. *f* ; gaṛhá. *m* ; gár. *f* ; khaḍḍ. *f* ;
CAVITY, *N.*
ṭoá. *m* ; khaḍá. *f* ;
in a wall. khuḍḍ. *f* ; khabbh. *f* ; morí. *f* ;
CAW, TO, *V. T.*
káṇ káṇ karná ; launá ;
CAWING, *N.*
káṇ káṇ. *m* ;
CAYENNE PEPPER, *N.*
lál mirch. *m* ;
CEASE, TO CAUSE, TO, *V. T.*
band karná ; rokná ; moṛná ;

CEASE, TO, *V. I.*
band honá ; mukkná ; khuṭṭ jáná ; lahiná ;
CEASELESS, *A.*
lagátár ; nitt ; ghaṛí múṛí ;
CEDAR, *N.*
deodár. *m* ; diár. *m* ; biár. *m* ;
CEILING, *N.*
chatt. *f* ; chatt baṇdí. *f* ;
CELEBRATE, TO, *V. T.*
manáuná ;
CELEBRATED, *A.*
manniá danniá; námí; jasí; jaswaṇt;
CELEBRATION, *N.*
yádgírí. *f* ;
CELEBRITY, *N.*
jas. *m* ; mashúr ádmí. *m* ;
CELERITY, *N.*
shatábí. *f* ; chustí. *f* ; phurtí. *f* ;
CELESTIAL, *A.*
asmání ;
CELIBACY, *N.*
majarradí. *f* ;
CELIBATE, *A.*
kuṇwárá ;
CELL, *N.*
1. a small prison. haválát. *f* ; kaṇjí haud. *m* ; bhorhá. *m* ;
2. a small room. hujrá. *m* ; koṭhṛí. *f* ;
CELLAR, *N.*
bhorhá. *m* ;
CEMENT, *N.*
símanṭ. *m* ;
CEMENT, TO, *V. T.*
joṛná ;
CEMETERY, *N.*
qabaristán. *m*, M ;
place where Hindu corpses are burnt. masán. *m* ; maṛhíáṇ. *f*, H ;
CENSURE, *N.*
jháṛ. *m* ; gilá gujárí. *f* ; jhiṛkí. *f* ;
CENSURE, TO, *V. T.*
malámat karní ; shikayat karní ; jháṛ karná ; gilá gujárí karní ; see REPROVE.
CENSURABLE, *A.*
malámat de laiq ;
CENSUS, *N.*
mardam shumárí. *f* ;
CENTIPEDE, *N.*
kann khajúrá. *m* ; kannkol. *m* ;
CENTRE, *N.*
waggá. *m* ; wichkár. *m* ; wichlá. *m* ;
CENTURY, *N.*
sáe waṛhe. *m* ; sadí. *f* ;
CEREMONY, *N.*
rít rasm. *f* ; rasm. *f* ; sagan bihár. *m* ;
CERTAIN, *A.*
zarúr ; pakká ; yaqíní ;
some. kaí ikk ;
CERTAINLY, *Adv.*
zarúr ; beshakk ; hor kí ; te hor kí ; nisaṇg ;
CERTAINTY, *N.*
yaqín. *m* ; nischá. *f* ; see BELIEF.
CERTIFICATE, *N.*
sártifikat. *m* ; neknámí dí chiṭṭhí. *f* ; sanad. *f* ;
CERTIFY, TO, *V. T.*
gawáhí deni ; sákhí deni ;
CERTITUDE, *N.*
yaqín. *m* ; partít. *m* ;
CESSATION, *N.*
bandí. *f* ;
CESSPOOL, *N.*
niáiṇ. *f* ; rúṛíáṇ. *f* ; ṛeally a retiring ground.
CHAFE, TO, *V. T.*
ambáuná ;
CHAFE, TO, *V. I.*
uchchná ; ragaṛ laggná ; ambná ;
CHAFF, *N.*
1. from corn. túṛí. *f* ; kakkh. *m* ;
2. from gram. missá bhoh. *m* ; bhoh. *m* ;
3. from rice. phakk. *f* ;
4. mocking. makhaul. *m* ; ṭhaṭṭhá. *m* ; hássá. *m* ; táná. *m* ;
CHAFF, TO, *V. T.*
ṭhaṭṭhá karná ; makhaul karná ;
CHAGRIN, *N.*
sharm. *f* ; saṇg. *f* ;
CHAIN, *N.*
1. small. jaṇjírí. *f* ;
2. larger. sanggal. *m* ; jaṇjír. *m* ;
3. on the door. kuṇḍí. *f* ;
CHAIR, *N.*
khursí. *f* ; chauṇkí. *f* ;
1. native chair with a back. píhṛá. *m* ;
2. native stool made of reeds, without back. muṛhá. *m* ;

CHAIRMAN, *N.*
sarpaṇch, *m* ; mír majlis, *m* ;
CHALICE, *N.*
piyálá. *m* ;
CHALK, *N.*
chák. *m* ; khaṛyá. *m* ;
CHALLENGE, *N.*
saddá. *f* ; lalkárá. *m* ;
CHALLENGE, TO, *V. T.*
lalkárná ;
CHAMBER, *N.*
koṭhrí. *f* ;
CHAMP, TO, *V. T.*
chabbná ;
CHAMPION, *N.*
palwárá. *m* ; balí. *m* ; mall. *m* ; súrbír. *m* ; surmá. *m* ;
CHANCE, *N.*
sabab. *m* ; dho. *m* ; sanjog. *m* ;
by chance. aiweṇ ; achának ; sabab nál ;
CHANCE, TO, *V. T.*
sabab nál ḍho ḍhukkná ;
CHANGE, *N.*
1. exchange. badlí. *f* ; badal. *m* ; waṭáṇḍrá. *m* ;
2. cash. bhán. *f* ; bhangaṛ. *m* ;
CHANGE, TO, *V. T.*
waṭáuná ; badal karná ; tabdíl karná ; adal badal karná ; waṭá dená ; waṭá lainá ; waṭáṇḍrá karná ; márchá karná OR márná ; waṭṭó saṭṭá karná ;
1. to change rupees or notes. toṛná ;
2. to give back. partáná ;
CHANGE, TO, *V. I.*
waṭ jáná ; badal jáná ;
to get changed. tuṛáná ; bhanáuná ; waṭáuná ;
CHANGEABLE, *A.*
dodilá ; kochcharí ; phirtú ghirtú ;
CHANNEL, *N.*
1. small. nálí. *f* ; khálí. *f* ; see CANAL.
2. large. nálá. *m* ; khál. *m* ;
CHAPEL, *N.*
girjá. *m* ;
CHAPLAIN, *N.*
pádrí sáhib. *m* ;
CHAPLET, *N.*
hár. *m* ;

CHAPTER, *N.*
kánd. *m* ; báb. *m* ;
CHAR, TO, *V. T.*
jhulas dená ;
CHARACTER, *N.*
chál chalan. *m* ; ḍhaṇg waṇg. *m* ; subhá. *m* ; subháo. *m* ;
CHARACTERISTIC, *N.*
gʻun. *m* ; sift. *f* ;
CHARCOAL, *N.*
kolá. *m* ; kole. *m* ;
CHARGE, *N.*
1. accusation. ilzám. *m* ; dosh. *m* ; nálish. *m* ;
2. custody. sapurdagí. *f* ; hawálá. *m* ; jummá. *m* ; hatth vichch ;
CHARGE, TO, *V. T.*
1. to accuse. ilzám láuná ; see ACCUSE.
2. to give in charge. uh de hawále karná ; de peṭe páuná ;
3. to exhort. hukm dená ; pakkí karná ; kah dená ;
CHARGES, *N.*
ḳharchá. *m* ;
CHARIOT, *N.*
rath. *m* ; gaḍḍí. *f* ;
an idol car with four wheels. rath. *m* ;
CHARITABLE, *A.*
dáyáwán ; mihrbán ; dáyálú ;
CHARITY, *N.*
dán. *m* ; dán punn. *m* ; khair ḳhairát. *f* ; punn. *m* ;
CHARM, *N.*
jádú. *m* ; tawít. *f* ; maṇtar jaṇtar. *m* ; jháṛá. *m* ; ṭuṇá ; *m* ; barwaṭṭá. *m* ; dhaggá. *m* ;
charms and spells. ṭoná ṭání. *f* ;
CHARM, TO, *V. T.*
1. to please. baṛá ḳhush karná ; man lainá ; see CAPTIVATE.
2. to bewitch. jádú karná ; maṇtar paṛhná ; mandarná ;
CHARMER, *N.*
jádúgar. *m* ; maṇtarí. *m* ; taṇtarí. *m* ;
CHARMING, *A.*
sohná ; suthrá ; mohní ; sundar ;
CHARPAI, *N.*
manjí. *f* ; manjá. *m* ; chárpái. *f* ;

CHART, *N.*
naqshá. *m* ; sáṇchá. *m* ;
CHASE, TO, *V. T.*
pichchá karná ; paiṛá karná ; maggar bhajjná ;
CHASM, *N.*
khuṇdhar. *f* ; khaḍḍ. *f* ;
CHASTE, *A.*
pák ; suddh ; sáf sutthrí ; satí ;
CHASTEN, TO, *V. T.*
sudhárná ; durust karná ; tambíh dená ; táṛná ;
CHASTISE, TO, *V. T.*
márná ; sazá dení ;
1. idioms. samjháuná ; iláj karná ;
2. sometime afterwards. milná ;
CHASTISEMENT, *N.*
sazá. *f* ; már. *f* ; már kuṭṭ. *f* ;
CHASTITY, *N.*
pákízagí. *f* ; pákdámaní. *f* ; jat sat. *m* ;
CHAT, *N.*
bát chít. *f* ; gal bát. *f* ; gallán bátáṇ. *f* ;
CHATTELS, *N.*
nikk sukk. *m* ; chíz wast. *f* ; chíz wastáṇ. *f* ; laṭá paṭá. *m* ; nikkar sukkar. *f* ; wast waleváṇ. *f* ;
CHATTER, *N.*
gapp. *f* ; gapp chaṛapp. *f* ; bahutíáṇ galláṇ. *f* ;
chatter of birds. chíṇ chíṇ. *f* ; chuṇ chuṇ. *f* ;
CHATTER, TO, *V. T.*
bakkná; ṭarṭar karná ; gapp mární ; chiṛ chiṛáuná ; ṭarṭráuná ; káṇ káṇ karná ; bataule márná ; kiṛ kiṛ karná ;
CHATTERER, *N.*
baṛbolá. *m* ; gappí. *m* ; khappí. *m* ; batuní. *m* ; bataulá. *m* ; batuṛá. *m* ; jatallí. *m* ; palálí. *m* ;
CHEAP, *A.*
sastá ; suwallá ; sast mullá ; miṭṭí de mull ;
CHEAPNESS, *N.*
sast, *m* ;
CHEAT, *N.*
ṭhagiá. *m* ; makkár. *m* ; dhoppebáj. *m* ; ṭhagg. *m* ; kapṭí *m* ; chhaliá. *m* ; dagebáj. *m* ;

CHEAT, TO, *V. T.*
ṭhaggná ; mutthná ; ṭhagí karní ; dhokhá dená ; dam jháṇsá dená ; chhalná ; muchchhná ; múṇdarná ; rond márná ; dagebájí karní ; see DECEIVE.
CHEATING, *N.*
fareb. *m* ; ṭhagí. *f* ; dhokhá. *m* ; dagebájí. *f* ; rond. *f* ; phauṛ. *m* ; phauh. *m* ;
CHECK, *N.*
rok. *m* ; rok tok. *m* ;
CHECK, TO, *V. T.*
rokná ; ḍáṭná ; dakkná ; aṭkáuná ;
CHEEK, *N.*
1. of the face. gallh. *f* ; gallháṇ. *f* ; plur ;
2. impudence. beadabí. *f* ; gustákhí. *f* ; berobí. *f* ;
CHEER, *N.*
jai jaikár. *m* ; lalkárá. *m* ;
CHEER, TO, *V. T.*
dalásá dená ; tasallí dení ; jí khush karná ;
CHEERFUL, *A.*
khush ; rází ; rází bází ; bág bág; magan ; anaṇd ; parsinn ;
CHEERFULLY, *Adv.*
dil nál ; khushí nál ; jí ján nál ; parsantá nál ; cháíṇ cháíṇ ; diloṇ wajhoṇ hoke ; dil lagáke ; manoṇ tanoṇ hoke ;
CHEERFULNESS, *N.*
anaṇdtáí. *f* ; khushí. *f* ; maṇggal. *m* ;
CHEESE, *N.*
panír. *m* ;
CHEMIST, *N.*
pasárí. *m* ;
CHEQUE, *N.*
chikk. *m* ; húndí. *f* ;
CHERISH, TO, *V. T.*
pálná posná ; parwastí karní ; sambhálná ;
CHERISHER, *N.*
pálaṇwálá. *m* ; pálanhár. *m* ;
CHERISHING, *N.*
parwastí. *f* ;
CHESS, *N.*
shatranj. *m* ;
1. to play chess. shatranj kheḍná;
2. chess board. basátí shatranj. *m* ; naqshá. *m* ;

3. chess men. nardáṇ. *f*; gotiáṇ. *f*;
4. king. bádsháh.
5. queen. wazír.
6. castle. ruk.
7. knight. ghoṛá.
8. bishop. fílá.
9. pawn. piádá.

CHEST, *N*.
sandúkrí. *f*;

CHEST, *N*.
hikk. *f*; chhátí. *f*;

CHESTNUT HORSE, *N*.
surang. *m*;

CHEW, TO, *V*. *T*.
chithná; dalná;
to chew grain. chabbná;

CHEWING, THE CUD, *N*.
ugálí. *f*; chugálí. *f*;

CHICANCERY, *N*.
shiltbiltí. *f*; chalákí. *f*;

CHICKEN, *N*.
chuchá. *m*; kukkṛí dá bachchá. *m*;

CHICKENPOX, *N*.
khasrá. *m*; kákṛá lákṛá. *m*;

CHIDE, TO, *V*. *T*.
ghuṛkí dení; jhiṛakná; táṛná; akkh wikháuná; khijhná;

CHIDING, *N*.
dábbá. *m*; dábbá dhássá. *m*; ghurkí. *f*; dhamkí. *f*; dabkí. *f*; jhiṛak. *f*;

CHIEF, *A*.
pahlá; baṛá; waḍḍá mukh; mahar;

CHIEF, *N*.
sálár. *m*; sardár. *m*;

CHIEFLY, *Adv*.
ḳháss karke;

CHILD, *N*.
bálak. *m*; bál. *m*; bachchá. *m*; jáyá. *m*; níṇgar. *m*; niáná. *m*; ayáná. *m*; ananá. *m*; bachṛá. *m*;
English child. báwá. *m*; báwí. *f*;

CHILDISH, *A*.
bholá bálá; nadán jehá; bachcheáṇ wargá;

CHILDHOOD, *N*.
bachchpaṇ. *m*; bálpaṇ. *m*; ayánpúná. *m*; bálakpúná. *m*; bál awasthá. *m*;

CHILDLESS, *A*.
auṇtará; beaulád; dhí puttar nahíṇ; auṇtrá niḳhattrá; beauládá; niḳhattrá; niputtá;
especially for a woman. bánjh, litbarren.

CHILDREN, *N*.
bál bachche. *m*; laṛke bále. *m*; níṇgar. *m*; jiájant. *m*; dhíáṇ puttar. *m*; dhíá puttá. *m*;

CHILL, *N*.
sít. *f*; ṭhaṇḍ. *f*; pálá. *m*;

CHILL, TO, *V*. *T*.
ṭhaṇḍá karná; ṭhárná;

CHILLINESS, *N*.
ṭhár. *m*; ṭharan. *f*;

CHILLY. *A*.
sít; sard; ṭhaṇḍá;
it was chilly. pálá paṇdá sí; baṛí sít pái;

CHIMNEY, *N*.
1. for lamp. chimní. *f*; shíshí. *f*;
2. for a house. aṇggíṭhí. *f*; burjí. *f*; dhuṇkash. *m*;
3. for sugar cane furnace. lúhmbhí. *f*; luhmbhá. *m*;

CHIMNEY PIECE, *N*.
parchattí. *f*;

CHIN, *N*.
ṭhoḍí. *f*;

CHINA, *N*.
1. country. Chín dá des. *m*;
2. crockery. chíní de bháṇḍe. *m*;

CHINESE, *N*.
Chín de lok. *m*;

CHINK, *N*.
1. a split. chir. *m*; darár. *m*; tareṛ. *f*;
2. a hole. chhek. *m*; see CRACK.

CHIP, *N*.
sakk. *m*; sakṛá. *m*; sakkaṛ. *f*; chillaṛ. *f*;
a piece of wood. tukṛá. *m*; ṭoṭá. *m*;

CHIP, TO, *V*. *T*.
chhillná;
to cut into small pieces. ṭoṭe ṭoṭe karná; tukṛe tukṛe karná;

CHIRP, TO, *V*. *T*.
chirkná; chíṇ chíṇ karní; chilúṇ chilúṇ karná; bolná;

CHIRP, *N*.
chíṇ chíṇ. *f*; chilúṇ chilúṇ. *m*;

CHISEL, *N*.
chhaiṇí. *f ;*
for roughing a mill stone. chakk ráhá. *m ;*
CHISEL, TO, *V. T*.
chhaiṇí nál waḍḍhná ;
CHITCHAT, *N*.
gal bát. *f;* bát chít. *f ;* gapp shapp. *f ;* gallán bátán. *f ;*
CHLOROFORM, *N*.
behosh karn dí dawá. *f ;*
CHOICE, *N*.
marzí. *f ;* marjí. *f ;* pasiṇd. *m ;* bhauná. *m ;* bhauní. *f ;*
CHOICE, *A*.
chaṇgá ; uttam ; see EXCELLENT.
CHOKE, TO, *V. T*.
gal OR saṇgh ghuṭṭná ; dam rokná OR ghuṭṭná ;
CHOKE, TO, *V. I*.
galghoṭu honá ; dam ghuṭṭiá jáná ;
CHOLERA, *N*.
ḍákí. *f ;* haizá. *m ;*
CHOOSE, TO, *V. T*.
pasiṇd karná ; cháhná ; dhárná ; chugná ; chuṇná; chháṇt kar lainá ;
CHOP, TO, *V. T*.
1. to chop wood into pieces. lakaṛ waḍḍhní ;
2. to split wood. lakaṛ phárṇá ;
3. to mince. kímá karná ;
CHOPPER, *N*.
ṭoká. *m ;* gandásá. *m ;*
CHOSEN, *A*.
chuniá hoyá ; manzúr ; dhariá hoyá ;
CHRIST, *N*.
Masíh. *m ;*
CHRISTEN, TO, *V. T*.
baptismá dená ;
CHRISTENING, *N*.
baptismá. *m ;*
CHRISTIAN, *N*.
Isáí. *m ;* Masíhí. *m ;*
CHRISTIANITY, *N*.
Isáí Dín. *m ;*
CHRISTMAS DAY, *N*.
waḍḍá din. *m ;* baṛá din. *m ;*
CHRONIC, *A*.
bahut chir dá ; puráná ;
CHUCKLE, TO, *V. I*.
guṭakná ;
CHUCKLING, *N*.
guṭak ;
CHURCH, *N*.
1. Christian. girjá. *m ;* bandagí dá ghar. *m ;* ibádat ḳháná. *m ;*
2. Cathedral. waḍḍá girjá. *m ;*
3. Jewish temple. haikal. *m ;*
4. Muhammadan mosque. masít. *f ;*
5. Hindu temple. mandir, *m ;* ṭhákar duárá. *m ;* shawálá. *m ;* síwálá. *m ;*
6. Sikh temple. gurdwárá. *m ;* dharmsálá. *m ;*
7. Sikh temple at Amritsar. darbár sáhib. *m ;*
8. body of Christians. kalísiá. *f ;*
CHURLISH, *A*.
karaṇgá ; bedhangá ; gaṇwár ; ujad ; saṛiá bhujiá ; khaṭṭá, muṭúṭá ;
CHURLISHNESS, *N*.
kall khorí. *f ;* tamsí. *f ;* gaṇwárpuṇá. *m ;*
CHURCHING, *N*.
auratáṇ dá shukaráná. *m ;*
CHURN, *N*.
chátti. *f ;*
churning stick. madhání. *f ;*
CHURN, TO, *V. T*.
riṛkná ;
CIGAR, *N*.
sharút. *m ;*
CIGARETTE, *N*.
sigraṭ. *f ;*
CINDER, *N*.
angiárí. *f ;*
CINNAMON, *N*.
dálchíní. *f ;*
C'RCLE, *N*.
gherá. *m ;* kuṇḍal. *m ;* gird. *m ;* dáirá. *m ;* chakkar. *m ;* gher. *f ;* gol dáirá. *m ;*
a circle for wrestling. piṛ. *m ;* akháṛhá. *m ;*
CIRCLE, TO, *V. T*.
gherá márná ; gherná ;
CIRCUIT, *N*.
chakkar. *m ;* pherá. *m ;* gerá. *m ;* ghumáú. *f ;* gird. *m ;*
to make circuits. waláwáṇ kháná ; chakkar márná ; walá páuná ;
CIRCULAR, *N*.
gol ; gol mol ;

CIRCULATE, TO, *V. T.*
phiráuná ; ghumáuná ;
CIRCULATE, TO, *V. I.*
ghumná ;
CIRCULATION, *N.*
ḳhun dá daurá. *m* ;
CIRCUMCISE, TO, *V. T.*
suntí baháuná ; sunnat karná ;
CIRCUMCISED, TO BE, *V. I.*
suntí baiṭhná ;
CIRCUMCISION, *N.*
suntí. *f* ; sunnat. *f* ; ḳhatná. *m* ;
CIRCUMFERENCE, *N.*
girdá. *m* ; gherá. *m* ; duálá. *m* ; gher. *f* ; gird. *m* ;
CIRCUMSPECT, *A.*
suchet ; chaukas ; hoshiyár ; gaurá ;
CIRCUMSTANCE, *N.*
hál. *m* ; hál hawál. *m* ; wákiá. *m* ; gal. *f* ; hálat. *f* ; bartánt. *m* ; hál haqíqat. *f* ; hál chál. *m* ; awasthá. *f* ; awastá. *f* ;
CISTERN, *N.*
chaubachchá. *m* ; hauj. *m* ;
CITADEL, *N.*
qilá. *m* ; koṭ. *m* ; burj. *m* ; gaṛhí. *f* ;
CITATION, *N.*
samman. *m* ;
CITIZEN, *N.*
shahrí. *m* ; shahriá. *m* ;
CITRON, *N.*
1. lemon. khaṭṭá. *m* ;
2. citron. galgal. *f* ;
3. another kind of citron. chakotrá. *m* ;
CITY, *N.*
shahr. *m* ; nagar. *m* ;
CIVIL, *A.*
1. polite. milansár ; ádarí ; ádar bháú wálá ; khulkí ;
2. not criminal. duání ;
3. pertaining to a city. shahrí ;
4. civil & military. mulkí te jangí ;
CIVILITY, *N.*
bhalmánsí. *f* ; ádar bháú. *m* ;
CIVILISATION, *N.*
ádmíat. *f* ;
CIVILIZE, TO, *V. T.*
ádmí OR manukkh banáuná ;
CIVILLY, *Adv.*
ádar man nál ;

CLAIM, *N.*
dává. *f* ;
right. haqq. *m* ;
CLAIM, TO, *V. T.*
dává karná ; nálish karná ;
CLAIMANT, *N.*
mudáí. *m* ; dávedár. *m* ;
CLAMOUR, *N.*
raulá. *m* ; shor. *m* ; dhum. *m* ; hugg. *f* ; gaugá. *m* ;
CLAN, *N.*
ját. *f* ; got. *f* ; koṛmá. *m* ;
CLANDESTINELY, *Adv.*
gujjhe gujjhe ; chup cháp ; akkh bachá ke ; chorí chorí karke ; luk ke ; chup ke ; uhle hoke ;
CLANKING SOUND, *N.*
shaṇkár. *m* ; jhaṇkár. *f* ;
CLAP, *N.*
tauṛí. *f* ; tálíáṇ. *f* ; giddhá. *m* ; táṛí. *f* ;
CLAP, TO, *V. T.*
tauṛí bajáuní ; tálíáṇ wajáuní ; táṛí mární ;
for women only. giddá páuná ; mángá márná ;
CLARIFY, TO, *V. T.*
1. to filter. nitárná ; punná ;
2. to sift. chhánná ;
CLARION, *N.*
surnáí. *f* ; turhí. *f* ; see TRUMPET.
CLASP, TO, *V. T.*
1. to embrace. japphá márná ; galle lagáuná ;
2. to clasp hands. hatth miláuná ;
3. to grasp a thing. phaṛí rakkhná ; phaṛná ; phagaṛná ;
CLASS, *N.*
1. assembly. jamát. *f* ; jalsá. *m* ;
2. kind. qism. *m* ; parkár. *m* ;
3. kind, for living things only. ját. *f* ;
4. railway class. darjá. *m* ;
CLASS FELLOW, *N.*
jamaití. *m* ; hamjholí. *m* ;
CLATTER, *N.*
shor. *m* ; raulá. *m* ; khaṛak kharáhat. *f* ;
CLAUSE, *N.*
fiqrá. *m* ;
CLAW, *N.*
panjá. *m* ;

CLAW, TO, *V. T.*
panjá márná ;
CLAY, *N.*
1. every kind of soil. miṭṭí. *f ;*
2. clay. chikní miṭṭí. *f ;*
3. mud used for mortar. gárá. *m ;*
CLEAN, *A.*
sáf ; safá ; suthrá ; nirmal ; ujjal ;
CLEAN, TO, *V. T.*
1. to clean corn. chhattná; kalauná;
2. to clean the mouth. karúlí karní;
3. to clean a metal vessel. mánjná ;
4. to wash a thing. dhoná ; khangghalná ;
5. to clean with a broom. huṇjná ;
6. to clean with a duster. jháṛná ;
7. to bathe. naháuná ; ashnán karná ;
8. to clean teeth with stick. M. miswák karná ; H. dátaṇ karná ;
9. to clean or brush clothes. punjhná ;
10. to clean cotton. jhambhná ;
11. to scrape clean. gharorná ;
12. to clean by shaking. chhaṇḍná ;
CLEANLINESS, *N.*
safáí. *f ;* suchamm. *m ;*
CLEANSING, *N.*
1. Muhammadan ceremonial. wazú. *m ;*
2. Hindu. ashnán. *m ;*
CLEAR, *A.*
1. clean. sáf ; suthrá ; nirmal ;
2. plain. záhir ;
CLEAR, TO, *V. T.*
1. to acquit. barí karná ; ráí karní ; riá karná ;
2. to clear the throat. khaṇgharná ; khaṇghurná ; saṇggh sawárná ; ghaṇgárná ; khaṇghná ;
CLEARLY, *Adv.*
safáí nál ; sáf sáf ; khullam khullhá ;
CLEAVE, TO, *V. T.*
chirná ; pháṛná ; see SPLIT.
CLEAVE, TO, *V. I.*
lag jáná ; chambaṛná ;
CLEMENCY, *N.*
narmí. *f ;* ráhm. *m ;* mihrbání. *f ;* mihrbánagí. *f ;*
CLENCH, TO, *V. T.*
mazbutí nál phaṛná ; japphí ghaṭṭná OR páuná ; see GRASP.
CLERGY, *N.*
pádrí lok. *m ;*
CLERGYMAN, *N.*
pádrí sáhib. *m ;*
CLERK, *N.*
munshí. *m ;* bábú. *m ;* muharrar. *m ;*
CLEVER, *A.*
dhangí ; hoshiyár ; sughar ; siáná ; phurtílá ; chátar ; suchet ;
CLEVERLY, *Adv.*
hoshiyárí nál ; chalákí nál ; baṛí ustádí nál ;
CLEVERNESS, *N.*
hoshiyárí. *f ;* chataráí. *f ;* phurtí. *f ;* ustádí. *f ;* chustí. *f ;* siánaf. *f ;*
CLEW, *N.*
patá. *m ;* khoj. *m ;* súh. *f ;*
CLIENT, *N.*
jagmán. *m ;* jan. *m ;*
CLIMATE, *N.*
wá. *f ;* hawá. *f ;*
CLIMB, *N.*
chaṛháí. *f ;*
CLIMB, TO, *V. T.*
chaṛh jáná ; uppar chaṛhná ;
CLING, TO, *V. I.*
chambaṛná ; laggá rahná ; see TO STICK.
CLIP, TO, *V. T.*
kaṭṭarná ;
CLIQUE, *N.*
firqá. *m ;* got. *f ;* ṭollí. *f ;* dhaṛá. *m ;*
CLOAK, *N.*
chogá. *m ;*
CLOCK, *N.*
ghaṛí *f ;*
CLOCKMAKER, *N.*
ghaṛísáz. *m ;*
CLOD, *N.*
ḍhemh. *f ;* ḍhelá. *m ;* ḍhím. *f ;* chil. *f ;*
CLOD CRUSHER, *N.*
suhágá. *m ;*
to break clods. ḍhemhá phehná ; chilán bhanná ;
CLOGGED ; *A.*
jaḍḍá ;
CLOSE, *Adv.*
neṛe ; pás ; kol ;
close together, sanghne

CLOSE, TO, *V. T.*
1. to shut. band karná;
2. to complete. púrá karná; naberná; mukáuná;
3. to close the eyes. míṭná; mích lená; míṭ lená;
4. to close the door. buhá márná OR dhoná OR bherná;

CLOSE, TO, *V. I.*
saṇggochná;

CLOSELY, *Adv.*
neṛe teṛe; kol kol; pás pás; láge láge;

CLOSET, *N.*
almárí. *f*;

CLOTH, *N.*
kapṛá. *m*; líṛá. *m*; kappaṛ. *m*; bastar. *m*; líṛá lattá. *m*;
1. coarse country made cloth. khaddar. *m*; subhar. *m*; gáṛhá. *m*; chauṇsí. *f*;
2. embroidered cloth. phulkárí. *f*;
3. colored cloth with white spots. daresh. *m*;
4. coarse embroidered cloth. bág. *m*;
5. red cloth. halwán. *m*;
6. cloth for carrying books. bastá. *m*;
7. cloth for carrying food. ponáṇ. *m*; jháṛaṇ. *m*;
8. velvet. makhmal. *n*; makhmakh. *m*;
9. muslin. malmal. *f*;
10. burial cloth. kafan. *m*;

CLOTHE, TO, *V. T.*
kapṛá páuná;

CLOTHES, *N.*
kapṛe. *m*; líṛe. *m*; bhes. *m*; baná. *m*; bastar. *m*; astar bastar. *m*; bharáwa. *m*; líṛá lattá. *m*;
used contemptuously, tallá. *m*;
clothes sent to a bride. jhaṛává, *m*;

WOMEN'S CLOTHES.
Loose trousers, tight at ankles. sutthaṇ. *f*; sutthuṇ. *f*; sulwár. *f*;
Loose trousers all the way down. gurárá. *m*;
Trousers tight to the knee. chúrídár sutthuṇ. *f*;
Waistcoat or overshirt. kurtí. *f*; phatúí. *f*;
Bodice for covering the breasts. cholí. *f*; aṇggí. *f*;
Petticoat. ghaggará. *m*; ghaggarí. *f*; lahiṇggá. *m*;
Bodice. jhaggí. *f*;
Tunic. jhaggá. *m*;
Skirt. ghaggará. *m*;
Length of cloth worn as a skirt. táhmaṇt. *m*;
Dress worn by Hindus and Parsees. sárhí *f*;
Shawl. chádar. *f*; chunní. *f*; líṛá. *m*;
Clothes given to bride by bridegroom's father. warí. *f*;
Stockings. jarábbán. *f*; massíán. *f*;
Shoe. juttí. *f*;
Wooden shoes. karáṇwán. *f*;
Colored threads for tying the hair. paráṇḍí. *f*;
Embroidered cloth. phulkárí. *f*;
Head dress. sirgá. *m*;
A suit of clothes. joṛá. *m*; teur. *m*;
Red cotton shawl with embroidered edge. chop. *m*;
Small coat for a child. kurtá. *m*; jhaggí. *f*;
A piece of cloth. lattá. *m*;

MEN'S CLOTHES.
Turban, small. pagṛí. *f*;
Turban, large. pagg. *m*; paggaṛ. *m*;
Turban, red. chírá. *m*;
Turban, red, with braided ends. gotíwálá chírá. *m*;
Turban with gold or silver fringe. jhálarwálá safá. *m*;
Scarf or cloth thrown over shoulder. dopattá. *m*;
Thick sheet. khes. *m*;
Khes, with coloured border. chútáí *f*;
Waistcoat. phatúí. *f*; wástkot. *m*;
Waistcoat with short sleeves. salúká. *m*;
Shirt, open with loose sleeves. kurtá. *m*; jhaggá. *m*; jhiggá. *m*;
Shirt with tight sleeves. kamíz. *m*;
Trousers with wide loose legs. tambá. *m*; tambí. *f*; pyjámá. *m*;
Trousers with tight fitting legs. churídár pyjámá. *m*;

Trousers, loose, but tight at ankle. silwár. *m ;*
Drawers worn bySikhs. kachchh.*f;* kachchárá. *m ;*
Loin cloth worn by Hindus. dhotti. *f ;*
Cloth worn round waist and legs by villagers. táhmat. *m ;*
Loin clothes or strips of cloth worn between legs. gahái. *f ;* langoṭṭí. *f ;* langoṭṭá. *m;* jhangiá. *m ;* súdná. *m ;* jhángírá. *m;* rumálí. *f ;* sáfá. *m ;*
Boots. but. *m ;*
Shoes. juttí. *f ;* annhe ghoṛe. *m ;*
Shoes, old and worn. chittar. *m ;*
Handkerchief. rumál. *m ;*
Socks. jurábáṇ. *f ;* moje. *m ;* massiáṇ. *f ;* jarebáṇ. *f ;*
Stockings. jurábáṇ. *f ;*
Stockings for children. massiáṇ. *f ;*
Vest. banáin. *f ;*
Coat. koṭ. *m ;*
Overcoat. brándí. *f ;*
Servant's coat. aṇgrakká. *m ;*
CLOTH MERCHANT, *N.* bajáj. *m ;*
CLOTTED, *A.* jamiá hoyá ;
CLOUD, *N.* baddal. *m ;* ghan. *m ;* ghaṭ. *f ;* baddalí. *f ;*
CLOUDINESS, *N.* baddal gubár. *m ;* haze. gahir. *f ;*
CLOUDLESS, *A.* nitriá hoyá ;
CLOUDY, *A.* ghaṭṭá ṭiṭ ; jhaṛ. *f ;*
1. very cloudy. baṛá baddal; gúhṛá baddal; gáhṛá baddal;
2. to be cloudy. jhaṛ ho jáná; baddal chhá jáná ; baddal á jáná ; ghaṭṭá áuní; ghaṭṭá chaṛhní; baddal ghuliá hoyá hai;
CLOVE, *N.* lauṇg. *f ;*
CLOVER, *N.* senjí. *f ;* lusan. *m ;*
CLOWN, *N.*
1. professional. nakliá. *m ;* bhaṇḍ. *m ;*

2. a foolish person. gaṇwár. *m ;* gawár. *m ;*
CLOWNISHNESS, N. gaṇwárpuṇá. *m ;*
CLUB, *N.* daṇḍá. *m ;* láṭṭhí. *f ;* ḍáṇg. *f ;* daṇgorí. *f ;* soṭṭá. *m ;* iron club. gurj. *m ;*
CLUB FOOTED, *A.* ḍuḍḍá ; ṭhibbá ;
CLUE, *N.* patá. *m ;*
CLUMP OF TREES, *N.* jhaṇgí. *f ;* zakhírá. *m ;*
CLUMSILY, *Adv.* búrí taráh nál;
CLUMSY, *A.* anáṛí ; beaql ; ḍaṇggar. bhaddá ;
CLUSTER, *N.* guchchhá. *m ;*
CLUTCH, *N.* muṭṭh. *f ;*
CLUTCH, TO, *V. T.* hatth nál phaṛná; guṭṭhná; phagaṛná ;
COADJUTOR, *N.* madatgár. *m;* sáṇjhí. *m ;* himaití.*m;* saṇgatí. *m ;* sáthí. *m ;* sharík. *m ;*
COACH HOUSE, *N.* baggí kháná. *m ;*
COACHMAN, *N.* sahís. *m ;* gaḍḍíwáṇ. *m ;*
COAGULATE, TO, *V. I.* jammná ; chakká honá ; phaṭ jáná ; phiṭ jáná ;
COAGULATION, *N.* jamáu. *f ;*
COAL., *N.* kolá. *m;* patthar dá kolá. *m;* small broken pieces of coal. kerí, *f ;*
COALESCE, TO, *V. I.* ikk ho jáná ; milná ;
COALESENCE, *N.*
1. union. miláp. *m ;*
2. join. joṛ. *m ;*
COARSE, *A.* moṭṭa ; sabbhar ; ṭhullhá ; as flour. dardará ; gargará ;
COAST, *N.* kaṇḍhá. *m ;* samundar dá bann *m;*

COAT, *N*.
koṭ. *m*; see CLOTHES.
COAX, TO, *V. T*.
ḳhush karke manáuná; dalásá dená; jháṇsná; puchkárná; see CAJOLE.
COB, *N*.
1. horse. ghoṛá. *m*;
2. of maize. challí. *f*; challí tukká. *m*;
COBBLER, *N*.
mochí. *m*;
COBRA, *N*.
phanyar sapp. *m*; khaṛappá. *m*; nág. *m*;
COBWEB, *N*.
jálá. *m*;
a single thread. tár. *f*;
COCK, *N*.
kukkaṛ. *m*;
1. a young cockerel. paṭṭhá. *m*;
2. a male chicken. chuchá. *m*;
COCK OF A GUN, *N*.
banduq dá ghoṛá. *m*;
COCKATOO, *N*.
totá. *m*;
COCKROACH, *N*.
ikk parkár dá kíṛá. *m*;
COCKCROW, *N*.
báng murg. *m*; taṛke. *m*; fajre. *m*; kukkuṛ dí báng. *f*; dhammí velá. *m*; sarghí velá. *m*; muṇh maṇhere. *m*;
COCKSCOMB, *N*.
kalgí. *f*;
COCOA, *N*.
koko. *f*;
COCOANUT, *N*.
khoppá. *m*; nalerá. *m*;
1. half a nut. ṭhuṭhí. *f*;
2. the kernel. girí. *f*; garí. *f*;
3. the shell. lalerí. *f*;
4. used as huqqá. lalerá. *m*;
COCOON, *N*.
resham de kíṛe dá khol. *m*;
CODDLE, TO, *V. T*.
gal nál láuná; pyár dená OR karná; láḍ karná;
COEQUAL, *A*.
barábar; ikko jehá;
COERCE, TO, *V. T*.
jabr karná; zoráwarí karní; jor páuná; dabáuná; tang karná; wáddhá karná;
COERCION, *N*.
jabardastí. *f*; julm. *m*; jor. *m*; dhigáná. *m*; jástí. *f*; wáddhá. *m*;
COFFEE, *N*.
káfí. *f*;
COFFEE POT, *N*.
káfidán. *m*;
COFFIN, *N*.
sandúq. *m*;
cloth used as coffin by Muhammadans. kafan. *m*;
COGITATE, TO, *V. T*.
sochná; soch wichár karná; dhián karná;
COGITATION, *N*.
soch. *m*; ḳhayál. *m*; gaur. *m*; chitmaní. *f*; chiṇtá. *f*;
COGWHEEL, *N*.
pinj dá árá. *m*;
COHABIT, TO, *V. T*.
garist karná; bhog karná; jamá karná;
COHABITATION, *N*.
garist. *m*; bhog. *m*; bhog balás. *m*;
COHERE, TO, *V. I*.
lipat jáná; lag jáná; chambaṛná; chambaṛ jáná;
COHESION, *N*.
mel. *m*; lugáo. *m*;
COIL, *N*.
kuṇḍal. *m*;
COIN, *N*.
sikká. *m*;
1. good coin. khará;
2. base coin. khoṭṭá;
COINCIDE, TO, *V. I*.
ralná; milná; ṭhík bahná;
COKE, *N*.
kolá. *m*;
COLANDER, *N*.
chhánní. *f*;
COLD, *N*.
pálá. *m*; sardí. *f*; ṭhaṇḍ. *f*; jáṛá. *m*; siál. *m*; thár. *m*; sít. *m*;
COLD, *A*.
ṭhaṇḍá; sard; ṭhaṇḍá sít;
it was cold. pálá paiṇdá sí;

COLD IN THE HEAD, *N.*
nazlá. *m ;*
to catch cold in the head. zakhám laggná ;

COLD BLOODED, *A.*
bedard ; beráhm ; betaras ; jálim ; karṛá ;

COLDNESS, *N.*
ṭhaṇḍak. *f ;*

COLD SEASON, *N.*
siál de din. *m ;* jáṛá. *m ;* pále de din. *m ;*

COLIC, *N.*
maroṛ. *m ;*
colic pains. waṭṭ. *m ;* sul. *m ;*

COLLAPSE, TO, *V. I.*
digg painá ; dhaih painá ;

COLLAR, *N.*
1. of a man. galbíná. *m ;* galamá. *m ;*
2. of a dog. paṭá. *m ;*
3. of a horse. halká *m ;*

COLLAR BONE, *N.*
hass. *m ;*

COLLEAGUE, *N.*
sáthí. *m ;* sáṇjhí. *m ;* bháíwál. *m ;* bhíál. *m ;*

COLLECT, *N.*
duá. *f ;*

COLLECT, TO, *V. T.*
joṛná ; kaṭṭhá karná ; jamá karná ;
to collect money. ugráhná ;

COLLECT, TO, *V. I.*
juṛná ; kaṭṭhe ho jáná ;

COLLECTED, *A.*
kaṭṭhe ;

COLLECTION, *N.*
1. of money. chandá. *m ;* dán. *m ;* pun. *m ;* pun dán. *m ;*
2. of people. kaṭṭh. *m ;* saṇgat. *f ;* mandalí. *f ;* ṭollí. *f ;* lukáí. *f ;* lokí. *f ;*
3. of dues. ugráhí. *f ;*

COLLEGE, *N.*
kálij. *m ;*

COLLIDE, TO, *V. I.*
khaih jáná ; bhiṛ jáná ; ṭakkar kháni ; khaih lag jáná ;

COLLISION, *N.*
ṭakkar. *f ;* khaih. *f ;*

COLLOQUIAL, *A.*
ám bolí vichch ; gal bát dá ;

COLLOQY, *N.*
gal bát. *f ;*

COLLUSION, *N.*
mansúbá. *m ;* saláh mashwárá. *m ;* matá. *m ;*

COLONEL, *N.*
karnail sáhib. *m ;* kamánier sáhib. *m ;*

COLONIST, *N.*
nawí abádí dá waskín. *m ;*

COLONIZE, TO, *V. T.*
wasáuná ; abád karná ;

COLONY, *N.*
nahr. *m ;* nawí abádí. *f ;* nawí wassoṇ. *m ;*

COLOSSAL, *A.*
bahut waḍḍá ; bhárá ;

COLOUR, *N.*
raṇg. *m ;* rup. *m ;*

LIST OF COLOURS.
fast colour. pakká ;
faint or light colour. phikká ; maddham ;
deep in colour. gúhṛá ; gúṛhá ; tez ; shokh ;
almond. badámí ;
black. kálá ; siáh ; níl ;
light blue. asmání raṇg; phikká nílá;
blue. nílá ;
light brown. badámí ;
reddy brown. fálsá ; bhúrá ;
dark brown. bhúsalá ;
leather colour. naswárí ;
crimson. ársí gulábí ; kíramchí ;
corn colour. gandamí ;
green. hará ; sabz ; hariá ; sáwá ;
light green. pastákí ;
flesh colour. gorá ;
bright red. lál ; surkh ; sodá ;
rattá ; rattaṛá ;
scarlet. suhá ;
dark red. guṛhá lál ;
purple. banjaní ; jáman ; káshní ;
orange. santrá raṇg ; gataí. naranjí ;
ochre. gerí ; bhagwá ; jogí raṇg ;
light pink. piází ; piájí ;
pink. gulábí ;
deep pink. átshí gulábí ;
grey. sáwá ;
yellow. basantí ; pílá ;
white. chittá ; súfed ; baggá ;
white, for hair only. dhaulá ;

COLOURS FOR HORSES.
bay. lohá ; kamait ; kamaid ;
black, with some red in it. mushkí ;
chesnut. lál ; phosalá ;
dun. samand ;
black. lákhá ; kálá ;
grey. sabzá ; kailá ;
iron grey, gorá ; sáwá ;
roan. garrá ;
piebald. ablak ; dabbá ;
white. baggá ; chittá ;
mouse coloured. ghasmailá ;
COLOURS FOR ANIMALS.
a black cow. lákhí ;
a brown cow. kaplá ;
reddish brown. lohá ; gorí ;
black. kálá ;
bluish grey. lílá ;
grey and black. kailá kaplá ;
white grey. baggá ;
white. daulá ;
deep red. rattá ;
COLOUR, TO, *V. T.*
rangná ; rang karná ;
to cause to be coloured. ranggáuná ;
COLOURED, *A.*
rangwálá ; rangdár ; rangbarang ;
COLOURING, *N.*
ranggat. *f ;* rang. *m ;*
COLT, *N.*
wachcherá. *m ;* bachcherá. *m ;*
COLUMN, *N.*
1. a pillar. kaulá. *m ;*
2. of a newspaper. khánǎ. *m ;*
COMA, *N.*
behoshí. *f ;* gúkí. *f ;*
COMB, *N.*
1. hair comb. kanghí. *f ;*
2. cock's comb. kalgí. *f ;* kalanggá. *m ;*
COMB, TO, *V. T.*
kanghá wáhuná OR karná OR pherná ;
COMBAT, *N.*
laṛáí. *f ;* ghol. *m ;*
of words. chunjaṛí. *f ;*
COMBATANT, *N.*
pahilwán. *m ;* ghuláṭiá. *m ;*
COMBINATION, *N.*
mel miláp. *m ;* ekká. *m ;*
COMBINE, TO, *V. T.*
joṛná ; miláuná ;
COMBINED, *A.*
miliá hoyá ; kaṭṭhe hoke ;
COME, TO, *V. I.*
pás OR neṛe OR kol OR lágge áuná ;
1. to come to oneself. surt vichch áuná ;
2. to come out. nikalná ;
3. the time has come. velá ḍhuk piá hai ;
COMELY, *A.*
shakalwálá ; darshaní ; sohná ; rupwálá ; mukhwálá ; joban ; sundar ;
COMET, *N.*
bodíwálá tárá. *m ;* puchhalwálá tárá. *m ;* púshwálá tárá. *m ;*
COMFORT, *N.*
tasallí. *f ;* dilásá. *m ;* dilásará. *m ;* ṭhanḍh. *f ;*
rest. armán. *m ;* rámán. *m ;* arám. *m ;* asog. *m ;*
COMFORT, TO, *V. T.*
tasallí dení ; dilásá dená ; dhirwás dená ;
COMFORTED, TO BE, *V. I.*
tasallí honí OR pauní ;
COMFORTABLE, *A.*
arám denwálá ;
COMFORTABLY, *Adv.*
arám nál ; sukh nál ;
COMFORTER, *N.*
tasallí denwálá. *m ;*
COMFORTLESS, *A.*
dukhí ; masosiá hoyá ;
COMING, *N.*
áuná. *m ;*
the second coming of Christ. Masíh dí dujjí ámad. *f ;*
COMMAND, *N.*
hukm. *m ;* ágiá. *m ;* tágíd. *f ;*
COMMAND, TO, *V. T.*
hukm dená ; hukm karná ; ágiá dená ; tágíd karná ;
COMMANDER, *N.*
faujdár. *m ;* kamaniár. *m ;*
commander-in-chief. jangí láṭ. *m ;*
COMMANDMENT, *N.*
Khudá dá hukm. *m ;*
COMMEMORATE, TO, *V. T.*
manáuná ; yád karná ;

COMMEMORATION, *N.*
yádgírí. *f ;*
COMMENCE, TO, *V. T.*
shurú karná ; árambh karná ; chohná ; shohná ; see BEGIN.
COMMENCEMENT, *N.*
ád. *m ;* shurú. *m ;* árambh. *m ;* muḍḍh. *m ;*
COMMEND, TO, *V. T.*
táríf karní ; shábásh dení ; saráhná ; guṇ gáuná ; saláhná ;
COMMENDABLE, *A.*
táríf de laiq ;
COMMENDATION, *N.*
1. recommendation. sifárish. *f ;*
2. praise. salauhat. *f ;* táríf. *f ;* waḍíáí. *f ;*
COMMENT, *N.*
raí. *f ;* gal. *f ;*
COMMENT, TO, *V. T.*
raí dení ; kujh bolná ;
COMMENTARY, *N.*
tafsír. *f ;*
COMMERCE, *N.*
buhár. *m ;* laiṇ deṇ. *f ;* vanj bipár. *m ;* vihár. *m ;* leká deká. *m ;* leká dekí, *f ;*
COMMINGLE, TO, *V. T.*
miláuná ; raláuná ;
COMMISERATE, TO, *V. T.*
dardí honá ; tars kháná ; rahm karná ; dilásá dená ; dukh waṇḍná ; dhirwás dená ;
COMMISERATION, *N.*
dáyá. *m ;* tars. *f ;* dardmandí. *f ;*
COMMISSION, *N.*
1. payment. dastúrí. *f ;* áhrat. *f ;* dalálí. *f ;*
2. authority. ikhtiyár. *m ;* wass. *m ;*
3. written authority. sanad. *f ;*
COMMISSION AGENT, *N.*
dalál. *m ;* áhratí. *m ;* áhratiá. *m ;*
COMMIT, TO, *V. T.*
1. to intrust. sauṇp dená ; hawále karná ;
2. to do. karná ;
3. to commit to memory. kaṇṭh karná ; múṇh zabání yád karná ; raṭ lená ; raṭṭná ;
COMMITTED, TO BE, *V. I.*
sauṇpiá jáná ;
COMMITTEE, *N.*
kameṭí. *f ;* paṇchait. *f ;* sabhá. *f ;*
COMMODITY, *N.*
1. goods. jins. *f ;* mál. *m ;* saudá. *m ;*
2. produce. paidáwárí. *f ;*
COMMON, *N.*
maidán. *m ;*
common village ground. baqáyá. *m ;* shámlát. *f ;*
COMMON, *A.*
ám ; mámulí ; aiweṇ aiweṇ ;
shared in common. sáṇjhá ;
COMMONLY, *Adv.*
aksar ; bahut wárí ;
COMMONPLACE, *A.*
mámulí ; ám ; aiweṇ keweṇ ;
COMMOTION, *N.*
raulá. *m ;* hal chal. *f ;* hullaṛ. *m ;* shor. *m ;* khap. *m ;* daṇggá fasád. *m;* khalhbalí. *f ;*
COMMUNE, TO, *V. T.*
1. to meditate. apne dil nál gallán karní ; soch wichár karná ; man OR dil vichch sochná ;
2. to talk. gallán bátáṇ karní ;
3. to confer. apo vichch saláh mashwará karná ;
COMMUNICATION, *N.*
khabar. *f ;* sanehá. *m ;*
COMMUNICATE, TO, *V. T.*
dassná ; kahná ; khabar dení ; sanehá ghallná ;
COMMUNICATE, TO, *V. T.*
Pák Rifáqat vichch shámil honá ; Ashá i Rabbání lainí ;
COMMUNION, *N.*
mel miláp. *m ;* saṇgat. *f ;*
the Holy Communion. Pák Rifáqat. *f ;* Ashá i Rabbání. *f ;*
COMMUNITY, *N.*
sáre lok. *m ;* qaum. *f ;* koṛmá. *m ;*
COMMUTE, TO, *V. T.*
badal lainá ; adal badal karná ; waṭáuná ; see EXCHANGE.
COMPACT, *N.*
qaul qarár. *m ;* nem. *m ;* bachan. *f ;*
COMPANION, *N.*
sáthí. *m ;* saṇgí. *m ;* sohbatí. *m ;* belí. *m ;* yár. *m ;* saṇgatí. *m ;* sajjan. *m ;* mere nál dá. *m ;* joṛídar. *m ;*

1. spoken by a woman of a woman. sahelí. *f*; sehlí. *f*; saríkaní. *f*;
2. spoken by a man of a woman. bhaiṇ. *f*;
3. who is your companion; tuháḍe nál dá ádmí kaun hai;

COMPANIONSHIP, *N*.
saṇgat. *f*; dostí. *f*; mel miláp. *m*; millat. *f*;

COMPANY, *N*.
jatthá. *m*; kaṭṭh. *m*; jamát. *f*; ṭollá. *m*; ṭollí. *f*; maṇḍlí. *f*; saṇg. *f*; jundí. *f*; saṇgat. *f*; taraṇḍí. *f*;
1. a business company. kampaní. *f*;
2. in companies. junḍíáṇ hoke;

COMPARE, TO, *V. T.*
miláke muqábalá karná; raláke muqábalá karná;
compared with. uh de muqábale vichch;

COMPARTMENT, *N*.
kamrá. *m*; kothṛí. *f*;

COMPASS, *N*.
1. circuit. gherá. *m*; chakkar. *m*;
2. instrument. kutabnumá. *m*;
3. boundary. hadd. *m*;

COMPASS, TO, *V. T.*
gáh márná;

COMPASSION, *N*.
ráhm. *m*; ráhmat. *f*; dáyá. *f*; kirpá. *f*; dardmandí. *f*; mihrbání. *f*; mihrbánagí. *f*;

COMPASSIONATE, *A*.
ráhmdil; narmdil; dáyáwáṇ; dayál; kirpál.
for God only. rahím;

COMPASSIONATELY, *Adv*.
dáyá karke; ráhm nál; ráhmdiil nál;

COMPATIBLE, *A*.
laiq; mildá juldá; ṭhík; see SUITABLE.

COMPEER, *N*.
sáthí. *m*; saṇgí. *m*;

COMPEL, TO, *V. T.*
láchár karná; dabáuná; jor páuná; taṇg karná; aukhíáṇ karná;

COMPENDIUM, *N*.
nichoṛ. *m*; ḳhalásá. *m*; arq. *m*;

COMPENSATE, TO, *V. T.*
harjá dená; harjánná dená; kasar bharní; waṭṭá dená;
to take revenge. badlá lená;

COMPENSATION, *N*.
harjá. *m*; badlá. *m*; waṭṭá. *m*; harjánná. *m*; ṭoṭ. *f*;
pay. mazdúrí. *f*; diháṛí. *f*;

COMPETE, TO, *V. T.*
rís karná; khaih karná; barábarí karní; muqábalá karná;

COMPETENT, *A*.
laiq; jog; samajhdár; tagṛá; kárígar;

COMPETITION, *N*.
muqábalá. *m*;

COMPETITOR, *N*.
rís karnwálá. *m*; muqábalá karnwálá *m*;

COMPILE, TO, *V. T.*
likhná; kitáb banáuní;

COMPLACENCY, *N*.
1. urbanity. narmí. *f*; ádar bhau. *m*;
2. satisfaction. tasallí. *f*; dharwás. *m*; tipat. *f*; dilásá. *m*; hauṇsilá. *m*;

COMPLACENT. *A*.
ḳhush; rájí; magan;

COMPLAIN, TO, *V. T.*
1. to accuse. shikayat karní; chuglí kháṇí; ilzám láuná; lutíáṇ láuná;
2. legal. nálish karná; dává karná; arjí páuṇí; faryád karná;

COMPLAINANT, *N*.
faryádí. *m*; fariádí. *m*; sawálí. *m*;
1. legal. nálashí. *m*; mudáí. *m*;
2. a tale bearer. chugal. *m*;

COMPLAINT, *N*.
shikayat. *f*; chuglí. *f*; fariád. *f*; durohí. *f*; duhái. *f*; chíṇ píṇ. *f*; sawál. *m*; hál pukár. *m*; uláhmá. *m*; ulámbhá. *m*;
legal. nálish. *f*; arjí. *f*; dává. *f*;

COMPLAISANCE, *N*.
bhalmánasí. *f*; narmí. *f*; bhalmansái. *f*;

COMPLETE, *A*.
púrá; tamám; sapuran; baṇiá banáiá; mukammal;

COMPLETE, TO, *V. T.*
púrá karná; naberná kar chhaḍḍná; sarájít karná; sire jhaṛáuná; mukáuná; sapuran karná;
COMPLETED, TO BE, *V. I.*
púrá honá; nibaṛ jáná; mukk jáná; sarájít honá;
COMPLETELY, *Adv.*
sáre dá sárá; pure taur nál; mullon; bilkull; ukká mukká; haddoṇ muḍḍhoṇ;
COMPLETION, *N.*
niberá. *m*; nibbaṛ tibbaṛ. *m*; nabáh. *m*;
COMPLEX, *A.*
pechwálá; wal pechwálá;
COMPLEXION, *N.*
raṇg. *m*; raṇg rup. *m*;
COMPLEXITY, *N.*
wal. *m*; pech. *m*; wal pech. *m*; her pher. *m*;
COMPLIANCE, *N.*
manzúrí. *f*; huṇgárá. *m*; hámí. *f*;
COMPLIANT, *A.*
narm; momdil; mihrbán;
COMPLICATE, TO, *V. T.*
wal páuná; pech páuná; phasáuná; gunjal páuná;
COMPLICATED, *A.*
gumgo; pechwálá; gol mol;
COMPLICATION, *N.*
ech pech. *m*; wal. *m*; pech. *m*; gunjal. *f*;
COMPLICITY, *N.*
sharárat karn vichch madat. *f*;
COMPLIMENT, *N.*
wadháioṇ. *f*; wadhái. *f*;
COMPLIMENT, TO, *V. T.*
wadháioṇ dení; waḍiái karní; mubárikbádí dení;
to praise. guṇ gáuná; táríf karní; saláhná; saláhuná;
COMPLY, TO, *V. T.*
1. to agree, accept. manná; manzúr karná; háṇ karní; qabúl karná; hámí bharní;
2. to obey. aggiákár karná;
COMPOSE, TO, *V. T.*
kitáb OR pustak banáuná; mazmun taiyár karná;
COMPOSED, *A.*
chup cháp; dhíraj máṇ; gambhír; dhírají; sabrwálá;
COMPOSER, *N.*
rág banáunwálá. *m*; shaihrí. *m*; saihrí. *m*;
COMPOSITION, *N.*
kabíshari. *f*;
COMPOSURE, *N.*
sáṇt. *f*; sáṇtagí. *f*; dhíraj. *f*; dil jamá. *m*; hauṇsilá. *m*; sabr. *m*;
COMPOUND, *N.*
1. enclosure. hátá. *m*; wehṛá. *m*;
2. mixture. miláwat. *f*; mel. *m*; miláo. *m*;
COMPOUND, TO, *V. T.*
miláuná; gholná; raláuná; to mix together (not liquids). massná;
COMPOUNDER, *N.*
dawá banáunwálá. *m*;
COMPREHEND, TO, *V. T.*
samajhná; malúm karná; bujjhná; ján lainá; lakhná; samajh áuní; nirwair karná;
COMPREHENSION, *N.*
samajh. *f*; aql. *f*; matt. *f*; buddh. *f*; hosh. *m*; thauh. *m*; bújh. *f*;
COMPRESS, TO, *V. T.*
1. to shorten. chhoṭá karná; ghaṭṭáuná; nichoṛ karná;
2. to squeeze. ghuṭṭná; dabná; napná;
COMPRESSION, *N.*
dabb. *f*; dabáu. *m*;
COMPRISE, TO, *V. I.*
samáuná; meuná;
COMPROMISE, TO, *V. T.*
rájínámá karná; suláh safái karní; faisalá karná;
COMPROMISE, *N.*
suláh. *f*; safái. *f*; suláh safái. *f*; legal. rázínámá. *m*;
COMPULSION, *N.*
jabar. *f*; zabardastí. *f*; vagárí. *f*; jorávarí. *f*; jástí. *f*; jálamí. *f*;
COMPULSORY, *A.*
zarúrí; jabaran; badobadí; jorájorí; dhakko dhakkí;
1. compulsory labour. wigár. *m*;
2. compulsory subject. lázmí;

COMPUNCTION, *N.*
hirkh. *m* ; pachtáwá. *m* ; pastáwá. *m* ; gam. *m* ; ranj. *m* ; gamí. *f* ; hamsos. *f* ;

COMPUTATION, *N.*
hisáb. *m* ; lekhá. *m* ; gintí. *f* ; hisáb kitáb. *f* ; lekhá pattá. *m* ; lekhá jokhá. *m* ;

COMPUTE, TO, *V. T.*
gin lainá ; hisáb karná OR joṛná ; lekhá lainá ; lekhá pattá karná ; to compute by weighing. háṛá lainá ;

COMRADE, *N.*
dost. *m* ; yár. *m* ; sáthí. *m* ; nál dá. *m* ; mittar. *m* ; sohbatí. *m* ; hamjolí. *m* ; sajjan. *m* ; pyárá. *m* ; saṇgatí. *m* ;

COMRADESHIP, *N.*
dostí. *f* ; yárí. *f* ;

CONCEAL, TO, *V. T.*
lukáuná ; chhipáuná ; uhlá karná ; dhappná ; napná ;
1. to conceal oneself. ghusáuná ; lukáuná ;
2. to cover anything. dhakkná ; kajjná ;

CONCEALED, TO BE, *V. I.*
lukná ; chhipná ;

CONCEALED, *A.*
gujjhá ; gujjhí ; gaib ;

CONCEALMENT, *N.*
lukáu. *m* ; chhipáu. *m* ; luká. *m* ;

CONCEDE, TO, *V. T.*
1. to grant. dená ; bakhshná ;
2. to admit. manná ; man lainá ;
3. to allow. ijázat dení ; ijan dená ;
4. to give up. chhaḍ dená ; ján dená ;

CONCEIT, *N.*
heṇh. *f* ; magrúrí. *f* ; gamrúrí. *f* ; hekaṛí. *f* ; baṭí. *f* ; mizáj. *f* ; damág. *m* ; báṇkápuná. *m* ; kibar. *m* ; ghamaṇḍ *m* ;

CONCEITED, *A.*
phiṭṭiá hoyá ; haṇkárí. *f* ; gamrúr ; báṇká ; ghamaṇḍ ; gumání ; magrúr ; báṇká ṭeḍhá ; damákí ;

CONCEITEDLY, *Adv.*
baṛe gumán nál ; baṛe damág nál ; ghamaṇḍ nál ;

CONCEIVE, TO, *V. T.*
1. to become pregnant. garbh rahná OR ṭhahrna ; garbhaní honá ; pair bhárí honá ; ḍhiḍḍh honá ;
2. for cattle only. áse honá OR laggná ;
3. to think. ḳhayál karná ; sochná ; soch wichárná ; chetná ;
4. to understand. samajhná ; bujjhná ;

CONCENTRATE, TO, *V. T.*
dhián karná ; kann dharke sochná ;

CONCENTRATION, *N.*
dhián. *m* ; gaur. *m* ; soch wichár. *m* ;

CONCEPTION, *N.*
1. thought. gumán. *m* ; wichár. *m* ; ḳhayál. *m* ; samajh. *f* ;
2. pregnancy. ummedwárí. *f* ; hamal. *m* ; garbh. *m* ; ḍhiḍḍh. *f* ;

CONCERN, *N.*
1. a work. kamm. *m* ; káj. *m* ; kár bár. *m* ;
2. care. anxiety. chintá. *m* ; parwáh. *f* ; hamsos. *f* ; fikr. *m* ; handeshá. *m* ; chitt chetá. *f* ;
3. connection. wástá. *m* ;

CONCERN, TO, *V. T.*
1. to be concerned about. fikr karná ;
2. to have connection with. wástá rakkhná ;

CONCERNING, *Prep.*
dí bábat ; de báre vichch ;

CONCERT, *N.*
gít gáun dá jalsá. *m* ; tamáshá. *m* ;

CONCERT, TO, *V. T.*
saláh mashwará karná ; ḍhaṇg sochná ; upáú labbhná OR karná ;

CONCESSION, *N.*
riayat. *f* ; ráí. *f* ;

CONCH, *N.*
saṇkh. *m* ;

CONCILIATE, TO, *V. T.*
rází karní ; manáuná ; suláh karáuní ; mel miláp karauná ; dhímá karná ; maṭṭhá karná ;

CONCILIATION, *N.*
mel miláp. *m* ; suláh. *f* ; suláh safáí. *f* ;

CONCILIATORY, *A.*
narm ; mulaim ;

CONCISE, *A*.
mukhtasar; ghaṭṭ; thoṛá;
CONCLAVE, *N*.
kameṭí. *f*; jalsá. *m*;
CONCLUDE, TO, *V. T*.
1. to finish. naberná; mukáuná;
2. to draw a conclusion. natíjá kaḍḍhná; gaveṛ karná; arq kaḍḍhná;
CONCLUDING, *A*.
ákhirí; mukk chaliá;
CONCLUSION, *N*.
1. result. natíjá. *m*; gaveṛ. *m*; hásil. *m*;
2. end. ákhir. *m*; anṭ. *m*; oṛak. *m*;
CONCOCT, TO, *V. T*.
1. to plan. saláh pakáuní; upáo labbhná;
2. to make. banáuná; ḍhaṇg sochná;
CONCOCTION, *N*.
1. a plan. tajwíz. *f*; saláh. *f*;
2. a mixture. miláwat. *f*; miláú. *m*;
CONCORD, *N*.
miláp. *m*; mel miláp. *m*; sanjog. *m*; ekká. *m*; ikkdilí. *f*; mel jol. *m*;
CONCOURSE, *N*.
kaṭṭh. *m*; jamát. *f*; samáj. *f*; mandlí. *f*; majlis. *f*; jalsá. *m*; ḍhání. *f*;
CONCUBINE, *N*.
benikáhí. *f*;
CONCUPISCENCE, *N*.
mastí. *f*; mastewáṇ. *m*; phaṭeváṇ. *m*: see LUST.
CONCUR, TO, *V. T*.
manná; manzúr karná; háṇ karní; huṇgárá dená; hámí bharní;
CONCURRENCE, *N*.
manzúrí. *f*; huṇgárá. *m*; hámí. *f*;
CONCURRENTLY, *Adv*.
nál hí; milkar;
CONCUSSION, *N*.
saṭṭ. *f*; ṭakkar. *f*; see SHOCK.
CONDEMN, TO, *V. T*.
mujrim karná; aib láuná; dosí ṭhahráuná; aibí banáuná; see CENSURE.
CONDEMNATION, *N*.
sazá dá hukm. *m*; sazá bolní. *f*;

CONDENSATION, *N*.
nichoṛ, *m*; arq. *m*;
CONDENSE, TO, *V. T*.
1. to epitomise. bayán ghaṭṭáuná; nichoṛ karná; arq kaḍḍhná;
2. to steam. simtáuná;
CONDESCEND, TO, *V. T*.
bakhshná; mihrbání karní; sir te hatth rakkhná OR dharná;
CONDESCENDING, *A*.
narm dil; mihrbán; dayál; milápará; milauṛá;
CONDESCENSION, *N*.
mihrbání. *f*; nirmáí, *f*; dáyá. *f*; tars. *f*;
CONDIMENT, *N*.
masálá. *m*;
CONDITION, *N*.
1. state. hál. *m*; hál hawál. *m*; hálat. *f*; hawál. *m*; hál chál. *m*; ḍaul chál. *f*; ḍauláṇ. *f*;
2. stipulation. sharat. *f*;
CONDITIONAL, *A*.
sharatí;
CONDOLE, TO, *V. T*.
1. to console. dukh waṇḍná; afsos karní; dilásá dená; dardí honá uh dá dard karná;
2. to visit in order to mourn and console. mukáṇí jáná;
CONDOLENCE, *N*.
dardmandí. *f*;
after a death. mukáṇ. *f*;
CONDONE, TO, *V. T*.
muáf karná; muáfí dení; bakhshná; jáṇ dená;
CONDUCT, *N*.
chál chalan. *m*; bol chál. *f*; dhaṇg. *m*; chál. *f*; lachchhan. *m*; salúk. *m*; taur taríqá. *m*; chál dhál. *f*;
CONDUCT, TO, *V. T*.
laí jáná; ráh dassná; pahuṇcháuná; chaḍḍ áuná; ráh malláuná; mohre chalná; agge chalná;
CONDUCTOR, *N*.
ágú. *m*; mohrí. *m*; see GUIDE.
CONDUIT, *N*.
1. a waterspout. parnálá. *m*;
2. a small channel or drain. nálí. *f*; morí. *f*; see DRAIN.

CONFABULATE, TO, *V. T.*
gal bát karní; saláh mashwará karná; see CONSULT.
CONFABULATION, *N.*
gallán bátán. *f*; bát chít. *f*;
CONFECTIONER, *N.*
halwáí. *m*; miṭháí wálá. *m*;
CONFECTIONERY, *N.*
miṭháí. *f*; see SWEETMEATS.
CONFEDERATE, *N.*
sáthí. *m*; sáṇjhí. *m*; madatgár. *m*; bhetí. *m*; saṇgatí. *m*; saháí. *m*;
ONFEDERATION, *N.*
juṇglá. *m*; ekká. *m*; kaṭṭh. *m*;
CONFER, TO, *V. T.*
1. to consult. saláh mashwará karná; matt lainí; ápo wichch gal bát karní;
2. to bestow. dená; bakhshná;
CONFERENCE, *N.*
kameṭí. *f*; paṇchait. *f*; jalsá; *m*;
CONFESS, TO, *V. T.*
iqrár karná; mann lainá;
CONFESSION, *N.*
iqrár. *m*; qaul qarár. *m*; qarár. *m*; man manautí. *f*;
CONFESSOR, *N.*
shahíd. *m*;
CONFIDANT, *N.*
bhetí. *m*; bhetáṇ. *f*; laṇgoṭiá yár. *m*;
CONFIDE, TO, *V. T.*
1. to tell. batláuná; dassná;
2. to trust. bharosá rakkhná; ásrá bharosá rakkhná; patíjná; ás rakkhní; wasáh karná; yaqín karná;
3. to believe in. yaqín karná; atbár karná;
CONFIDENCE, *N.*
atbár. *m*; bharosá. *m*; ásrá. *m*; partít. *f*; sardhá. *f*; wasáh. *m*; biswás. *m*;
CONFIDENT, *A.*
bekhauf; befikr;
CONFIDENTIAL, *A.*
1. trusty. atbárí; motabar; wihárí; hatth dá suchchá;
2. private. parde dí gal; nij dí gal; ghar dí gal;
CONFIDENTLY, *Adv.*
yaqín de nál; bekhauf; púrá bharosá karke; dáwe nál; bedharak;

CONFIDING, *A.*
sáddá; bholá; siddhá sáddá;
CONFIGURATION, *N.*
ḍaul. *f*; shakal. *f*; rúp. *m*;
CONFINE, TO, *V. T.*
1. to imprison. qaid kárná; bannh lainá;
2. to restrain. rokná; aṭkáuná;
CONFINED, *A.*
saurá; taṇg; bhíṛá;
CONFINEMENT, *N.*
qaid. *f*;
CONFIRM, TO, *V. T.*
1. to establish. mazbut karná; pakká karná; pakkeáṇ karná; sábit karná;
2. to ratify. háṇ vichch háṇ miláuní; háṇ nál háṇ miláná; háṇ ṭhík ákhná;
CONFIRMATION, *N.*
1. proof. sabút. *f*;
2. evidence. gawáhí. *f*; sákhí. *f*;
CONFIRMED, *A.*
mustaqím; pakká; mazbút; to be confirmed. mustaqím ho jáná; pakkeáṇ ho jáná;
CONFISCATE, TO, *V. T.*
jabt karná; khoh lainá;
1. by legal process. kurk karná;
2. to be confiscated. jabt honá;
CONFISCATION, *N.*
jabtí. *f*; jabt. *m*;
legal. kurkí. *f*;
CONFLAGRATE, TO, *V. T.*
jaláuná; sáṛná; phukná;
CONFLAGRATION, *N.*
agg. *f*; bháṇbar. *m*; bhámrí. *f*;
CONFLATE, TO, *V. T.*
miláuná; kaṭṭhá karná; raláuná;
CONFLICT, *N.*
laṛáí. *f*; jhagṛá. *m*; fasád. *f*; see QUARREL.
CONFLICT, TO, *V. I.*
khiláf ho jáná; nahíṇ milná;
CONFLICTING, *A.*
1. contrary. ápo vichch nahíṇ raldá; khiláf;
2. hostile. ḍhíṭh; háṭhá; jhakkí;
CONFLUENCE, *N.*
1. junction of streams. joṛ. *m*;
2. crowd. bhíṛ. *f*; baṛí khilqat. *f*;

CONFLUX, *N.*
katṭh. *m;* see CONCOURSE.
CONFORM, TO, *V. T.*
1. to make uniform. ikk ḍaul karná; ralá milá dená;
2. to obey. manná; ákkhe laggná;
CONFORMATION, *N.*
ḍaul. *f;* surat. *f;* shakal. *f;*
CONFORMITY, *N.*
mel. *m;* mel jol. *f;*
CONFOUND, TO, *V. T.*
1. to amaze. pareshán karná; ghabrá dená; hakká bakká karná; harán karná;
2. to abash. sharmáuná; lajáuná; ṭhíṭṭh karná;
CONFOUNDED, TO BE, *V. I.*
ghábar jáná; ghábarna; ghabráuná; hakká bakká ho jáná; afarí dafarí paí jáná;
CONFRATERNITY, *N.*
barádrí. *f;* bhái chárá. *m;* bhái bandí. *f;* koṛmá. *m;*
CONFRONT, TO, *V. T.*
sáhmane karná; múṇh te ákhná; múṇh barúh honá;
CONFUSE, TO, *V. T.*
1. to make disorder. raulá páuná; gaṛbaṛí páuní; shor macháuná; hullaṛ macháuná;
2. to abash. sharmáuná; ṭhíṭṭh karná; lajáuná;
3. to embarrass. ghabráuná;
CONFUSED, *A.*
gaḍḍ maḍḍ; biákul;
CONFUSED, TO BE, *V. I.*
ghábar jáná; ghabarná; biákul honá; hafarí dafarí paí jáná; hafará dafarí vichch paí jáná;
CONFUSION, *N.*
raulá. *m;* shor. *m;* gaṛbaṛí. *f;* ḍaṇḍ. *f;* hulaṛ. *m;* khapp. *f;* raulí. *f;* harolí. *f;* afará dafarí. *f;* to be in confusion. khapp mach jáná;
CONFUTATION, *N.*
khaṇḍaṇ. *m;* jawáb. *m;*
CONFUTE, TO, *V. T.*
jhuṭhá sábit karná; jhuṭheáṇ karná; raddná; kise dá múṇh band karná; mukhráuná;

CONGEAL, TO, *V. I.*
jammná; jamm jáná;
CONGENIAL, *A.*
1. suitable. wáṇguṇ; wargá;
2. affable. hass mukhá; milauṛá; milápará; milaṇwálá;
CONGEST, TO, *V. T.*
ḍher lagáuná;
CONGLOMERATION, *N.*
1. an accumulation. ḍher. *m;* ḍherí. *f;*
2. a mixture. jamáú. *m;*
CONGRATULATE, TO, *V. T.*
badhái dení; wadháioṇ dení; mubárikbádí dení;
I congratulate you. maiṇ tuháḍá dhanbád karná háṇ;
CONGRATULATION, *N.*
badhái. *f;* waḍái. *f;* wadháioṇ. *f;*
CONGREGATE, TO, *V. I.*
kaṭṭhá honá; jamá honá;
CONGREGATION, *N.*
jamát. *f;* mandalí. *f;* sabhá. *f;* saṇgat. *f;*
CONGRESS, *N.*
jalsá. *m;* kaṭṭh. *m;*
CONGRUITY, *N.*
mel. *m;* mel jol. *f;* mel miláp. *m;* ekká. *m;*
CONJECTURAL, *A.*
ḳhayálí; kiásí; waihmí;
CONJECTURE, *N.*
ḳhayál. *m;* takk. *f;* kiás. *m;*
CONJECTURE, TO, *V. T.*
andázá láuná; ḳhayál karná; bujjhná; ṭewá láuná; tukká láuná; háṛá lainá;
CONJOINT, *A.*
sáṇjhá; bhanjál;
CONJOINTLY, *Adv.*
milke; kaṭṭhe hoke; ralke; mil julke;
CONJUNCTION, *N.*
mel. *m;* miláuṇí. *f;* wástá. *m;* sanjog. *f;*
CONJURE, TO, *V. T.*
1. to show tricks. kheḍ wikháuní; tamáshá dikhláuná;
2. to exercise. jháṛá karná; jháṛá páuná; jádú karná; ṭúná karná

CONJURER, *N.*
madárí. *m*; jaṇtarí. *m*; madáraṇ. *f*; jogí. *m*; jogaṇ. *f*; bázígar. *m*;
CONNECT, TO, *V. T.*
joṛná; miláuná; lagáuná; raláuná;
CONNECTION, *N.*
1. relationship. rishtá. *m*; mel. *m*; sák aṇg. *m*; rishtedárí. *f*; sákadárí. *f*; náttá sák. *m*;
2. union. wástá. *m*; láká. *m*;
CONNIVANCE, *N.*
madat. *f*;
CONNIVE, TO, *V. T.*
akkh mární;
CONQUER, TO, *V. T.*
jittná; haráuná; sar karná; see OVERCOME.
CONQUERED, TO BE, *V. I.*
pachhaṛ jáná; pachhaṛná;
CONQUEROR, *N.*
jittaṇwálá; jetu. *m*;
CONQUEST, *N.*
fathá. *f*; jit. *f*; jet. *f*;
CONSCIENCE, *N.*
dil. *m*; andar dá chánan. *m*; dil dí awáj. *f*;
my conscience does not allow me. merá dil gawáhí nahíṇ dendá;
CONSCIENTIOUS, *A.*
ímándár; sachchá; díndár; dharmí; hatth dá suchchá; wihárí;
CONSCIENTIOUSLY, *Adv.*
rástí nál; dil nál; sachchíáí nál;
CONSCIOUS, *A.*
hosh vichch;
CONSCIOUSLY, *Adv.*
ján bujh ke; soch samajh ke;
CONSCIOUSNESS, *N.*
hosh. *m*; sudh. *f*;
CONSECRATE, TO, *V. T.*
ghol ghumáuná; Khudá de nám utte dená; ghumáuná; makhsus karná; pawittar karná; mansná;
CONSECRATION, *N.*
ghol ghattí. *f*; ghol ghumáí. *f*;
CONSECUTIVELY. *Adv.*
ikk ikk karke; barábar; aggaṛ pichchhaṛ;
CONSENSUS, *N.*
ekká. *m*; mel jol. *f*; mel miláp. *m*;
CONSENT, TO, *V. T.*
man lainá; manzúr karná; qabulná; háṇ karní; hámí bharní; hungárá OR huṇgúrá karná; rází honá;
CONSENT, *N.*
marzí. *f*; qarár. *m*; hámí. *f*; huṇgárá. *m*; manautí. *f*;
CONSEQUENCE, *N.*
natíjá. *m*; phal. *m*; asar. *m*; gaveṛ. *m*;
CONSEQUENTLY, *Adv.*
is sabab karke; is káran; is laí; is wáste;
CONSERVE, *N.*
1. sweet. murabbá. *m*;
2. salted. achár. *m*;
CONSERVE, TO, *V. T.*
bacháuná; rákkhí karní; rachchiá karná; sambhálná;
CONSIDER, TO, *V. T.*
chitárná; sochná; soch wichár karná; dhíán karná; gaur karná; dhíánaná; kiás karná;
CONSIDERABLE, *A.*
bahut; bahutere; ḍher; bahut sárá;
CONSIDERABLY, *Adv.*
bahut;
CONSIDERATE, *A.*
mihrbán; dhírá; dhírajmáṇ; surtílá; sochmán;
CONSIDERATION, *N.*
1. thought. soch. *m*; soch wichár. *m*; dhíán. *m*; gaur. *m*; chitwaṇí. *f*; wichár. *m*;
2. sake. wáste. *m*; káran. *m*; khátir. *f*; liház. *m*;
CONSIDERING, *Prep.*
is khayál nál;
CONSIGN, TO, *V. T.*
sauṇp dená; hawále karná; supurd karná;
CONSIGNMENT, *N.*
mál. *m*;
CONSIGNMENT NOTE, *N.*
biltí. *f*;
CONSIST, TO, *V. I.*
honá;
CONSISTENCE, *N.*
1. agreement. mel. *m*; mel jol. *f*;
2. density. gáṛhá. *m*; gahiṛ. *f*; guṛhá. *m*;

CONSISTENT, *A.*
pakká ; mildá juldá ;
CONSISTENTLY, *Adv.*
ikk chál nál ; ikk ḍhaṇg nál ;
CONSOLATION, *N.*
tasallí. *f ;* dilásá. *m ;* dilásrá. *m ;* dhirwás. *m ;*
mourning and consoling. mukán. *f ;*
CONSOLE, TO, *V. T.*
tasallí dení ; dilásá dená ; sahárná ; dil ḳhush karná ; dhirwás dená ;
CONSOLIDATE, TO, *V. T.*
jamáuná ; pakká banáuná ;
CONSPICIOUS, *A.*
1. clear. záhir ; sáf ;
2. famous. mashhúr ; námí ; maniá daniá ;
CONSPIRACY, *N.*
juṇglá. *m ;* chálá. *m ;* ekká. *m ;* ghaí. *f ;*
CONSPIRATOR, *N.*
bágí. *m ;* sarkár de barḳhiláf. *m ;* ákí. *m ;*
CONSPIRE, TO, *V. T.*
goreáṇ guṇdná ; ḳhiláf gal pakáuní ; sájish karná ; saláh pakáuní ;
CONSTABLE, *N.*
sipáhí. *m ;* polís dá sipáhí. *m ;*
CONSTANCY, *N.*
1. patience. dhíraj. *f ;* sabr. *m ;*
2. fidelity. wafáí. *f ;* sachchíáí. *f ;*
CONSTANT, *A.*
1. patient. dhírá ; dhírají ;
2. loyal. wafádár ; khará ;
3. resolute. pakká ; pakk paká ;
CONSTANTLY, *Adv.*
sadá de laí ; har vele ; har dam ; hameshá ; nitt ;
CONSTERNATION, *N.*
hairánagí. *f ;* haṛbaṛá. *f ;* habṛá dabṛí. *f ;* gaṛbaṛí. *f ;* habaṛ dabaṛ. *m ;* afará dafarí. *f ;*
fear. ḍar. *m ;*
CONSTIPATION, *N.*
girá. *f ;*
CONSTITUTE, TO, *V. T.*
thapná ; ṭhahráuná ; muqarrar karná ;
CONSTRAIN, TO, *V. T.*
láchár karná ; aukhiáṇ karní ; dabáuná ; jor páuná ; taṇg karná ;
CONSTRAINT, *N.*
jor. *m ;* zabardastí. *f ;* zoráwarí. *f ;* dabáú. *m ;*
CONSTRICT, TO, *V. T.*
1. to tie tightly. kassná ;
2. to collect together. sameṭná ; waleṭná ;
CONSTRICTION, *N.*
sauṛ. *f ;*
CONSTRUCT. TO, *V. T.*
1. to make. banáuná ;
2. to build. usárná ;
CONSTRUCTION, *N.*
usárí. *f ;* banauṭ. *f ;*
CONSTRUE, TO, *V. T.*
máne OR matlab kaḍḍhná ; samjháuná ;
CONSULT, TO, *V. T.*
1. to consult together. saláh lainí ; saláh mashwará karná ;
2. to ask advice. mat lainí ; raí lainí ; puchchná ;
3. to plot together. matá pakáuní ;
CONSULTATION, *N.*
saláh. *f ;* saláh mashwará. *m ;* mat. *f ;* gurmatá. *m ;* ghálá málá. *m ;* ráí. *f ;*
CONSUME, TO, *V. T.*
1. to burn. sáṛna ; jaláuná ;
2. to eat. kháná ;
3. to eat greedily. haṛapp shaṛapp kháná ;
CONSUMMATE, TO, *V. T.*
púrá karná ; naberná ; siddh karná ; kar chhaḍḍná ; mukáuná ; bhugtáná ;
CONSUMPTION, *N.*
tap dikk. *m ;*
CONTACT, *N.*
lagáu. *m ;*
with illness, or with one of a lower caste. chhút. *f ;*
CONTAIN, TO, *V. I.*
áuná ; samáuná ; painá ;
I could not contain myself ; maiṇ phulliá samáundá nahíṇ ;
CONTAMINATE, TO, *V. T.*
ḳharáb karná ; wigáṛná ; gaṇdá karná ; palít karná ; chhút laggní ; bhiṭṭ dená ;

CONTAMINATION, *N.*
chhút. *f;* nápákí. *f;* palídagí. *f;* palítí. *f;* bhiṭṭ. *f;*
CONTEMN, TO, *V. T.*
niṇdiá karná; haqír jánná; nachíj samajhná; haṇkár karná; máṛíáṇ jánná;
CONTEMPLATE, TO, *V. T.*
sochná; dhián karná; chitamná; soch wichár karná; gaur karná; dhiánaná;
CONTEMPLATION, *N.*
soch wichár. *m;* dhián. *m;* chitwaní. *f;* ḳhayál. *m;*
CONTEMPLATIVE, *A.*
wichárak;
CONTEMPT, *N.*
hiqárat. *f;* niṇdiá. *f;* ghin. *f;* nafrat. *f;* karáhat. *f;*
CONTEMPTIBLE, *A.*
kamíná; búrá; máṛá; náchíz; hochchá; ních; tuchchh; chaṇḍál; nikammá; chhuchhohrá; chotná;
CONTEMPTUOUS, *A.*
magrúr; majájí; haṇgkárí; gamrúr; ghamaṇḍí;
CONTEND, TO, *V. T.*
1. to wrangle. jhagaṛná; laṛná;
2. to argue. dalíláṇ láuní; khaihná; bahisná;
3. to vie. muqábalá karná; jutná; rís karná; barobarí karní;
CONTENT, *N.*
ḳhushí. *f;* parsiṇtáí. *f;* saṇtokh. *m;*
CONTENTED, TO BE, *V. I.*
ḳhush OR rází honá; parsinn ho jáná; rajj jáná; sabr karná; saṇtokh karná;
CONTENTED, *A.*
ḳhush; rází; befikr; rajiá pujiá; sukhí;
CONTENTEDLY, *Adv.*
ḳhushí nál; ḳhush hoke;
CONTENTIOUS, *A.*
daṇggáí; laṛáka; fasádí; jhagṛálú; jhagṛáú; hujjatí;
CONTENTIOUSLY, *Adv.*
badobadí; laṛke; jhagṛá karke;
CONTENTION, *N.*
1. dissension. náittifáqí. *f;* bakheṛá. *m;* aṇbaṇ. *f;* khaṭá páṭí. *f;* khaṭṭ paṭṭ. *f;*
2. debate. bahs. *f;* hujjat. *f;* khapp. *f;*
3. quarrel. jhagṛá. *m;* laṛáí. *f;* reṛká. *m;*
CONTENTMENT, *N.*
sukh. *m;* saṇtokh. *m;* befikrí. *f;* taript. *f;* tipat. *f;* anaṇd. *f;*
CONTEST, *N.*
1. conflict. laṛáí. *f;* fasád. *f;* khap. *f;*
2. competition. muqábalá. *m;* rís. *f;*
CONTEST, TO, *V. T.*
1. to dispute. jhagaṛná; laṛná;
2. to emulate. rís karná; muqábalá karná; khaihná; jutná;
CONTIGUITY, *N.*
neṛ. *f;* najíkí. *f;*
CONTIGUOUS, *A.*
kol; pás; nál dá; miliá hoyá; nazdík; neṛe;
CONTINENCE, *N.*
parej. *m;* rakkh shakkh. *f;* parejí. *f;*
CONTINENT, *A.*
parejgár; sáf; jatí satí;
CONTINENTLY, *Adv.*
parejgárí nál; jat sat nál;
CONTINGENCY, *N.*
dho. *m;*
CONTINUAL, *A.*
barábar; har vele; nitt;
CONTINUALLY, *Adv.*
har ghaṛí; har dam; hameshá; nitt; nitt diháṛí; sadá; har vele; continually coming. ghaṛí muṛí áuná;
CONTINUE, TO, *V. I.*
chhiṛná; rahná; ṭhahrná;
CONTINUOUS, *A.*
lagátár; barábar; roz diháṛí;
CONTINUOUSLY. *Adv.*
lagátár; barábar; rawáṇ; nitt; muṛ muṛ;
CONTORT, TO, *V. T.*
maroṛná; tarafná; kalmaláuná; ákaṛná;
to crouch down. kuṇggaṛ jáná; guchchhá honá;
CONTORTION, *N.*
maroṛ. *m;* maroṛá. *m;*
CONTOUR, *N.*
ḍaul. *f;* shakal. *f;* surat. *f;*

CONTRABAND, *N.*
nájaiz mál. *m ;*
CONTRACT, *N.*
1. work. ṭheká. *m ;*
2. agreement. qaul qarár. *m ;* bachan. *m ;*
3. covenant. nem. *m ;*
CONTRACT, TO, *V. T.*
1. to lessen. kamtí karní ; ghaṭṭ karná ; ghaṭáuná ; saṇggochná ;
2. to take a contract. ṭheká lainá ;
3. to give a contract. ṭheká dená ;
CONTRACTED, *A.*
bhíṛá ; sauṛá ; taṇg ;
CONTRACTION, *N.*
ghaṭau. *m ;*
CONTRACTOR, *N.*
ṭhekedár. *m ;*
CONTRADICT, TO, *V. T.*
barḳhiláf bolná ; jhuṭhláuná ; to deny. *f ;* mukkarná ; inkár karná ; gal moṛní ; jhuṭhiá karná ; hutt karní ;
CONTRADICTION, *N.*
ṭálá. *f ;* náṇh mukkar. *m ;* inkár. *m ;* mukkar. *m ;* hutt. *f ;*
CONTRADICTORY, *A.*
1. opposite. ulṭá ;
2. given to contradicṭ. ziddí ; háṭhá ; khappí ; jhakkí ;
CONTRARIETY, *N.*
1. obstinacy. ḍhíṭh. *f ;* jidd. *f ;* zidd. *f ;* ghessu. *f ;*
2. opposition. dushmaní. *f ;* ḍhuchchar. *m ;* muḳhálifat. *f ;* náittifáqí *f ;*
CONTRARILY, *Adv.*
1. in a contrary manner. zidd de nál ; khár nál ;
2. on the other hand. sagoṇ ;
CONTRARINESS, *N.*
jidd. *f ;* náittifáqí. *f ;*
CONTRARIOUS, *A.*
ziddí ; haṭhílá ; jiddal ; see OBSTINATE.
CONTRARY, *A.*
ziddí ; jiddí ; ḍhíṭh ; háṭhá ; barḳhiláf ; jhakkí ;
on the contrary. sagoṇ ;
CONTRAST, *N.*
farq. *m ;*
CONTRAST, TO, *V. T.*
raláke muqábalá karná ; ápo vichch muqábalá karná ;
CONTRAVENE, TO, *V. T.*
1. to oppose. sámhná karná ; muḳhálifat karní ; zidd karná ;
2. to transgress. hukm ṭorná ; ṭál dená ;
CONTRAVENTION, *N.* .
1 opposition. muḳhálifat. *f ;* virodh. *m ;*
2. transgression. gunáh. *m ;* qusúr. *m ;* aparádh. *m ;* hukm udúlí. *f ;*
CONTRIBUTE, TO, *V. T.*
dená ; chandá dená ; pún karná ; dán karná ;
CONTRIBUTION, *N.*
chandá. *m ;* madat. *f ;*
given by guests at a wedding. neuṇdrá. *m ;* neuṇdá. *m ;*
CONTRITE, *A.*
ájiz ;
CONTRITELY, *Adv.*
ájizí nál ; taubá karke ; pachhtá pachhtáke ;
CONTRITION, *N.*
ranj. *m ;* gam. *m ;* see COMPUNCTION.
CONTRIVANCE, *N.*
jugat. *f ;* banaut. *f ;* upáo. *m ;* hoshiyàrí. *f ;*
CONTRIVE, TO, *V. T.*
sajáuná ; intizám karná ;
he will contrive something. uh kujh upáo kareṇgá ;
CONTROL, TO, *V. T.*
qábú vichch rakkhná ; lagám dená ; rokná ; dabáuná ; iḳhtiyár rakkhná ;
CONTROL, *N.*
iḳhtiyár. *m ;* wass. *m ;* hatth. *m ;* qábú. *m ;*
he is not under anyone's control. uh kise de ákhe vichh nahíṇ ;
CONTROVERSIAL, *A.*
ziddí ; laṛáká ; bahisí ; jhagṛálú ;
CONTROVERSY, *N.*
bahs. *f ;* see DISPUTATION.
CONTROVERT, TO, *V. T.*
1. to deny. inkár karná ; mukkarná ; jhuṭhá sábit karná ;
2. to dispute. dalíl karná ; dalíláṇ láuná ;

CONTUMACIOUS, *A*.
ziddí ; ḍhíṭh ; ḍhíṭhá ; háṭhá ; haṭhílá ; jhakkí ; jiddal ;
CONTUMACY, *N*.
ghamaṇḍ. *m* ; jidd. *f* ; ghes. *f* ; ghesal. *f* ; húṛh. *f* ;
CONTUMELY, *N*.
1. scurrilous language. gál. *f*; gálí. *f*; see ABUSE.
2. contemptuousness. beizzatí. *f* ; bijjtí. *f* ; beqadrí . *f* ;
CONTUSE, TO, *V. T*.
daraṛná ; ragaṛná ;
CONTUSION, *N*.
1. bruise. choṭ. *f* ; saṭṭ. *f* ; jarb. *f* ;
2. abrasion. ragaṛ. *f* ; jharíṭ. *f* ;
CONUNDRUM, *N*.
pahelí. *f* ;
CONVALESCE, TO, *V. I*.
tagṛá OR wall OR achchhá ho jáná ; arám páuná ;
CONVALESCENCE, *N*.
bímárí de pichchoṇ armán. *m* ;
CONVALESCENT, *A*.
wall ; tagṛá ; takṛá ;
CONVENE, TO, *V. T*.
kaṭṭhá karná ; jamá karná ; jalsá karná ;
CONVENIENCE, *N*.
1. comfort. arám. *m* ; ramán. *m* ; armán. *m* ; sukh. *m* ;
2. opportunity. mauqá. *m* ; ṭhík waqt. *m* ;
CONVENIENT, *A*.
ṭhík velá ; vele sir ;
at a convenient time, mauqá vekh ke ;
CONVENIENTLY, *Adv*.
asání nál ; arám nál ; sukhále ; saukhe ;
CONVENT, *N*.
auratáṇ dá mat. *m* ;
CONVENTION, *N*.
jalsá. *m* ; kaṭṭh. *m* ;
CONVERSANT, *A*.
guṇí ; wáqif ; wáqab ;
CONVERSATION, *N*.
gal bát. *f* ; galláṇ bátáṇ. *f* ; bol chál. *f* ; bát chít. *f* ; gal katth. *f* ; charchá wártá. *m* ; bachan bilás. *m* ;
CONVERSE, TO, *V. T*.
gal bát karní ; galláṇ karní ; bát chít karní ; bolná ;
CONVERSE, *A*.
ulṭá ;
upside down. úṇḍhá ; mudhá ; puṭṭhá ;
CONVERSION, *N*.
dil dí tabdílí. *f* ; nawe siroṇ jammná. *m* ;
CONVERT, TO, *V. T*.
mannáuná ; Isáí karná ; Isáí banáuná ; dín vichch miláuná ;
CONVEY, TO, *V. T*.
laí jáná ; ḍhoná ; chukkná ; pahuṇcháuná ; chukk ke le jáná ;
CONVEYANCE, *N*.
gaḍḍí. *f* ;
CONVICT, *N*.
qaidí. *m* ;
CONVICT, TO, *V. T*.
qusúr sábit karná ; jurmí banáuná ; qusurí karná OR banáuná.
CONVICTION, *N*.
yaqín. *m* ; ímán. *m* ; ḳhayál. *m* ; partít. *f* ;
CONVINCE, TO, *V. T*.
manáuná ; samjháuná ; yaqín karáuná ; yaqín diláuná ;
CONVINCED, TO BE, *V. I*.
qail honá ;
CONVINCING, *A*.
pakká ; mannan jog ;
CONVIVIAL, *A*.
maují, hass mukhá ;
CONVIVIALITY, *N*.
ḳhushí. *f* ; mauj. *f* ;
CONVOKE, TO, *V. T*.
lokáṇ núṇ kaṭṭhá karná ; jalsá karná ;
CONVOY, TO, *V. T*.
pahuṇcháná ; nál jáná ; nál chalná ; laí jáná ;
CONVULSE, TO, *V. T*.
1. to contract violently, maroṛná ;
2. to shake. hiláuná ;
3. to disturb. ghabráuná; ghábarná;
CONVULSION, *N*.
maroṛ. *m* ;
CONEY, *N*.
sahá. *m* ;

COO, TO, *V. T.*
guṭakná;
COOING, *N.*
guṭak. *f;*
COOK, *N.*
ḳhánsámáh. *m;* báwárchí. *m;* rasoiá. *m;* see BAKER.
COOK, TO, *V. T.*
pakáuná; rasoí karní; rihinnaná; chauṇká bháṇḍá karná;
COOK, TO, *V. I.*
1. for dál, etc. gal jáná;
2. is the meat cooked, *i. e.*, with water. gosht gal gayá ki nahíṇ;
COOKED, *A.*
pakká; pakkí pakáí;
COOKING, *N.*
pakáí. *f;*
COOKING PLACE, *N.*
for Hindus. chauṇká. *m;*
COOKING VESSELS, *N.*
bháṇḍe. *m;* háṇḍí. *f;*
COOL, *A.*
ṭhaṇḍá ṭhaṇḍá; sítal;
COOL, TO, *V. T.*
ṭhaṇḍá karná; ṭhárná;
COOLIE, *N.*
mazdúr. *m;* kúlí. *m;* beldár. *m;*
COOLNESS, *N.*
ṭhaṇḍhak. *f;* sít. *m;* thár. *m;*
to cause coolness between two friends; phikk páuná;
CO-OPERATE, TO, *V. T.*
nál ralke kamm karná; milke kamm karná;
CO-OPERATION, *N.*
madat. *f;* saṇjog. *m;* ikk dujje dí madat;
COPING, *N.*
banerá. *m;*
COPIOUS, *A.*
bahut; batherá; bahut sárá; ḍher; wadhík;
COPPER, *N.*
trámmá. *m;* támbá. *m;* missí. *f;*
COPPER SMITH, *N.*
ṭhaṭhiár. *m;* ṭhaṭherá. *m;*
COPSE, *N.*
jhanghí. *f;* zakhírá. *m;*
COPULATE, TO, *V. T.*
chodná;
of cattle. gaṛh páuná; gaṛháuná; phaláuná; ásse karáuṇá;
COPULATION, *N.*
chod. *m;*
of cattle. gaṛh. *m;*
COPY, *N.*
naql. *f;*
COPY, TO, *V. T.*
naql karní; naql utárná; sáṇghláuná;
to copy from another boy. naql mární;
COPY BOOK, *N.*
kápí. *f;*
COPYIST, *N.*
likkhaṇwálá. *m;* kátib. *m;* naql nawís. *m;*
COQUET, TO, *V. T.*
nakhrá karná; majáz karná; laṭak nál ṭurná;
COQUETRY, *N.*
laṭak *f;* chochlá. *m;* choj. *m;* nakhrebájí. *f;* maṭak. *f;* láḍ. *m;* lachká. *m;*
COQUETTE, *N.*
mohní. *f;* nakhre karnwálí. *f;* nakhrelí. *f;* chojan. *f;* nakhrebáj. *f;*
CORD, *N.*
rassá. *m;* rassí. *f;* ḍorá. *m;* bannhan. *m;* see ROPE.
CORDIAL, *N.*
dawá. *f;* dawái. *f;* dárú. *m;*
CORDIAL, *A.*
hass mukhá; chaṇge dil wálá; dilí; milauṛá; milápaṛá; milápí;
CORDIALITY, *N.*
narmdilí. *f;*
CORDIALLY, *Adv.*
dil te ján nál; ḳhushí nál; jí ján nál; diloṇ wajhoṇ hoke; see HEARTILY.
CORE, *N.*
girí. *f;* gúddá. *m;* dal. *m;*
CORIANDER, *N.*
dhanían. *f;*
CORK, *N.*
daṭṭá. *m;* kág. *f;* kák. *f;* ḍakk *m;*
CORK, TO, *V. T.*
daṭṭ láuná; ḍakk láuná; bujjá dená;

CORKSCREW, *N.*
pechkass. *m ;*
CORN, *N.*
1. wheat. kannak. *f ;* anáj. *m ;* gallá. *m ;* dáná phakká. *m ;*
2. on the foot. bhaurí. *f ;* magrorí. *f ;*
CORNBIN, *N.*
1. round. bharolá. *m ;*
2. square. koṭhí. *f ;*
CORNMILL, *N.*
1. small, worked by hand. chakkí. *f ;*
2. large, worked by oxen or engine. kharás. *m ;*
CORNER, *N.*
1. of a room. nukkar. *f ;* khúṇj. *f ;* khúṇjá. *m ;*
2. of a sheet, used to tie up money, &c. kanní. *f ;*
3. whole end of sheet. pallaṛá. *m ;* pallá. *m ;*
4. corner stone. guṭṭh dá sir. *m ;*
5. from the four corners of the earth. chauháṇ kútáṇ thoṇ ;
6. corner of a field. guṭṭh. *f ;* guṭṭhá. *m ;*
CORNET, *N.*
dhútú. *m ;* turam. *m ;* tútí. *f ;*
CORNICE, *N.*
chhajjá. *m ;*
CORONATION, *N.*
tájposhí. *f ;*
CORONET, *N.*
táj. *m ;* muṭak. *m ;* mukaṭ. *m ;*
CORPORAL, *N.*
naik. *m ;*
CORPOREAL, *A.*
sarírik ;
CORPSE, *N.*
loth. *f ;* maiyat. *f ;*
CORPULENCY, *N.*
moṭái. *f ;*
CORPULENT, *A.*
moṭṭá tájá ; moṭṭá ; ḍhiḍḍhu ; gogaṛ ; gogaṛiá ; ḍhiḍḍhal ; ṭhullhá ;
CORRECT, *A.*
ṭhík ; durúst ; sahí ; suddh ;
CORRECT, TO, *V. T.*
ṭhík ṭhák karná ; durúst karná ; sodhná ; sahí karní ; sudhráuná ; to correct character. sudhárná ;
CORRECTION, *N.*
sudhár. *m ;* sudhái. *f ;*
CORRECTLY, *Adv.*
ṭhík ṭhík ; durústí nál ; hu bahú ; ṭhíkam ṭhík ; ṭhík ṭhák ;
CORRECTNESS, *N.*
suddhtái. *f ;* durústí. *f ;*
CORRESPOND, TO, *V. T.*
chiṭṭhí likhní ;
they began to correspond. ápe vichch chiṭṭhíáṇ áwan jáwan lagíáṇ.
CORRESPOND, TO, *V. I.*
milná ; ralná ;
CORRESPONDENCE, *N.*
likhat. *f ;* likhat paṛhat. *f ;* likhái. *f ;*
CORRIDOR, *N.*
barámadá. *m ;*
CORROBORATE, TO, *V. T.*
tasdíq karná ; pakká karná ;
CORROBORATION, *N.*
sabút. *m ;*
CORRODE, TO, *V. T.*
galáuná ;
CORRODE, TO, *V. I.*
gal jáná ;
CORROSION, *N.*
galáo. *m ;*
CORRUPT, *A.*
ḳharáb ; badzát ; badját ; bharisht ; máṛá ;
CORRUPT, TO, *V. T.*
ḳharáb karná ; gaṇdá karná ; wigáṛná ; palít karná ; ját bharisht karná ;
CORRUPTED, *A.*
wigaṛiá hoyá ; vichalíá hoyá ;
CORRUPTION, *N.*
palídagí. *f ;* palítí. *f ;* nápákí. *f ;* gaṇdagí. *f ;* saṛihán. *f ;*
CORRUPTLY, *Adv.*
beímání nál ; bewafái nál ; beímán hoke ;
COST, *N.*
mull. *m ;* lágat. *f ;* kharíd de mull. *m ;* moḳh. *m ;* dám. *m ;*
legal costs. ḳharchá. *m ;*
COST, TO, *V. I.*
mull lagná ; lágat áuní ;
COSTIVENESS, *N.*
girá. *f ;* qabz. *m ;* qabzí. *f ;* qabaj. *m ;*

COSTLY,
bahut máhṇgá ; bháre mull dá ; máhaṇg mullá ;
COSTUME, *N*.
bhes. *m* ; poshák. *m* ; libás. *m* ;
COT, *N*.
panghúrá. *m* ; see CRADLE.
COTTON, *N*.
1. sewing cotton. sut. *m* ; sutar. *m*;
2. raw cotton. kapáh. *f* ;
3. seeded cotton. rúṇ. *f* ;
4. cotton plant. kapáh da búṭá. *m* ;
5. cotton seed. warewáṇ. *m* ; wanewáṇ. *m* ;
6. cotton stalks after picking. manchittí. *f* ;
7. cotton bud. tiṇḍá. *m* ;
8. cotton flower. phul. *m* ;
9. cotton pod. gográ. *m* ; chundí. *f*;
10. cotton press. welní. *f* ; rúṇ dá pech. *m* ;
11. cotton carding machine. peṇjá. *m* ;
12. gathering cotton. kapáh chugná OR chunná ;
13. cotton carder. peṇjá. *m* ; táréwálá. *m* ;
14. to seed cotton. welná ;
15. ball of cotton ready for spinning. gohrá. *m* ;
16. a small portion pulled out from the gohrá. púní. *f* ;

COUGH, *N*.
khaṇgh. *f* ; kháṇsí. *f* ; útthú. *m* ;
a slight cough. khulkí. *f* ;
COUGH, TO, *V. T*.
khaṇghná ; útthú áuná ;
1. to cough slightly. saṇgh swárná ; khaṇgárná ; khaṇgúrná ;
2. to cough hoarsely. khauṇ khauṇ karná ;
COUNCIL, *N*.
kameṭí. *f*; kaunsal. *f*; paṇchayat. *f*; majlis. *m* ; paṇch. *m* ;
COUNSEL, *N*.
saláh. *f* ; mattá. *f* ; math. *f* ; saláh mashwará. *m* ; ghálámálá. *m* ; gurmatá. *m* ; see ADVICE.
COUNSEL, TO, *V. T*.
matt dení ; saláh dení ; nasíhat dení ;

COUNSELLOR, *N*.
matt denwálá. *m* ; saláhkár. *m* ; see ADVISER.
COUNT, TO, *V. T*.
ginná ; gin lainá ; joṛná ; gintí-karní ; lekhá karná ;
COUNTENANCE, *N*.
rup. *m* ; múṇh. *m* ; s̱hakal. *f* ;
COUNTER, *N*.
mez. *f* ;
COUNTER, *A*.
1. antagonistic. ḳhiláf ; virodh ;
2. reversed. ultá ;
COUNTERACT, TO, *V. T*.
ṭokná ; rokná ;
COUNTERACTION, *N*.
rok. *f* ; muqábalá. *m* ;
COUNTERFEIT, *A*.
khoṭṭá ; naklí ; banáutí ; jhuṭhá ; forged. jáhlí ;
COUNTERFEIT, TO, *V. T*.
naql karná ;
COUNTERMAND, TO, *V. T*.
hukm band karná ; hukm moṛná ; see CANCEL.
COUNTERPANE, *N*.
1. above. razáí. *f* ; lef. *f* ; jaráí. *f* ;
2. underneath. niháli. *f* ; tuláí. *f* ; wicháuná. *m* ; gudaṛí. *f* ;
COUNTING, *N*.
gintí. *f* ;
COUNTLESS, *A*.
aṇgint ; beoṛak ; behisáb ; anek ;
COUNTRY, *N*.
des. *m* ; mulk. *m* ; watan. *m* ; dhartí. *f* ;
1 country side. giráṇwáṇ. *f* ;
2. country of birth. jaman bhon. *f* ;
COUNTY, *N*.
zilá. *m* ; iláqá. *m* ;
COUPLE, *N*.
joṛá. *m* ; joṛí. *f* ;
in couples. do do karke ;
COUPLE, TO, *V. T*.
joṛná ; miláuná ; raláuná ;
COUPLET, *N*.
dohrá. *m* ; dohá. *m* ; bait. *f* ;
COUPLING, *N*.
joṛ. *m* ; bandhan. *m* ;

COURAGE, *N.*
himmat. *f;* hausilá. *m;* dilerí. *f;* dilaurí. *f;* bahádurí. *f;* jigará. *m;* jí. *m;* pursharath. *m;* dalelí. *f;*
COURAGEOUS. *A.*
diler; dilaur; diláwar; himmatwálá; bahádur; dil wálá; hausilewálá;
COURAGEOUSLY, *Adv.*
dilerí nál; bahádurí nál; sher hoke;
COURSE, *N.*
ráh. *f;* rastá. *m;*
1. race course. ghoṛ dauṛ. *m;*
2. arena. akháṛá. *m;* daṇggal. *m;* piṛ. *m;*
3. of course. beshakk; hor kí;
COURT, *N.*
1. law court. kacherí. *f;* adálat. *f;*
2. royal court. darbár. *m;*
COURTEOUS, *A.*
milansár; milauṛá; milápaṛá; milaṇwálá; komal;
COURTEOUSLY, *Adv.*
ádar man nál;
COURTESAN, *N.*
kanjarí. *f;* kasbí. *f;* see PROSTITUTE.
COURTESY, *N.*
bháu. *m;* ádar bháú. *m;* muláhjá. *m;* milansárí. *f;* bháú bhagat. *f;* jí sadke. *m;* ḳhátar tawájjá. *m;* komaltái. *f;*
COURTIER, *N.*
darbárí. *m;* musáhab. *m;*
COURTYARD, *N.*
walgan. *m;* wehṛá. *m;* beṛhá. *m;*
COUSIN, *N.*
bhará. *m;*
elder cousin. lálá. *m;*
COVENANT, TO, *V. T.*
1. to promise. iqrár karná;
2. to write. likh dená;
3. to make a covenant. nem bannhná OR karná;
COVENANT, *N.*
qaul qarár. *m;* nem. *m;* bachan. *m;*
COVER, *N.*
ḍhakan. *m;*
1. for earthern pots. chapní. *f;* chhuní. *f;*
2. of a book. gattá. *m;*

COVER, TO, *V. T.*
ḍhakkná; ḍhappná; kajjná; chipáuná; ḍhakk lainá;
to cover oneself with ashes. bhabút láuná;
COVERLET, *N.*
lef. *m;*
a cotton sheet. chádar. *m;* see BEDDING.
COVERTLY, *Adv.*
chupp cháp; chorí chorí karke; chup kítián;
COVET, TO, *V. T.*
lálach karná; lobh karná; chauhná; hirs karní; tama karná; lalchauná;
COVETOUS, *A.*
lobhí; lálachí; lobhan; hirsí; lenjh; lobbí;
covetous of wealth. máyá dá lobhí;
COVETOUSLY, *Adv.*
lálach karke; hirs nál; tama nál;
COVETOUSNESS, *N.*
lobh. *m;* lálach. *m;* hirs. *f;* laulá. *m;* tama. *m;* labb. *m;*
COVEY, *N.*
ḍár. *f;*
COW, *N.*
gáu. *f;* gáṇ. *f;* gai. *f;*
1. a cow not yet calved. wahr. *f;* wachchí. *f;*
2. a milch cow. lawerí. *f;*
3. a cow that gives rich milk. gheulí. *f;* gheul. *f;* ghiál. *f;*
4. a cow that kicks. chhaṛílí. *f;*
COWARD, *N.*
ḍarú. *m;* ḍarákal. *m;* ḍaraṇwálá. *m;* bhagaurá. *m;* giddar. *m;*
COWDUNG, *N.*
erná. *m;* erná gohá. *m;* gohá gattá. *m;*
1. flat cakes of cowdung. pátthiáṇ. *f;*
2. large cakes of cowdung. dhakkale. *m;*
3. small cakes of cowdung. thápiáṇ. *f;*
COWHERD, *N.*
wágí. *m;* cherú. *m;* ijaṛí. *m;* ájarí. *m;* guálá. *m;* ḍánggarí. *m;*
milkman. dodhí. *m;*
COWHOUSE, *N.*
kuṛh. *f;* gaushálá. *m;*

COWARDICE, *N.*
kamhimmatí. *f;* namardi. *f;*
COWARDLY. *A.*
ḍarákal; ḍarú; ḍaráká; kair; gídí;
CO-WIFE, *N.*
saukaṇ. *f;*
COWRIE, *N.*
kauḍí. *f;*
COXCOMB, *N.*
ṭeḍhá báṇká. *m;* báṇká. *m;*
CRACK, *N.*
darár. *m;* teṛ. *f;* tareṛ. *f;* ghápá. *m;* jhít. *f;*
1. in the foot. beái. *f;*
2. in wood. chír. *m;*
CRACK, TO, *V. T.*
ṭirkáuná; tiṛáuná; bhuṛakná;
CRACK, TO, *V. I.*
tiṛná; treṛ painí;
of wood. karkná; ṭirk jáná; kark jáná;
CRADLE, *N.*
panghúṛá. *m;* bhagúṛá. *m;*
CRAFT, *N.*
1. trade. kamm. *m;* kár. *m;*
2. deceit. chaláki. *f;* hilebájí. *f;* dhokhebájí. *f;* chhaliá. *m;*
CRAFTINESS, *N.*
chaláki. *f;* see CRAFT.
CRAFTY, *A.*
chalák; farebí; dagábáj; dhokhebáj;
CRAG, *N.*
chatán. *m;*
peak. ṭisí. *f;* choṭṭí. *f;*
CRAM, TO, *V. T.*
wárná; dhúhná; bharná; dhusná; ghuserná;
CRAMP, *N.*
bakhor. *m;*
to get cramp. bakhor páiná;
CRAMPED, *A.*
sauṛá;
CRANE, *N.*
kunj. *f;* baglá. *m;* lamḍhíng. *m;*
CRANIUM, *N.*
khoprí. *f;* kapál. *m;*
CRASH, *N.*
dhaṛáká. *m;*
CRASH, TO, *V. T.*
ḍiggná; ḍigg páiná;

CRAVE, TO, *V. T.*
arz karní; minnat karní; bentí karní; ardás karuá, sawál karná;
CRAVEN, *N.*
ḍarpokṛá. *m;* see COWARD.
CRAWL, TO, *V. T.*
riṛhná; surláuná; haulí haulí chalná; goḍeáṇ bhár turná;
as a worm. julakná;
CRAZY, *A.*
kamlá; págal; jhallá; shudáí; kamlá ramlá;
to become crazy. shudáí ho jáná; shudá ho jáná;
CREAK, TO, *V. I.*
chíṇ chíṇ karní; chikuṇ chíkuṇ karná.
as new shoes. múṛkná;
CREAM, *N.*
malái. *f;*
to skim the cream. malái láuná;
CREASE, *N.*
waṭṭ. *m;* bhann. *m;*
in palm of hand or foot. rekh. *f;* rekhá. *f;*
CREASE, TO, *V. T.*
waṭṭ páuná;
CREASE, TO, *V. I.*
waṭṭ paí jáná; bhann páiná;
there is a crease in the carpet. waṭṭ darrí vichch paí gayá;
CREATE, TO, *V. T.*
paidá karná; rachná; sirjáná; utpat karná; utpann karná; banáuná;
to create dissension. páṭṭak páuná;
CREATION, *N.*
paidaish. *f;* rachná. *f;* utpattí. *f;* utpat. *f;* utpann. *f;*
CREATOR, *N.*
kartár. *m;* ḳháliq. *m;* sirjanhár. *m;* paidákaranwálá. *m;*
CREATURE, *N.*
janaur. *m;* jánwar. *m;* jaṇtu. *m;*
CREDENCE, *N.*
yaqín. *m;* partít. *m;* atbár. *m;* bharosá. *m;*
CREDIBLE, *A.*
mannanwálí gal; yaqíní; atbárí;
CREDIT, *N.*
1. credence. yaqín. *m;* partít. *m;*
2. on credit. udhár. *m;* karaz. *m;*

CREDIT, TO, *V. T.*
1. to believe. yaqín karná ; manná ; • atbár karná ;
2. to give credit. udhár dená ;
CREDITABLE, *A.*
táríf de laiq ;
CREDITOR, *N.*
laindár. *m ;*
CREDITS, *N.*
laihná. *m ;*
CREDULITY, *N.*
bholápaṇ. *m ;* sáddagí. *f ;*
CREDULOUS, *A.*
siddhá sáddá ; bholá ; sáddá ;
CREED, N.
aqídá. *m ;* kalamá. *m ;* dharm. *m ;*
CREEK, *N.*
nálá. *m ;* nạdí. *f ;* kháṛí. *f ;*
CREEP, TO, *V. I.*
riṛhná ; surláuná ; sahij sahij chalná ;
CREEPING THINGS, *N.*
kíṛe makoṛe. *m ;*
CREMATE, TO, *V. T.*
phukná ; dáh dená ; sáṛná ;
CREMATION, *N.*
dáh. *m ;* sáṛan. *m ;*
CRESCENT, *N.*
dúj dá chaṇd. *m ;*
CREST, ON A BIRD, *N.*
kalgí. *f ;* kalaṅggá. *m ;*
CRESTFALLEN, *A.*
udás ; bedil ; sogmáṇ ; dil bujhiá hoyá ; man máriá hoyá ;
CREVICE, *N.*
daraj. *f ;* tareṛ, *f ;* jhít. *f ;* see CRACK.
CRIB, *N.*
1. cot. panghúrá. *m ;*
2. manger. khurlí. *f ;*
CRICKET, *N.*
1. insect. bíṇḍá. *m ;* ṭiḍḍí. *f ;*
2. game. krikaṭ. *m ;*
CRIME, *N.*
jurm. *m ;* dosh. *m ;* hattiá. *m ;* aparádh. *m ;*
CRIMINAL, *N.*
dosí. *m ;* gunáhí. *m ;* pápí. *m ;* hattiárá. *m ;* aparádhí. *m ;* buríár. *m ;*
CRIMINAL CASE, *N.*
faujdárí muqadamá. *m ;*

CRIMSON, *A.*
suhá ; kirmchí ;
CRINGE, TO, *V. I.*
jhijakná ; hichkaná ; jakkná ;
CRIPPLE, *N.*
luhlá. *m ;* lunjá. *m ;* langṛá. *m ;* piṇggalá. *m ;*
CRISIS, *N.*
názak waqt. *m ;*
CRISP, *A.*
khastá ; bhurbhará ;
CRITICISM, *N.*
raí. *f ;*
CRITICIZE, TO, *V. T.*
nuqs kaḍḍhná ; dosh dassná ;
CROCODILE, *N.*
sansár. *m ;* magar machh. *m ;*
CROOK, *N.*
wal. *m ;* moṛ. *m ;* ḍiṇg. *m ;*
CROOKED, *A.*
viṇgá ; ḍiṇgá ; ṭeḍhá ; ḍiṇg phaṛiṇgá ; viṇgg tariṇggá ;
CROOKEDNESS, *N.*
wiṇgg. *m ;* ḍiṇg. *m ;* ṭeḍh. *f ;* kabb. *f ;* kaj. *f ;*
CROP, *N.*
fasal. *m ;* gallá. *m ;*
1. spring crop. háṛhí. *f ;* rabbí. *f ;*
2. autumn crop. sauní. *f ;* kharíf. *f ;*
CROP, TO, *V. T.*
kaṭṭná ; katarná ;
CROSS, *N.*
salíb. *f ;*
a stake, on which men were transfixed ; súlí. *f ;*
CROSS, *A.*
náráz ; rinj ; chhiṛhmí ; lusiá hoyá ; avaiṛíá ;
CROSS, TO, *V. I.*
langhná ; pár honá;
CROSS, EXAMINE TO, *V. T.*
jirá karná ; sawál karná ;
CROSS EYED, *A.*
bhaiṅggá ;
CROSSING, *N.*
chauráhá. *m ;*
CROSS LEGGED, TO SIT, *V. I.*
chauṅkrí márke baihná ;
CROSS ROADS, *N.*
chauk. *m ;*

CROUCH, TO, *V. I.*
dabakná ; kuṇggaṛná. ; guchchhá honá ;
CROUCHING, *A.*
daṛakká ; dabak. *m* ;
CROUP, *N.*
khaṇgh. *m* ;
CROW, *N.*
káṇ. *m* ; káún. *m* ; kág. *m* ; kúá. *m* ; kaúá. *m* ;
a young crow. káṇgrá. *m* ;
CROW, TO, *V. T.*
1. as a cock. báṇg dení ;
2. to boast. sheḳhí mární ; taṛ taṛ karní ; apná rág gáuná ; dam márná ; phauṛ karná ;
CROWD, *N.*
bhíṛ. *f* ; ṭollá. *m* ; kaṭṭh. *m* ; jatthá. *m* ; ṭcllí. *f* ; ḍháṇí. *f* ; ghaṛmass. *f* ; baṛí ḳhalqat. *f* ;
CROWDED, *A.*
gachch pachch ; gaṭṭ paṭṭ ; bhíṛ bhaṛ ;
CROWING, *N.*
báṇg. *f* ; kukkrúṇghúṇ. *m* ;
CROWN, N.
táj. *m* ; muṭak. *m* ; mukaṭ. *m* ;
CROWN, OF THE HEAD, *N.*
tálú. *m* ; khoprí. *f* ; kapál. *m* ;
CROWN, TO, *V. T.*
ráj tilak dená ; táj rakkhná ;
CRUCIFIX, *N.*
salíb. *f* ;
CRUCIFIXION, *N.*
salíb chaṛháuṇ dí hálat. *f* ;
CRUCIFY, TO, *V. T.*
salíb dená ; salíb chaṛháuná ;
CRUDE, *A.*
asṭá ; asaṭṭhá ; anpakk ; moṭṭá ; kachchá ;
CRUEL, *A.*
saḳht ; beráhm ; zálim ; kaṭhor ; betaras ; khuṭaṛ ; khuṭṛá ; haiṇsiárá ; nirdáí ;
CRUELLY, *Adv.*
beráhmí nál ; saḳhtí nál ;
CRUELTY, *N.*
julm. *m* ; saḳhtí. *f* ; beráhmí. *f* ; rakhaspuṇá. *m* ; loṛhá. *m* ;
CRUMB, *N.*
bhorá. *m* ; chúr bhúr. *m* ; chúrá. *m* ; chúrá bhúrá. *m* ; bhorá chúrá. *m* ;
CRUMBLE, TO, *V. T.*
chúr chúr karná ; bhore bhore karná ;
CRUMPLE, TO, *V. T.*
waṭṭe páiná ;
CRUNCH, TO, *V. T.*
chúr karná ; chúrá chúrá karná ; kuṛkuná ; kuṛakná ;
CRUPPER, *N.*
dumbchí. *f* ; sákhatí. *f* ;
CRUSADE, *N.*
dín dí laṛáí. *f* ; jahád. *m* ;
CRUSE, *N.*
kaṭorí. *f* ;
CRUSH, TO, *V. T.*
chitthná ; phihná ; dabáuná ; chíthalná ; chathílná ; bhur bhuráuná ; to grind in a vessel. ghotná ;
CRUSH, *N.*
1. a crowd. bhíṛ. *f* ;
2. a squeeze. ṭákkar. *f* ; khaih. *f* ;
CRUST, *N.*
chhilká. *m* ;
CRUTCH, *N.*
láṭṭhí, *f* ;
CRY, *N.*
chík. *f* ; shor. *m* ; kuk. *f* ; hek. *f* ; áwáz. *f* ; chhiláuná. *m* ; chirláuná. *m* ; kurlát *m* ;
CRY, TO, *V. T.*
1. to call loudly. ḍanḍ páuní ; chíkáṇ mární ; kuk mární ; chichláuná ; uchchí uchchí ákhná ;
2. to weep. roná ; wilkná ; phusphus karná ; bubháṇ márná ;
3. she began to weep and cry. pher báṇh ulár ulár piṭṭan te ron lagí ;
4. don't cry. kujh rudhan ná karná ;
5. to cry and scream. chík chiháṛá páuná ;
CRYING, *N.*
roná. *m* ; chíhábaṭṭ. *m* ; rudhan. *m* ; roní. *f* ;
CRYSTAL, *N.*
bilaur. *m* ; phatak. *m* ;
CUB, *N.*
bachchá. *m* ;
CUBIT, *N.*
hatth. *m* ;

CUCKOO, *N.*
bambíhá. *m ;*
CUCUMBER, *N.*
khírá. *m ;* tar. *f ;*
CUD, *N.*
jugálí. *f ;*
to chew the cud. ugálí karní ;
CUDDLE, TO, *V. T.*
godí vichch baiṭháná;
CUDGEL, *N.*
ḍáṇg. *f ;* ḍáṇgá. *m ;* láṭṭhí. *f ;* soṭṭá. *m ;*
CUE, *N.*
patá. *m ;*
CUFF, *N.*
chapeṛ. *f ;* dhapphá. *m ;*
with clenched fist. húrá. *m ;*
CUFF, TO, *V. T.*
chapeṛ márná ;
with fist. húrá márná ;
CULLENDER, *N.*
chháṇní. *f ;*
CULMINATE, TO, *V. I.*
uchchiái par apaṛná ;
CULPABILITY, *N.*
qusúr. *m ;*
CULPABLE, *A.*
qusúrwár ; dosí ; malámat de laiq ;
CULPRIT, *N.*
dosí. *m ;* gunahgár. *m ;* gunáhí. *m ;* asámí ; *m ;* jurmí. *m ;*
CULTIVATE, TO, *V. T.*
wáhí karní ; khetí karní ; kásht karná ; wáhuná ; hal chaláuná ;
CULTIVATED, *A.*
bíjí hoí zamín ; gaḍḍí hoí zamín ;
CULTIVATION, *N.*
káshtkárí. *f ;* wáhí. *f ;* khetí. *f ;* jimídárí. *f ;*
CULTIVATOR, *N.*
zamindár. *m ;* jaṭṭ. *m ;* jimídár. *m ;* káshtkár. *m ;* asámí. *m ;* sámi. *m ;*
CULTURE, *N.*
shaistagí. *f ;*
CULTURED, *A.*
paṛhiyá hoyá ; likhiá paṛhiá hoyá ;
CULVERT, *N.*
pul. *m ;* pulí. *f ;*
CUMBERSOME, *A.*
bhárí ;
CUMMIN, *N.*
zíre. *m ;*
CUMULATE, TO, *V. T.*
kaṭṭhá karná ; joṛná ; ḍher lagáuná;
CUNNING, *A.*
chalák ; chátar ; dhokhebáz ; farebí ; makkár ; podhá ;
CUNNING, *N.*
chalákí. *f ;* hílebází. *f ;* ghágá. *m ;* mukkárí. *f ;* chatarái. *f ;*
CUP, *N.*
piyálá. *m ;* kásá. *m ;*
1. clay cup. ṭhuṭhá ; *m ;*
2. brass cup. kaṭorá. *m ;* bhabká. *m ;* chhanná. *m ;* kaul. *m ;*
CUPIDITY, *N.*
lálach. *m ;* lobh. *m ;* hirs. *f ;* tamá. *m ;*
CUPOLA, *N.*
gumbaz. *m ;*
CUR, *N.*
kuttá. *m ;*
CURB, *N.*
1. bridle. lagám. *m ;*
2. anything that hinders. rok. *f ;*
CURB, TO, *V. T.*
lagám dená ; qábú karná ; rokná ; bág khichchná ;
to curb the passions. jí márná ;
CURD, *N.*
dahíṇ. *f ;*
CURDLE, TO, *V. T.*
dahíṇ jamáuná ;
CURE, *N.*
iláj. *m ;* láj. *m ;* duá dárú. *m ;*
CURE, TO, *V. T.*
wall karná. achchhá karná ; chaṇgá karná ; iláj karná ;
CURED, TO BE, *V. I.*
achchhá ho jáná ; tagaṛá ho jáná ;
CURELESS, *A.*
láiláj ; bachan dí ummed nahíṇ ;
CURIOUS, *A.*
aṇokhá ; ajíb ; acharaj ;
CURL, *N.*
bodá. *m ;*
CURRANT, *N.*
manakká. *m ;*
CURRENT, *N.*
vahn. *m ;* laṭ. *f ;*
CURRENT, *A.*
vartárá ;

CURRIER, *N.*
chamár. *m* ; chammrang. *m* ;
CURRY, *N.*
kári. *f* ; gosht chaul. *m* ;
CURRY COMB, *N.*
kharkhará. *m* ;
CURSE, *N.*
lánat. *f* ; duré. *m* ; badduá. *f* ; saráp. *m* ; dhikkár. *m* ; phiṭkár. *f* ; hardú lánat. *f* ; phiṭak. *f* ; phiṭṭ. *f* ;
CURSE, TO, *V. T.*
lánat dení ; saráp dená ; sarápná ; duṛ duṛ karná ; bad duá dení ; kosná ; phiṭkárná ;
CURSED, *A.*
lánatí ; lánatan ; sarápí ; dhirig ;
CURT, *A.*
biṇsoche ;
CURTAIL, TO, *V. T.*
ghaṭṭ karná ; ghaṭáuná ; kamtí karní ;
CURTAIN, *N.*
paṛdá ; *m* ;
CURTLY, *Adv.*
gusse nál ;
CURVE, *N.*
moṛ. *m* ; wiṇgg. *m* ;
CURVE, TO, *V. T.*
moṛná ; lafáuná ; lachkáuná ;
CUSHION, *N.*
gaddí. *f* ; sirháná. *m* ;
CUSTODY, *N.*
supurdagí. *f* ; qaid. *m* ; hawálá. *m* ;
CUSTOM, *N.*
rít. *f* ; rasm. *f* ; rawáj. *f* ; dastúr. *m* ; ḍhaṇg. *m* , buhár. *m* ; rawaiyá. *m* ; lokáṇ chárí. *f* ;
habit. gejh. *f* ; ádat. *f* ;
CUSTOMARY, *A.*
rawáji ; rasamí ;
CUSTOMER, *N.*
gáhk. *m*; lainwálá. *m* ; kharídár. *m* ;
CUSTOM DUES, *N.*
mahsúl. *m* ;
CUT, *N.*
káṭ. *f* ; chír. *m* ; phaṭṭ. *m* ;
CUT, TO, *V. T.*
waḍḍhná ; waḍḍh suṭṭná ; kaṭṭná ; baḍḍhná ;
1. to cut grass. khotarná ;
2. to cut short. ghaṭṭáuná ; ghaṭṭ karná ;
3. to be cut to the heart. dil vijh jáná ;
4. to chop up grass. kutarná ;
CUTE, *A.*
chalák ; hoshiyár ; síáná ;
CUTTING, *N.*
kalam. *f* ;
CYCLE OF YEARS, *N.*
jugg. *m* ;
CYCLONE, *N.*
zor dá hanerá. *m* ; parlú. *m* ; see TEMPEST.
CYMBAL, *N.*
khaṇjarí. *f* ;
CYPRESS, *N.*
sarú. *m* ;

D

DAB, *N.*
dhappá. *m* ; thápí. *f* ; thapp. *m* ;
DAB, TO, *V. T.*
1. to damp. gillá karná ; bheuná ;
2. to smear. chopaṛná ; lagáuná ;
3. to tap. ṭakorná ; thápaṛná ;
DABBLE, TO, *V. T.*
1. to moisten. gillá karná ; tar karná ; bhigáuná ;
2. to play in water. páni vichch kheḍná ;
DABCHICK, *N.*
ḍubkú. *m* ; jalkukkaṛí. *f* ; murgábí. *f* ;
DACOIT, *N.*
ḍákú. *m* ; dháṛví. *m* ; luṭerá. *m* ;
DACOITY, *N.*
ḍáká. *m* ; dháṛá. *m* ;
to commit a dacoity. ḍáká márná ;
DAEMON, *N.*
bhút. *m* ; see DEMON.
DAFT, *A.*
kamlá ; págal ; murakh ; shudáí ;
DAGGER, *N.*
chhurá. *m* ; kaṭár. *f* ; ḳhanjar. *m* ; worn by Sikhs. kirpán. *f* ; khaṇḍá. *m* ;
DAILY, *A.*
roz diháṛe ; nit ; dinbadin ;
daily labour. diháṛí. *f* ;
DAINTIES, *N.*
padárath. *m* ; chaṇgá parshád. *m* ; gahre gapphe. *m* ; tardá tardá mál. *m* ; chaṇgíáṇ chaṇgíán khán díáṇ chízáṇ. *f* ;

DAINTINESS, *N.*
ḳhubsuratí. *f;*
DAINTY, *A.*
1. pretty. ḳhubsurat; shakalwálá; sohná; sundar;
2. tasty. mazedár; sawádlá; sawádí;
DAIRY, *N.*
dudh makkhan dí dukán. *f;*
DAIRYMAN, *N.*
gujjar. *m;* dodhí. *m;* see MILKMAN.
DALE, *N.*
ghâṭṭí. *f;* wádí. *f;*
mountain pass. dará. *m;* see VALLEY.
DALLIANCE, *N.*
der. *f;* chir. *m;* see DELAY.
DALLY, TO, *V. T.*
chir láuná; der láuní; ajj kal karná; velá ṭálná;
DAM, *N.*
bannh. *m;* baṇḍí. *f;*
a dam in a canal. jhál. *m;*
DAM, TO, *V. T.*
baṇd karná; bannh márná; baṇḍí páuní;
DAMAGE, *N.*
nuqsán. *m;* harj. *f;* gháṭṭá. *m;* wigáṛ. *m;* ṭoṭ. *f;*
DAMAGES, *N.*
1. legal. harjá. *m;* ḳharchá. *m;* harj. *m;*
2. ordinary compensation. harjánná. *m;* iwzánná. *m;*
DAMAGE, TO, *V. T.*
nuqsán karná; ḳharáb karná; harjá páuná; bigáṛná; wigáṛná; wichálná;
DAMAGED, *A.*
wigaṛá hoyá;
to be damaged. V. I. wichalná;
DAMP, *A.*
gillá; tar; silhá; wattará;
the salt is damp. luṇ te sill ghattá hai;
DAMP, *N.*
silháb. *f;* salábh. *f;* sill. *f;* gill. *f;* wattar. *m;* sejjal. *f;* namí. *f;*
DAMP, TO, *V. T.*
bheonná; bhagoná; gillá karná;
DAMP, TO, BECOME, *V. I.*
sill OR sejjal chaṛhná;

DAMPNESS, *N.*
wattar. *m;* tarí. *f;* watt. *f;* giláulá. *m;* sill. *f;* see DAMP.
DAMSEL, *N.*
kuṛí. *f;* kákí. *f;* laṛkí. *f;* bálṛí. *f;* kanníáṇ. *f;* bálkí. *f;*
DAMSON, *N.*
alúchá. *m;*
DANCE, *N.*
1. general. nách. *m;*
2. dancing by women of ill repute. mujrá. *m;*
3. dancing by men only. bhaṇgrá. *m;*
4. dancing by Jangalis. dhamál. *m;* luddí. *f;*
DANCE, TO, *V. T.*
nachchná; mujrá karná; bhaṇgrá páuná;
by Jangalis. dhamál páuná; thaí thaí karná;
dancing and clapping of hands by women. giddhá márná; see DANCE.
DANCER, *N.*
náchá. *m;* náchú. *m;*
DANCING, *N.*
nách. *m;* mujrá. *m;* see DANCE.
DANCING GIRL, *N.*
nachí. *f;* kaṇchaní. *f;* lolí. *f;*
DANDLE, TO, *V. T.*
uchhálná; láḍ karná OR laḍáuná; parkáuná; lorí dená;
DANDRUFF, *N.*
sikkaṛí. *f;*
DANDY, *N.*
báṇká. *m;* shukín. *m;* ákkaṛ ḳhán. *m;*
DANGER, *N.*
ḳhatrá. *m;* ján jokhoṇ. *m;*
DANGEROUS, *A.*
ḍaráuná; ḳhatrewálá; ján jokhoṇ dá;
DANGLE, TO, *V. T.*
jhuláuná;
DANGLE, TO, *V. I.*
lamakná;
DANK, *A.*
gillá; tar; wattá;
DARE, TO, *V. T.*
1. to venture. dil kaḍḍhná; jurat karní; himmat karní; hauṇsilá karná; dilerí karní;

2. to defy. ákaṛná; laṛan núṇ tiyár honá;
DARING, *A*.
diler; diláwar; dilaur; bahádur; takṛá; himmatí;
DARING, *N*.
dilerí. *f*; himmat. *f*; dilaurí. *f*; jurat. *f*; jigará. *m*;
DARINGLY, *Adv*.
dilerí nál; sher hoke; bahádurí nál; tagṛeáṇ hoke;
DARK, *A*.
hanerá; ghupp;
very dark. ghupp gher; anher ghupp gher;
DARK, TO GET, *V. I*.
hanerá painá;
DARKEN, TO, *V. T*.
hanerá karná;
to get dark. hanerá painá; ghub gher ho jáná;
DARKNESS, *N*.
anerá. *m*; hanerá. *m*; haner. *f*;
thick darkness. ghupp anher. *f*;
DARKSOME, *A*.
dhuṇḍlá; see DARK.
DARLING, *N*.
pyárá. *m*; laḍlá. *m*; lál. *m*; láḍo. *m*; láḍlí. *f*;
DARLING, *A*.
pyárá; dulárí; dulárá;
DARN, TO, *V. T*.
punná; tupp karná; rafú karná;
DARNING, *N*.
tupp. *m*; rafú. *m*;
DART, *N*.
nok. *f*; chunj. *f*; kaní. *f*;
an arrow. tír. *m*; kaní. *f*; báṇ. *m*;
a thorn. kaṇḍḍá. *m*;
DART, TO, *V. T*.
1 to dart towards. lapakná;
2. to throb. phaṛakná;
3. to grab at. chapattá márná;
DASH, *N*.
1. a collision. ṭakkar. *f*;
2. a push. dhakká. *m*;
3. a rush. jhapaṭ. *f*;
DASH, TO, *V. T*.
1. to knock violently. ṭakkar márná; khaihná;
2. to throw down. suṭṭná; paṭkáuná;
3. to run at. dháuná; ṭuṭṭke painá;
4. to dash along. sir toṛ bhajjná;
DATARD, *N*.
ḍarákal. *m*; ḍarú. *m*; ḍaranwálá. *m*; bhagaurá. *m*;
DATE, *N*.
1. tree. khajúr. *f*;
2. unripe dates. ḍoke. *m*;
3. ripe dates. khajúr. *f*;
4. dried dates. chhuhárá. *m*;
5. of the month. taríkh. *f*; mití. *f*;
DAUB, TO, *V. T*.
1. to plaster walls with mud plaster. limbná; lembíkarní; lapáí karní; lep karná; limb dená;
2. to smear floors with cowdung. pochá dená;
DAUGHTER, *N*.
dhí. *f*; laṛkí. *f*; bálṛí. *f*; jaí. *f*; chhokrí. *f*;
1. step daughter. matreí dhí. *f*;
2. daughter in law. núṇh. *f*;
3. daughter's daughter. dohtrí. *f*; dohtí. *f*;
DAUNT, TO, *V. T*.
ḍaráuná; dhamkáuná; ḍar páuná; kachráuná;
DAUNTLESS, *A*.
diler; bahádur; tagaṛá; dilaur; himmatwálá; bekhauf; bedhaṛak; himtál; dilwálá;
DAUNTLESSLY, *Adv*.
dilerí nál; baṛí himmat nál; sher banke;
DAUNTLESSNESS, *N*.
dilerí. *f*; bahádurí. *f*; dilaurí. ; jigará. *m*; diláwarí. *f*;
DAWDLE, TO, *V. T*.
susṭí karní; kál watáuná OR batáuná; velá guáuná; aiweṇ kamm karná; ghusáí márná;
DAWDLER, *N*.
sust ádmí; *m*; kammchor. *m*; daliddarí. *m*;
DAWN, *N*.
taṛká. *m*; din charhe. *m*; sájhará. *m*; múṇherá. *m*; múṇh muṇherá. *m*; sarghíwelá. *m*; pahí phatí. *f*;
at dawn. dhammí velá. ṭhaṇḍe thaṇḍe; din chaṛhde hí;

DAWN, TO, *V. I.*
pauh phuṭná; din chaṛhná; pahí phuṭní;
DAY, *N.*
din. *m;* dihárá. *m;* roz. *m;*
1. the next day. agle bhalak; dujje bhalak;
2. day before yesterday. parsoṇ. *m;*
3. day by day. roz diháṛe;
4. day and night. dine rát; rátíṇ dine;
5. by day. dine;
6. day of the month. táríkh. *f;*
7. a day's wages. diháṛí. *f;*
DAY BOOK, *N.*
rokaṛ. *f;* see ACCOUNT BOOK.
DAYBREAK, *N.*
din chaṛhe. *m;* taṛke. *m;* see DAWN.
DAY LABOURER, *N.*
mazdúr. *m;* diháṛedár. *m;*
DAYLIGHT, *N.*
lo. *f;* roshní. *f;*
DAYTIME, *N.*
din dá velá. *m;*
DAZZLE, TO, *V. T.*
lishkáuná; chamak dikhláuná;
DAZZLE, TO, *V. I.*
chamakná; jhalkná; lishkná;
DAZZLING, *A.*
raunaqwálá;
DEACON, *N.*
pádrí. *m;*
DEAD, *N.*
murdá. *m;* moyá hoyá. *m;*
1. corpse. loth. *f;*
2. tree. khaṛsukk;
DEADBEAT, *A.*
thakká máṇḍá; chúr hoyá; ṭuṭṭiá hoyá; thakká ṭuṭṭiá hoyá;
he was deadbeat with the journey. paiṇḍá kardeáṇ kardeáṇ thakkiá hoyá;
DEAD DRUNK, *A.*
sharáb píke behosh;
DEAF, *A.*
bolá; ḍorá; uchchá sunná; ṭauṇá;
1. stone deaf. bolá baddal;
2. I am deaf. maiṇ uchchá sundá hán, *i. e.*, I hear loud.
DEAFEN, TO, *V. T.*
bolá karná; gaugá karná;

DEAL, TO, *V. T.*
1. to divide. waṇḍná; waṇḍ dená; hissá karná;
2. to scatter. khiṇḍáuná; kerná; khilárná; chhatá dená;
3. to deal cards. tásh waṇḍná;
4. to trade. laiṇ deṇ karná; wanj bipár karná; saudágarí karní;
DEALER, *N.*
bipárí. *m;* saudágar. *m;* baniá. *m;*
1. wholesale dealer. thok farosh. *m;*
2. dealer in grain, groceries, &c. parchúniá, *m;*
DEALING, *N.*
1. buying and selling. laiṇ deṇ. *m;* saudágarí. *f;* wanj bipár. *m;*
2. intercourse. wartáu. *m;* kamm. *m;* uṭṭhaṇ baiṭhaṇ. *m;* láká. *m;*
DEAR, *A.*
1. expensive. baṛá máhṇgá; pyárá; tez; máhaṇg mullá; aṇmull;
2. beloved. pyárá; dulárá; hejlá; láḍlá;
DEARNESS, *N.*
máhṇgíái. *f;* tejí. *f;*
DEARTH, *N.*
kál. *m;* auṛ. *f;*
DEATH, *N.*
maut. *f;* wafát. *f;* faut. *f;* kál. *m;* nás. *m;* barbádí. *f;* surgwás. *m;*
1. angel of death. jammdút. *m;*
2. after death. maraṇ de pichche;
DEBACLE, *N.*
jhissí. *f;* jhijkí. *f;*
DEBAR, TO, *V. T.*
1. to stop. rokná; aṭkáuná;
2. to forbid. maná karná; ṭhákná; warajná;
3. to turn back. moṛná.
4. to excommunicate. khárij karná; chhekná; alag karná; huqqá páni band karná;
DEBASE, TO, *V. T.*
1. to spoil. wigáṛná; chauṛ kar dená; wichálná;
2. to abase. bepat karná; beizzat karní; pat láhuná; sharmindá karná;
3. to adulterate. khoṭ pauná; chaṇgí chíz wichch khoṭṭí chíz ralá dení;

DEBASED, *A*.
1. despicable. nikammá ; máṛá ; bhaiṛá ; kamíná ;
2. adulterated. khoṭṭá ;
DEBASEMENT, *N*.
beizzatí. *f* ; bijjtí. *f* ; namoshí. *f* ; bepatí. *f* ;
DEBASING, *A*.
nikammá ; kamíná ;
DEBATEABLE, *A*.
shakk shubhe dí gal ; bharmílá ;
DEBATE, *N*.
bahis. *f* ;
DEBATE, TO, *V. T*.
bahisná ; qánún chháṇtná ; dalíláṇ láuní ; jhagaṛná ; hujjat karní ; in one's heart. soch wichárná ; dil vichch sochná;
DEBATER, *N*.
bahis karnwálá. *m* ;
DEBAUCH, TO, *V. T*.
wigáṛná ; ḳharáb karná ; gaṇdá karná ; palít karná ;
DEBAUCHED, *A*.
1 of bad morals. luchchá ; uchakká ; dúsht ; guṇḍá ;
2. drunken. sharábí ; nashebáj ; nasháí ;
DEBAUCHEE, *N*.
badkár. *m* ; nále dá ḳharach. *m* ; ḳharábatí. *m* ; chudákal. *m* ; nasháí. *m* ;
DEBAUCHERY, *N*.
nashebájí. *f* ; luchchpúṇá. *m* ; badkárí. *f* ; badí. *f* ; uchakkpúná. *m* ;
DEBENTURE, *N*.
1. a bond. tamassak. *m* ; iqrárnámá. *m* ;
2. a stamped document. asṭám. *m* ;
DEBILE, *A*.
kamjor ; lissá ; máṛá ; ruṛhiá ;
DEBILITATE, TO, *V. T*.
kamjor karná ; nirbal karna ;
DEBILITATED, *A*.
kamjor ; mareṛá ;
DEBILITATION, *N*.
kamjorí. *f* ; nirbaltáí. *f* ;
DEBILITY, *N*.
kamjorí. *f* ; marattaṇ. *m* ; durbaltáí. *f* ;
DEBIT, TO, *V. T*.
qarz likhná ; udhár dená ;

DEBRIS, *N*.
malbá. *m* ; iṭṭáṇ waṭṭe. *m* ;
DEBT, *N*.
udhár. *m* ; hudár. *m* ; qarz. *m* ; deṇdárí. *f* ; lahiná. *m* ;
to contract a debt. qarz chaṛhná ; udhár chhukkná ;
1. I am greatly in debt. merá lekhá paháṛ ho gayá hai.
2 to get out of debt. surkhru honá ;
DEBTOR, *N*.
deṇdár. *m* ; qarzáí. *m* ;
DECALOGUE, *N*.
Ḳhudá de das hukm. *m* ;
DECAMP, TO, *V. T*.
chaliá jáná ; nassná ; naṭṭhná ; bhajj jáná ; ṭur jáná ; chupp chupítá nass jáná ; khisk jáná ;
DECAPITATE, TO, *V. T*.
sir waḍḍhná ; sir láh dená ; dhaṛ thoṇ sir utárná ;
for Sikhs slaughtering goats. jhaṭká karná ;
DECAY, *N*.
sáṛá. *m* ;
DECAY, TO, *V. I*.
tarakkná ; garjáná ; garná ; saṛná ; gal jáná ; kujjná ;
as fruit. chalná ; tarakkná ;
DECAYED, *A*.
as fruit. chaliá hoya ; galiá hoyá ;
DECEASE, *N*.
maut. *f* ; see DEATH.
DECEIT, *N*.
fareb. *m* ; dhokhá. *m* ; dagá. *m* ; makár. *m* ; makkár. *m* ; chhal. *m* ; chalákí. *f* ; ṭhaggí. *f* ; khoṭ. *m* ; pakhaṇd. *m* ; ech pech. *m* ; phauṛ. *m* ; chhal bal. *m* ; dhohípuṇá. *m* ; farfej. *m* ; her pher. *m* ; jháṇsá. *m* ; phergher. *m* ; dhoppá. *m* ; ghusái. *f* ; dhakwanj. *m* ; dhokhebájí. *f* ; pahimání. *f* ; pahimánagí. *f* ; kapaṭ. *m* ; farebdárí. *f* ; dharoh. *m* ;
DECEITFUL, *A*.
makkár ; farebí ; dagebáj ; dhokhebáj ; ṭhagg ; khoṭ dilá ;
a deceitful woman. siápe dí naíṇ. *f* ;
DECEITFULLY, *Adv*.
dhokhebájí nál ; chhal nál ; fareb nál ; dage nál ;

DECEITFULNESS, *N.*
dhokhebájí. *f*; see DECEIT.
DECEIVE, TO, *V. T.*
dhokhá dená; fareb dená; ṭhaggná; chhal lainá; bahkáuná; jhāṇsá dená; dhauṇs dení; dhoppá dená; ghusáuná; bhuchláuná; chhal khedṇá; phauṛ márná; mutthná; bharmáuná; bhuláuná; phaṇdná; wal chhal karná;
1. he deceived me. uh mainúṇ chhal gayá;
2. you cannot deceive me. ṭuháḍe ṭhaggíáṇ maiṇ ṭhagiá nahíṇ jáṇdá;
3. to deceive a horse. bhaláwará páuná;
4. to deceive in weighing. ṭhúṇgá márná; gibbí dená;
DECEIVED, TO BE, *V. I.*
fareb OR dhokhá OR dhoppá khāná; fareb OR dhauṇs vichch áuná;
I continued to be deceived by him. maiṇ us te apne ápnúṇ bhutáundá rihá.
DECEIVER, *N.*
farebí. *m*; makár. *m*; ṭhagg. *m*; dambáj. *m*; chhaliá. *m*; farfejí. *m*; dhoppebáj. *m*; kapṭí. *m*; ṭhaggiá. *m*; khoṭṭá. *m*; dharohí. *m*;
DECEMBER, *N.*
poh. *m*;
DECENCY, *N.*
háyá. *m*; sharm. *f*; saṇg. *f*; láj. *f*;
DECENTLY, *Adv.*
laiq taur nál;
DECEPTION, *N.*
dhokhá. *m*; farfej. *m*; see DECEIT.
deception in weighing. ṭhúṇga. *m*;
DECEPTIVE, *A.*
farebí; dhokhebáj;
DECEPTIVELY, *Adv.*
chhal nál; fareb nál;
DECERN, TO, *V. T.*
1. to discern. malúm karná; bujjh lainá; bujjhná; táṛná;
2. to decree. faisalá karná; hukm dená;

DECIDE, TO, *V. T.*
1. to determine. faisalá karná; mitháuná; nitárná;
2. to end. naberṇá; nibṛáuná;
DECIDED, TO BE, *V. I.*
nibbaṛná;
DECIDED, *A.*
pakká;
DECIDELY, *Adv.*
baṛí safái nál; jarúr; muloṇ;
DECIMATE, TO, *V. T.*
halák karná; már suṭṭná; sattiá nás karná; thánoṇ már suṭṭná;
DECIPHER, TO, *V. T.*
matlab kaḍḍhná; paṛhná;
DECISION, *N.*
faisalá. *m*; hukm. *m*; naberá. *m*;
legal decree. ḍigrí. *f*;
DECISIVE, *A.*
pakká; púrá;
DECK, TO, *V. T.*
saṇgár karná; suárná; see DECORATE.
DECLAIM, TO, *V. T.*
wáz karná; nasíhat dení; bayán karná; parchár karná;
DECLAMATION, *N.*
wáz. *m*; nasíhat. *f*; wák. *m*; bachan. *m*; zikr. *m*;
DECLARATION, *N.*
iqrár. *m*; bayán. *m*; qaul. *m*; dalíl. *f*; bachan. *m*;
DECLARE, TO, *V. T.*
bayán karná; záhir karná; dassná; bolná; dhomáuná; tagíd nál bolná; pargaṭ karná;
DECLENSION, *N.*
1. deterioration. ḳharábí. *f*;
2. refusal. inkár. *m*; hutt. *f*; sukká jawáb. *m*; náh. *f*;
DECLINE, *N.*
tap dikk. *m*;
DECLINE, TO, *V. T.*
1. to deny. inkár karná; náh karná; mukkarná; hutt karní; ná manná;
2. the day to decline. din ḍhalná; din lah jáná;
3. the day is declining. din lah gayá hai;

DECLIVITY, *N.*
utarái, *f;* utárá. *m;* ḍhál. *f;* ḍháyá. *m;* see SLOPE.
DECOCTION, *N.*
doshánḍá. *m;* jusánḍá. *m;* dosánḍá. *m;* káṛhá. *m;*
DECOMPOSE, TO, *V. I.*
saṛná; tarakkná;
DECOMPOSITION, *N.*
sáṛá. *m;*
DECORATE, TO, *V. T.*
sajáwat karní; suárná; ṭíp ṭáp karná; shangárná; sanwárná; sajáná; sájná; phabáuná;
DECORATED, *A.*
sajjiá hoyá;
DECORATION, *N.*
1. ornament. shangár. *m;*
2. medal. takmá. *m;* tagmá. *m;*
3. ornamenting. sajáwat. *f;*
DECOROUS, *A.*
hayáwálá; dhírajmán;
DECOROUSLY, *Adv.*
hayá nál;
DECORUM, *N.*
hayá. *m;* láj. *f;* sang. *f;*
DECOY, *N.*
dhokhá. *m;* lalchá. *m;*
DECOY, TO, *V. T.*
lálach dená; khichchná; lubháuná; lalcháuná; tama dená; bhuláuná;
for a horse. bhaláwará páuná;
DECREASE, *N.*
thuṛ. *m;* gháṭṭá. *m;* kamí. *f;* kasar. *m;* híná. *f;* ghápá. *m;*
DECREASE, TO, *V. T.*
ghaṭṭ karná; ghaṭáuná; thoṛá karná;
DECREASE, TO, *V. I.*
ghaṭṭ honá; thuṛ jáná; nakhuṭṭ jáná; ghaṭṭná;
DECREE, *N.*
1. order. hukm. *m;* ágiá. *m;*
2. legal. ḍigrí. *f;*
DECREE, TO, *V. T.*
hukm dená; faisalá karná; raí dení; nabeṛná;
legal. ḍigrí dení;
DECREPIT, *A.*
buḍḍhá; kamjor; máṛá; jahíf; buḍḍhrá; bahut umrwálá;
DECREPITUDE, *N.*
buḍḍhepá. *m;* kamjorí. *f;*
DECRY, TO, *V. T.*
badnám karná; nindiá karná; aiblauná;
DEDICATE, TO, *V. T.*
chaṛháuná; arpan karná; wakhrá karná; see CONSECRATE.
DEDICATION, *N.*
ghol ghattí. *f;* ghol ghumáí. *f;*
DEDUCE, TO, *V. T.*
natíjá kaḍḍhná;
DEDUCT, TO, *V. T.*
kaṭṭná; ghaṭṭáuná; thoṛá karná; mujrá dená;
DEDUCTION, *N.*
1. abatement. káṭ. *f;* gháṭṭá. *m;*
2. discount. mujrá. *m;*
3. inference. natíjá. *m;*
DEED, *N.*
1. an act. kamm. *m;* kamm káj. *m;* kartabb. *m;* káraj. *m;* kartut. *f;* karní. *f;*
2. a writing. likhat. *f;* tamassak. *m;* sanad. *f;*
3. bad deed. khoṭṭá karm. *m;*
4. good deed. subh karm. *m;* changá kamm. *m;* nek kamm. *m;* sukarm. *m;*
DEEM, TO, *V. T.*
ḳhayál karná; sochná; soch wichár karná; faisalá karná; dhiánaná;
DEEP, *A.*
ḍunghá ḍunghṛá; gahirá;
in colour. guhṛá; gúṛhá;
DEEP, *N.*
samundar. *m;*
DEEPEN, TO, *V. T.*
ḍunghá karná;
DEEPNESS, *N.*
ḍunghíáí. *f;* ḍungh. *f;* ḍummh. *m;*
in colour. guṛh. *m;* guṛhtáí. *f;*
DEER, *N.*
haran. *m;* harní. *f;*
DEFACE, TO, *V. T.*
rup wigáṛná; chauṛ chapaṭṭ kar dená;
DEFALCATE, TO, *V. T.*
chorí karní; chuṛáuná

DEFALCATOR, *N.*
chor. *m;* choṭá. *m;* chorṭá. *m;* chorṭerá. *m;*

DEFAMATION, *N.*
badnámí. *f;* tohmat. *m;* niṇdiá. *m;* chuglí. *f;*

DEFAME, TO, *V. T.*
niṇdiá karná; dosh láuná; chhaṭṭná; badnám karná; mehná launá; táná dená; baṇgoná; nahaqq bolná; chuglí karní; aib láuná; náṇ wigáṛná; bhaṇḍná; see CALUMINATE.

DEFAMER, *N.*
chuglí ḳhor. *m;* niṇdak. *m;* tohmatí. *m;*

DEFAULT, *N.*
qusur. *m;* jurm. *m;* gunáh. *m;* aib. *m;*

DEFAULTER, *N.*
chor. *m;* jurmí. *m;*

DEFEAT, *N.*
hár. *f;* bháṇj. *f;*
defeat at cards. khalál. *m;* kot. *m;*

DEFEAT, TO, *V. T.*
jittná; jitt láuná; haráuná; jet milní;

DEFEATED, TO BE, *V. I.*
hár jáná; hárná;

DEFECT, *N.*
nuqs. *m;* kasar. *f;* waṭṭá. *m;* kamí. *f;* augún. *m;* dos. *m;* kaj. *f;* illat. *f;* káṇ. *f;* dokh. *m;* see FAULT.

DEFECTION, *N.*
1. disobedience. náfarmáni. *f;*
2. desertion. tark. *f;* taj. *m;*

DEFECTIVE, *A.*
nákas; adhúrá; kachchá; aibí; defective in some organ. kojhá; káṇá; see DEFORMED.

DEFECTIVENESS. *N.*
kamí. *f;* kasar. *f;* khoṭ. *f;*

DEFENCE, *N.*
1. guard. bacháo. *m;* bachá. *m;* rákkhí. *f;* dhir. *f;* rakkhiá. *f;* saran. *f;*
2, statement. bayán. *m;* uzr. *f;*

DEFENCELESS, *A.*
beásrá; anáth; máṛá; besáyá; behathiyárá; wachárá;

DEFEND, TO, *V. T.*
bacháuná; rákkhí karní;

DEFENDANT, *N.*
mudáilá. *m;* sámí. *m;*

DEFENDER, *N.*
hamáití. *m;* rákkhá. *m;* madadgár. *m;* ráchchhiá. *m;*

DEFENSIBILITY, *N.*
bacháo. *m;*

DEFER, TO, *V. T.*
1. to postpone. ṭálná; multaví karní; ṭál shál kar chhaḍḍná; ṭál maṭolá kar dená; urá pará kar dená;
2. to submit. manná; manzúr karná; qabulná;

DEFERENCE, *N.*
ádar. *m;* izzat. *f;* liház. *m;* bháu. *m;* ḳhátir. *f;*

DEFERENTIAL, *A.*
adab karnwálá; ṭahl karnwálá;

DEFERMENT, *N.*
ḍhill. *f;* ḍhill maṭṭh. *f;* see DELAY.

DEFIANCE, *N.*
gustáḳhí. *f;* dilerí. *f;* magrúrí. *f;* burá bol. m; bhaiṛá bol. *m;*

DEFIANT, *A.*
gustáḳh; magrúr; diler; besharm;

DEFIANTLY, *Adv.*
gustáḳhí nál; dileri nál; hausale nál;

DEFICIENCY, *N.*
ghátṭá. *m;* kasar. *m;* kamí. *f;* ṭoṭ. *f;* ghápá. *m;* híṇ. *f;* ṭoṭṭá. *m;* híṇaṭ *f;* thuṛ. *m;*

DEFICIENT, *A.*
kassá; ghaṭṭ;

DEFICIT, *N.*
ghátṭá. *m;* ghát. *m;* see DEFICIENCY.

DEFILE, TO, *V. T.*
mailá OR palít OR gaṇdá karná; wigáṛná; chutt laggní; ḳharáb karná; bhiṭṭ dená; bhiṭ chhaḍḍná;

DEFILED, TO BE, *V. I.*
palít ho jáná; chhutt laggní; bhiṭṭ jáná;

DEFILED, *A.*
gaṇdhlá; palít; napák;
as food, &c., bhiṭṭ; bhiṭṭaṛ;

DEFILEMENT, *N.*
palídagí. *f*; palítí. *f*; gaṇdagí. *f*; napákí. *f*: chhutt. *f*;
DEFINE, TO, *V. T.*
samjháuṇá; ṭhík dassná; bakháuná;
DEFINITE, *A.*
ḳháss; ṭhík;
DEFINITELY, *Adv.*
ṭhík ṭhák; ḳháss karke;
DEFINITION, *N.*
bayán. *m*; matlab. *m*;
DEFLECT, TO, *V. T.*
1. to make return. moṛná; pherná;
2. to cause to revolve. geṛná;
DEFLECTION, *N.*
moṛ. *m*; ger. *f*;
DEFORM, TO, *V. T.*
rup wigáṛná; baḍaul karná; badshakal banáuná;
DEFORMATION, *N.*
kaj. *f*; baj. *f*;
DEFORMED, *A.*
lulá; kojhá;
1. without a hand. ṭuṇḍá;
2. one eyed. káná; akknoṇ láwáṇ;
3. six fingered. chháṇggá. *m*;
4. club footed. páṇggulá; ḍuḍḍá; ṭhibbá; phiḍḍá; paṇgalá;
5. bandy legged. ḍuḍḍá; ḍuḍḍíáṇ lattàṇwálá; báṇḍá;
6. a man with a harelip. khaṇḍá. *m*;
7. humpbacked. kubbá;
8. squint eyed. ṭírá; bhaiṇggá;
9. a cripple. piṇggalá. *m*;
10. toothless. pappá;
11. lame. luṇjá;
DEFORMITY, *N.*
kaj. *f*;
DEFRAUD, TO, *V. T.*
haqq OR hissá márná; haqq dabàuná; pet kaṭṭná; ṭhaggná; mutthná; see CHEAT.
DEFRAUDER, *N.*
ṭhagiá. *m*; ṭhagg. *m*; chhaliá, *m*; dagebáj. *m*; dhoppebáj. *m*;
DEFRAY, TO, *V. T.*
bharná; tárná;
to pay for another. chukáuná; see PAY.

DEFT, *A.*
siáná; chatúr; hoshiyár; phurtílá; guṇí;
DEFTLY, *Adv.*
chaṇgí taráh nál; hoshiyárí nál;
DEFUNCT, *A.*
murdá; moyá;
DEFY, TO, *V. T.*
ákaṛná; laṛan núṇ taiyár honá;
DEGENERACY, *N.*
wigáṛ. *m*; ḳharábí. *f*;
DEGENERATE, *A.*
ḳharàb; kamíná; sharír; luchchá; nikammá;
DEGENERATE, TO, *V. I.*
wigaṛná; ḳharáb ho jáná;
DEGENERATION, *N.*
wigáṛ. *m*; kamínpuṇà. *m*;
DEGRADATION, *N.*
1. dishonour. bepatáí. *f*; baizzatí. *f*; bijjtí. *f*; nimoshí. *f*;
2. baseness. ḳharábí. *f*;
DEGRADE, TO, *V. T.*
darjá ghaṭṭáuná; uhde thoṇ ḍegná; toṛná; taṛoṛná; ḍigáuná; bepatí karní; apmán karná; see DISGRACE.
DEGRADED, *A.*
bharisht; see DEGENERATE.
DEGRADING, *A.*
kamíná;
DEGREE, *N.*
darjá. *m*; uhdá. *m*; rutbá. *m*;
by degrees. haule haule; hundeáṇ hundeáṇ;
to such a degree. itthoṇ tík;
DEIFY, TO, *V. T.*
Ḳhudá dá rutbá dená;
DEIGN, TO, *V. T.*
baḳhshná; mihrbání karní;
DEITY, *N.*
1. God. Ḳhudá. *m*, M; Rabb. *m*, M; Alláh *m*, M;
2. a heathen deity. deotá. *m*, H;
3. divinity. ḳhudàí. *f*;
DEJECT, TO, *V. T*
udás karná; bedil karná; mar toṛná; ḍuláuná;
DEJECTED, TO BE, *V. I.*
gam karná; udás hoṇ bedil honá; dil chhaḍḍná;

DEJECTED, *A*.
udás ; bedil ; sogmán ; dil ḍhaṭṭhá ; masosiá hoyá ;
DEJECTEDLY, *Adv*.
gam nál ; udás hoke ;
DEJECTION, *N*.
udásí. *f* ; gam. *m* ; afsos. *m* ; dilgírí. *f* ; bedilí. *f* ; gamdilí. *f* ;
DELATE, TO, *V. T.*
ilzám láuná ; nálish karná ; see ACCUSE.
DELATION, *N*.
ilzám. *m* ; see ACCUSATION.
DELAY, TO, *V. T.*
1. to linger. chir láuná ; gall ghiṇge páuná ; ghaul karná ; ajj bhalak karná ; ḍhill maṭṭh karní ;
2. to stop one. rokná ; aṭkáuná ;
3. to keep another waiting. naṭṭí baháná ;
DELAY, *N*.
chir. *m* ; der. *f* ; derí *f* ; ḍhill. *f* ; ḍhill maṭṭh. *f* ; ghaul. *f* ; aver. *f* ; averá. *m* ; ghasar masar. *f* ; that which delays. rukávat. *f* ;
DELAY, TO, *V. I.*
chir laggní ; der láuní ; raḥ jáná ; why are you delaying. chir kánúṇ lánná e?
DELAYED, *A*.
avere ;
DELECTABLE, *A*.
man bhauná ; dilpasiṇḍ ;
DELEGATE, *N*.
diligeṭ. *m* ; wakíl. *m* ; an agent. muḳhtiár. *m* ;
DELEGATE, TO, *V. T.*
wakíl ṭhahráuná ;
DELETE, TO, *V. T.*
miṭáuná ; meṭná ; kalam pherní ; harf kaṭṭná ; láhná ;
DELETED, TO BE, *V. I.*
kaṭṭiá jáná ; miṭ jáná ;
DELETRIOUS, *A*.
nuqsán karnwálá ; nuqsání ; dukhdái ;
DELETION, *N*.
káṭ kúṭ. *f*, káṭ cháṇt. *f* ; kát waḍḍh. *f* ;
DELIBERATE, TO, *V. T.*
1. to consider. soch wichár karná ; wichárná ; gaur karná ; dhiánáná ;
2. to consult. saláh mashwará karná ; matá pakáuní ;
DELIBERATE, *A*.
dhírajmáṇ ; dhírá ; gaurá ; sochwaṇd ;
DELIBERATELY, *Adv*.
1. knowingly. ján bújhke ; soch samajh ke ; jánke ; hoshiyárí nál ;
2. slowly. haule haule ; dhíre dhíre ; tharáke ; matthe matthe ; saije saije ;
DELIBERATENESS, *N*.
dhíraj. *f* ; saij. *f* ;
DELIBERATION, *N*.
1. thoughtful consideration. soch. *m* ; wichár. *m* ; ḳhayál. *m* ;
2. caution. hoshiyárí. *f* ;
3. counsel. masaudá. *m* ;
DELICACY, *N*.
padárath. *m* ; parshád. *m* ; niámat. *f* ; bhog. *m* ;
DELICATE, *A*.
nájak ;
DELICIOUS, *A*.
suádí ; suádlá ; mazedár ;
DELICIOUSNESS, *N*.
suád. *m* ; mazá. *m* ;
DELIGHT, *N*.
ḳhushí. *f* ; anaṇd. *m* ; bhauná. *m* ; parsintáí. *f* ; magantáí. *f* ; shantí. *f* ;
DELIGHT, TO, *V. T.*
1. to please another. ḳhush karná ; anaṇd karná ;
2. to make one laugh. khiṛ ḳhiráuná ; hassáuná ;
DELIGHT, TO, *V. I.*
ḳhush honá ; rájí honá ; anaṇd honá. bhág bhág honá ;
DELIGHTED, *A*.
ḳhush ; rájí ; nihál ; jam jam ; bhág bhág ; parsinn ; anaṇd ; magan ;
DELIGHTFUL, *A*.
rasílá ;
DELIMIT, TO, *V. T.*
hadd banáuná ; banná páuná ;
DELINEATE, TO, *V. T.*
taswír khichchná ; naqshá banáuná ;

DELINEATION, *N.*
naqshá. *m ;* taswír. *f ;* murat. *f ;* shakal. *f ;*
DELINQUENCY, *N.*
qusúr. *m ;* dosh. *m ;* bhull. *f ;* galatí. *f ;* bhulekhá. *m ;*
DELINQUENT, *N.*
qusurwár. *m ;* doshí. *m ;* taqsírí *m ;* jurmí. *m ;*
DELIRIOUS, *A.*
besudh ; behoshí vichch bakná ;
DELIRIUM, *N.*
1. condition. sarsám. *m ;*
2. delirious talk. bakaṛwát. *f ;* bakaṛwás. *f ;* bakaṛwá. *f ;*
DELIVER, TO, *V. T.*
1. to save. chhuḍáuná ; bacháuná ; chhuṭkárá dená ; rihái dení ;
2. to hand over. sauṇp dená ; dená ; hawále karná ; phaṛáuná ;
3. to utter. bolná ; bayán karná ; káhná ; dassná ;
DELIVERANCE, *N.*
chhuṭkárá. *m ;* bacháo. *m ;* rihái. *f ;* ḳhálásí. *f ;*
DELIVERER, *N.*
bacháunwálá. *m ;* naját denwálá. *m ;* muktídátá. *m ;* chhuḍáunwálá. *m ;*
DELL, *N.*
khaḍḍ. *f ;*
DELUDE, TO, *V. T.*
dhokhá dená ; dam vichch láuná ; jháṇsá dená ; see DECEIVE.
DELUGE, *N.*
jal parláo. *f ;* parlo. *f ;* parlú. *f ;*
DELUSION, *N.*
dhokhá. *m ;* jhánsá. *m ;* waihm. *m ;* see DECEPTION.
DELUSIVE, *A.*
farebí ; dhokhebáj ;
DELVE, TO, *V. T.*
khodná ; puṭṭná ; khaṭṭná ;
DEMOGOGUE, *N.*
bakháunwàlá. *m ;*
DEMAND, *N.*
darḳhást. *f ;* arz. *f ;* dává. *f ;* máng. *f ;*
DEMAND, TO, *V. T.*
maṇgná ; darḳhást karní ; arz karní ; arjí páuní ;
DEMARCATION, *N.*
hadd. *f ;* kanárá. *m ;* banná. *m ;* waṭṭ. *f ;*
DEMEANOUR, *N.*
ḍaul. *f ;* ḍhang. *m ;* bol chál. *m ;* chàl chalan. *m ;*
DEMENT, TO, *V. T.*
jichch karná ; págal banáuná ; sir khapáuná ; satáuná ; sir khá jáná ;
DEMENTED, *A.*
págal ; kamlá ; sudáí ; kamlá ramlá ; jhallá ;
DEMENTIA, *N.*
sháudá. *m ;* jhall. *m ;* kamal. *m ;*
DEMERIT, *N.*
1. fault. jurm. *m ;* aib. *m ;*
2. defect. kasar. *m ;* nuqs. *m ;*
DEMISE, *N.*
maut. *f ;* see DEATH.
DEMISSION, *N.*
jawáb. *m ;* istífá. *m ;*
DEMIT, TO, *V. T.*
jawáb dená ; istífá dená ; chhaḍḍ dená ;
DEMOLISH, TO, *V. T.*
ḍháh dená ; ḍháhná ; ḍegná ; ḍháuná ; pachháṛná ;
DEMOLITION, *N.*
ḍháh. *f ;*
DEMON, *N.*
bhút. *m ;* paret. *m ;* deú. *m ;* rakas. *m ;* rakhas. *m ;* bhútnà. *m ;* badrúh. *f ;*
DEMONIAC, *N.*
uh jeh de utte badrúh chambaríá ;
DEMONSTRATE, TO, *V. T.*
1. to prove. sábit karná ; nitárnà;
2. to show. záhir karná ; dikhláuná ; see SHOW.
DEMONSTRATION, *N.*
1. proof. sabút. *m ;* dalíl. *f ;*
2. manifestation. pargaṭ. *f ;* dikhlàí. *f ;*
DEMORALISATION, *N.*
badchalní. *f ;* badkárí. *f ;* ḳharábí. *f ;*
DEMORALIZE, TO, *V. T.*
wigáṛná ; ḳharáb karná ; jhàṇsná ; ujáṛnà ;
DEMORALIZED, TO BE, *V. I.*
wigaṛná ; bigaṛ janá ;

DEMULCENT, *A.*
narm ; mulaim ;
DEMUR, *N.*
jirá. *m* ; uzr. *f* ; bahána. *m* ; pajj. *m* ; ṭhuṇá. *m* ; see EXCUSE.
DEMUR, TO, *V. T.*
hujjat kaḍḍhní ; itaráj karná ; uzr karní ; ṭokkná ; chú chará karní ; kusakná ;
DEMURE, *A.*
hayáwálá ; matthekajjí ; sharmwalí ;
DEMURELY, *Adv.*
saṇg de nál ; hayá nàl ;
DEMURENESS, *N.*
hayá. *m* ; sharm. *m* ; láj. *f* ; saṇg. *f* ;
DEMURRAGE, *N.*
harjá. *m* ;
DEN, *N.*
1. wild beasts' den. khuṇdhar. *f* ; ghurhá. *m* ; ghurná *m* ; ghurh. *m* ;
2. den of thieves. dhárwíáṇ dà khoh. *m* ; dhárwíáṇ dá gupphá. *m* ;
DENIAL, *N.*
inkár. *m* ; mukkar. *m* ; hutt. *f* ; ṭálá. *f* ; náṇh mukkar. *m* ;
DENIER, *N.*
munkar. *m* ; inkárí. *m* ;
DENOMINATE, TO, *V. T.*
náṇ dená ; náṇ rakkhná ;
DENOTE, TO, *V. T.*
batláuná ; dikhláuná ;
DENOUNCE, TO, *V. T.*
dos láuná ; ilzám láuná ; hikayat karní ; nálish karná ; see ACCUSE.
DENOUNCEMENT, *N.*
ilzám, *m* ; shikayat. *f* ;
DENSE, *A.*
1. thick. gaṛhá ; gahirá ;
2. of trees or population. saṇhná.
DENSITY, *N.*
moṭṭáí. *f* ; gahir. *f* ;
DENT, *N.*
chibb. *m* ;
DENTED, *A.*
chibbá ;
DENUDE, TO, *V. T.*
naṇgá karná ; kapṛe utár lená ; kapṛe láh dená.

DENY, TO, *V. T.*
inkár karná ; mukkarná ; hutt karní ; kann te hatth rakkhná ; mukkar jáná ;
to deny oneself. jí márná ; man márná ; see ABSTAIN.
DEODAR, *N.*
diár. *m* ;
DEODORIZE, TO, *V. T.*
1. to make clean. safá karná ;
2. to apply fresh cowdung to the floor. pochá pherná ;
DEPART, TO, *V. I.*
1. to leave. ṭurná ; ṭur jáná ; challiá jáná ; khisk jáná ; sidhárná.
2. to die. mar jáná ; guzar jáná ;
DEPARTMENT, *N.*
mahikamá. *m* ;
DEPARTURE, *N.*
rawángí. *f* ; rukhsat. *f* ;
DEPEND, TO, *V. T.*
ásrá rakkhná ; bharosá rakhná ; patíjná ; yaqín karná ; patiáuná ;
I am depending on you. maiṇ tuháḍe gochará háṇ ;
DEPENDENCE, *N.*
atbár. *m* ; bharosá. *m* ; ásrá. *m* ; dhijá. *m* ; ás. *f* ; dhijáu. *m* ; patiárá. *m* ;
DEPENDENT, *A.*
gochará ;
DEPICT, TO, *V. T.*
bayán karná ; zikr karná ; dikhláuná ; bakháuná ; dassná ;
DEPLETE, TO, *V. T.*
ḳhálí karná ; vehlá karná ;
DEPLETION, *N.*
gháṭṭá. *m* ;
DEPLORABLE, *A.*
bhaiṛá ; ḳhajjal ḳharáb ;
DEPLORE, TO, *V. T.*
hamsos karná ; roná ; kurláuná ; phús phús karná ;
I deplore it greatly. mainúṇ uh dá baṛá afsos hai ;
DEPOPULATE, TO, *V. T.*
ujáṛná ;
DEPOPULATION, *N.*
ujáṛá. *m* ;
DEPORT, TO, *V. T.*
mulkoṇ báhar kaḍḍh dená ; laí jáná ;

DEPORTATION, *N.*
des nikálá. *m ;*
DEPORTMENT, *N.*
chál chalan. *m;* bol chál. *m;* ḍaul. *f;* ḍhang chál. *m ;* lachchhan. *m ;*
DEPOSAL. *N.*
mauqúfí. *f ;* chhuṭṭí. *f ;*
DEPOSE, TO, *V. T.*
1. to dismiss. chhuṭṭí dení ; jawáb dená ; haṭá dená ; kaḍḍhná ;
2. to state on oath. sauṇh kháke bayán karná ; sauṇh kháke gawáhí dení ;
DEPOSIT, *N.*
1. anything entrusted to the care of another. amánat. *f ;*
2. an advance of the price to be paid. sáí. *f ;*
DEPOSIT, TO, *V. T.*
amánat rakkhní ; sáí dení ;
DEPOSITION, *N.*
bayán. *m ;* gawáhí. *f ;* shahádat. *f ;*
DEPOSITOR, *N.*
amánat rakkhaṇwálá. *m ;*
DEPOT, *N.*
ḍipú. *m ;*
DEPRAVATION, *N.*
wigáṛ. *m ;* ḳharábí. *f ;*
DEPRAVE, TO, *V. T.*
wigáṛná ; ḳharáb karná ; gaṇḍá karná ;
DEPRAVED, *A.*
sharír ; luchchá ; dusht ; ḳharáb ; uchakká ; beháyá ; badmásh ; luṇḍá ; guṇḍá ; bhaiṛá ;
DEPRAVATY, *N.*
badkárí. *f ;* besharmí. *f ;* ních kamm. *m ;* kamínpuṇá. *m ;* chandál puṇá. *m ;* sharárat. *f ;* badí. *f ;*
DEPRECATE, TO, *V. T.*
uzr karná ; see DEMUR.
DEPRECATION, *N.*
uzr. *m ;* see DEMUR.
DEPRECIATE, TO, *V. T.*
badnàm karná ; niṇdiá karná ; búrá kahná ;
DEPRECIATION, *N.*
1. deficiency. ghaṭáú. *f ;* kasar. *m ;* kamí. *f ;* gháṭṭá. *m ;*
2. dishonour. badnámí. *f ;* namoshí. *f ;* bijjatí. *f ;*

DEPREDATION, *N.*
ḍáká. *m ;* chorí. *f ;* már dháṛ. *f ;*
DEPREDATOR, *N.*
luṭerá. *m ;* ḍákú. *m ;* dháṛví. *m ;* chor. *m ;*
DEPRESS, TO, *V. T.*
1. to make sorry. bedil karná ; man toṛná ; gamdil karná ;
2. to press down. dabáuná ;
3. to humble. níwíáṇ karná ; ních bṇanáuná ; níwáṇ karná ;
DEPRESSED, *A.*
udás ; sogmáṇ ; sogí ; dukhí ; dukhiá ; masosiá hoyá ;
DEPRESSION, *N.*
udásí. *f ;* gam. *m ;* bedilí. *f ;* dilgírí *f ;* sog. *m ;* ranj. *m ;*
DEPRIVATION, *N.*
mauqufí. *f ;* chhuṭṭí. *f ;* jawàb. *m ;*
DEPRIVE, TO, *V. T.*
kho lená ; láhná ; luṭṭná ;
to deprive of dignity. mikk jháṛní ;
DEPTH, *N.*
ḍunghiáí. *f ;* ḍuṇgh. *f ;* tháh. *f ;* háth. *m ;*
DEPUTE, TO, *V. T.*
mukhtiár banáuná ;
DEPUTY, *N.*
mukhtiár. *m ;* wakíl. *m ;*
of a shopkeeper. gumáshtá. *m ;*
DERANGE, TO, *V. T.*
sarkáuná ; ulaṭ pulaṭ karná ; uladdná ;
DERANGEMENT, *N.*
betartíbí. *f ;* kasút. *m ;*
DERELICTION, *N.*
1. unfaithfulness. beimání. *f ;* beimánagí. *f ;* bewafái. *f ;*
2. abandonment. tark. *f ;* chhaḍdáwá. *m ;*
DERIDE, TO, *V. T.*
ṭhaṭṭhé vichch uḍáuná ; maḳhaul karná ; hassná ; jugat karná ;
DERISION, *N.*
maḳhaul. *m ;* ṭhaṭṭhá. *m ;* maskarí. *f ;* hássí. *f ;* hássá. *m ;* bollí ṭhollí. *f ;* bakheṛá. *m ;* hássá bakheṛá. *m ;* hasáí. *f ;*
DEROGATE, TO. *V. T.*
badnám karná ; níṇdíá karná; náhaqq bolná ; ujjláuná ;

DESCANT, TO, *V. T.*
bayán karná ; kahná ; kujh bolná ; samjháuná ;
DESCEND, TO, *V. I.*
uttarná ; heṭháṇ áuná ; lahiná ;
DESCENDANT, *N.*
aulád. *f ;* nasl. *f ;* bachchá. *m ;* descendants. parwár. *m ;*
DESCENT, *N.*
utarái. *f ;* utár. *m ;* ḍhál. *f ;* lahái. *f ;* ḍháyá. *m ;* see SLOPE.
DESCRIBE, TO, *V. T.*
bayán karná ; zikr karná ; dassná ;
DESCRIPTION, *N.*
bayàn. *m ;* zikr. *m ;* hál. *m ;* bakhán. , *m ;*
DESCRY, TO, *V. T.*
vekhná ; malúm karná ; takkná ;
DESECRATE, TO, *V. T.*
palít karná ; nápák karná ; wigáṛná ; labeṛná ;
DESECRATION, *N.*
nápákí. *f ;* palidagí. *f ;* palítí. *f ;*
DESERT, *N.*
thal. *m ;* ujáṛ. *f ;* ban. *m ;* jangal. *m ;* rohí. *f ;*
DESERT, TO, *V. T.*
1. to relinquish. chhaḍḍná ; tiágná ;
2. to run away. bhajjná ; nassná ; dauṛná ; naṭṭhná ;
DESERTED, *A.*
sunj ; wirán ; ujjaṛiá hoyá ;
DESERTER, *N.*
bhagaurá. *m ;*
DESERTION, *N.*
taj. *m ;*
DESERVE, TO, *V. I.*
laiq honá ;
he deserves. uhdá haqq hai ;
DESERVEDLY, *Adv.*
haqq mujib ;
DESERVING, *A.*
laiq ; jog ; haqqdár ;
DESIDERATE, TO, *V. T.*
cháhuná ; see DESIRE.
DESIGN, *N.*
1. plan. naqshá. *m ;* ḍaul. *f ;* sáṇchá. *m ;*
2. intention. matlab. *m ;* dalíl. *f ;* irádá. *m ;* gaun. *m ;* marjí. *f ;* manorath. *m ;*
DESIGNATE, TO, *V. T.*
náṇ rakkhnà ; ṭhahráuná ; muqarrar karná ;
DESIGNATION, *N.*
1. name. náṇ. *m ;*
2. rank. rutbá . *m ;* darjá. *m ;* uhdá *m ;*
DESIGNEDLY, *Adv.*
ján bujh ke ; jánke ; samajhke ; soch samajhke ;
DESIGNING, *A.*
chalák ; farebí ; kapṭí ; chhaliá ; matbalí ; matbaliá ; matlabí ; mat labíá ;
DESIRABLE, *A.*
1. necessary. cháhidá ; zarúrí ; munásib ;
2. pleasing. man bháuṇdá ;
DESIRE, *N.*
cháh. *f ;* lochá. *f ;* ríjh. *f ;* shauq. *m ;* táṇgh *f ;* cháu. *m ;* loch. *f ;* manorath. *m ;* ichchhiá. *f ;* bháunà. *m ;* bháuní. *f ;* teh. *f ;* bhának. *f ;*
1. I have lost my desire for rice. chauláṇ te merí bháṇak gaí hoí hai.
2. sensual desire. kámṇá. *f ;*
DESIRE, TO, *V. T.*
jí karná ; sháuq rakkhná ; jí cháhuná ; cháhná ; lochná ; loṛná ; cháh karní ; tarasná ; talakná ; jhurkná ; lalcháuná ; dil karná; táṇgh karná ;
1. to desire that which is improper or impossible. ṭharakná ;
2. I have no desire. maiṇúṇ koí ichchiá nahíṇ ;
DESIST, TO, *V. T.*
lámbhe ho jáná ; báj ráhná OR áuná ; chhaḍḍ dená ; ṭal jáná. muṛná ; haṭ jáná ;
DESK, *N.*
mez. *f ;*
DESOLATE, *A.*
ujáṛ. wirán ; ujjaṛ pujjaṛ. sunn masunn ;
DESOLATION, *N.*
chauṛ. *m ;* ujáṛ. *f ;*
the ruins of an old village. theh. *m ;*
DESPAIR, *N.*
náummedí. *f ;* udásí. *f ;* bedilí. *f ;* **nirás. *f ;***

DESPAIR, TO, *V. I.*
nirás honá ; náummed honá ; ṭhaṇḍá paí jáná ;
DESPAIRING, *A.*
nirás ; kujh ummed nahíṇ ; bedil ; lachár ;
DESPAIRINGLY, *Adv.*
bedil hoke ; ghábar ke ;
DESPATCH, *N.*
1. letter. ḳhatt. *m* ; chhiṭṭí. *f* ;
2. small note. rukká. *m* ; purjá. *m* ;
3. haste. káhlí. *f* ; shatábí. *f* ;
DESPATCH, TO, *V. T.*
1. to send. ghallná ; toṛná ; pahuṇcháná ; bhejná ;
2. to kill. már suṭṭná ; ḳhun karná ; waḍḍhná ;
3. to finish a work. púrá karná ; naberná ; mukáuná ;
DESPERATE, *A.*
beás ; lachár ; aukhá ; bedil ;
DESPICABLE, *A.*
ních ; máṛá ; nikammá ; ghináuná ; chaṇḍál ; nachíj ; shodá ; namáṇná ; chaṇḍálaní ; maháṇ ních ;
DESPICABLENESS, *N.*
chaṇḍálpuṇá. *m* ;
DESPISE, TO, *V. T.*
niṇdiá karná ; niṇdná ; kise núṇ máṛeáṇ jánná ; túchchh samajhná ; haqír jánná ; nachíz samajhná ; kujh ná samajhná ;
to despise a thing. us núṇ hauliáṇ jánná ; dí hiqárat karní ;
DESPITE, *N.*
wair. *m* ; dushmaní. *f* ; adávat. *f* ; virodh. *m* ; kíná. *m* ; khijh. *f* ; kauṛ. *m* ;
DESPITEFULLY, *Adv.*
sakhtí nál ;
DESPOIL, TO, *V. T.*
luṭṭná ; kho lená ; dháṛá márná ; már dháṛ karnà ; chorí karní ;
DESPOILATION, *N.*
chorí. *f* ; luṭṭ. *f* ; luṭái. *f* ; ḍáká. *m* ; dháṛá. *m* ;
DESPOND, TO, *V. I.*
bedil honá ; udás honá ;
DESPONDENCY, *N.*
bedilí. *f* ; gam *m* ; gamí. *f* ; nirás. *f* ;
DESPONDENT, *A.*
bedil ; lachár ; nirásá ; náummed ;
DESPOT, *N.*
jálim. *m* ; waḍḍá haner. *m* ;
DESPOTIC, *A.*
jálim ; saḳhtdil ; saḳht ; beráhm ; zabardast ; kaṛrá ;
DESPOTISM, *N.*
julm. *m* ; zabardastí. *f* ; saḳhtí. *f* ; anher. *m* ; jástí. *f* ;
DESTINATION, *N.*
ṭhikáná. *m* ; jagáh. *f* ;
DESTINE, TO, *V. T.*
muqarrar karná ; ṭhahráuná ;
DESTINY, *N.*
lekh. *m* ; bhág. *m* ; bháná. *m* ; nasíb. *m* ; qismat. *f* ; karm. *m* ;
DESTITUTE, *A.*
garíb ; muhtáj ; bechárá ; miskín ; máṛá ; láchár ; ájiz ; kaṇggál ; damáṇḍol ;
DESTITUTION, *N.*
muhtájí. *f* ; láchárí. *f* ; garíbí. *f* ; taṇgí. *f* ; kaṇggálí. *f* ;
DESTROY, TO, *V. T.*
barbád karná ; ujáṛ dená ; nishṭ karná ; nás karná ; dháṛá márná ; roṛhná ; chaṭṭam karná ; sattiá nás karná ; jaṛ puṭṭná ; chauṛ karná ; nighárná ; satyanás karná ; bíj dur karná ; khanḍná ; saṇgghárná ;
DESTROYED, TO BE, *V. I.*
barbád ho jáná ; nigghar jáná ; tabáh ho jáná ; taraṭṭí chauṛ honí ; ujjaṛ pujjaṛ jáná ;
DESTROYED, *A.*
chauṛ ; ujáṛ ; barbád ; khastáh ;
DESTRUCTION, *N.*
barbádí. *f* ; satyanás. *m* ; nás. *m* ; nuqsán. *m* ; tabáhí. *f* ; ḍhá. *f* ; chauṛ. *m* ; nishṭ. *f* ; ḍobbá sokká. *m* ; bhang. *f* ; nisṭ. *f* ; saṇgghár. *m* ;
DESTRUCTIVE, *A.*
nuqsánkaranwálá ;
DESULTRY, *A.*
aiweṇ ;
DETACH, TO, *V. T.*
1. to separate. wakkh karná ; chhekná ; aḍḍ karná ; nakherná alag karná ;
2. to open. kholná ;

DETACHED, *A.*
wakkh ; alag ; anjo anj ; wakkhrá ; wakkho wakkh ;
DETACHMENT, *N.*
1. of an army. dastá. *m* ;
2. separation. judáí. *f* ;
DETAIL, *N.*
bayán. *m* ; tafsíl. *f* ;
in detail. sárián gallán. *f* ; waddián nikkián gallán. *f* ;
DETAIL, TO, *V. T.*
púrá bayán karná ; sárá hál dassná ;
DETAIN, TO, *V. T.*
rokná ; ján ná dená ; báj rakkhná ; ḍakkná ; baháí rakkhná ; khalhárí rakkhná ;
DETECT, TO, *V. T.*
maιúm karná ; wekh lainá ; pargaṭ karná ; jách lainá ; táṛ lainá ;
DETECTION, *N.*
khoj. *m* ;
DETECTIVE, *N.*
khojjí. *m* ;
DETENTION, *N.*
1. imprisonment. qaid. *f* ;
2. stoppage. aṭkáú. *m* ;
DETER, TO, *V. T.*
rokná ; ḍakkná ; aṭkàuná ; band karná ; udráuná ;
DETERIORATE, TO, *V. I.*
ḳharáb ho jàná ; wigaṛná ; farq áuná ;
DETERIORATION, *N.*
ḳharábí. *f* ; wikárí. *f* ;
DETERMINATE, *A.*
pakká ; qaim ; kabbá ;
DETERMINATION, *N.*
1. purpose. dilí irádá. *m* ; dalíl. *f* ;
2. judgment faisalá. *m* ; niáún. *m* ;
DETERMINE, TO, *V. T.*
1. to purpose. pakká irádá karná ; dhárná ; dalíl karná ; ṭhaṭhná ; thánná ;
2. to decide. faisalá karná ;
3. to terminate. nibeṛná ; mukáuná ;
DETERMINED, *A.*
pakká ; kabbá ;
DETEST, TO, *V. T.*
nafrat áuní ; ghiṇ áuni ; dur rahná ; karáhat áuní ; karích áuná ;
DETESTABLE, *A.*
bahut burá ; palít ; máṛá ; ghiṇauná ; bhaiṛá ;
DETESTATION, *N.*
nafrat. *f* ; ghiṇ. *f* ; karáhat. *f* ;
DETHRONE, TO, *V. T.*
gaddí thoṇ utárná OR láhná ; taḳhtoṇ haṭáuná ;
DETRACT, TO, *V. T.*
badnám karná ; see DEFAME.
DETRACT, TO, *V. I.*
beizzat honá ;
DETRACTION, *N.*
badnámí. *f* ; namoshí. *f* ; beqadrí. *f* ; chuglí. *f* ; badgoí. *f* ;
DETRACTOR, *N.*
tohmatí. *m* ; chuglíḳhor. *m* ; niṇdak. *m* ;
DETRIMENT, *N.*
nuqsán. *m* ; harj. *m* ; gháṭṭá. *m* ; kasar. *m* ;
DETRIMENTAL, *A.*
nuqsání ;
DEVASTATE. TO, *V. T.*
ujáṛná ; wirán karná ; ḳharáb karná ; barbád karná ; nishṭ karná ; see DESTROY.
DEVASTATION, *N.*
satiánás. *m* ; nás. *m* ; tabáhí. *f* ; barbádí. *f* ;
DEVELOP, TO, *V. T.*
1. to unfold. kholná ;
2. to enlarge. waddháuná ; moklá karná ;
DEVELOP, TO, *V. I.*
khulná ;
DEVELOPMENT, *N.*
waddh. *f* ; waddháu. *m* ;
DEVIATE, TO, *V. I.*
1. to wander. phirná ;
2. to swerve. muṛná ; bhaunná ;
3. to change. waṭ jáná ; tabdíl ho jáná ; waṭṭná ;
4. to stray from the path of duty. bhul jáná ; kuráh jáná ;
DEVIATION, *N.*
gumráhí. *f* ; badráhí. *f* ; kuráh. *m* ; bhull. *f* ; bhulekhá. *m* ;
DEVICE, *N.*
1. contrivance. kalá. *f* ; upáú. *m* ;
2. purpose. irádá. *m* ; níyat. *f* ; manshá. *m* ; matlab. *m* ;

DEVIL, *N*.
1. Satan. Shaitán. *m*; Iblís. *m*;
2. an evil spirit. bhut. *m*; badrúh. *f*; palíd átmá. *m*; pareṭ. *m*; bhutṇá. *m*;

DEVILISH, *A*.
shaitání; dozakhí; sharír; dusht; dojakhí;

DEVILRY, *N*.
sharárat. *f*; badí. *f*; shaitání kamm. *m*;

DEVIOUS, *A*.
pechdár; pechwálá;

DEVISE, TO, *V. T*.
1. to invent. hikmat karní; gharṇá; sajáuná.
2. to imagine. sochná;
3. to concoct. ḍhaṇg sochná; upáú labbhná OR karná;

DEVISER, *N*.
bání. *m*;

DEVOLVE, TO, *V. T*.
hawále karná; saunpná;

DEVOLVE, TO, *V. I*.
hattho hatthí áuná;

DEVOTE, TO, *V. T*.
chaṛháuná; de dená; najar dení; arpan karná;
1. to devote oneself. ghamáuná;
2. to devote time. ḳharach karná;

DEVOTE, TO, *V. I*.
wárí jáná; ghol ghumáuná; sadke jáná;

DEVOTED, *A*.
sargarm; joshwálá; shukín; gairatí;
a devoted servant. hatthíṇ baddhíṇ gulám. *m*;

DEVOTEDNESS, *N*.
sargarmí. *f*; josh. *m*; shauq. *m*;

DEVOTEE, *N*.
1. Muhammadan. saíṇ. *m*; Alláh lok. *m*; faqír. *m*; walí Ḳhudá dá. *m*; Rabb dá púrá ádmí. *m*; namájí. *m*;
2. Hindu. bhagat. *m*; jogí, *m*; saṇt. *m*; abdhút. *m*; muní *m*; sádh. *m*; sádhú. *m*; tapassí. *m*; tappassaṇ. *f*; parm bhagtí. *m*;
3. Sikh. nitt nemí. *m*;

DEVOTION, *N*.
1. worship. baṇdagí. *f*, *H*: ibádat. *f*, *M*; bhaktí. *f*, *H*; pujá. *f*; *H*: pujá pát. *f*, *H*; bhagtí. *f*; *H*; bhagtái. *f*, *H*; namáz. *f*, *M*;
2. austere devotions. tapassiá. *f*;
3. zeal. sargarmí. *f*; josh. *m*: shauq. *m*;

DEVOUR, TO, V. T.
khá lainá; ragaṛ lainá; pháṛ kháná; leṛ márná;

DEVOUT, A.
1. Hindu; dharmí; bhagat;
2. Muhammadan; nimájí; díndár;

DEVOUTLY, *Adv*.
baṛí ájizí nál; baṛe adab nál;

DEW, *N*.
tarel. *f*;
dew to fall. tarel painí;

DEWDROPS, *N*.
tarel de choe. *m*; tarel de tubke. *m*;

DEXTERITY, *N*.
tezí. *f*; chustí. *f*; chalákí. *f*; hoshiyárí. *f*; ustádí. *f*; hatth chalákí. *f*; phurti. *f*; chatarái. *f*; júgat. *f*; siánaf. *m*:

DEXTEROUS, *A*.
hoshiyár; phurtílá; guṇíkár; guṇí; siáná; hikmatí; jugatí; dáná;

DEXTEROUSLY, *Adv*.
hoshiyárí nál; hikmat nál;

DIABOLIC, *A*.
shaitání; sharír; dusht;

DIADEM, *N*.
táj. *m*; muṭak. *m*;

DIAGNOSIS, *N*.
bimárí dí jáṇch. *f*; nadáṇ. *f*;

DIAGRAM, *N*.
naqshá. *m*;

DIALECT, *N*.
bolí. *f*; zabán. *f*;

DIALOGUE, *N*.
sawál te jawáb. *m*; galláṇ bátáṇ. *f*;

DIAMETER, *N*.
muṭí. *f*;

DIAMOND, *N*.
hírá. *m*;

DIARRHŒA, *N*.
dast. *m*; maroṛ. *m*;

DICE, *N*.
páshá. *m*; dáná. *m*; nard. *f*; pásá. *m*; chauṇpaṭ. *m*; kumár. *m*;

DICE, TO, *V. T.*
páshá suṭṭná ; gune páuná ; sár páshá kheḍná; páshá páuná ;
DICTATE, TO, *V. T.*
1. to order. hukm dená OR karná ;
2. to cause to be written. imlá likháuná ;
DICTATION, *N.*
imlá *f ;*
DICTATORIAL, *A.*
jálim ; zabardast ; karṛá ;
DICTIONARY, *N.*
lugát. *f ;*
DICTUM, *N.*
bayán. *m ;* bachan. *m ;*
DIDACTIC, *A.*
tálímí ;
DIDDLE, TO, *V. T.*
dhokhá dená ; see DECEIVE.
DIE, *N.*
ṭhappá. *m ;* chhápp. *m ;*
DIE. TO, *V. I.*
marná ; mar jáná ; dam dená ; guzar jáná ; purá honá ; razá-ho jáná ; prán chhaḍḍná ; prán de dená ;
1. to die childless. auṇt mar jáná ; auṇtrá nakhattrá mar jáná ;
2. of trees. sukkh jáná ;
DIET, *N.*
ḳhurák. *f ;* bhojan. *m ;* gizá. *f ;* kháná. *m ;* roṭí. *f ;* khádh ḳhurák. *f ;* khájj. *m ;*
DIETING, *N.*
rakkh. *f ;*
DIFFER, TO, *V. T.*
farq painá ;
DIFFER, TO, *V. I.*
farq honá ; ná ralná ; ná milná ;
DIFFERENCE, *N.*
farq. *m ;* verwá. *m ;* bhinn bhed. *m ;* nikheṛá. *m ;*
1. great difference. asmán zamín dá farq. *m ;*
2. slight difference. rawál ku farq. *m ;*
DIFFERENT, *A.*
wakkhrá ; hor ; alag ; wakkho wakkh ; niárá ;
1. different kinds. bhánṭ bhánṭ de ;
2. different places. tháíṇ tháíṇ. *f ;*
DIFFERENTIATE, TO, *V. T.*
farq painá ;
DIFFERENTIATION, *N.*
farq. *m ;*
DIFFICULT, *A.*
mushkil ; aukhá ; saḳht ; bikhṛá ; sauṛá ; dubbar ; dubbhar ;
DIFFICULTY, *N.*
aukh. *m ;* phettí. *f ;* kastaní. *f ;* ech pech. *m ;* aukkaṛ. *f ;* sauṛ. *f ;* jafar. *f ;*
1. with difficulty. masíṇ ; masáṇ masáṇ ; marke ; mase kíweṇ ;
2. one who causes difficulty. jaṇjálí. *m ;* jaṇjálan. *f ;*
3. the difficulty has disappeared . bárá khul gayá hai.
DIFFIDENCE, *N.*
1. bashfulness. sharm. *f ;* saṇg. *f ;* láj. *f ;* hayá. *m ;*
2. timidity. ḍar. *m ;*
DIFFIDENT, *A.*
hayáwálá ; kanaudá ;
DIFFIDENTLY, *Adv.*
hayá nál ;
DIFFUSE, *A.*
bahut ; bathere ; bahut sárá ;
DIFFUSE, TO, *V. T.*
khinḍáuná ; khilárná ;
DIFFUSELY, *Adv.*
bahut karke ; bahutait nál ;
sown thickly. sanghne ;
DIFFUSION, *N.*
phailáu. *m ;* wistár. *f ;*
DIG, TO, *V. T.*
1. with spade, deeply. khaṭṭná ; puṭṭná ;
2. on the surface. godná ; polí karní ;
3. to dig through the roof. muggh karná ;
4. to dig hole in the ground. ṭoá kaḍḍhná OR márná ;
5. to cause to be dug. khudwáuná ;
DIGEST, TO *V. T,*
házmá kar lainá ; pachá lená ; hazm kar lainá ;
DIGEST, TO, *V. I.*
házmá honá ; pach jáná ; hazm ho jáná ;
DIGESTIBLE, *A.*
narm ;

DIGESTION, *N*.
házmá. *m*; hájamá. *m*; pachan. *m*;
DIGGING, *N*.
khudáí. *f*;
DIGIT, *N*.
1. finger. uṇgglí. *f*;
2. little finger. chíchí. *f*;
3. thumb. aṇgguṭhá. *m*;
DIGNIFY, TO, *V. T*.
izzat dení; darjá dená; uchchá karná; uchchíáṇ karná;
DIGNITY, *N*.
1. honour. izzat. *f*; buzurgí. *f*; ádar. *m*; ro. *f*; ṭháṇs. *f*;
2. rank. darjá. *m*; uhdá. *m*; padwí. *f*;
DIGRESS, TO, *V. I*.
phirná; waṭ jáná; see DEVIATE.
DIKE, *N*.
1. water course. khál. *m*; kassí. *f*; nálá. *m*; áḍ. *f*;
2. pit. ṭoá. *m*;
DILAPIDATE, TO, *V. T*.
ujáṛná; barbád karná; wigáṛná;
DILAPIDATION, *N*.
barbádí. *f*; ḍhaháí. *f*; ujáṛ. *m*; a dilapidated building. kholá. *m*;
DILATE, TO, *V. T*.
kholná; wadháuná;
DILATE, TO, *V. I*.
khul jáná;
DILATORILY, *Adv*.
sustí nál; ḍhill nál; haule haule;
DILATORINESS, *N*.
sustí. *f*; ghaul. *f*; ḍhill. *f*; ḍhill maṭṭh. *f*; álas. *m*; álak. *m*;
DILATORY, *A*.
sust; ḍhillá; ghaulaṇ; ghaulí; ghauliá; maṭṭhá; postí; surliá hoyá;
DILEMMA, *N*.
aukh. *m*; aukhíáí. *f*;
DILIGENCE, *N*.
1. exertion. mihnat. *f*; uddam. *m*; koshish. *f*; himmat. *f*;
2. care. hoshiyárí. *f*;
3. attention. dhián. *m*; ḳhayál. *m*;
DILIGENT, *A*.
mihnatí; sargarm; uddamí; shukín.
DILIGENTLY, *Adv*.
uddám nál; mihnat karke; dil lagáke;
DILLY DALLY, TO, *V. T*.
chir láuní; ajj bhalak karná OR dassná;
DILUTE, TO, *V. T*.
patlá karná; halká karná; haulá karná;
DILUTED, *A*.
halká; patlá;
DIM, *A*.
maṭṭhá; maddham; dhuṇdlá; jhaulá; ghusmusá; sáf nahíṇ; dim sighted. chunnhá;
DIM, TO, *V. T*.
hanerá karná; dhuṇdlá karná;
DIMENSION, *N*.
náp. *m*; mintí. *f*;
DIMINISH, TO, *V. T*.
ghaṭṭáuná; ghaṭṭ karná; thoṛá karná;
DIMINISH, TO, *V. I*.
ghaṭṭná; ghaṭṭ honá; khuṭṭ jáná;
DIMINUTION, *N*.
gháṭṭá. *m*; see DECREASE.
DIMINUTIVE, *A*.
chhoṭá; chhoṭá jehá;
DIMLY, *Adv*.
sáf nahíṇ;
DIMNESS, *N*.
dhuṇd. *f*; dhuṇdúkár. *m*; dhúr. *f*; haze. gahir. *f*;
DIN, *N*.
raulá. *m*; shor. *m*; hugg. *f*; ḍanḍ. *f*; gaugá. *m*; khap. *m*; see CONFUSION.
DIN, TO MAKE, *V. T*.
raulá páuná; shor macháuná; khap páuná; ḍanḍ páuná;
DINE, TO, *V. T*.
roṭí kháná; parshádá shakaná; dining room. kháná kamrá. *m*;
DINGY, *A*.
mailá; mailá kuchailá;
DINNER, *N*.
rasoí. *f*; parshádá. *m*; roṭí. *f*; bhojan. *m*; annpání. *m*;
DIP, TO, *V. T*.
1. plunge. gotá márná; ḍob dená; ḍobná; chubbhí láuní;
2. to ladle out. páuná;

DIP, *N.*
ḍob. *f*; ḍobbá. *m*; ḍubb. *m*; ḍubkí. *f*; chubbhí. *f*;
DIPHTHERIA, *N.*
khunáq. *m*;
DIPLOMA, *N.*
chiṭṭhí. *f*; sanad. *f*;
DIPLOMACY, *N.*
pallasí. *f*; hikmat. *f*;
DIRE, *A.*
ḍaráuná; ḍaráú;
DIRECT, *A.*
siddhe;
DIRECT, TO, *V. T.*
1. to point out. ráh dassná; patá dená;
2. to order. hukm dená OR karná; kah dená; ágiá dená;
3. to regulate. intizám karná;
DIRECTION, *N.*
1. towards. taraf. *f*; wal. *f*; pásse. *m*; dá. *f*; hatth. *m*; rukkh. *m*;
2. guidance. hidayat. *f*; nasíhat. *f*;
3. command. hukm. *m*; ágiá. *f*;
4. address. pind pír. *m*; náṇ patá. *m*; atá patá. *m*; tháṇ sitá. *m*;
DIRECTLY, *Adv.*
huṇe; jhaṭ phaṭ;
DIRECTNESS, *N.*
siddh. *f*; sed. *f*; sedh. *f*;
DIRGE, *N.*
aláuná. *m*; siápá. *m*;
DIRT, *N.*
mailá. *m*; gaṇd. *m*; gaṇdagí. *f*; ghuṇ. *m*; mal. *m*; mail kuchail. *f*; chiṭak. *f*; kasut. *m*;
dirt in a well. khíṇ. *m*; chíṇáṇ. *f*;
DIRT, TO, *V. T.*
mailá karná; gaṇdá karná; wigáṛná; see SOIL
DIRTINESS, *N.*
gaṇdagí. *f*; chiṭak. *f*; see DIRT.
DIRTY, *A.*
mailá; gaṇdá; malín; mailá kuchailá; kasutà; kasutrá; ghasmailá;
dirty person. kuchajjá; kuchajjí;
DISABILITY, *N.*
láchárí. *f*; kamjorí. *f*;
DISABLE, TO, *V. T.*
bekár karná;
DISADVANTAGE, *N.*
harj. *m*; nuqsán. *m*; gháṭṭá. *m*; kasar. *m*;
DISAFFECTED, *A.*
badníyat; virodhí;
DISAGREE, TO, *V. T.*
manzúr ná karná; zidd karná; nahíṇ manná; farq painá; wiṭṭarná;
DISAGREEABLE, *A.*
1. unpleasant. búrá; kharáb;
2. not agreeable. khiláf;
DISAGREEMENT, *N.*
1. discord. náittifáqí. *f*; phuṭṭ. *f*; jhagrá. *m*; aṇ baṇ. *f*; tanázá. *m*; anjoṛ. *m*;
2. difference. farq. *m*; verwá. *m*;
DISALLOW, TO, *V. T.*
ná hon dená; náh karná; radd karná; ṭhák dená; maná karná;
DISAPPEAR, TO, *V. I.*
luk jáná; chip jáná; nazroṇ ghuss jáná; cháiṇ máiṇ ho jáná;
DISAPPOINT, TO, *V. T.*
náummed karná; nirás karná; bedil karná;
DISAPPOINTED, *A.*
nirásá;
DISAPPOINTMENT, *N.*
nirás. *f*; náummedí. *f*; námurádí. *f*;
DISAPPROBATION, *N.*
malámat. *f*; shikayat. *f*;
DISAPPROVAL, *N.*
námanzúrí. *f*;
DISAPPROVE, TO, *V. T.*
1. to censure. qusur baṭláuná; shikayat karní; jháṛ karná;
2. to reject. radd kar dená; manzúr nahíṇ karná;
3. to complain. gilágujárí karní;
4. to be displeased with. muṇhoṇ utárná;
DISARM, TO, *V. T.*
hathiyár laí lainá;
DISARRANGE, TO, *V. T.*
ulaṭ pulaṭ karná, rkáuná; ulad pulad karná; tháṇ tháṇ karná;
DISARRANGED *A.*
kusútá; tháṇ tháṇ; upar thalí;

DISARRANGEMENT, *N.*
kusút. *m;* betartíbí. *f;*
DISARRAY, TO, *V. T.*
khillar pullar karná; betartíb karná; see DISARRANGE.
DISARRAY, *N.*
betartíbí. *f;*
DISASTER, *N.*
musíbat. *f;* áfat. *f;* balá. *f;* biptá. *f;* haner. *m;* bijj. *f;*
DISAVOW, TO, *V. T.*
1. to refuse to own. ná manná;
2. to deny. inkár karná; mukkarná; hutt karní;
DISAVOWAL, *N.*
inkár. *m;* mukkar. *m;* ṭálá. *f;* namukkar. *m;*
DISBAND, TO, *V. T.*
náṇwáṇ kaṭṭṇá; jawáb de dená;
DISBELIEF, *N.*
shakk. *m;* shubhá. *m;* shakk shubhá. *m;* bharm. *m;* jak. *f;* jhakk. *m;* bepartítí. *f;* wiswás. *m;*
DISBELIEVE, TO, *V. T.*
ná manná; shakk karná; bharm karná; yaqín ná karná;
DISBELIEVER, *N.*
munkar. *m;* namukkar. *m;* ámoṛ. *m;*
DISBURSE, TO, *V. T.*
ḳharach karná; hisáb kitáb naberṛ dená;
DISBURSEMENT, *N.*
ḳharach. *m;* lágat. *f;* lággá. *m;*
DISCARD, TO, *V. T.*
suṭṭṇá; chhaḍḍ dená; nikál dená;
DISCERN, TO, *V. T.*
malúm karná; vekhná; záhir karná; pahchhánná;
DISCERN, TO, *V. I.*
samajhná; vekhná; jáchná;
DISCERNIBLE, *A.*
záhir; malúm;
DISCERNING, *A.*
hoshiyár; siáná; suchet; aqlwálá; dáná;
DISCERNMENT, *N.*
hoshiyárí. *f;* buddh. *f;* pahchán. *f:* chaukasí. *f;*
DISCHARGE, TO, *V. T.*
1. to dismiss. jawáb de dená; haṭá dená; náṇ kaṭṭná; kaḍḍhná; chhuṭṭí dení;
2. to release. azád karná; chhaḍḍ dená; ḳhalásí karní; rihá karná;
3. to perform. púrá karná; naberṇá; muká dená;
4. to fire a gun. banduq chaláuná;
5. to be discharged, dismissed. jáwáb milná;
DISCHARGE, *N.*
1. dismissal. chuṭṭí. *f;* jawáb. *m;*
2. release. chhuṭkárá. *m;* rihá. *m;* ḳhalásí. *f;*
3. of a gun. fail. *m;*
DISCIPLE, *N.*
shagird. *m;* chelá. *m;* muríd. *m;* chelará. *m;* dás. *m;* bálká. *m;* sikh. *m;* sikhní. *f;*
fellow disciple. gur bhái. *m;*
DISCIPLESHIP, *N.*
shágirdí. *f;*
DISCIPLINE, *N.*
in order, arrangement. rahit bahit. *f;* intizám. *m;*
DISCIPLINE, TO, *V. T.*
tálím dení; sikhláuná; paṛháuná; durúst karná;
DISCLAIM, TO, *V. T.*
mukkarná; inkár karná;
DISCLOSE, TO *V. T.*
1. to tell. batláuná; záhir karná; dassná; bayán karná;
2. to open out. ughárṇá; ugheṛná; pholná;
DISCLOSURE, *N.*
bayán. *m;*
DISCOLOUR, TO, *V. T.*
raṇg wigáṛná;
DISCOLOURATION, *N.*
dág. *m;*
DISCOLOURED, *A.*
badraṇg;
to become discoloured. raṇg uḍḍ jáná;

DISCOMFIT, TO, *V. T.*
1. to disconcert. sharmáuná; jhár suṭṭná OR chaḍḍná; ghabrá dená;
2. to defeat. jittná; haráuná;
DISCOMFITTED, *A.*
sharm dá máriá; háyá dá máriá; to be discomfited. lajjiá áuní;
DISCOMFITURE, *N.*
hár. *f;* namoshí. *f;* sharmindagí. *f;*
DISCOMFORT, *N.*
taklíf. *f;* beárámí. *f;* dukh. *f;* aukh. *f;* aukhíáí. *f;*
DISCOMFORT, TO, *V. T.*
dukhdená; satáuná; taklíf dení; aukhián karní; sir khapáuná;
DISCOMPOSE, TO, *V. T.*
dabkáuná; ghabrá dená;
DISCOMPOSURE, *N.*
bechainí. *f;* hairánagí. *f;* beárámí. *f;* beqarárí. *f;*
DISCONCERT, TO, *V. T.*
sharmáuná; ṭhíṭṭh karná; lajáuná;
DISCONNECT, TO, *V. T.*
alag karná; judá karná; wakkh karná; aḍḍ karná;
DISCONNECTED, *A.*
alag; aḍḍ.; wakkh;
DISCONSOLATE, *A.*
udás; masosiá hoyá; bechain; gamgín; sogmáṇ; sasdil; nimújhán;
DISCONTENT, *N.*
narázagí. *f;* bechainí. *f;* besabrí. *f;* asantokhí. *f;* khár. *f;*
DISCONTENTED, *A.*
rází nahíṇ; to be discontented. awájár honá;
DISCONTINUANCE, *N.*
bandí. *f;*
DISCONTINUE, TO, *V. T.*
band karná; rokná;
DISCONTINUE, TO, *V. I.*
band ho jáná; mukkná; khuṭṭ jáná;
DISCORD, *N.*
náittifáqí. *f;* phuṭṭ. *f;* jhagrá. *m;* aṇ baṇ. *f;* tanázá. *m;* aṇjoṛ. *m;*
DISCORDANT, *A.*
besurá;

DISCOUNT, *N.*
mujráí. *f;* mujrá. *m;*
DISCOUNT, TO, *V. T.*
mujrá lainá;
DISCOUNTENANCE, TO, *V. T.*
1. to shame. sharmáuná; lajjáuná; ṭhíṭṭh karná;
2. to refuse. inkár karná; manzur nahíṇ karná; mukkar painá;
DISCOURAGE, TO, *V. T.*
dil toṛná; ḍuláuná; bedil karná; thiṛáuná; udráuná;
DISCOURAGEMENT, *N.*
náummedí. *f;* bedilí. *f;*
DISCOURSE, *N.*
naṣíhat. *f;* wáz. *m;* kalám. *m;* bayán. *m;* bachan. *m;* parsang. *m;* vakhyán. *m;* parchár. *m;* sikkhiá. *f;*
religious or philosophical. gián gosaṭ. *f;* gián godarí. *f;*
DISCOURSE, TO, *V. T.*
bayán karná; kahná; wáz karná; nasíhat dení;
DISCOURTEOUS, *A.*
gustákh; ḍhíṭh; ḍhíṭhá; see RUDE.
DISCOURTEOUSLY, *Adv.*
gustákhí nál; beadabí nál;
DISCOURTESY, *N.*
beadabí. *f;* chámalí. *f;*
DISCOVER, TO, *V. T.*
malúm karná; patá launá; bhálná; labbhná; kaḍḍhná;
DISCREDIT, TO, *V.*
1. to distrust. atbár nahíṇ karná; shakk karná;
2. to disgrace. badnám karná bepat karná; lajáuná;
DISCREDITABLE, *A.*
bahut búrí gal;
DISCREET, *A.*
siáná; hoshiyár; aqlwálá; suchet; chaukas; suján;
DISCREETLY, *Adv.*
hoshiyárí nál; khabardárí nál; hosh nál;
DISCREETNESS, *N.*
hoshiyárí. *f;* buddh. *f;* see DISCRETION.

DISCREPANCY, *N.*
farq. *m*; verwá. *m*;
DISCREPANT, *A.*
galat; ṭhík nahíṇ;
DISCRETION, *N.*
aql. *f*; samajh. *f*; hosh. *m*; hoshiyárí. *f*; buddh. *f*; sújh. *f*; surt. *f*; chaukasí. *f*; síáṇaf. *f*; síánap. *f*; síáṇapá. *m*; síáṇpat. *f*; síáṇpuṇá. *m*;
authority. iḳhtiyár. *m*;
DISCRIMINATE, TO, *V. T.*
pahchhánná; farq karná; nakheṛá karná;
DISCRIMINATION, *N.*
samajh. *f*; pahchán. *f*; jách. *f*; aql. *f*; buddh. *f*;
DISCUS, *N.*
worn by Akalis. chakkar. *m*;
DISCUSS, TO, *V. T.*
bahis karná; gall karní; saláh karní; saláh mashwará karná; bahisná; apo vichch galláṇ bátáṇ karní;
DISCUSSION, *N.*
bahis. *f*;
religious or philosophical. gián gosaṭ. *f*; gián godarí. *f*;
DISDAIN, TO, *V. T.*
haqír jánná; nachíz samajhná; haṇkár karná; niṇdiá karná;
DISDAIN, *N.*
ghiṇ. *f*; niṇdiá. *f*; hiqárat. *f*;
DISDAINFUL, *A.*
magrúr; see HAUGHTY.
DISEASE, *N.*
bimárí. *f*; rog. *m*; marz. *f*; auhar. *f*;
1. contagious disease. acchút bimárí. *f*; laganwálí bimárí. *f*;
2. fatal disease. már denwálí bimárí. *f*;
DISEASED, *A.*
bimár; rogí; rogaṇ;
DISEMBARK, TO, *V. T.*
jaház thoṇ utárná;
DISEMBARK, TO, *V. I.*
jaház thoṇ utarná;
DISEMPLOY, TO, *V. T.*
jawáb de dená; haṭá dená; kaḍḍhná; chhuṭṭí dení;
DISENGAGE, TO, *V. T.*
1. to separate. wakkh karná; aḍḍ karná; nakheṛná;
2. to open. kholná;
DISENGAGED, *A.*
1. out of work. vehlá; bekár;
2. at liberty. ikaṇt;
DISENGAGEMENT, *N.*
ḳhalásí. *f*; chhuṭkárá. *m*; chhuṭṭí. *f*;
DISENTANGLE, TO, *V. T.*
kholná;
DISFAVOUR, *N.*
narázagí. *f*; nápasaṇdí. *f*; gussá. *m*; rinjgí. *f*;
DISFIGUARTION, *N.*
kaj. *f*; badsuratí. *f*;
DISFIGURE, TO, *V. T.*
rup wigáṛná; chauṛ kar dená;
DISGORGE, TO, *V. T.*
kaḍḍh dená;
DISGRACE, *N.*
beizzatí. *f*; bijjtí. *f*; bepatí. *f*; namoshí. *f*; badnámí. *f*; múkálá. *m*; hattak. *f*; anádar. *m*; lík. *f*; lajjá. *f*;
DISGRACE, TO, *V. T.*
beizzatí karní; ijjat láhuní; badnám karná; durkár suṭṭná; niádarí karní; mikk jháṛní; beqadr karná; ḍigáuná; múṇhkálá karná; ḳhák uḍáuná; pat láh suṭṭná; múṇhoṇ utár dená; ijjat utár dení; pagg láhuní; múkálá karná; miṭṭí palít karná; bepatí karní; bepat karná;
you have disgraced me. tuṇ sáḍe sir utte miṭṭí pái hai;
DISGRACEFUL, *A.*
sharm dí gal; ṭhíṭṭh; búrá; máṛá; ních; thiṇdá sharmiṇdá;
DISGRACEFULLY, *Adv.*
bahut búrí taráh nál;
DISGUISE, *N.*
bhes. *m*; bhekh. *m*; sáṇg. *m*;
DISGUISE, TO, *V. T.*
bhes waṭáuná OR banáuná OR badalná;
DISGUST, *N.*
nafrat. *f*; karáhat. *f*; ghiṇ. *f*; súg. *f*;

DISGUST, TO, *V. T.*
ghiṇ karná;
to feel physical disgust. karích áuná; súg karní;

DISH, *N.*
thálí. *f;* rakábí. *f;* bháṇḍá. *m;* bartan. *m;* thál. *m;*
1. shallow brass drinking dish. chhanná. *m;*
2. brass kneading dish. parát. *f;*
3. earthenware kneading dish. kunál. *m;*

DISHEARTEN, TO, *V. T.*
bedil karná; man toṛná;

DISHEARTENED, TO BE, *V. I.*
hausalá chhaḍḍná; dil chhaḍḍná;

DISHEARTENED, *A.*
bedil; udás; ghábriyá hoyá; sogmáṇ;

DISHEVEL, TO, *V. T.*
wál ḍhá dená; wál ḳharáb karná;
for women only. wál khilárná;

DISHEVELLED, TO BE, *V. I.*
ḍháe jáná; wál ḳharáb ho jáná;
for women only. wál khilar jáná;

DISHONEST, *A.*
beímán; badniyat; dagabáz; farebí; namak harám; choṭá; dhokhebáz; ṭhagg; chálbáj; kapaṭṭá;
to prove dishonest. imán guáuná;

DISHONESTY, *N.*
beimání. *f;* beímángí. *f;* luṇ harámí; dagábájí; kabáhat. *f;*

DISHONOUR, *N.*
beızatí. *f;* bijjtí. *f;* namoshí. *f;* hattak. *f;* see DISGRACE.

DISHONOUR, TO, *V. T.*
pat láhuná; láj láhuná; múṇh kálá karná; ṭhíṭṭh karná; apmán karná; niṇdiá karná; bijjtí karní; durkárná; ijjat láhuní; bhaṇḍná; see DISGRACE.

DISHONOURABLE, *A.*
ṭhíṭṭh; búrá; ních; kupaṭṭa;

DISHONOURABLY, *Adv.*
to act. jhakh márná;

DISINCLINATION, *N.*
ghiṇ. *f;*

DISINCLINED, TO BE, *V. I.*
múṇh pherná; jí nahíṇ karná; dil nahíṇ karná;

DISINFECT, TO, *V. T.*
1. to clean. safá karná;
2. to plaster afresh with cowdung. pochá pherná;
3. to sprinkle phenyle. fanail taráukná;
4. to fumigate. dhúkh dená; gandhak dhukháuná;

DISINHERIT, TO, *V. T.*
haqq márná; hissá kho lená;

DISINTER, TO, *V. T.*
qabr vichchoṇ murdá kaḍḍhná;

DISINTERESTED, *A.*
begaraj;

DISINTERESTEDNESS, *N.*
begarají. *f;*

DISJOIN, TO, *V. T.*
alag karná; aḍḍ karná; adho adhí karná; wakkhrá wakkhrá karná;

DISJOINED, *A.*
alag; aḍḍ;

DISJOINT, TO, *V. T.*
baṇd baṇd aḍḍ karnà; toṛná;

DISLIKE, *N.*
nafrat. *f;* ghiṇ. *f;*

DISLIKE, TO, *V. T.*
búrá jánná; búrá laggná; karáhat karní; ghiṇ karná; achchhá nahíṇ laggná; bhaiṛá laggná;

DISLOCATE, TO, *V. T.*
baṇd baṇd aḍḍ karná;

DISLOCATED, TO BE, *V. I.*
moch áuná; utar jáná; nikal jáná;

DISLOCATED, *A.*
ṭaḷiá hoyá; utarí hoí;

DISLOCATION, *N.*
moch. *f;* joṛ dá utar jáná. *m;*

DISLODGE, TO, *V. T.*
haṭá dená; ulṭá dená; sarkáuná; ḍeg dená;

DISLOYAL, *A.*
ákí; luṇ harám; nimak harám; harámí;

DISLOYALTY, *N.*
beímání. *f;* nimak harámí. *f;* luṇ harámí. *f;*

DISMAL, *A.*
1. doleful. udás; masosiá hoyá; sogmáṇ;
2. dreary. ḍaráuná;
3. dismal looking. roní shakal;

DISMANTLE, TO, *V. T.*
ḍháh dená ; ḍháhná ; ḍegná ;
DISMAY, *N.*
ḳhauf. *m* ; ḍar. *m* ; bhau. *m* ; haul. *m* ; bhaí. *f* ; handeshá. *m* ; haráni. *f* ; haṛbaṛí. *f* ;
DISMAY, TO, *V. T.*
ghabrá dená ; ḍaráuná ; ḍar páuná ; sáyá páuná ;
DISMAYED, *A.*
ghábar gayá ; ḍar paí gáyá ;
DISMEMBER, TO, *V. T.*
joṛ wakkh karná ; aṇg kaṭṭná ;
DISMISS, TO, *V. T.*
jawáb de dená ; chhuṭṭi de dení ; haṭá dená ; ṭor dená ; maqúf karná ; kaḍḍhná ; dur karná ;
1. to send away. vidiá karná ;
2. to dismiss a suit. dává ḳhárij karná ;
3. to be dismissed. jawáb milná ;
DISMISSAL, *N.*
chhuṭṭí. *f* ; maqufí. *f* ; jawáb. *m* ;
DISMOUNT, TO, *V. T.*
utárná ; láhuná ;
DISMOUNT, TO, *V. I.*
utarná ; láih páiná ;
DISOBEDIENCE, *N.*
náfarmání. *f* ; hukm udulí. *f* ; ágiá bhaṇg. *f* ; ákhá moṛná, *m* ; aṇágiákárí. *f* ; ulaṇgghaṇ. *m* ;
DISOBEDIENT, *A.*
ákí ; náfarmán ; bemukkh ; nábar ;
DISOBEY, TO, *V. T.*
ákkhe nahíṇ laggná ; hukm OR gal nahíṇ manná ; hukm udúlí karná ; ákhá moṛná ; hukm báhar jáná ; udúl karná ; ulaṇgghaṇ karná ;
DISORDER, *N.*
1. tumult. shor. *m* ; raula. *m* ; gaṛ baṛ. *m* ; gaṛbaṛí. *f* ; gaugá. *m* ; khapp. *f* ; ḍanḍ. *m* ;
2. illness. bimárí. *f* ; rog. *m* ;
3. derangement. betartíbí. *f* ; badintijámí. *f* ; kusútá kamm. *m* ;
DISORDERLY, *A.*
ulṭá pulṭá ; tháṇ tháṇ ; uppar thalí ; ure pare ; khillár pullár ;
DISORGANISATION, *N.*
gaṛbaṛí. *f* ;
DISORGANIZE, TO, *V. T.*
intizám ḳharáb kar dená ; ulat pulaṭ karná ;
DISOWN, TO, *V. T.*
mukkarná ; inkár karná ; ná manná ;
DISPARAGE, TO, *V. T.*
badnám karná ; niṇdiá karná ; aib láuná ; búrá kahná ; qadr ghaṭṭáuná ;
DISPARAGEMENT, *N.*
badnámí. *f* ; namoshí. *f* ; beqadrí. *f* ;
DISPARITY, *N.*
farq. *m* ; verwá. *m* ;
DISPASSIONATELY, *Adv.*
bináṇ tarafdárí de ; insáf nál ;
DISPEL, TO, *V. T.*
dur karná ; haṭá dená ;
DISPENSABLE, *A.*
loṛ nahíṇ ; loṛídá nahíṇ ;
DISPENSARY, *N.*
haspitál. *m* ; dák ḳháná. *m* ; dawái ḳháná. *m* ;
DISPENSATION, *N.*
muáfí. *f* ;
DISPENSE, TO, *V. T.*
waṇḍná ; waṇḍ dená ; dená ;
1. to dispense medicine. dawáíáṇ banáuná ;
2. to dispense justice. adálat karní ; munsabí karṇí ;
3. to dispense with services. haṭá dená ; jawáb dená ;
DISPERSE, TO, *V. T.*
1. to scatter. khinḍáuná ; khilárná ; uráṇ paráṇ karná ;
2. to distribute. waṇḍná ; waṇḍ dená ;
DISPERSE, TO, *V. I.*
khillar jáná ; khinḍná ; uḍ-puḍ jáná ;
DISPERSION, *N.*
wistár. *f* ;
DISPIRITED, *A.*
bedil ; udás ; sogmáṇ ;
DISPLACE, TO, *V. T.*
ulaṭ pulaṭ karná ; haṭá dená ; sarkáuná ;

DISPLACEMENT, *N.*
uh dí ṭhík jagáh nahíṇ;
DISPLAY, *N.*
1. a show. tamáshá. *m;*
2. a manifestation. dikhává. *m;* dikhlái. *f;* dikhlává. *m;*
3. pomp. saj dhaj. *f;* shúká shákí. *f;* chiṛhat. *f;*
DISPLAY, TO, *V. T.*
wikhálná; dikhláuná; záhir karná; dikhá dená;
DISPLEASE, TO, *V. T.*
naráz karná; dil kha ṭṭá karná; gussá diláuná; chheṛná; rusáuná; akáuná; bhakháuná;
DISPLEASED, TO BE, *V. I.*
múṇh waṭṭná; akkná;
DISPLEASED, *A.*
naráj; ḳhafá; náḳhush; witreá hoyá;
DISPLEASING, *A.*
búrá; náḳhush karnwálí shaí;
DISPLEASURE, *N.*
narázagí. *f;* ḳhafgí. *f;* rossá. *m;* kop. *m;* karodh. *m;* gussá. *m;*
DISPORT, TO, *V. T.*
kheḍná;
DISPOSABLE, *A.*
kamm dá;
DISPOSAL, *N.*
1. settlement. naberá. *m;* faisalá. *m;*
2. control. iḳhtiyár. *m;* wass. *m;*
3. I am at your disposal. maiṇ tuháḍe laṛ laggá;
4. O true Guru, our lives and wealth are present, *i. e.*, at your disposal. he sat gurú, sáḍḍá ján mál hájar hai.
DISPOSE, TO, *V. T.*
1. to sell. vechná; mull dená;
2. to settle. naberná; faisalá karná; ṭhahráuná;
DISPOSITION, *N.*
1. character. mazáj. *f;* subhau. *m;* tabíát. *f;* subhá. *m;* síl. *f;* lachchhan. *m;*
2. habit. ádat. *f;* chajj chál. *m;*
3. arrangement. intijám. *m;*
4. a good disposition. sumatt. *f;*
5. having a good disposition. sulagg;

DISPOSSESS, TO, *V. T.*
1. to turn out. kaḍḍh dená;
2. to seize. kho lainá; see SEIZE.
DISPROPORTIONATE, *A.*
aṇmel;
DISPROVE, TO, *V. T.*
galat OR jhuṭhá sábit karná; jhuṭháuná; mukhráuná; kise dá múṇh band karná; raḍḍná;
DISPUTABLE, *A.*
tark jog;
DISPUTANT, *N.*
takrárí. *m;* bahis karnwálá. *m;* jhagṛálú. *m;*
DISPUTATION, *N.*
takrár. *m;* jhagṛá. *m;* laṛái. *f;* bakheṛá. *m;* hujjat. *f;* reṛká. *m;* patháṛá. *m;* bahis. *f;* jhambelá. *f;* khapáṛá. *f;* khapp. *f;* puáṛá. *m;* aṇbaṇ. *f;*
DISPUTE, *N.*
fasád. *f;* takrár. *m;* see DISPUTATION.
DISPUTE, TO, *V. T.*
1. to quarrel. jhagṛá karná; laṛái karní; laṛná; jhagaṛná; taraṛáuná; chakarí karní;
2. to discuss. bahis karní; see DEBATE.
DISQUALIFICATION, *N.*
náláiqí. *f;* nuqs. *m;* áib. *m;*
DISQUALIFY, TO, *V. T.*
náṇ kaṭṭná; náwáṇ láhná;
DISQUIET, TO, *V. T.*
ghabrá dená;
DISQUIETITUDE, *N.*
beárámí. *f;* bechainí. *f;* fikr. *m;* beqarárí. *f;* chiṇtà. *m;* jahimat. *f;*
DISREGARD, *N.*
láparwáhí. *f;* gáfalí. *f;* sustí. *f;* ghaul. *m;* anádar. *m;*
DISREGARD, TO, *V. T.*
liház nahiṇ karná; láparwáhí karní; nahíṇ manná;
DISREGARDFUL, *A.*
gáfal; láparwáh; ḍhillá; ghaulá;
DISREPUTABLE, *A.*
lukká;
DISREPUTE, *N.*
badnámí. *f;* see DISGRACE.

DISRESPECT, *N.*
beadabí. *f;* beizzatí. *f;* bijjtí. *f;* beqadrí. *f;* anádar. *m;* gustáḳhí. *f;* namoshí. *f;* berobí. *f;* shoḳhí. *f;*
DISRESPECT, TO, *V. T.*
beadabí karní; bijjtí karní; berobí karní; namoshí karní; gustáḳhí karní;
DISRESPECTFUL, *A.*
baṛbolá. *m;* magrúr; shoḳh;
DISRESPECTFULLY, *Adv.*
beadabí nál; shoḳhí nál;
DISSATISFACTION, *N.*
1. displeasure. narázagí. *f;*
2. impatience. besabrí. *f;*
3. uneasiness. beqarárí. *f;*
DISSATISFIED, TO BE, *V. I.*
awá jár honá;
DISSATISFY, TO, *V. T.*
naráz karná; dil khaṭṭá karná; see DISPLEASE.
DISSECT, TO, *V. T.*
chír pháṛ karná; chírná;
DISSECTION, *N.*
chír pháṛ. *m;*
DISSEMBLE, TO, *V. T.*
1. to disguise. bhes badalná OR waṭáuná;
2. to feign. dhokhá dená; makr karná;
DISSEMBLER, *N.*
pakhaṇḍí. *m;* makkar. *m;* bhaglá bhagat. *m;* see DECEIVER.
DISSEMBLING, *N.*
faréb. *m;* riyákárí. *f;*
DISSEMINATE, TO, *V. T.*
bakheṛná; khilárná; phailáuná;
DISSENSION, *N.*
fasád. *f;* náittifáqí. *f;* phuṭṭ. *f;* jhagṛá. *m;* laṛáí. *f;* takrár. *m;* bahis. *f;* bikháṇd. *m;* aṇbaṇ. *f;* tanázá. *m;* páṭak. *m;*
DISSENT, TO, *V. T.*
manzúr nahíṇ karná; farq painá; nahíṇ manná;
DISSERTATION, *N.*
bayán. *m;* wáz. *m;* nasíhat. *f;*
DISSERVICE, *N.*
nuqsán. *m;* harj. *f;*

DISSEVER, TO, *V. T.*
alag karná; wakkh karná; aḍḍ karná;
DISSIMILAR, *A.*
judá; wakkh; alag; wakkhrá; barábar nahíṇ; ikko jehá nahíṇ;
DISSIMILARITY, *N.*
farq. *m;*
DISSIMULATION, *N.*
fareb. *m;* dhokhá. *m;* see DECEIT.
DISSIPATE, TO, *V. T.*
1. to waste. záyá karná; ḳharáb karná; wigáṛná;
2. to squander. guá dená; ḳharach karná;
3. to scatter. khilárná;
DISSIPATION, *N.*
badchalní. *f;* luchchpuṇá. *m;* bhaiṛápaṇ. *m;* badí. *f;*
DISSOLUBLE, *A.*
jehṛá pání wángar ho jáwe;
DISSOLUTE, *A.*
badkár; luchchá; badmásh; sharír; lukká; guṇḍá; bhaiṛá;
DISSOLUTELY, *Adv.*
badkárí vichch; mastewáṇ nál;
DISSOLUTENESS, *N.*
badkárí. *f;* badchalní. *f;* sharárat. *f;* luchchpuṇá. *m;* badí. *f;* mastewáṇ. *m;*
DISSOLUTION, *N.*
1. separation. judáí. *f;* wachoṛá. *m;*
2. death. maut. *f;*
3. destruction. barbádí. *f;* nás. *f;* sattiá nás. *f;*
DISSOLVE, TO, *V. T.*
khorná; khárná; golná;
DISSOLVE, TO, *V. I.*
gallná; khurná; kharná;
DISSUADE, TO, *V. T.*
rokná; aṭkáuná; báj rakkhná; moṛná; maná karná; samjháuná; warjná;
DISTANCE, *N.*
paiṇḍá. *m;* paṇdh. *m;* dureḍá. *m;* dúr. *m;* wát. *f;*
1. distance between space. witth *f*
2. at a great distance. duráḍḍá;
3. at a short distance. kukkaṛ udárí.

DISTANCE, TO, *V. T.*
pichche chhaḍḍná; wadh jáná; agge nikal jáná;
DISTANT, *A.*
dúr; duráḍḍá; dureḍe; pare; dúrwár;
DISTASTE, *N.*
ghin. *f;* nafrat. *f;*
DISTASTE, TO, *V. I.*
búrá laggná; búrá jánná; changá nahíṇ laggná; ghiṇ áuní;
DISTASTEFUL, *A.*
1. evil. búrá; ghiṇáhdá; bharist; bhaiṛá;
2. not tasty. kusawád;
DISTEMPER, *N.*
kutte dí bimárí. *f;*
DISTEND, TO, *V. T.*
1. to open out. kholná;
2. to enlarge. wadháuná; phailáuná;
3. to spread out. pasárná;
4. to inflate. phuláuná;
DISTEND, TO, *V. I.*
khul jáná; phull jáná;
DISTIL, TO, *V. T.*
arq kaḍḍhná; sat kaḍḍhná;
DISTILLER, *N.*
kalál. *m;*
DISTILLERY, *N.*
sharáb banáuṇ dá makán. *m;*
DISTINCT, *A.*
1. different. hor;
2. separate. wakkh; niárá; wakkhrá; aḍḍ; alag; judá; wakkho wakh;
3. clear. nirmal;
DISTINCTION, *N.*
farq. *m;* verwá, *m;* nirwá. *m;* nirwáṇ. *m;* nikheṛá. *m;* bhinn bhed. *m;*
DISTINCTIVE, *A.*
ḳháss;
DISTINCTLY, *Adv.*
sáf sáf; safáí nál; changí taráh;
DISTINCTNESS, *N.*
safáí. *f;*

DISTINGUISH, TO, *V. T.*
pachhánná; farq kaḍḍhná; nakheṛá karná; chháṇtná; to distinguish truth from falsehood. nitárná;
DISTINGUISHED, *A.*
mashhúr; námí; manniá danniá;
DISTORT, TO, *V. T.*
wigáṛná;
DISTORTION, *N.*
kaj. *f;* badsúratí. *f;*
DISTRACT, TO, *V. T.*
khapáuná; hairán karná; chheṛná; jich karná; dikk dená; aukhiáṇ karní; taṇg karná; see DISTRESS.
DISTRACTED, *A.*
págal; kamlá; shudái; januní; besúdh; jhallá;
DISTRACTED, TO BE, *V. I.*
aql chakkar kháná; ghábar jáná;
DISTRACTION, *N.*
sir khapáí. *f;* bechainí. *f;* beqarárí. *f;* dubdhá. *f;* dhaṛká. *m;*
DISTRAIN, TO, *V. T.*
kurk karáuná;
DISTRAINT, *N.*
kurkí. *f;*
DISTRESS, *N.*
1. pain. dukh. *m;* pír. *f;* dard. *f;* aukh. *m;* dukhṛá. *m;* kasálá. *m;*
2. calamity. musíbat. *f;* taklíf. *f;* biptá. *f;* kasṭaní. *f;* áfat. *f;* balá. *f;* kashṭ. *m;* khechal. *f;*
3. poverty. taṇgí. *f;* garíbí. *f;* taṇgsí. *f;* kaṇgálí. *f;*
DISTRESS, TO, *V. T.*
dukh dená; taṇg karná; satáuná; dukháuná; taklíf karní; kashṭ dená; aukhiáṇ karní; kasálá karná; see DISTRACT.
DISTRESSED, TO BE, *V. I.*
aukhá OR taṇg honá; hussaṛná; ranj honá;
DISTRESSED, *A.*
aukhá; taṇg; dukhí; dukhiá; khwár; ḳhajjal ḳharáb;
DISTRIBUTARY, *N.*
of river, canal. báhá. *m;*

DISTRIBUTE, TO, *V. T.*
waṇḍ dená; hissá karná; wartáuná;
among two only. adho adh karná;
DISTRIBUTION, *N.*
hissá. *m*; waṇḍ. *f*; pattí. *f*;
DISTRICT, *N.*
iláqá. *m*; halká. *m*; tappá. *m*; Government districts. zilá. *m*; tahsíl. *f*; zail. *f*;
DISTRUST, *N.*
shakk. *m*; shubhá. *m*; shakk shubhá. *m*; bharm. *m*; jhakk. *m*; jann. *m*;
DISTRUST, TO, *V. T.*
shakk karná; atbár nahíṇ rakhná; jhakkná; bharm karná;
DISTRUSTFUL, *A.*
bharmí; shakkí; gumání; janní;
DISTRUSTFULLY, *Adv.*
shakk karke;
DISTRUSTFULNESS, *N.*
shakk. *m*; bharm. *m*; see DISTRUST.
DISTURB, TO, *V. T.*
1. to quarrel. jhagaṛná; raulá páuná; karudh páuná;
2. to agitate. ghabrá dená;
3. to shake. hiláuná;
4. to raise a disturbance. agg láuná;
DISTURBANCE, *N.*
1. quarrel. raulá. *m*; karudh. *m*; fasád. *f*; rattá. *m*; ḍanḍ. *f*; reṛká. *m*; daṇggá fasád. *f*; bakheṛá. *m*; halchal. *f*; rohlí. *f*;
2. agitation. bechainí. *f*; beqarárí. *f*; beárámí. *f*; afrá dafrí *f*;
DISTURBED, *A.*
bechain; gháúṇ máúṇ; beárám; aukhá; betáb;
DISTURBER, *N.*
fasádí. *m*; daṇggáí. *m*; laṛáká. *m*; kapṭí. *m*;
DISUNION, *N.*
aṇjor. *m*; náittifáqí. *f*; judáí. *f*; phuṭṭ. *f*; aṇ baṇ. *f*; phaṭ. *m*; jhagṛá; *m*; khapp. *f*; puáṛá. *m*;

DISUNITE, TO, *V. T.*
wakkh wakkh karná; alag karná; chhekná; aḍḍ karná; nakheṛná; wichoṛ dená;
DISUSAGE, *N.*
bekárí. *f*;
DISUSE, TO, *V. T.*
kamm vichch nahíṇ leáuná;
DITCH, *N.*
khaí. *f*; ṭoá. *m*; nálí. *f*; gaṛhá. *m*; khál. *m*; khaḍḍ. *f*; khuḍḍal. *f*; challá. *m*;
trench for troops. morchá. *m*;
DITCH, TO, *V. T.*
khái puṭṭná; ṭoá kaḍḍhná;
DITTY, *N.*
gít. *m*;
DIVE, *N.*
gotá. *m*; ḍubkí. *f*; chubbhí. *f*; ḍubb. *m*; ṭubbí. *f*;
DIVE, TO, *V. T.*
gottá márná; chubbhí láuní; ṭubbí launí OR mární;
DIVER, *N.*
ṭobhá. *m*; chubbhí máranwálá. *m*; ḍuboliá. *m*;
DIVERGE, TO, *V. I.*
farq painá;
DIVERGENCE, *N.*
farq. *m*; verwá. *m*;
DIVERGENT, *A.*
wakkho wakkh; anek;
DIVERSION, *N.*
rág raṇgg. *m*; parchává. *m*;
DIVERS PLACES. *N.*
tháíṇ tháíṇ. *f*;
DIVERSITY, *N.*
farq. *m*;
DIVERT, TO, *V. T.*
1. to amuse. dil parcháuná; dil bhaláuná; khush karná; bahiláuná; baráuná;
2. to turn aside. moṛná;
DIVEST, TO, *V. T.*
naṇgá karná; kapṛe utárná OR láhná; naṇg dhaṛ karná;
DIVIDE, TO, *V. T.*
waṇḍ dená; hissá karná; wartáuná;
amongst two only. adho adh karná;
DIVIDED, TO BE, *V. I.*
khulná; alag ho jáná;

DIVIDENDS, *N*.
biáj. *m* ;
DIVINATION, *N*.
fál. *m* ;
DIVINE, *A*.
1. belonging to God. iláhí; Ḳhudá dá; Rabb dá; Parmeshwar dá;
2. excellent. uttam;
3. heavenly. ásmání; swargí;
DIVINE, TO, *V. T*.
agetre dassná; tír tukká márná;
DIVINER, *N*.
manṭarí. *m* ; janṭarí. *m* ; raul. *m* ; ramlá. *m* ;
DIVING, *N*.
chubbhí. *f* ; goṭṭá. *m* ; ḍob. *f* ;
DIVINITY, *N*.
Ḳhudáí. *f* ; Ishúrtáí. *f* ;
DIVISION, *N*.
1. distribution. paṭṭí. *f* ; waṇḍ. *f* ;
2. division of a book. káṇḍ. *m* ;
3. party. ṭollí. *f* ; fariq. *m* ; jatthá. *m* ;
4. dissension. páṭak *m* ; phuṭṭ. *f* ;
DIVORCE PAPER, *N*.
taláq námá. *m* ; likhat. *f* ; tiág pattrí. *f* ;
DIVORCE, TO, *V. T*.
taláq námá de dená; tiágná; tiág dená; likhiá de dená; likhat paṛhat dení; taláqná; chhaḍḍ dená;
bill of divorcement. taláq námá. *m* ; tiág pattrí. *f* ; likhat paṛhat. *f* ; likhat. *f* ;
DIVULGE, TO, *V. T*.
bhet dassná; zikr karná; batláuná;
DIZZINESS, *N*.
gherní. *f* ; chakkar. *m* ; bhauṇ. *m* ; hanerní. *f* ;
DIZZY, *A*.
sir bhaundá; sir dakk dakk kardá;
DO, TO, *V. T*.
karná; kar lainá; amal karná;
to do what one is compelled to do. gal piá ḍhol bajáuná; see PERFORM.

DOCILE, *A*.
1. obedient. tábedár; ágiákár; ṭahldár. mannanwálá.
2. yielding. garíb; asíl; adhín; mulaim; maskín;
DOCILITY, *N*.
garíbí. *f* ;
DOCK, TO, *V. T*.
dumb waḍḍhná
DOCTOR, *N*.
dáktár. *m* ; dágdár. *m* ; hakím. *m* ; baid. *m* ; waid. *m* ;
DOCTRINE, *N*.
1. teaching. tálím. *f* ; sikkhiá. *f* ; dharm updesh. *m* ;
2. creed. aqídá. *m* ;
3. one point of doctrine. maslá. *m* ;
DOCUMENT, *N*.
sanad. *f* ; tamassak. *m* ;
file of papers. misal. *f* ;
DODGE, *N*.
dhokhebájí. *f* ; see TRICK.
DODGE, TO, *V. T*.
1. to avoid. ṭálná; múṇh lukáuná;
2. to trick. dhokhá dená; see DECEIVE.
DOE, *N*.
harní. *f* ;
DOER, *N*.
kartá. *m* ; karnwálá. *m* ;
DOFF, TO, *V. T*.
láhná; láh dená; láh suṭṭná;
DOG, *N*.
kuttá. *m* ; kuttí. *f* ;
1. mad dog. halká. *m* ; halkáyá. *m* ;
2. a small dog. khaṇḍá. *m* ; katúrá. *m* ; gular. *m* ;
DOGCART, *N*.
baggí. *f* ; tamtam. *f* ;
DOGKEEPER, *N*.
ḍoriá. *m* ;
DOGMA, *N*.
1. creed. aqídá. *m* ;
2. one point of creed. maslá. *m* ;
DOINGS, *N*.
kamm. *m* ; karm. *m* ; amal. *m* ; karní. *f* ;
DOLE, *N*.
dán punn. *m* ;

DOLEFUL, *A.*
udás ; sogmán ; gamgín ; nimújhán ; masosiá hoyá ;
DOLEFULNESS, *N.*
udásí. *f ;* gam. *m ;* ranj. *m ;* hamsos. *f ;* gamí. *f ;*
DOLL, *N.*
guḍḍí. *f ;*
DOLER, *N.*
gam, *m ;* see DOLEFULNESS.
DOLOROUS, *A.*
udás ; gamgín ;
DOLT, *N.*
ḍaṇggar. *m ;* ḍaṇggarí. *m ;* ḍaṇggarú. *m ;* beaql. *m ;*
DOMAIN, *N.*
iláqá. *m ;* ráj. *m ;*
DOME, *N.*
gumṭí. *f ;* burjí. *f ;* gammaṭ. *m ;*
DOMESTIC, *N.*
naukar. *m ;* ṭahliyá. *m ;* chákar. *m;*
DOMESTIC, *A.*
ghar dá ; gharoká ;
DOMICILE, *N.*
1. house. ghar. *m ;* makán, *m ;*
2. country. des. *m ;*
DOMINATION, *N.*
bádsháhí. *f ;* hukúmat. *f ;* julm. *m ;*
DOMINEER, TO, *V. T.*
hukúmat karní ; dhamkáuná ; julm karná ; jabardastí karní ; jástí karní ; wass rakhná ;
DOMINION, *N.*
ráj. *m ;* bádsháhí. *f ;*
1. dominion of sin. páp dí wáh. *f ;*
2. to exercise dominion. hukúmat karní ; ráj karná ; bádsháhí karní ; wass rakhná ;
DONATE, TO, *V. T.*
chandá dená ; pun karná ; dán karná ;
DONATION, *N.*
chandá. *m ;* dán. *m, H ;* pun. *m, H. ;* ḳhairát. *f, M ;*
DONE, *P. P.*
ho gayá ;
DONKEY, *N.*
khottá. *m ;* gadhá. *m ;* gaddá. *m ;*
DONKEY OWNER, *N.*
ghamiár. *m ;* kumhár. *m ;*
DONOR, *N.*
denwálá. *m ;* dátá. *m ;*
DOOM, *N.*
qismat. *f ;* nasíb. *m ;* lekh. *m ;* bhág. *m ;* karm. *m ;* parálabhat. *f ;*
DOOR, *N.*
buhá. *m ;* darwázá. *m ;* dúár. *m ;*
1. a single leaved door. bhit. *m ;* khiṛk. *m ;*
2. made of reeds. khiṛkí. *f ;*
3. an open door. latthá buhá ; buhá latthá hoyá hai ; buhá khulá hoyá hai ; buhá khulá hai ;
DOOR FRAME, *N.*
chaugát. *m ;*
DOOR KEEPER, *N.*
darbán. *m ;*
DOORSTEP, *N.*
sardal. *f ;*
DORMOUSE, *N.*
chuhí. *f ;*
DOSE, *N.*
ikk ḍaṇg. *f ;* khurák. *f ;*
DOT, *N.*
binḍí. *f ;* ṭikká. *m ;*
DOTAGE, *N.*
buḍḍhepá. *m ;* waḍḍápaṇ. *m ;*
DOUBLE, *A.*
duṇá ; dohrá ; dugaṇá ;
1. double barreled. dunálí ;
2. double faced. doruká ; dorukhá ;
3. double minded. do dilá ; duhittá ;
4. double tongued. do jibbhá ; nagallá ; dubájrá ;
5. double dealing. dagábájí. *f ;* fareb bájí. *f ;*
DOUBLE, TO, *V. T.*
duganá karná ; duṇá karná ;
DOUBT, *N.*
shakk. *m ;* shubhá. *m ;* shakk shubhá. *m ;* bharm. *m ;* jhakk. *m ;* khaṭká. *m ;* sainsá. *m ;* bepartítí. *f ;* dubdhá. *m ;*
without doubt. nishaṇg ; beshakk ; nisaṇg ;
DOUBT, TO, *V. T.*
shakk karná ; bharm karná ; yaqín nahíṇ áuná ; dhaṛakná ; atbár nahíṇ rakkhná ; dalíláṇ vichch painá.

DOUBTFUL, *A.*
shakkí; bharmí; dubhde vichch; bharm dí;
DOUBTFULLY, *Adv.*
shakk karke;
DOUBTLESS, *A.*
beshakk; nishaṇg. nisaṇg;
DOUBTLESSLY, *Adv.*
biná shakk de; jarúr;
DOUGH, *N.*
tauṇ. *f;*
dough in which there is no yeast. patír. *m;*
DOUGHTY, *A.*
diler; bahádur; see BRAVE.
DOVE, RING, *N.*
ghuggí. *f;* ghuggú. *m;*
turtle dove. ṭoṭrú. *m;*
DOVE COTE, *N.*
1. on the ground. kumbhal. *m;* ghumail. *f;* khuḍḍ. *m;*
2. roosting place at top of pole. chhattaṛí. *f;*
DOWER, *N.*
dáj. *f;* dát. *f;* khaṭ. *m;*
DOWN, *N.*
rúṇ. *f;* ruí. *f;*
DOWN, *Prep.*
heṭháṇ; níchhe;
DOWNCAST, *A.*
udás; bedil; gamgín; masosiá hoyá; sasdil;
DOWNFALL, *N.*
nás. *m;* barbádí. *f;*
DOWNWARDS, *Adv.*
heṭháṇ wal;
DOWNY, *A.*
narm; kullhá;
DOWRY, *N.*
dáj. *f;* dát. *f;* khaṭ. *m;*
DOZE, *N.*
uṇggh. *f;* níṇdar. *m;* kachchí níṇd. *f;*
DOZE, TO, *V. I.*
uṇgghná; uṇgghláuná;
DOZEN, *N.*
darjan. *m;* bárah. *m;*
DRAFT, *N.*
huṇḍí. *f;*
of a deed. masaudá. *m;*
DRAFT, TO, *V. T.*
kháká banáuná;

DRAG, TO, *V. T.*
ghasíṭná; khichchná; reṛhná; dhiṛná; dhuhná; dharúhná;
DRAGGING, *N.*
ghasíṭ. *f;* khichchwái. *f;*
DRAIN, *N.*
1. large. khál. *f;*
2. small. nálí. *f;* vaihṇí. *f;* khálí. *f;*
DRAIN, TO, *V. T.*
páni kaḍḍhná; nichoṛná;
DRAKE, *N.*
batak. *m;*
DRAMA, *N.*
rás. *f;* náṭak. *m;*
DRAPE, TO, *V. T.*
kapṛeáṇ nál sajáuná;
DRAPER, *N.*
bajáj. *m;*
DRAPERY, *N.*
bajájí. *f;*
DRAUGHT, *N.*
1. a current of air. jhoṇká. *m;*
2. a drink. ghuṭṭ. *m;*
DRAW, TO, *V. T.*
1. to sketch. naqshá banáuná; taswír khichchná;
2. to drag. khichchná; dhúhná; ghasíṭná; dhíṛná;
3. to receive. lená; qabulná;
4. to draw from a well. bharná;
5. to draw off an infusion. nitárná;
DRAWBACK, *N.*
nuqs. *m;*
DRAWER, *N.*
kháná. *m;* dráz. *f;* rakhná. *m;* golak. *f;*
lit. a box. ḍabbá. *m;*
DRAWERS, *N.*
1. men's. kachchh. *f;*
2. women's. sutthaṇ. *f;* see CLOTHES.
DRAWING, *N.*
taswír. *f;* murat. *f;*
plan or map. naqshá. *m;*
DRAWING ROOM, *N.*
gol kamrá. *m;*
DRAWL, TO, *V. T.*
haule haule bolná; saije saije bolná; maṭṭhá maṭṭhá bolná;

DREAD, *N.*
ḍar. *m;* ḳhauf. *m;* haul. *m;* bhaí. *f;* bhaú. *m;* ḍaráwá. *m;* jhakk. *m;* sahim. *m;*
DREAD, TO, *V. T.*
ḍarná; andeshá karná; ḍar laggná; haul karná; jhakkná; sahimaná;
DREADFUL, *A.*
ḍaráuná; ḍaráká; bhayának;
DREADFULY, *Adv.*
ḍar ke;
DREAM, *N.*
sufná. *m;*
DREAM, TO, *V. T.*
sufne vichch vekhná; sufná áuná;
DREAMER, *N.*
sufne wekhanwálá. *m;* khábí. *m;*
DREAMINGLY, *Adv.*
sustí nál; ḍhillá hoke;
DREAMY, *A.*
uh ádmí wahmí hai.
DREARINESS, *N.*
ujáṛ. *f;*
DREARY, *A.*
ujáṛ; wirán:
DREDGE, *N.*
jál. *m;*
DREGS, *N.*
lagg labeṛ. *f;* phog. *m;*
DRENCH, TO, *V. T.*
1. to cause to drink. piláuná; piálná;
2. to wet. bheunná; bhigoná;
DRESS, *N.*
kapṛe. *m;* lírá. *m;* báná. *m, S;*
DRESS, TO, *V. T.*
kapṛe pauná; báná pauná. *S;* to dress a wound. malam paṭṭí karní; paṭṭí bannhná; phiáh láná;
DRIBBLE, TO, *V. I.*
wagná; choná;
DRIED, *A.*
sukkiá hoyá; sukk marukk; of a tree. kharsukk;
DRIFT, TO, *V. I.*
waggná;
DRILL, *N.*
kawaid. *m;*
DRILL, TO, *V. T.*
1. to exercise. kawaid karná; warjish karná; wardash karná;
2. to make a hole. chhek kaḍḍhná; see PIERCE.
DRINK, *N.*
1. intoxicating drink. sharáb. *m;* nashá. *m;*
2. a draught. ghuṭṭ. *m;*
DRINK, TO, *V. T.*
píná; pí laíná;
1. to cause to drink. piálná; piáná; piláuná;
2. to drink without taking breath. gaṭ gaṭ karke pí jáná;
DRINKING VESSEL. *N.*
gilás.
1. small. garví. *f;*
2. large. gaḍwá. *m;*
3. shallow. of brass. channá. *m;*
4. metal glass. kaṭorá. *m;*
DRIP, TO, *V. I.*
choná; waggná;
DRIPPING, *N.*
chowá. *m;*
DRIVE, TO, *V. T.*
hik dená; hakkná; chaláuná; ṭorná; dhassná; hakkí jánná;
1. to drive away. haṭáuná; haṭá dena; jháṛ suṭṭná;
2. for cattle. hakáuná;
3. to drive off an enemy. bhájaṛ páuná; bhajá dená;
DRIVEL, *N.*
1. spittle. thukk. *m;* ráláṇ. *f;*
2. nonsense. gapp. *f;* bak jhak. *f;* bak. *m;* bakwás. *m;* wáhiyátí gal. *f;*
DRIVEL, TO, *V. I.*
1. to slaver. ráláṇ waggná; láráṇ waggná;
2. to talk nonsense. gapp márná; bakwás karná;
DRIVER, *N.*
hikaṇwálá. *m;* hakwaiyá. *m;* hakwáí. *m;*
DRIVING, *N.*
hakáí. *f;*
DROZZLE, *N.*
phakk. *f;* phúhar. *f;* bhúr. *m;*
DRIZZLE, TO, *V. I.*
phakk OR phúhar painí

DROLLERY, *N.*
ṭhaṭṭhá ; *m* ; ṭhaṭṭhebází. *f* ; hássá. *m* ;
DROOP, TO, *V. I.*
kamláuná ;
DROP, *N.*
búṇd. *f* ; choá. *m* ; tubká. *m* ; chiṭṭ *f* ;
drop of rain. kaṇí. *f* ; kiṇí *f* ;
DROP, TO, *V. T.*
giráuná ; ḍiggaṇ dená ;
DROP, TO, *V. I.*
kir jáná ; ḍiggná ; painá ; gir painá ;
DROPPING, *N.*
ṭapak. *f* ; ṭapakiáṇ. *f* ;
DROPSY, *N.*
jalodhar. *m* ;
DROSS, *N.*
khoṭ. *f* ; khoṭáí. *f* ; phog. *m* ;
DROUGHT, *N.*
kál. *m* ; aúṛ. *f* ; sokká. *m* ; sokká dobbá. *m* ; roṛá. *m* ; sokṛá. *m* ;
DROVE, *N.*
heṛh. *f* ; wagg. *m* ; see HERD.
DROWN, TO, *V. I.*
dubná ; dubbke marná ; ruṛh ke marná ; nigghar jáná ;
DROWSILY, *Adv.*
sustí nál ;
DROWSINESS, *N.*
uṇggh. *f* ; kachchí nínd. *f* ; ṭúl. *f* ;
DROWSY, TO BE, *V. I.*
uṇgghná ; uṇgghláuná ; jhokáṇ lainá ; ṭúlaná ;
DRUB, TO, *V. T.*
márná ; see BEAT.
DRUDGE, *N.*
begárí. *f* ;
labourer. mazdúr. *m* ; naukar. *m* ;
DRUDGE, TO, *V. T.*
naukarí karní ; mihnat mashaqqat karní ; mihnat karní ;
DRUDGERY, *N.*
begár. *m* ; mazdúrí. *f* ; naukarí. *f* ; mihnat. *f* ;
DRUG, *N.*
dárú. *m* ; dawá. *f* ; dawáí. *f* ;
DRUGGIST, *N.*
atár. *m* ; pasárí *m* ; hakím. *m* ;

DRUM, *N.*
ḍhol. *m* ; ḍholak. *f* ; dhauṇsá. *m* ;
1. small drum. ḍholkí. *f* ; chhikká. *m* ;
2. double drums. table. *m* ;
3. large, placed on ground. nagárá. *m* ;
4. drum stick. ḍagá. *m* ; ḍaṇká. *m* ;
DRUM, TO, *V. T.*
wajáuná ; ḍhol bajáuná ;
DRUMMER, *N.*
pirhái. *m* ; ḍholkiá. *m* ; ḍholá. *m* ; tambúrchí. *m* ; ḍholwálá. *m* ;
DRUNK, *A.*
nashe vichch ; mastáná ; khíwá ; matwálá ; guṭṭ ; see INTOXICATED.
DRUNKARD, *N.*
sharábí. *m* ; matwálá. *m* ; sharáb kabábí. *m* ;
DRUNKENESS, *N.*
nashebájí. *f* ; nasebájí. *f* ;
DRY, *A.*
sukká ; rukkhá ; rukkhí ; sukká pukká ;
DRY, TO, *V. T.*
sukáuná ; dhuppe páuná ;
DRYNESS, *N.*
sokṛá *m* ; sokká. *m* ;
DUBIOUS, *A.*
shakkí ; bharmí ;
DUBIOUSNESS, *N.*
shakk. *m* ; shubhá. *m* ; bharm. *m* ;
DUCK, *N.*
batak. *m* ;
wild duck. murgábí. *f* ;
DUE, *N.*
haqq. *m* ;
DUE, *A.*
cháhidá ; jarúrí ;
DUG, *N.*
thaṇ. *m* ;
DULL, *A.*
1. dim. dhuṇdlá ; sáf nahíṇ ;
2. stupid. khuṇḍhá ; bewaqúf ; see STUPID.
DULLARD, *N.*
bewaqúf. *m* ; jáhil. *m* ;
DULNESS, *N.*
1. stupidity. bewaqúfí. *f* ; beaqlí. *f* ; hochchhápuṇa. *m* ;
2. dimness. dhuṇd. *f* ; gahir. *f* ;

DULY, *Adv.*
laiq ; munásib ; jog ; ṭhík ;
DUMB, *A.*
guṇgá ;
DUMB BELL, *N.*
mugdar. *m ;* bugdar. *m ;* mugdarí. *f ;*
Indian club. munglí. *f ;*
DUN, *A ;*
samaṇd ;
DUN, TO, *V. T.*
taṇg karná ; aukhiáṇ karní ; pichchhe páuná ;
DUNCE, *N.*
bewaqúf ;
DUNG, *N.*
lid. *f ;* gohá. *m ;*
1. horse-dung. lid. *f ;*
2. cow-dung. gohá. *m ;* gohá gaṭṭá. *m ;*
3. buffaloe-dung. dhadd. *f ;*
4. cow or buffalo-dung freshly cast. phos phosí. *f ;*
5. dried dung lying in jungle. erná. *m ;* gohtá. *m ;*
6. human excreta. jháṛá. *m ;* guṇh. *m ;*
7. birds' excreta. wiṭṭh. *f ;* biṭṭh. *f ;*
8. cow-dung cakes for fuel.
(*a*) flat. páttíáṇ. *f ;*
(*b*) small, shaped. ṭhápíáṇ. *f ;* páttíáṇ. *f ;*
(*c*) large. ḍhakkle. *m ;*
9. goats' and sheep-dung. meṇgnáṇ. *f ;* meṇgṇí. *f ;* míṇg. *f ;* ríkh. *m ;*
10. dogs' excreta. guṇh. *m ;*
11. to make cakes of cow-dung. patthná ;
12. stack of dried cow-dung cakes. gahírá. *m ;* guhárá. *f ;*
DUNGEON, *N.*
1. prison
hawálát. *f ;* kaṇjí haud. *m ;* jel. *m ;* baṇdí ḳháná. *m ;*
2. cellar or pit. bhorhá. *m ;*
DUNGHILL, *N.*
rúṛí. *f ;*
small heaps in fields. dheṛíáṇ. *f ;*
DUPE, *N.*
dhokhá khánwálá. *m;*
DUPE, TO, *V. T.*
ṭhaggná ; ṭhaggí karní ; dhokhá dená ; dagebájí karní ; fareb dená ; see DECEIVE.
DUPLEX, *A.*
duṇá ; dúhrá ; dugṇá ;
DUPLICATE, *N.*
sáṇgh. *m ;* naql. *f ;*
DUPLICATE, TO, *V. T.*
sáṇgh láuná OR utárná ; naql utárná ; naql karní ;
DUPLICITY, *N.*
chalákí. *f ;* fareb. *m ;* dhokhá. *m ;* see DECEIT.
DURABILITY, *N.*
pakkíáí. *f ;* mazbutí. *f;*
DURABLE, *A.*
pakká ; handan sár ;
DURANCE, *N.*
qaid. *f ;*
DURATION, *N.*
chir. *m ;* velá. *m ;*
DURBAR, *N.*
darbár. *m ;*
DURESS, *N.*
1. imprisonment. qaid. *f ;*
2. constraint. dubáu. *m ;*
DURING, *Prep.*
jis vele ; jad ; jis waqt ;
DUSK, *N.*
takáláṇ. *f ;* tarkáláṇ. *f;* shám. *f ;*
DUSKY, *A.*
dhuṇdlá ; kálá jehá ;
DUST, *N.*
ghaṭṭá. *m ;* dhúṛ. *f ;* miṭṭí. *f ;* gardá. *m;* kheh. *f;* dhuddal. *f ;* gard. *f ;* dhuṛá. *m ;* ghaṭṭá miṭṭí. *f;*
1. black dust storm. kálí bolí hanerí. *f ;* annhí hanerí. *f ;*
2. haze. gahir. *f ;*
3. dust of dust storm. gubárí. *f ;* See STORM.
DUST, TO, *V. T.*
jháṛ dená ; jháṛ poch karná ; dhúṛ jhárná ;
1. to raise the dust. gard uḍáuná ;
2. to throw dust. ghaṭṭá ghattná ;
DUSTER, *N.*
jháṛan. *m ;* parolá. *m ;*
DUSTY, *A.*
gahirá ;

DUTIFUL, *A.*
1. obedient. tábedár; farmánbardár; ágiákár;
2. faithful. wafádár;
3. respectful. adabwálá; nekbaḳht; bhalámánas;
4. a dutiful son. suputt. *m*;

DUTIFULLY, *Adv.*
farz samajhke; wafáí nál;

DUTIFULNESS, *N.*
1. duty. farz. *m*;
2. obedience. farmánbardárí. *f*; ágiákárí. *f*;

DUTY, *N.*
1. service. naukarí. *f*; kamm. *m*; chákarí. *f*;
2. obedience. farmánbardárí. *f*; ágiákárí. *f*;
3. obligation. farz. *m*;

DWARF, *N.*
gaiṇá. *m*; giṭṭhá. *m*; giṇḍhá. *m*; ṭhiṇgná. *m*; giṭṭhú. *m*; giṭṭh muṭhiá. *m*; wáuná. *m*;

DWARFISH, *A.*
madhrá jehá; giṭṭhá jehá; chhoṭá jehá; ṭhiṇggná; wáuná;

DWELL, TO, *V. I.*
rahná; wassná; ṭikná; bás karná; baserá karná;

DWELLER, *N.*
wásí. *m*; rahanwálá. *m*;

DWELLING, *N.*
ghar. *m*; makán. *m*; ḍerá. *m*; jagáh. *f*; ṭhikáná. *m*; vaserá. *m*; vasebbá. *m*;

DWINDLE, TO, *V. I.*
ghaṭṭná; ghaṭṭ honá; thoṛá OR kam honá; nakhuṭṭ jáná;

DYE, *N.*
raṇg. *m*;
for the hair. wasmá. *m*;

DYE, TO, *V. T.*
raṇgná; raṇg karná; ḍob dená; raṇg chaṛhná;
to cause to be dyed. raṇggáuná;

DYER, *N.*
lalárí. *m*; nalárí. *m*;

DYEING, *N.*
raṇgái. *f*; raṇgwái. *f*;

DYING, *A.*
maranwálá; maranhárá;

DYNAMITE, *N.*
ikk qism dá bárúd. *m*;

DYNASTY, *N.*
jaddí pushtí. *f*; bádsháhí ghar. *m*;

DYSENTRY, *N.*
pechash. *m*; dast. *m*; pechas. *m*;
with griping pains. maroṛ. *m*;

DYSPEPSIA, *N.*
badhazmí. *f*;

DYSPEPTIC, *A.*
házámá ḳharáb;

E.

EACH, *Pro.*
har ikk;
1. to each man. ikk ikk ádmí núṇ;
2. two each. do do karke;

EAGER, *N.*
joshwálá; sargarm; joshílá; tez; jataní; shukín;

EAGERLY, *Adv.*
shauq nál; ríjh nál; josh nál; diloṇ wajhoṇ; jí ján nál; dil khol ke;

EAGERNESS, *N.*
shauq. *m*; josh. *m*; sargarmí. *f*; cháu. *m*; ríjh. *f*;

EAGLE, *N.*
ukáb. *m*;

EAR, *N.*
kann. *m*;
1. with the ears. kanníṇ;
2. ears of corn. siṭṭe. *m*;

EARACHE, *N.*
kann píṛ. *f*;

EARLY, *Adv.*
taṛke; múṇh anhere; fajre; savere; waḍḍí fajr; ghusmusé; waḍḍe vele; sájhre; sawaḳhte; prabát de vele; savere tere; mián dí báng nál; kukkaṛ dí báng nál;
very early. waḍḍe taṛke; wahḍe vele; bahut taṛke;

EARN, TO, *V. T.*
kamáuná; ḍhann khaṭṭná; kamáí karní; khaṭná kamáuná; khaṭṭ lainá; gujárá karná;

EARNER, *N.*
kamáunwálá. *m*; khaṭṭú. *m*;

EARNEST, *A.*
sargarm; joshwálá; jataní; tez; uddamí;
in earnest. sachchí muchchí;

EARNESTLY, *Adv.*
sargarmí nál; dil nál; diloṇ wajhoṇ; ríjh nál; uddam nál;
EARNEST MONEY, *N.*
sáhí. *f*; sáí. *f*; biáṇá. *m*;
EARNESTNESS, *N.*
jatan. *m*; josh. *m*; dilí shauq. *m*; sargarmí *f*; ríjh. *f*;
to do with great earnestness. dil lagáná; ríjh nál karná; chá nál karná;
EARNINGS, *N.*
khaṭṭí. *f*; kamáí. *f*;
EAR RING, *N.*
bálá. *m*; ḍogá. *m*; duṛ. *m*; wálí. *f*; jhubká. *m*; muṇdar. *m*; muṇdará. *m*; buṇḍá. *m*; bír bhallíáṇ. *f*; see ORNAMENTS.
EARTH, *N.*
1. world. dhartí. *f*; dunyá. *f*; jahán. *m*; dharat. *f*; zamín. *f*;
2. soil. miṭṭí. *f*; bhoṇ. *f*; zamín. *f*; bhúṇ. *f*; ghaṭṭá. *m*;
EARTHEN, *A.*
miṭṭí dá;
an earthen vessel. miṭṭí dá bháṇḍá. *m*;
EARTHENWARE, *N.*
bháṇḍe. *m*; bartan. *m*;
earthen cooking vessel. háṇḍí. *f*;
EARTHLY, *A.*
1. of clay. miṭṭí dá;
2. wordly. dunyáví; saṇsárí; saṇsárik; dunyá dá;
EARTHQUAKE. *N.*
bhuṇchál. *m*;
EARTHWORK, *N.*
miṭṭí dá kamm. *m*;
trench. morchá; *m*;
EARTHWORM, *N.*
gaṇḍoá. *m*;
EARWAX, *N.*
kann dí mail. *f*;
EARWIG, *N.*
kíṛá. *m*;
EASE, *N.*
arám. *m*; armán. *m*; rámán. *m*; asání. *f*; sukh. *m*; chain. *f*; saukh. *m*; asog. *m*;
1. with ease. sukhále; saukh nál; see EASILY.
2. at ease. maze vichch; maze nál; sukhí;
EASE, TO, *V. T.*
1. to help. madat dení; sahárá karná; arám dená; uprálá karná;
2. to lighten. maṭṭhá karná; dhímá karná; hauliáṇ karná;
3. to ease oneself. jháṛe phirná; jangal jáná;
EASILY, *Adv.*
asání nál; arám nál; sukhále; saukh nál; háíṇ máíṇ;
gently, slowly. sahije sahije; haule haule;
EASINESS, *N.*
asání. *f*;
EAST, *N.*
chaṛhdá. *m*; purab. *m*;
EAST, *A.*
chaṛhde pásse;
EASTER, *N.*
Íd-i-Qiámat. *f*;
EASTERLY, *A.*
chaṛhde pásse; chaṛhde wall;
EASY, *A.*
sukhálá; saukhá; sahal; sawalá sawalaṛá; suhelá; sukhulá;
EASY CHAIR, *N.*
arám dí chaukí. *f*;
EAT, TO, *V. T.*
kháná; bhojan karná; parshád shakaná; ann páṇí wartná;
1. to eat greedily. leṛ márná; harapp karná;
2. to eat an orange or sugar cane. chupná;
3. to eat parched grain, &c., chabbná;
4. to taste. sawád chhakná;
5. to eat the air. wá bhakkhná OR kháná;
6. to cause to eat. khuáná; khiláuná;
EATABLE, *A.*
khán de laiq;
EATABLES, *N.*
ann páṇí. *m*; ann jal. *m*; bhojan. *m*; roṭí. *f*; khájjá. *m*; khádh; ḳhurák. *f*; parshádá. *m*;
EATING, *N.*
kháná.. *m*;

EATING HOUSE, *N.*
laṇgar. *f* ;
EAVES, *N.*
banerá. *m* ; chhajjá. *m* ;
EAVESDROPPING, TO, *V. T.*
chorí sunná ; kann láke sunná, luk ke sunná ;
EAVESDROPPPER, *N.*
chorí sunnanwálá. *m* ;
EBB, *N.*
láh chaṛhá. *m* ;
EBB, TO, *V. I.*
daryá uttarná ;
EBULLITION, *N.*
ubál. *f* ; ubálá. *f* ;
animation. josh. *m* ;
ECCENTRIC, *A.*
1. strange. nirálá ; laihrí ; awallá ;
2. somewhat mad. págal jehá ;
ECCENTRICITY, *N.*
ṭenḍh. *m* ;
ECCLESIASTIC, *N.*
pádrí sáhib. *m* ; pír pádrí. *m*; ḳhádim ud dín. *m* ;
ECCLESIASTICAL, *A.*
mazhabí ; kalísiá dá ;
ECHO, *N.*
gaṛuṇj. *f* ; gaṛ gajj. *m* ;
ECHO, TO, *V. I.*
duhrí awáz áuní ; guṇjná ; guṇj uṭṭhná ;
ECLIPSE, *N.*
suraj garahn. *m* ;
ECONOMICAL, *A.*
sarfewálá ; shum ; saṇjuhṛí. *f* ; saṇjuhṛá ;
ECONOMIZE, TO, *V. T.*
kam ḳharach karná ; ḳharach ghaṭṭáuná ; soch wichár ke ḳharach karná ;
ECONOMY, *N.*
sarfá ; *m* ; ghaṭṭ ḳharach. *m* ; kam ḳharach. *m*; marjádá. *m* ;
EXSTASY, *N.*
waḍḍí ḳhushí. *f* ; josh. *m* ; mauj. *f* ;
EXZEMA, *N.*
lúṭ. *f* ;
EDDY, *N.*
ghumman gher. *f*; ghumman gherí. *f* ;
EDEN, *N.*
bág-i-Adan. *m* ;
EDGE, *N.*
1. of a river, &c., kanḍhá. *m* ; kanárá. *m* ; lámbh. *m* ; banná. *m* ;
2. of a blade. dhár. *f* ;
3. margin of a page. chupherá. *m* ; háshiá. *m* ; kanḍhá. *m* ;
4. of a garment. kanní. *f* ;
EDIBLE, *A.*
khán de laiq ;
EDICT, *N.*
hukm. *m* ; ágiá. *m* ;
EDIFICATION, *N.*
faidá. *m* ;
EDIFICE, *N.*
makán. *m* ;
EDIFY, TO, *V. T.*
faidá pahuṇcháuná ; faide de wáste samjháuná ;
EDIFYING, *A.*
faidemand ; chaṇgá ; man bháuná ;
EDUCATE, TO, *V. T.*
paṛháuná ; sikháuná ;
EDUCATED, *A.*
paṛhiá hoyá ; ilmwálá ; siáná : viddiáwáṇ ; likhiá paṛhiá ;
EDUCATION, *N.*
paṛhái. *f* ; ilm. *m* ;
EDUCE, TO, *V. T.*
kaḍḍhná ; nikálná ; nikásná ;
EFFACE, TO, *V. T.*
miṭáuná ; meṭná ; láhná ; kalam pherní ; harf kaṭṭná ; miṭá dená ; bujháuná ;
EFFECT, *N.*
asar. *m* ; natíjá. *m* ; anjám. *m* ; phal. *m* ;
of none effect, awírthá ;
EFFECT, TO, *V. T.*
1. to produce. paidá karná ; karná;
2. to complete. purá karná ; naberná ; mukáuná ;
EFFECTIVE, *A.*
kamm dá ; kamm de laiq ;
EFFECTIVELY, *Adv.*
pure taur nál ; pakke taur nál ;
EFFEMINATE, *A.*
namard ;
1. a eunuch. khosrá ;
2. an effeminate man. janáná jehá ; janánṛá ;
EFFERVESCE, TO, *V. T.*
ubbalná ;

EFFERVESCENCE, *N.*
ubál. *f ;* ubálá. *f ;*
EFFETE, *A.*
1. exhausted. kamjor ; máṇdá ;
2. barren. báṇjh ;
3. useless. kise kamm dá nahíṇ. nikammá ; akárath ; nikárá ;
EFFICACIOUS, *A.*
tagṛá ; mazbut ; táqatwálá ; asarwálá ; suphal ;
EFFICACIOUSLY, *Adv.*
jor nál ; mazbutí nál ;
EFFICACY, *N.*
jor. *m ;* bal. *m ;* jabar. *m ;* shaktí.
EFFICENCY, *N.*
liyáqat. *f ;*
EFFICIENT, *A.*
laiq ; tagṛá ; pakká ; kamm dá ;
EFFICIENTLY, *Adv.*
pakkí taráh ;
EFFIGY, *N.*
miṭṭi dá mádho. *m ;* putlá. *m ;*
1. small doll. guḍḍí. *f ;*
2. large doll. guḍḍá. *m ;*
EFFLUVIUM, *N.*
badbú. *f ;* see STINK.
EFFORT, *N.*
uddam. *m ;* koshish. *f ;* mihnat. *f ;* jatan. *m ;* hílá. *m ;* till. *m ;* jor. *m ;* wajháp. *m ;* chestá. *m ;*
EFFRONTERY, *N.*
besharmí. *f ;* behayáí. *f ;* magrurí. *f ;* chámalí. *f ;* beadabí. *f ;* haṇkár. *m ;* ḍhíṭháí. *f ;* ḍhíṭhpuṇá. *m ;* kharmastí, *f ;*
EFFULGENCE, *N.*
1. lustre. chamkát. *f ;* chamak. *f ;* chamkárá. *m ;* jhalká. *m ;* chilkárá. *m ;*
2. splendour. raunaq. *f ;* jagmag. *f ;* partáp. *m ;* tej. *m ;*
EFFULGENT, *A.*
chamakdár ; chamkílá ; chamkanwálá ; lishkdár ; lishkanwálá ;
EGG, *N.*
aṇḍḍá. *m ;* aṇḍá. *m ;* aṇḍṛá. *m ;*
1. white of egg. sufedí. *f ;*
2. yoke of egg. zardí. *f ;*
3. egg shell. aṇḍḍe dá chhilká OR kholar OR chhill. *m ;*
EGG ON, TO, *V. T.*
uksáuná ; sikhláuṇá ; chukkná ; see INCITE.
EGG, PLANT, *N.*
batáún. *m ;* waiṇaṇ. *m ;* bhaṭṭhá. *m ;*
EGOTISM, *N.*
haṇkár. *m ;* ḳhudí. *f ;*
EGOTISTICAL, *A.*
haṇkárí ; gamrúr ; phiṭṭiá hoyá ;
EGREGIOUS, *A.*
ajíb ; aṇokhá ; nirálá ;
EGRESS, *N.*
guzar. *f ;* ráh. *f ;* rastá. *m ;*
EGYPT, *N.*
Misr. *m ;*
EIGHT, *A.*
áṭh ;
EIGHTEEN, *A.*
aṭhárán ;
EIGHTEENTH, *A.*
aṭháráwáṇ ;
EIGHTH, *A.*
aṭhwán ;
EIGHTIETH, *A.*
assíwáṇ ;
EIGHTY, *A.*
assí ;
eighty-one. ikássí;
eighty-two. biássí;
eighty-three. tirássi ;
eighty-four. churássí ;
eighty-five. pachássí ;
eighty-six. chhiássí ;
eighty-seven. satássí ;
eighty-eight. aṭhássí ;
eighty-nine. unánweṇ ;
EIKON, *N.*
murat. *f ;* putlá. *m ;*
EITHER, *Pron. & A.*
jáṇ ; yá-yá ; athwá ; cháhe- cháhe ; bháweṇ-bháweṇ ;
EJACULATE, TO, *V. T.*
jhaṭ bolná ; áh áh karná ;
EJACULATION, *N.*
áh. *f ;*
EJECT, TO, *V. T.*
kaḍḍh dená ; haṭá dená ; chhekná ; nakheṛná ;
EJECTION, *N.*
1. excommunication. nakheṛ. *m ;* chhek. *m ;*
2. dismissal. chhuṭṭí. *f ;* jawáb. *m ;*
EKKA, *N.*
yakká ; *m ;*

ELABORATE, TO, *V. T.*
mihnat nál banáuná ; sajáuná ;
ELABORATE, *A.*
sajjiá hoyá ;
ELABORATELY, *Adv.*
mihnat nál ;
ELABORATION, *N.*
mihnat. *f ;*
ELAPSE, TO, *V. T.*
bítná ; langhná ; gujarná ; gujar jáná ;
ELASTIC, *N.*
rabbar. *m ;*
ELASTIC, *A.*
lifanwálá ;
ELASTICITY, *N.*
lachak. *f ;*
ELATE, TO, *V. T.*
1. to puff up. phuláuná ;
2. to exalt. uchchiáṇ karná ; taraqqí dení ; wadiáuná ;
ELATED, *A.*
baṛá ḳhush ;
the man was very elated. uh bandá ḳhushí nál phull gáyá ;
ELATION, *N.*
baṛí ḳhushí. *f ;*
ELBOW, *N.*
arak. *f ;*
ELBOW, TO, *V. T.*
arak mární ;
ELDER, *N.*
buzurg. *m ;* bábá. *m ;*
ELDER, *A.*
waḍḍá ; buzurg ; daulí ḍáṛhí ;
elder brother. lálá. *m ;* bhaiyá. *m ;*
ELDERLY, *A.*
buḍḍhá ; buzurg ;
ELDEST, *A.*
sabh thoṇ waḍḍá ;
ELECT, *A.*
chuniá hoyá ; pyárá ; pák log ; Ḳhudá núṇ pahuṇche hoe lok ; pahuṇcháyá hoyá ;
ELECT, TO, V. T.
1. to choose. chunná ; chhánaná ;
2. to express an opinion. raí dení ;
ELECTOR, *N.*
voṭ denwálá. *m ;* voṭar. *m ;* raí denwálá. *m ;*
ELECTRICITY, *N.*
bijlí. *f ;*

ELEGANCE, *N.*
ḳhubí. *f ;* gun. *m ;* hundar. *m ;* suthráí. *f ;* sugharpuṇá. *m ;*
ELEGANT, *A.*
suthrá ; guní ; sohná ; ḳhubsurat ; ḳhub ; man mohan ; sughaṛ ;
ELEMENT, *N.*
tatt. *m ;*
ELEMENTARY, *A.*
asán ;
ELEPHANT, *N.*
háthí. *m ;* háthní. *f ;*
ELEPHANT DRIVER, *N.*
hathwáṇ. *m ;*
ELEVATE, TO, *V. T.*
uchchiáṇ karná ; chaṛháuná ; taraqqí dení ; darjá dená ;
ELEVATION, *N.*
1. height. uchchíáí. *f ;* lambáí. *f ;*
2. advance. taraqqí. *f ;*
ELEVEN, *A.*
yáráṇ ; giáráh ;
ELEVENTH, *A.*
yáráwáṇ ; giáráhwáṇ ;
ELF, *N.*
bhút. *m ;* jinn. *m ;* bhutṇá. *m ;*
ELICIT, TO, *V. T.*
malúm karná ; natíjá kaḍḍhná ; nikásná ;
ELIDE, TO, *V. T.*
kalam pherní ; meṭná ; miṭáuná ; miṭá dená ;
ELIGIBILITY, *N.*
laiqí. *f ;* liyáqatí. *f ;*
ELIGIBLE, *A.*
laiq ; jog ;
ELIMINATE, TO, *V. T.*
kaḍḍhná ; nikál dená ; kaṭṭná ; waḍḍhná ;
ELIMINATION, *N.*
káṭ kúṭ. *f ;* káṭ chánṭ. *f ;*
ELIXIR, *N.*
áb-i hayát. *f ;*
ELK, N.
báráh singgá. *m ;*
ELONGATE, TO, *V. T.*
lammá karná ; wadháuná ; lambáuná ; lambíáuná ;
ELONGATION, *N.*
wadháú. *m ;* lambáí. *f ;*
ELOPE, TO, *V. I.*
nass jáná ; udhalná ;

ELOPE, TO, *V. T.*
udhál jáná ; udhál le jáná ;
ELOPEMENT, *N.*
udhálá. *m ;*
ELOPER, *N.*
udhálú. *m ;*
ELOQUENT, *A.*
far far karke bolná ; sohníáṇ galláṇ karnwálá ;
ELOQUENTLY, *Adv.*
far far karke ; tarák tarák bolke ; to speak eloquently. suáhre bolná ;
ELSE, *A. & Adv.*
hor;
ELUCIDATE, TO, *V. T.*
samjháuná ; kholke dassná ; arth karná ; matlab dassná ;
ELUCIDATION, *N.*
bayán. *m ;* bakháṇ. *m ;* matlab. *m;*
ELUDE, TO, *V. T.*
dhokhe nál nikalná ; nikal jáná ; muṇh lukáuná ; katráuná ; matthe ná laggná ;
ELUSION, *N.*
dhokhá. *m ;* see DECEIT.
ELUSIVE, *A.*
dhokhebáz ; see DECEITFUL.
EMACIATED, *A.*
lissá ; baṛá máṛá ; lín ; kamjor ; jahmatí ; jhíkkh ; sukkaṛ ; sukṛú ;
EMACIATION, *N.*
kamjorí. *f ;*
EMANATE, TO, *V. I.*
nikalná ;
EMANCIPATE, TO, *V. T.*
azád karná ; chaḍḍáuná ; bacháuná ; riháí dení ;
EMANCIPATION, *N.*
ḳhalásí. *f ;* chuṭkárá. *m ;* riháí. *f ;*
EMASCULATE, TO, *V. T.*
1. to castrate. khassí karní ;
2. to deprive of virility. namard banáuná ;
3. to weaken. kamjor karná ; nirbal karná ;
EMBANKMENT, *N.*
bannh. *m ;* baṇd. *m ;*
EMBARGO, *N.*
báṇḍh. *f ;*
EMBARK, TO, *V. T.*
jaház utte chaṛhná ;
to embark on an enterprise. chhiṛná ;
EMBARKATION, *N.*
jaház dí sawárí. *f ;*
EMBARASS, TO, *V. T.*
1. to confuse one. ghabráuná ;
2. to abash. sharmáuná ; lajáuná ; sharmindiá karná ;
3. to trouble one. dikk dená ; dukh dená ; taṇg karná; sir khapáuná;
EMBARASSED, *A.*
gaḍḍ maḍḍ ;
to be embarassed. bakal jáná ;
EMBARASSMENT, *N.*
1. astonishment. pashemání. *f ;* ghabrát. *f;* hairání. *f;* beqarárí. *f;* hairánagí. *f ;*
2. trouble. dikkat. *f ;* jinjál. *m ;*
EMBELLISH, TO, *V. T.*
shaṇgárná ; suárná ; sudhárná ; sajáuná ; ṭíp ṭáp karná ; hár saṇgár karná ; phabáuná ;
EMBELLISHMENT, *N.*
shaṇgár. *m ;* sajáut. *f ;* sajáu . *f ;*
EMBER, *N.*
1. large. aṇggíár. *m ;*
2. small. aṇggiárí. *f ;* chaṇggiárí. *f ;*
EMBEZZLE, TO, *V. T.*
rupáe kháná ; hatth márná ; chorí karní ; bhorná ; mál kháná ; mál márná ; ḍakárná ;
EMBEZZLEMENT, *N.*
chorí. *f ;* chorí chakárí. *f ;*
EMBITTER, TO, *V. T.*
dil khaṭṭá karná ; bhaṛkáuná ; agg láuná ; russáuná ;
EMBLEM, *N.*
nishán. *m ;* nishání. *f ;*
EMBODY, TO, *V. T.*
miláuná ; joṛná ; raláuná ;
EMBOLDEN, TO, *V. T.*
dilerí dení ; dil wadháuná ; takṛáí karná ;
EMBOSS, TO, *V. T.*
ṭhappná ; ṭhappá lagáuná ;
EMBRACE, *N.*
japphá. *m ;* japphí. *f ;* jámbhaṛí. *f;*
EMBRACE, TO, *V. T.*
japphí páuní ; japphá páuná OR márná ; chhátí nál láuná ; aṇgg lagáuná ; hikk nál láná ; gal nál láná ; galaphṛí páuná ;

EMBROCATION, *N.*
málish karan dí dawá. *f* ;
EMBROIDER, TO, *V. T.*
kasídá kaḍḍhná ;
1. on shoes. namolí karní ;
2. with silk. paṭṭ pherná ;
EMBROIDERY, *N.*
kasídákárí. *f* ; phulkárí. *f* ; bág. *m*; chop. *m* ;
1. embroidery on net. jálí. *f* ;
2. Swiss embroidery. fítá. *m* ;
EMBROIL, TO, *V. T.*
phasáuná ; dukh vichch páuná ;
EMBROILMENT, *N.*
raulá. *m* ; bakheṛá. *m* ; hujjat. *f* ; jhagṛá. *m* ; taṇṭá. *m* ;
EMBRYO, *N.*
garbh. *m* ; hamal. *m* ; ḍhiḍḍh. *f* ;
EMEND, TO, *V. T.*
durust karná ; ṭhík ṭhák karná ; sodhná ; sahí karná ; sudhár karná;
EMENDATION, *N.*
durustí. *f* ; sudhár. *m* ;
EMERALD, *N.*
panná. *m* ; jamrútí. *f* ;
EMERGE, TO, *V. I.*
nikalná ;
for wheat. &c. nissarná ;
EMERGENCY, *N.*
loṛ. *f* ;
EMETIC, *N.*
ulṭí liáunwálí dawá. *f* ;
EMIGRATE, TO, *V. T.*
des chhaḍḍ dená ; dujje des vichch já wassná ;
EMINENCE, *N.*
1. height. uchchiáí. *f* ;
2. greatness. buzurgí. *f* ; waḍiáí. *f*;
EMINENT, *A.*
manniá danniá ; mashhúr ; waḍḍá ; ghukiá hoyá ; minniá ginniá ;
EMISSARY, *N.*
wakíl. *m* ;
for a wedding. lággí. *m* ;
EMIT, TO, *V. I.*
nikalná ;
EMOLUMENT, *N.*
mazdurí. *f*; kamáí. *f* ; talab. *f* ; lábh. *m* ; ámdaní. *f* ; diháṛí. *f* ;
EMOTION, *N.*
josh. *m* ; lahir . *f* ;
1. of love. pyár. *m* ; muhabbat. *f* ; teh. *f* ;
2. of fear. ḍar. *m* ; ḳhauf. *m* ; jhakk. *f* ;
EMPEROR, *N.*
sháhanshán. *m* ; bádsháh. *m* ; qaisar. *m* ; máharájá. *m* ; adhíráj. *m* ;
EMPHASIS, *N.*
jor. *m* ;
EMPHASIZE, TO, *V. T.*
kise lafz de utte zor dená ;
EMPHATICALLY, *Adv.*
zor de nál ;
EMPIRE, *N.*
ráj. *m* ; bádsháhí. *f* ; riyásat. *m* ;
EMPLOY, TO, *V. T.*
kamm vichch láuná OR lagáuná ; wartná ;
EMPLOYEE, *N.*
naukar. *m* ; chákar. *m* ; ṭahliyá. *m* ;
1. farm labourer. kámá. *m* ; sepí. *m* ;
2. daily labourer, cooly. mazdúr. *m* ;
EMPLOYER, *N.*
málik. *m* ;
EMPLOYMENT, *N.*
naukarí. *f* ; kamm. *m* ; kár. *m* ; dhaṇdá. *m* ; chákarí. *f* ; báná. *m* ;
EMPOWER, TO, *V. T.*
iḳhtiyár dená ; muḳhtiár banáuná ;
EMPRESS, *N.*
rání. *f* ; begam. *f* ; mahárání. *f* ;
EMPTY, *A.*
ḳhálí ; sakkhná ; vehlá ; sunní ; sunyán ; sunj ; ṣunn ;
1. empty handed. hatthal ; sakkhne hatth ; sakkhniáṇ ; sakkhní hatthíṇ ; khulmakhulí ;
2. hollow. khokhlá ;
EMPTY, TO, *V. T.*
ḳhálí karná ; vehlá karná ;
EMPTY TO, *V. I.*
ḳhálí ho jáná ;
EMULATE, TO, *V. T.*
rís karná ; muqábalá karná ; barábarí karní ;
EMULATION, *N.*
rís. *f* ; muqábalá. *m* ; jatan. *m* ; khaih. *f* ;

ENABLE, TO, *V. T.*
táqat dení ; madat dení OR karní ; mazbut karná ; sahárá karná ;

ENACT, TO, *V. T.*
hukm dená ; naberná ; qánún banáuná ; thahráuná ;

ENACTMENT, *N.*
1. order. hukm. *m* ; ágiá. *m* ;
2. legal decree. digrí. *f* ;

ENAMOUR, TO, *V. T.*
bará khush karná ; parcháuná ; anand karná ; moh lainá ;

ENCAMP, TO, *V. T.*
derá khará karná ; derá láuná ; uttarná ; makám karná ;

ENCAMPMENT, *N.*
derá. *m* ; utárá. *m* ;

ENCHANT, TO, *V. T.*
dil khush karná ; moh lená ; parcháuná ;

ENCHANTED, *A.*
bara khush ;

ENCHANTMENT, *N.*
jádú. *m* ; mantar. *m* ; tuná. *m* ; jádugarí. *f* ;

ENCHANTER, *N.*
jádugar. *m* ; mantarí. *m* ;

ENCIRCLE, TO, *V. T.*
gherá márná ; gherná ; walná ;

ENCLOSE, TO, *V. T.*
gherná ; gherá pá lainá ; murhná ; wár dená ;

ENCLOSURE, *N.*
hátá. *m* ; angan. *m* ; wehrá. *m* ;
1. for sheep. wárá. *m* ; bárá. *m* ;
2. for cattle. havelí. *f* ; derá. *m* ;
3. for poultry. khuddá. *m* ;

ENCOMIUM, *N.*
táríf. *f* ; wadíáí. *f* ;

ENCOMPASS, TO, *V. T.*
gherná ; gherá páuná ; duále gherá pá lainá ;

ENCOUNTER, *N.*
1. quarrel. laráí. *f* ; jhagrá. *m* ; danggá fasád. *m* ;
2. meeting. mulaqát. *f* ; milní. *f* ; mel gel. *f* ; darshan-parshan. *m* ;

ENCOUNTER, TO, *V. T.*
milná ; dí mulaqát karní ; darshan karná matthe laggná ; takkarná ;

ENCOURAGE, TO, *V. T.*
dilásá dená ; jí kaddhná ; dil wadháuná ; dilerí dení ; takrá karná ; jagáuná ; ásrá dená ; patiáná ;

ENCOURAGEMENT, *N.*
dilásá. *m* ; dilbarí. *f* ; dilerí. *f* ;

ENCROACH, TO, *V. T.*
dakhal dená ; apní hadd thon wadh jáná ; dhakke nál kho lainá ;

ENCROACHMENT, *N.*
ziyádatí. *f* ; jástí. *f* ;

ENCUMBER, TO, *V. T.*
rok chhaddná ; atkáuná ; dhakkná ;
to stop anyone. thákná ;

ENCUMBRANCE, *N.*
1. load. bojh. *m* ; bhár. *m* ;
2. hindrance. rok tok. *f* ; rukávat. *f* ;

END, *N.*
orak. *m* ; ákhar. *m* ; ant. *m* ; hadd. *m* ;
1. extremity. sirá. *m* ; akhír. *m* ; dhur. *m* ;
2. result. natíjá. *m* ; ant. *m* ;
3. close. akhír. *m* ; chhekar. *m* ; orak. *m* ; ákhar. *m* ;
4. to the end that. tán jo ;
5. in the end we must die. ant nún marná hai ;

END, TO, *V. T.*
band karná ; rokná ; muká dená ; chukáuná ; kar chhaddná ; see FINISH.

END, TO, *V. I.*
khutt jáná ; mukk jáná ; nibbar jáná ;

ENDANGER, TO, *V. T.*
khatre vichch leáuná ;

ENDEARMENT, *N.*
pyár. *m* ; lád. *m* ;

ENDEAVOUR, *N.*
1. effort. mihnat. *f* ; koshish. *f* ; jatan. *m* ;
2. aim. irádá. *m* ; gaun. *m* ;
3. endeavours. ohur pohur. *m* ; till. *m* ; uddam. *m* ; hílá. *m* ;

ENDING, *N.*
natíjá. *m* ; ant. *m* ;

ENDLESS, *A.*
beant ; behadd ; bebahá ; anant ;

ENDORSE, TO, *V. T.*
1. to approve. manzur karná; qabulná; pasiṇd karná;
2. to sign. dastkhatt dená; apná náwáṇ dená; sehí páuná;
3. to affix thumb mark. aṇgguṭhá láuná;

ENDORSEMENT, *N.*
1. approval. manzurí. *f;*
2. signature. dastkhatt. *m;*
3. thumb mark. aṇgguṭhá. *m;*

ENDOW, TO, *V. T.*
dená; dán punn dená;

ENDUE, TO, *V. T.*
dená; inayat karní;

ENDURABLE, *A,*
sahn jog;
strong. pakká; mazbut; sábtá;

ENDURANCE, *N.*
1. patience. sabr. *m;* sabúrí. *f;*
2. strength. táqat. *f;* jor. *m;* sábtí. *f;* wáh. *f;*

ENDURE, TO, *V. T.*
sahárná; jhallná; sabr karná; saih lainá; jarná;

ENDURE, TO, *V. I.*
1. to bear. jhallná; sahárná. saihná; khimá karná;
2. to remain. rahná;

ENEMY, *N.*
dushman. *m;* wairí. *m;* dútí. *m;* galím. *m;* bairí. *m;* dút. *m;* lágú. *m;* virodhí. *m;* wairan. *f;* deadly enemy. ján dá márú. *m;* lahú dá tiháyá. *m;*

ENERGETIC, *A.*
uddamí; mihnatí; tagṛá; himmat-wálá; himmatí; himtál; laṭṭhá;

ENERGETICALLY, *Adv.*
uddam nál; mihnat nál; dil lagáke;

ENERGISE, TO, *V. T.*
himmat dení; tagṛeáṇ karná; josh duáuná;

ENERGY, *N.*
josh. *m;* sargarmí. *f;* himmat. *f;* jor. *m;* pursharath. *m;*

ENERVATE, TO, *V. T.*
kamjor banáuná OR karná; nirbal karná; máṛíáṇ banáuná; lissíáṇ karná;

ENERVATION, *N.*
kamjorí. *f;* miṛittan. *m;* ṭoṭṭá; *m;*

ENFEEBLE, TO, *V. T.*
kamjor karná;

ENFEEBLED, *A.*
kamjor; máṛá; lissá; jahimatí;

ENFOLD, TO, *V. T.*
1. to encircle. gherná; gherá márná;
2. to embrace. japphí mární OR páuní; gulaphṛí páuná;

ENFORCE, TO, *V. T.*
dabáuná; jor páuná; lachár karná; aukhíáṇ karná;

ENFORCEMENT, *N.*
joráwarí. *f;*

ENGAGE, TO, *V. T.*
1. to employ a servant. naukar rakkhná;
2. to attack. dhává karná; hamlá karná; hallá karná;
3. to promise. wádá dená; háṇ karná; bachan dená; qarár karná;

ENGAGED, TO BE, *V. I.*
rujhná; runnhná; ruddhná;
engaged in business. kamm vichch baiṭhná; kamm vichch rujjhná; jutná; ḍaihná;

ENGAGEMENT, *N.*
1. betrothal. maṇgní. *f;* kuṛmái. *f;*
2. battle. laṛáí. *f;* juddh. *m;* raṇ. *m;*
3. business. kamm. *m;* láṇjhá. *m*

ENGENDER, TO, *V. T.*
paidá karná; jamná;

ENGINE, *N.*
injan. *m;*

ENGLISH, *A.*
angrezí; wilaití;

ENGLISH, *N.*
1. people. angrej. *m;* angrez. *m;*
2. language. angrezí bolí. *f;*

ENGRAFT, TO, *V. T.*
peuṇd lagáuná;

ENGRAVE, TO, *V. T.*
ukkaṛná; ghaṛná;

ENGRAVER, *N.*
nakásh. *m;* ṭhathiár. *m;*

ENGULFED, TO BE, *V. I.*
garq ho jáná; dubb jáná;
in mud. khubbh jáná; dhas jáná;

ENHANCE, TO, *V. T.*
wadháuná; mull wadháuná;

ENIGMA, *N.*
pahelí. *f;*
ENJOIN, TO, *V. T.*
hukm dená; kah dená; tágíd karná; ágiá dená;
ENJOY, TO, *V. T.*
mauj manná OR karná; anaṇd karná; ḳhushí karní; maujáṇ uḍáuná; mauj bahárāṇ karná; suád lená; sukh bhogná;
ENJOYMENT, *N*
ḳhushí. *f;* mazá. *m;* suád. *m;* anaṇdtáí. *f;* maṇggal. *m;* mauj. *f;* sukh. *m;*
ENKINDLE, TO, *V. T.*
bhaṛkáuná; chukkná; josh dená; phuláuná; tapáuná;
ENLARGE, TO, *V. T.*
wadháuná; cháuṛá karná;
to be enlarged. khullhá ho jáná;
ENLARGEMENT, *N.*
wáddhá. *f;* waddh. *f;*
ENLIGHTEN, TO, *V. T.*
roshan karná; samjháuná;
ENLIGHTENED, *A.*
samajhwálá; siáná; dáná; hoshiyár; aqliá; buddhmáṇ;
ENLIGHTENMENT, *N.*
1. light. roshní. *f;*
2. knowledge. ilm. *m;* viddiá. *m;* gián. *m;*
ENLIST, TO, *V. T.*
bhartí karní;
ENLISTED, TO BE, *V. I.*
bhartí ho jáná;
ENLISTMENT, *N.*
bhartí. *f;*
ENLIVEN, TO, *V. T.*
ḳhush karná; jí kaḍḍhní; jor te tázagí dení;
ENMITY, *N.*
wair. *m;* dushmaní. *f;* aṇ baṇ. *f;* khár. *f;* adáut. *f;* kiṛ. *f;* kíná. *m;* virodh. *f;* khaṭṭpat. *f;* khaṭápatí. *f;*
to create enmity. páṭṭak páuná;
ENORMITY, *N.*
ních kamm. *m;* ḳharábí. *f;* chaṇdálpuṇá. *m;*

ENORMOUS, *A.*
bahut waḍḍá; waḍḍá sárá; moṭá tagaṛá;
ENORMOUSLY, *Adv.*
bahut ziyádá; wadhík;
ENOUGH, *A.*
bas; batherá; bahutá; bahterá; káfí;
enough and to spare. loṛ thoṇ waddh;
ENQUIRE, TO, *V. T.*
daryáft karná; patá puchchná; bhál karná; suh karná; parchol karná; gavcr karná; partál karná;
1. to enquire about a thing. us gal núṇ chheṛná;
2. to enquire about anyone. patá puchchná;
ENQUIRY, *N.*
parchol. *f;* partál. *f;*
having made careful enquiry. puchch gichchke;
ENRAGE, TO, *V. T.*
russáuná; khijáuná; gussá duwáuná; chheṛná; agg láuná; gusse karná; luhná;
ENRAGED, *A.*
karodhí; gusse; bhuhe; baṛá naráz; ruṭṭhiá hoyá; karopí; russiá hoyá;
ENRICH, TO, *V. T.*
máldár banáuná OR karná; dhanní karná;
ENROLL, TO, *V. T.*
bhartí karná;
ENSAMPLE, *N.*
namúná. *m;* vaṇgí. *f;*
ENSIGN, *N.*
jhaṇḍá. *m;* jhaṇḍí. *f;* dhal. *f;* dhajá. *f;*
ENSLAVE, TO, *V. T.*
gulám banáuná;
ENSLAVEMENT, *N.*
gulámí. *f;*
ENSNARE, TO, *V. T.*
jál OR phaṇde OR pháhí vichch phasáuná; paháuná; pháhná;
ENSUE, TO, *V. I.*
ho jáná; ban jáná;
ENTANGLE, TO, *V. T.*
phasáuná; wal páuná; pech páuná; pháhná; dáláuná;

paháuná ; aṛáná ;
ENTANGLED, TO BE, *V. I.*
phas jáná ; aṛ jání ; pháh paí jáná ;
as a thread. pilch jáná ; guṇjal paí jáná ; wal paí jáná ;
ENTANGLEMENT, *N.*
guṇjal. *f* ; magrorí. *f* ;
ENTER, TO, *V. I.*
waṛná ; andar jáná ; ghusaṛ jáná ;
at entering. waṛdeáṇ sár ;
ENTERIC, *N.*
mohrká táp. *m* ;
ENTERPRISE, *N.*
1. bravery. himmat. *f* ; dilerí. *f* ; bahádurí. *f* ;
2. difficult work. aukhá kamm. *m* ;
ENTERPRISING, *A.*
himmatí ; chalák ; hoshiyár ; bahádur ;
ENTERTAIN, TO, *V. T.*
1. to amuse. ḳhush karná ; war-áuná ; parcháuná ; bahiláuná ; manáuná ;
2. to feast. baṛá kháná karná ; bhojan karná ; jagg pakáuná OR karná ; deg pakáuná ; roṭí pakáuní ;
ENTERTAINMENT, *N.*
1. exhibition. tamáshá. *m* ; rág-raṇgg. *m* ; parchává. *m* ; parch parchá. *m* ;
2. banquet. mamáhní. *f* ; ziyáfat. *f* ;
ENTHRONE, TO, *V. T.*
gaddí te bithálná ;
ENTHUSIASM, *N.*
josh. *m* ; sargarmí. *f* ; shauq. *m* ; tejí. *f* ; áṛ. *m* ; ríjh. *f* ;
ENTHUSIAST, *N.*
sargarm ádmí. *m* ;
ENTHUSIASTIC, *A.*
shukín ; sargarm ; josh wálá ; tez ;
ENTICE, TO, *V. T.*
tamá dená ; lobh páuná ; lálach dená ; lalcháuná ;
ENTICEMENT, *N.*
tamá. *m* ; hirs. *f* ; lálach. *m* ; lobh. *m* ;
ENTIRE, *A.*
sárá ; sábit ; sabh ; baniá banáiá ; sábtá ; sabútá ; samulchá ;
ENTIRELY, *Adv.*
muloṇ muḍḍhoṇ ; haddoṇ muḍ-ḍhoṇ ; ukká mukká ;
ENTIRETY *N.*
purantáí. *f* ;
ENTITLE, TO, *V. T.*
náṇ rakkhná ; ṭhahráuná ; haqq dená ;
ENTITLED, *A.*
haqqdár ;
ENTOMB, TO, *V. T.*
dafn karná ; dabb dená ; napná.
ENTRAILS, *N.*
ándṛáṇ. *f* ;
ENTRANCE, *N.*
1. admission. daḳhal. *f* ;
2. door. bhuhá. *m* ; darwázá. *m* ;
3. path. ráh. *f* ; galá. *m* ; rastá. *m* ;
4. room at entrance. deuhṛí. *f* ;
ENTRAP, TO, *V. T.*
jál OR phaṇde OR pháhí vichch phasáuná ;
ENTREAT, TO, *V. T.*
bentí OR minnat OR arz OR duá OR kajá karní ; darḳhást karní ; tarle minnat karní ; maṇgná ; pichche páuná ; wáste páuná ; girgaṛáuná ;
ENTREATY, *N.*
arz. *f* ; bentí. *f* ; duá. *f* ; minnat. *f* ; ardás. *f* ; tarlá. *m* ; tarle minnat. *f* ; árjú. *f* ;
ENTRENCH, TO, *V. T.*
waṭṭ kaḍḍhní ;
ENTRUST, TO, *V. T.*
sauṇp dená ; hawále karná ;
ENTRY, *N.*
galá. *m* ; see ENTRANCE.
ENUMERATE, TO, *V. T.*
1. to tell. bayán karná ; dassná ;
2. to count. ginná ; joṛná ; gintí karní ; hisáb karná ;
ENUMERATION, *N.*
bayán. *m* ; hisáb. *m* ; gintí. *f* ;
ENUNCIATE, TO, *V. T.*
bayán karná ; batláuná : dassná ; bolná ;
ENUNCIATION, *N.*
1. statement. bayán. *m* ; qaul. *m* ; bachan. *m* ;
2. speech. bolí. *f* ;

ENVELOP, TO, *V. T.*
1. to enwrap. lapeṭná;
2. to cover. kajjná; dhakkná;
ENVELOPE, *N.*
lafáfá. *m;*
ENVENOM, TO, *V. T.*
chheṛná; agg láuná; dil khaṭṭá karná; bhaṛkáuná; gussá chaṛháuná; russáuná;
ENVIOUS, *A.*
lálachí; lobhí; saṛiá baliá;
don't be so envious. aiḍá lab OR lobh ná kariá kar;
ENVIOUS, TO, BE, *V. I.*
khár karná; saṛná;
to be consumed with envy. sáṛe nál saṛ jáná;
ENVIOUSLY, *Adv.*
lálach karke; khár nál; rís nál;
ENVIRON, TO, *V. T.*
gherná; gherá pá lainá; walná;
ENVIRONMENT, *N.*
áṇḍh guáṇḍh. *m;* chár chauphere. *m;*
ENVIRONS, *N.*
guáṇḍh. *m;*
ENVOY, *N.*
elchí. *m;*
messenger. lággí. *m;* halkárá. *m;* sandesí. *m;*
ENVY, *N,*
lálach. *m;* khár. *f;* sáṛá. *m;* jalan. *f;* cheṛ. *f;* kíná. *m;* ḍáh. *f;*
through envy. khár de máre;
ENVY, TO, *V. T.*
lálach karná; sáṛá áuná; khár karná;
EPICURE, *N.*
peṭú. *m;* kháú. *m;* chaskebáj. *m;* chaṭorá. *m;*
EPIDEMIC, *N.*
bawál. *f;* balá. *f;* tapálí. *f;*
EPILEPSY, *N.*
mirgí. *f;*
EPIPHANY, *N.*
íd-i-zuhúr. *m;*
EPISODE, *N.*
ḍho. *m;* hál. *m;* wáqiá. *m;* wárdát. *f;*
EPISTLE, *N.*
1. letter. ḳhatt. *m;* chiṭṭhí. *f;*
2. note. rukká. *m;* purjá. *m;*
EPITHET, *N.*
náuṇ. *m;*
EPITOME, *N.*
nichoṛ. *m;* arq. *m;*
EPITOMIZE, TO, *V. T.*
nichoṛ kaḍḍhná; arq kaḍḍhná; bayán chhoṭá karná; bayán ghaṭṭáuná;
EPOCH, *N.*
jugg. *m;* samá. *m;* sammat. *m;*
EPSOM SALTS, *N.*
jaláb. *m;*
EQUAL, *A.*
barábar; ikko jeḍá; ikko jeḍí; uh de tull; ikk raṇg; ikko jehá; sáwán; hání;
EQUALITY, *N.*
barábarí. *f;* barobarí. *f;*
EQUALIZE, TO, *V. T.*
ikko jehá banáuná OR karná; sáwáṇ karná;
EQUALLY, *Adv.*
barábar; unnáṇ hí; usí taráh;
EQUANIMITY, *N.*
chain. *m;*
EQUESTRIAN, *N.*
sawár. *m;* aswár. *m;*
EQUINOX, *N.*
sanjog. *m;*
EQUIP, TO, *V. T.*
sárá asbáb dená; sabho kujh dená;
EQUIPMENT, *N.*
asbáb. *m;* samíán. *m;*
EQUITABLE, *A.*
ádal; niáíṇ; insáfwálá; see JUST;
EQUITY, *N.*
insáf. *m;* niáúṇ. *m;* niáí. *f;* adálat. *f;* haqq. *m;*
EQUIVALENCE, *N.*
barábarí. *f;* barobarí. *f;*
EQUIVALENT, *A.*
barábar; ikko jehá;
EQUIVOCAL, *A.*
gol mol;
EQUIVOCATE, TO, *V. T.*
jabán badalní; ṭálná; ṭál moṭolá karná; jhuṭh bolná; ále ṭále karná;
EQUIVOCATION, *N.*
ṭál. *f;* ṭálá. *m;* ghasal masal. *m* ṭálá bálá. *m;* baháná. *m;*

ERA, *N*.
sammat. *m* ; jugg. *m* ; samá. *m* ; waqt. *m* ; velá. *m* ;
ERADICATE, TO, *V*. *T*.
1. to pull up by the roots. jaṛ puṭṭná ; ukháṛná ; ukheṛná ;
2. to cross out. meṭná ; kalam pherní ; miṭáuná ; miṭá dená ;
3. to expel. kaḍḍhná ; chhekná ;
ERADICATION, *N*.
barbádí. *f* ; nás. *f* ; satiánás. *f* ;
ERASE, TO, *V*. *T*.
harf kaṭṭná ; kalam pherní ; meṭná ; miṭáuná ; láhná ; miṭá dená ; bujhá dená ;
ERASEMENT, *N*.
káṭ kúṭ. *f* ;
ERASER, *N*.
rabar. *m* ;
ERASURE, *N*.
káṭ kúṭ. *f* ;
ERECT, *A*.
khalotiá hoyá ;
ERECT, TO, *V*. *T*.
1. to rear. khaliárná ;
2. to make. banáuná ;
3. to build : usárná ;
ERECTION, *N*.
makán. *m* ; ghar. *m* ; koṭhí. *f* ;
ERR, TO, *V*. *T*.
qusur karná ; bhullná ; bhullná chukkná ; ghuss jáná ; ukk jáná ; gunáh karná ; bhulekhá lagná ; khuṇjhná ; thiṛakná ; bahikná ; to cause to err. bahikáuná ;
ERRAND, *N*.
1. message. sanehá. *m* ; sanáh. *m* ; sandes. *m* ;
2. business. kamm. *m* ;
ERRATIC, *A*.
págal jehá ; bauntar ;
ERRATUM, *N*.
bhulekhá. *m* ; bholává. *m* ; see ERROR.
ERRING, *A*.
bhullanwálá ; bhullanhár ;
ERRONEOUS, *A*.
galat ; ṭhik nahíṇ ; ulṭá ; ulaṭ pulaṭ ;
ERRONEOUSLY, *Adv*.
bhull bhulekhe ; bhulekhe nál ; galatí nál ; wissar bholle ;
ERROR, *N*.
galatí. *f* ; bhull. *f* ; bhull chukk. *f* ; bhulekhá. *m* ; bholává. *m* ; augun. *m* ; bholá. *m* ; bholí. *f* ; wissar bhollá. *m* ;
ERUCTATION, *N*.
dakár. *m* ;
ERUDITE, *A*.
siáná ; hoshiyár ; dáná ; widdiáwán ; buddhwán ; ilmwálá ;
ERUDITION, *N*.
ilm. *m* ; gián. *m* ; widdiá. *f* ;
ERUPTION, *N*.
1. large. phoṛá. *m* ; gaṛ. *m* ; uthá. *m* ;
2. small. phimhní. *f* ; barúrí. *f* ; barúlí. *f* ;
ESCAPE, *N*.
bacháo. *m* ; chhuṭkárá. *m* ; rihái. *f* ; ḳhalásí. *f* ;
ESCAPE, TO, *V*. *I*.
chhuṭṭ jáná ; bhajj jáná ; bach jáná ; bach nikalná ;
ESCORT, *N*.
nál de bande. *m* ; rákkhe. *m* ;
ESCORT, TO, *V*. *T*.
nál laí jáná ; nál chalná ; pahuṇcháuná ;
ESPECIAL, *A*.
ḳháss ; uchechá ;
ESPECIALLY, *Adv*.
ḳháss karke ; uchechá ; bahut karke ;
ESPIONAGE, *N*.
jásúsí. *f* ; suh. *f* ; mukhbarí. *f* ;
ESPOUSAL, *N*.
kurmái. *f* ; mangní. *f* ; náttá. *m* ;
ESPOUSE, TO, *V*. *T*.
1. to help. madat dení ;
2. to engage. náttá karná ; maṇgní OR kurmái karní ;
3. to marry. shádí karní ; wiáháuná ; wiáh karná ;
ESPY, TO, *V*. *T*.
duroṇ wekhná ; pahchánná ; takkná ; táṛná ;
ESSAY, N.
1. a composition. bakhán. *m* ; bayán. *m* ;
2. an attempt. koshish. *f* ;
ESSAY, TO, *V*. *T*.
koshish karní ; jatan karná OR láuná ; mihnat karní ; hílá karná ;

ESSENCE, *N.*
1. substance. asl. *m ;*
2. scent. mihak. *f ;* hamkár. *m ;*
ESSENTIAL, *A.*
zarúrí ; loṛídá hai ; baṛí loṛ ;
ESSENTIAL, *N.*
aslíat. *f ;* aslí. *f ;*
ESSENTIALLY, *Adv.*
asl vichch ;
ESTABLISH, TO, *V. T.*
1. to appoint. láuná ; muqarrar karná ;
2. to make firm. pakká karná ; mazbut karná ; asthír karná ;
ESTABLISHED, *A.*
pakká ;
ESTABLISHMENT, *N.*
1. house. ghar. *m ;* makán. *m ;* koṭhí. *f ;*
2. servants. naukar chákar. *m ;* ṭahlie ṭuhlie. *m ;*
3. field servant. kámá. *m ;* sepí. *m ;*
ESTATE, *N.*
jaedád. *f ;* jagír. *m ;* milḳh. *f ;* málkí. *f ;*
ESTEEM, *N.*
ádar. *m ;* izzat. *f ;* qadr. *f ;* ádar bháu. *m ;*
ESTEEM, TO, *V. T.*
qadr karná ; adab karná ; ádar karná OR dená ; achchhá samajhná ; liház karná ;
ESTIMATE, *N.*
háṛá. *m ;* hisáb. *m ;* giṇtí. *f ;* jách. *f ;* see COMPUTATION.
ESTIMATE, TO, *V. T.*
háṛá lainá ; takk láuná ; hisáb karná ; tewá láná ; andázá launá ; jách kar lainá ;
ESTIMATION, *N.*
1. esteem. qadr. *f ;* see ESTEEM.
2. account. hisáb. *m ;* lekhá. *m ;* giṇtí. *f ;* háṛá. *m ;*
3. opinion. ḳhayál. *m ;* raí. *f ;*
ESTRANGE, TO, *V. T.*
apne wallon dil khaṭṭá karná ; manon chaṛháuná ;
ESTRANGEMENT, *N.*
judáí. *f ;* phuṭṭ. *f ;*
ETCETRA, *Adv.*
lalú panjú ; wagairá ; airá wagairá ;

ETERNAL, *A.*
sadá dá ; hameshá dá ; abadí ; sadípak ; mudaimí ; nitt ;
eternal life. sadípak jíún. *m ;*
ETERNALLY, *Adv.*
sadá ; nitt ; hameshá ; hamesh ; sadípak ; sadípkál :
ETERNITY, *N.*
hameshgí. *f ;* sadíp. *m ;*
ETIQUETTE, *N.*
uṭṭhan baihn dá ḍhaṇg. *m ;*
custom. dastúr. *m ;*
EUCHARIST, *N.*
Ashá-i-Rabbání. *f ;* Pák Rifáqat. *f ;*
EULOGIZE, TO, *V. T.*
táríf karní ; waḍíái karní ; waḍíáuná ; guṇ gáuná ; sarháuná ; saláhuná ;
EULOGY, *N.*
táríf, *f ;* waḍíái. *f ;* maihmá. *f ;* salauhat. *f ;*
EUNUCH, *N.*
khusrá. *m ;*
EURASIAN, *N.*
doglá. *m ;*
EUROPE, *N.*
Wiláyat. *f ;*
EUROPEAN, *A.*
angrejí ;
EVACUATE, TO, *V. T.*
1. to make empty. ḳhálí karná ; vehlá karná ; sakkhná karná ;
2. to leave. chhaḍḍ deṅá ; nikal jáná ; khisk jáná ;
EVADE, TO, *V. T.*
1. to avoid a person. muṇh lukáuná ; luk jáná ; muṇh moṛná ;
2. to avoid a subject in conversation. ṭál maṭolá karná ; baháná karná ; dhuchchar launá ; aí gaí karná ; suṭṭ súṭṭní ;
EVANGEL, *N.*
Injíl. *f ;*
EVANGELIST, *N.*
manád. *m ;*
EVANGELISATION, *N.*
manádí. *f ;*
EVANGELIZE, TO, *V. T.*
manádí karní ; Injíl dá ḍhaṇḍorá dená ;

EVAPORATE, TO, *V. I.*
sukk jáná;
EVASION, *N.*
ṭál. *f;* ṭálá. *m;* álá ṭálá. *m;* baháná. *m;* ṭálmaṭol. *m;* ṭhuṇá. *m;*
EVASIONS, *N.*
híl hujjat. *f;* uzr. *f;* ánná baháná. *m;* ṭál maṭól. *m;*
EVE, *N.*
shám. *f;* tarkáláṇ. *f;* takáláṇ. *f;*
EVEN, *Adv.*
bháṇweṇ; bhí; ví; sagoṇ; arth-át;
EVEN, *A.*
1. equal. sáwán; barábar;
2. flat. paddhrá; sawáhrá;
EVENING, *N.*
shám. *f;* sánjh. *f;* takáláṇ de vele. *m;* khaupíyyá. *m;* takál sandhiá. *m;*
toward evening. shám ho challí hai, sánjh páiáṇ;
EVENLY, *Adv.*
1. equally. barábar;
2. fairly. insáf nál; munsabí nál;
EVENNESS, *N.*
barábarí. *f;* barobarí. *f;*
EVENT, *N.*
ḍho. *m;* wáqiá. *m;* gall. *f;* wárdát. *f;*
EVENTUALLY, *Adv.*
phir; akhír; oṛak núṇ;
EVER, *Adv.*
1. at any time. kadí;
2. for all time. hameshá tík; oṛak; sadá tík; júggoṇ júgg;
EVERLASTING, *A.*
sadá; hameshá; sanátan; abadí;
EVERLASTING LIFE, *N.*
sadá dí zindagí. *f;* hameshá dí jíun. *f;* sadípak jíun. *f;*
EVERMORE, *Adv.*
sadá de laí; oṛak tíkar;
EVERY, *A.*
sarbatt; har ikk; har; sáre;
1. from every side. chároṇ taraf; sabhníṇ pássíṇ; chauhíṇ guṭṭhíṇ; chawallí;
2. everybody. hár ikk;
3. every now and then. kadí kadí;
4. everything. sabh kujh; sabho kujh;
5. everywhere. sabhníṇ pássíṇ; har jagáh; har tháṇ; jitthe kitthe; sabhnáṇ tháíṇ; har kite;
6. everyday. har roz; har díháṛe;
7. every other day. ikk din chhaḍḍke; ikk din with páke;
8. every time. har bár; har wár; har wárí;
EVICT, TO, *V. T.*
kaḍḍh dená; nikál dená; chhek dená;
EVIDENCE, *N.*
gawáhí. *f;* ugáhí. *f;* sákhí. *f;* proof. sabút. *m;* dalíl. *f;*
EVIDENCE, TO GIVE, *V. T.*
gawáhí dení; ugáhí dení; sákhí dení;
EVIDENT, *A.*
malúm; ujágár; sáf; sáf záhir; záhir;
EVIDENTLY, *Adv.*
1. clearly. sáf;
2. certainly. jarúr; zarúr;
EVIL, *N.*
1. depravity. badí. *f;* kharábí. *f;* sharárat. *f;* buriáí. *f;* badchal-ní. *f;* luchchpuṇá. *m;*
2. misfortune. áfat. *f;* biptá. *f;* musíbat. *f;* badnasíbí. *f;*
3. harm. nuqsán. *m;* harj. *m;* kasar. *m;*
EVIL, *A.*
kharáb; burá; bhaiṛá; máṛá; sharír; chaṇḍál; chaṇḍrá; nakárá; nikammá;
evil things. awalliáṇ galláṇ. *f;*
EVILDOER, *N.*
gunáhgár. *m;* pápí. *m;* badkár. *m;* badmásh. *m;* dusht. *m;* buriár. *m;* gunáhí. *m;* shatán. *m;* taqsírí. *m;*
EVIL SMELLING, *A.*
gandá; tarakkiá hoyá; saṛiá; galliá hoyá;
EVIL SPIRIT, *N.*
badrúh. *f;* bhut. *f;* bhutná. *m;* báhirle. *m;*
the Evil One. Shatán. *m;*

EVINCE, TO, *V. T.*
1. to show. záhir karná; dikhláná;
2. to prove. sábit karná;

EVOKE, TO, *V. T.*
saddná; buláuná;

EVOLVE, TO, *V. T.*
1. to unfold. kholná;
2. to disclose. ughárná;
3. to create. paidá karná; banáuná;

EWE, *N.*
bheḍ. *f*; bheḍí. *f*;

EXACERBATE, TO, *V. T.*
naráz karná; chheṛná; rassáuná; bhaṛkáuná; agg láuná; dil khaṭṭá karná; gussá chaṛháuná OR dilwáuná;

EXACT, *A.*
ṭhík; durust; sahí; sál; suddh; bilkul ṭhík; jatharath;
exact time. vele sir;

EXACT, TO, *V. T.*
1. to collect money. ugráuhná;
2. to extort. joriṇ lainá; kho lainá; jichch karná; aukhiáṇ karké lainá;

EXACTION, *N.*
1. levy. ugráhí. *f*;
2. extortion. zabardastí. *f*; sakhtí. *f*; jástí. *f*;

EXACTLY, *Adv.*
ṭhík ṭhík; ṭhík ṭhák; ṭhíkam ṭhík; saṇwárke;

EXACTNESS, *N.*
durustí. *f*; sahí. *f*;

EXAGGERATE, TO, *V. T.*
gal wadháuná; lún mirch lagáuná; masále láke dassná;
you exaggerate. túṇ hadd karní hai;

EXAGGERATION, *N.*
wáddhá. *m*;

EXALT, TO, *V. T.*
1. to raise. uchchá karná; ijjat dení; darjá dená; chaṛháuná; uchchiáṇ karná;
2. to extol. waḍiái karní; táríf karní; saráhná; saláhná; guṇ gáuná;

EXALTATION, N.
buzurgí. *f*; izzat. *f*; darjá. *m*;

EXALTED, *A.*
buzurg; maháṇ; álá;

EXAMINATION, *N.*
1. test of candidates. imtihán. *m*; toh. *f*; parekhá. *m*;
2. scrutiny of books. partál. *f*;
3. examination in court. peshí *f*;
4. search of house by police. taláshí *f*;

EXAMINE, TO, *V. T.*
1. to test. imtihán lená; parakhná; partáuná; gákhná; johná; tohná.
2. to enquire. hál hawál puchchná; daryáft karná; puchch páchch karná;
3. to look for a thing. dekh bhállná;
4. to examine books. partál karná;
5. to examine a school. muainá karná;
6. to search a house. taláshí karná;
7. to examine medically. muláhzá karná; vekhná;
8. to cross examine. jírhá karná;

EXAMINED, TO BE, *V. I.*
imtihán dená;

EXAMINER, *N.*
imtihán lenwálá. *m*;

EXAMPLE, *N.*
namúná. *m*; misál. *f*;
for example. masalaṇ.;

EXASPERATE, TO, *V. T.*
chheṛná; dil khaṭṭá karná; agg láuná; gussá chaṛháuná; gussá diwáuná; bhaṛkáuná; russáuná; luhná; rerrná;

EXASPERATION, *N.*
gussá. *m*; jhall. *m*; roh. *m*; kop. *m*; narázagi. *f*;

EXCAVATE, TO, *V. T.*
jamín puṭṭná; khodná; polí karní; ṭoá márná; khaḍá khodná;

EXCAVATION, *N.*
ṭoá. *m*; khaḍá. *m*; khol. *m*; khaḍ. *f*;
excavation by side of pond or river from which water is taken for irrigation, jhalár. *f*;

EXCEED, TO, *V. T.*
wadháuná; pichche páuná;

EXCEED, TO, *V. I.*
wadh jáná ;
EXCEEDINGLY, *Adv.*
ḍáḍhí ; att ; pujke ;
EXCEL, TO, *V. T.*
wadh jáná ;
EXCELLENCE, *N.*
ḳhubí. *f* ; guṇ. *m* ; bhaliái. *f* ; buzurgí. *f* ; suthrái. *f* ; khariái. *f* ; chaṇggiái. *f* ; uttamtái. *f* ;
EXCELENT, *A.*
uttam ; baṛá chaṇgá ; suthrá ; sohná ; ḳhub ; umdá ; bhalá ; chaṇggerṭá ; bhalá chaṇgá ; ḳháskí ; for a person. dáná pardháná ;
EXCELLENTLY, *Adv.*
chaṇgí taráh nál ; banáke ; saṇwárke ;
EXCEPT, *Prep.*
de siwá ; bájhoṇ ; biná ;
EXCEPTION, *N.*
qaide de ḳhiláf ; qaide de ulṭ ;
EXCEPTIONAL, *A.*
ḳháss ;
strange. awallá ; anokhá ;
EXCEPTIONALLY, *Adv.*
ḳháss karke ;
EXCESS, *N.*
1. abundance. wáddhá ; *f* ; wadhíkí ; *f* ; dher. *m* ;
2. dissipation. badparejí. *f* ; badchalní. *f* ; luchchpuṇá.
EXCESSIVE, *A.*
haddoṇ waddh ; hadd thoṇ báhar ; wadhík ; wadherá ; aṇgiṇt ; ḍher ; wádhú ;
spare. wáfar ;
EXCESSIVELY, *Adv.*
bahut ziyádá ; bahutait nál ;
EXCHANGE, *N.*
badlá. *m* ; badal. *m* ; adal badal. *m* ; badalí. *f* ; waṭáṇḍrá. *m* ; márchá. *m* ; vaṭṭá saṭṭá. *m* ;
in exchange. badle ;
EXCHANGE, TO, *V. T.*
1. to change. waṭáuná ; badal karná ; adal badal karná ; waṭá dená ; márchá karná ; vaṭṭo saṭṭá karná ;
2. to trade. leṇ deṇ karná ; bapár karná ;
EXCHEQUER, *N.*
ḳhajáná. *m* ;
EXCISE, *N.*
1. octroi. mahsúl. *f* ;
2. tax. tákas. *m* ;
3. revenue. muámlá. *m* ;
EXCISEMAN, *N.*
mahsúliá. *m* ; mahsúl lainwálá. *m* ;
EXCITE, TO, *V. T.*
1. to animate. josh duáuná ; chukkná ; uksáuná ; hil jhul macháuná ;
2. to provoke. chheṛná ; agg bhaṛkáuná ; luhná ; bhaḅkáuná ;
EXCITED, *A.*
lohá lákkhá.
EXCITEMENT, *N.*
1. agitation. josh. *m* ;
2. an inducement. ulárá. *m* ; tamá. *m* ;
3. noise. raulá. *m* ; gaṛbaṛ. *f* ; hill jhul. *f* ; raulá gaulá. *m* ;
EXCLAIM, TO, *V. T.*
shor macháuná ; wáz mární ; uchchí bolná ; bol uṭṭhná ;
EXCLAMATION, *N.*
1. a voice. awáz. *f* ; chík chihárá. *m* ;
2. outcry. raulá. *m* ; shor. *m* ; hugg. *f* ; ḍand. *f* ;
EXCLUDE, TO, *V. T.*
báhar kaḍḍh dená ; chhekná ; nakheṛná ; alag karná ; haṭá dená ; ḳhárij karná ; huqqá pání band karná ;
EXCLUDED, *A.*
ḳhárij ;
EXCLUSION, *N.*
nakheṛ. *m* ; tark. *f* ;
EXCLUSIVE, *A.*
ḳháss ; alag ;
EXCOMMUNICATE, TO, *V. T.*
chhekná ; nakheṛná ; huqqá pání band karná ; ḳhárij karna ; chhek chhaḍḍná ;
EXCOMMUNICATE, *A.*
ḳhárij ;
EXCREMENT, *N.*
1. human. jháṛá. *m* ;
2. of a buffalo. dhadd. *f* ; see DUNG.

EXCRUCIATE, TO, *V. T.*
dukháuná ; jichch karná ; see TROUBLE.

EXCRUCIATING, *A.*
aukhá ; dukhí ; dukhdáí ;

EXCULPATE, TO, *V. T.*
barí karná ; sachchá sábit karná ; rihá karná ;

EXCURSION, *N.*
1. a walk. sail. *m ;*
2. a tour. daurá. *m ;*
3. a journey. safar. *m ;* paiṇḍá. *m ;*

EXCUSABLE, *A.*
muáf karn de laiq ;

EXCUSE, *N.*
pajj. *m ;* baháná. *m ;* uzr. *f ;* hílá. *m ;* híl hujjat. *f ;* ánná baháná. *m ;* ṭhuṇá. *m ;* dhuchchar. *m ;* ṭál maṭol. *f ;* huṭṭar. *m ;*

EXCUSE, TO, *V. T.*
1. to excuse onese lf. gallon láuná ; baháná karná ; uzr karná ;
2. to forgive. muáf karná ; muáfí dení ; ján dená ; khimá karná ; bakhshná ;
3. thou art without excuse. tere láí koí pajj nahíṇ ;

EXECRABLE, *A.*
palít ; ghiṇáuná ; bahut búrá ; máṛá ; bhaiṛá ;

EXECRATE, TO, *V. T.*
1. to curse. lánat dení ; saráp dená ; dos láuná ;
2. to abhor. ghiṇáuná ; nafrat karní ; karích áuná ;

EXECRATION, *N.*
lánat. *f ;* bad duá. *f ;* saráp. *m ;*

EXECUTE, TO, *V. T.*
1. to fulfil. purá karná ; naberná ; nabáhuná ; kar lainá ; bajá láuná ; niṛbáhuná ; kar chhaḍḍná ;
2. to put to death. pháṇsí dená ; pháhe dená ;

EXECUTE, TO, *V. I.*
purá honá ; nibbaṛ jáná ;

EXECUTION, *N.*
pháṇs í *f ;*

EXECUTIONER, *N.*
jalád. *m ;* jaṇdár. *m ;*

EXECUTIVE, *A.*
intizámí ;

EXEGISIS, *N.*
1. account. bayán. *m ;*
2. interpretation. tafsír. *m ;*
3. meaning. matlab. *m ;* matbal. *m ;* arth. *m ;*

EXEMPLAR, *N.*
namuná. *m ;*

EXEMPLARY, *A.*
umdá ;

EXEMPLIFY, TO, *V. T.*
misál dení ; namuná dikhláuná ; misál deke samjháuná ;

EXEMPT, *A.*
muáf ;

EXEMPT, TO, *V. T.*
muáf karná ; ján dená ; chhaḍḍ dená ; bakhsh dená ;

EXEMPTION, *N.*
muáfí. *f ;* riháí. *f ;* chhuṭkárá. *m ;* khalásí. *f ;*

EXERCISE, *N.*
1. bodily. warzish. *f ;* chestá. *m ;*
2. practice. mashak. *f ;*
3. military. qawaid. *m ;*

EXERCISE, TO, *V. T.*
ṭahiláuná ;
1. to take exercise. ṭahilná ; warzish karná ;
2. to exercise a horse. ṭahiláuná ; pherná ; phiráuná ;

EXERT, TO, *V. T.*
mihnat karní ; uddam karná ; hílá karná ; jor láuná ; jor márná ; jatan karná ;

EXERTION, *N.*
mihnat. *f ;* uddam. *m ;* koshish. *f ;*

EXHALATION, *N.*
1. air. wá. *f ;*
2. vapour. bháf. *f ;*

EXHALE, *TO, V. T.*
phukná ;

EXHAUST, TO, *V. T.*
thakáuná ; hapháuná ; haráuná ;

EXHAUSTED, *A.*
máṇḍá thakkiá hoyá ;
I am exhausted. maiṇ thakke chúr ho gáyá ; merá bhochhá nikal gáyá ;

EXHAUSTION, *N.*
kamjorí. *f;* thakewáṇ. *m;*
EXHIBIT, TO, *V. T.*
dikhláuná; wikháuná; see SHOW.
EXHILIRATE, TO, *V. T.*
ḳhush karná; jí kaḍḍhná; zor te tázagí dená;
EXHILARATION, *N.*
ḳhushí. *f;* mauj. *f;* anaṇdtái. *f;*
EXHORT, TO, *V. T.*
nasíhat dení; samjháuná; tágíd karná; jatáuná; chitárná; pakkí karná; see ADMONISH.
EXHORTATION, *N.*
1. admonition. nasíhat. *f;* tambíh. *f;* samjhautí. *f;* samjhává. *m;*
2. discourse. wáz. *m;* updes. *m;*
EXHORTER, *N.*
updesak. *m;* updesí. *m;* nasíhat denwálá. *m;*
EXHUME, TO, *V. T.*
qabr vichchoṇ kaḍḍhná;
EXIGENCY, *N.*
loṛ. *f;* parojaṇ. *m;*
EXIGENT, *A.*
baṛí jarúrí; loṛídá;
EXIGUOUS, *A.*
1. small. chhoṭá; nikká;
2. thin. patlá;
EXILE, *N.*
des nikálá. *m;*
EXILE, TO, *V. T.*
mulkoṇ báhar kaḍḍhná; nikál dená; nikálá dená;
EXIST, TO, *V. I.*
1. to be. honá;
2. to live. rahná;
EXISTENCE, *N.*
hoṇ. *f;* hoyá. *m;*
EXISTENT, *A.*
jíundá; házir;
EXIT, *N.*
1. way. ráh. *m;* rastá. *m;*
2. departure. ṭurnáṇ. *m;*
EXODUS, *N.*
kúch *m.*
EXONERATE, TO, *V. T.*
barí karná; chhaḍḍ dená; see ACQUIT.
EXONERATION, *N.*
safái. *f;* rihái. *f;*

EXORBITANCY, *N.*
jástí. *f;* wáddhá. *m;* wadhíkí. *f;*
EXORBITANT, *A.*
wadhík; bahut; ziyádá;
EXORCISE, *V. T.*
jháṛá karná; dhúní dhukháuná; bhút kaḍḍhná;
EXORCISER, *N.*
maṇtarí. *m;* jaṇtari. *m;* jádúgar. *m;* taṇtarí. *m;*
EXORCISM, *N.*
jháṛá. *m;* jádú. *m;* jádúgarí. *f;* jháṛá phukkí. *f;* ṭuṇá. *m;*
EXPAND, TO, *V. T.*
kholná; wadháuná; phailáuná;
EXPAND, TO, *V. I.*
khul jáná; wadh jáná; phail jáná; pasárná;
EXPANSION, *N.*
wistár. *m;* phalár. *m;*
EXPATIATE, TO, *V. T.*
bahút kujh bolná;
EXPECT, TO, *V. T.*
uḍíkná; ráh takkná; ráh wekhná;
EXPECTANCE, *N.*
ummed. *f;* uḍík. *f;* ás. *f;*
EXPECTANT, *A.*
ummedwár; áswaṇd;
EXPECTATION, *N.*
uḍík. *f;* intazárí. *f;* ás. *f;* ásá. *f;* ummed. *f;*
to raise expectations. ummed dení;
EXPECTORATE, TO, *V. T.*
thukkná; khaṇghár márná;
EXPECTORATION, *N.*
thukk. *f;* khaṇghár. *m;*
EXPEDIENCY, *N.*
jarurat. *f;* loṛ. *f;*
EXPEDIENT, *A.*
jarurí; munásib; cháhidá;
EXPEDIENT, *N.*
upáu. *m;* kal. *f;*
expedients. ohuṛ pohuṛ. *m;*
EXPEDITE, TO, *V. T.*
1. to cause to go quickly. dauráuná; chhetí ṭuráuná;
2. to hasten. chhetí karní; jaldí karní; shatábí karní; hatth pair pai jáná;

EXPEDITION, *N*.
1. march. kúch. *m*;
2. haste. tezí. *f*; shatábī. *f*;
3. for war. lám. *m*;
EXPEDITIOUS, *A*.
tez; káhlá; utaulá; trikkhá; tikkhá;
EXPEDITIOUSLY, *Adv*.
jhaṭ paṭ; jaldí; chhetí nál; shatábí nál; see QUICKLY.
EXPEL, TO, *V. T*.
chhekná; khaderná; nikál dená; kaḍḍhná; chhek chhaḍḍná;
EXPEND, TO, *V. T*.
kharch karná; kharchná; wartná;
EXPENDITURE, *N*.
kharch. *m*; lággá. *m*; lágat. *f*;
EXPENSES, *N*.
kharchá. *m*; lágat. *f*;
1. legal expenses. harjá. *m*;
2. marriage disbursements to servants. lág. *m*; lág paṭhá. *m*;
3. at my expense. mere peṭoṇ; mere palleoṇ;
EXPENSIVE, *A*.
máhngá; pyárá; bháre múll dá; waḍḍe mull dá; waḍḍ mullá;
EXERCISE, *N*.
mashq. *m*;
EXERCISE, TO, *V. T*.
mashq karná; zor karná;
EXORCIST, *N*.
jháṛá phukanwálá. *m*;
EXPERIENCE, *N*.
tajrabá. *m*;
EXPERIENCE, TO, *V. T*.
gákhná; wartná; bhogná;
I have experienced. haḍd vítí;
EXPERIENCED, *A*.
síáná; tajrabekár; haṇḍhiá wartiá hoyá; khuráṇd.
EXPERIMENT, *N*.
ḍhaṇg. *m*;
EXPERT, *A*.
tagṛá; hoshiyár; laiq; phurtílá; kárígar; siáná; hikmatí; suchet; ustád; huṇdarí;
EXPERTLY, *Adv*.
hoshiyárí nál; baṛí ustádí nál;
EXPERTNESS, *N*.
hoshiyárí. *f*; liyáqat. *f*; jách. *f*; chalák. *f*;

EXPIATE, TO, *V. T*.
balídán dená; hadiá dená;
EXPIATION, *N*.
badlá. *m*; paráhchit. *f*, H; kafárá. *m*, M; paráschitt. *m*, H;
EXPIRATION, *N*.
maut. *f*; see DEATH.
EXPIRE, TO, *V. I*.
mar jáná; dam dená; see DIE.
EXPIRY, *N*.
hadd. *f*; aṇt. *m*;
EXPLAIN, TO, *V. T*.
samjháuná; khol ke dassná; matlab dassná; arth karná; batláuná;
EXPLANATION, *N*.
bayán. *m*; vikhyán. *m*; bakhán. *m*; nirná. *m*;
EXPLICATE, TO, *V. T*.
kholná; see EXPLAIN.
EXPLICIT, *A*.
bilkul sáf;
EXPLICITLY, *Adv*.
safái nál; sáf sáf;
EXPLODE, TO, *V. I*.
páṭṭná;
EXPLOIT, *N*.
baháduri dá kamm. *m*;
EXPLORE, TO, *V. T*.
labbhná; dekh bhál karná; talásh karní;
EXPLOSION, *N*.
tháh. *m*;
EXPONENT, *N*.
ustád. *m*; samjháuṇwála. *m*;
EXPORT, TO, *V. T*.
ikk des thoṇ dujje des asbáb bhej dená;
EXPOSE TO, V. T.
záhir karná; khol dená; naṇgá karná; wikhálná; samjháuná; pargaṭ karná;
EXPOSED, *A*.
naṇgá;
EXPOSITION, *N*.
bayán. *m*; tafsír. *m*; matlab. *m*; arth. *m*; nirná. *m*;
EXPOSTULATE, TO, *V. T*.
jhiṛakná; warajná;
EXPOSTULATION, *N*.
jhiṛak. *f*;
EXPOSURE, *N*.
dikháú. *f*;

EXPOUND, TO, *V. T.*
samjháuná; batláuná; záhir karná; dikhláuná;
EXPOUNDER, *N.*
of omens. sagṇú. *m;*
EXPRESS, TO, *V. T.*
batláuná; ákhná;
EXPRESSION, N.
1. speech. bolí. *f;* bayán. *m;*
2. appearance. muṇh. *m;* ḍhaṇg. *m;* shakal. *f;*
EXPROPRIATE, TO, *V. T.*
kaḍḍh dená; nikál dená;
EXPUNGE, TO, *V. T.*
kalam pherní; harf kaṭṭná; meṭnà; miṭá dená; see CANCEL.
EXPURGATE, TO, *V. T.*
1. to purge. safá karná;
2. to strike out. kalam pherní; miṭáuná; meṭná;
EXQUISITE, *A.*
uttam; sohná; umdá; ḳhub; ḍáhḍá sohná;
EXTEND, TO, *V. T*
wadháuná; phailáuná; lambáuná; lammá karná;
EXTENSION, *N.*
wadh. *f;* wadháó. *m;* pasárá; *m;* phailáun. *f;* wistár. *m;*
EXTENSIVE, *A.*
lammá chauṛá; moklá; waḍḍá sárá; khullhá; gaṇdhál;
EXTENT, *N.*
guṇjaish. *f;* lambái chauṛái. *f;* samái. *f;* pujj. *m;* lám. *f;* in length. lambái. *f;* lamái. *f;*
EXTENUATE, TO, *V. T.*
1. to lessen. ghaṭáuná; thoṛá karná; ghaṭṭ karná;
2. to palliate. uzr karná; baháná karná;
EXTENUATION, *N.*
uzr. *f;* baháná. *m;* see EXCUSE.
EXTERIOR, *A.*
báhar; báharlá;
EXTERMINATE, TO, *V. T.*
nás karná; sattiá nás karná; ujáṛná;
EXTERMINATION, *N.*
sattiá nás. *m;* tabáhí. *f;* barbádí. *f;* ujáṛ. *f;*
EXTERNAL, *A.*
báhar;
EXTINGUISH, TO, *V. T.*
1. to quench. bujháuná;
2. to destroy. barbád karná; sattiá nás karná; ujáṛná;
3. to put out lamp. dívá waḍhá kar dená;
EXTINGUISHER, *N.*
ḍhakná. *m;*
EXTIRPATE, TO, *V. T.*
sattiá nás karná. see DESTROY.
EXTIRPATION, *N.*
barbádí. *f;*
EXTOL, TO, *V. T.*
waḍiáí karní; táríf karní; gun gáuná; saráhná; saláhná; mahímá karná;
EXTORT, TO, *V. T.*
joríṇ lainá; kho lainá; jich karná; aukhiáṇ karná;
EXTORTION, *N.*
jástí. *f;* julm. *m;* saḳhti. *f;* dabá. *m;*
EXTORTIONATE, *A.*
saḳht; jabardast; jálim; patthar dil;
EXTORTIONER, *N.*
luteṛa. *m;* ḍá már. *m;*
EXTRA, *A.*
wádhú;
something extra. jhuṇgá. *m;*
EXTRACT, *N.*
nichoṛ. *m;* arq. *m;*
EXTRACT, TO, *V. T.*
kaḍḍhná; nichoṛná;
EXTRACTION, *N.*
nichoṛ. *m;* kaḍḍh. *f;*
EXTRAORDINARY, *A.*
ajíb; anokhá; acharaj; awallá;
EXTRAVAGANCE, *N.*
fajúlí. *f;*
EXTRAVAGANT, *A.*
fazul ḳharach;
EXTRAVAGANTLY, *Adv.*
behisábí nál;
EXTREME, *N.*
hadd. *f;* aṇt. *m;* sirá. *m;*
EXTREMELY, *Adv.*
att; vaddhiá; ḍáḍhí; bahutá; wadhík;

EXTREMITY, *N.*
dhuṛ. *m ;*
1. beginning. muḍḍh. *m ;*
2. head. sirá. *m ;*
3. boundary. hadd. *f ;*
EXTRICATE, TO, *V. T.*
kaḍḍhná ; kholná ;
EXUBERANCE, *N.*
ḍher. *m;* bahut sárá. *m;* bahutaít. *f ;*
EXUBERANT, *A.*
bahut sárá ; bahterá ; bahutá ; wáfar ; wadhík ;
EXUDE, TO, *V. I.*
simmná ; ras choná ; nikalná ;
EXULT, TO, *V. T.*
ḳhushí manáuná ; baṛá bágán karná ; dandanáuná ; jaí jaí kár karná ;
EXULTANT, *A.*
baṛá ḳhush ;
EXULTATION, *N.*
baṛí ḳhushí. *f;* hulás. *f ;* hulásá. *m ;*
EYE, *N.*
akkh. *f ;* akkhí. *f ;* díddá. *m ;* nain. *f ;* netar. *m ;*
1. needles eye. suí dá nakká. *m ;*
2. one eyed. kániáṇ hoke ; káná ;
EYE BALL, *N.*
ḍelhá. *m ;* ánáṇ. *m ;*
EYE BROWS, *N.*
bharwaṭṭe. *m ;* bhawán. *f ;*
EYE LASHES, *N.*
jhimníáṇ. *f ;* pipníáṇ. *f ;*
EYE LID, *N.*
palak. *m ;* akkh dá chhatt. *m ;*
EYE SIGHT, *N.*
nazr. *f ;* jotná. *f ;*
EYE WITNESS, *N.*
gawáh. *m ;*

F.

FABLE, *N.*
bát. *f ;* kathá . *f ;* kathiá. *f ;*
FABRIC, *N.*
kapṛá. *m ;*
FABRICATE, TO, *V. T.*
jhuṭh bolná. kachch márná ; ḍhangge láuná ;
FABRICATION, *N.*
jhuṭh. *m ;* ḍhanggá. *m ;*
FABULOUS, *A.*
jhuṭhá ; baniá hoyá

FACE, *N.*
múṇh. *m ;* mukh. *m ;* mukhṛá. *m ;* muhándrá. *m ;*
1. face to face. dúbadú ; áhme sáhme ; áhmo sáhme ;
2. to his face. uh de múṇh te ;
FACETIOUS, *A.*
ṭhaṭṭhebáj ; maskará ; hassanwálá ; maḳhauliá ; hass mukhá ;
FACETIOUSLY, *Adv.*
hássí nál ; hass ke ;
FACILE, *A.*
1. easy. saukhá ; sukhálá ; sukhalá ; sahal ;
2. dexterous. hoshiyár ; chalák see DEXTEROUS.
FACILITATE, TO, *V. T.*
saukhá karná ; sukhálá karná sahal karná ;
FACILITY, *N.*
1. ease. asání. *f;* saukh. *m;* sahal.
2. dexterity. hoshiyárí. *f ;* chalraí. *f ;*
FACSIMILE, *N.*
naql. *f ;*
FACT, *N.*
asl gal. *f ;* haqqí gal. *f ;* sachchí gal. *f ;* purí gal *f ;*
FACTION, *N.*
1. party. fasád karnwálá jatthá. *m ;* dhir. *f ;* dhará, *m ;*
2. dissension. phuṭṭ. *f ;* ajoṛ *m* wigáṛ. *f ;* aṇ baṇ. *f ;*
FACTIOUS, *A.*
fasádí ; daṇggáí ; jhagṛáú ; jhagṛálú ; jhánjiá ; laṛáká ; pasádiá ; pasádí ;
FACTIOUSLY, *Adv.*
fasád karke ; laṛke ; badobadí ;
FACTITIOUS, *A.*
banautí ; jáhalí ;
FACTOR, *N.*
muḳhtiár. *m ;*
for a shopkeeper. gumáshtá. *m ;*
FACTORY, *N.*
kár ḳháná. *m ;* mashínáṇ. *m ;*
FACULTY, *N.*
1. capability. liyáqat. *f ;* táqat. *f ;* shakhtí. *f ;*
2. skill. gúṇ. *m ;* jách. *f ;*

FADE, TO, *V. T.*
1. for plants. kamláuná
2. for material, &c., raṇg uttarná; raṇg uḍḍ jáná; paṛ jáná; raṇg phiṭṭ jáná;

FADED, *A.*
1. for plants, men, &c., kamlá gayá;
2. for material. badraṇg;

FAGGED, TO BE, *V. I.*
huss jáná; thakk jáná; chur ho jána; hussar jáná
I am fagged out. merá ḍhilak nikal gayá; merá bhochhá nikal gayá;

FAIL, TO, *V. I.*
1. to be wanting. ghaṭṭ jáná; thuṛ jáná; rah jáná; muk jáná;
2. to miss success. ukk jáná, purá ná uttarná; kujh ná banná; rah jáná;
3. to be defeated. hár jáná;
4. to become bankrupt. dawálá nikalná;
5. to fail in exam. fel ho jáná;

FAILING, *N.*
augan. *m*; kamí. *f*; kasar. *m*; nuqs. *m*; aib. *m*; kamjorí. *f*; see FAULT.

FAILURE, *N.*
1. non success. nákámyábí. *f*;
2. bankruptcy. dawálá. *m*;
3. defeat. hár. *f*;

FAINT, *N.*
gash. *f*; gashí. *f*; murchhá. *f*; behoshí. *f*; daṇdaṇ. *f*;
giddy. bhauṇ. *m*;

FAINT, TO, *V. I.*
gash áuní; gash kháṇí; jí ḍubbná; ḍob painá; jí khussná; khussdá jáná; daṇdaṇ paí jáná; behosh ho jáná; murchhá kháná OR ho jáná;
1. to feel faint. dil chhappná; dil ghaṭṭná;
2. I feel faint from the blow. saṭṭ laggan nál merá dil haulá ho gayá hai;

FAINT, *A.*
kamjor; bewas; máṛá; máṛuá; lissá;
of colour. phikká;

FAINTHEARTED, *A.*
bedil; ḍarú; ḍarákal; kam himmat;

FAINTNESS, *N.*
behoshí. *f*; gashí. *f*; see FAINT.

FAIR, *A.*
1. just. niáiṇ; ádal;
2. middling. ḳhásá;
3. light coloured. phikká; gorá;
4. fair haired. kakká;

FAIR, *N.*
melá. *m*; jalsá. *m*;

FAIRLY, *Adv.*
insáf nál; ímán nál; dharm nál; rástí nál;

FAIR MINDED, *A.*
niáiṇ; khará; vihárí;

FAIRNESS, *N.*
insáf. *m*; rástí. *f*; bhalmánsí *f*; bhalmánsaú. *f*;

FAIRY, *N.*
parí. *f*;

FAITH, *N.*
ímáṇ. *m*; dharm. *m*; mán. *m*; biswás. *m*; vishwás. *m*; partít. *m*; ímándárí. *f*; nehchá. *m*;
to have faith. nehchá karná; ímán le áuná;

FAITHFUL, *A.*
ímándár; dharmí; khará; lun halál; ímánwálá; atbárí;
1. the faithful. momin. *m*;
2. one faithful to his promise. gal dá pakká. *m*; qaul dá pakká. *m*; qaul dá purá. *m*;

FAITHFULLY, *Adv.*
ímán nál; ímándárí nál; dharm nál; dharmo dharmí;

FAITHFULNESS, *N.*
ímándárí. *f*; sachchiái. *f*; rástí. *f*; wafádárí. *f*;

FAITHLESS, *A.*
beímán; bedharm; beatbár; jhuṭhá; lun harám; khoṭṭá; chalbáz; bepartítá;

FAITHLESSLY, *Adv.*
beímání nál;

FAITHLESSNESS, *N.*
beímání. *f*; bedharmí. *f*; beatbárí. *f*
kudharmí. *f*; bepartítí. *f*;

FAKIR, *N.*
sádhú. *m* ; faqír. *m* ;
1. a Hindu faqir with filthy habits. aughar. *m* ;
2. a faqir smeared with ashes. bhabútiá. *m* ; nangá jogí. *m* ; nángá sant. *m* ; nángá. *m* ;

FALCON, *N.*
báj. *m* ; lagaṛ. *m* ;

FALCONER, *N.*
bájdár. *m* ; shikárí. *m* ;

FALCONRY, *N.*
bájdárí. *f* ;

FALL, *N.*
1. tumble. ḍiggan ḍigáo. *m* ;
2. defeat. hár. *f* ;

FALL, TO, *V. I.*
ḍiggná ; ḍigg painá ; ḍháí painá ; ḍhainá ; ḍhaṭh jáná ;
1. as seed. kir jáná ; jhaṛná ; kirná ;
2. fruit, leaves, &c., falling. kirná ; jhaṛná ; ḍiggná ;
3. to fall under. heṭh painá ;
4. to fall into evil ways. kuráh painá ;
5. to fall from a height. ullarná ; ḍig painá ;
6. liquid. &c., duhl jáná ;

FALLACIOUS, *A.*
1. incorrect. galat ; ṭhík nahíṇ ;
2. deceptive. jhuṭhá ;

FALLACY, *N.*
galati. *f* ; bhulekhá. *m* ; bholá. *m* ;

FALLEN, *A.*
ḍiggiá hoyá ; ḍhaṭṭhiá hoyá ;

FALLOW, *A.*
piá hoyá ; banjjar piá ;
the land is lying fallow. jamín paí hoí hai ;

FALSE, *A.*
jhuṭhá ; beímán ; khoṭṭá ; kúṛá ; makarhatthá ; lapáṭiá ;
1. false reports. jhuṭhiáṇ galláṇ. *f* ; kuṛiáṇ galláṇ. *f* ; gappáṇ. *f* ;
2. false hopes. dam dalásá. *m* ;
3. counterfeit. jáhlí ; khoṭṭá ; banautí ;

FALSEHEARTED, *A*
beimán ; khoṭṭá ; see DECEITFUL.

FALSEHOOD, *N.*
jhuṭh. *m* ; phauṛ. *m* ; kuṛ. *m* ; jhuṭh muṭh. *m* ; jhakk. *f* ; phaphṛe. *m* ; asatt. *m* ;

FALSELY, *Adv.*
jhuṭhá hoke ; jhuṭhí muṭhí kuṛí mirchchí ; kuṛí muṛí ;

FALSENESS, *N.*
dhokebází. *f* ; see DECEIT.

FALSIFY, TO, *V. T.*
jhuṭh sachch kahná OR bolná jabán badalná ;

FALSITY, *N.*
jhuṭh. *m* ; see FALSEHOOD.

FALTER, TO, *V. I.*
1. to tremble. kambná ; thar thar kambná ;
2. to hesitate. hichkaná ; jakná jhakkná ; jhijakná ;

FAME, *N.*
1. renown. awáí. *f* ; mashhúrí. *f* ; charchá. *m* ;
2. honour. izzat. *f* ; partáp *m* ; jas. *m* ;

FAMED, *A.*
manniá danniá ; mashhúr ; see FAMOUS.

FAMILIAR, *A.*
wáqab ; wáqif ;
to be too familiar, cheeky. bhúhe honá OR charhná ; machchharná ;

FAMILIARITY, *N.*
gárhí yárí. *f* ; dostí. *f* ; wáqbí. *f* ; mittartái.

FAMILIARIZE, TO, *V. T.*
gijháuná ; ádat páuní, báṇ páuní ; ádat pái jáná ;

FAMILY, *N.*
ghar de log. *m* ; ṭabbar. *m* ; gharáná. *m* ; ṭabbar kabílá. *m* ; kuṛmáṇ. *m* ; bál bachche. *m* ;
ancestral family. jad. *f* ; kul. *f* ; píṛí. *f* ;

FAMILY MAN, *N.*
ṭabbarwálá. *m* ; bál bachchedár. *m* ; kabíldár. *m* ;

FAMINE, *N.*
kál. *m* ; auṛ. *f* ;

FAMISH, TO, *V. I.*
bhukhá honá ; bhukh laggní ;

FAMOUS, *A.*
mashhúr ; waḍḍá námí ; ujágar ; ghukiá hoyá ; manniá danniá ; manniá parmanniá ; jaswant ;
to make famous. dhumáuná ; mashhúr karná ; dhum pá dená ;

FAN, *N*.
pakkhá. *m*; pakkhí. *f*; jhallá. *m*;
FAN, TO, *V. T*.
jhallná; jhall márná; to pull a pankah. jhall márná; pakkhá khichchná;
FANATIC, *N*.
baṛá josh wálá. *m*;
FANATICISM, *N*.
baṛá josh. *m*;
FANCIFUL, *A*.
ḳhayálí; aiweṇ kiweṇ; lorí; man-maují;
FANCY, *N*.
waihm. *m*; lallhu. *m*; ḳhayál. *m*; lahir. *f*; lall. *f*; man mauj. *f*;
FANCY WORK, *N*.
kasídá kárí. *f*;
FANG, *N*.
daṇd. *m*;
FANTAIL, *N*.
lakká. *m*;
FAQIR, *N*.
faqír. *m*; see FAKIR.
faqir's rosary. málá. *f*; tasbá. *m*; tasbí. *f*;
faqir's bag. baglí. *f*;
faqir's cloak. kafní. *f*;
faqir's hut. jhuggí. *f*; kuṭhiá. *m*.
FAR, *A*.
dúr; duráḍḍá; dureḍá;
FARE, *N*.
1. food. bhojan. *m*; roṭí. *f*; ann pání. *m*; parshádá. *m*;
2. price of passage. bháṛá. *m*; karáyá. *m*;
FAREWELL, *Interj*.
salám. *m*; bandagí. *f*;
to say farewell. widiá karná;
FARM, *N*.
jamín. *f*; murabbá. *m*;
FARM, TO, *V. T*.
wahí karní; kásht karná;
FARMER, *N*.
jaṭṭ. *m*; jamíndár. *m*; murabbe-dár. *m*; jaṭṭ búṭ. *m*;
legal term. káshtkár. *m*;
FARM LABOURER, *N*.
kámá. *m*; sepí. *m*;
FARMING, *N*.
wáhí. *f*; káshtkárí. *f*;
FARMYARD, *N*.
hátá. *m*; hawelí. *f*; ḍerá. *m*;
FARRIER, *N*.
1. shoeing smith. khuriáṇ láun wálá. *m*;
2. vet. salotarí. *m*;
FARTHER, *Adv*.
hor dúr; ziyádá dúr; pare; dureḍá;
FASCINATING, *A*.
mohní; sohní;
FASCINATION, *N*.
moh. *m*;
FASHION, *N*.
1. custom. dastúr. *m*; dhaṇg. *m*; riwáj. *f*; rawaiyá. *m*;
2. shape. ḍaul. *f*; shakal. *f*; rupp. *m*; ḍhab. *m*;
3. mode of dress. pahráwá. *m*; pahináwá. *m*;
FASHION, TO, *V. T*.
ghaṛná; ḍhálná; banáuná;
FAST, *A*.
1. swift. káhlá; tikkhá; tarikkhá;
2. not loose. kassiá hoyá;
3. fast colour. pakká;
FAST, *N*.
Muhammadan Fast. rozá. *m*;
Hindu Fast. wart. *m*; barat. *m*; niráhár. *m*;
FAST, TO, *V. T*.
rozá rakkhná; M, wart rakkhná, H; bhukhá rahná;
one who fasts. wartí. *m*; H; roze-wálá. *m*, M;
FASTEN, TO, *V. T*.
bannhná; gaṇḍhná; joṛná;
to tighten. kassná;
FASTENED, TO BE, *V. I*.
bajjhná;
FASTENED, *A*.
baddhá hoyá;
FASTENING, *N*.
1. anything which binds. bannh. *m*; jotar. *f*;
2. wooden bolt. billí. *f*;
3. iron staple. kuṇḍá. *m*;
FASTNESS, *N*.
kilá. *m*; koṭ. *m*; gaṛh. *m*;
FAT, *N*.
charbí. *f*; thiṇḍá. *m*;

FAT, *A.*
moṭa ; moṭá tájá ; daṭṭá ; sabbhar ; ḍhiḍḍhú ; ṭhullhá ;
very fat. ghuchch múchch ; jhoṭaṛ ; sunn munn ; tair ṭhullhá ; tahiṛ ṭhullhá ; phiṭṭá hóyá ;

FATAL, *A.*
maranwálá ;

FATE, *N.*
qismat. *f*, M, taqdír. *f*. M; nasíb, *m*; M ; bháná. *m* ; karam. *m* ; lekh, *m* H ; bhág. *m* ; bháwí. *f* ; pará lavat. *f* ; honí. *f* ;
in the course of fate. karmáṇ dí gatí. *f* ; nasíbáṇ dí márí ;

FATHER, *N.*
báp. *m*, pitt. *m* ; pitá. *m* ; pio. *m* ; bháíá. *m* ; cháchchá. *m* ; báppú. *m*; lálá *m* ;
1. father's elder brother. táiá. *m* ; bábá. *m* ;
2. father's younger brother. cháchchá. *m* ;
3. used by daughters, especially in marriage songs. bábal. *m* ;

FATHER-IN-LAW, *N.*
sauhrá. *m* ;

FATHERLESS, *A.*
pio mahiṭṭar ; yatím ;

FATHERLY, *A.*
báp jehá ; pewán wargá ;

FATHOM, TO, *V. T.*
1. to sound the bottom, tháh lainí ; hátth lainí ;
2. to comprehend. samajhná ;

FATIGUE, *N.*
thakkewáṇ. *m* ;

FATIGUE, TO, *V. T.*
thakkáuná ;

FATIGUED, TO BE, *V. I.*
thakk jáná ; huss jáná ;

FATIGUED, *A.*
mándá ; thakkiá hoyá ;
1. fatigued with the journey ; painḍá kardeáṇ kardeáṇ thakkiá hoyá ;
2. easily fatigued, thakelá ;

FATNESS, *N.*
moṭái. *f* ; muṭápá . *m* ; ṭhullh. *f* ;

FATTY, *A.*
1. greasy. thinḍá ;
2. obese. moṭá ;

11

FATTISH, *A.*
muṭerá ;

FATUITY, *N.*
bewaqufí. *f* ; beaqlí. *f* ; nadání. *f* ;

FAULT, *N.*
qusúr. *m* ; dosh. *m* ; augun. *m* ; illat. *f* ; páp. *m* ; bhull. *f* ; chukk. *f* ; galatí. *f* ; kasar. *m* ; gáfalí. *f* ; aparádh. *m* ; see FAILING.
to find fault. boliáṇ mární ;

FAULTINESS, *N.*
buríáí. *f* ; badí. *f* ; sharárat. *f* ; khoṭáí. *f* ;

FAULTLESS, *A.*
bequsur ; beaib ; begunáh ; bedos ; bedosá ; nirdokh ; betaqsírá ;

FAULTY, *A.*
1. defective. nakárá ; nákas ;
2. bad. kharáb ; nikammá ; khoṭṭá. máṛá ;

FAVOUR, *N.*
1. kindness. mihrbání. *f* ; kirpá. *f* ; dáyá. *f* ; narmí. *f* ; upkár. *m* ;
2. help. madad. *f* ; sahárá. *m* ;
3. prejudice. tarafdárí. *f*; pakh. *m*;

FAVOUR, TO, *V. T.*
1. to show kindness. kirpá karní ; dáyá karní ; mihrbání karní ; múṇh lagáuná ; lábh páuná ;
2. to help. madad dení OR karní ; sahárá dená ;
3. to show partiality. pakh karná ;

FAVOURABLE, *A.*
faidedár ; nafewálá ; nafewaṇd ;

FAVOURABLY, *Adv.*
dostí nál ; mihrbání nál ;

FAVOURED, *A.*
piárá ; pasiṇd ;
1. ill favoured. badsurat ; beḍaul ; berúp ;
2. well favoured. khubsurat ; sohná ; mohná ; sundar ;

FAVOURITE, *N.*
pyárá. *m* ; parítam. *m* ; láḍlá. *m* ; lál. *m* ; láḍlí. *f* ; láḍo. *m* ;

FAVOURITE, *A.*
pyárá ; láḍlá ; láḍlí ;

FAWN, *N.*
hiran dá bachchá. *m*;
harnoṭá. *m* ; chakárá. *m* ;

FAWN, TO, *V. T.*
phuláuná ; cháplusí karní ; parmáuná ; lallo patto karná ; gaddoṇ khurkí karní ;
FAETUS, *N.*
gabbh. *m* ; garbh. *m* ;
FEALTY, *N.*
wafádárí. *f* ; farmánbardárí. *f* ; diyánatdárí. *f* ;
FEAR, *N.*
ḍar. *m*; ḳhauf. *f*; haul. *m*; bhau. *m* ; bhái. *f* ; ḍaráwá. *m* ; jhakk. *m* ; handeshá. *m* ; saiṇsá. *m*; khaṭká. *m* ;
FEAR, TO, *V. T.*
ḍarná ; ḍar laggná ; andeshá karná ; haul karná ; sahimná ; bhau áuná ;
FEARFUL, *A.*
1. dreadful. ḍaráká ; ḍaráuná ;
2. timid. ḍarákal. ; kamm himmat ; bujjhe dil wálá ;
FEARFULLY, *Adv.*
ḍar nál ; ḍar ke ; sahim ke ;
FEARFULNESS, *N.*
sahim. *m* ; ḍar. *m* ; see FEAR
FEARLESS, *A.*
niḍar ; bedhaṛak ; diler ; nichiṇt ; beḍar ; naḍar ; himmatwálá ; himmatí ; himtál ; bejhakk ; nidhaṛak ;
FEARLESSLY, *Adv.*
baṛí dilerí nál ; diler hoke ; sher banke ; bedhaṛak ;
FEARLESSNESS, *N.*
dilerí. *f* ; see BOLDNESS.
FEASIBLE, *A.*
sukhálá ; saukhá ; ho sakdá ;
FEAST, *N.*
1. banquet. jiáfat. *f* ; majmání. *f* ; mamáhní. *f* ; dhám. *f* ;
2. a feast of fat things. tará tarí khánā. *m* ;
3. festival. din. *m* ; íd. *f* ;
4. a feast for Brahmans and poor. jagg. *m* ;
5. to observe a festival. íd manauní ; ḳhushí manáuní ;
FEAST, TO, *V. T.*
roṭí pakáuní ; bhojan karná ; deg pakáuná ; baṛá kháná karná ;
1. to give a feast after the death of an aged person. kaṭṭh karná ;
2. to feast Brahmans and poor. jagg karná OR pakáuná ;
FEAST, TO, *V. I.*
roṭí kháná ;
FEAT, *N.*
kamm. *m* ; bahádurí dá kamm. *m* ; muhimm. *f* ;
FEATHER, *N.*
khambh. *f* ; par. *m* ;
FEATURE, *N.*
shakal. *f* ; rupp. *m* ;
FACES, *N.*
1. dregs. lagg labeṛ. *f* ; júṭh. *f* ; phog. *m* ;
2. excrement. mailá. *m* ; jháṛá. *m* ; see DUNG.
FECUND, *A.*
phalwálá ; phaldár ; phaliá phuliá ;
FEE, *N.*
1. pay for labour. mazdúrí. *f* ; dihárí. *f* ;
2. reward. inám. *m* ;
3. entrance fee. dáḳhalá. *m* ;
4. fees given to servants at weddings. lág. *m* ;
FEEBLE, *A.*
máṛá ; kamjor ; lissá ; bewas ; huttiá hoyá ; híṇáṇ ;
FEEBLE, RATHER, *A.*
maṛerá ; máṛúá ; huttiá hoyá ;
FEEBLENESS, *N.*
kamjorí. *f* ; nátáqatí. *f* ; thiṛ. *m* ; nirbaltái. *f* ;
FEED, TO, *V. T.*
1. to feed anyone. khuláuná ; bhojan karáuná ; khán núṇ dená ; chhakáuná ; khuwáuná ; khuáná ; khuálná ;
2. to feed dogs, &c. ṭukkar páuná ;
3. to feed poultry. chugáná ;
4. to feed cattle. paṭṭhe páuná ; gháh páuná ;
FEEL, TO, *V. T.*
chhuhná ; hatth láuná ; tohná ; chhohná ; ṭúh ṭúh karná.
1. to feel about. ṭolá ṭálí karná ;
2. to feel the pulse. nabz wekhní ;
FEELING, *N.*
1. touching. chhuhái. *f* ; chhút. *f* ;
2. sympathy. dard. *f* ; rahmdilí. *f* ;
FEET, *N.*
pair. *m* ; charn. *m* ;

FEIGN, TO, *V. T.*
dhokhá dená; see DECEIVE.
to feign ignorance, machláuná;
FEIGNED, *A.*
jhuṭhá; jáhilí; banautí;
FEINT, *N.*
dhokhá. *m;* chhal. *m;* fareb. *m;*
in wrestling. dáṭ. *m;* see PRETENCE.
FEINT, TO, *V. T.*
pech kheḍná; dá kheḍná; see PRETEND.
FELICITY, *N.*
ḳhushí. *f;* ḳhushhálí. *f;* sukh. *m;*
bhágwání. *f;*
FELL, TO, *V. T.*
ḍegná; ḍigáuná; ḍháná;
FELLOW, *N.*
sáthí. *m;* dost. *m;* jamaití. *m;*
see COMPANION.
FELLOWSHIP, *N.*
1. friendship. dostí. *f;* yárí. *f;*
2. partnership. sáṇjh. *m;* bhanjálí. *f;*
bháíwálí. *f;*
FELON, *N.*
dosí. *m;* hattiárá. *m;* buriár. *m;*
jurmí. *m;*
FELONY, *N.*
jurm. *m;* dosh. *m;* hattiá. *m;*
aparádh. *m;*
FEMALE, *N.*
janání. *f;* tímí. *f;* buḍḍhí. *f;*
nár. *f;*
1. a female friend. dubhain. *f;*
sahelí. *f;*
2. a female servant. dásí. *f;*
bandí. *f;* ṭahilaṇ. *f;*
FEMALE, *A.*
janáná;
of animals. madín;
FENCE, *N.*
jangalá. *m;*
of thorns. wáṛ *f;* see HEDGE.
FENCE, TO, *V. T.*
gherná; wáṛ gaḍḍná;
FENCER, *N.*
gatkebáj. *m;* palatthebáj. *m;*
FENCING, *N.*
gatkebájí. *f;* palatthebájí. *f;*
FERMENT, *N.*
1. leaven. ḳhamír. *m;*
2. quarrel. fasád. *f;* jhagṛá. *m;*
laṛáí. *f;*
3. excitement. josh. *m;*
FERMENT, TO, *V. I.*
ḳhamírá ho jáná; ḳhamír uṭṭhná
OR phulná;
FERMENTATION, *N.*
ubálá. *f;*
to rot. saṛná;
FEROCIOUS, *A.*
saghtá; beráhm; karṛá; kharwá;
FEROCIOUSNESS, *N.*
saḳhtí. *f;* julm. *m;* jabardastí. *f;*
beráhmí. *f;* jástí. *f;*
FEROCITY, *N.*
julm. *m;* saḳhtí. *f;* beráhmí. *f;*
FERREL, *N.*
sám. *f;* shám. *f;*
FERRY, *N.*
gháṭ. *m;* pattaṇ. *m;*
FERRYMAN, *N.*
wáṇjhí. *m;* mulláh. *m;*
FERTILE, *A.*
phaldár; phal denwálá;
FERVENCY, *N.*
josh. *m;* shauq. *m;* sargarmí. *f;*
tezí. *f;*
FERVENT, *A.*
joshwálá; sargarm; tez; jataní;
FESTIVAL, *N.*
1. a fair. melá. *m;* jalsá. *m;*
2. holiday. chhuṭṭí. *f;*
3. religious festival. din. *m;* íd. *f*, M; teohár. *m*, H;
FESTIVITY, *N.*
ḳhushí. *f;* mauj, *f;* rág nách. *m;*
rág raṇg. *m;*
FESTOON, *N.*
málá. *f;* hár. *m;*
for a bridegroom. sehrá. *m;*
FETCH, TO, *V. T.*
le áuná; le lená;
FETID, *A.*
gandá; mailá; palít;
FETLOCK, *N.*
ghoṛe de gitte de pichhle wál. *m;*
gámchí. *f;*
FETTERS, *N.*
1. for feet. beṛíáṇ. *f;*
2. for hands. hatthkaṛíáṇ. *f;*
FETTER, TO, *V. T.*
beṛíáṇ páuná; jakaṛná;

FEUD, *N.*
1. quarrel. jhagṛá. *m ;* laṛái. *f ;* pathāṛá. *m ;*
2. hatred. dushmaní. *f ;* wair. *m ;* virodh. *f ;*
FEVER, *N.*
táp. *m ;* tap. *m ;* kass. *f ;* bukhár. *m ;*
1. remittent fever. netkí. *f ;* teyá táp. *m ;*
2. one who has fever. tápí. *m ;* tápaṇ. *f ;*
3. to get fever. pindá bhaḳhaná ; tap chaṛhná ;
4. to lose fever. tap utarná ; tap lah jáná ;
5. he got fever. uhnúṇ tap ho gayá ;
FEW, *A.*
thoṛe ; ghaṭṭ ; virle ; do chár ; ghaṭṭ waddh ; ghaṭṭie ; koí koí ; virlá virlá ;
FEWNESS, *N.*
kamí. *f ;* kamtí. *f ;*
FEZ, *N.*
lál topí. *f ;* Rúmí topí. *f ;*
FIANCEE, *N.*
maṇg. *f ;*
FIASCO, *N.*
nákámyábí. *f ;*
FIAT, *N.*
hukm. *m ;* ágiá. *f ;*
FIB, *N.*
jhuṭh. *m ;* jhuṭh muṭh. *m ;* phauṛ. *m ;* kúṛ. *m ;*
FIB, TO, *V. T.*
jhuṭh bolná OR márná ; kúṛ bolná OR márná ;
FIBRE, *N.*
tár. *m ;* sút. *m ;* tágá. *m ;*
FICKLE, *A.*
do dilá ; man dá bhur bhurá ; to be fickle minded. do dilá honá ;
FICKLENESS, *N.*
kachch pakk. *m ;*
FICTION, *N.*
1. a story. kahání. *f ;* gal. *f ;*
2. a fabrication. banáutí gal. *f ;*
3. a lie. jhuṭh. *m ;* phauṛ. *m ;*
FICTITIOUS, *A.*
jhuṭhá ; banáutí ;
FIDDLE, *N.*
saraṇgí. *f ;*
FIDDLE STICK, *N.*
saraṇgí dá gaz. *m ;*
FIDDLE STRING, *N.*
saraṇgí dá tár. *m ;*
FIDELITY, *N.*
wafádárí. *f ;* ímándárí. *f ;* ímán. *m ;* sachchái. *f ;* diyánatdárí. *f ;*
FIDGET, *N.*
bearámí. *f ;* see RESTLESSNESS.
FIGET, TO, *V. T.*
chulbuláuná ; kulbaláuná ; chulchuláuná ; hilná jullná ;
FIDGETY, *A.*
nachallá ;
FIE, FIE, *Interj.*
tobá tobá ;
FIELD, *N.*
khet. *m ;* khelar. *m ;*
1. a ploughed field. wáhṇ. *m ;*
2. part of a field. kiárá. *m ;*
FIEND, *N.*
bhút. *m ;* paret. *m ;* deu. *m ;*
FIE, *Interj.*
abe tabe ;
FIERCE, *A.*
tez ; saghtá ; waihshí ; ḍáhḍá ; to be fierce. ghuṛná ; ghuṛakná ; jhiṛakná ;
FIERCELY, *Adv.*
baṛí saḳhtí nál ; gusse nál ;
FIERCENESS, *N.*
tezí. *f ;* saḳhtí. *f ;* baṛá gussá. *m ;*
FIERY, *A.*
tez ; zabardast ; joshwálá ; jhallá ;
FIFE, *N.*
1. flute. bauṇsarí. *f ;* báṇsarí. *f ;*
2. double flute. mattíán. *f ;*
3. large flute. wanjhli. *f ;*
FIFTEEN, *A.*
paṇdráhá ;
FIFTEENTH, *A.*
paṇdráhwáṇ ;
FIFTH, *A.*
paṇjwáṇ ;
FIFTHLY, *A.*
paṇjweṇ ;
FIFTY, *A.*
paṇjáh ;
fifty one. ikwaṇjá ;
fifty two. bawaṇjá ;
fifty three. tarwaṇjá ;
fifty four. churiṇjá ;

fifty five. pachwaṇjá ;
fifty six. chhawiṇjá ; chhapiṇjá ;
fifty seven. satwaṇjá ;
fifty eight. aṭhwaṇjá ;
fifty nine. unáhṭh ;

FIG, *N.*
phagwáṛá. *m ;*

FIGHT, *N.*
laṛáí. *f ;* jhagṛá. *m ;* már kuṭái. *f.* jhagṛá fasád. *f ;* dangá fasád *f ;*
1. of cattle. bhiṛáí. *f ;*
2. battle. juddh. *m ;*

FIGHT, TO, *V. T.*
laṛáí karní ; jhagṛá karná ;
1. to fight amongst yourselves. áp vichch dí laṛná ;
2. of buffaloes. bhiṛná ;
3. as cocks. jhaṛaf márná ;

FIGMENT, *N.*
banaut. *f ;* jhuṭh. *m ;*

FIGURATIVELY, *Adv.*
misál de taur nál ; misál deke ;

FIGURE, *N.*
1. form. rupp. *m ;* shakal. *f ;* surat. *f ;*
2. statue. murat. *f ;* butt. *m ;*
3. number. hinsá. *m ;*
4. price. mull. *m ;*
5. type. namuná. *m ;* misál. *f ;*

FILCH, TO, *V. T.*
churáuná ; chorí karní ; khaṛá jáná ;

FILE, *N.*
retí. *f ;*

FILE, TO, *V. T.*
retná ; retí karní ;

FILL, TO, *V. T.*
bharná ; bhar dená ; purá karná ; ḍhusná ;
to the brim. múṇhoṇ múṇh bharná ; múṇhá múṇh bharná ; ladná ; ledná ;

FILL, TO, *V. I.*
bhar jáná ;

FILLED, *A.*
bharía hoya ;

FILLY, *N.*
wacheṛí. *f ;*

FILTER, *N.*
chhanní. *f ;*

FILTER, TO, *V. T.*
punná ; nitárná ;

FILTERED, *A.*
Initariá hoyá ;

FLTH, *N.*
gaṇdagí. *f ;* mail. *f ;* gaṇd. *m ;* palítí. *f ;* mal. *m ;* mail kuchail. *f ;* malíntái. *f ;* gaṇd maṇd. *m ;*

FILTHY, *A.*
gaṇdá ; palít ; mailá ; malíṇ ;

FILTRATION, *N.*
chhanáí. *f ;* punnáí. *f ;*

FINAL, *A.*
áḳhirí ; chekaṛlá ; oṛak de ;

FINALLY, *Adv.*
oṛak núṇ ; áḳhar ; chekaṛ núṇ ; chekṛe ;

FIND, TO, *V. T.*
1. to meet with. hatth lagná ; labbhná ; milná ; labbh painá ;
2. to perceive. malúm karná ; bujhná ; wekhná ;
3. to find fault. boliáṇ márná ; jháṛ karná ; lán tán karná ;

FINDING, *N.*
1. judgment. faisalá. *m ;*
2. order ; hukm. *m ;* ágiá. *m ;*
3. legal decree. digṛí. *f ;*

FINE, *N.*
jurmáná. *m ;* chaṭṭí. *f ;* ḍann. *m ;* jarimáná. *m ;*

FINE, *A.*
1. excellent. uttam ; suthrá ; baṛá chaṇgá ; sundar. baṛá sohná ;
2. delicate. mahín ; patlá ; baríк ; nájak ;

FINE, TO, *V. T.*
jurmáná karná ; ḍann láná ; chaṭṭí láuní ;

FINGER, *N.*
uṇgglí. *f ;* uṇggal. *f ;*
little finger. chíchcí. *f ;*

FINGER, TO, *V. T.*
hath láuná ; chhuhná ; chheṛná ; tohná ;

FINGER RING, *N.*
1. a plain ring. chhallá. *m ;* aṇguṭhí. *f ;*
2. a signet ring. chháp. *f ;*

FINGER TIP, *N.*
uṇgglí dá potá. *m ;*

FINISH, *N.*
aṇt. *m ;* nibeṛá. *m ;* nabáh. *m ;* áḳhír. *m ;*

FINISH, TO, *V. T.*
nabeṛná ; mukáuná ; purá karná ; bhugtáná ; kar haṭná ; kar chhaḍḍná ;

FINISH, TO, *V. I.*
nibaṛ jáná ; khuṭṭná ; muk jáná ; purà ho jáná ; nibhná ; sarájít honá ;

FINISHED, *A.*
purá ; ḳhatam ; taiyár ; sarájít ; baniá banáiá ;

FIRE, *N.*
agg. *f*; agní. *f*; agan. *f*; bháṇbar. *m*; bhámrí. *f*; bhá. *m* ;

FIRE, TO, *V. T.*
1. to kindle a fire. agg bálná ; agg láuná ; agg dená ; agg bhakháuná ;
2. to inspire. chukkná ; dilerí dení ; josh duáuná ; bhaṛkánná ;
3. to discharge a gun. banduk chaláuná ; golí mární.

FIREBRAND, *N.*
kapṭí. *m* ;

FIREFLY, *N.*
ṭiṭáṇá. *m* ; tiḍáná. *m* ; jugṇú. *m* ; ṭanáṇá. *m* ;

FIREPLACE, *N.*
chulha. *m*; chulh. *m*;

FIREWOOD, *N.*
bállaṇ. *m* ; lakkaṛ. *f* ;

FIREWORKS, *N.*
astbází. *f* ;
1. crackers. paṭáke. *m* ;
2. bombs. gole. *m* ;
3. sky rockets. hawáíáṇ. *f* ;

FIRM, *N.*
pakká ; takṛá ; tagṛá ; qaim ; sabútá ; sábtá ; ná hillanwálá ; asthar ; ashthír ; astháwar ;

FIRMAMENT, *N.*
asmán. *m* ; ákás. *m* ; puláṛ. *m* ;

FIRMLY, *Adv.*
mazbuṭí nál ; takaṛái nál ; tagṛái nál ;

FIRMNESS, *N.*
pakkíái ; *f*; sábtí. *f*; ghaliár. *f*; khalihár. *f* ;
of will. siḍḍ. *m* ;

FIRST, *A.*
1. foremost. pahláṇ ; moharlá ; aglá ;
2. exalted. buzurg ; waḍḍá ; manniá danniá ; manniá parmanniá ; turdá ádmí ;
3. at first. paund saṭṭe ;

FIRSTBORN, *A.*
pahleṭhí dá ;

FIRSTCLASS, *A.*
avval darje dá ;

FIRST FRUIT, *N.*
pahlá phal. *m* ;

FIRSTLY, *Adv.*
pahile ;

FIRST RATE, *A.*
chaṇgá ; álá ; umdá ; khará ;

FISH, *N.*
machchí. *f* ;

FISH, TO, *V. T.*
machchí phaṛná ;

FISHERMAN, *N.*
máchchí. *m* ;

FISH HOOK, *N.*
kuṇḍí. *f* ;

FISHING LINE, *N.*
ḍor. *f* ;

FISHING NET, *N.*
machchíáṇ phaṛanwálá jál. *m* ;

FISHING ROD, *N.*
bánsí. *f* ; charhí. *f* ;

FISHMONGER, *N.*
machchíáṇ wechanwálá. *m* ;

FISSURE, *N.*
teṛ. *f* ;

FIST, *N.*
mukká. *m* ; muṭṭh. *f* ; hurá. *m* ; ghusunn. *m* ; mukkí. *f* ;
to double the fist. muṭṭh ghuṭṭná ; hurá waṭṭná ; muṭṭh míṭná ; mukkí waṭṭní ;

FIT, *N.*
gash. *f* ; behoshí. *f* ; murchhá. *f* ; dandan. *f* ;
giddiness. chakkar. *m* ; bhaun. *m* ;

FIT, *A.*
de laiq ; de jog ; de gochrá ; ṭhík ; munásib ; kamm chalàú ;

FIT, TO, *V. T.*
ṭhík ṭhák karná ; durust karná ; sajáuná ; suháuná ;

FIT, TO, *V. I.*
sajná ; ṭhík áuná ; milná ;
for clothes, &c., púrá áuná OR honá ;

FITNESS, *N.*
laiqí *f ;*
FITTINGLY, *Adv.*
laiq taur nál ;
FIVEFOLD, *A.*
panj guṇá
FIVE, *A.*
paṇj ;
FIX, *N.*
aukh. *m ;*
FIX, TO, *V. T.*
lá dená ; ṭaṇg dená ;
1. to fix a day. din miṭná ;
2. to fix the ground. gaḍḍáuná ;
3. to determine. ṭhaṭhná ; ṭhahráuná ; muqarrar karná ; makáuná
FIXED, *A.*
qaim ; nichhal ;
FLABBINESS, *N.*
narmí. *f ;*
FLABBY, *A.*
ḍhilkiá hoyá ; más palamdá ; pilpilá ;
FLACID, *A.*
pilpilá ;
FLAG, *N.*
jhaṇḍá. *m ;* jhaṇḍí *f ;* dhajá. *f ;* dhujjá. *f ;*
1. flag on sikh temples. nishán sáhib. *m ;*
2. water flag. dabbh. *m ;*
FLAME, *N.*
1. small. lát. *f ;*
2. large. lamb. *f ;*
3. lamp to flame up. láṭ nikalní ;
4. fire to flame up ; bhaṛk uṭṭhná ; bhámbaṛ uṭṭhná ;
FLAMINGO, *N.*
lamḍhíng. *f ;*
FLANK, *N.*
pásá. *m ;*
of an animal ; wakkhí. *f ;* pásá. *m ;*
FLANNEL, *N.*
falálain. *f ;*
FLAP TO, *V. T.*
1. to flutter. par márná ;
2. to shake. hiláuná ; see FLUTTER.
FLAP, TO, *V. I.*
hilná ;
FLARE, TO, *V. I.*
bhaṛakná ;
FLASH, *N.*
chamak. *f ;* lishk. *f ;* lishkárá. *m ;* chamkárá. *m ;*
FLASH, TO, *V. T.*
lishkná ; chamakná ;
FLASK, *N.*
botal. *m ;*
FLAT, *N.*
paddhrá ; suáhrá ; raṛá ; chauṛá ;
FLATIRON, *N.*
istrí. *f ;*
FLATNESS, *N.*
paddharáí. *f ;*
FLATTEN, TO, *V. T.*
paddhará karná ; saṇwárá karná ;
FLATTER. TO, *V. T.*
gaddá khurkí karná ; lollo poppo karná ;
lallo patto karná ; parmáuná ; phuláuná ; leṭ phaṛná ;
FLATTERER, *N.*
jholí chuk. *m ;* jháṇsebáj. *m ;* cháplús. *m ;*
FLATTERY, *N.*
lallo patto. *f ;* leṭí peṭí. *f ;* choj. *m ;* chochlá. *m ;* lollo poppo. *f ;* phaphṛe. *m ;*
FLATULENCY, *N.*
báddí. *f ;* bak bakká. *f ;*
FLAUNT, TO, *V. T.*
majáj karná ; shekhí mární ;
FLAVOUR, *N.*
suád. *m ;* majá. *m ;*
FLAVOURLESS, *A.*
besuád ; besúádá ;
without salt. aluná ;
FLAVOURED, *A.*
suádlá ;
FLAW, *N.*
nuqs. *m ;* dág. *m ;* see FLEMISH.
FLATLESS, *A.*
bedág ; see UNBLEMISHED.
FLAX, *N.*
alsí. *f ;*
FLAY, TO, *V. T.*
chamm udheṛná OR láuná ; dhaṛí udeṛní OR láh suṭṭní ; khall láuní ;
FLE, *N.*
júṇ. *f ;* pissú. *m ;*

FLECK, *N.*
dág. *m* ; chitak . *f* ;
FLEE, TO, *V. I.*
bhajjná ; nassná ; naṭṭhná ; dauṛná ; piṭṭh dení ;
1. an army to flee. bhájaṛ kháná ;
2. to cause to flee. nassáuná ;
FLEECE, *N.*
bheḍáṇ dí un. *f* ;
FLEECE, TO, *V. T.*
1. to shear. katarná ;
2. to rob. luṭṭná ; kho lainá ;
FLEECY, *A.*
unní ;
FLEET, *A.*
tez ; káhlá ; trikkhá ; tikkhá ;
FLEETING, *A.*
ikk pal dá ;
FLEETNESS, *N.*
tejí. *f* ; shatábí. *f* ;
FLESH, *N.*
1. food. más. *m* ; gosht. *m* ; tarkárí. *f* ; goshat. *m* ;
2. human race. insán. *m* ; manukkh. *m* ;
FLESHY, *A.*
moṭṭá ; moṭṭá tázá ; subbhar ; ṭhullhá ;
FLEXIBILITY, *N.*
lachak. *f* ;
FLEXIBLE, *A.*
lifanwálá ;
FLIGHT, *N.*
1. of an army. bhájaṛ. *f* ; bhánj. *f* ;
2. an army to flee. bhájaṛ kháná ;
3. of birds. uḍárí. *f* ; ḍár. *f* ;
FLIMSY, *A.*
kamjor ; patíl ; haulá ; see FRAGILE.
FLINCH, TO, *V. I.*
sí sí karní ; hichkaná ;
FLING, TO, *V. T.*
suṭṭná ; paṭkáuná ; bhuánke márná ; vagáhuná ;
FLINT, *N.*
pathrí. *f* ;
FLIPPANCY, *N.*
shokhí. *f* ;
FLIPPANT, *A.*
tur turá ; lutará ;

FLIRT, *N.*
nakhrebáj. *f* ; chojan. *f* ; matakáṇ karnwálí. *f* ; maṭak karnwáli. *f* ;
FLIRTATION, *N.*
nakhrá. *m* ; nakhrebájí. *f* ; aṭak maṭak. *f* ; maṭakáṇ. *f* ;
FLIT, TO, *V. I.*
1. to go. jáná ;
2. fly. uḍḍná ;
FLOAT, TO, *V. I.*
tarná; pání de upar tarná; ṭhillhná;
FLOCK, *N.*
1. of goats, sheep, &c. ijjaṛ. *m* ;
2. of birds. ḍár. *f* ; taranḍá. *m* ;
FLOG, TO, *V. T.*
baiṇt márná ; chábak nál márná ; koṭle márná ;
FLOOD, *N.*
haṛh. *m* ; parlu. *m* ; chhall. *m* ; káṇg. *f* ; parlo. *m* ;
FLOOD, TO, *V. T.*
pání dená OR waddhná OR láuná OR sinjná ;
FLOOR, *N.*
farsh. *m* ;
FLOORING, *N.*
farsh. *m* ;
FLOUNDER, TO, *V. I.*
hatth pair márná ; loṭná ; loṭ poṭ honá ;
FLOUR, *N.*
áṭá . *m* ; áṭṭá. *m* ; maidá. *m* ;
FLOURISH, TO, *V. I.*
phalná phúlná ; phailárná ; waddhna ; lai lai karná ; chhai chhai karná ;
FLOURISHING, *A.*
harí bharí ; ghupiá hoyá ;
happy. nihál ; rází bází ;
FLOUT, TO, *V. T.*
láparwái karní ; makhaul karná ;
FLOW, *N.*
dhál. *m* ; báhar. *m* ; pání dá wagná. *m* ;
FLOW, TO, *V. I.*
wagná ; bahiná ;
FLOWER, *N.*
phul. *m* ;
of cotton plant. phul guddi.
FLOWER, TO, *V. T.*
phulná ;
of crops. nissarná ;

FLOWER BED, *N.*
kiárí. *f* ; khil. *f* ;
FLOWER GARDEN, *N.*
bagíchá. *m* ; bág. *m* ;
FLOWER POT, *N.*
gamlá. *m* ;
FLOWER VASE, *N.*
phuldán. *m* ;
FLOWERY, *A.*
phullanwálá ;
FLUCTUATE, TO, *V. I.*
1. to move. waddhná ghaṭṭná ; hilná ;
2. to vacillate. hichkaná ;
FLUENCY, *N.*
múṇh dí chalákí. *f* ;
FLUENT, *A.*
shapal ; far far karke boldá ; muṇh dá baṛá chalák ;
FLUENTLY, *Adv.*
far far karke ; shapal shapal karke ; shapá shap ;
to speak fluently. suáhre bolná ;
FLUENTNESS, *N.*
muṇh dí chalákí. *f* ;
FLUFF, *N.*
rúṇ dá tuṇbá. *m*; OR phaṇbá. *m* ;
FLUFFY, *A.*
ruṇwálá ;
soft. kulá ;
FLUID, *N.*
pání wargí patlí chíz *f*;
FLUSH, *N.*
lállí. *f* ;
FLUSH, TO, *V. I.*
múṇh lál honá ;
FLUSTER, *N.*
raulá. *m* ; beqarárí. *f* ; bechainí. *f* ; gaṛbaṛí. *f* ;
FLUSTER, TO, *V. T.*
ghabrá dená ; see EMBARASS.
FLUSTERED, TO BE, *V. I.*
ghábar jáná ; ghabráuná ;
FLUTE, *N.*
bauṇsarí. *f* ; báṇsarí. *f* ; báṇslí. *f* ; waṇjhlí. *f* ;
a double flute. mattíáṇ. *f* ;
FLUTTER, TO, *V. I,*
1. as a bird. kambh márná; chulchuláuná ; chulbuláuná ;
2. to palpitate. phaṛkná ; dhaṛakná ; kalphanná ; taṛafná ;
FLY, *N.*
makkhí. *f* ; makkh. *m* ;
FLY, TO, *V. I.*
uḍḍná ;
FLY, TO, *V. T.*
uḍḍáuná ;
FLYER, *N.*
uḍḍanwálá. *m* ;
FLYING, *N.*
uḍárí. *f* ;
FLYFLAP, *N.*
tamáchá. *m* ;
FOAL, *N.*
wachcheṛá. *m* ; bachcheṛí. *f* ;
FOAM, *N.*
jhagg. *m* ; kaf. *f* ; jhigg. *m* ;
FOAM, TO, *V. I.*
1. from the mouth. jhagg chhaḍḍní ;
2. on water, &c. jhagg á jáná ;
FODDER, *N.*
paṭṭhe. *m*; gháh pattá. *m*; chárá. *m*; paṭṭhá dathá. *m* ; túṛí. *f* ; khájjá. *m* ;
mixed food given to cows to increase their milk. gutává. *m* ;
waṇḍ wareveṇ. *f* ; waṇḍ. *m* ;
FOE, *N.*
dushman. *m* ; wairí. *m* ; dutí. *m* ; bairí. *m* ; lágú. *m* ;
FOG, *N.*
dhuṇd. *f* ;
haze. gahir. *f* ; gaihr. *f* ;
FOGGY, *A.*
dhuṇdlá ;
FOIL, TO, *V. T.*
haráuná ; aṭkáuná ; ḍakkná ; rokná ;
FOLD, *N.*
1. pleat. bhann. *m* ; waṭṭ. *m* ;
2. sheep fold. wáṛá. *m* ;
FOLD, TO, *V. T.*
waleṭná ; taih karná ;
1. into two. dohrá karná ;
2. into three. trehrá karná;
FOLIAGE, *N.*
patte. *m* ; pattar. *m* ; haríaul. *m* ;
FOLK, *N.*
lok. *m* ; baṇde. *m* ; ḳhilqat. *f* ; manukkh. *m* ; baṛá ádmí. *m* ; lokí. *m* ;

FOLLOW, TO, *V. I.*
magar chalná ; pichchhe ṭurná OR jáná OR chalná ; pichchhe lag painá ; pichchhe ho jáná ; khahiṛe painá ; magare magar jáná ; magar ṭur painá ;
FOLLOWER, *N.*
1. disciple. chelá. *m*, H ; shagird. *m* ; bálká. *m* ; sikh. *m* ; muríd. *m*. M ;
2. servant. naukar. *m* ; naukar chákar. *m* ; ṭahliá. *m* ;
FOLLOWING, *A.*
dujjá ;
FOLLY, *N.*
bewaqufí. *f* ; beaqlí. *f* ; nadání. *f* ; múrakhtái. *f* ; durmatt. *f* ;
FOMENT. TO, *V. T.*
1. with a warm brick. sek dená ;
2. with damp hotcloths. ṭakor karná ;
3. to foment a quarrel. laṛáí wadháuní ;
FOMENTATION, *N.*
ṭakor. *f* ; sek. *m* ;
FONDLE, TO, *V. T.*
sir te hatth pherná ; piyár dená ; lád karná ;
FONDLING, *N.*
hej. *m* ;
FONDLY, *Adv.*
piyár nál ; prem nál ;
FONDNESS, *N.*
piyár. *m* ; prem. *m* ; ríjh. *f* ; moh. *m* ; muhabbat. *f* ;
FONT, *N.*
baptismá dá hauz. *m* ;
FOOD, *N.*
ann páni. *m* ; roṭí. *f* ; parshád. *m* ; bhojan. *m* ; ann jal. *m* ; khájj. *m* ; ṭukk. *m* ; rozí. *f* ; gijá. *f* ; ṭukkar. *m* ; roṭí ṭukkar. *m* ; khánά dáná. *m* ; roṭi jhoṭí. *f* ; khádh khurák. *f* ;
1. food for animals. chárá. *m* ; khájjá. *m* ; gutává. *m* ; patte. *m* ;
2. food for birds. choggá . *m* ;
3. food and clothes. roṭí kapṛá. *m* ; khánά páhiná. *m* ; khánά-handháuná. *m* ; ann páni te kapṛá lattá. *m* ;
4. food offered to gods. parshád. *m* ;
5. midday food taken to workers. bhattá. *m* ;
6. daily allowance of food for dog. roṭí. *f* ; ṭukk. *m* ;
FOOL, *N.*
murakh. *m* ; guár. *m* ; jhallá. *m* ; aql dá annhá. *m* ; dhuchchal. *m* ; buḍḍhu. *m* ; jhuḍḍu. *m* ; aql dá púrá. *m* ; paglá. *m* ;
FOOLERY, *N.*
wahiyátí. *f* ; nadání. *f* ; beaqlí. *f* ;
FOOLHARDINESS, *N.*
beaqlí. *f* ; nadání. *f* ;
FOOLHARDY, *A.*
jaldbáz ; jáṇbáz ;
FOOLISH, *A.*
1. senseless. bewaqúf ; beaql ; murakh ; guwár; besamajh; ujaḍḍh ; paglá; kaiṇdh ; kulann ; buddhín; kuchajjá ; kuchajjí ; durmatt ;
2. simple. anján ; nadán ; bholá bhálá ; siddh paddhará ; kamlá ;
3. a foolish person. ullú. *m* ; dhuchchal. *m* ;
FOOLISHLY, *Adv.*
bewaqúfí nál ; biná soche samjhe ; nadání nál ;
FOOLISHNESS, *N.*
bewaqúfí. *f* ; beaqlí. *f* ; nadání. *f* ; agiáṇ. *m* ; anárviddiá. *f* ;
FOOT, *N.*
1. of a person. pair. *m* ; charn. *m* ;
2. of a bird. paṇjá. *m* ;
3. of a bed table, &c., páwá. *m* ; puándí. *f* ;
4. on foot. pairíṇ ṭurdá ;
5. fore part of the foot. pabb. *m* ;
FOOTBALL, *N.*
fatbál. *m* ;
small. khiddo. *m* ; khenu. *m* ;
FOOTFALL, *N.*
pairáṇ dá khaṛak. *m* ;
FOOTHOLD, *N.*
cut in a wall. &c. pauḍḍá. *m* ;
FOOTMARK, N.
khurá. *m* ; khuṛá. *m* ; khoj. *m* ;
FOOTNOTE, *N.*
háshiá dí likhat. *f* ;
FOOTSOLDIER, *N.*
sipáhí. *m* ;
FOOTSTEP, *N.*
khurá. *m* ;
the sound of footsteps. paichhaṛ. *f* ;

FOOTSTOOL, *N.*
pīṛhī. *f ;*
FOOTPATH, *N.*
ḍaṇḍī. *f ;* ráh. *m ;* rastá. *m ;* paihá. *m ;*
FOP, *N.*
bāṇká. *m ;* shukín. *m ;*
FOPPISHNESS, *N.*
maṭakpúṇá. *m ;*
FOPPISH, *A.*
báṇkí chál ; maṭakwálá ;
FOR, *Prep.*
káran ; de laí ; de wáste ; de badle ; dí khátir ;
FOR, *Conj.*
is laí ; kyuṇ jo ; is laí ;
FORAGE, *N.*
chárá. *m ;* see FODDER.
FORAGE, TO, *V. T.*
chárá labbhná ;
FORAY, *N.*
dháwá. *m ;* chaṛhái. *f ;*
FORBEAR, TO, *V. T.*
ján dená ; saihná ; jhallná ;
FORBEAR, TO, *V. I.*
lámbhe ho jáná ; bachiá rahná ; báj rahná ; muṇh moṛná ;
FORBEARANCE, *N.*
sabr. *m ;* dhíraj. *f ;* saṇjam. *m ;* hauṇsilá. *m ;* khímá. *f ;*
FORBEARING, *A.*
dhírajwálá ; nigghá ;
FORBID, TO *V. T.*
ṭhák dená ; maná karná ; warajná ; rokná ; moṛná ;
God forbid. kade nahíṇ ;
FORBIDDEN, *A.*
harám ;
FORCE, *N.*
1. power. jor. *m ;* táqat. *f ;* bal. *m ;*
2. violence. zabardastí. *f ;* julm. *m ;* dhakká. *m ;* jorí. *f ;* jabar. *m ;*
3. by force. badobadí ; dhakke nál ; sikhá sháhí ; zorozorí ; yoroyorí ; hikk dí tarán. *f ;*
FORCE, TO, *V. T,*
1. to coerce. taṇg karná ; aukhiáṇ karná ; lachár karná ;
FORCED LABOUR, *N.*
begár. *f ;* wagár. *f ;*
FORCED LABOURER, *N.*
begárí. *m ;* wagárí. *m ;*

FORCEPS, *N.*
jambúr. *m ;*
FORCIBLE, *A.*
jorávar ; táqatwálá ;
FORCIBLY. *Adv.*
badobadí ; malomalí ; dhakko dhakkí ; jor nál ; baṛá ṭill láke ; ṭill nál dabb ke ; zabardastí nál ; zorá zorí ; jorá jorí ; taṇo taṇí ; dhakká shaí ; see VIOLENTLY.
FORD, *N.*
pattan. *m ;* ghát. *m ;*
FORD, TO, *V. I.*
pattan laṇghná ;
FORE, *A.*
agge ;
FOREARM, *N.*
víní. *f ;* bíní *f ;*
FOREBODING, *N.*
lakháú. *m ;*
FOREFATHER, *N.*
piudádá. *m ;* waḍerá. *m ;*
FOREFINGER, *N.*
uṇggal. *m ;*
FOREGO, TO, *V. T.*
ján dená ; chhaḍḍ dená ;
FOREHEAD, *N.*
matthá. *m ;*
FOREIGN, *A.*
oprá ; gair ; paráiá ; begáná ; horí mulk dá ;
for foreign goods. disaurí ;
FOREIGNER, *N.*
pardesí. *m ;*
FORELAND, *N.*
jamín dí nukkar. *f ;*
FOREMAN, *N.*
sardár. *m ;*
FOREMOST, *A.*
aglá ; moharlá ; pahilá ;
FORENOON, *N.*
subhá. *m ;*
FORESEE, TO, *V. T.*
pahle thoṇ wekhná ;
FORESIGHT, *N.*
agamm. *m ;* lammí soch. *f ;*
FORESKIN, *N.*
khallarí. *f ;*
FOREST, *N.*
ban. *m ;* jangal. *m ;* ujáṛ. *m ;*
FORESTALL, TO, *V. T.*
agge thoṇ karná ;

FORETELL, TO, *V. T.*
agamm báchchná OR wáchchná; pahle batláuná; pahle jatáuná; agamm dí khabar dená;
FORETELLING, *N.*
ṭewá. *m*;
FOREVER, *Adv.*
sadá de laí; oṛak tíkar;
FORFEITURE, *N.*
kurkí. *f*; jabtí. *f*; jabt. *f*;
FORGE, *N.*
bhaṭṭhí. *f*;
FORGE, TO, *V. T.*
1. to counterfeit. naqlí dastkhatt karná; jhuṭhá kágat banáuná;
2. to make by hammering. kuṭ ke banáuná;
FORGED, *A.*
jhuṭhá; jáhlí;
FORGER, *N.*
jál sáj. *m*;
FORGERY, *N.*
jálsájí. *f*;
FORGET, TO, *V. T.*
wisárná; bhulá dená; bhuláuná; yád ná rakkhná; thauh ná rakkhná;
FORGET, TO, *V. I.*
bhul jáná; wisar jáná;
I forgot it. mainúṇ uh dá thauh nahíṇ rihá;
FORGETFUL, *A.*
gáfal; ḍhillá; bholu;
FORGETFULNESS, *N.*
wisárá. *m*; bhull chukk. *f*; ḍhill. *f*; aṇchiṇtá. *m*; bhulekhá. *m*; gáfalí. *f*;
FORGIVE, TO, *V. T.*
muáf karná; bakhshná; chhaḍḍná; muáfí dení; ján dená; khímá karná;
FORGIVENESS, *N.*
muáfí. *f*; khímá. *f*; chhuṭkárá. *m*; khalásí. *f*; riháí. *f*;
FORGIVING, *A.*
ráhmdil; narm;
for God. rahím;
FORK, *N.*
1. for table. káṇṭá. *m*;
2. pitchfork, with two forks. dusáṇgaṛ. *f*; dusáṇgí. *f*; sáṇgá. *m*;
3. with five or more forks. tangalí. *f*;
FORLORN, *A.*
1. friendless. beyár; bechárá;
2. unfortunate. badnasíb; benasíb;
3. solitary. akallá;
4. sorrowful. udás; namáná; masosiá hoyá;
FORM, *N.*
ḍaul. *f*; surat. *f*; sarúp. *m*; shakal. *f*; chhab. *f*; rúp. *m*;
FORM, TO, *V. T.*
banáuná; rachná; ghaṛná;
FORMAL, *A.*
rawájí;
FORMALITY, *N.*
dastúr. *m*; rít. *f*; tariqá. *m*;
FORMALLY, *Adv.*
dastúr de mutábiq;
FORMATION, *N.*
ḍaul. *f*; see FORM.
FORMER, *A.*
aglá;
FORMERLY, *Adv.*
pahláṇ; agetare; agge; chirokná; pahloṇ hí;
FORMIDABLE, *A.*
ḍaráú; ḍaráúná; ḍaráúnwálá;
FORNICATE, TO, *V. T.*
janáh karná; harámkárí karní; badkárí karní; yárí láuná;
FORNICATION, *N.*
zinákárí. *f*; badkárí. *f*; badfelí. *f*; harámkárí. *f*; janáh. *m*; chhinálá. *m*;
FORNICATOR, *N.*
harámkár. *m*; zinákár. *m*; járná. *m*; janáhí. *m*;
FORNICATRESS, *N.*
kaṇjarí. *f*; chaṇḍál. *f*; kasbí. *f*; badkár. *f*;
FORSAKE, TO, *V. T.*
chhaḍḍná; tark karná; tiágná;
FORSAKEN, *A.*
a deserted wife. chhaḍ; chuṭṭar;
FORSWEAR, TO, *V. T.*
1. to renounce. sauṇh kháke chhaḍḍná; tark karná;
2. to perjure. jhuṭhí gawáhí dení;
FORT, *N.*
qilá. *m*; gaṛh. *m*;
FORTH, *Adv.*
sáhmne; agge; báhar;
FORTHCOMING, *A.*
áunwálá;
FORTHWITH, *Adv.*
huṇe; jhaṭ paṭ; jhabde; jhaṭá jhaṭ;

FORTIETH, *A.*
chálíwáṇ;
FORTIFICATION, *N.*
qilá. *m;*
a trench. morchá. *m;*
FORTIFY, TO, *V. T.*
to fortify with defences. morchá bannhná;
2. to strengthen. mazbut banáuná; jor dená;
FORTITUDE, *N.*
1. courage. dilerí. *f;*
2. patience. sabr. *m;* dhíraj. *f;*
FORTNIGHT, *N.*
do hafte. *m;*
FORTRESS, *N.*
qilá. *m;*
FORTUITOUS, *A.*
aiweṇ; eweṇ; itifáqí;
FORTUITOUSLY, *Adv.*
sabab nál; aiweṇ; eweṇ;
FORTUITOUSNESS, *N.*
ḍho. *m;*
FORTUNATE, *A.*
bhágwán; sulakkhná; bhágáṇwálá; sukhí; partápwálá; dhannbhág; karmáwálá; sulachchná;
FORTUNATELY, *Adv.*
bhágáṇ nál; ḳhushnasíbí nál;
FORTUNE, *N.*
1. chance. bhág. *m;* karm. *m;* qismat. *f;* nasíb. *m;* lekh. *m;*
2. good fortune. partáp. *m;* ; nekbaḳhtí. *f;*
3. bad fortune. badnasíbí. *f;* benasíbí. *f;*
4. wealth. mál. *m;* daulat. *f;* dhan. *m;* máyá. *f;*
FORTUNE TELLER, *N.*
raul. *m;* ramlá. *m;* majúsí. *m;* ramlí. *m;* páṇḍhá. *m,* H; páṇḍá. *m,* *H;*
FORTUNE TELLING, *N.*
najúm. *m;* ramal. *m;* phál. *f;*
FORTY, *A.*
chálí;
forty-one. iktálí;
forty-two. batálí;
forty-three. tartálí;
forty-four. chutálí;
forty-five. paiṇtálí;
forty-six chhatálí;
forty-seven. saiṇtálí;
forty-eight. aṭhtálí;
forty-nine. uninjá;
FORUM, *N.*
1. court. adálat. *f;*
2. centre of village, meeting place. chauṇk. *m;*
FORWARD, *A.*
1. cheeky. ḍhíṭh; besharm; athrá;
2. in front. agge; sáhmne; agárí agháṇ; muhre; aggáṇ;
FORWARDNESS, *N.*
besharmí. *f;* ḍhíṭhpúṇa. *m;* beadabí. *f;*
FOSTER, TO, *V. T.*
1. to bring up. pálná posná; parwastí karní;
2. to forward. dil wadháuná; dilásá dená; takṛá karná;
FOSTER BROTHER, *N.*
dudh bháí. *m;*
FOSTERING, *N.*
parwastí. *f;*
FOUL, *A.*
mailá; gaṇḍá; palít; ghináuná; mailá kuchailá;
FOUL, TO, *V. T.*
mailá karná; gaṇḍá karná; palít karná; wigáṛná;
FOUL, TO BECOME, *V. I.*
bigaṛ jáná; palít OR gaṇḍá ho jáná; chhút laggní; ḳharáb ho jáná;
for water. ganghal jáná;
FOULLY, *Adv.*
búrí taráh nál;
FOUL MOUTHED, *A.*
gaṇdi zabán; bol bagáṛú; bol bagáṛ;
to use foul language. jabán gaṇḍí karní; muṇh gaṇḍá karná;
FOULNESS, *N.*
1. filthiness. napákí. *f;* palídagí. *f;* gaṇḍagí. *f;* gaṇḍ. *m;*
2. treachery. beímání. *f;* beímánagí. *f;* dagá. *m;*
FOUND, *P. P.*
labbh liyá; mil gayá;
FOUND, TO, *V. T.*
1. to lay the base. níṇh dharní OR rakkhní;

2. to establish. mazbut OR pakká OR qaim karná ; ṭhahráuná ;
3. to originate. muḍḍh bannhná ; shurú karná ;
4. to found a town. abád karná

FOUNDATION, *N.*
1. base. níṇh. *f* ; bunyád. *f* ; muniád. *f* ;
2. origin. muḍḍh. *m* ; shurú. *m* ; jaṛ. *f* ;

FOUNDER, *N.*
banáunwálá. *m* ; shurú karnwálá. *m* ;

FOUNDER, TO, *V. I.*
khubbh jáná ;

FOUNDERY, *N.*
kár ḳháná. *m* ;

FOUNDLING, *N.*
láwáris bachchá. *m* ; máṇ pio mahiṭṭar. *m* ; yatím. *m* ;

FOUNTAIN, *N.*
sotá. *m* ; sumb. *m* ;

FOUR, *A.*
chár ;
1 all four. cháre ;
2. from the four corners. chauháṇ kútáṇ thoṇ ;

FOUR ANNA PIECE, *N.*
chauanní. *f* ;

FOUR DAYS AGO, *N.*
chauth. *f* ;

FOUR FOLD, *A.*
chauguná ; chauná ;

FOUR FOOTED, *A.*
chaupáiá ;

FOUR SCORE, *A.*
assí ;

FOUR SQUARE, *A.*
chauras ; chaunukrá ;

FOURTEEN, *A.*
chaudáṇ ;

FOURTEENTH, *A.*
chaudáṇwáṇ ;

FOURTH, *A.*
chauthá ;
the fourth day, past or future. chauth. *f* ;

FOWL, *N.*
kukkaṛi. *f* ;

FOWLER, *N.*
chiṛímár. *m* ; pháṇḍhí. *m* ;

FOWLING PIECE, *N.*
banduq. *f* ;

FOX, *N.*
lumbaṛ. *m* ; lumṛí. *f* ; lumbaṛí. *f* ;

FOX HOUND, *N.*
shikárí kuttá. *m* ;

FOXY, *A.*
chalák ; farebí ; makkár ;

FRACAS, *N.*
laṛái. *f* ; daṇggá fasád. *m* ; jhagṛá. *m* ; see FRAY.

FRACTION, *N.*
1. moment. pal. *m* ;
2. piece. tukṛá. *m* ; ṭoṭá *m* ;
3. break. ṭúṭṭ. *f* ;

FRACTIOUS, *A.*
kauṛá ; laṛáká ; jhagṛálú ; fasádí ; upádí OR fasád karnwálá ;

FRACTIOUSLY, *Adv.*
jhagṛá karke ; laṛke ;

FRACTIOUSNESS, *N.*
narázagí. *f* ; ḳhafgí. *f* ; khaṭṭ phaṭṭí. *f* ; jhiṛká jhiṛkí. *f* ;

FRACTURE, *N.*
ṭuṭṭ. *f* ;

FRACTURE, TO, *V. T.*
toṛná ; bhan suṭṭná ; taroṛná ;
to cause to be broken. bhanáuná ;

FRAGILE, *A.*
kamjor ; nájuk ; kachchá ; ṭuṭṭanwálá ; bhurbhurá ;

FRAGILITY, *N.*
kamjorí. *f* ; nájakí. *f* ;

FRAGMENT, *N.*
churá. *m* ; tukṛá. *m* ; chakná-chúr. *m* ; páṛchhá. *m* ;
1. fragments of food. chúr bhúr. *m* ; rihá khihá. *m* ;
2. fragment of broken earthenware. ṭhikrí. *f* ; babbarí. *f* ;

FRAGRANCE, *N.*
ḳhushbo. *f* ; maihak. *f* ; hamkár. *m* ;

FRAGRANT, *A.*
ḳhushbowálá ; ḳhushbodár ; sugaṇdhí ;

FRAIL, *A.*
kamjor ; nájuk ; kachchá ; bhurbhurá ;

FRAILTY, N.
kamjorí. *f* ; nájakí. *f* ; natákatí. *f* ; nirbalí. *f* ;

FRAME, *N*.
ḍháṇchá. *m*; ḍaul. *f*;
1. frame on which wall of well is built. chakk. *m*;
2. frame for door, picture, &c. chugáṭh. *f*;
3. a fráme of wood, drawn by oxen, in treading out corn. phalhá. *m*;
FRAME, TO, *V. T.*
banáuná; gharná;
to frame a charge in court. fard lagáuná;
FRAMEWORK, *N*.
ḍháṇchá. *m*
FRANK, *A*.
sáf dil; khullam khullhá;
FRANKINCENSE, *N*.
dhúp. *f*; lubán. *m*;
FRANKLY, *Adv*.
safái nál; sáf sáf; sáf dilí nál; dil kholke; nitárke; khullam khullhá; chaṇgí taráh;
FRANKNESS, *N*.
safái. *f*; sáf dilí. *f*; sáf sáf ákhná. *m*;
FRANTIC, *A*.
janúní; besudh; págal; shudái;
FRANTICLY, *Adv*.
besudh hoke;
FRATERNAL, *A*.
barádaráná;
FRATERNALLY, *Adv*.
barádaráná taur nál;
FRATERNITY, *N*.
barádarí. *f*; bháíbandí. *f*; bháíchárá. *m*;
FRATERNIZE, TO, *V. T.*
wartná; bháíbandí karní; mel rakkhná; milná;
FRAUD, *N*.
chhal. *m*; dagabází. *f*; dhoppá. *m*; dhokkhá. *m*; jháṇsá. *m*; her pher. *m*; parfej. *m*; pech. *m*; dá. *m*; see DECEIT.
FRAUDELENCY, *N*.
dhoppebází. *f*; kapaṭ. *m*; dhokhá. *m*;
FRAUDULENT, *A*.
farebí; dagebáj; ṭhagg; kapaṭṭí; jhuṭhá; beímán; chálbáj; lapáṭiá;
FRAUDELENTLY, *Adv*.
chhal nál; chalákí nál; dhokhebájí nál;

FRAY, *N*.
fasád. *m*; daṇggá fasád. *m*; laṛái. *f*; rattá. *m*; haugámá. *m*; már kuṭṭái. *f*; jhagṛá. *m*;
FRAY, TO, *V. T.*
ragaṛná; ghasáuná;
FREAK, *N*.
aṇokh. *m*; lahir. *f*;
FREAKISH, *A*.
aṇokhá;
FREE, *A*.
1. at liberty. azád; khullhá dhullhá; vehlá; nirbhaṇd;
2. without price. muft; nirmull;
FREE, TO, *V. T.*
azád karná; chhaḍḍ dená; bacháuná; rihái dení; chhuṭkárá dená; chhuḍáuná; ḳhalásí dení;
FREE, TO BE, *V. I.*
azád honá; chhuṭ jáná;
FREEBOOTER, *N*.
luteṛá. *m*; ḍákú. *m*; dháṛví. *m*;
FREEDOM, *N*.
chhuṭṭí. *f*; ḳhalásí. *f*; azádagí. *f*; azádí. *f*; rihái. *f*; chhuṭkárá. *m*;
FREEHANDED, *A*.
dilwálá; man chalá; diler;
FREEHEARTED, *A*.
dilwálá; mihrbán;
FREEHOLD, *N*.
jágír. *m*; milkíyat. *f*; jaedát. *f*;
FREEHOLDER, *N*.
málik. *m*;
FREELIVER, *N*.
guṇḍá. *m*; luchch. *m*; badkár. *m*;
FREELY, *Adv*.
jí kholke; khullhe dil nál;
FREENESS, *N*.
azádí. *f*; azádagí. *f*; see FREEDOM.
FREESPOKEN, *A*.
khullam khullhá; See FRANKLY.
FREETHINKER, *N*.
kufrí. *m*; káfir. *m*; daihriá. *m*;
FREETHINKING, *N*.
kufr. *m*; bedíní. *f*;
FREEZE, TO, *V. I.*
ṭhaṇḍ nál jam jáná; korá jam jáná;
FREEZING, *A*.
baṛá ṭhaṇḍá; baṛí ṭhaṇḍ;
FREIGHT, *N*.
1. load. asbáb. *m*; bojhá. *m*; bhár. *m*;

2. cargo. jaház dí bhartí. *f*;
3. charge for cartage. karáyá. *m*; dhulwáí. *f*;

FREIGHT, TO, *V. T.*
laḍḍná;

FREIGHTAGE, *A.*
dhulwáí. *f*; mál dá karáyá, *m*; bhárá. *f*;

FRENZIED, *A.*
1. mad. págal; diwáná; kamlá ramlá;
2. enraged. russiá hoyá; ruṭṭhiá hoyá;

FRENZIEDLY, *Adv.*
besudh hoke;

FRENZY, *N.*
jhall. *m*; kamal. *m*; sudá. *m*;

FREQUENCY, *N.*
kaí wár. *f*; bahut wárí. *f*;

FREQUENT, *A.*
askar; bahut dafá; ghaṛí muṛí; ghaṛí ghaṛí; bahut wárí;

FREQUENT, TO, *V. I.*
ghaṛí ghaṛí áyá jáyá karná; ghaṛí muṛí áuná; ghaṛí ghaṛí áuná;

FREQUENTLY, *Adv.*
ghaṛí ghaṛí; kaí wár; baṛí wárí; bahut wárí; bár bár; ghaṛí muṛí; askar;
this is frequently the case. ih aksar hoyá kardá hai; see REPEATEDLY.

FRESH, *A.*
1. not stale. tájá; sajjrá;
2. green. hariá; hará; hariáulá;
3. vigorous. tagṛá; takṛá; haṭṭá kaṭṭá;

FRESHEN, TO, *V. T.*
tájá karná;

FRESHNESS, *N.*
hariá. *m*; hariával. *f*; ṭahik. *f*;

FRET, *N.*
1. anxiety. chiṇtá. *m*; fikr. *m*; saiṇsá. *m*;
2. anger. ḳhafgí. *f*; narázagí. *f*; waṭṭ. *m*; kauṛ. *m*;

FRET, TO, *V. I.*
kuṛhná; masosná; udás honá; khijhná; akkná; uktáuná;

FRETFUL, *A.*
kauṛá; ḳhafá; naráz; nakchaṛhá; múṇh ṭuṭṭá; khaṭṭá; rukkhá; kirnwálá; chiṛhanwálá;

FRETFUL, TO BE, *V. I.*
jhunjláuná;

FRETFULLY, *Adv.*
ḳhafá hoke;

FRETFULNESS, *N.*
narázagí. *f*;
of children. rihár. *f*;

FRICASSEE, *N.*
sálan. *m*;

FRICTION, *N.*
ragaṛ. *f*; ghasar. *f*; khasar. *m*; ghássí. *f*; ghássá. *m*;
massage. málish. *f*; muṭṭhí chápí. *f*;

FRIDAY, *N.*
Júmá, *m*, *M*; Shukarwár. *m*, *H*; Sukkarwár. *m*, *H*;

FRIEND, *N.*
dost. *m*; yár. *m*; yár básh. *m*; mittar. *m*; sajjan. *m*; millatí. *m*; milápí. *m*; surjan. *m*; belí. *m*; pyárá. *m*; sáthí. *m*; melí. *m*; premí. *m*; wáqab. *m*; parítam. *m*;
1. a great friend. guṛhá dost. *m*;
2. a female friend. sahelí. *f*; sahelrí. *f*;

FRIENDLESS, *A.*
akallá; bechárá; garíb; kanggál; beyár;

FRIENDLESSNESS, *N.*
beyárí. *f*; bechárgí. *f*;

FRIENDLINESS, *N.*
dostí. *f*; milansárí. *f*; muhabbat. *f*; prít. *f*; mittarchárí. *f*; melí gelí. *f*; mel jol. *f*;

FRIENDLY, *A.*
melí; milanwálá; dostáṇ wáṇgar;

FRIENDSHIP, *N.*
dostí. *f*; mel. *m*; prem. *f*; miláp. *m*; mittartáí. *f*; millat. *f*; hej. *m*; see FRIENDLINESS.
female friendship. sahelpuṇá. *m*;

FRIGHT, *N.*
ḍar. *m*; bhau. *m*; haul. *m*; khaṭká. *m*; ḍaráwá. *m*; dhuṛká. *m*; ghabrá. *m*; sahim. *m*; jhakk. *m*;

FRIGHTEN, TO, *V. T.*
ḍaráuná; dar páuná; ghabrá dená; ḳhauf vichch páuná; akkh wikháuná; padíṛná;

FRIGHTENED, TO BE, *V. I.*
ḍarná; ghábar jáná; sahimaná; sahim jáná;

FRIGHTFUL, *A*.
ḍaráuná ; ḍaráú ;
FRIGHTFULLY, *Adv*.
ḍaráké ; búrí taráh nál;
FRIGHTFULNESS, *N*.
ḍaráwá. *m* ; saḳhtí. *f* ;
FRIGID, *A*.
1. cold. ṭhaṇḍá ;
2. unsympathetic. rukkhá ; khaṭṭá ; bedard ;
3. dull. sust ; ḍhillá ; ḍhillá maṭṭhá ; álasí ;
FRILL, *N*.
jhálar. *f* ;
FRINGE, *N*.
jhálar. *f* ; balkhí. *f* ; aughí. *f* ; turrá. *m* ;
a fringe of leather, &c., placed above horses' eyes to keep flies off. makherná. *m* ;
FRISK, TO, *V*. *T*.
kalol karná ; bhurkaná ; chálán márná ; kuddná ; nachná ; ṭappná ; khedná ;
FRISKINESS, *N*.
kalol. *f* ; kheḍ kháḍ. *f* ; kheḍ. *f* ;
FRISKY, *A*.
ḳhush ; rází ; khiḍárí ;
FRITTER, *N*.
galgalá. *m* ; pakauṛá. *m* ;
these are sweet cakes fried in ghi. málhpuṛá. *m* ;
FRITTER AWAY, TO, *V*. *T*.
1. to waste. ḳharáb kar dená ; gawáuná ; wigáṛná ;
2. to mince. kímá karná ;
FRIVOLITY, *N*.
1. levity. hássí. *f* ; ṭhiskarí. *f* ; ṭhaṭṭhá. *m* ; maskarí. *f* ;
2. foolishness. beaqlí. *f* ;
FRIVOLOUSLY, *Adv*.
aiweṇ ; eweṇ ;
FRIVOLOUSNESS, *N*.
1. foolishness. bewaqúfí. *f* ; beaqlí. *f*.
2. levity. hássí. *f* ; hássá. *m* ; ṭhiskarí. *f* ;
FRO, *Adv*.
utthoṇ ;
FROCK, *N*.
frák. *m* ;
FROG, *N*.
ḍaḍḍ. *f* ; ḍaḍḍú. *m* ;

FROLIC, *N*.
kheḍ. *f* ; kalol. *f* ; ḳhushí. *f* ;
FROLIC, TO, *V*. *I*.
kheḍná ; ḳhushí manáuní ; kuddná ; kalol karní ;
FROLICSOME, *A*.
ḳhush ; khill diwání ; khiḍárí ;
FROM, *Prep*.
thoṇ ; walloṇ ; thíṇ ;
FRONT, *N*.
agwáṛá. *m* ; aggá. *m* ; sámhná. *m* ; aget. *m* ;
in front. muhre ; agáre ; agárí ; sáhmne ; agháṇ ; agge ; muharlá ;
FRONT, TO, *V*. *T*.
sámhná karná ;
FRONT, TO COME TO THE, *V*. *I*.
agge áuná ;
FRONTAGE, *N*.
agwáṛá. *m* ;
FRONTIER, *N*.
hadd. *f* ; sarhadd. *f* ;
FROST, *N*.
kakkar. *m* ; korá. *m* ;
FROSTY, *A*.
baṛá ṭhaṇḍá ; sard ;
FROTH, *N*.
jhagg. *f* ; kaf. *f* ; jhigg. *m* ;
FROTH, TO, *V*. *I*.
1. at the mouth. jhagg chhaḍḍní ; faiṇ áuná ; múṇh vichch jhagg le áuní ;
2. on water, &c. jhagg á jáná ;
FROTHY, *A*.
jhaggdár ;
FROWARD, *A*.
ziddí ; bhuhe ; ḍhíṭhá ; gamrúr ; see PERVERSE.
FROWARDLY, *Adv*.
beadabí nál ; gustáḳhí nál ;
FROWARDNESS, *N*.
ghamaṇḍ. *m* ; zidd. *f* ; kabb. *f* ; ghes. *f* ; ghassú. *f* ; haṇkár. *m* ; ḍhíṭhái. *f* ; beadabí. *f* ;
FROWN, *N*.
ghúr. *m* ; ghúrí. *f* ; ghúrkí. *f* ; tiuṛí. *f* ; ghurákiá. *f* ; waṭṭ. *m* ; waṭṭu. *m* ;
FROWN, TO, *V*. *T*.
ghurakná ; ghur dená ; táṛná ; ghúrí waṭṭní ; matthe waṭṭ páuná ; ghurakíáṇ kaḍḍhná ;

FROZEN, *A.*
ṭhaṇḍ nál jamiá hoyá;
FRUCTIFEROUS, *A.*
phaldár; phaldenwálá; phaliá phuliá; hariá bhariá;
FRUCTIFICATION, *N.*
phaldárí. *f*;
FRUCTIFY, TO, *V. T.*
phal dená;
FRUCTIFY, TO, *V. I.*
phal lagná;
FRUGAL, *A.*
sarfewálá; kafaití; sanjuhṛá; sanjuhṛí;
FRUGALITY, *N.*
sarfá. *m*; ghaṭṭ ḳharach. *m*;
FRUGALLY, *Adv.*
sarfá karke; thoṛá ḳharach karke;
FRUIT, *N.*
phal. *m*; mevá. *m*;
FRUIT, TO, *V. T.*
phalná; phal páiná;
to be fruitful. hariá bhariá ráhná;
FRUITAGE, *N.*
phal. *m*;
FRUITERER, *N.*
phal vechanwálá. *m*;
FRUITFUL, *A.*
phaldár; phaldaik; phalwálá; phaliá phuliá; hariá bhariá;
a fruitful vine. phullí hoí dákh. *f*;
FRUITFULNESS, *N.*
phaldárí. *f*;
FRUITION, *N.*
1. result. anjám. *m*; natíjá. *m*; gaveṛ. *m*; aṇt. *m*;
2. pleasure. ḳhushí. *f*; anaṇdtái. *f*; parsintái. *f*;
FRUITLESS, *A.*
befaidá; apphal; bephal; wirthá; birthá; akárath; bearth; nisphal;
FRUITLESSLY, *Adv.*
akárath; befaidá;
FRUIT TREE, *N.*
meve OR phal dá rukkh. *m*;
FRUSTRATE, TO, *V. T.*
1. to stop. rokná; ḍakkná; aṭkáuná;
2. to defeat. haráuná; jitt láuná;
FRUSTRATION, *N.*
hár. *f*; bháṇj. *f*;
FRY, TO, *V. T.*
tálná; tal dená; bhunná; taṛakná;
FRYING PAN, *N.*
kaṛáhí. *f*; tawá. *m*;
FUDDLE, TO, *V. T.*
mast karná; sharáb píáke behosh karná;
Fudge, *N.*
bakwás. *m*; wáhiyát gallán. *f*; wáfrí. *f*; wáfar gallán. *f*;
FUEL, *N.*
bálan. *m*; lakkaṛ. *f*;
FUGITIVE, *N.*
bhagauṛá. *m*;
FUGITIVE, *A.*
nassanwálá; nassiá hoyá;
FULFIL, TO, *V. T.*
purá karná; nabáhuná; kar chhaḍḍná; mukáuná; suddh karná; naberná; nirbáuná;
to fulfil a promise. qaul nabáhuná; bachan OR gal pálná.
FULF ILMENT, *N.*
1. com pletion. niberá. *m*; nibbaṛ tibbaṛ. *m*; nabáh. *m*;
2. accomplishment. puraṇtái. *f*; sanpuran. *m*;
FULGENCY, *N.*
chamak. *f*; bháh. *f*; chilkárá. *f*; chamkáṭ. *f*; chilak. *f*; chamkárá. *m*; lishak. *m*; bhaṛak. *f*; jhalak. *f*;
FULGENT, *A.*
chamkílá; chamakdár; chamkanwálá;
FULL, *A.*
bhariá hoyá; múṇho múṇh; ḍakkáḍakk; nakko nakk;
full moon. puranmáshí. *f*;
FULLY, *Adv.*
mulloṇ; ukká mukká; pure taur nál;
FULMINATE, TO, *V. T.*
dhamkáuná; ghurakná; ḍaráuná; see THREATEN.
FULMINATION, *N.*
dhamkí. *f*; ḍarává. *m*; dhauṇs. *f*; dábbá. *m*; dhássá. *m*; ghurkí. *f*;
FULNESS, *N.*
bharpúrí. *f*; puraṇtái. *f*;
FUMBLE, TO, *V. I.*
ṭohná;
FUME, *N.*
1. smoke. dhúán. *m*; dhún. *m*;

2. rage. gussá. *m;* karodh. *m;* roh. *m;* kop. *m;*

FUMIGATE, TO, *V. T.*
safá karná; dhukh dená; dhuf dená; guggal dhukháná; dhúní dená;

FUMIGATION, *N.*
dhúní. *f;*

FUN, *N.*
ṭhaṭṭhá. *m;* hássí. *f;* khushí. *f;* ṭhiskarí. *f;* maskarí. *f;* ṭhaṭholí. *f;*
a game. kheḍ. *f;*

FUNCTION, *N.*
1. duty. kamm. *m;* farz. *m;*
2. ceremony. darbár. *m;*

FUND, *N.*
púṇjí. *f;* rás. *f;* thauṇí. *f;*

FUND, TO, *V. T.*
rupae jamá karná; rupae kaṭṭhe karná;

FUNDAMENTAL, *N.*
asl. *m;* jaṛ. *f;* aslíat. *f;*

FUNDAMENTAL, *A.*
jarúrí; loṛídá; cháhidá;

FUNERAL, *N.*
1. Muhammadan. janázá. *m;*
2. Hindu. kiryá karm. *m;*
3. Hindu. for a married or aged person. babán. *m;*
4. Hindu. for an unmarried person. siṛhí. *f;*

FUNGUS, *N.*
ullí. *f;*

FUNNEL, *N.*
nál. *m;*
of an engine, steamer, &c. lumbí. *f;*

FUNNILY, *Adv.*
hasske; hásse nál;

FUNNY, *A.*
hassanwálá; maskará; khill diwání; khiḍárí;

FUR, *N.*
jatt. *f;* pasham. *f;* khall. *f;*
lit. hide.

FURBISH, TO, *V. T.*
chilkáuná; chamkáuná; jhalkáuná; lishkáuná;

FURIOUS, *A.*
baṛe gusse vichch; sakht naráz; jaliá baliá; ruṭṭhiá hoyá;
to get furious. tap ke lál honá; russiá hoyá;

FURIOUSLY, *Adv.*
gusse nál; baṛí sakhtí nál; russke;

FURIOUSNESS, *N.*
gussá. *m;* karodh. *m;* roh. *m;* kop. *m;* waṭṭ. *m;*

FURL, TO, *V. T.*
valeṭná;

FURLED, TO BE, *V. I.*
urjhná;

FURLONG, *N.*
míl dá athwáṇ hissá. *m;*

FURLOUGH, *N.*
chhuṭṭí. *f;*

FURNACE, *N.*
1. for baking bricks. bhaṭṭhá. *m;*
2. for cooking food. taṇdúr. *m;*
3. for boiling cane juice. chumbá. *m;*

FURNISH, TO, *V. T.*
samián dená;
to decorate. sajáuná; ṭíp ṭáp karná; saṇwárná; sájná;

FURNISHED, *A.*
sajjiá hoyá;
furnished and ready. wichháyá te saṇwáriá hoyá;

FURNITURE, *N.*
ghar dá asbáb. *m;* mez kursíáṇ *f;* wál walevá. *m;* samián. *m;* samán. *m;*

FURORE, *N.*
1. enthusiasm. josh. *m;* sargarmí. *f;* ríjh. *f;* shauq. *m;*
2. rage. gussá. *m;* karodh. *m;* roh. *m;* waṭṭ. *m;*
3. commotion. khalhbalí. *f;* raulá. *m;* hal chal. *f;* shor. *m;*

FURRIER, *N.*
chámár. *m;*

FURROW, *N.*
hal dá siár. *m;* rahil. *f;* oṛá. *f;*

FURTHER, *Adv.*
agge; pare; ziyádá dúr;

FURTHER, TO, *V. T.*
madat dení; see HELP.

FURTHERANCE, *N.*
madat. *f;* see HELP.

FURTHERMORE, *Adv.*
nále; is te biná; eh de siwá;

FURTHEST, *A.*
parle pár;

FURTIVELY, *Adv.*
chorí chorí karke; chupp cháp; akkh bachá ke; chupp chupátá;
FURY, *N.*
gussá. *m*; see FURIOUSNESS.
FUSE, TO, *V. T.*
pighláuná;
FUSILLADE, *N.*
rábbá. *m*;
FUSION, *N.*
galáu. *m*; pighláu. *m*;
FUSS, *N.*
raulá. *m*; shor. *m*; raṭṭá. *m*; hill jull. *f*;
FUSS, TO, *V. T.*
raulá páuná; shor macháuná; raṭṭá páuná; reṛká páuná;
to make a fuss. ṭíṭne márná; lit, to kick up the hind legs.
FUSSY, *N.*
nachallá; chiṛchiṛá; ghábariá hoyá;
FUSTY, *A.*
bássí; behí;
FUTILE, *A.*
nakárá; befaidá; raddí; nikammá; kise kamm dá nahíṇ;
FUTILELY, *Adv.*
aiweṇ; eweṇ; befaidá;
FUTURE, *A.*
honwálá;
in the future. agge núṇ; aidoṇ agge; agáháṇ núṇ;
FUTURITY *N.*
agamm. *m*;
the next world. parlok. *m*;

G.

GABBLE, *N.*
bak. *m*; fajúl galláṇ. *f*; gapp shapp. *f*; bak jhak. *f*;
GABBLE, TO, *V. T.*
bak bak karná; magaz márná; lutar lutar karní; khap páuní; bataule márná; ṭaiṇ ṭaiṇ karná;
GABBLER, *N.*
bakwásí. *m*; lutará. *m*; khappí. *m*; batuṛa. *m*; bataulá. *m*;
GAIETY, *N.*
ḳhushí. *f*; anaṇd mangal. *m*; anaṇdtái. ; mauj. *f*; hássí. *f*;
GAILY, *Adv.*
baṛí ḳhushí nál; ḳhush hoke; cháíṇ cháíṇ;
GAIN, *N.*
faidá. *m*; lábh. *m*; hásal. *m*; kamái. *f*; khaṭṭí, *f*; láh. *m*; parápat. *m*; labhat. *f*;
GAIN, TO, *V. T.*
1. to acquire. khaṭṭná; hásil karná; hatth laggná; kamáuná; kamái karní; khaṭṭ lainá; parápat karná;
2. to win. jittná; bází jitt lainá; haráuná;
3. to reach. appaṛná; pahuṇchná; pujjná;
GAIN, TO, *V. I.*
hásil honá; parápat honí; taraqqí milní; mallná; hatth áuná; napp lainá;
GAINSAY, TO, *V. T.*
1. to contradict. gall moṛní; jhuṭhiá karná; hutt karná; barḳhiláf bolná; jhuṭhláuná;
2. to deny. inkár karná; mukkarná;
GAIT, *N.*
chál. *f*; ṭor. *f*;
GALE, *N.*
jhakkaṛ. *m*; hanerí. *f*; anherí. *f*; jhánjhá. *m*;
a great gale. káli bolí hanerí. *f*; annhí anherí. *f*;
GALL, *N.*
chhállá. *m*;
1. on the back of an animal. lággá. *m*;
2. to be galled on back, from saddle. lággá lagná; piṭṭh laggní;
3. to be galled on hands, from work. chhállá painá;
GALLANT, *A.*
diler; takṛá; bahádur; hauslewálá;
GALLANTLY, *Adv.*
dilerí nál; bahádurí nál; sher hoke;
GALLANTRY, *N.*
dilerí. *f*; himmat. *f*; jurat. *f*; hausilá. *m*; súrbírtá. *f*; surmápuṇá. *m*; surtái. *f*; variámgí. *f*;
GALLOP, *N.*
1. fast gallop. sarpaṭṭ. *f*; dapaṭ. *m*;
2. gentle gallop. poiá. *m*;

GALLOP, TO, *V. T.*
poiá páuná OR ṭorná; dapṭáuná; ghoṛá dauṛáuná; dapaṭ dená; bág ḍhillí chhaḍḍ dená; sarpatt dauṛáná;
GALLOP, TO, *V. I.*
dapaṭná; poiá ṭurná; bág chhuṭ dauṛná; tin pairán chalná; hand gallop. sarpaṭṭ ṭurná;
GALLOWS, *N.*
pháhí. *f;* pháṇsí. *f;*
an impaling stake. súlí. *f;*
GAMBLE, TO, *V. T.*
juá kheḍná;
GAMBLER, *N.*
juáriá. *m;* juárí. *m;* juwárí. *m;* juáraṇ. *f;*
GAMBLING, *N.*
juá. *m;*
GAMBOL, *N.*
kalol. *f;*
GAMBOL, TO, *V. T.*
kalol karní; bhurkná; see FRISK.
GAME, *N.*
kheḍ. *f;*
1. to win a game. bází jittní;
2. to lose a game. bází hární;
GAME, *N.*
shikár. *m;*
GAME, *A.*
diler; bahádur;
GAMESTER, *N.*
juárí. *m;* see GAMBLER.
GANDER, *N.*
batká. *m;*
GANG, *N.*
jatthá. *m;* ṭollá. *m;* ṭollí. *f;*
GAP, *N.*
khappá. *m;* vel. *m;*
GAPE, *N.*
abásí. *f;*
GAPE, TO, *V. T.*
abásí áuní OR lainí;
GARB, *N.*
kapṛe. *m;* bhes. *m;* líṛá. *m;* bharáwá. *m;*
GAREEN, *N.*
bág. *m;* bagíchá. *m;*
garden bed. kiárí. *f;*
GARDENER, *N.*
málí. *m;* bágwán. *m;*
GARDENING, *N.*
bág dá kamm. *m;* bágbání. *f;*
GARGLE, TO, *V. T.*
garárá karná; chúlí karní; karúlí karní;
GARGLING, *N.*
garárá. *m;*
used by Sikhs. kurlá. *m;* karulí. *f;*
GARLAND, *N.*
phuláṇ dá hár. *m;*
for a bridegroom. phuláṇ dá sehrá. *m;*
GARLIC, *N.*
thom. *f;* lasan. *m;*
GARMENT, *N.*
kapṛá. *m;* bastar. *m;* bhes. *m;* ṭallá. *m;*
GARNISHED, *A.*
sajiá hoyá; jhāṛiá suáriá; wicháyá te saṇwáriá hoyá;
GARRISON, *N.*
qile dí fauj. *f;*
GARRULITY, *N.*
bahu bachan. *m;*
GARRULOUS, *A.*
gappí; batuní. *m;* batuṛá. *m;* bataulá; lutará. *m;* see TALKATIVE.
GASH, *N.*
jakham. *m;* ghá. *m;* ṭakk. *m;* phaṭṭ. *m;*
GASP, *N.*
sáh. *m;* hatkorá. *m;* hauṇkṇí. *f;* sukanná. *m;*
GASP, TO, *V. T.*
hauṇkná; zor nál sáh lainá; dam lainá; sahikná; hatkore lainá; lamme lamme sáh lainá;
GASTRITIS, *N.*
peṭ dí soj. *f;*
GATE, *N.*
pháṭak. *m;*
door for house, &c. darwájjá. *m;*
GATEKEEPER, *N.*
chowkídár. *m;*
GATHER, TO, *V. T.*
kaṭṭhá karná; sámbh lainá; jamá karná; ḍher láuná; joṛná;
GATHERED, TO BE, *V. I.*
jamá honá; sámbhiá jáná; kaṭṭhá honá;
GATHERING, *N.*
kaṭṭh. *m;* jalsá. *m;* maṇḍlí. *f;*

GAUDINESS, *N.*
dikháwá. *m;*
GAUGE, TO, *V. T.*
1. to measure. mápná; minná;
2. to estimate. háṛá lainá; takk láuná; tewá láná;
GAUNT, *A.*
lissá; máṛá;
GAUZE, *N.*
malmal. *f;* bahut mahín kapṛá. *m;*
GAUZY, *A.*
mahín; barík;
GAY, *A.*
ḳhush; rájí; rájí bájí; magan; anaṇd;
GAZE, *N.*
takk. *f;* jhamáká. *m;* jháká. *f;*
GAZE, TO, *V. T.*
takkná; wekhná; takk láuní; jhákná; johná; jhamáká láuná;
GAZELLE, *N.*
hiran. *m;* hirní. *f;*
GEAR, *N.*
samán. *m;* asbáb. *m;* mál. *m;* wast waleveán. *f;* daṇg dawál. *m;*
GELDING, *N.*
ghoṛá. *m;* khassí ghoṛá. *m;*
GEM, *N.*
ratan. *m;*
GENEALOGICAL, *A.*
naslí;
GENEALOGY, *N.*
kursí námá. *m;* kullpattrí. *f;* vansáulí. *f;*
GENERAL, *A.*
mámúlí; ámm;
GENERAL, *N.*
jarnail sáhib. *m;*
GENERALIZE, TO, *V. T.*
matlab kaḍḍhná;
GENERALLY, *Adv.*
askar; bahut karke; bahut wárí;
GENERATE, TO, *V. T.*
1. to create. paidá karná;
2. to give birth to. janná; jamná;
GENERATION, *N.*
piṛhí. *f;*
from generation to generation. piṛhíoṇ piṛhí;
GENERATIVE ORGANS, *N.*
faláṇ thok. *m;*
GENEROSITY, *N.*
parupkár. *m;* síl. *f;* murabbat. *f;*
GENEROUS, *A.*
dilwálá; khush dil denwálá; dátá; sakhí; parupkárí; sílwant;
Proverb. The generous gives, but the steward grieves. dátá de, bhaṇḍárí dá peṭ phaṭe; used of those who become jealous when they see another prospering.
GENEROUSLY, *Adv.*
dil kholke; khullhe dil nál; waḍḍe dil nál; khullhí hatthoṇ;
GENESIS, *N.*
1. origin. jaṛ. *f;* muḍḍh. *m;* shurú. *m;*
2. book. Paidaish dí kitáb. *f;*
GENIAL, *A.*
hass mukhá; milanwálá; milansár;
GENIALITY, *N.*
ḳhushmizájí. *f;*
GENITAL ORGANS.
faláṇ thok. *m;* indrí. *f;*
GENIUS, *N.*
gúṇí. *m;*
GENTEEL, *A.*
sharíf;
GENTILE, *N.*
gair Yahudí. *m;*
GENTILITY, *N.*
bhalmánasí. *f;*
GENTLE, *A.*
1. well born. sharíf; buzúrg;
2. quiet. asíl; garíb; narm; síl sabhaú;
3. kind. bhalamánas; mihrbán; dhímá; hitwálá; kirpál;
GENTLEMAN, *N.*
bhalamánas. *m;* raís. *m;* supattá. *m;*
GENTLENESS, *N.*
narmí. *f;* dhíraj. *f;* komaltáí. *f;* nirmáí. *f;*
GENTLY, *Adv.*
haulí haulí; sáhije sáhije; áste áste; dhíre; malkaṛe malkaṛe;
GENUINE, *A.*
ṭheṭh; áslí; ṭhík; ḳhális; khará; chokkhá; suddh;
GENUINENESS, *N.*
khariáí. *f;*

GIDDINESS, *N.*
chakkar. *m;* bhauṇ. *m;* gherní. *f;* nerní. *f;* gardaní. *f;*
GIDDY, *A.*
sir bhauṇḍá;
GIFT, *N.*
1. present. dhoá. *m;* sugáth. *m;* inám. *m;* inám kinám. *m;* dát. *f;*
2. virtue. gúṇ. *m;* chaṇgíáí. *f;*
3. gift for wedding expenses. neuṇdrá. *m;* neuṇdá. *m;* neotá. *m;*
4. gifts to servants at weddings. lág. *f;* ráṭhá chárí. *f;* lág patar. *m;*
5. dowry to daughter at wedding. dáj. *f;*
GIFTS, *N.*
inám kinám. *m;* dhoe. *m;*
GIFTED, *A.*
gúṇí; gúṇwáṇ; hoshiyár;
GIGANTIC, *A.*
baṛá; bahut waḍḍá; waḍḍá sárá; moṭá tagaṛá; kaddáwar;
GIGGLE, *N.*
ṭhaṭṭhá. *m;* háṇsí. *f;* hássá. *m;*
GIGGLE, TO, *V. T.*
hassná; chohul karná; kih kih karná; daṇd kaḍḍhná;
GILD, TO, *V. T.*
jhál pherná; gilt chaṛháuná; soná chaṛháuná; jhol karná; mulammá karná;
to paint. raṇg karná;
GILDED, *A.*
mulammá;
GILDER, *N.*
mulammásáj. *m;*
GIMLET, *N.*
warmá. *m;*
GIN, *N.*
sharáb. *f;*
GINGER, *N.*
adhrak. *f;* suṇḍh. *f;*
Proverb. To show that a low person cannot appreciate a noble sentiment. What does the monkey know of the taste of ginger? Bándar kí jáne adhrak dá sawád?
GINGHAM, *N.*
garbhí. *f;*

GIRD, TO, *V. T.*
lakk bannhná; kamar kassná;
GENUS, *N.*
parkár. *m;* bháṇt. *m;* jins. *f;*
GEOGRAPHY, *N.*
jugráfiá. *m;*
GERMINATE, TO, *V. I.*
1. to burst out. phuṭṭṇá;
2. to be born. jammná;
GESTATION, *N.*
hamal, *m;* garbh. *m;*
GESTICULATE, TO, *V. T.*
báṇhwáṇ márná;
GESTURE, *N.*
sainat. *f;* ishárá. *m;*
GET, TO, *V. T.*
1. to obtain. labbhná; hatth lagná; laí lainá;
2. to earn. kamáuná; khaṭṭṇá; jamáuná; hásil karná;
3. to get ready. taiyár karná;
4. to get up. uṭṭhná;
5. to get wet. bhijjná;
6. to get out. parháṇ jáná; haṭṭ jáná;
7. to get hurt. choṭ laggní OR kháná;
8. to get an opportunity. dá laggná;
GET, TO, *V. I.*
milná; hatth lagná; ho jáná;
What will you get from him? uh de koloṇ kí faidá honá hai?
GEWGAW, *N.*
1. toy. khiḍáuná. *m;*
2. small things. nikk sukk. *m;* alaṛ palaṛ. *m;*
GHEE, *N.*
gheú. *m;*
GHOST, *N.*
bhút parít. *m;* jinn. *m;* parít. *m;* parítni. *f;*
the Holy Ghost. Pák Rúh. *m;* Pavittar Átmá. *m;*
GIANT, *N.*
dánno. *m;* daṇt. *m;*
a goblin or demon. rákas. *m;*
GIBBET, *N.*
pháhí. *f;* pháṇsí. *f;*
an impaling stake. súlí. *f;*
GIBE, *N.*
táná. *m;* mehná. *m;* ṭhaṭṭhá. *m;* bollí ṭhollí. *f;* ṭhaṭholí. *f;*

GIBE, TO, *V. T.*
táne márná; maḳhaul karná; ṭhaṭṭhe vichch uḍáuná;
GIRDER, *N.*
1. wooden. shatír. *m;* toṛá. *m;*
2. steel. gárḍar. *m;*
3. wooden beam for a well. laṭṭh. *m;* see BEAM.
GIRDLE, *N.*
peṭí. *f;* paṭká. *m;*
GIRL, *N.*
kurí. *f;* kákí. *f;* laṛkí. *f;* kanníáṇ. *f;* játakrí. *f;* bálrí. *f;*
GIRTH, *N.*
farákí. *f;* taṇg. *m;*
GIST, *N.*
asl matlab. *m;* ḳhulásá. *m;* nichoṛ. *m;*
GIVE, TO, *V. T.*
dená; baḳhshná; pún dán karná; dán karná;
1. to give up. chhaḍḍ dená; ján dená; tajná;
2. to give in charge. pharáuná;
3. to cause to be given. duáuná; diwáuná; dawá dená;
4. to give to a beggar. ḳhair páná;
5. don't give up. madán ná chhaḍḍo. lit. don't quit the field of battle.
GIVER, *N.*
dátá. *m;* denwálá. *m;* denhárá. *m;* dání. *m;* daik. *m;* datárí. *m;*
GLAD, *A.*
ḳhush; rájí; anaṇd; magan; parsinn; nihál;
to be glad. phullná; ḳhush honá;
GLADDEN, TO, *V. T.*
rájí karná; ḳhush karná; magan karná; phuláuná;
GLADLY, *Adv.*
ḳhushí nál; ḳhush hoke; jam jam; parsantá nál; chaiṇ chaiṇ;
GLADNESS, *N.*
ḳhushí. *f;* anaṇd. *m;* anandtáí. *f;* shántí *f;* kallíáṇ. *f;* magantáí. *f;*
GLANCE, *N.*
jhák. *f;* jháká. *m;* takk. *m;* jhamáká. *m;*

GLANCE, TO, *V. T.*
takkná; tikk tikkí láuní; jhákná; wekhná; jhamáká láuná;
GLAND, *N.*
gilṭí. *f;*
GLARE, *N.*
1. dazzling light. chamak. *f;* damak. *f;* jagmag. *f;* chamkárá. *m;* chilkárá. *m;*
2. look. ghúrá ghárí. *f;* gurkhí. *f;* ghurákí. *f;*
GLARE, TO, *V. T.*
ghúrákí kaḍḍhná; ghúr dení; ghúrná;
GLASS, *N.*
1. for windows. kachch. *m;*
2. looking glass. shíshá. *m;* darpan. *m;*
3. drinking vessel. gilás. *m;*
4. metal drinking cup. kaṭorá. *m;* kaṭorí. *f;*
GLEAM, *N.*
chamak. *f;* jot. *f;* lishk. *f;* jhalak. *f;* chamkárá. *m;* lishkárá. *m;*
GLEAM, TO, *V. I.*
chamakná; jhalkná; chilakná; lishkná;
GLEAN, TO, *V. T.*
silá chúgná;
GLEE, *N.*
ḳhushí. *f;* anaṇd táí. *f;* shántí. *f;*
GLIB, *A.*
múchattarí;
GLIBNESS, *N.*
múṇh chhattaráí. *f;*
GLIDE, TO, *V. I.*
ghisarná;
GLIMMER, *N.*
jot. *f;* nimmú roshní. *f;*
GLIMPSE, *N.*
jhák. *f;* takk. *f;*
GLISTEN, TO, *V. I.*
chamakná; jhalkná; lishkná;
GLISTERING, *A.*
chamkanwálá;
GLITTER, TO, *V. I.*
chamakná; jhalakná; jhamakná; chilakná; jhilmal jhilmal karná; jagmagáuná;

GLITTER, *N.*
chamak. *f;* jhamak. *f;* chamkárá. *m;* dubhak dubhak. *f;* lát. *f;* bhaṛak. *f;* chilkárá. *m;* chamkáṭ. *f;*

GLITTERING, *A.*
chamakdár; jagmag jagmag; jalmal jalmal;

GLOAT, TO, *V. I.*
akkh laṛáuná; táṛná; takk láuní; akkhiáṇ maṭkáuná;

GLOBE, *N.*
golá. *m;*
of a lamp. háṇḍí. *f;*

GLOBULAR, *A.*
gol mol;

GLOOM, *N.*
1. darkness. dhuṇd. *f;* hanerá. *m;* parchháwán. *m;*
2. grief. rinjí. *f;* gamí. *f;* gam. *m;* santáp. *m;* birláp. *m;* wirláp. *m;*
3. haze. gahir. *f;* jhaṛ. *m;*

GLOOMY, *A.*
1. dim. jhaulá; dhuṇdlá;
2. sad. masosiá hoyá; sogí; sogmáṇ; udás; nimújhán;

GLORIFICATION, *N.*
táríf. *f;* sitáish. *d;* waḍíáí. *f;*

GLORIFY, TO, *V. T.*
waḍíáí karní; táríf karní; sitáish karní; máhimá karná; saláhná; saráuhná;

GLORIOUS, *A.*
shánwálá; jalálí; partápí; tejwáṇ;

GLORY, *N.*
waḍíáí. *f;* jalál. *m;* buzurgí. *f;* izzat. *f;* tej. *m;* ṭhaṭh. *f;* partáp. *m;* sunhapp. *m;* máhimá. *f;* pat. *f;* shán te bhaṛk. *f;* upmán. *m;*

GLORY, TO, *V. T.*
ghamaṇḍ karná;

GLOSSINESS, *N.*
chamak. *f;* bhaṛak. *f;* lishk. *m;*

GLOSSY, *A.*
chamakwálá; bhaṛakwálá; chamakdár; chíkná;
varnished. roganí;

GLOVE, *N.*
dastáná. *m;*

GLOW, *N.*
chilak. *f;*

GLOW, TO, *V. I.*
chamakná; chilakná; lishkaná;

GLOWING, *A.*
1. warm. tattá; garm;
2. shining. chamakdár; bhaṛakwálá; chamkanwálá;
3. ardent. joshwálá; sargarm; shukín; árí;

GLOW WORM, *N.*
ṭiḍáná. *m;* jugnú. *m;*

GLUE, *N.*
suresh. *f;*

GLUE, TO, *V. T.*
suresh nál joṛná; suresh láuná;

GLUM, *A.*
nimújhán; gamgin; udás; masosiá hoyá; sogmáṇ;

GLUT, TO, *V. T.*
láh karná; leṛ márná; bahut kháná; to eat quickly. bhasar bhasar kháná; see GORGE.

GLUTINOUS, *A.*
lesalá;

GLUTTON, *N.*
kháu; *m;* peṭú. *m;* nadídá. *m;* chaṭṭú. *m;*

GLUTTONOUS, *A.*
peṭú; kháu;

GNASH, TO, *V. T.*
daṇd píhná; karaṛ karaṛ karná; kichkicháuná; jhagáuná;

GANSHING OF TEETH. *N.*
kachíchí. *f;*

GNAT, *N.*
machchar. *m;* guttí. *f;*

GNAW, TO, *V. T.*
chabbná;

GO, TO, *V. I.*
jáná; chaliá jáná; ṭurná; chalná;
1. to go in. waṛná;
2. to go out. nikalná;
3. to go back. haṭṭná; agge thoṇ haṭṭná; muṛná;
4. to go about. phirná;
5. to go astray. bhullná; khuṇjhná; ghussná;
6. to go abroad. wáṇḍhe jáná;
7. to go before. agge vadh jáná; agáhán ṭurná; muhre jáná;
8. to go from door to door. dar dar phirná;
9. I cannot go. maithoṇ nahíṇjáídá;

GOAD, *N.*
  parání. *f;*
GOAD, TO, *V. T.*
  hul mární;   hujj mární;
GOAL, *N.*
  1. objective. ṭhikáná. *m;*
  2. goal posts. gol. *m ;* dáí. *f;*
GOAT, *N.*
  bakrá. *m ;* bakrí. *f ;* bakkará. *m ;*
  bakroṭá. *m ;*
  1. young goat. paṭhorá. *m ;*
  bakroṭ. *m ;*
  2. young goat not yet milked.
  paṭṭh. *f;*
  3. goat that has been offered to a
  deity. balbakrá. *m;*
  4. a goat kept for breeding pur-
  poses. bok. *m ;*
GOATHERD, *N.*
  ajaṛí. *m ;* ijaṛí. *m ;* chheṛú. *m ;*
GOBBLE, TO, *V. T.*
  bhasar bhasar kháná ; leṛ márná ;
GOBETWEEN, *N.*
  wicholá. *m ;* dalál. *m ;*
GOBLET, *N.*
  kaṭorá. *m ;* kaṭorí. *f ;* piyálá. *m ;*
  gilás. *m ;*
GOBLIN, *N.*
  bhút. *m ;* jinn. *m ;* bhutná. *m ;*
GOD, *N.*
  1. Muhammadan terms. Khudá. *m;*
  Rabb. *m ;* Alláh. *m ;*
  2. Hindu and Sikh terms. Sarab
  Shaktímán. *m ;* Sarjanhár. *m ;*
  Bhagwán. *m ;* Parmeshur. *m ;*
  Kartár. *m ;* Kartár Purakh. *m ;*
  Ishwar. *m ;* Nirankár. *m ;*
  Parmátmá. *m ;* Wáh Gúrú. *m ;*
GOD, *N.*
  deotá. *m ;* devtá. *m :*
GODDESS, *N.*
  deví. *f ;* mátá. *f ;* dewí rání. *f ;*
GODFATHER, *N.*
  dharm báp. *m ;*
GODLESS, *A.*
  adharmí ; bedín ;
GODLESSNESS, *N.*
  bedíní. *f ;* kufr. *m ;*
GODLINESS, *N.*
  díndárí ; *f ;* nekí. *f ;* rástí. *f ;*
  rástbází. *f ;* dharmtáí. *f ;*

GODLY, *A.*
  díndár ; dharmí ; bhagat ; sant ;
  baṛá nek;
GODMOTHER, *N.*
  dharm máṇ. *f ;*
GODOWN, *N.*
  bhaṇḍár. *m ;* koṭhí. *f ;*
GODSON, *N.*
  dharm puttar. *m ;*
GOING, *N.*
  chál. *f ;* ṭor. *f;*
GOITER, *N.*
  gillaṛ. *m ;*
GOLD, *N.*
  soná. *m ;* kanchan. *m ;*
  1. unalloyed fine gold. kundaṇ. *m ;*
  2. gold thread. tillá. *m ;*
  3. gold lace. goṭá. *m ;*
GOLDEN, *A.*
  sone dá ; sunehrí ;
GOLDSMITH, *N.*
  suniárá. *m ;* suniár. *m ;*
  wife of goldsmith. suníáraṇ. *f ;*
GONE, TO BE, *V. I.*
  chaliá gayá ;
GONG, *N.*
  ghaṛiál. *m ;* ghanṭá. *m ;* ghanṭí. *f ;*
GONORRHAEA, *N.*
  bád. *m ;* bád farang. *m ;* parme. *m ;*
GOOD, *A.*
  1. excellent. baṛá chaṇgá ; baṛá
  achchhá ; uttam ; sohná ; bhalá ;
  khará ; chaṇggerá ; suchcham ;
  2. pious. nek ; bhagat ; chaṇgá ;
  bhalamánas ;
  3. kind. mihrbán; kirpál; dáyáwán;
  4. good things. sawalíáṇ gallán. *f ;*
  5. it is no good to me. ih chíz
  mere kamm dí nahíṇ;
  6. Proverb. If you are good
  yourself, the world is good.
  áp bhalá, jagg bhalá ;
GOOD, *N.*
  fáidá. *m ;* bhadraká. *m ;* bhadkará. *m ;*
  1. what good can be expected
  from him? is te kí bhadraká
  honá hai ;
  2. to do good. bhalá karná ;
GOODBYE, *Interj.*
  salám ;
  1. By Christians and Muhammadans. salám ;

2. By Hindus. bandagí; Rám Rám;
3. By Sikhs. wáh gurú jí ki fateh;

GOOD FORTUNE, *N.*
nekbakhtí. *f;*

GOOD FRIDAY, *N.*
Mubárik Júme dá Din. *m;*

GOODHUMOUREDLY, *Adv.*
khushí nál; khush hoke; jam jam; hass ke;

GOOD LOOKING, *A.*
sohná; sundar; phabiá; darshaní; shakalwálá;

GOOD MAN, *N.*
khará ádmí. *m;*

GOOD NATURED, *A.*
khulkí; hass mukhá; mihrbán;

GOODNESS, *N.*
bhaliáí. *f;* nekí. *f;* bhalá. *m;* mihrbání. *f;* khariáí. *f;* changiáí. *f;* diyálgí. *f;*

GOODS, *N.*
asbáb. *m;* mál. *m;* mál matá. *m;* nikk sukk. *m;* latá patá. *m;* valuable goods. tardá tardá mál. *m;*

GOODS TRAIN, *N.*
mál gaḍḍí. *f;*

GOOD TEMPERED, *A.*
khulkí; hass mukhá;

GOOD WILL, *N.*
kirpá. *f;* dáyá. *f;* khairkháhí. *f;*

GOOSE, *N.*
bataká, *m;* batakh. *f;*
wild goose. maggh. *m;*

GOOSEBERRY, *N.*
ṭipárí. *f;*

GORE, TO, *V. T.*
sir márná; duddh márná; ṭakkar márná;

GORE, *N.*
ratt. *f;* lahú. *m;* khun. *m;*

GORGE, TO, *V. T.*
1. to glut oneself. leṛ márná; dapphná; khá jáná; áppharná;
2. to eat quickly and greedily. bhasar bhasar kháná; gulk gulk kháná;
3. to gorge another. aphráuná; rajjáuná;

GORGEOUS, *A.*
raunaqí; uttam; tejwán;
1. gorgeous apparel. chamak dí poshák. *f;*
2. to live gorgeously. waḍḍí shán vichch rahná;

GORMAND, *N.*
peṭú. *m;* kháú. *m;* nadídá. *m;* chaṭṭú. *m;*

GORMANDIZE, TO, *V. T.*
leṛ márná; dapphná; see GORGE.
Idiom, for one who gormandises. terá bhart nahíṇ bhardá; *i.e.*, your belly does not fill.

GORY, *A.*
ratt o ratt;

GOSPEL, *N.*
Injíl. *f;* Mangal Samáchár. *f;*

GOSSIP, *N.*
1. idle talk. gapp. *f;* gapp shapp. *f;* wádhíáṇ galláṇ. *f;* bak jhak. *f;*
2. tattler. gappí. *m;* bakwásí. *m;* lutrá. *m;* khappí. *m;*
3. Proverb concerning the way women waste their time gossiping at spinning parties. átan dí rann ná kár ná kamm;

GOSSIP, TO, *V. T.*
bakná; ṭarṭar karná; taiṇ ṭaiṇ karná; bataule márná;

GOUGE, *N.*
naháṇ. *m;*

GOURD, *N.*
laukí. *f;*

GOUT, *N.*
gaṇṭhiá. *m;*

GOVERN, TO, *V. T.*
ráj karná; bádshahí karní; hukúmat karní;

GOVERNESS, *N.*
ustádní. *f;*

GOVERNMENT, *N.*
1. administration. sirkár. *f;*
2. state. ráj. *m;*
3. the act. hukúmat. *f;* hákamí. *f;*

GOVERNMENT, *A.*
sirkárí;

GOVERNOR, *N.*
hákim. *m;* málik. *m;* lát sáhib. *m;*

GOWN, *N.*
chogá. *m;*

GRAB, TO, *V. T.*
phaṛná; pakaṛná; jhaṛap márná; napp lainá; jhapat mární; jharát márná; phagaṛná;

GRACE, *N*.
fazl. *m*; fajl. *m*; dáyá. *f*; kirpá. *f*;
GRACE, TO, *V. T*.
1. to favour. kirpá karná; dáyá karná;
2. to adorn. sajáuná; suárná; shaṇgárná;
3. to honour. izzat dení; waḍíáuná; kise dí waḍíái karní;
GRACEFUL *A*.
ḳhubsurat; sohní; sundar; shakalwálí;
GRACELESS, *A*.
máṛá; burá; bhaiṛá;
GRACIOUS, *A*.
dayál; mihrbán; kirpál; dáyáwán; to be gracious. dáyá karná;
GRACIOUSLY, *Adv*.
dáyá nál; kirpá nál; fazl nál;
GRACIOUSNESS, *N*.
mihrbání. *f*; kirpá. *f*; dáyá. *f*;
GRADATION, *N*.
ḍhang. *m*;
GRADE, *N*.
darjá. *m*; uhdá. *m*;
GRADIENT, *N*.
chaṛhái. *f*;
GRADUALLY, *Adv*.
haule haule; dhíre dhíre; áste áste; ṭharáke; huṇḍiáṇ huṇḍiáṇ; sahije sahije; huṇde huṇde;
GRAFT, TO, *V. T*.
peuṇd chaṛháuná OR karná OR láuná;
GRAFT, *N*.
peuṇd. *f*;
GRAIN, *N*.
dáná. *m*; anáj. *m*; dáná duṇká. *m*; ann. *m*; dáná phakká, *m*;
1. grain coarsely ground. dalyá. *m*;
2. parched barley grain. dháhṇ. *m*;
3. grain measure. ṭoppá. *m*;
GRAM, *N*.
chhole. *m*;
GRAMMAR, *N*.
viakaran. *m*; sarfonáv. *m*;
GRANARY, *N*.
koṭhá. *m*; khattá. *m*;
Proverb. In whose granary is grain his fools are also wise. jehdí koṭhí vichch dáne uh de kamle ví siáne;

GRAND, *A*.
uttam; partápí; shándár; shánwálá;
GRANDCHILD, *N*.
1. daughter's son. dohtará. *m*;
2. son's son. pohtará. *m*;
GRANDDAUGHTER, *N*.
1. daughter's daughter. dohtarí. *f*; dohtí. *f*;
2. son's daughter. potrí. *f*;
GRANDEE, *N*.
máldár. *m*; amír. *m*;
GRANDEUR, *N*.
shán. *m*; raunaq. *m*; mahimá. *f*;
GRANDFATHER, *N*.
1 paternal. dáddá. *m*;
2. maternal. nánná. *m*;
3. paternal great grandfather. paṛdádá. *m*;
GRANDMOTHER, *N*.
1. paternal. dáddí. *f*;
2. maternal. nánní. *f*;
3. paternal great grandmother. paṛdáddí. *f*;
GRANDSON, *N*.
1 son's son. potrá. *m*;
2. daughter's son. dohtrá, *m*;
3. great grandson. paṛotá. *m*;
GRANT, *N*.
sirkárí madat. *f*; gránt. *m*; amdád. *f*;
GRANT, TO, *V. T*.
dená; baḳhshná;
GRANULATED, *A*.
dáne dár;
GRAPE, *N*.
dákh. *f*;
Proverbs. 1. Do men gather grapes of thorns? kanḍḍeáṇ thoṇ dákh ikaṭṭheáṇ karde ne?
2. What! can a dry thorn bush bear eggs? sukká ḍhingar ánneṇ lahâwe?
3. The fox and sour grapes. The jackal could not reach the grapes, so said Pooh, they are sour. giddar dákh na appaṛe, thúh, kaurí;
GRAPHIC, *A*.
baṛá sáf;
GRAPPLE, TO, *V. T*.
phagaṛná; phaṛ lainá; japphí paúni; japphí ghaṭṭṇí;

GRASP, TO, *V. T.*
phagaṛná; napp lainá; phaṛi rakkhní; phaṛná; phaṛ lainá; see CATCH.
GRASP, *N.*
pakaṛ. *f*; phaṛáí. *f*;
embrace. japphí. *f*; japphá. *m*; jámbhaṛí. *f*;
GRASPING, *N.*
labbí; lobhí; leṇjh; lálchí;
GRASS, *N.*
gháh. *m*;
GRASS CUTTER, *N.*
ghąhí. *m*;
wife of grass cutter. ghásaṇ. *f*; ghásí. *f*; ghasiáraṇ. *f*;
GRASS HOPPER, *N.*
ṭiḍḍí. *f*; ṭiḍḍá. *m*;
large green vareity. akk ṭiḍḍá. *m*;
GRATE, *N*.
chulhá. *m*; chulh. *m*; aṇggíṭhí. *f*;
GRATE, TO, *V. T.*
ragaṛná;
GRATEFUL, *A.*
shukrguzár;
GRATEFULLY, *Adv.*
shukrguzárí nál;
GRATEFULNESS, *N.*
shukrguzárí. *f*;
GRATER, *N.*
retí. *f*;
GRATIFICATION, *N.*
tasallí. *f*; ḳhushí. *f*; anaṇd. *m*; tipat. *f*; taript. *f*; shántí. *f*;
GRATIFY, TO, *V. T.*
ḳhush karná; nihál karná; rájí karná; phuláuná; rijháuná; taṛáuná;
to be gratified. ḳhush honá; ríjhná;
GRATIS, *A.*
mukht; nirmull; aiweṇ;
GRATITUDE, *N.*
shukrguzárí. *f*; shukr. *m*;
GRATUITOUS, *A.*
mukht;
GRATUITOUSLY, *Adv.*
aiweṇ; eweṇ;
GRATUITY, *N.*
baksís. *f*; baḳhshísh. *f*;
GRAVE, *N.*
1. Muahmmadan. qabr. *f*; also ḳhángáh. *f*; lit. a monastery.
2. Hindu. maṛhí. *f*; samádh. *f*; these are edifices erected on the places where dead bodies have been burned.
GRAVE, *A.*
dhírá; dhírajmán; gaurá;
GRAVEL, *N.*
bájrí. *f*;
made from broken bricks. kankri. *f*;
GRAVITY, *N.*
dhíraj. *f*; sanjídagí. *f*;
GRAVY, *N.*
shorá. *m*; kaṛhí. *f*; grebí, *f*;
GRAZE, TO, *V. T.*
charáuná; chugáuná; chárná;
GRAZE, TO, *V. I.*
1. to feed. charná; chugná;
2. to abrase. ragaṛná; chhillná;
GRAZIER, *N.*
wággí. *m*; pálí. *m*; chheṛú. *m*; ijjaṛí. *m*; ḍáṇggarí. *m*;
GREASE, N.
charbí. *f*;
to grease the wheels of a cart. wáṇggná; báṇggná; choppaṛná;
GREASINESS, *N.*
thiṇdiáí. *f*; chikunáí. *f*;
GREASY, *A.*
thiṇdá; chikná; chikuná;
greased hair. thiṇde wál. *m*;
GREAT, *A.*
1. large. waḍḍá; baṛá; baḍá; waḍḍá sárá;
2. illustrious. waḍḍá námí; manniá danniá; waḍerá; manniá parwanniá;
GREATER, *A.*
waḍerá; waddh; adhak;
GREATEST, *A.*
sáreáṇ de náloṇ waḍḍá; **waḍerá**;
GREATLY, *Adv.*
bahut; att;
GREATNESS, *N.*
buzúrgí. *f*; waḍiáí. *f*; **mahimá**. *f*;
GREECE, *N.*
Yunán dá des. *m*;
GREEDILY, *Adv.*
baṛí cháh nál;
1. to eat greedily. leṛ **marna**; **ghappar ghappar kháná**;
2. to eat quickly. bhasar **bhasar kháná**; harapp garapp **kháná**;

GREEDINESS, *N.*
1. covetousness. lálach. *m*; lobh. *m*; tamá. *m*; hirs. *f*; laulá. *m*;
2. gluttony. nadídpuṇá. *m*;

GREEDY, *A.*
1. covetous. lálachí; lobbí; lenjh; hirsí;
2. gluttonous. peṭú; kháú; baṛá bhukkhá; nadídá; lenjh; ṭheṭhar; ṭarkáú;
3. Proverb—concerning the greedy. He wants two slices, and those buttered. do do, nále chopaṛíáṇ;

GREEK, *A.*
Yunání;

GREEN, *A.*
hará; hariá; haṛiálá; sáwá; hare bhare; hariáulá;
1. green grass. hare hare gháh *m*;
2. green fields. sawe sawe khet. *m*; haríáṇ haríáṇ pailíáṇ. *f*;

GREENNESS, *N.*
hariául. *f*; hariá. *m*; sabjí. *f*; hariáí. *f*;

GREENS, *N.*
ság. *m*; sabjí. *f*; ság patt. *m*;

GREET, TO, *V. T.*
salám karná; bandagí karní; pairíṇ painá; matthá ṭekná;
1. greet him for me and say. uh núṇ mere hatth joṛke parnám karo te ákho;
2. he greeted him and enquiring about his health said. uh ne hatth joṛke parnám kítí, te sukh sáṇd puchch puchch ke ákhiá;

GREETING, *N.*
salámí. *f*;
give my greeting to him. uh núṇ merí bandagí kaheṇ;

GREY, *A.*
kailá;

GREY HAIR, *N.*
dhaulá; *m*;

GREYHOUND, *N.*
shikárí kuttá. *m*;

GRIDDLE, *N.*
tawá. *m*; tawí. *f*;

GRIEF, *N.*
ranj. *m*; afsos. *f*; sog. *m*; gamí. *f*; jhorá. *m*; hamsos. *f*; súl. *m*; udásí. *f*; birláp. *m*; jhurewá. *m*; jhor. *m*; herwá. *m*; santáp. *m*; varm. *m*;
1. intense grief. sall. *m*;
2. there is always grief when friends are separated. wichhoráṇ dá herwá táṇ zarúr hí lagdá hai.

GRIEVANCE, *N.*
1. trouble. taklíf. *f*; khechal. *f*; áukh. *f*; janjál. *m*;
2. complaint. shikayat. *f*; gilá gujárí. *f*; fariád. *f*; duháí. *f*; durohí. *f*;

GRIEVE, TO, *V. I.*
gam karná; udás honá; masosná; karáhná; jhurná; dukhí honá;
1. it grieved me very much. merá andar saṛ gayá OR merá kalejá tap gayá OR mainúṇ waḍḍá sog hoyá;
2. to weep. roná;

GRIEVE, TO, *V. T.*
satáuná; dukháuná; sáṛná;
1. don't grieve me. sáḍá kalejá ná sal;
2. he grieved me very much. uh ne mainúṇ bahut sáṛiá;
3. if I have grieved you please forgive me. je maithoṇ koí tuháḍí ranjídagí dí gal yá ná ṭhík ṭhik satkár hoyá howe, táṇ mainúṇ bakhshná;

GRIEVED, *A.*
udás; dil ḍhaṭṭhá; masosiá hoyá;

GRIEVOUS, *A.*
dukhí; aukhá; taṇg;

GRIEVOUSLY, *Adv.*
baṛí taṇgí nál; aukhá hoke;

GRIEVOUSNESS, *N.*
dukh. *m*; aukh. *m*;

GRIM, *A.*
sakht; ḍaráuná;

GRIMACE, *N.*
bhairá múnh. *m*; ron hákká. *m*;
a grin. guṭak. *f*;

GRIMACE, TO, *V. T.*
múṇh bhaiṛá banáuná;

GRIME, *N.*
mail. *f*; gand. *m*; mal. *f*;

GRIN, *N.*
guṭak. *f*;

GRIN, TO, *V. T.*
daṇd wikháuná; daṇd kaḍḍhná; guṭakná; guṭak painná; khikhiáuná;

GRIND, TO, *V. T.*
chakkí jhoná; chakkí píhná;
1. to grind coarsely. dalná;
2. to grind drugs. kharal karná;
3. to grind the teeth. daṇdir waṭṭní;

GRINDER, *N.*
1. one who grinds. písanwálá. *m*; chakkí píhnwálí. *f*;
2. a molar. dáhṛ. *f*; haṇṇho. *f*;

GRINDING, *N.*
píhái. *f*;
wages for grinding. píhái. *f*; dalái. *f*;

GRINDSTONE, *N.*
parúá. *m*; púṛ. *m*;
for grinding knives, &c. sáṇ. *f*;

GRIPES, *N.*
maroṛá. *m*; maroṛ. *m*;

GRISTLE, *N.*
paṭṭhá. *m*;

GRIT, *N.*
1. dust. ghaṭṭá. *m*; dhuṛ. *f*; gardá. *m*; gard. *f*; miṭṭí. *f*; dhul. *f*; dhuddal. *f*;
2. pluck. dilerí. *f*; himmat. *f*; bahádurí. *f*;

GRITTING THE TEETH, *N.*
kachíchí. *f*;
to grit the teeth. daṇd karíchchná:

GROAN, *N.*
haí. *f*; húṇgá. *m*;

GROAN, TO, *V. T.*
1. from sorrow. ḍháh mární;
2. from pain. húṇgná;
3. to gasp. hauṇkná;
4. to gasp at point of death. hatkore lainá;

GROANING, *N.*
húṇgá. *m*; húṇg. *f*;

GROCER, *N.*
paṇsárí. *m*;

GROG, *N.*
sharáb. *m*;

GROIN, *N.*
chaḍḍhá. *m*;

GROOM, *N.*
sais. *m*; sahís. *m*;

GROOM, TO, *V. T.*
1. to rub. malná; málish karná;
2. to brush. jháṛná;

GROOVE, *N.*
1. a track. lík. *f*; líh. *f*;
2. a furrow. siár. *m*; oṛá. *m*;
3. a channel. nálí. *f*;

GROPE, TO, *V. T.*
tohná;

GROSS, *A.*
moṭṭá; bhárá; ṭhullhá; see FAT;

GROSSNESS, *N.*
moṭái. *f*; muṭápá. *m*;

GROTESQUE, *A.*
ajíb; anokhá; acharaj;

GROUND, *N.*
bhoṇ. *f*; jamín. *f*; dhartí. *f*;
1. on the ground. bhuṇje; bhoṇweṇ; bhoṇ utte; bhuṇe;
2. ground from which the crop has been reaped. vaḍḍh. *m*; vaḍḍhu. *m*;

GROUNDLESS, *A.*
bebunyád; jhuṭhá; khashufá;

GROUND RENT, *N.*
karáyá jamín. *f*;

GROUP, *N.*
1. of people. kaṭṭh. *m*; ḍhání. *f*;
2. of boys. muṇḍeáṇ dí ikk ḍhání. *f*;
3. of trees. jhaṇgí. *f*;

GROUP, TO, *V. T.*
kaṭṭhá karná;

GROUSE, *N.*
bhaṭiṭṭar. *m*;

GROVE, *N.*
1. small. jhaṇgí. *f*;
2. large. jhaṇg. *m*; jhiṛí. *f*;

GROVEL, TO, *V. I.*
apne ápnúṇ ních banáuná;

GROW, TO, *V. I.*
1. to increase in size. waddhná; wadhdá jáná;
2. to take root. uggná;
3. to emerge. nikalná;
4. to spread. phailárná;
5. to grow fat. bhardá jáná;

GROW, TO. *V. T.*
bíjná; boná; lagáuná;

GROWL, *N.*
ghurk. *m*;

GROWL, TO, *V. I.*
ghurná;

GROWTH, *N.*
wadháú. *m*;

GRUB, *N.*
kíṛá. *m;*
GRUDGE, *N.*
khár. *m;* kiṛ. *f;* adávat. *f;* wair. *m;* dushmaní. *f;*
GRUDGE, TO, *V. T.*
hasad karná; khár karná; sáṛná; sáṛá áuná;
GRUDGINGLY, *Adv.*
khár nál; dil nál nahíṇ; tuṭṭe dil nál; aukhá hoke;
GRUEL, *N.*
dalliá. *m;* kaṛhí. *f;*
GRUFF, *A.*
karṛá; rukkhá; kauṛá;
GRUFFLY, TO SPEAK, *V. T.*
baṛhkaná; galá ḳhushk ho jáná;
GRUFFNESS, *N.*
ḳhushkí. *f;*
GRUMBLE, TO, *V. T.*
buṛbuṛáuná; kuṛhná; chíṇ píṇ karná;
GRUMBLE, *N.*
buṛ buṛ. *f;* kuṛ kuṛ. *f;*
GRUNT, *N.*
súr dí awáj. *f;* ghur ghur. *m;*
GUARANTEE, *N.*
1. security. jamánat. *f;*
2. responsibility. zammewárí. *f;* jummewárí. *f;*
3. guarantor. jámin. *m;* jummewár. *m;*
GUARANTEE, TO, *V. T.*
jumme lainá;
I will guarantee. achchhá, eh mere peṭe hai.
GUARANTOR, *N.*
jámin. *m;* jummewár. *m;*
GUARD, *N.*
rakhwálí. *m;* rákkhá. *m;* pahiredár. *m;* chaukidár. *m;* pahrewálá. *m;* a village chaukidár. rabtiá. *m;*
GUARD, TO, *V. T.*
rákkhí karní; pahrá dená; chaukidárí karní; chaukí pahrá dená;
GUARDIAN, *N.*
wálí wáris. *m;* pálanwálá. *m;* jaiz wálí. *m;*
GUARDIANSHIP, *N.*
parwastí. *f;* rákkhí. *f;* rakhwálí. *f;*
GUAVA, *N.*
amrúd. *m;*

GUESS, *N.*
takk. *f;* ṭewá. *m;* háṛá. *m;* andázá. *m;* wichár. *m;* tír tukká. *m;* by guess. takk takk; mere takk vichch;
GUESS, TO, *V. T.*
táṛ lainá; takkná; ṭewá lainá; andázá karná; háṛá lainá; bujhná;
GUEST, *N.*
mamán. *m;* majmán. *m;* paráhuná. *m;* melí. *m;* dáutí. *m;* jiyáfatí. *m;* ágat. *m;*
1. for a wedding. melwálá. *m;*
2. Proverb on the uncertainty of life. Life is but the guest of a moment. koí dam dá paráhuná hai;
GUIDANCE, *N.*
agwáhí. *f;* nasíhat. *f;* hidayat. *f;* matt. *f;*
GUIDE, *N.*
ágú. *m;* ráhbar. *m;* agwán. *m;* agwáhá. *m;* dauṛáhá. *m;* mohrí. *m;*
1. religious guide of Sikhs. gur. *m;* gurú. *m;*
2. religious guide of Muhammadans. pír. *m;* murshid. *m;*
3. the true guide. satgúr. *m;*
GUIDE, TO, *V. T.*
ráh dassná; patá dená; agwáí karní; ráh malláuná; laí jáná;
GUILD, *N.*
1. company. jammát. *f;* jatthá. *m;*
2. brotherhood. bháíbandí. *f;*
GUILE, *N.*
dhokhá. *m;* fareb. *m;* makkár. *m;* see DECEIT.
GUILEFUL, *A.*
ṭhagg; farebí; riyákár;
GUILELESS, *A.*
siddhá sádá; bholá bálá; siddh paddhrá;
GUILT, *N.*
jurm. *m;* qusúr. *m;* gunáh. *m;* páp. *m;*
GUILTLESS, *A.*
begunáh; bequsúr; bedosá; nirparádh; nirparádhí;
GUILTLESSNESS, *N.*
begunáhí. *f;*
GUILTY, *A.*
mujrim. *m;* muljim; jurmí;

GUISE, *N.*
bhes. *m ;*
GUITAR, *N.*
1. with three strings. sitár. *f ;*
2. with one string only. kiṇg. *f ;*
GULF, *N.*
khalíj. *m ;*
GULLET, *N.*
gal dí nálí. *f ;* saṇggh. *m ;* saṇggh dí churí. *f ;* saṇgghá. *m ;*
GULLY, *N.*
nálá. *m ;* nálí. *f ;*
GULP, *N.*
1. of water. ghuṭṭ. *m ;*
2. of food. burkí. *f ;* giráh. *m ;*
GULP, TO, *V. T.*
happú chappú kháná ; haṛapp karná ; gulak gulak karná ;
GUM, *N.*
1. juice. lákh. *f ;* gúnd. *f ;*
2. of the mouth. masúṛhá. *m ;*
3. toothless gums. buṭṭ. *m ;*
GUM, TO, *V. T.*
gúṇd nál joṛná ;
GUN, *N.*
bandúk. *f ;*
GUN CARRIAGE, *N.*
top kháná. *m ;*
GUNPOWDER, *N.*
dárú. *m ;* barúd. *m ;*
GURGLE, *N.*
garálá. *m ;*
GURGLE, TO, *V. T.*
garála karná ;
to rinse the mouth. karulí karní ;
GURGLE, TO, *V. I.*
páṇí gusse nál wagná ; phiṇ-phaṇáuná ;
GUSH OUT, TO, *V. I.*
jor nál waggná ; uchchal nikalná ; uchchal painá ;
to spill out. chhalakná ;
GUSSET, *N.*
bagal. *m ;*
GUST, *N.*
1. a blast. jhoká. *m ;* jhok. *f ;*
2. relish. mazá. *m ;* suwád. *m ;*
GUTS, *N.*
áṇdráṇ. *f ;*
GUTTER, *N.*
morí. *f ;* nálí. *f ;*
a watercourse. khál. *m ;*

GYMNAST, *N.*
bájígar. *m ;*
GYMNASTICS, *N.*
bájígarí. *f ;*
GYPSY, *N.*
pakkhíwás. *m ;* **tapríwás.** *m ;* gaṇdhílá. *m ;*
jugglers who wander about. naṭṭ. *m ;*

H.

HA, *Interj.*
ahá ; áh ;
HABERDASHERY, *N.*
maniárí dá saudá. *m ;*
HABILIMENT, *N.*
kapṛe. *m ;* bastar. *m ;* see CLOTHES.
HABIT, *N.*
ádat. *f ;* kho. *f ;* sabhá. *m ;* chál. *f ;* chálá. *f ;* ṭharak. *m ;* hiltar. *f ;* jhass. *m;* rahit. *f ;* chajj. *m;* gejh. *f;* helat. *f;* ḍhab. *m ;*
1. bad habit. bán. *f;* búrí wáddí. *f;* bhaiṛ. *f ;* wáddaṛí. *f ;* lát. *f ;* illat. *f ;* paikáṛá. *m ;*
2. what a bad habit you have! tainúṇ kí búrí wáddí paí gayi hai.
HABITABLE, *A.*
rahaṇ jogg ;
HABITANT, *N.*
rahanwálá. *m ;* waskín. *m ;* wásí. *m ;*
HABITATION, *N.*
ghar. *m ;* makán. *m ;* tháṇ. *m ;* jagáh. *f ;* ḍerá. *m ;* buṇggá. *m ;* in which many people live ; also the name of the costly buildings erected round the Golden Temple at Amritsar.
HABITUAL, *H.*
rawájí ;
HABITUALLY, *Adv.*
barábar ; har dam ; har vele ; har gharí ; nitt ; sadá ;
HABITUATE, TO, *V. T.*
sádhná ; gijháuná ; haláná ; ádat páuní ;
1. to be habituated, ádát paí jáná ;
2. to become a habit with. gijj jáná ;

HACK, *N.*
ghoṛá. *m* ; ghoṛí. *f* ;
HADES, *N.*
ruháṇ dá jahán. *m* ;
HAFT, *N.*
dastá. *m* ; muṭṭh. *f* ; gúhí. *f* ; see HANDLE.
HAG, *N.*
buḍḍharí. *f* ; buḍḍharí terhí. *f* ; lit. a witch or female goblin. ḍáiṇ. *f* ;
HAGGARD, *A.*
lissá ; máṛá ;
HAGGLE, TO, *V. T.*
mull dí bábat jhagaṛná ;
HAIL, *N.*
1. salutation. salám. *m* ; bandagí. *f* ; rám rám. *m* ;
2. a voice. awáz. *f* ;
HAIL, *N.*
gaṛe. *m* ; chandre bhaiṛe. *m* ;
to hail. gaṛe warhná ;
HAIL, TO, *V. T.*
pukárná ; buláuná ; awáz mární ; hák mární ; kúk márná ;
HAIR, *N.*
bál. *m* ; wál. *m* ;
1. long hair of the Sikhs. kes. *m* ;
2. knot of hair of the Sikhs. júṛá. *m* ;
3. matted hair of faqirs. jaṛáu. *m* ; babríyáṇ. *f* ; jupph. *m* ; babráná. *f* ; jaṭáṇ. *f* ; jaṛáwáṇ. *f* ;
4. greased hair. bhinne wál. *m* ; masse wál. *m* ;
5. long hair of a woman. jháṭṭá. *m* ; chhatte. *m* ;
6. woman's hair plaited and hanging down. gutt. *m* ;
7. hair matted with grease and dirt. laṭṭáṇ. *f* ; plur ;
8. Hindu lock of hair. boddí. *f* ; choṭṭí. *f* ;
9. plaited hair. meḍhí. *f* ; miḍhí. *f* ; menḍhí. *f* ;
10. hair of horse or animal. lúṇ. *f* ; púsh. *m* ;
11. hair on the body. rom. *m* ; lúṇ. *f* ;
12. pudendal hair. jháṇṭ. *f* ; jháṇṭh. *f* ; jhúṇ. *f* ; jhúṇh. *f* ;
13. white hair. dhaule OR chiṭṭe OR bagge wál. *m* ;
14. grey hair. karṛ barṛe wál. *m* ;
15. one whose hair is of medium length. jhanḍúlá. *m* ;
16. a man with curly hair. julfú. *m* ;
17. a curl. boddá. *m* ;
18. beardless. khoddá ;
19. to do the hair. sindhiyá kar lená ; wál suárná ;
20. line of parting the hair. wilí. *f* ;
21. hair of a camel, goat, etc. jatt. *m* ;
22. topknot of hair of old woman. chonḍá. *m* ;
23. topknot of hair of young woman. júṛá. *m* ;
24. circle of hair round the head when crown is shaved. girdá. *m* ;
25. to plait hair. gunḍná ;
26. small knot of hair on head of a child. chunḍí. *f* ;
27. having hair disheveled. jhaṭáṇ khillriáṇ OR khinḍiáṇ hoyiáṇ ;
28. hair about the privities. jháṇṭh. *f* ; pákí de bál. *m* ;
29. entirely shaved. roḍá bhoḍá ;
30. cleaning the hair of vermin. rol dení OR páuní ;
HAIRY, *A.*
jatáulá ; jatailá ;
HALE, *A.*
wall ; rájí bájí ; tagaṛá ;
HALF, *A.*
addhá ; addh ; addho addh ;
1. half and half or approximately. addhá pachaddhá ; addh pachaddh ;
2. Proverb. Half at home is better than the whole elsewhere. ghar dí addhí báhar dí sárí náloṇ changí hai ;
HALF, *N.*
addh. *m* ; addhá. *m* ;
nearly half. addh pachaddhá ;
HALF DEAD, *A.*
addh moyá ;
HALF DONE, *A.*
adhurá ;
HALF HEARTED, *A.*
bújjhe dilwálá ;
HALF READY,
adhurá ;

HALF WAY, *A.*
addhwáṭṭe;
HALL, *N.*
baiṭhak. *f;*
HALLOW, TO, *V. T.*
1. to make holy. pák OR pavittar karná;
2. to consecrate. ghol ghumáuná; makhsus karná;
HALLUCINATION, *N.*
bhulekhá. *m;*
HALO, *N.*
parwár. *m;*
halo round the moon. parwár. *m;* piṛ. *m;*
HALT, *N.*
paṛá. *m;* paṛáo. *m;* makám. *m;*
HALT, TO, *V. I.*
ṭhahrná; uttarná; makám karná;
1. to order a halt. makám bolná;
2. to halt to take breath. sáh lainá;
3. to stand. khalo jáná; khalotá rahná;
HALT, *A.*
langṛá; langá;
HALTER, *N.*
1. for horse. talihárá. *m;*
2. for cattle. gallá khorí. *f;* mohrak. *f;*
3. a bit, also bridle. lagám. *m;*
4. reins. bágḍorí. *f;* bág. *m;*
5. for hanging. pháhí. *f;*
HALVE, TO, *V. T.*
addho addhí karná; addho addh karná;
HAMMER, *N.*
hathoṛá. *m;*
1. small hammer. hathoṛí. *f;*
2. sledge hammer. badán. *m;* wadán. *m;*
3. mason's hammer. tessí. *f;*
4. carpenter's adze used as a hammer. tessá. *m;*
HAMMER, TO, *V. T.*
ṭhokná;
to hammer in poles. gaḍḍná;
HAMPER, *N.*
paṭár. *m;* ṭokrá *m;*
HAMPER, TO, *V. T.*
rokná; ṭhákná; aṭkáuná;
HAND, *N.*
hatth. *m;*
1. palm of the hand. hathelí. *f;* tallí. *f;* hathállí. *f;*
2. hand of watch or clock. suí. *f;*
3. hand's breadth. chappá. *m;*
4. by hand. dastí; hatthíṇ;
HAND, TO, *V. T.*
1. to deliver unto. dená; sauṇpná; hawále karná;
2. to pass. phaṛáná; dená;
HANDCUFFS, *N.*
hatthkaṛíáṇ. *f;*
HANDCUFF, TO, *V. T.*
hatthkaṛíáṇ márníáṇ; sangaláṇ nál bannh lainá;
HANDFUL, *N.*
1. single handful. lapp. *f;* chúlí bhar. *f;*
2. small handful. muṭṭhí *f;* chuṭkí. *f;* muṭṭh. *f;*
3. full handful. rugg. *m;* chuṭká. *m;*
4. double handful. bukk. *m;*
5. handfuls. ruggáṇ de rugg. *m;* bukko bukk;
HANDICRAFT, *N.*
dastkárí. *f;*
HANDIWORK, *N.*
karígarí. *f;* kamm. *m;*
HANDKERCHIEF, *N.*
rumál. *m;*
a small towel for drying, &c. parná. *m;*
HANDLE, *N.*
dastá. *m;* guhí. *f;* muṭṭh. *m;* hatthá. *m;*
1. for a door. kuṇḍá. *m;*
2. knob or button of a lid. láṭú. *m;* ḍúḍḍaṇ. *m;*
3. of a plough. janghí. *f;*
4. of a fan. ḍaṇḍí;
HANDLE, TO, *V. T.*
chhuhná; hatth láuná; tohná;
HANDLESS, *A.*
ṭuṇḍá; luṇjá;
HANDMAID, *N.*
ṭahlaṇ *f;* gollí. *f;* dássí. *f;* lauṇḍí. *f;*
HANDMILL, *N.*
chakkí. *f;*
HANDSAW, *N.*
árí. *f;*
HANDS & FEET, *N.*
hatth pair. *m;*

HANDSOME, *A*.
sundar ; sohná ; raṇgraṇgilá ; soháwará ; shakalwálá ; darshaní ;
very handsome. ḍáḍhá sohná ;
HANDWRITING, *N*.
likháí. *f* ; likhautí. *f* ; likhávat. *f* ;
HANDY, *A*.
1. ready. taiyár ;
2. near. neṛe ; kol ; pás ;
3. skilful. guṇí ; hoshiyár ; chalák ; chust ; siáná ;
HANG, TO, *V. T*.
1. to suspend. ṭaṇggná; ṭaṇg dená ;
lamkáuná ; palmá dená ; laṭkáuná ; palmáuná ;
2. to execute. pháe dená ; pháṇsí
dená ; pháhí dená ; ṭaṇggná ;
3. to hang oneself. áp pháh
lainá ;
4. he hanged himself. uh ápoṇ pháh
laike mar gayá ;
HANG, TO, *V. I*.
laṭakná ; lamakná ; palmaná ;
HANGER ON, *N*.
mukht khor. *m* ; mukht chaṭṭú. *m* ;
nakhaṭṭú. *m* ;
Proverb. Where goes the bridegroom there go the hangers on.
jidhar gayá dulhá udhre lág ar lúg;
HANGING, *N*.
laṭkáú. *m* ;
HANGING, *P. P*.
lamkiá hoyá ;
HANK, *N*.
1. hank of yarn, &c. chhallí. *f* ;
sutt dá gaṭṭh. *m* ;
2. a hank so wound that the
threads cross each other at
each turn. aṭṭí. *f* ;
HANKER, TO, *V. T*.
cháhuná ; cháh karní ; shauq rakkhná ; tarasná ; lochná ; jí karná ;
táṇgh karná ; jhurkná ; dil baṛá
karná ;
HAP, *N*.
sanjog. *m* ; ḍho. *m* ; sabab. *m* ;
fate. qismat. *f* ;
HAPLESS, *A*.
bechárá ; lachár ; bewass ; see
HELPLESS.
HAPLY, *Adv*.
shayad ; achának ; aiweṇ ; eweṇ ;
sabab nál ;
lest haply. khabare ; kite ná ;
HAPPEN, TO, *V. I*.
honá ; bítná ; michná ; bápná ;
báparná ;
1. tell me what happened. bhalá,
tuṇ dass khán, kí gal hoí ?
2. what has happened. ih kí hon
lag piá ?
3. I hope it won't happen so to me.
matáṇ mere nál ví koí eho jehí
gall ná ho jáve ;
HAPPILY, *Adv*.
baṛí khushí nál ; cháh nál ; bhágáṇ
nál ; chaiṇ chaiṇ ; sukh sáṇd nál ;
HAPPINESS, *N*.
khushí. *f* ; mauj. *f* ; anaṇd. *m* ;
sukh. *m* ; anaṇdtái. *f* ; kallíáṇ. *f* ;
HAPPY, *A*.
khush ; rájí ; rájí bájí ; magan ; jam
jam ; parsinn ; sukhí ; anaṇd ;
bág bág ; nihál ; dhann ; mubárik ;
sulakkhná ; sulachchná ;
HARANGUE, TO, *V. T*.
wáz karná ; samjháuná ;
HARANGUE, *N*.
wáz. *m* ; nasíhat. *f* ; wák. *m* ;
HARASS, TO, *V. T*.
chheṛná ; taṇg karná ; dukh dená ;
taklíf dení ; dikk dená ; satáuná ;
hakáuná ; dukháná; aukhíáṇ karní ;
sáṛná ; miṭṭí kharáb karná ; sir
khapáuná ; gal painá ;
HARBOUR, *N*.
1. shelter. sáyá. *m* ; panáh. *f* ;
ṭhikáná. *m* ; saran. *f* ;
2. port. jaházáṇ dá paṛáo. *m* ;
bandargáh. *f* ;
HARBOUR, TO, *V. T*.
panáh dení ; rákhí karní ; bacháuná ; sambhálná ;
HARBOUR, TO, *V. I*.
ṭikná ; rahná ;
HARD, *A*.
1. firm. pakká ; niggar ;
2. difficult. aukhá ; bikhṛá ; sauṛá ;
dubbar ;
3. cruel. karṛá ; sakht ; beráhm ;
hattiárá ; patthar dil ; khuṭaṛ ;
4. resolute. karakht ; karaṛá;

HARDEN, TO, V. T.
sakht karná; pakkí karná;
HARDEN, TO, V. I.
jamm jáná; sakht ho jáná;
to be hardened in heart. man
sunn honá;
HARDHEARTED, A.
karṛá; beráhm; sakht; sakhtdil; betaras; jálim; patthar dil;
haṇsiárá;
HARDIHOOD, N.
1. bravery. dilerí. f; himmat. f;
diláwarí. f; wariámgí. f;
2. audacity. gustákhí. f; magrúrí. f;
beadabí. f; berobí. f;
HARDINESS, N.
dilerí. f; bahádurí. f; himmat. f;
hauṇsilá. m;
HARDLY, Adv.
1. labouriously; masíṇ; masíṇ
masíṇ; aukhá hoke; mushkil nál;
2. harshly. beráhmí nál; sakhtí
nál;
HARDNESS, N.
sakhtí. f; beráhmí. f; karṛáí. f;
kaṭhortá. m;
HARDSHIP, N.
1. trouble. taklif. f; dukh. m;
kashṭ. m; biptá. m; jafar. f;
2. severity. julm. m; sakhtí. f;
jástí. f; see OPPRESSION.
HARDY, A.
diler; takṛá; dilávar; himtál;
himmatí;
HARE, N.
saihá. m; sehá. m; sahiá. m;
HARK, Interj.
sun; suno;
HARLOT, N.
kasbí. f; kaṇjarí. f; jární. f;
bazárí aurat. f; laṭí. f; kaṇchaní. f;
weswá. f; guṇḍí rann. f;
Proverb. A thief and   a pick-
pocket are chaudharis and a harlot
a leader. chor uchakká chaudhari
te guṇḍí rann pardháṇ;
HARLOTRY, N.
zinákárí. f; yárí. f; badkárí. f;
kaṇjráú. m;
HARM, N.
nuqsán. m; harj. m; kasar. m;

HARM, TO, V. T.
nuqsán karná; harjá páuná; bigáṛná; kharáb kar dená;
HARMFUL, A.
nuqsání; nuqsánkarnwálá;
HARMFULNESS, N.
nuqsán. m; harj. m;
HARMLESS, A.
bechárá; bholá bhálá; sádá;
siddh paddhará; asíl; siddhá;
baṛá gao; garíb;
HARMLESSNESS, N.
sádápaṇ. m; asílí. f;
HARMONIOUSLY, Adv.
sur miláké; thík sur nál;
HARMONIZE, TO, V. T.
1. to make tuneful. sur karná; sur
miláuná;
2. to reconcile. miláuná; raláuná;
suláh karáuná;
HARMONIZE, TO, V. I.
milná; ralná; ikk mikk honá;
HARMONY, N.
1. concord. mel. m; mel jol. m;
mel miláp. f; ekká. m;   ikkdilí. f; millat. f; bháí bandhí. f;
2. musical. sur. m; rág. m;
3. in harmony. thík sur nál;   sur
raláke;
HARNESS, N.
sáj. m; sáz. m;
HARNESS, TO, V. T.
jo dená; sáj páuná; joná;
HARNESSED, TO BE, V. I.
juttná;
HARROW, N.
suhágá. m; really a heavy beam
of wood for breaking clods and
levelling fields.
a wooden rake. daṇdálí. f;
HARROW, TO, V. T.
1. to draw a harrow. suhágá pherná
OR márná;
2. to harass. satáuná; chheṛná;
taklíf dení; aukhíáṇ karná;
HARRY, TO, V. T.
ujáṛná; lúṭṭná; see HARASS.
HARSH, A.
kauṛá; sakht; karṛá; rukkhá;
kharhwá; beráhm; haiṇsiáṛá;
hattiárá; patthar dil;

HARSHNESS, *N*.
sakhtí. *f*; beráhmí. *f*; jástí. *f*; jorávarí. *f*; loṛhá. *m*; hattiá. *m*; ghát. *f*;

HART, *N*.
haran. *m*; chankárá. *m*;

HARVEST, *N*.
1. crop. fasl. *m*; khetí. *f*;
2. cutting of crops. váḍhí. *f*;

HARVEST, TO, *V. T*.
vaḍḍhná; váḍhí karní; váḍhíáṇ karní;

HARVESTER, *N*.
váḍhá. *m*; waḍhává. *m*;

HARVESTING, *N*.
vaḍhái. *f*; váḍhí. *f*;

HASH, *N*.
astiú. *m*;

HASP, *N*.
kuṇḍá. *m*;

HASSOCK, *N*.
múṛhá. *m*;

HASTE, *N*.
shatábí. *f*; chhetí. *f*; káhlí. *f*; utaulí. *f*; chaṭpaṭí. *f*; káhl. *f*;
1. in haste. phurtí nál;
2. Proverb. More haste less speed. aggá rauṛ, pichchhá chauṛ;

HASTEN, TO, *V. T*.
jaldí karní; shatábí karní; hílá karná; dhauná; káhlá ṭurná; hatth pair paí jáná; harfalí painá; to cause to go quickly. dauṛáná; chhetí ṭuráuná;

HASTILY, *Adv*.
1. quickly. jhapájhap; jaldí; chhetí nál; shatábí; jhaṭṭ paṭṭ; káhlí nál; utaulá; jhaṭá jhaṭ;
2. without thinking. biná soche samjhe; bin soche;

HASTINESS, *N*.
josh. *m*; jaldbází. *f*;

HASTY, *A*.
káhlá; utaulá; jaldbáz; joshwálá; Proverb re hasty friendships. That man becomes ghí and khichchrí in a moment. Uh ádmí pal vichch gheu khichchrí ho jándá hai;

HAT, *N*.
ṭopí. *f*;

HATCH, TO, *V. T*.
1. to concoct. ḍhaṇg sochná; saláh pakáuní; upáo karná OR labbhná; goreáṇ guṇḍná; ḍoríáṇ guṇḍná; see PLOT.
2. to produce young. bachche kaḍḍhná; páṛe bahiná; seuná;

HATCHET, *N*.
kuhárá. *m*; kuhárí. *f*;
1. small hatchet for cutting twigs for tooth brushes. ṭakúá. *m*;
2. chopper for cutting up fodder. gaṇḍásá. *m*;

HATE, *N*.
ḍáh. *m*; dushmaní. *f*; dusmaní. *f*; wair. *m*; adávat. *f*; kauṛ. *m*; dushmanái. *f*; khár. *f*; kiṛ. *f*; bakháṇḍh. *f*;
dislike. nafrat. *f*; ghiṇ. *f*;

HATE, TO, *V. T*.
adávat karní OR rakkhní; wair rakkhná; karáhat karní; ghiṇáuná; nafrat auní; khár kární; kiṛ rakkhní;

HATEFUL, *A*.
ghiṇáuná; bahut búrá; bhaiṛá; máṛá;

HATRED, *N*.
adávat. *f*; khár. *f*; see HATE.

HAUGHTILY, *Adv*.
ákaṛ nál; haṇkár nál; majáj nál; magrúrí nál;

HAUGHTINESS, *N*.
haṇkár. *m*; damák. *m*; ákkaṛ. *f*; abhimán. *m*; gamrúrí. *f*; heṇh. *f*; ghamaṇd. *m*; magrúrí. *f*; mazáj. *f*;

HAUGHTY, *A*.
magrúr; haṇgkárí; haṇkárá; gamrúr; majájí; ḍhíṭh; nárá; ḍhíṭhá; ghamaṇḍí; gusták; phiṭṭiá hoyá; akaṛbáj; nak chaṛhiá; magrá; hekaṛí;

HAUL, *N*.
khichch. *m*; khichch ghasíṭ. *f*;

HAUL, TO, *V. T*.
khichchná; dhuhná; dhirná; ghasíṭná; dharuhná; ghasírná;

HAUNCH, *N*.
chúlá. *m*; chungná. *m*;

HAUNT, TO, *V. I*.
ghaṛí ghaṛí áyá jáyá karná; muṛ muṛ áuná; ghaṛí muṛí áuná; to stick to one. chambaṛná; chammaṛná;

HAUTEUR, *N.*
ákkaṛ. *f ;*
HAVE, TO, *V. I.*
de kol honá ;
1. to have in common. sabh kujh sánjhe rakkhná ;
2. I have no fear. mainúṇ koí ḍar nahíṇ ;
3. I have two sons. mere do putt han ;
HAVEN, *N.*
1. shelter. sáyá. *m ;* panáh. *f ;* ṭhikáná. *m ;* saran. *f ;*
2. port. bandargáh. *f ;*
HAVERSACK, *N.*
jholá. *m ;* jholí. *f ;*
HAVILDAR, *N.*
havaldár. *m ;*
HAVOCK, *N.*
chauṛ. *m ;* sokká. *m ;* barbádí. *f ;* tabáhí. *f ;* nuqsán. *m ;* satía nás. *m ;* nisṭ. *f ;* saṇgghár. *m ;*
HAWK, *N.*
báj. *m ;* turmatí. *f ;* illar. *m ;* dámí. *f ;* lagaṛ. *m ;*
HAWK, TO, FOR SALE, *V. T.*
chhábṛí dhoní OR wahuní ;
HAWKER, *N.*
chhábṛíwálá. *m ;*
HAWKING, *N.*
bájdárí. *f ;*
HAWSER, *N.*
rassá. *m ;* lajj. *f ;* see ROPE.
HAY, *N.*
sukká ghá. *m ;*
HAZARD, *N.*
1. chance. ḍho. *m ;* dá. *f ;*
2. danger. ḳhatrá. *m ;* ján jokhoṇ. *f ;*
HAZARDOUS, *A.*
ḳhatrewálá ; ḍaráuná ;
HAZE, *N.*
1. from heat. gahir. *f ;*
2. mist. dhuṇḍ. *f ;* dhuṇḍúkár. *m ;*
HAZY, *A.*
1. misty. jhaulá ; dhuṇḍlá ;
2. dusty. gahirá ;
3. not clear. sáf nahíṇ ;
HE, *Pro.*
eh ; uh ;
HEAD, *N.*
sir. *m ;*
1. of inanimate things. sirá. *m ;*
2. of a bed. sarhándí. *f ;* serú. *m ;*
3. of a canal, múṇdh. *m ;*
4. Proverb. A poor man at the head of a canal is as good as a rich man at the tail. múṇdh dá faqír te páṇdh dá amír ;
HEAD, TO, *V. T.*
1. to lead. laí jáná ; mohre chalná ; agge chalná ;
2. to stop. rokná ; ḍakkná ; aṭkáuná ; khaliárná ;
3. to turn anyone or thing. moṛná ;
HEADACHE, *N.*
sir píṛ. *f ;* sir dard. *m ;* ull. *f ;* sir ulṭiá. *m ;* seláṇ. *f ;*
HEADING, *N.*
surḳhí. *f ;*
HEADLAND, *N.*
zamín dí nukkar. *f ;*
HEADLONG, *Adv.*
1. quickly. káhile nál ; chhetí ; hillke ; jhapájhap ;
2. falling headlong. múṇh paṛne ḍiggke.
HEADMAN, *N.*
lambardár. *m ;* chaudharí. *m ;*
HEADQUARTERS, *N.*
hedkuátar. *m ;* sadr maqám. *m ;*
HEADSHIP, *N.*
1. authority. iḳhtiyár. *m ;* sardárí. *f.* hukúmat. *f ;* pardhántái. *f ;*
2. office of lambardár or headman of village. lambardárí. *f ;*
HEADSTONE, *N.*
nukkar dá sirá. *m ;* khúnje dá sirá. *m ;*
HEADSTRONG, *A.*
aṛyal ; jiddí ; kabbá ; ḍhíṭh ; haṭhá ; avaiṛá ; jiddal ; aṛbangá ;
HEADWAY, *N.*
1. success. kámyábí. *f ;*
2. progress. taraqqí. *f ;* wáddhá. *f ;*
HEAL, TO, *V. T.*
changá OR wall karná ; naroíáṇ karná ; changíáṇ karná ; achchhá karná ; arog karná ;
HEAL, TO, *V. I.*
rájí OR changá OR wall honá ;
HEALING, *N.*
iláj. *m ;* láj. *m ;* duá dáru. *m ;*
HEALTH, *N.*
arogtá. *f ;*

HEALTHY, *A.*
wall; naroá; changá; tagaṛá; achchhá; changá bhallá; naweáṇ naroiáṇ, nirog; nirogí;

HEAP, *N.*
ḍher. *m*; ḍherí. *f*; daṇḍá. *m*; kunnú. *m*; kusak. *m*; thok. *m*;
1. very large heap. ganj. *m*;
2. heap of sugar cane. &c., plastered over. dhar. *f*;
3. heap of straw. palarí. *f*;
4. heap of wheat. dáníáṇ dá bohal. *m*; khalwár. *m*;
5. small heap of grain. bohlí. *f*; bohulí. *f*;
6. heap of cowdung cakes for fuel. gohárá. *m*; gahúrá. *m*; gírá. *m*;
7. heap of sand. tibbá. *m*;
8. Proverb. The hungry ass has charge of the heap of corn. bhukkhá gaddon bohal dá rakkhwálá;

HEAP, TO, *V. T.*
ḍherí láuní; kunnu láuná; kusak láuná; ḍher láuná;

HEAR, TO, *V. T.*
sunná; kann láuná; dhíán karná;
1. to be heard. awáz áuní;
2. to be hard of hearing. uchchá sunná;
3. I am hard of hearing. maiṇ uchchá sundá háṇ;
4. at the time of hearing. sunde sár;

HEARER, *N.*
sunnanwálá. *m*;

HEALING, *N.*
sunáí. *f*;
1. of a lawsuit. peshí. *f*;
2. in the hearing of the people. sáre lokáṇ de sundíáṇ;
3. I am hard of hearing. maiṇ uchchá sundá háṇ;

HEARSAY, *N.*
suní sunáí gal. *f*; suníáṇ galláṇ. *f*; awáí. *f*;

HEART, *N.*
dil. *m*; man. *m*; chitt. *m*; hirdá. *m*; ridá. *m*;
1. after my heart. apne man bháundá;
2. I know this by heart. ih mere kaṇth hai; ih mainúṇ kaṇth ho gayá;

HEART BROKEN, *A.*
udás; dil ḍhaṭṭhá; masosiá hoyá; to be cut to the heart. dil vichch saṛ jáná;

HEARTBURN, *N.*
kalíje di saṛan. *f*; jí kachchá honá. *m*;

HEARTBURNING, *N.*
khár. *f*; sáṛá. *m*; jalan. *f*;

HEARTEN, TO, *V. T.*
dilásá dená; dilerí dení; see ENCOURAGE.

HEARTH, *N.*
chullá. *m*;

HEARTILY, *Adv.*
dil nál; manoṇ; man nál; dil lagáke; josh nál; jí ján nál; shauq nál; diloṇ wajhoṇ hoke; dil kholke; manoṇ tanoṇ hoke; chitt nál;

HEARTINESS, *N.*
shauq. *m*; cháh. *f*; jatan. *m*; uddam. *m*; sargarmí. *f*; ríjh. *m*;

HEARTLESS, *A.*
beráhm; sakht; karṛá; betaras; bedard; patthardil;

HEARTLESSLY, *Adv.*
beráhmí nál; sakhtí nál;

HEATLESSNESS, *N.*
sakhtí. *f*; beráhmí. *f*;

HEART RENDING, *A.*
dukhí; dil chiranwálí;

HEARTSICK, *A.*
udás; sogmán; dil ḍhaṭṭhá; masosiá hoyá;

HEARTY, *A.*
dilí; joshwálá; sargarm; jataní; himmatí;

HEAT, *N.*
1. warmth. waṭṭ. *m*; garmí. *f*; tá. *m*; garmáí. *f*; tapís. *f*;
2. rage. gussá. *m*; waṭṭ. *m*; karodh. *m*; roh. *m*; rossá. *m*;
3. ardour. josh. *m*; shauq. *m*; sargarmí. *f*; jatan. *m*; ríjh. *m*;
4. scorching heat. tapish. *f*;
5. heat of spices. jhál. *f*;
6. heat in the body. pittu. *f*;

HEAT, TO, *V. T.*
tattá karná; garm karná; táná; tapáuná;
to warm oneself. sekná;
HEATED, TO BE, *V. I.*
garm honá; tapná; tattá honá;
HEATH, *N.*
maidán. *m;*
HEATHEN, *N.*
butparast lok. *m;* muratí pujak. *m;* miṭṭí pujak. *m;*
HEATHENISM, *N.*
butparastí. *f;*
HEAVE, TO, *V. T.*
suṭṭná; vagháuná;
HEAVEN, *N.*
1. sky. asmán. *m;* akás. *m;*
2. Paradise. bihist. *m* M; surag. *m*, H; swarag. *m*, H; biakunṭh.
HEAVENLY, *A.*
asmáni; suragí; surgwásí; surgí; swargí;
HEAVILY, *Adv.*
udás hoke; gam nál;
raining heavily. dham dham; jhamájham; sham sham;
HEAVINESS, *N.*
1. weight. bhár. *m;* bojh. *m;*
2. dejection. gam. *m;* rinjí. *f;* udásí. *f;* jhurevá. *m;* birláp. *m;* gamráí. *f;*
HEAVY, *A.*
bhárí; bhárá; ḍhaṭṭá; bojhal; niggar;
rather heavy. bharerá;
HEAVY HEARTED, *A.*
udás; nimújhán; masosiá hoyá; dil ḍhaṭṭá; sasdil;
HEBREW, *N.*
Yahudí. *m;* Ibrání. *m;*
HECKLE, TO, *V. T.*
1. to annoy. chheṛná; kharáb karná; aukhíáṇ karná;
2. to question. sawál karná;
HECTOR, TO, *V. T.*
dhamkáuná; dabkáuná; dhamkí dená; ghurakná;
HEDGE, *N.*
wár. *m;* jháṛíáṇ. *f;* chháppá. *m;*
1. of cut branches. khittí. *f;*
2. hedge, fence or wall enclosing ground. walgan. *f;*
HEDGE, TO, *V. T.*
wár dená; khittí de dená; chháppá dená;
HEDGEHOG, *N.*
jháh chuhá. *m;* jháṛ chuhá. *m;* kanḍailá. *m;*
HEED, *N*
dhíán. *m;* surt. *f;* gaur. *m;* gauh. *m;* birtí. *f;* khabardárí. *f;*
HEED, TO, *V. T.*
1. to attend to. gaur karná; dhíán karná; sochná; man láuná; chaukasí karní; táṛ rakkhná; gauh karná; hosh karná;
2. to obey. manná; ákkhe laggná; sir matthe dharná; sir púr dharná;
HEEDFULLY, *Adv.*
dhíán nál; soch wichárke; gauh nál; soch samajh ke;
HEEDFULNESS, *N.*
dhíán. *m;* chettá. *m;* chittá. *m;* birtí. *f;* chaukasí. *f;*
HEEDLESS, *A.*
gáfal; ḍhillá maṭṭhá; ghaulí; beparwáh; sullhá; surliá hoyá;
HEEDLESSLY, *Adv.*
biná soche samjhe; ghaul nál; gáfalí nál;
HEEDLESSNESS, *N.*
gáfalí. *f;* ḍhill. *f;* ghaul. *f;* beparwáhí. *f;*
HEEL, *N.*
aḍḍí. *f;* eḍ. *f;* pásṇá. *m;*
HEIFER, *N.*
wahṛ. *f;* wachchhí. *f;*
HEIGHT, *N.*
1. of a person. qadd. *m;* lamáí. *f;* uchchíáí. *f;* qaddshán. *m;*
2. of a place. uchchíáí. *f;*
3. a high place. uchcháṇ. *m;*
HEIGHTEN, TO, *V. T.*
uchchá karná;
HEINOUS, *A.*
máṛá; bhaiṛá; ghiṇáuná;
HEINOUSNESS, *N.*
buríáí. *f;* chanḍálpúṇá. *m;* ních kamm. *m;* kharábí. *f;*
HEIR, *N.*
wáris. *m;* váras. *m;* málik ban gayá; adhkárí. *m;*

HEIRESS, *N.*
wárisní. *f*; wárisá. *f*; haqqwálí. *f*;
HEIRSHIP, *N.*
hissá. *m*; waṇḍ. *m*; haqq. *m*;
HELL, *N.*
dozakh. *m*, M; jahanam. *m*, M; nark. *m*, H; narag. *m*, H;
HELLISH, *A.*
dozakhí; narakí;
devilish. shaitání;
HELMET, *N.*
ṭopí. *f*;
HELP, *N.*
madad. *f*; madat. *f*; sahárá. *m*; sahaitá. *f*; sahái. *f*; chárá. *m*;
1. help in a lawsuit, &c. riá. *m*; jháll. *m*;
2. he was calling out for help. uh te hál hál piá pándá si;
HELP, TO, *V. T.*
madat dení; madat karní; sahaitá karná; sahárá dená; jháll lainá; báhuṛná; jhállú banná; uprálá karná; pakkhurná;
HELPER, *N.*
belí. *m*; madatgár. *m*; himaití. *m*; saháik. *m*; sámbhú. *m*;
partner. sharík. *m*; sáṇjhí. *m*; sáthí. *m*; wáhrú. *m*; panjhál. *m*; bhiál. *m*; hissedár. *m*;
HELPFUL, *A.*
kamm dá; faidedár; upkárí;
HELPLESS, *A.*
bechárá; wachárá; ájaz; bewas; anáth; abass; lachár; bepar; máṛá; adhíṇ; besahárá;
I am helpless. maiṇ thuṛiá hoyá háṇ;
HELPLESSLY, *Adv.*
lachár hoke;
HELPMATE, *N.*
sáṇjhí. *m*; sahaití. *m*; see HELPER and PARTNER.
HELPLESSNESS, *N.*
lachárí. *f*; natákatí. *f*; bewasí. *f*;
HEM, *N.*
kinárá. *m*; kanní. *f*;
HEM, TO, *V. T.*
1. to hem on another piece of cloth. kanní lagáuní; magzí láuní; saṇjáf láuní.
2. to hem the same piece of cloth, alerná;
3. to hem on embroidery. goṭṭá láuná;
HEMORRHAGE, *N.*
lahú wag turná. *m*;
HEMORRHOIDS, *N.*
khuní bawásír. *f*;
HEMP, *N.*
saṇ. *f*; saṇu. *f*; saṇkukṛá. *m*;
intoxicating hemp. bhaṇg. *f*; charas. *f*;
HEN, *N.*
kukkaṛí. *f*;
HENCE, *Adv.*
1. from this place. itthoṇ;
2. for this reason. is káran; is sababoṇ;
HENCEFORTH, *Adv.*
huṇ thoṇ; aidoṇ agge; agge núṇ;
HENNA, *N.*
menḍhí. *f*;
HER, *Pro.*
uh;
HERALD, *N.*
elchí. *m*;
HERALD, TO, *V. T.*
khabar dení; ḍhaṇḍorá dená; hoká dená; ḍauṇḍí piṭṭṇá OR pherní;
HERBS, *N.*
1. medicinal. buṭí. *f*;
2. culinary. tarkárí. *f*; ság. *m* sabzí. *f*; ság patt. *m*;
3. herbage. hariaul. *f*;
HERBAGE, *N.*
ság pattá. *m*;
HERD, *N.*
1. of cattle. heṛh. *f*; wagg. *m*; chauṇá. *m*;
The herd has gone to graze. chauṇá chhiṛ gayá hai;
2. of buffaloes. khaṇḍhá. *m*;
3. of elephants. jhuṇḍ. *m*;
4. of sheep or goats. iyyaṛ. *m*; gallá. *m*;
HERDSMAN, *N.*
pálí. *m*; ḍáṇggarí. *m*; gujjar. *m*; chhaunewálá. *m*; wággí. *m*; chheṛú. *m*; ijjaṛí. *m*;
of buffaloes. máhí. *m*; májjhí. *m*;
HERE, *Adv.*
itthe; ure; iddhar; ettal;

HEREABOUT, *Adv.*
kite kite; kitale kitale; kidhare kidhare;
HEREAFTER, *Adv.*
huṇ thoṇ; ih de pichchoṇ; ih de magaroṇ;
HEREBY, *Adv.*
is thoṇ; is káran;
HEREDITARY, *A.*
jaddí; naslí; maurúsí;
HEREIN, *Adv.*
ih de vichch;
HERESY, *N.*
bidat. *f*; jhuṭhí tálím. *f*; kufr. *m*;
HERETIC, *N.*
bidatí. *m*; káfir. *m*; kufrí. *m*;
HERETICAL, *A.*
bidatí;
HERETOFORE, *Adv.*
is thoṇ pahle;
HEREWITH, *Adv.*
ih de nál;
HERITABLE, *A.*
wirse jogg;
HERITAGE, *N.*
wirsá. *m*; milkíat. *f*; málakí. *f*;
HERMIT, *N.*
tiágí. *m*; baṇwási. *m*;
1. to become a hermit. tap karná; lit. to do penance.
2. one who practises tap, devotions connected with austerities and penances. tapí. *m*; tapiá. *m*;
3. wandering Hindu devotees. faqír. *m*; wairágí. *m*;
HERMITAGE, *N.*
ásram. *m*;
HERO, *N.*
surá. *m*; súrmá. *m*; bahádur. *m*;
HEROIC, *A.*
súrmáṇ; dilaur; diláwar; diler; bahádur;
HEROICALLY, *Adv.*
baṛí dilerí nál; sher hoke; be-dhaṛak; naḍar hoke;
HEROISM, *N.*
súrbírtá. *m*; bahádurí. *f*; súr-mápuṇá. *m*; baṛí dilerí. *f*; variámgí. *f*; súrtai, *f*; mardáu. *m*;
HERON, *N.*
dhíṇg. *m*;
1. white heron. baglá. *m*;
2. grey heron. waḍḍá baglá. *m*; narí. *f*;
HESITANCY, *N.*
1. doubt. bharm. *m*; shakk. *m*; saṇdeh. *m*; wiswás. *m*; saiṇsá. *m*; dhuṛakná. *m*; durpá. *m*;
2. vacillation. kachch pak. *m*; jakko takk. *f*;
HESITATE, TO, *V. T.*
jakko takk karná; hichkaná; jakná; jhijhakná; jhakkná; dhaṛakná; ṭhahr jáná; aṭkanná; shakk vichch rahná; rukkná; in speech. malkaláuná;
HESITATINGLY, *Adv.*
shakk nál; dubdhe nál;
HESITATION, *N.*
dubdhá. *m*; saṇdeh. *m*; bharm. *m*; dhuṛakná. *m*; wiswás. *m*; see HESITANCY:
HEW, TO, *V. T.*
ṭoṭe karná; chírná;
HEWER, *N.*
lakkaṛ chíranwálá. *m*; lakkaṛ páṛ. *m*;
HIBERNAL, *A.*
siál dá;
HICCUP, *N.*
hirkí. *f*; hichkí. *f*; hiḍkí. *f*;
HICCUP, TO, *V. T.*
hichkí áuní; hichkí láiní; hiḍkí áuní OR lagní;
HIDDEN, *A.*
gupt; gujjhí; uhle vichch; gaib; paṛde vichch;
hidden sin. gujjhe gunàh. *m*;
HIDE, TO, *V. T.*
lukáuná; chhipáuná; ḍhappná; ohle karná; luká lainá;
1. to hide a thing. luká rakkhná;
2. to be hidden. lukkná; gaib honá;
3. to cover. ḍhakkná; kajjná;
HIDE, *N.*
chamm. *m*; dhauṛí. *f*; khall. *f*; chamṛá. *m*; khallaṛí. *f*;
a dry hide. khallaṛ. *m*; khallaṛí. *f*;
HIDE & SEEK, *N.*
lukan michái. *f*; lukmíchí. *f*;
HIDEOUS, *A.*
1. horrible. ḍaráuná; ḍaráú; bhayának;

2. detestable. ghiṇáuná; bahut búrá;
3. ugly. baḍaul; kojhá; badshakal; kurúp; kushakal;

HIDEOUSNESS, *N.*
1. ugliness. badsuratí. *f*; baḍaulí. *f*; beḍhangí. *f*;
2. detestation. karáhat. *f*; nafrat. *f*; ghin. *f*;

HIDING, *N.*
chhipáú. *m*;

HIDING PLACE, *N.*
kuṇj gosá. *m*; kuchchh. *f*; chhahí. *f*; kuṇj. *m*;

HIGH, *A.*
uchchá;
rather high. uchcherá;

HIGHBORN, *A.*
uchchí zát dá; uchchí zátwálá; baṛe lok;

HIGHEST, *A.*
upparle uppar;

HIGH-HANDED, *A.*
jabardast; sakht; jálim; khuṭar;

HIGHLAND, *N.*
paháṛí mulk. *m*;

HIGHMETTLED, *A.*
diler; bahádur; himmatí; himtál;

HIGHMINDED, *A.*
phiṭṭiá hoyá; magrúr; gamrúr; see PROUD.

HIGHNESS, *N.*
uchchiái. *f*;

HIGHPRICED, *A.*
waḍḍe mull dá; máhngá; piyárá;

HIGHROAD, *N.*
pakkí saṛak. *f*;

HIGHSPIRITED, *A.*
joshwálá; jushíla; diler; himmatí;

HIGHWAY, *N.*
waḍḍí saṛak. *f*; pakkí saṛak. *f*;

HILARIOUS. *A.*
magan; ḳhush; anaṇd; ranggí;

HILARITY, *N.*
chohul. *m*; ḳhushí. *f*; hássí. *f*; hulás. *f*; chohul mohul. *m*;

HILL, *N.*
parbat. *m*; ṭibbá. *m*;
ant hill. warmí. *f*;

HILLOCK, *N.*
ṭibbá. *m*; ṭillá. *m*;
a mound. the remains of an old village. theh. *m*;

HILLTOP, *N.*
choṭṭá. *m*; choṭṭí. *f*; sirá. *m*; ṭísí. *f*;

HILLY, *A.*
paháṛí;

HILT, *N.*
dastá. *m*; guhí. *f*; muṭṭh. *f*; hatthá. *m*;

HIM, *Pro.*
uh núṇ;

HIMSELF, *Pro.*
áp;

HIND, *N.*
hirní. *f*;

HINDER, TO, *V. T.*
rokná; ḍakkná; ṭhákná; ḍáṭná; ṭokná; warajná; aṭkáuná; thammhná; haṭakná ḍakká dená;

HINDERANCE, *N.*
rok ṭok. *f*; ṭok ṭák. *f*; ṭok. *f*; rok *f*; bándhá. *m*; aṭká. *m*; aṭak. *f*; rukáu. *m*; ḍakk. *m*; ḍakká. *m*;

HINDERED, TO BE, *V. I.*
rukiá rahná; ḍakkiá rahná;

HINDERER, *N.*
rokanwálá. *m*; ḍakhanwálá; ḍakáu. *m*;

HINDMOST, *A.*
sáreaṇ náloṇ pichche;

HINDRANCE, *N.*
rukhávat. *f*; rok. *f*; see HINDERANCE.

HINDU, *N.*
hindú. *m*; hindwání. *f*;

HINDUISM, *N.*
hindú dharm. *m*;

HINGE, *N.*
qabjá. *m*; qabzá. *m*;

HINT, *N.*
1. sign. sainat. *f*; ramaj. *f*;
Proverb. a hint is enough to an aráki horse, but a stick for a donkey. aráki núṇ sainat, gaddhe núṇ soṭṭá;
2. information. patá. *m*; ḳhabar. *f*. súh. *f*; uggh suggh. *f*;

HINT, TO, *V. T.*
patá dená; sainat mární;
HIP, *N.*
kúllá. *m*; chuklá. *m*; chukṇá. *m*; chúlá. *m*; chungná. *m*; ḍhák. *f*;
HIRE, *N.*
1. rent. karáyá. *m*; bháṛá. *m*; ṭheká. *m*;
2. wages. talab. *f*; kamáí. *f*; mazdurí. *f*;
3. on hire. bháṛe utte; karáye utte;
4. to take on hire. karáye te lená; muhárí lení;
HIRELING, *N.*
majúr. *m*; mazdúr. *m*; kąmáṇ. *m*;
HIS, *Pro.*
uh dá;
HISS, *N.*
phúk. *f*;
of a snake. sapp dí phúk. *f*; phuṇkárá. *m*; phuṇkár. *m*;
HISS, TO, *V. T.*
phuṇkárná; shúkaná; shukarná; as a snake. súṇ súṇ karní;
HISTORIAN, *N.*
tawaríkh likhanwálá. *m*;
HISTORICAL, *A.*
tawaríkhí;
HISTORY, *N.*
tawaríkh. *f*; vikhiá. *m*; bartant. *m*; story. kahání. *f*; bát. *f*;
HIT, *N.*
már. *f*; choṭ. *f*; hujj. *f*; saṭṭ. *f*; see BLOW.
HIT, TO, *V. T.*
márná; dhraul mární; duhatthaṛ márná; chapeṛe márná;
HIT, TO BE, *V. I.*
lagná;
HITCH, *N.*
rukáu. *m*; aṭkáu. *m*; aṭak. *f*; see HINDERANCE.
HITCH, TO, *V. T.*
1. to fasten. lagáuná; juṛná; bannhṇá;
2. to háng. ṭaṇggná; lamkáuná; laṭkáuná;
HITCH, TO, *V. I.*
phas jáná; aṛak janá; aṛ jáná;
HITHER, *Adv.*
ure; itthe; uráṇ; urháṇ;
HITHERTO, *Adv.*
ajje; huṇ tík; ajj tík; ajj tíkar;
HIVE, *N.*
makkhíáṇ dà chhajjá OR khaggá. *m*;
swarm of bees. makkhíáṇ dá chhattá. *m*;
HOARD, *N.*
khajáná. *m*; máyá. *f*; rás. *f*;
HOARD, TO, *V. T.*
mál kaṭṭhá karná; máyá sameṭná; máyá kaṭṭhí karní; máyá jamá karná;
HOARFROST, *N.*
kakkar. *m*; korá. *m*;
HOARINESS, *N.*
chiṭṭé wál. *m*; dhaule wál. *m* bagge wál. *m*;
HOARSE, *A.*
ghaggá; bhárí awáz;
1. to be hoarse. awáz bhárí honá; galá OR wáz OR saṇgh baihná; awáj baiṭhná;
2. I have become hoarse. merá saṇgh baih gayá hai;
HOARY, *A.*
chiṭṭá; dhaulá;
HOAX, *N.*
dhokhá. *m*; chhal. *m*; see TRICK.
HOAX. TO, *V. T.*
buttá márná; ṭhagná; dhokhá dená; see DECEIVE.
HOBBLE, TO, *V. T.*
1. to walk lamely. laṇgṛáuná; laṇgná;
2. to tie horse's feet. ḍhaṇgná; dáuná;
HOBGOBLIN, *N.*
bhaú. *m*; bhút. *m*; bhutná. *m*;
HOCKEY, *N.*
khunḍí. *f*; hákí. *f*;
HOCUS POCUS, *N.*
ṭuná ṭání. *f*;
HOE, *N.*
1. native spade. kahí. *f*;
2. native trowel. rambá. *m*;
HOE, TO, *V. T.*
goḍḍí karní; goḍná;
to cause to be hoed. guḍáuná;
HOEING, *N.*
goḍḍí. *f*;

HOG. *N.*
sur. *m;* badd. *m;*
HOIST, TO, *V. T.*
cháṛhná; chukkná; uṭháuná; chaṛháuná;
HOLD, *N.*
qábu. *m;* phaṛái. *f;* pakaṛ. *f;*
HOLD, TO, *V. T.*
ghuṭṭ lená; ghuṭṭke phaṛná; phaṛí rakkhná; tagṛeāṇ karke phaṛná; phagaṛná;
1. to hold up. thammhná; khaliárná;
2. to hold out. tagná;
3. to keep. rakkhná; sámbná; sámbh lainá;
4. to think. ḳhayál karná; sochná; soch wichárná;
HOLE, *N.*
chhek. *m;* morí. *f;*
1. hole in roof. mogh. *m;* maggh. *m;*
2. hole in wall made by thief. san. *f;* sannh. *f;*
3. hole of snake. khuḍḍ. *f;*
4. hole of mouse. ruḍḍ. *f;* ḍuḍḍ. *f;* morí. *f;*
5. hole of an animal. ghurná. *m;*
6. hole in wall made by rain. gharl. *m;* gharálá. *m;*
7. hole in bank made by water. taroṭá. *m;* rauṇd. *m;* ghukká. *m;*
HOLIDAY, *N.*
1. festival. din. *m.* M; íd. *f, M;* tihár. *m, H;*
2. leave. chhuṭṭí. *f;*
HOLINESS, *N.*
pákízagí. *f;* suddhtái. *f;* rástí. *f;* nekí. *f;*
HOLLOW, *A.*
khokhlá; khulkhulá; kholá; khokhrá;
HOLLOW, *N.*
1. a pit. ṭoá. *m;* bhorhá. *m;* see PIT.
2. very deep pit, as an old well. khaḍ. *f;* khuḍḍal. *f;*
3. hollow where there is much grass. jhal. *f;*
4. hollow of one hand. lapp. *f;*
5. hollow of two hands. bukk. *m;*
HOLLOWNESS, *N.*
pol. *m;* khol. *m;*
HOLY, *A.*
pák; pavittar; nek; másúm; suddh; sanṭ;
1. very holy. att pavittar;
2. a holy man. sain. *m, M;* faqír. *m, M;* sádhú. *m, H;* gusain. *m, H;* joggí. *m, H;*
HOLY DAY, *N.*
din. *m, M;* íd. *f, M;* tihár. *m, H;*
HOLY GHOST, *N.*
Pák Rúh. *m;* Pavittar Átmá. *m;* Ruhul Quds. *m;*
HOLY SCRIPTURE. *N.*
Kalám Ulláh. *m;* Pak Kalám. *m;* Injíl. *f;* Baibal Sharíf. *m;* Ḳhudá dá Kalám. *m;*
HOMAGE, *N.*
1. worship. bandagí. *f;* ibádat. *f;* ustút. *f;* see WORSHIP.
2. reverence. adab. *f;* máṇ. *m;* ádar. *m;* bháú bhagat. *f;*
3. to pay homage to. pairíṇ painá;
HOME, *N.*
ghar. *m;* makán. *m;* jagáh. *f;*
1. at home. ghare;
2. how are things at home? tere ghar bhár dá kí hál hai;
HOMELESS, *A.*
nathávan; beghar; awárá;
HOMEMADE, *A.*
ghar dá; nijj dá; gharoká; gharokí;
HOME RULE, *N.*
swaráj. *m;*
HOME SICKNESS, *N*
udrewáṇ. *m;*
HOMICIDE, *N.*
ḳhun. *m;*
HOMILY, *N.*
wáz. *m;* nasíhat. *f;* tálím. *f,* updesh. *m;*
HONEST, *A.*
hatth dá suchchá; ímánwálá; ímándár; sachchá; khará; bhalamánas;
HONESTLY, *Adv.*
dharm nál; ímán nál; rástí nál;
HONESTY, *N.*
ímándárí. *f;* sachchiái. *f;* rástí. *f;*

HONEY, *N*.
shahd. *m*; makhír. *m*; mákhí. *f*; mákho. *m*; shahit. *m*;

HONEYCOMB, *N*.
chhallí. *f*;
the droppings of the honeycomb. chhallí de butke. *m*; makhír díáṇ ṭapkíáṇ. *f*;

HONORARIUM, *N*.
inám. *m*;

HONORARY, *A*.
beṭankháh; khushí nál mukht kam kardá;

HONOUR, *N*.
izzat. *f*; ijjat. *f*; ádar. *m*; lajj. *m*; lajjiá. *m*; láj. *m*; patt. *f*; abrú. *f*; mán. *m*;

HONOUR, TO, *V. T.*
izzat dení OR karní; ádar karní; adab karní; múṇh láuná; pairíṇ painá;

HONOURABLE, *A*.
izzatwálá; manniá danniá; manniá parwanniá; dáná pardháná; su-pattá abrudár; paṭwaṇt; surkhrú;

HOOD, *N*.
of a cobra. phaṇ. *f*; phaṇú;

HOODWINK, TO, *V. T*.
ṭhagná; dhokhá dená; see DECEIVE.

HOOF, *N*.
1. uncloven. summ. *m*; somb. *m*; pauṛ. *m*;
2. cloven, large. khur. *m*;
3. cloven, small. khurí. *f*;

HOOF MARK, *N*.
khurá. *m*; khoj. *m*;

HOOK, *N*.
1. for clothes, &c. kuṇḍá. *m*;
2. fish hook. kuṇḍí. *f*;

HOOKAH, *N*.
huqqá. *m*;

HOOP, *N*.
reṛhá. *m*; chakkar. *m*;

HOOPING COUGH, *N*.
kutte khaṇg. *m*;

HOOPOE, *N*.
chakkí ráhá. *m*; ṭokká. *m*;

HOOT, *N*.
táná. *m*; makhaul. *m*;

HOOT, TO, *V. T*.
táná dená OR márná; oe oe karná;

HOP, *N*.
ṭapái *f*; ṭaposí. *f*;

HOP, TO, *V. T*.
ṭapná; ṭaposíáṇ márniáṇ; burakná; ṭapesná;

HOPE, *N*.
ás. *f*; ásá. *f*; dharwás. *m*; ummed. *f*,

HOPE, TO, *V. T*.
ás rakkhní; ummed rakkhní; ásrá bharosá rakkhná;

HOPEFUL, *A*.
áswaṇd; ummedwár;

HOPEFULNESS, *N*.
ummed. *f*; ás. *f*;

HOPELESS, *A*.
náummed nirásá; bedil; lachár; niásrá;
1. I am hopeless. merá jí ḍhaindá hai;
2. I became hopeless. merá maṇ phal gayá; maiṇ bedil ho gayá;

HOPELESSNESS, *N*.
bedilí. *f*; náummedí. *f*; nirás. *f*;

HOPPLE, *N*.
paukhuṛ. *m*; paiṇkaṛ. *m*;

HORDE, *N*.
ṭollá. *m*; ṭollí. *f*; mahain. *m*; dal. *m*; sainá. *f*; bhíṛ. *f*; jatthá. *m*; ghaṛmass. *f*; ḍháṇí. *f*;

HORIZON, *N*.
uh tháṇ jitthe asmán te zamín mile hoe dissde han;

HORN, *N*.
siṇgg. *m*;

HORNED, *A*.
siṇgganwálá;

HORNET, *N*.
ḍehmú. *f*;

HOROSCOPE, *N*.
janampattrí, *f*; kuṇḍálí. *f*;

HORRIBLE, *A*.
ḍaráuná; see HIDEOUS.

HORRIBLY, *Adv*.
bahut burí taráh nál;

HORRID, *A*.
ḍaráuná; bhayának;

HORRIDLY, *Adv*.
bahut burí taráh nál;

HORRIFY, TO, *V. T*.
ghabrá dená; ḍaráuná; ḍar páuṇá;

HORROR, *N.*
haul. *m*; ḍar. *m*; ḳhauf. *m*; harbarí. *f*; dhaṛak. *m*;
HORSE, *N.*
ghoṛá. *m*;
HORSE ARTILLERY, *N.*
top ḳháná. *m*;
HORSEBACK, *A.*
ghoṛe te sawár;
HORSEBREAKER, *N.*
chábuksawár. *m*;
HORSECLOTH, *N.*
bhúrá. *m*; jhull. *m*;
HORSEDEALER, *N.*
ghoṛeáṇ dá baṇárí. *m*;
HORSEDOCTOR, *N*;
salotrí. *m*;
HORSEDUNG, *N.*
lidd. *f*;
HORSEFAIR, *N.*
ghoṛeáṇ dí mandí. *f*;
HORSEFLY, *N.*
makkh. *f*;
HORSEHAIR, *N.*
lúṇ. *f*;
HORSEMAN, *N.*
sawár. *m*;
HORSEMANSHIP, *N.*
ghoṛe dí sawárí. *f*;
HORSE RACE. *N.*
háṭh. *f*; ghoṛ dauṛ. *f*;
a pony worth a damrí and he runs races! damṛí dá ṭaṭṭú, te háṭháṇ bhane;
HORSE SHOE, *N.*
khurí. *f*; nál. *f*;
HORSE SOLDIER, *N*.
rasálá. *m*; sawár. *m*;
HORSE WHIP, *N*,
1. English whip. chábuk. *m*;
2. native, with leather thong only. chháṇṭá. *m*; chábuk. *m*;
3. used by Jats for bullocks, puráni. *f*;
HORTICULTURE, *N.*
bágbání. *f*;
HORTICULTURIST. *N.*
málí. *m*;
HOSE, *N.*
1. stockings. moje. *m*; jurábáṇ. *f*; massíáṇ. *f*; messíáṇ. *f*;
2. a pipe.. chamṛe dí nálí. *f*;

HOSPITABLE, *A.*
ḳhátir karnwálá; musáfiráṇ dá ṭahl karnwálá; ṭahl tawájjiá karnwálá;
HOSPITABLY, *Adv.*
ḳhátirdárí nál; ṭahl sewa nál;
HOSPITAL, *N.*
haspattál. *m*; dák ḳháná. *m*;
HOSPITALITY, *N.*
mamání. *f*; ṭahl tawájjiá. *m*; ádar pá. *m*; ḳhátirdárí. *f*; ḳhátir tawájjiá. *m*; sewá. *m*; paráhuṇchárí. *f*;
Proverb, used concerning niggardly hospitality. I ate and drank of my own, he gave me a mere "Good morning." kháná píná ápná, nirí salám álek;
HOST, *N.*
1. army. phauj. *f*; sainá. *f*;
2. crowd. dal. *m*; mahain. *m*; jatthá. *m*; ṭollí. *f*;
3. one who entertains. ḳhátir tawájjiá karnwálá. *m*;
HOSTEL, *N.*
bording. *m*;
HOSTILE, *A.*
virodhí; ḳhiláf;
they were hostile to him. uh uh de saḳht wairí sáṇ;
HOSTILITY, *N.*
vair. *m*; dushmaní. *f*; adávat. *f*; kíná. *m*; jidd. *f*; virodh. *m*; kauṛ. *f*;
HOT, *A.*
tattá; garm;
1. hot tempered. bhuhe; jhalla;
2. to be hot. tap jáná; tattá ho jáná;
3. I was very hot. maiṇnúṇ baṛá waṭṭ lagá hoiá; maiṇnúṇ baṛá waṭṭ chaṛhiá hai;
HOTBLOODED, *A.*
tez; joshwálá; jhallá;
HOTEL, *N.*
hoṭal. *m*;
HOTHEADED, *A.*
tez; gusse vichch; joshwálá; bhuhe; jhallá;
HOTLY, *Adv.*
1. violently. badobadí; zor nál; taṇo taṇí; dhakko dhakkí; malomalí;

2. ardently. baṛe josh nál; ríjh nál;

HOTNESS, *N.*
tá. *m;* waṭṭ. *m;* garmái. *f;* garmí. *f;*

HOT TEMPERED, *A.*
tez; tattá; jhallá;

HOUND, *N.*
kuttá. *m;*

HOUR, *N.*
ghaṛí. *f;* ghaṇṭá. *m;*

HOURI, *N.*
parí. *f;* húr. *f;*

HOURLY, *A.*
ghaṛi ghaṛí;

HOUSE, *N.*
1. residence. ghar. *m;* koṭhí. *f;* koṭhṛí. *f;* makán. *f;* koṭhá. *m;* outside the house. gharoṇ banne;
2. household. gharáná. *m;* gharbár. *m;* ṭabbar. *m;* khándán. *m;* qabílá. *m;* kormá. *m;*
3. descendants. ṭabbar. *m;* aulád. *f;* bál bachche. *m;*
4. dilapidated house. kholá. *m;*
5. house of ill fame, brothel. chaklá. *m;*

HOUSEHOLDER, *N.*
gharwála. *m;* ghar dá málik. *m;* ṭabbardár. *m;* málik makán. *m;*

HOUSEKEEPING, *N.*
ghar dá kamm. *m;*

HOUSEMAID, *N.*
ṭahlan. *f;* launḍí. *f;*

HOUSESTEWARD. *N.*
mukhtiár. *m;* gumástá. *m;*

HOUSEWIFE. *N.*
gharwálí. *f;* ṭabbarwálí. *f;* bál bachchewálí. *f;* wahutí. *f;* tímí. *f;* janání. *f;* patní. *f;* ṭabbar. *f;*

HOVEL, *N.*
kholá. *m;* kullí. *f;* jhuggí. *f;* see HUT.

HOVER, TO, *V. I.*
uḍḍí phirná; bhaunḍé phirná;

HOW, *Adv.*
1. of manner. kahnúṇ; kis taráh; kíkar; kíkkúṇ;
2. of porportion. kinná;
3. how big? ke ḍá ku?
4. how big is your son? tuháḍá puttar keḍá kú hai?
4. how far? kinní dur?
5. how often? kinní wári?
6. how much more? kinná wadhík?
7. how long? kad táiṇ? kad tíkar?
8. how are you? kí ḍaul hai? kí hál hai.
9. how are you all at home? apne gharbár dí koí gal sunáo?

HOWBEIT, *Adv.*
tad ví;

HOWDAH, *N.*
haudá. *m;*

HOWEVER, *Adv.*
khair; lekin; par; tad ví; parantu;

HOWL, *N.*
chíkh. *f;* wáwelá. *m;* kuk. *f;* hek. *f;*

HOWL, TO, *V. T.*
1. to cry or weep. roná; kurlauná; chík chiháṛá páuná;
2. to bark. bhauṇkná;
3. jackals barking or howling. hawáṇkná; hawáṇgná;

HOWSOEVER, *Adv.*
tad ví;

HUB, *N.*
pahiye dí nábh. *f;* puṭṭhí. *f;*

HUBBLE BUBBLE, *N.*
guṛguṛ. *f;*

HUBBUB, *N.*
halchal. *f;* hullar. *m;* khalhbalí. *f* raulá. *m;* gaugá. *m;* khap. *m;*

HUDDLE, TO, *V.* I.
1. to crowd together. bhíṛ bháṛ honá;
2. to sit huddled up. guchchhá honá;

HUE, *N.*
rang. *m;*

HUFF, *N.*
waṭṭ. *m;* hirkh. *m* kauṛ. *m;* roh. *m;*

HUFFY, *A.*
naráz; gusse; russià hoyá; witariá hoyá; bhuhe;

HUG, *N.*
japphá. *m;* japphí. *f;* galaphṛí. *f;*

HUG, TO, *V. T.*
japphá márná OR páuná; galle láuná; híkk nál láná;

HUGE, *A.*
bahut waḍḍá; baṛá bhárá; moṭá tagaṛá; waḍḍá sárá; kaddáwar;
HUM, *N.*
bhiṇ bhiṇ. *f*;
HUM, TO, *V. T.*
bhiṇ bhiṇ karná; makkhiáṇ bhiṇakná;
HUMAN, *A.*
insání;
HUMANE, *Adj.*
rahmdil; narmdil; dáyáwán; dáyáwant;
HUMANITY, *N.*
insáníyat. *f*; insángatí. *f*; insángat. *f*;
kindness. sil. *f*; mihrbání; *f*; murabbat. *f*;
HUMBLE, *A.*
ájiz; garíb; halím; maskín; ájaj; adhiṇ;
HUMBLE, TO, *V. T.*
níwíáṇ karná; ních banáuná; beqadr karná; ḍigáuná; dháhuná; níwáṇ karná; heṭháṇ karná; see HUMILIATE.
to humble oneself. neuná;
HUMBLENESS, *N.*
ájijí. *f*; halímí. *f*; garíbí. *f*; maskíní. *f*;
HUMBLY, *Adv.*
ájijí nál; garíbí nál; minnat nál;
HUMBUG, *N.*
1. hoax. dhokhá. *m*; fareb. *m*; chhal. *m*;
2. a cheat. ṭhagg. *m*; chhaliá. *m*; makkár. *m*;
HUMBUG, TO, *V. T.*
dhokhá dená; chhal karná; see DECEIVE.
HUMDRUM, *A.*
aiweṇ; eweṇ;
HUMID, *A.*
sillhá; gillá; tar;
HUMIDITY, *N.*
wattar. *m*; gill. *f*; tarí. *f*; sill. *f*; gilaulá. *m*; galerá. *m*;
HUMILIATE, TO, *V. T.*
pat láhuná; laj láhuná; múṇh kálá karná; ijjat láhuní; sharmindiá karná; see HUMBLE,

HUMILIATION, *N.*
beijjatí. *f*; bijjtí. *f*; bepatí. *f*; namoshí. *f*;
to feel humiliated. namoshí áuná; see DISGRACE.
HUMILITY, *N.*
ajizí. *f*; maskíní. *f*; halímí. *f*;
HUMOUROUS, *A.*
hassanwálá; hass mukhá; makhauliá; maskará; khill diwání;
HUMOUROUSLY, *Adv.*
hásse nál; hasske;
HUMOUROUSNESS, *N.*
hássá. *m*; hássí. *f*; chohul. *m*; chohul mohul. *m*;
HUMP, *N.*
1. a hunch back. kubbá. *m*; kubṛá. *m*;
3. hump of a camel. bann. *m*;
2. hump of a bullock. bann. *m*;
HUMPBACKED, *A.*
kubbá; kubṛá;
HUNDRED, *A.*
saikṛá; sau;
hundreds. saikṛe;
HUNDREDFOLD, *A.*
sau guná;
HUNDREDTH, *A.*
sauwáṇ;
HUNG, TO BE, *V. I.*
palmaná;
HUNGER, *N.*
bhukkh. *f*;
Pro verb. He who holds the spoon dies of hunger. jeh de hatth ḍoí bukkh mare soí;
HUNGER, TO, *V. I.*
bhukkh laggní; hábaṛ jáná;
HUNGRY, *A.*
bhukkhá; hábaṛiá hoyá; bhukháulá;
Proverb. The neighbour of a river is never hungry or thirsty. daryá dá hamsáyá ná bhukkhá ná tarháyá;
HUNT, TO, *V. T.*
shikár kheḍná;
HUNT, *N.*
1. hunting. shikár. *m*;
2. search. bhál. *f*; ḍhúnḍ. *f*; ṭol bhál. *m*;
3. search by police. taláshí. *f*;

HUNTER, *N.*
shikárí. *m ;*
HUNTING, *N.*
shikár. *m ;*
HURDLE, *N.*
wár. *f ;*
HURL, TO, *V. T.*
suṭṭná ; wagá ke márná ; ghattná ; vagháuná ;
HURRAH, *Interj.*
jaí jaí ; wáh wáh; shábásh ;
HURRICANE, *N.*
kálí bolí hanerí. *f ;* annhí bolí hanerí. *f ;*
HURRIEDLY, *Adv.*
shapá shap ; jaldí ; chhetí ; shatábí ;
HURRY, *N.*
shatábí. *f ;* chhetí. *f ;* shap. *m ;* káhlí. *f ;* utáulí. *f ;* chohulí. *f ;* to be in a hurry. sauṛá painá ; káhl painí ;
HURRY, TO, *V. T.*
hílá karná ; káhlá OR chhetí turná ; jaldí OR shatábí karní ;
1. to cause one to run. dauṛáuná ;
2. why does he not hurry ? hallke kyuṇ nahíṇ chaldá ?

HURRYINGLY, *Adv.*
hallke ; hillke ; jhapájhap ; shapá shap ;
HURT, *N.*
1. wound. ghá. *m ;* jaḳhm. *m ;*
2. bruise. saṭṭ. *f ;* choṭ. *f ;*
3. loss. nuqsán. *m ;* harj. *m ;* gháṭṭá. *m;* kasar *m ;* bhánggá. *m ;*
4. a hurt to the eye. chobh. *m ;*

HURT, TO, *V. T.*
bigáṛná. ḳharáb kar dená ; dukh dená ; chheṛná ; taklíf dení ; to hurt one's fellings. dil dukháuná;
HURTFUL, *A.*
nuqsání ; nuqsán karnwálá;
HUSBAND, *N.*
ádmí. *m;* ḳháwind. *m;* khasam. *m ;* kauṇt. *m ;* patí. *m ;* málik. *m ;* gabhrotá. *m ;* gabhrú. *m ;* bhartá. *m ;* suámí. *m ;*
1. husband and wife. miáṇ bibí. *m ;*
2. husband's younger brother, deor. *m ;*
3. husband's elder brother. jeṭh. *m;*
4. husband's sister. nanan. *f ;*

HUSBANDLESS, *A.*
raṇḍí ; bekauṇt ; bekauṇtí ;
HUSBANDMAN, *N.*
jaṭṭ. *m ;* jamíndár. *m ;* zamíndár. *m ;* khetíwálá. *m ;* legal term. káshtkár. *m ;*
HUSBANDRY, *N.*
wáhí. *f ;* khetí bárí. *f ;* káshtkárí. *f ;* wáhí jottí. *f ;*
Proverbs connected with husbandry and farming.

1. Plough hard and eat your full. Dabb ke wáh, rajj ke khá.
2. Farming is an empire, but if there are no crops it is a halter to be hung with. Wáhí bádsháhí, ná thíwe te gal vichch pháhí.
3. Worthless bullock with a bad driver, the one goads the other kicks. Lindá bald kabindá hálí, weh dendá chuṇgá. wuh dendá chhálíṇ.
4. If the landlord be friends his tenants then the latter will cultivate well. Málik je kare riáyat páhí, táṇ uh kardá chaṇgí wáhí.
5. Sow big wheat and give manure, and you will go home rejoicing. Ḍagan gad, te mallar pá, aishán kardá ghar núṇ já.
6. When he puts the reaper to the harvest the farmer claims to be a king. Pakkí khetí láe láwe, jaṭṭ kare bádsháhí de dáwe.
7. He who has a milk giving animal in his house is best of all. Jis de ghar lawerá, uh sabh thoṇ chaṇgerá.
8. Land ploughed by old cattle grows only spear grass and reeds; buḍḍhíáṇ ḍhaggíáṇ dí wáhí, ugge dabbh te káhí.
9. The weak ox is liable to all kinds of diseases. Máṛá ḍhaggá sabbhe rog.
10. The manure is to the field what the army is to the raja Dalíṇ rájá, malíṇ khetí.
11. Plough the land and (you will be able to afford to) eat sugar, rice and milk. Jamín nún wáh, te khaṇḍ khír khá.

12. Plough the land after manuring it, and if God pleases the profit will be double. Páh ghatt de pichchoṇ wáh sáin chahe te dohrá láh.
13. When drought comes the crops are destroyed. Laggí auṛ, te khetí chauṛ.
14. He who has manure has (firm) foundations. Jed dí rúṛí us dí múṛí.

HUSH, TO, *V. T.*
chupp karáuná;
to quiet a child. lorí dení;

HUSH, TO, *V. I.*
chupp ráhná;

HUSK, *N.*
chhill. *f;* chhilká; *m;* chhillaṛ. *m;*
of rice or barley. toh. *m;* tuh. *m;* bhoh. *m;*

HUSKINESS, *N.*
ḳhushkí. *f;* ḳhushk gallá. *m;*

HUSKY, *A.*
ghaggá; bhárí awáz;

HUSTLE, TO, *V. T.*
dhakelná; dhakká dená; ṭakkar láuní;

HUT, *N.*
kúṭiá. *f;*
1. faqir's hut. jhuggá. *m;* jhuggí. *f;* gufá. *m;*
2. thatched hut. chhapprí. *f;* chhappar. *m;* ḍhárá. *m;*
3. a hut of grass or reeds. kakkháṇ dí jhuggí. *f;* kullí *f;*

HYDROPHOBIA, *N.*
halak. *m;* halkái. *f;*

HYAENA, *N.*
bijjú. *m;* bhadáwá. *m;*

HYMN, N.
bhajan. *m;* gít. *m;* gauṇ. *f;*

HYPOCRISY, *N.*
makkár. *m;* pakhanḍ. *m;* fareb. *m;* dhokhá. *m;* makar. *m;* makárí. *f;* chalá. *m;* kapaṭ. *m;*

HYPOCRITE, *N.*
pakhanḍí. *m;* nakhrebáj. *m;* makkár. *m;* farebí. *m;* kapṭí. *m;* baglá bhagat. *m;*
Proverbs concerning hypocrites.
1. His beard is that of a priest's, but his acts are those of the devil. Dáṛhí sheḳháṇ dí, te kamm Shaitán de;
2. He appears a believer, but is a heretic at heart. Shakal mominán dí, te andar káfaráṇ dá;
3. A scavenger's house and he calls it a temple. Ghar chuhṛáṇ dá, nám dharmsálá;
4. A paddy bird in appearance, but really a guzzler of fishes. Dissaṇ dá baglá te machchhíáṇ dá ṭarkáú;
5. The Quran under his arm and his eye on the bullock (to see if he can steal it). Kachch tale Qurán, nazar ḍhagge te;
6. A whitened grave and the dead a heretic. chiṭṭí qabr te murdá beímán;
7. He is good to look at, but evil in deeds. dissán dá chaṇgá, amláṇ dá ḳharáb

HYPOCRITICAL, *A.*
farebí; dhagabáj; makarhatthá; pakhanḍí;

HYPOTHESIS, *N.*
ḳhayál. *m;* aṇmáṇ. *m;*

HYPOTHETIC, *A.*
ḳhayálí; kiásí;

HYSSOP, *N.*
zufá. *m;*

HYSTERIA, *N.*
vaihm. *m;*

I.

IBIS, *N.*
bojá. *m;*

ICE, *N.*
barf. *f;*
hail. kakkar. *m;* korá. *m;*

ICE CREAM, *N.*
malái dí barf. *f;*

ICY, *A.*
baṛá ṭhanḍá; baṛí ṭhanḍ;

IDEA, *N.*
ḳhayál. *m;* wichár. *m;* soch. *m;*
1. vain idea. lall. *f;*
2. I have no idea. mainúṇ kakkh ví patá nahíṇ lagdá;

IDEAL, *A.*
ḳhayálí;

IDENTICAL, *A.*
ikko jehá; vaggmán;

IDENTIFICATION, *N.*
pachchán. *f* ;

IDENTIFY, TO, *V. T.*
pachchánná ; sihánná ; sanjhánná ; sujánná ;

IDENTITY, *N.*
barábarí. *f* ; barobarí. *f* ;

IDIOCY, *N.*
págalpuṇá. *m* ; kamal. *m*; shudá. *m*; see INSANITY.

IDIOM, *N.*
muhávrá. *m* ; bolaṇ dá ḍhang. *m* ;

IDIOMATIC, *A.*
ṭheṭh ;

IDIOMATICALLY, *Adv.*
muhávare de mutábiq ;

IDIOT, *N.*
paglá ; *m* ; ḍaú. *m* ;

IDIOTIC, *A.*
1. insane. págal ; kamlá ; dawáná ;
2. foolish. bewaqúf ; besamajh ; beaql ; nadán ; kamlá ;

IDLE, *A.*
1. lazy. surliá hoyá ; sust ; ḍhillá ; ḍhillí ; machall; nikammá; ḍhailá; payyal ; álasí ; jillhá ; kammchor; nikesal; kammkos ; ḍhillá maṭṭhá; daliddarí ;
2. out of work. vehlá ; berozgár ; bekár ;
3. an idle word. wádhí gal. *f* ;
4. Proverb. The industrious son comes and is respectful, the idle son comes and is quarrelsome. khaṭṭú áwe ḍardá, nakhaṭṭú áwe laṛdá

IDLE, TO, *V. T.*
susṭí karní ; álas karná ;

IDLENESS, *N.*
sustí. *f* ; jillh. *f* ; álas. *m* machalpuṇá. *m* ; ḍhill. *f* ; daliddar. *m* ;

IDLER, *N.*
mankhaṭṭú. *m* ; phosar. *m* ;

IDLY, *Adv.*
1. lazily. sustí nál ; láparwáhí nál; ghaul nál ;
2. unprofitably. befaidá ; aiweṇ ; eweṇ ;

IDOL, *N.*
murat. *f* ; but . *m* ; miṭṭí dá putlá. *m* ; ṭhákúr. *m* ; murtí. *f* ;

IDOLATER, *N.*
butparast. *m* ; deupujak. *m* ; miṭṭí pujak. *m* ;

IDOLATRY, *N.*
butparastí. *f* ; murtípujá. *m* ; deupujá. *m* ;

IDOLIZE, TO, *V. T.*
láḍ karná ; bahut piyár karná ;

IF, *Conj.*
je ; jekar ; agar ;

IGNITE, TO, *V. T.*
bálná ; jalá dená ; agg láuná magháuná ;

IGNITE, TO, *V. I.*
balná ;
to smoke. dhukhná ;

IGNOBLE, *A.*
nikammá ; chanḍál ; bhaiṛá ; máṛá

IGNOMINIOUS, *A.*
ních ; ghiṇáuná ;

IGNOMINY, *N.*
láj. *f* ; bhanḍí. *f* ; namoshí. *f*. : sharm. *m* ; sharmindagí. *f* ; badnámí. *f* ; lík. *f* ; líh. *f* ;

IGNORAMUS, *N.*
jáhil ádmí. *m* ; bewaquf bandá. *m* ; nadán. *m* ;

IGNORANCE, *N.*
beilmí. *f* ; nadání. *f* ; húṛh. *f* ; bekhabarí. *f* ; besamajhgí. *f* ;
1. of religious matters. aggián. *m*;
2. one who feigns ignorance. machlá.

IGNORANT, *A.*
1. untaught. anpaṛh ; jáhil ; nadán. ; anján ; beilm ; kowallá ; nirbuddh ; ansikkhiá ; asujh ;
2. foolish. beaql ; bewaqúf ; kamlá ;

IGNORANTLY, *Adv.*
nadání nál, bekhabrí nàl ;

IGNORE, TO, *V. T.*
khayál ná karná ; láparwáhí karní; nahíṇ manná ;
to ignore a friend. akkh chuṛáuní ; khikhiáuná ; katráuná ;

IGUANA, *N.*
goh. *m* ;

ILL, *A.*
bimár ; mandá ; wall nahíṇ ; rogí ; dukhiá ; kasrí ; azárí ; maleá hoyá ; tagaṛá nahíṇ ;
to be ill. azár ho jáná ; bimár ho jáná ; mal ghattná ;

ILL BLOOD, *N.*
wair. *m;* adávat. *f;* kíná. *m;* dushmaní. *f;* virodh. *f;* khár. *m;* khaṭá paṭí *f;* khaṭṭ paṭṭ. *f;*

ILL BRED, *A.*
badját; kuḍhanggá; kamíná; kuḍhang; kuḍhabá;

ILL DISPOSED, *A.*
badníyat; darohí; dokhí; kuchal; sharír;

ILLEGAL, *A.*
nájaiz; niṇd; qánun de ḳhiláf;

ILLEGALITY, *N.*
jurm. *m;* qasúr. *m;*

ILLEGALLY, *Adv.*
nájaiz; bejá; sirkárí hukm de ḳhilát;

ILLEGIBLE, *A.*
raddí likhiá; ghasíṭiá hoyá; jo paṛhiá nahíṇ jándá;

ILLEGITIMACY, *N.*
harámzádagí. *f;* harám. *m;*

ILLEGITIMATE, *A.*
harám dá; harámí; harám jádá; gaibí golá;
an illegitimate child. harám dá bachchá. *m;*

ILLFATED, *A.*
chaṇdará; kalaihná; abhágí; badnasíb;

ILLFAVOURED, *A.*
badsurat; kasohná; ḳuḍhab; badshakal; kojhá; kojhrá;

ILLFORMED, *A.*
karúp; beḍaul; badsurat; kulann; kuḍhabb;

ILL GOTTEN WEALTH, *N.*
harám dá mál. *m;*

ILL HUMOUR, *N.*
narázagí. *f;* waṭṭ. *m;* chhiṛham. *f;*

ILL HUMOURED, *A.*
muṇh ṭuṭá;

ILLIBERAL, *A.*
chiṛhá; taṇgdil; kanjús; marjiú; marjírá;

ILLICIT, *A.*
nájaiz; bejá;
illicit intercourse. badfelí. *f;* harámkárí. *f;*

ILLIMITABLE, *A.*
aṇgiṇt; behadd; behisáb;

ILLITERACY, *N.*
beilmí. *f;*

ILLITERATE, *A.*
aṇpaṛh; ansikkhiá; beilm; ṭhuṭh; besamajh; jáhal;

ILL LUCK, *N.*
abhág. *m;* kambaḳhtí. *f;* benasíbí. *f;* bad saganí. *f;* shámat. *f;*

ILLMANNERED, *A.*
jáhal; guṇwár; nak chaṛhá; kuḍhanggá; kuḍhab; baṛbolá; ujjad; kuḍhabá; kuḍhang; hoshá; ḍhíṭh; ḍakkará;

ILLNATURE, *N.*
ḍhíṭhái. *f;* badmajájí. *f;* kusíltáí. *f;*

ILLNATURED, *A.*
ḍhíṭh; ziddí; kusíl; badmajájí; saṛú; saṛúká; majáj dá máriá hoyá;

ILLNESS, *N.*
bímárí. *f;* mándagí. *f;* rog. *m;* zahmat. *f;*
plague. bimárí. *f;* manno. *f;* táún. *f;*

ILL OMEN, *N.*
kulachhaṇ. *m;* badsaganí. *f;*

ILLOMENED, *A.*
abhágí; kambaḳht;

ILLSEASONED, *A.*
phuklá; phauklá;

ILLSTARRED, *A.*
badnasíb; abhágí;

ILLTEMPERED, *A.*
rukkhá; kauṛá; khaṭṭá; múṇh ṭúṭá; nakk chaṛhá; awallá; chanḍá; kulakkhní; kulaihná; badmajáj; avaiṛá;

ILLUMINATE, TO, *V. T.*
1. to give light. roshní dení; chánan karná; lo karní;
2. to explain. samjháuná; matlab batláuná; kholke dassná;

ILLUMINATION, *N.*
1. light. lo. *f;* roshní. *f;* roshnáí. *f;*
2. knowledge. viddiá. *m;* ilm. *m;* gián. *m;*

ILLUSAGE, *N.*
saḳhtí. *f;* badsalukí. *f;*

ILL USE, TO, *V. T.*
dhakká márná; ḳharábí karní; burá saluk karná;

ILLUSION, *N.*
1. deception. dhokhá. *m*; fareb. *m*; pakhaṇḍ. *m*; dhoppá. *m*; chhal. *m*;
2. hallucination. lall. *f*; waihm. *m*; ḳháb ḳhayál. *m*; pher gher. *m*;

ILLUSIVE, *A.*
jhuṭhá; farebí; see DECEITFUL.

ILLUSTRATE, TO, *V. T.*
misál deke samjháuná; arth karná; bayán karná;

ILLUSTRATION, *N.*
misál. *f*; daristáṇt. *f*;

ILLUSTRIOUS, *A.*
1. renowned. waḍḍá námí; manniá danniá; manniá parwanniá; minniá ginniá; parnámí; ghukiá hoyá; mahá;
2. glorious. jalálí; partápí; shánwálá;
3. noble. sharíf; amír;

ILLUSTRIOUSNESS, *N.*
buzurgí. *f*; waḍíáí. *f*; jalál. *m*; partáp. *m*;

ILL WILL, *N.*
dushmaní. *f*; wair. *m*; kíná. *m*; adávat. *f*; virodh. *m*; khár. *m*; waṭṭ. *m*; kauṛ. *f*; ḍáh. *m*; khaṭápatí. *f*; see HATE.

IMAGE, *N.*
murat. *f*; but. *m*; putalá. *m*; murtí. *f*;

IMAGE WORSHIP, *N.*
butparastí. *f*; pujá. *m*; murtí-pujá. *m*; pujá pát. *f*;

IMAGINARY, *A.*
ḳhayálí gal; farzí gal; sufne dí gal;

IMAGINATION, *N.*
1. thought. ḳhayál. *m*; soch. *m*; soch wichár. *m*;
2. fancy. waihm *m*; lall. *f*; lallhú. *m*; manmauj. *f*;

IMAGINE, TO, *V. T.*
ḳhayál karná; sochná; dhián karná; soch wichár karná; wichárná;
to imagine vain things. kuṛe ḳhayál karná;

IMBECILE, *A.*
págal; see IDIOTIC.

IMBECILITY, *N.*
págalpuṇá. *m*; kamal. *m*; saudá. *m*; foolishness. beaqlí. *f*; nádání. *f*; bewaqúfí. *f*;

IMBIBE, TO, *V. T.*
1. to drink. píná.
2. to suck. chupná; chup lainá;

IMITATE, TO, *V. T.*
naql karná OR láuná OR utárná; sáṇg wikháuná;

IMITATION, *N.*
sáṇg. *m*; naql. *f*;

IMMACULATE, *A.*
1. without fault. beaib; bejurm; bedosá;
2. without spot. bedág; ne kalank;
3. holy. pák; pák sáf; pavittar; suchcham; such pavittar;

IMMATERIAL, *A.*
1. of no consequence. koí bát nahíṇ; kujh parwá nahíṇ;
2. incorporeal. niraṇkár; nirúp; nirúpá;

IMMATURE, *A.*
1. young. niáná; bachchá; anján;
2. not of legal age. nabálig;
3. unripe. kachchá; lillá; ḍaḍ-ḍará; gaḍḍará;

IMMEASUREABLE, *A.*
1. boundless. behadd; haddoṇ waddh; beoṛak;
2. not to be reckoned. behisáb;
3. innumerable. aṇgiṇt; beshumár;
4. very great. bahut waḍḍá; haddoṇ waddh;

IMMEDIATELY, *Adv.*
jhaṭ phaṭ; turt; turt phurt; huṇe; turant; jhabde; uweṇ; ikk dam; chhetí chhetí; jhaṭá jhaṭ;
immediately on reading the letter. chiṭṭhí paṛhdiáṇ sár hí;

IMMENSE, *A.*
haddoṇ waddh; baṛá waḍḍá; waḍḍá sárá;

IMMERSED, TO BE, *V. I.*
in work. rujjhná; kamm vichch laggá honá;

IMMOBILE, *A.*
ná hillanwálá; nihchall;

IMMODERATE, *A*.
wadhík ; ḍher ; wadherá ; haddoṇ wadh ; bahutá ; hadd thoṇ báhar ;

IMMODERATELY, *Adv*.
bahut ziyádá ; wadhík ;

IMMODEST, *A*.
behayá ; besharm ; belajjá ; guṇḍá ; belaháj ;

IMMODESTLY, *Adv*.
besharmí nál ;

IMMODESTY, *N*.
behayái. *f* ; bepaṛdagí. *f* ; besharmí. *f* ; belahájí. *f* ;

IMMOLATE, TO, *V. T.*
qurbání chaṛháuní ; balidán karná ; bheṭ chaṛháuní ;

IMMOLATION, *N*.
qurbání. *f* ; balídán. *m* ; balí bheṭ. *f* ; sadká. *m* ;

IMMORAL, *A*.
bhaiṛá ; palít ; maṇḍá ; burá ; luchchá ; guṇḍá ; luṇḍá ; adharmí ; aibí ; lukká ;
immoral practice. lat. *f* ;

IMMORALITY, *N*.
badchalní. *f* ; badkárí. *f* ; badí. *f* ; badfelí. *f* ; palídagí. *f* ; janáh. *m* ; yárí. *f* ;

IMMORTAL, *A*.
akál ; abnásí ; amiṭ ; amar ;

IMMORTALITY, *N*.
hameshgí. *f* ; beaṇt zindagí. *f* ;
Lt. food of the gods. amratt. *m* ; amritt. *m* ;

IMMOVABLE, *A*.
qaim ; sábat ; aṇdol ; jehṛá nahíṇ hilldá ; nihchall ; asthar ; nichall ; achall ; ná hillanwála ; asthávar ;
to be immovable. thahí rahná ; ṭhahr rahná ; ṭikkná ;

IMMUNITY, *N*.
chhuṭkárá. *m* ; khalásí. *f* ;

IMMUTABILITY, *N*.
sábatí. *f* ;

IMMUTABLE, *A*.
sábat ; qaim ; aṭall ;

IMP, *N*.
bhút. *m* ; shaitán. *m* ;

IMPACT, *N*.
ṭakkar. *f* ;
a push. dhakká. *m* ;

IMPAIR, TO, *V. T.*
kharáb kar dená ; wigáṛná ; nuqsán karná ; harjá páuná ; pheṛná ;

IMPALPABLE, *A*.
bahut mahín ; barík; kappaṛ chháṇ;

IMPARITY, *N*.
farq. *m* ; vervá. *m* ;

IMPART, TO, *V. T.*
1. to give. dená ; bakhshná
2. to reveal. dikhláuná ; batláuná ; záhir karná ; dassná ;

IMPARTIAL, *A*.
begarj ; niáiṇ ; tarafdár nahíṇ ; beriyá ; belág ;
to be impartial. sabhnáṇ núṇ ikkí akkh nál vekhná ; rástí nál faisalá karná ; kise dá pakh ná karná ;

IMPARTIALITY, *N*.
begarjí. *f* ; insáf. *m* ;

IMPARTIALLY, *Adv*.
rástí nál ; insáf nál ; ímán nál ;

IMPASSABLE, *A*.
bikhṛá ; awallaṛá ; laṇghaṇwálá nahíṇ ;

IMPASSIONED, *A*.
joshwálá ; tez ;

IMPASSIVE, *A*.
beján ; sunn ;

IMPATIENCE, *N*.
besabrí. *f* ; betábí. *f* ; sauṛ. *f* ; utáulí. *f* ;

IMPATIENT, *A*.
besabr ; besabrá ; betáb ; joshwálá ; káhlá ; sauṛá ; tarikkhá ;
to be impatient. uktáuná ; besabrí honá ;

IMPATIENTLY, *Adv*.
besabrí nál; káhle nál ;
to be impatient. hauṇsilá ná karná ; sabr ná karná ; káhle painá ; uktáuná ;

IMPEACH, TO, *V. T.*
ilzám láuná ; aib láuná ; dosh láuná ; shikayat karní ;

IMPEACHMENT, *N*.
1. accusation. ilzám. *m* ; ujj. *f* ;
2. legal charge. dává. *f* ; nálish. *f* ;
3. complaint. chuglí. *f* ; shikayat. *f* ; fariád. *f* ; uláhmá. *m* ;

IMPECUNIOUS, *A*.
garíb ; kaṇgál; maskín ; jis de palle vichch kujh bhí nahíṇ ;

IMPEDE, TO, *V. T.*
rokná ; ṭhákná ; aṭkáuná ;
ḍakkná ; ḍátná ; ṭokná ;
IMPEDIMENT, *N.*
rok ṭok. *f;* rukávat. *f;* see HINDERANCE.
IMPEL, TO, *V. T.*
1. to incite. chukkná ; uksáuná ; lárá dená ; see INCITE.
2. to cause to go. chaláuná; ṭuráuná;
IMPENDING, *A.*
honwálá ; neṛe ;
IMPENETRABLE, *A.*
bikhṛá ; laṇghaṇwálá nahíṇ ;
IMPENITENCE, *N.*
1. obduracy. sakhtdilí. *f;* haṭh *f;*
2. hard heartedness. beráhmí. *f;* lohṛá. *m;*
3. shamelessness. besharmí. *f;* behayáí. *f;*
4. presumption. ḍhíṭháí. *f;* asṭáí. *f;* haṇkár. *m;*
IMPENITENT, *A.*
sakhtdil ; magrá ; patthar dil ; háṭhá ;
IMPERATIVE, *A.*
jarúrí ; zarúrí ;
IMPERCEPTIBLE, *A.*
1. not to be perceived. anḍiṭṭh ; andekhí ;
2. fine. bahut barík ; mahín ; kappaṛ chháṇ ;
IMPERFECT, *A.*
kachchá ; nakárá ; khoṭṭá ; adhurá ; mukká nahíṇ ;
IMPERFECTION, *N.*
1. want of perfection. kachchíáí. *f;* káṇ. *f;* kasar. *m;* kamjorí. *f;*
2. fault. augun. *m;* nuqs. *m;* kamí. *f;* aib. *m;*
IMPERIAL, *A.*
bádsháhí ; sháhí ;
IMPERIL, TO, *V. T.*
khatre vichch leáuná ; jokhoṇ vichch páuná ;
IMPERIOUS, *A.*
1. arrogant. gustákh ; gamrúr ; haṇkárí ; haṇkárá ; gabbar ; phiṭṭiá hoyá ; magrá ; majájí ; ghamaṇḍí ; ḍhíṭh ; hekaṛí ;
2. domineering. jabardast ; karṛá ; hákamáná ;
IMPERIOUSLY, *Adv.*
jabardastí nál ; jástí nál ;
IMPERIOUSNESS, *N.*
haṇkár. *m;* abhimán. *m;* jabardastí. *f;* gamrúrí. *f;* jástí. *f;*
IMPERISHABLE, *A.*
abnásí ; amiṭ ; amar ;
IMPERSONATE, TO, *V. T.*
bhes badalná OR waṭáuná ; sáṇg wikháuná ;
IMPERSONATION, *N.*
sáṇg. *m;* naql. *f;*
IMPERTINENCE, *N.*
beadabí. *f;* gustákhí. *f;* haṇkár. *m;* ḍhíṭháí. *f;* chauṛ. *f;* besharmí. *f;* kharmastí. *f;*
IMPERTINENT, *A.*
besharm ; gustákh ; hekaṛ ; ḍhíṭhá ; shokh ; akkhaṛ kháṇ ; bemukh ; baṛbolá ; akkhaṛkháṇḍ ;
IMPERTINENTLY, *Adv.*
gustákhi nál ; shokhí nál ; kharmastí nál ;
IMPERTURABLE, *A.*
dhírá ; dhírají ; dhírajmáṇ ; nigghá ;
IMPERVIOUS, *A.*
sakht ;
IMPETUOSITY, *N.*
tezí. *f;* josh. *m;* sargarmí. *f;*
IMPETUOUS, *A.*
tikkhá ; sargarm ; joshwálá ;
IMPETUOUSLY, *Adv.*
josh nál ; jhapájhap ; dhakko dhakkí ; badobadí ; chhetí chhetí ; dúbadú ; jhaṭá jhaṭ ;
IMPETUS, *N.*
chalan dá jor. *m;*
IMPIETY, *N.*
bedíní. *f;* adharm. *m;* adharmtáí. *f;* abhagtí. *f;*
IMPINGE, TO, *V. T.*
1. to strike. márná ; ṭhokná ;
2. to dash against. ṭakkar mární ;
IMPIOUS, *A.*
bedín ; adharmí ;
IMPIOUSLY, *Adv.*
bedíní nál ;
IMPLACABILITY, *N.*
sakhtí. *f;* dushmaní. *f;* adávat. *f;* wair. *m;*

IMPLACABLE, *A.*
sakht; beráhm; patthar dil; karṛá; jálim;

IMPLANT, TO, *V. T.*
1. to instil. páuná;
2. to sow. bíjná;
3. to fix. gaḍḍná; láuná;

IMPLEMENT, *N.*
aujár. *m;* hathiyár. *m;*

IMPLICATE, TO, *V. T.*
phasáuná; uljháuná; wal páuná; pech páuná; pháhí vichch páuná;

IMPLICATION, *N.*
matlab. *m;* arth. *m;*

IMPLICIT, *A.*
1. clear. sáf;
2. believable. mannan jog;
3. settled. pakkí gal;

IMPLICITLY, *Adv.*
yaqín nál; atbárí nál;

IMPLORE, TO, *V. T.*
girgaṛáuná; wáste páuná; duá karní; minnat karní; bentí karní; parárthná karná; arz karní; raiṇ raiṇ karná; tarle minnat karní;

IMPLY, TO, *V. T.*
dassná; ishárá karná; batláuná; matlab kaḍḍhná;

IMPOLITE, *A.*
jáhal; akkhaṛ ḳhán; nakk chaṛhiá; kuḍhabá; baṛbolá;

IMPOLITIC, *A.*
bemukkh; bewaqúf; nadán; beaql; ujjad;

IMPORT, *N.*
1. meaning. matlab. *m;* arth. *m;*
2. goods. mál. *m;* dasaur. *m;*

IMPORT, TO, *V. T.*
1. opposed to export. dujje des thoṇ samán leáuná;
2. to signify. arth karná;

IMPORTANCE, *N.*
qadr. *f;*

IMPORTANT, *A.*
baṛí jarúrí; bhárí;

IMPORTED GOODS, *N.*
dasaurí mál. *m;*

IMPORTUNATE, *A.*
besharm; ḍhíṭh;

IMPORTUNATELY, *Adv.*
baṛí minnat nál; tarle minnat karke;

IMPORTUNE, TO, *V. T.*
pichchhe painá; kíjá karní; tarle minnat karní; úká karní; giṛgaṛáuná; takorná; kijháuná; aukkhíáṇ karná; taṇg karná; taṇgí dení; see ENTREAT.

IMPORTUNITY, *N.*
1. entreaty. tarle minnat. *f;* tagádá. *f;*
2. shamelessness. behayáí. *f;* besharmí. *f;*

IMPOSE, TO, *V. T.*
1. to deceive. dhokhá dená; ṭhaggná; chhal lainá; bhuláuná;
2. to appoint. ṭhahráuná; muqarrar karná;

IMPOSING, *A.*
shándár; partápí;

IMPOSITION, *N.*
1. fine. ḍaṇḍ. *m;* chaṭṭí. *f;* jurmáná. *m;* jurimáná. *m;*
2. burden. bojh. *m;* bhár. *m;*
3. trick. dhokhá. *m;* chhal. *m;* pakhaṇḍ. *m;* chalittar. *m;*

IMPOSSIBILITY, *N.*
aṇhoní gal *f;*
1. Proverb used of an impossibility. A string of camels is passing through the needle's eye. suí dí duk vichchoṇ katár uṭṭháṇ dí laṇghí waiṇdhí;
2. A bhang smoker cannot give up smoking bhang. amalíáṇ thoṇ amal nahíṇ haṭáyá jáṇdá;

IMPOSSIBLE, *A.*
aṇhoyá; aṇhoní; aṇhoná; ho nahíṇ sakdá;
1. Even the impossible becomes possible. aṇhoní ví honí ho sakdí hai;
2. to attempt the impossible. lohṛá márná; gajab márná;
3. Proverb. To attempt the impossible. bhunne tittar uḍaune. *i. e.*, to fly roasted partridges;
4. exclamation. majál e; taubá; tobbá;

IMPOST, *N.*
1. tax. takas. *m;*
2. octroi. mahsúl. *m;*
3. land revenue. muámlá. *m;*

IMPOSTER, *N*.
makkár. *m* ; see CHEAT.
IMPOSTURE, *N*.
fareb. *f*; dhokhá. *m*; dagá. *f*; dambájí. *f*; see DECEIT.
IMPOTENCE, *N*.
1. weakness. kamjorí. *f*; nirbaltáí. *f*; thiṛ. *m* ;
2. want of power of procreation. námardí. *f*;
IMPOTENT, *A*.
1. weak. kamjor; bewas; máṛá; fachch;
2. destitute of power of procreation. namard; nisphal;
IMPOTENTLY, *Adv*.
baṛí kamjorí nál;
IMPOUND, TO, *V. T*.
qabzá kar lainá;
IMPOVERISH, TO, *V. T*.
garíb OR kaṇgál kar dená;
IMPRACTICABILITY, *N*.
aṇhoní gal. *f*;
IMPRACTICABLE, *A*.
bikhṛá; aṇhoní; mahál; dur labbh;
IMPRECATE, TO, *V. T*.
saráp dená; bad duá dení; lánat dení; duṛú duṛú dená;
IMPRECATION, *N*.
lánat. *f*; bad duá. *f*; duṛú. *m*; saráp. *m*; dhikkár. *m*; phiṭkár; *f*; dhitkár. *m*;
IMPREGNATE, TO, *V. T*.
gabbhaṇ karná; pet karná; gaib karná;
IMPRESS, TO, *V. T*.
1. to inculcate. pakkí karní; ḳhub samjháuná;
2. to seal. mohr láuní; thappná;
3. to force one to work. begár pharná;
IMPRESSION, *N*.
1. effect. asar. *m*; tásír. *f*;
2. that produced by pressure. naqsh. *m*; nishán. *m*; chháppá. *m*;
3. influence on organs of sense. asar. *m*;
4. thought. ḳhayál. *m*;
IMPRESSIVE, *A*.
man bhaundá;
IMPRISON, TO, *V. T*.
qaid karná; bandí ḳháne páuná; to be imprisoned. qaid honá; bajjhná;
IMPRISONMENT, *N*.
qaid. *f*;
IMPROBABILITY, *N*.
aṇhoní gal. *f*;
IMPROBABLE, *A*.
aṇhoní;
IMPROBABLY, *Adv*.
shayad; ummed nahíṇ;
IMPROBITY, *N*.
beímání. *f*; bad diyánatí. *f*; beímángí. *f*;
IMPROMPTU, *A*.
1. without thinking. besoche samjhe;
2. at once. jhaṭṭ paṭṭ; paund saṭṭe; hune; paindí saṭṭe;
IMPROPER, *A*.
bejá; nalaiq; námunásib; náwájab;
IMPROPERLY, *Adv*.
náwájabí nál; burí taráh nál;
IMPROPRIETY, *N*.
námunásib gal. *f*; burí gal. *f*;
IMPROVE, TO, *V. T*.
1. to advance. taraqqí karní;
2. to advance another. taraqqí dení;
3. to rectify. sudhárná; suárná; ṭhík ṭhák karná; sádhná; durust karná;
IMPROVE, TO, *V. I*.
chaṇgá ho jáná; wall ho jáná; saurná; sudharná;
IMPROVEMENT, *N*.
taraqqí. *f*;
in illness. arám. *m*; armán. *m*; ramán. *m*; sabehtá. *m*;
IMPROVIDENCE, *N*.
fazul ḳharch. *m*;
IMPROVIDENT, *A*.
nikhaṭṭú; mankhaṭṭú; ujáṛú; gawáú;
IMPROVIDENTLY, *Adv*.
fazul ḳharchí nál;
IMPRUDENCE, *N*.
nadání. *f*; beaqlí. *f*; beḳhabrí. *f*;
IMPRUDENT, *A*.
beaql; sochdá nahíṇ; bewaquf; gáfal; nadán; daullá maullá; annhá dhuṇd;

IMPRUDENTLY, *Adv.*
biná soche samjhe; besoche samjhe;
IMPUDENCE, *N.*
kharmastí. *f*; gustákhí. *f*; besharmí. *f*; beadabí. *f*; chauṛ. *f*; ḍhítháí. *f*; haṇkár. *m*; see IMPERTINENCE.
IMPUDENT, *A.*
ḍhíṭh; ḍhíṭhá; hekaṛ; magrá; kuḍhab; kuḍhabá; chák; magrur; shokh; kulajj; behayá; chámaliá hoyá;
IMPUDENT, TO BE, *V. I.*
damág vigaṛná;
IMPUDENTLY, *Adv.*
shokhí nál; gustákhí nál; besharmí nál; beadabí nál; ákaṛ ke;
IMPUGN, TO, *V. T.*
jhuṭhláuná; gal moṛní; barkhiláf bolná; jhuṭheáṇ karná;
IMPULSE, *N.*
matlab. *m*; garaz. *m*; cháh. *f*; táṇgh. *f*;
IMPULSIVE, *A.*
jaldbáz; káhlá;
IMPURE, *A.*
1. unholy. napák; asuddh; nikhiddh;
2. unclean. palít; gaṇḍá;
3. sinful. pápí; gunáhí;
4. vicious and debauched. luchchá; bharisht; badkár; luṇḍá; guṇḍá; nikhiddh;
5. adulterated. khoṭṭá;
6. polluted, as food, etc. bhiṭṭ; bhiṭṭaṛ; palít;
IMPURELY, *Adv.*
napákí nál;
IMPURITY, *N.*
1. unholiness. napákí. *f*;
2. filth. gaṇdagí. *f*; palítí. *f*; mail kuchail. *f*;
3. adulteration. khoṭái. *f*;
4. debauchery. badfelí. *f* badkárí. *f*; nikhiddh kamm. *m*; luchchpuṇá. *m*; uchakkpúṇá. *m*;
5. impurity of the blood. maláí. *f*; gaṇdá lahú. *m*;
IMPUTATION, *N.*
ilzám. *m*;
IMPUTE, TO, *V. T.*
1. to ascribe. ṭhahráuná; mithná;
2. to accuse. ilzám láuná; see ACCUSE.
IN, *Prep.*
vichch; vikhe; vichkár;
INABILITY, *N.*
lachárí. *f*; kamjorí. *f*; ájazí. *f*;
INACCURACY, *N.*
bhulekhá. *m*; bhull. *f*; bholáwá. *m*; galatí. *f*;
in accounts. bholá. *m*; bholí. *f*;
INACCURATE, *A.*
galat; ghutthá; ṭhík nahíṇ;
INACCURATELY, *Adv.*
bhulekhe nál; galatí nál; ṭhík nahíṇ;
INACTION, *N.*
sustí. *f*; jillh. *f*; álas. *m*; álasí. *f*; álakí. *f*;
INACTIVE, *A.*
sust; jillhá; ḍhillá; kammchor; kam koss; machall; ghauliá; ḍhillar; ḍhillá maṭṭhá; postí; surliá hoyá;
INACTIVITY, *N.*
álas. *m*; sustí. *f*; see LAZINESS.
INADEQUACY, *N.*
1. insufficiency. kasar. *f*; ghāṭṭá *m*; kamtí. *f*;
2. defect. nuqs. *m*; kasar. *f*;
INADEQUATE, *A.*
kassá; thoṛá; ghaṭṭ; káfí nahíṇ; ajog;
INADEQUATELY, *Adv.*
pure taur nál nahíṇ; adhurá;
INADMISSIBLE, *A.*
námanzúr; náwájib;
INADVERTENCE, *N.*
gáfalí. *f*; ghaul. *f*; láparwáí. *f*;
INADVERTENT, *A.*
1. careless. láparwáh; sust; gáfal; ḍhillá;
2. accidental. takdírí; itifáqí; haiṇ maiṇ;
INADVERTENTLY, *Adv.*
1. carelessly. gáfalí nál; láparwáí nál; aiweṇ; eweṇ;
2. accidentally. sabab nál; itifáq nál;
INANE, *A.*
bewaqúf; behudá; nadán; beaql;

INANIMATE, *A.*
bején ; sunn ; nirjív ;
INAPPLICABLE, *A.*
ṭhík nahíṇ ; námuwáfiq ; ajog ;
INAPPROPRIATE, *A.*
ṭhík nahíṇ ;
INAPT, *A.*
naqábil ; anján ; nawáqif ; nadán ; ajog ;
INAPTITUDE, *N.*
1. ignorance. náwáqfí. *f ;* náwáqabí. *f ;* beilmí. *f ;*
2. unfitness. nálaiqí. *f ;*
INARTICULATE, *A.*
1. dumb. guṇggá ;
2. stutterer. thathá ; thathdlá ;
INASMUCH, *Adv.*
kyuṇ jo ;
INATTENTION, *N.*
ḍhill. *f ;* gáfalí. *f ;* ghaul. *f ;* aṇchintá. *m ;* bechittí. *f ;*
INATTENTIVE, *A.*
gáfal ; ḍhillá ; bemukkh ; ghauliá ; ghaulí ; ḍhillá maṭṭhá ; ghesalá ; dhiáu nahíṇ kardá ;
INATTENTIVELY, *Adv.*
gáfalí nál ; ghaul nál ; biná soche samjhe ;
INAUGURATE, TO, *V. T.*
shurú karná ; ád karná ; tumná ; rawáṇ karná ;
INAUSPICIOUS, *A.*
benasíb ; abhágí ; durbhág ; kusubh ; chaṇdará ;
INAUSPICIOUSLY, *Adv.*
benasíbí nál ;
INCALCULABLE, *A.*
aṇgiṇt ; behisáb ; beoṛak ;
INCANTATION, *N.*
maṇtar. *m ;* maṇtar jaṇtar. *m ;* kalám. *m ;*
to perform incantations. maṇtar jaṇtar paṛhná ; hál khedná ; sir márná ;
INCAPABLE, *A.*
ájaz ; kamjor ; kamm de laiq nahíṇ ;
INCAPACITATE, TO, *V. T.*
kamjor karná ; bekár karná ; nikammá karná ;
INCAPACITY, *N.*
kamjorí. *f ;* lachárí. *f ;*

INCARCERATE, TO, *V. T.*
qaid karná ; bandí kháne páuná ;
INCARCERATION, *N.*
qaid. *m ;*
INCARNATE, *A.*
deh dhárí ;
to become incarnate. deh dhárí honá ; janam lainá OR dhárná ; autár dhárná ;
INCARNATION, *N.*
autár. *m ;* autárí. *f ;*
INCAUTIOUS, *A.*
daullá maullá ; annhá dhuṇd ; láparwá ;
INCAUTIOUSLY, *Adv.*
láparwáí nál ; sochan de biná ; besoche samjhe ;
INCENSE, *N.*
dhúp. *f ;* dhúf. *f ;* dhukh. *m ;* khushbo. *f ;* guggal. *m ;* sugaṇdhtá *f ;*
to burn incense. dhupná ; dhup dená ; dhup dhukháuná ; guggal dhukháuná ;
INCENSE, TO, *V. T.*
luhná ; russáuná ; chheṛná ; gussá diláuná OR chaṛháuná ; dil khaṭṭá karná ; agg láuná ;
INCENTIVE, *N.*
wajáh. *f ;* sabab. *m ;* see INCITEMENT.
INCEPTION, *N.*
shurú. *m ;* ád. *m ;*
INCERTITUDE, *N.*
shakk shubhá. *m ;* bharm. *m ;* dubdhá. *f ;* dhuṛká. *m ;*
INCESSANT, *A.*
lagátár ; barábar ; har vele ; aṭhe pahar ; har dam ;
INCESSANTLY, *Adv.*
har dam ; dam dam ; hamesh ; ghaṛí ghaṛí ; ghaṛí muṛí ; jhaṭe jhaṭe ; niraṇtar ;
INCEST, *N.*
badkárí. *f ;* badfelí. *f ;* zinákárí. *f ;* mastí. *f ;* bahir. *m ;* jom. *m ;*
INCESTUOUS, *A.*
badkár ; luchchá ; zinákár ; záni ; luṇḍá ; guṇḍá ;
INCH, *N.*
inchí. *f ;*

INCIDENT, *N.*
dho. *m*; wáqiá. *m*; gal. *f*; hál. *m*; incidents. wárdátán. *f*;
INCIDENTAL, *A.*
aiweṇ; eweṇ; kade kade; ittifáqí;
INCIDENTALLY, *Adv.*
aiweṇ; eweṇ; kade kade;
INCINERATE, TO, *V. T.*
sáṛná; jaláuná; magháuná; bálná;
INCISE, TO, *V. T.*
kaṭṭná; waḍḍhná;
INCISION, *N.*
1. cut. káṭ. *f*;
2. wound. jakham. *m*; ghá. *m*;
INCITE, TO, *V. T.*
chukkná; jagáuná; lárá dená; dilerí dení; bhaṛkáuná; bhuhe chaṛháuná; bhahiká dená; kann vichch phukkná; uksáuná; uchálá dená; bhiṛáuná; machráuná; kalá jagáuní;
INCITEMENT, *N.*
lárá. *m*; chukk. *f*; uchálá. *m*;
INCIVILITY, *N.*
beadabí. *f*; shoḳhí. *f*; chámalí. *f*; kharmastí. *f*;
INCLEMENCY, *N.*
jástí. *f*; saḳhtí. *f*; beráhmí. *f*; jorávarí. *f*;
INCLEMENT, *A.*
beráhm; bedard; saḳht; kauṛá; karṛá; rukkhá; karárá;
INCLINATION, *N.*
chau. *f*; cháh. *f*; shauq. *m*; laulá. *m*; liwalá. *m*; táṇgh. *f*; see DESIRE.
INCLINE, TO, *V. T.*
1. to bend. jhukáuná;
2. to wish. cháhná; rúh OR jí OR dil karná;
INCLINE, *N.*
utarái. *f*; utárá. *m*; ḍhál. *f*; salámí. *f*;
INCLOSE, TO, *V. T.*
1. to surround. gherná; walná; gherá pá lainá;
2. to close. band karná; see SHUT.
INCLUDE, TO, *V. T.*
shámil karná; raláuná; miláuná; vichch páuná;
INCLUSIVE, *A.*
nál; saṇg; shámil karke; de sane; vichch páke; raláke;
INCOHERENCE, *N.*
1. noise. gaugá. *m*;
2. delirium. bakaṛwádh. *m*; bakaṛwá. *f*; bakaṛwás. *f*; bakaṛwát. *f*;
INCOME, *N.*
ámdaní. *f*; parápat. *f*; khaṭṭí. *f*; lábh. *m*; áundaṇ. *f*; ámadan. *f*; a good income. chaṇgá guzárá. *m*;
INCOME TAX, *N.*
tákas. *m*;
INCOMMENSURATE, *A.*
ghaṭṭ; thoṛá; kassá; káfí nahíṇ;
INCOMMODE, TO, *V. T.*
taṇg karná; aukhíáṇ karná; taklíf dení; satáuná; dukháuná; dukkh dená; dikk dená OR karná;
INCOMMODOUS, *A.*
bhíṛá; taṇg; sauṛá;
INCOMPARABLE, *A.*
uttam; álá; baṛá chaṇgá;
INCOMPATIBILITY, *N.*
aṇjoṛ. *m*; náittifáqí. *f*; aṇmel. *m*;
INCOMPATIBLE, *A.*
aṇmel; mildá juldá nahíṇ; ulṭá; wakkhrá; viruddh; phabbdá nahíṇ;
INCOMPETENT, *A.*
yabbal; kamjor; anján; laiq nahíṇ; nahíṇ kar sakdá;
INCOMPETENTLY, *Adv.*
burí taráh nál;
INCOMPLETE, *A.*
adhurá; nákas; purá nahíṇ;
INCOMPREHENSIBLE, *A.*
samajh thoṇ báhar; samajh vichch nahíṇ áundá; agamm;
INCONCEIVABLE, *A.*
samajh thoṇ pare; agamm; asoch;
INCONCLUSIVE, *A.*
adhurá;
INCONGRUITY, *N.*
aṇjoṛ. *f*; kusaṇg. *m*;
INCONGRUOUS, *A.*
raldá nahíṇ; phabbdá nahíṇ; námuwáfiq;
INCONSIDERABLE, *A.*
thoṛá; chhoṭá; haulá;

INCONSIDERATE, *A.*
1. hasty. káhlá; joshwálá; tez;
2. thoughtless. aṇchiṇt; sochdá nahíṇ;

INCONSISTENCE, *N.*
1. difference. farq. *m;* vervá; *m;*
2. dishonesty. beímání. *f;* beímángí. *f;*

INCONSISTENT, *A.*
mildá juldá nahiṇ; viruddh;

INCONSOLABLE, *A.*
nimújhán; gamgín; masosiá hoyá; chupp kítá hoyá;

INCONSPICUOUS, *A.*
lukí hoí; gupt; gujjhí;

INCONSPICIOUSLY, *Adv.*
luk ke;

INCONSTANCY, *N.*
kachch pakk. *m;*

INCONSTANT, *A.*
do dilá; do chittí; man dá bhur bhurá;

INCONTESTABLE, *A.*
pakkí; jih de laí koí hál hujjat ná ho sake;

INCONTESTABLY, *Adv.*
sachchí muchchí; biná shakk de;

INCONTINENCE, *N.*
mastí. *f;* nafs. *f;* badparejí. *f;*

INCONTINENT, *A.*
luchchá; badkár; badját; mastáná; guṇḍá;

INCONTINENTLY, *Adv.*
badparejí nál; badkárí nál;

INCONTROVERTIBLE, *A.*
bilá shakk; bilá hujjat;

INCONVENIENCE, *N.*
1. trouble. taklíf. *f;* janjál. *m;* jichch. *f;* jahimat. *f;*
2. uneasiness. bearámí. *f;* betábí. *f;* bechainí. *f;*

INCONVENIENCED, *A.*
ḳhajjal ḳharáb; ḳhajjal ḳháṛ; aukhá; taṇg;

INCONVENIENT, *A.*
1. difficult. aukhá; mushkil; dubbar; sauṛá;
2. inopportune. kuvele; bemauqá; kumauqá;
3. It is inconvenient just now. huṇ wehlak nahíṇ; ṭhík waqt nahíṇ;

INCONVENIENTLY, *Adv.*
kuvele;

INCORPORATE, TO, *V. T.*
miláuná; raláuná; shámil karná;

INCORPOREAL, *A.*
niraṇkár; nirúp; nirúpá; jisdá sarír ná howe;

INCORRECT, *A.*
galat; ṭhík nahíṇ; ulṭá; durust nahíṇ; ghutthá;

INCORRECTLY, *Adv.*
bhulekhe nál; galatí nál;

INCORRECTNESS, *N.*
bhulekhá. *m;* galatí. *f;* bhulá. *m;* bhulí. *f;*

INCORRIGIBLE, *A.*
baṛá sharír; ḍhíṭh; uh mandá nahíṇ;

INCORRUPT, *A.*
pák; rást; baṛá nek; hatth dá suchchá;

INCORRUPTIBILITY, *N.*
ímándárí. *f;*

INCORRUPTIBLE, *A.*
1. upright. sachchá; hatth dá suchchá; suddh;
2. that cannot corrupt or decay. jo nás ná howe; awanás;

INCORRUPTION, *N.*
anás. *m;* awínás. *m;*

INCREASE, *N.*
1. augmentation. wadháu. *m;* taraqqí. *f;* wáddhá. *m;* wadhíkí. *f;* wádh. *f;*
2. extension. phailáu. *m;* phailár. *m;* pasárá. *m;*

INCREASE TO, *V. T.*
wadháuná; taraqqí dení; bahuṭá karná; see AMPLIFY.

INCREASE, TO, *V. I.*
wadhná; taraqqí karní; phailarná; wadhdá jáná; báhlá honá;

INCREDIBILITY, *N.*
beatibárí. *f;* beyaqíní. *f;*

INCREDIBLE, *A.*
beatibár; anokhá; yaqín de laiq nahíṇ; mannanwálí gal nahíṇ;

INCREDULITY, *N.*
bharm. *m;* shakk *m;* shubhá. *m;* bepartítí. *f;* shakk shubhá. *m;* jhakk. *m;*
an exclamation of incredulity. hekkháṇ; wekkháṇ;

INCREDULOUS, *A*.
bharmí; shakkí; beatibár; bepartítá;
INCREDULOUSLY, *Adv*.
shakk karke; bharm nál;
INCREMENT, *N*.
taraqqí. *f*; wádhá. *m*;
INCRIMINATE, TO, *V. T*.
ilzám láuná; dos láuná; see ACCUSE
INCUBATE, TO, *V. T*.
bachche kaḍḍhná; paṛe bahiná; seuná;
INCULCATE, TO, *V. T*.
sikhláuná; samjháuná; updesh dená; paṛháuná;
INCUMBENT, *A*.
jarúrí; cháhidá hai; loṛídá hai;
INCURABLE, *A*.
láiláj; bedárú; koí iláj nahíṇ; bedawá;
INCURSION, *N*.
hallá. *m*; chaṛhái. *f*; dháwá. *m*;
INDEBTED, *A*.
1. debtor. deṇwár. *m*; qarzdár. *m*; qarzái. *m*;
2. obliged. balihár; baliháraṇ;
INDEBTEDNESS, *N*.
qarzdárí. *f*; deṇdárí. *f*;
INDENCY, *N*.
1. shamelessness. bahayái. *f*; besharmí. *f*; bhaṇḍí. *f*;
2. uncleanness. gaṇdagí. *f*; palítí. *f*; mail kuchail. *f*;
INDECENT, *A*.
1. shameless. behayá; besharm; belajjá; asaṇg; ḍhíṭh;
2. in talk. fohsh;
3. sensual. guṇḍá; luchchá; laṭpaṭá; khíwá;
INDECENTLY, *Adv*.
besharmí nál; behayái nál;
INDECISION, *N*.
shakk. *m*; dochittí. *f*; bharm. *m*;
INDECISIVE, *A*.
dochitt; dochittá; dodilá;
INDECOROUS, *A*.
behayá; fohsh; belajjá;
INDECOROUSLY, *Adv*.
behayái nál; beadabí nál; besharmí nál; kharmastí nál;
INDECORUM, *N*.
behayái. *f*; besharmí. *f*; kharmastí. *f*;

INDEED, *Ad*.
sachche muchche; sachch sachch; as an exclamation of surprise. halá;
INDEFATIGABLE, *A*.
aṇthakk; himtál; baṛá himmatí; mihnatí;
INDEFINABLE, *A*.
jih dá bayán ná ho sake; bayánoṇ báhrá;
INDEFINITE, *A*.
kachch pakk; kachchí gal; ṭhík patá nahíṇ;
INDEFINITELY, *Adv*.
aiweṇ kiweṇ;
INDELIBLE, *A*.
amiṭ;
INDELICACY, *N*.
behayái. *f*; bepaṛdagí. *f*; besharmí. *f*;
INDELICATE, *A*.
besharm; behayá; belajjá;
INDEMNIFY, TO, *V. T*.
ḳharchá dená; nuqsán bharná; kasar bharní;
INDEMNITY, *N*;
ḳharchá. *m*; see DAMAGES.
INDENT, *N*.
hisáb. *m*;
INDENTED, *A*.
chibbá;
INDEPENDENCE, *N*.
azádí. *f*;
INDEPENDENT, *A*.
1. free. azád;
2. not needing anything. bemutháj;
3. not subject to control. áp hí málik hai; ḳhudmuḳhtár;
4. to be independent. apní nínd sáuná, apní nínd uṭṭhná;
INDEPENDENTLY, *Adv*.
ápoṇ áp; apní marzí nál;
INDESCRIBABLE, *A*.
bayán karan thoṇ báhar; bayánoṇ báhrá;
INDESTRUCTIBLE, *A*.
abinásí;
INDEX, *N*.
firist. *f*;
INDIA, *N*.
Hindustán. *m*;
INDIAN, *N*.
Hindustání. *m*;

INDIAN CORN, *N.*
makkí. *f;* makkái. *f;* juár. *f;* jowár. *f;*
INDIARUBBER, *N.*
rabbar. *m;*
INDICATE, TO, *V. T.*
1. to tell. batláuná; dassná; zikr karná;
2. to shew. dikhláuná; wikháuná; dikhálná;
INDICATION, *N.*
1. a sign. ishárá. *m;* sainat. *f;*
2. a mark. nishán. *m;* lík. *f;* ládh. *f;*
INDICT, TO, *V. T.*
1. to accuse. ilzám láuná; dos láuná; butáṇ láuná; gilá karná;
2. to prosecute. nálish karná; arzí páuní; dává karní;
3. to frame a charge under the I. P. Code. fard lagáuná;
INDICTMENT, *N.*
ilzám. *m;* dos. *m;* ujj. *f;*
INDIFFERENCE, *N.*
láparwái. *f;* beparwái. *f;* sustí. *f;* gáfalí. *f;* ḍhill. *f;* aṇchiṇtá. *m;*
INDIFFERENT, *A.*
ḍhillá maṭṭhá; bemukkh; láparwá; gáfal; daullá; daullá maullá; mastmaláná;
Idiom applied to those who are careless and indiffererent as to loss or gain. sháh ví dhaulí, te duddh ví dhaulá, *i. e.*, buttermilk is white and milk is white;
INDIFFERENTLY, *Adv.*
1. carelessly. láparwái nál; dhián nál nahíṇ;
2. impartially. biná ro; insáf nál; ímán nál;
INDIGENCE, *N.*
kaṇgálí. *f;* garíbí. *f;* taṇgí. *f;* maskíní. *f;* taṇgsí. *f;*
INDIGENOUS, *A.*
desí; mulkí;
INDIGENT, *A.*
kaṇgál; garíb; lachár; see POOR.
INDIGESTIBLE, *A.*
nahíṇ pachí; pachdá nahíṇ; saḳht; duspach;
do not eat this, it is indigestible. ih chíz ná kháíṇ, bhárí hai;

INDIGESTION, *A.*
badhazmí. *f;* aṇpáchá. *m;*
to suffer from indigestion. jíriá jáná; jírná;
INDIGNANT, *A.*
baṛá naráz; baṛe gusse vichch;
to be indignant. khij jáná; see ANGRY.
INDIGNANTLY, *Adv.*
naráz hoke; gusse nál; ṛusske;
INDIGNATION, *N.*
gussá. *m;* karodh. *m;* hirkh. *m;* waṭṭ. *m;* rossá. *m;*
INDIGNITY, *N.*
beadabí. *f;* namoshí. *f;* bijjtí. *f;* búrí báb. *f;* bapatí, *f;*
INDIGO, *N.*
níl. *m;* líl. *m;*
INDIRECT, *A.*
ṭeḍhá; waldár; siddhá nahíṇ;
INDIRECTLY, *Adv.*
wal nál;
by way of induendo. lapeṭwíṇ;
INDISCREET, *A.*
bemukh; besamajh; beaql;
1. disrespectful. belaház; baṛbolá;
2. foolish. beaql.; besamajh; nadán;
INDISCREETLY, *Adv.*
1. foolishly. nadání nál; beaqlí nál;
2. without thinking. biná soche samjhe; besoche samjhe;
INDISCRETION, *N.*
nadání. *f;* beaqlí. *f;*
INDISCRIMINATELY, *Adv.*
1. without thinking. besoche samjhe;
2. without distinction. biná ro; adal nál; insáf nál;
INDISPENSABLE, *A.*
jarúrí; loṛídá hai;
INDISPENSABLY, *Adv.*
jarúr;
INDISPOSED, *A.*
1. somewhat ill. bamár; sust; tagṛá nahíṇ; wall nahíṇ;
2. unwilling. rází nahíṇ; badhá rudhá;
INDISPOSITION, *N.*
bamárí. *f;* máṇdagí. *f;* rog. *m;* marj. *f;*

INDISPUTABLE, *A*.
ṭhík ; durust ; sach ; haqqí gal ;
INDISPUTABLY, *Adv*.
biná shakk de ; sachchí muchchí ;
INDISSOLUBLE, *A*.
jehṛá gal ná sake ; sakht ;
INDISTINCT, *A*.
dhuṇdhlá ; sáf nahíṇ ; maddham ;
ghichch michch ;
INDISTINCTLY, *Adv*.
ghichch michch ;
1. to speak indistinctly. ghichch michch bolná ;
2. to write indistinctly. ghichch michch likhná ;
INDISTINGUISHABLE, *A*.
besián ; bepahchán ;
INDIVIDUAL, *N*.
manukkh. *m* ; bandá. *m* ; janá. *m* ;
ádmí. *m* ;
INDIVIDUALLY, *Adv*.
ikk ikk karke ; alagg alagg ; wakho wakh ;
INDIVISIBLE, *A*.
sábit ; akhaṇd ;
INDOLENCE, *N*.
sustí. *f* ; ḍhill. *f* ; álas. *m* ; áhlak. *f* ;
INDOLENT, *A*.
sust ; jillhá ; ḍhillá maṭṭhá ; ḍhillá ;
see LAZY.
an indolent person. postí. *m* ;
áhlakí. *m* ; áhlakaṇ. *f* ;
INDOLENTLY, *Adv*.
sustí nál ; láparwái nál ; ghául nál ;
INDOMITABLE, *A*.
baṛá tagṛá ; bahádur ; baṛá sher ;
himmatí ;
INDOMITABLY, *Adv*.
baṛí dilerí nál ; baṛí himmat nál ;
uddam nál ;
INDOOR, *A*.
andarwár ; buhe OR ghar de andar ;
ghare ;
INDUBITABLE, *A*.
biná shakk de ; pakkí gal ;
INDUCE, TO, *V. T*.
chukkná ; bhiṛáuná ; manáuná ;
bharmáuná ;
INDUCEMENT, *N*.
tamá. *m* ; ulárá. *m* ; lábh *m* ;
lálach. *m* ;

INDUCT, TO, *V. T*.
qabzá de dená ; láuná ; see INSTALL.
INDULGE, TO, *V. T*.
khush karná ; láḍ karná ;
INDULGENCE, *N*.
láḍ. *m* ; narmí. *f* ;
INDULGENT, *A*.
narmdil ; mihrbán ;
INDULGENTLY, *Adv*.
narmí nál ; dayá nál ;
INDUSTRIOUS, *A*.
tagṛá ; uddamí ; chust ; phurtílá ;
mihnatí ; himmatí ;
Proverb. The industrious son comes and is respectful, the idle son comes and is quarrelsome. khaṭṭú áwe ḍardá, nakhaṭṭú áwe laṛdá ;
INDUSTRIOUSLY, *Adv*.
uddam nál ; mihnat nál ; himmat nál ; diloṇ wajhoṇ ;
INDUSTRY, *N*.
mihnat. *f* ; uddam. *m* ;
INDWELL, TO, *V. T*.
vichch rahná ;
INEBRIATE, TO, *V. T*.
mast karná ; nashái karní ;
INEBRIETY, *N*.
nashebází. *f* ; nashá. *m* : nasebájí. *f* ;
INEFFABLE, *A*.
bayánoṇ báhar ; bebayáṇ ;
INEFFECTIVE, *A*.
beasar ; betásír ; bekár ; nikammá ;
birthá ;
fruitless. apphal ;
INEFFECTIVELY, *Adv*.
beasarí nál ;
INEFFECTIVENESS, *N*.
betásírí. *f* ; beasarí. *f* ;
INEFFECTUAL, *A*.
befaidá ; bearth ; birthá ; see INEFFECTIVE.
INEFFICACIOUS, *A*.
beasar ; betásír ; nikammá ; kise kamm dá nahíṇ ;
INEFFICIENCY, *N*.
1. that which effects nothing. betásírí. *f* ;
2. incompetency. kamjorí. *f* ;
INEFFICIENT, *A*.
yabbal ; allhaṛ ; see INEFFECTIVE.

INEFFICIENTLY, *Adv.*
burí taráh nál; besamajhgí nál;

INELEGANCE, *N.*
badsuratí. *f;* beḍaulí. *f;*

INELEGANT, *A.*
kusohná; see UGLY.

INELIGIBILITY, *N.*
nálaiqí. *f;*

INELIGIBLE, *A.*
laiq nahíṇ;

INELOQUENT, *A.*
bolan dá ḍhaṇg nahíṇ; bolan dí jách nahíṇ;

INEPT, *A*
1. useless. nikammá; nakárá; kise kamm dá nahíṇ;
2. clumsy. bhaddá; allhaṛ;

INEPTLY, *Adv.*
beaqlí nál; burí taráh nál; besamajhgí nál;

INEQUALITY, *N.*
farq. *m;* vervá. *m;*

INEQUITY, *N.*
beinsáfí. *f;* námunsafí. *f;* julm. *m;* beniáíṇ. *f;* hikk dá dhakká. *m;*

INERT, *A.*
1. lazy. sust; ḍhillá; ghauliá; álasí; surliá hoyá; daliddarí;
2. lifeless. beján; murdá;

INERTIA, *N.*
sustí. *f;* álas. *m;* ḍhill. *f;* daliddar. *m;*

INERTNESS, *N.*
sustí. *f;* ghaul. *f;*

INESTIMABLE, *A.*
aṇmul; aṇmullá; amolak;

INEVITABLE, *A.*
jarúrí; aṭall; amoṛ;

INEVITABLY, *Adv.*
jarúr ba jarúr;

INEXACT, *A.*
ṭhík nahíṇ; durust nahíṇ;

INEXCUSABLE, *A.*
na bakhshan jogg;
you are without excuse. tuháḍá kujh uzr nahíṇ;

INEXHAUSTIBLE, *A.*
nakhuṭṭ; aṇgiṇt; behadd; aṇmukk; beoṛak; akhuṭṭ;
an inexhaustible storehouse. akhuṭṭ bhaṇḍár. *m;*

INEXORABLE, *A.*
beráhm; betaras; patthar dil; karṛá; jálím;

INEXPEDIENT, *A.*
nawájib; námunásib;

INEXPENSIVE, *A.*
suwallá; sastá; thoṛe mull dá;

INEXPERIENCE, *N.*
khámí. *f;* beḍhang. *m;*

INEXPERIENCED, *A.*
allhaṛ; aṇsikkh; aṇsikkhiá; beḍhaṇgá;
in an abusive sense. yabbal;

INEXPERT, *A.*
gawár; nadán; beaql; allhaṛ; kachchá;

INEXPLICABLE, *A.*
samajh thoṇ pare;

INEXPRESSIBLE, *A.*
bayán thoṇ báhar;

INFALLIBLE, *A.*
uh jis thoṇ bhulekhá ná ho sake; chátar;

INFAMOUS, *A.*
bhaiṛá; badját; kupattá; ṭhíṭṭh;

INFAMOUSLY, *Adv.*
baṛí kharábí nál;

INFAMY, *N.*
bhaṇḍí. *f;* apajas. *m;* baṛí shará-rat. *f;*

INFANCY, *N.*
ayánpuṇá. *m;* bálpaṇ. *m;* bach pan. *m;*

INFANT, *N.*
ayáná. *m;* bachchá. *m;* bachchṛá. *m;* bachchṛí. *f;* buchungṛá. *m;*
infant marriage. gúḍḍíáṇ dá viáh. *m;*

INFANTRY, *N.*
piádá fauj. *f;*

INFATUATE, TO, *V. T.*
aql már dení;

INFATUATED, *A.*
diwáná; paglá; baurá; kamlá;

INFATUATION, *N.*
baurápaṇ. *m;* diwánagí. *f;* págalpuṇá. *m;*

INFECT, TO, *V. T.*
chhut láuná;

INFECTED, TO BE, *V. I.*
chhut laggní; bhiṭṭiá jáná; chhoh jáná;
to be polluted, as food. bhiṭṭ jáná;

INFECTION, *N*.
lagganwálí bimárí. *f*; chhútt dí bimárí. *f*;
INFECTIOUS, *A*.
lagganwálá;
INFECUND, *A*.
1. of a woman. báṇjh; sanḍh;
2. of a tree. bephal; apphal;
3. of land. banjjar; kallar;
4. of cow or buffalo. phanḍar;
INFELICITY, *N*.
gam. *m*; gamí. *f*; ranj. *m*;
INFER, TO, *V. T*.
1. to deduce. matlab OR natíjá kaḍḍhná; arq OR nichoṛ kaḍḍhná;
2. to perceive. malúm karná; bujjhná; vekhná;
INFERENCE, *N*.
1. result. natíjá. *m*; nichoṛ. *m*;
2. meaning. matlab. *m*; arth. *m*;
INFERIOR, *A*.
adná; náqas; nikammá;
INFERIORITY, *N*.
adhíṇí. *f*; ghaṭṭiá. *m*;
INFERNAL, *A*.
1. hellish. dozakhí;
2. devilish. shaitání;
INFERTILE, *A*.
banjjar; see INFECUND.
INFERTILITY, *N*.
apphaltái. *f*;
INFEST, TO, *V. T*.
chheṛná; taṇg karná; thakáuná; dukháuná; aukhíáṇ karní;
INFIDEL, *N*.
káfir. *m*; munkar. *m*; kufrí. *m*; dahriá. *m*;
INFIDELITY, *N*.
1. unbelief. bepartítí. *f*; kufr. *m*; bedíní. *f*;
2. unfaithfulness. beímání. *f*; beímángí. *f*;
INFINITE, *A*.
1. boundless. beaṇt; behadd; haddoṇ waddh; beoṛak;
2. bottomless. atháh;
INFINITELY, *Adv*.
att;
INFIRM, *A*.
kamjor; márá; lissá; bewas; durbal;
INFIRMARY, *N*.
haspaṭál. *m*; dák ḳháná. *m*;
INFIRMITY, *N*.
kamjorí. *f*; rog. *m*; bamárí. *f*; dúrbaltái. *f*;
INFLAME, TO, *V. T*.
tapáuná; agg bhaṛkáuná; josh duáná; hil jhul macháuná; chukkná; uksáuná;
to be inflamed. sujjná;
INFLAMMABLE, *A*.
bhabkaunwálá;
INFLAMMATION, *N*.
saṛan. *f*;
1. inflammation in the eyes. raṛak. *f*;
2. to be inflamed. V.I. sujjná; soj painá;
INFLATE, TO, *V. T*.
phuláuná;
to inflate a tyre, phukk bharní;
INFLATED, *A*.
phulliá hoyá; sujjiá hoyá;
INFLATION, *N*.
phuláu. *m*;
INFLECT, TO, *V. T*.
áwáz waṭáuná;
INFLEXIBILITY, *N*.
1. stubbornness. haṭh. *m*;
2. quality of being inflexible. karṛápaṇ. *m*; sakhtí. *f*;
INFLEXIBLE, *A*.
1. strong. sábat; pakká; sabal; sanḍhá; musṭanḍá;
2. obstinate. aṛyal; kabbá; ḍhíṭhá; háṭhá;
INFLICT, TO, *V. T*.
1. to punish. sazá dení; táṛná;
2. to fine. jurmáná karná; ḍann láná; ḍannaná;
INFLICTION, *N*.
1. punishment. sazá. *f*;
2. calamity. balá. *f*; garauh. *m*; biptá. *f*;
3. trouble. taklíf. *f*; janjál. *m*; aukh. *f*; jichch. *f*;
INFLUENCE, *N*.
pokho. *m*; asar. *m*; chháiá. *m*;
INFLUENCE, TO, *V. T*.
asar karná; dabáú páuná; pokho páuná OR dená;

INFLUENTIAL, *A.*
manniá danniá; ịkhtiyárwálá; jorwálá; dáná pardháná; manníá parwanníá;

INFORM, TO, *V. T.*
dassná; sunáuná; ḳhabar dení; jatáuná; chitárná; kah dená; janáuná; pargaṭ karná;
to inform by message. sunehá ghallná;

INFORMAL, *A.*
1. not according to rule. beqaidá;
2. simple. rache miche hoe;

INFORMANT, *N.*
bhetí. *m;* ḳhabar denwálá. *m;* suhá. *m;*

INFORMATION, *N.*
ḳhabar. *f;* suh. *f;* taláh. *f;* samáchár. *f;* ḍáh. *m:* uggh suggh. *f;* attá pattá. *m;* bhákiá. *m;*

INFORMER, *N.*
bhetí. *m;* suhá. *m;* jásús. *m;* bhediá. *m;*

INFRACTION, *N.*
1. breakage. ṭúṭ. *f;* toṛ. *m;*
2. violation. khanḍan. *m;*

INFREQUENT, *A.*
kade kade; vele kuvele;

INFREQUENTLY, *Adv.*
ghaṭṭ waddh; kade kade; ghaṭṭ;

INFRINGE, TO, *V. T.*
hukm udúlí karní; hukm toṛ dená; ná manná;

INFRINGEMENT, *N.*
jurm. *m;* hukm udúlí. *f;* qusúr. *m;*

INFURIATE, TO, *V. T.*
russáuná; bhaṛkáuná; gussá diláuná; chheṛná; rerrná;

INFURIATED, *A.*
karodhí; baṛe gusse vichch; bhuhe; jaliá balíá; russiá hoyá; with flies, &c. makhiáiá hoyá; akhiyá hoyá; khijjiá hoyá;

INFUSE, TO, *V. T.*
páuná; ḍálná;

INFUSION, *N.*
dushánḍá. *m;*

INGATHERING, *N.*
fasl. *m;* wáḍhí. *f;*

INGENIOUS, *A.*
ḍhangí; guṇí; hikmatí; hoshiyár; sujan; chattar; usṭandí;

INGENIOUSLY, *Adv.*
hoshiyárí nál;

INGENIOUSNESS, *N.*
hoshiyárí. *f;* guṇ. *m;* chatarái. *f;*

INGENUITY, *N.*
hunḍar. *m;* hoshiyárí. *f;* hikmat. *f;* usṭanḍ. *m;*

INGLORIOUS, *A.*
ṭhíṭṭh; búrá; máṛá;

INGRAFT, TO, *V. T.*
píunḍ cháṛhná; peunḍí karní; peunḍ láuní;

INGRATITUDE, *N.*
náshukrí. *f;* lunharámí. *f;* nimakharámí. *f;* náshukrguzárí. *f;* beshukrí *f;* kirat ghanṭá. *m;*
Proverbs to express ingratitude.
1. when his house was built he forgot the carpenter. Koṭṭhá ussariá, te tarkhán wissariá;
2. when the wish was satisfied, the carpenter was forgotten. tamá latthá te tarkhán wissariá;

INGRESS, *N.*
rastá. *m;* ráh. *f;* galá. *m;*

IṆGULFED, TO BE, *V. I.*
1. entirely, ḍubb janá;
2. somewhat. dhasná; dhas chalná: khubbhná;

INHABIT, TO, *V. T.*
wassná; ráhná; ṭikná;

INHABITANT, *N.*
rahanwálá. *m;* waskín. *m;* wásí. *m;* wasník. *m;* wassanwálá. *m;*
legal term. sákin. *m;*

INHABITED, *A.*
ábád;

INHALE, TO, *V. T.*
1. to breathe. dam láiná; sáh láiná;
2. to smell. súṇgghaná;

INHARMONIOUS, *A.*
betál; besurá;

INHERIT, TO, *V. T.*
málik ho jáná; wáris banná; wirsá milná;

INHERITANCE, *N.*
wirsá. *m;* paṭṭí. *f;* milkíyat. *f;* málaki. *f;* jáedát. *f;*

INHERITOR, *N.*
haqqdár. *m;* wáris. *m;* adhkárí. *m;*

INHIBIT, TO, *V. T.*
1. to forbid. warajná ; maná karná ; ṭhák dená ;
2. to check. rokná ; ṭhák dená ; aṭkáuná ;
INHIBITION, *N.*
manáhí. *f;* rok. *f;* bandish. *f;*
INHUMAN, *A.*
1. hard. saḳht ;
2. unmerciful. beráhm ; betaras ; patthar dil ;
3. tyrannical. jálim ; jabardast ;
4. stoneyhearted. patthar dil ; hattiárá ; haiṇsiárá ;
INHUMANITY, *N.*
saḳhtí. *f;* beráhmí. *f;* julm. *m;* jástí. *f;*
INHUMANLY, *Adv.*
saḳhtí nál ; baṛí beráhmí nál ;
INHUME, TO, *V. T.*
dabb dená ; gaḍáuná ; dafan karná ;
INIMICAL, *A.*
1. hostile. virodh ; ḳhiláf ;
2. harsh. rukkhá ; haiṇsiárá ; hattíará ;
3. hurtful. nuqsání ; nuqsán karnwálá ;
INIQUITIOUS, *A.*
burá ; sharír ; bhaiṛá ; adharmí ;
INIQUITOUSLY, *Adv.*
sharárat nál ;
INIQUITY, *N.*
buríáí. *f;* sharárat. *f;* hattiá. *m;* páp. *m;* gunáh. *m;* dosh. *m;* adharm. *m;*
INITIAL, *A.*
pahlá ;
INITIAL, *N.*
náṇ dá páhlá akkhar. *m;*
INITIAL, TO, *V. T.*
sehí páuná ; akkhar karná ;
to affix thumbmark. aṇgguṭhá láuná ;
INITIATE, TO, *V. T.*
1. to begin. shurú karná ; ád karná ;
2. to introduce. miláuná ;
3. to tell. batláuná ; kah dená ; dassná ;
4. to teach. sikhláuná ; paṛháuná ;
INITIATION, *N.*
1. entrance. daḳhal. *f;*
2. beginning. muḍḍh. *m;* shurú. *m;* ád. *m;*
INJECT, TO, *V. T.*
ṭikká lagáuná ;
INJECTION, *N.*
ṭikká, *m;*
INJUDICIOUS, *A.*
besamajh ; bemukkh ; nadán ;
INJUDICIOUSLY, *Adv.*
besamjhí nál ;
INJUDICIOUSNESS, *N.*
beaqlí. *f;* nadání. *f;*
INJUNCTION, *N.*
1. advice. hidáyat. *f;* saláh. *f;* matt. *f;* gurmatt. *m;*
2. order. hukm. *m;* ágiá. *m;* tágíd. *m;*
INJURE, TO, *V. T.*
1. to spoil. nuqsán karná ; wigáṛná ; ḳharáb kar dená ; harjá páuná ; pheṛná ;
2. to give pain to. dukh dená ; taklíf dení ; dil dukháuná ;
3. to harass. satáuná ; aukhíáṇ karní ; chheṛná ;
4. to injure one's enemy. lahú dá ghuṭṭ píná ;
INJURED, TO BE, *V. I.*
kaṇghá honá ; nuqsán ho jáná ;
INJURIOUS, *A.*
nuqsání ; dukhdái ;
INJURY, *N.*
nuqsán. *m;* gháṭṭá. *m;* harj. *f;* harjá. *m;* dakhlá. *m;* bijj. *f;*
a bruise. choṭ. *f;* jarb. *f;* saṭṭ. *f;*
INJUSTICE, *N.*
beinsáfí. *f;* anniá. *m;* hikk dá dhakká. *m;* beniáín. *f;* julm. *m;* anher. *m;*
INK, *N.*
sháhí. *f;* siáhí. *f;*
red ink. rattí sháhí. *f;* lál sháhí. *f;*
INKLING, *N.*
súh. *f;* patá. *m;* ḳhabar. *f;* uggh suggh. *f;*
INKSTAND, *N.*
bugtá. *m;* dawát. *f;* duát. *f;* maswání. *f;* sawání. *f;*
INLAY, TO, *V. T.*
mínákárí karní ;
INLET, *N.*
khálí. *f;* nálá. *m;* nadí. *f;*

INMATE, *N*.
rahanwálá. *m*; wásí. *m*; waskín. *m*;

INMOST, *A*.
andarlá;

INN, *N*.
1. for native travellers. sarán. *f*;
2. for European travellers. dák bangalá. *m*;
3. connected with temples. dharmsálá. *m*; gurdwárá. *m*; thákardawárá. *m*;

INNER, *A*.
andarlá; vichlá;

INNINGS, *N*.
wár. *f*;

INNKEEPER, *N*.
saránwálá. *m*; bhaṭhiyárá. *m*;

INNOCENCE, *N*.
begunáhí. *f*; bedosí. *f*; bequsurí. *f*; sádgí. *f*;

INNOCENT, *A*.
bedos; begunáh; bequsúr; betaqsírá; suddh; nirdos; bedosá;
simple minded. bholá bhálá;

INNOCENTLY, *Adv*.
begunáhí nál; siddhíáí nál;

INNOCUOUS, *A*.
bholá bhálá; garíb; sádá; siddhá; siddh paddhará;

INNOVATE, TO, *V. T*.
nawín taráh karná;

INNOVATION, *N*.
nawín gall. *f*;

INNOXIOUS, *A*.
1. harmless. bechárá; maskín;
2. free from mischievious qualities. sádá; siddhá; siddh paddhará; bholá bhálá;

INNUMERABLE, *A*.
angiṇt; behisáb; beshumár;

INOBSERVANT, *A*.
gáfal; annhá; bemukh; ḍhillá maṭṭhá;

INOCULATE, TO, *V. T*.
ṭikká lagáuná OR láuná;

INOCULATOR, *N*.
ṭikká lagáunwálá. *m*; dágdár. *m*;

INOFFENSIVE, *A*.
bholá bhálá; garíb; bechárá; maskín; siddhá; siddh paddhará; baṛá gáo;

INOPERATIVE, *A*.
nikammá; kamm nahíṇ dendá; láhásal;

INOPPORTUNE, *A*.
bemauqá; kumauqá; kuvele; bewaqt; ṭhík waqt nahíṇ;
Proverb concerning inopportune arrivals. The wretch came at midnight like a lump of clay for a pillow and a clod in one's mouth. sunjáṇ áyá adhí rát, dilh sarándí, waṭe wát;

INOPPORTUNELY, *Adv*.
kuvele; velo sir ná;

IN ORDER THAT.
táṇ jo;

INORDINATE, *A*.
haddoṇ waddh; wadhík; wadherá; behadd;
inordinate desire. lobh. *m*;

INQUIRE, TO, *V. T*.
puchchná; parchol karná; daryáft karná; bhálná; patá karná; khojná; khabar láiní;
after one's health. dí surt láiní; dá patá karná; puchchná;

INQUIRER, *N*.
iqrárí. *m*; mutaláshí. *m*;

INQUIRY, *N*.
partál. *f*; bhál. *f*; parchol. *f*; khoj. *m*; puchch gichch. *f*; puchchh páchchh. *m*;
inquiring at a shrine. puchchh. *f*;

INQUISITIVE, *A*.
aiweṇ laṭṭ aṛáunwálá;

INROAD, *N*.
dháwá. *m*; hallá. *m*; chaṛháí. *f*;

INSALUBRIOUS, *A*.
gaṇdá; námuwáfiq;

INSANE, *N*.
baurá; kamlá; kamlí; págal; diwáná; sudáí; kamlá ramlá; jhallá;

INSANITY, *N*.
saudá. *m*; págalpuṇá. *m*; jhall. *m*; kamal. *m*;

INSCRIBE, TO, *V. T*.
likhná;

INSCRIPTION. *N*.
likhat. *f*; harf. *m*;

INSCRUTABLE, *A*.
samjhoṇ pare; aqloṇ pare;

INSECT, *N.*
kíṛá. *m*; makauṛá. *m*; káḍhá. *m*;
INSECURITY, *N.*
ḳhatrá. *m*;
INSENSATE, *A.*
beaql; bewaqúf; kuṇḍá; hochchhá; kamaql; murakh; kamlá;
INSENSIBILITY, *N.*
1. unconsciousness. behoshí. *f*; ghúkí. *f*;
2. apathy. sustí. *f*; ghúkí. *f*; ḍhil maṭṭh. *f*;
INSENSIBLE, *A.*
behosh;
INSEPARABLE, *A.*
jehṛa aḍḍ ná ho sake;
inseparable friend. langoṭiá yár. *m*; jání dost. *m*;
INSERT, TO, *V. T.*
1. to include. dáḳhal karná; shámil karná;
2. to write. likh dená;
INSERTION, *N.*
dáḳhalá. *m*;
INSIDE, *A.*
andar;
INSIDE, *N.*
andar. *m*;
INSIDIOUS, *A.*
dagábáj; beímán; khoṭṭá; kapṭí;
INSIDIOUSNESS, *N.*
dagábájí. *f*; beímánagí. *f*;
INSIGHT, *N.*
aql. *f*; samajh. *f*; buddh. *f*; chaukasí. *f*;
INSIGNIA, *N.*
1. medal; takhmá. *m*;
2. badge of chaprasi. chaprás. *f*;
INSIGNIFICANCE, *N.*
beqadrí. *f*; alpatá. *f*;
INSIGNIFICANT, *A.*
haulá; chhoṭá; náchíz; kujh nahíṇ; haqír; náqas;
INSIGNIFICANTLY, *Adv.*
beqadrí nál;
INSINCERE, *A.*
dagábáj; jhuṭhá; kapṭí;
INSINCERELY, *Adv.*
dagábájí nál; chhal nál; beímání nál;
INSINCERITY, *N.*
makkárí. *f*; dhokhebájí. *f*; chhal. *m*; kapaṭ. *m*;
INSINUATE, TO, *V. T.*
1. to backbite. chuglí karní; nindiá karná; kann bharná; lutíáṇ láuná; bhagí karní;
2. to fill the ear. kann bharná;
INSINUATION, *N.*
chuglí. *f*; lutí. *f*; ujj. *f*;
INSIPID, *A.*
1. unsalted. alúṇá; miṭhluṇá; miṭhsalúná;
2. without taste. besuádá; bemajá; bakbaká; phikká; phuklá; phoklá;
3. without sauce, &c. rukkhá; phikká;
INSIPIDNESS, *N.*
besuádí. *f*; rukkhái. *f*; phikk. *m*;
INSIST, TO, *V. T.*
haṭh karná; de magar painá; kijá karní; de gal painá; siḍḍá karná;
INSISTENT, *A.*
jiddí; pakká; aṇmoṛ; kabbá;
INSISTENCY, *N.*
kijá. *f*; haṭh. *m*; haṭh dharmí. *m*; chih. *m*;
INSOBRIETY, *N.*
nashebájí. *f*; nashá. *m*;
INSOLENCE, *N.*
kharmastí. *f*; shoḳhí. *f*; chauṛ. *f*; astái. *f*; see IMPERTINENCE.
INSOLENT, *A.*
magrur; magrá; bhuhe; astá; ḍhíṭh; see IMPUDENT.
táne máranwálá; chák;
INSOLENTLY, *Adv.*
akaṛke; beadabí nál; shoḳhí nál;
INSOLUBILITY, *N.*
ná ghullaṇ dí sift. *f*;
INSOLUBLE, *A.*
ná ghullaṇwálá; ná pagghraṇwálá;
INSOLVENCY, *N.*
dawálá. *m*;
INSOLVENT, *A.*
dawálá;
INSOMUCH, *Adv.*
itthoṇ tík;
INSPECT, TO, *V. T.*
parakhná; partáuná; pherá márná; wekhná; tohná;
1. to inspect books. partál karná;

2. to inspect a school. muáiná karná ;
3. to look closely, níjh láuná ;
INSPECTION, *N.*
partál. *f* ; imtehán. *m* ;
1. medical inspection. muláhzá. *m* ;
2. close inspection. níjh. *f* ;
INSPECTOR, *N.*
inspiktar. *m* ;
INSPIRATION, *N.*
ilhám. *m* ;
INSPIRE, TO, *V. T.*
josh duáuná OR diláuná ; ummed dení ; tagṛeáṇ karná ; ubhárná ; agg bhaṛkáuná ;
INSTABILITY, *N.*
besábatí, *f* ; nápaidárí. *f* ;
INSTABLE, *A.*
pakká nahíṇ ; kachchá ;
INSTALL, TO, *V. T.*
1. to seat. biṭhálná ; jagáh dení ;
2. to enthrone. gaddí utte baháuná ; takht utte baháuná ;
3. to appoint to some rank. uhde utte chaṛháuná ;
INSTALMENT, *N.*
kisht. *f* ;
INSTANCE, *N.*
1. example. misál. *f* ;
2. pattern. namuná. *m* ; váṇgi. *f* ; bannagí. *f* ;
3. for instance. maslan ; arthát ; jíweṇ ; jíkar ;
INSTANT, *N.*
dam. *m* ; pall. *m* ; jhaṭ. *m* ;
INSTANTANEOUS, *A.*
ikk dam ; jhaṭ paṭ ; use vele ;
INSTANTLY, *Adv.*
turt ; turant ; jhaṭ paṭ ; turt phurt ; huṇe ; jhaṭá jhaṭ ; dabádab ;
INSTEAD, *Adv.*
de badle ; de tháṇ ;
INSTIGATE, TO, *V. T.*
chukkná ; bhiṛáuná ; uchálá dená ; see EXCITE & INCITE.
INSTIGATION, *N.*
uchálá. *m* ; lárá. *m* ; chukk. *f* ; tamá. *m* ;
INSTIGATOR, *N.*
bakáunwálá. *m* ;
INSTIL, TO, *V. T.*
samjháuná ; see INSTRUCT.
INSTINCT, *N.*
janauráṇ dí aql. *f* ;
INSTINCTIVE, *A.*
qudratí ;
INSTINCTIVELY, *Adv.*
malomalí ; kháh makháh ; ápí áp ;
INSTITUTE, TO, *V. T.*
láuná ; muqarrar karná ; ṭhahráuná ; qaim karná ;
INSTRUCT, TO, *V. T.*
samjháuná ; sikhláuná ; paṛháuná ; sabaq dená ;
INSTRUCTION, *N.*
paṛhái. *f* ; tálím *f* ; matt. *f* ; sikkhiá. *f* ; updes. *m* ; sikkh matt. *f* ; nasíhat. *f* ; sikhautí. *f* ; sikhauṭí. *f* ; sikhláut. *f* ; religious instruction. gián. *f* ; dharm updesh. *m* ;
INSTRUCTIVE, *A.*
tálímí ; sikkhiá denwálí ;
INSTRUCTOR, *N.*
1. school teacher. ustáḍ. *m* ;
2. religious teacher. Sikh. giání. *m* ; updesak. *m* ; updesí. *m* ; gurú. *m* ; gúr. *m* ; updeshí. *m* ;
3. religious teacher, Muhammadan. maulví. *m* ; murshad. *m* ;
4. religious teacher, Hindu. pandit. *m* ; bráhman. *m* ;
INSTRUMENT, *N.*
hathiyár. *m* ; ṛachch. *m* ;
1. a means. wasílá. *m* ;
2. a machine. kalá. *m* ;
3. musical instrument. bájá. *m* ; wájá. *m* ;
INSTRUMENTALITY, *N.*
wasílá. *m* ;
INSUBORDINATION. *N.*
náfarmání. *f* ; hukmudulí. *f* ; ágyá bhaṇg. *f* ;
INSUFFERABLE, *A.*
ná sahan jogg ;
INSUFFICIENCY, *N.*
ghaṭṭá. *m* ; kasar. *m* ; kamí. *f* ; thuṛ. *f.* see DEFICIENCY.
INSUFFICIENT, *A.*
ghaṭṭ ; kassá ; thoṛá ; káfí nahíṇ ;
INSUFFICIENTLY, *Adv.*
adhurá ; thoṛá ; ghaṭṭ ;

INSULT, *N.*
namoshí. *f;* bijjtí. *f;* beadabí. *f;* búrí báb. *f;* bepatí. *f;* beizzatí. *f;* apmán. *m;*

INSULT, TO. *V. T.*
ijjat láhuní; pat láhuná; muṇh kálá karná; durkárná; ṭhiṭṭh karná;
1. to insult a woman. hatth páuná;
2. he insults me. sáḍí niṇdiá kardá hai; sáḍí pat láhúndá hai; sánúṇ beizzat kardá hai.
3. he insulted me. uh ne merí pat láh suṭṭí.

INSULTING *A.*
bad jabán; magrá; hekaṛbáj; bijjtí karnwálá;

INSUPERABLE, *A.*
waḍḍá aukhá;

INSURANCE, *N.*
bímá. *m;*

INSURE. TO. *V. T.*
bímá karáuná;

INSURGENT, *N.*
ákí. *m;* bágí. *m;* daṇggáí. *m;*

INSURRECTION, *N.*
gadar. *m;* balwá. *m;* phatúr. *m;*

INTACT, *A.*
1. complete. sábat; purá; sárá; sabutá; sábtá; samúchchá;
2. uninjured. bachiá hoyá;

INTEGRITY, *N.*
ímándárí. *f;* sachchíáí. *f;* sidhíáí. *f;* bhalmánsí. *f;*

INTELLECT, *N.*
aql. *f;* samajh. *f;* see INTELLIGENCE.

INTELLECTUAL, *A.*
samajhdár; ilmdár; paṛhiá hoyá;

INTELLIGENCE, *N.*
1. understanding. buddh. *f;* aql. *f;* samajh. *f;* siánaf. *f;* chajj. *m;* chárbájí. *f;*
2. news. ḳhabar. *f;* suh. *f;* suggh. *f;* uggh suggh. *f;*

INTELLIGENT, *A.*
siáná; hoshiyár; aqlwálá; buddhwán; samajhdár; gíání; surtíuá;

INTEMPERANCE, *N.*
badparejí. *f;*

INTEMPERATE. *A.*
badparej; aṇrakkhá;
1. in drink. mastáná;
2. in food. peṭú; kháú;

INTEMPERATELY, *Adv.*
mastewen nál;

INTEND, TO, *V. T.*
cháhuná; irádá karná; níat karní; thánná; jí karná; dháṛná;

INTENSE, *A.*
behadd; ḍáḍhá; bahut ziyádá; wadhík;

INTENSIFY, TO, *V. T.*
wadháuná;

INTENSITY, *N.*
jor. *m;* tezí. *f;*

INTENT, *A.*
suchet; shukín;

INTENTION, *N.*
níat. *f;* irádá. *m;* matlab. *m;* dalíl. *f;* garaj. *f;* arath. *m;* phurná. *m;* marzí. *f;* manshá. *m;* muddá. *m;* murád. *f;* gauṇ. *m;*
a good intention. suarath. *m;*

INTENTIONALLY, *Adv.*
ján bujh ke; uchechá; soch samajhke;

INTER, TO, *V. T.*
gaḍḍná; dabb dená;

INTERCEDE, TO, V. T.
dí sifárish karná;

INTERCEDER, *N.*
sháfí. *m;* hámí bharanwálá. *m;* sifárish karnwálá. *m;* wicholá. *m;*

INTERCEPT, TO, *V. T.*
ràh vichch phaṛná;

INTERCESSION, *N.*
1. mediation. sifárish. *f;*
2. prayer. bentí. *f;* minnat. *f;* duá. *f;* parárthṇá. *f;*

INTERCESSOR, *N.*
sifárish karnwálá. *m;* sifárishí. *m;* wicholá. *m;*

INTERCESSORY, *A.*
sifárishí;

INTERCHANGE, TO, V. T.
waṭṭo saṭṭá karná; waṭáuná; waṭá dená; márchá karná;

INTERCHANGEABLE, *A.*
waṭṭ salaṭ jog;

INTERCOURSE, *N.*
wartává. *m*; milní gilní. *f*; mel jol. *f*; saṇgat. *f*; leká deká. *m*; leká dekí. *f*; warat sarat. *m*; uṭṭhaṇ baiṭhaṇ. *m*; láká. *m*; wáh. *m*; bannat. *f*; bol chál. *f*;
to have sexual intercourse. chodná;

INTERDICT, TO, *V. T.*
warajná; rokná; ṭhák dená; aṭkáuná; maná karná;

INTEREST, *N.*
1. usury. biáj. *m*; wiáj. *m*; sud. *m*;
2. intercourse. láká. *m*; wástá. *m*;

INTEREST, *N.*
man bhauná. *m*; ríjh. *f*;

INTERESTED, *A.*
1. seeking advantage. matlabí yár;
2. having an interest. man bhaundá;

INTERFERE, TO, *V. T.*
dakhal dená; dhasná; ghusná; ghusaṛná; hatth páuná; painá; pair aṛáuná; láká dená; bháṇjí mární;

INTERFERENCE, *N.*
dakhal. *f*; laṭṭ márná. *m*; láká. *m*; bháṇjí. *f*;
Proverb used of an interfering person. Neither invited or consulted, yet she is the mother of the bridegroom! saddí ná puchchhí nausho dí ammáṇ;

INTERIOR, *N.*
andarwár. *m*;

INTERIOR, *A.*
andarlá; vichlá

INTERLOPE, TO, *V. T.*
dakhal dená; see INTERFERE.

INTERMARRIAGE, *N.*
waṭṭe dá sákk. *m*;

INTERMARRY, TO, *V. T.*
waṭṭe dá sákk karná; waṭṭá karná;

INTERMEDDLE, TO, *V. T.*
dakhal dená: see INTERFERE.

INTERMINABLE, *A.*
behadd; beoṛak;

INTERMINGLE, TO, *V. T.*
miláuná; raláná;

INTERMISSION, *N.*
1. a breath. sáh. *m*;
2. interval. arsá. *m*; waqt. *m*; chir. *m*;

INTERNAL, *A.*
vichlá; andarlá; wichkárlá;

INTERPOSE, TO, *V. T.*
dakhal dená; see INTERFERE.

INTERPRET, TO, *V. T.*
1. to explain, matlab samjháuná; arth karná;
2. to translate. tarjamá karná;

INTERPRETATION, *N.*
matlab. *m*; arth. *m*; bayán. *m*;

INTERPRETER, *N.*
tarjamá karnwálá. *m*;

INTERROGATE, TO, *V. T.*
sawál karná; puchchná; patá puchchná;

INTERROGATION, *N.*
sawál. *m*;

INTERROGATOR, *N.*
sawálí. *m*;

INTERRUPT, TO, *V. T.*
gal kaṭṭní; ṭhák dená; gal ṭokní; bháṇjí mární;

INTERRUPTION, *N.*
1. hindrance. aṭak. *f*; rukaut. *f*;
2. intervention. dakhal. *f*; khaṇdat. *f*; bháṇjí. *f*; khalal. *m*;

INTERSECT, TO, *V. T.*
aḍḍ aḍḍ karná; wakkh karná;

INTERTWINE, TO, *V. T.*
gundaná;

INTERVAL, *N.*
muhlat. *f*; chir. *m*;

INTERVENE, TO, *V. T.*
dakhal dená; pair aṛáuná;

INTERVENTION, *N.*
dakhal. *f*;

INTERVIEW, *N.*
darshan. *m*; milní, *f*; mulaqát. *f*; melá. *m*; mel jol. *m*;

INTERVIEW, TO, *V. T.*
darshan karná; dídár lainá; malaqát karní; milná;
to grant an interview. darshan dená.

INTERWEAVE, TO, *V. T.*
gundaná;

INTERWOVEN, *A.*
pechwálá; miliá juliá hoyá;

INTESTINES, *N.*
andríáṇ. *f*; andaráṇ. *f*;

INTIMACY, *N.*
wáqabí. *f*; dostí. *f*; gáṛhí dostí. *f*; mel jol. *f*;

INTIMATE, *A*.
wáqab; kháskí;
INTIMATE, TO, *V. T.*
ḳhabar dení; dassná; kah dená;
INTIMATION, *N*.
ḳhabar. *f*; patá. *m*; suh. *m*; ládh. *f*;
INTIMIDATE, TO, *V. T.*
ḍar dená OR páuná; jor wikháuná; ḍaráuná; dhamkáuná; dabb dení; dabká márná; dhauṇsná;
INTIMIDATION, *N*.
dhamkí. *f*; ghuṛkí. *f*; jhiṛak. *f*; dhauṇs. *f*; bhabkí. *f*;
INTO, *Prep*.
vichch; vikhe;
INTOLERABLE, *A*.
ná sahan jog; julm dí gal;
INTOLERANCE, *N*.
jabardastí. *f*; haṭṭ. *f*; jástí. *f*;
INTOLERANT, *A*.
jabardast; ziddí; karṛá;
INTONATION, *N*.
bolí. *f*;
INTOXICATE, TO, *V. T.*
mast karná; nasháí karná; behosh karná;
to be intoxicated. guṭṭ ho jáná; chhakná;
INTOXICATED, *A*.
mast; nashe vichch; mastáná; matwálá; madhmáttá;
intoxicated with bhang. bhaṇgeriá hoyá;
INTOXICATION, *N*.
mastí. *f*; nashá. *m*; behoshí. *f*;
INTRACTABLE, *A*.
ḍhíṭhá; khachrá; ziddí; karṛá;
INTRACTABILITY, *N*.
haṭṭ. *m*; zidd. *f*;
INTRANQUILITY, *N*.
bechainí. *f*; bearámí. *f*;
INTRENCH. TO, *V. T.*
morchábaṇdí karní;
INTRENCHMENT, *N*.
morchá. *m*; ṭoá. *m*;
INTREPID, *A*.
dilaur; diler; diláwar; tagṛá; himmatí; himtál; hauslewálá; beḍharak; himmatwálá;
INTREPIDITY, *N*.
dilaurí. *f*; dilerí. *f*; diláwarí. *f*; himmat. *f*; hausalá. *f*; súrbírtá. *m*; surmápuṇá. *m*; variámagí. *f*; surtáí. *f*;
INTREPIDLY, *Adv*.
dilerí nál; hausale nál; himmat nál;
INTRICACY, *N*.
wal. *m*; pech. *m*; wal pech. *m*; pech ghech. *m*; uljháu. *m*;
INTRICATE, *A*.
pechdár; pechwálá;
difficult. aukkhá; mushkil;
INTRIGUE, *N*.
chalá. *m*; mansúbá. *m*; saláh. *f*;
INTRIGUE, TO, *V. T.*
mansúbá bannhná OR gharná; saláh pakáuná; gall pakání; saláh gundní; saláhán karní; matá pakáuná;
INTRODUCE, TO, *V. T.*
miláuná; wáqabí karáuní; mulaqát karáuní; mel karáuná;
INTRODUCTION, *N*.
1. meeting. mulaqát. *f*; mel. *m*; darshan. *m*; milní. *f*;
2. preface of a book. bhúmiká. *m*;
INTRUDE, TO, *V. T.*
daḳhal dená; ghusaṛná; ghusná;
INTRUDER, *N*.
daḳhal denwálá. *m*;
INTRUSION, *N*.
ghuss. *m*; daḳhal. *f*;
INTRUST, TO, *V. T.*
sauṇp dená; hawále karná; phaṛáuná; amánat rakkhná;
INTUITION, *N*.
aql. *f*; samajh. *f*; sújh. *f*; buddh. *m*;
INUNDATE, TO, *V. I.*
jal thal ho jáná. see FLOOD.
INUNDATION, *N*.
haṛh. *m*; chhall. *m*;
INVADE, TO, *V. T.*
hallá karná; chaṛháí karní; dháwá karná;
INVALID, *N*.
bamár. *m*;
INVALID, *A*.
1. ill. bamár; tagṛá nahíṇ;
2. not allowable. asiddh;
INVALIDATE, TO, *V. T.*
raddná; radd kar dená;

INVALUABLE, *A.*
aṇmull; amolak; waḍḍe mull dá;
INVARIABLE, *A.*
aṭal;
INVARIABLY, *Adv.*
sadá; hameshá;
INVASION, *N.*
dháwá. *m;* hallá. *m;* chaṛhái. *f;* dháuṇí. *f;* dhái. *f;*
INVECTIVE, *N.*
gálí. *f;* gál. *f;* gaṇdíáṇ gallán. *f;* gálí galoch. *f;* phakkaṛ. *f;* phiṭak. *f;*
INVEIGLE, TO, *V. T.*
ṭhaggná; wargaláuná; lárá dená; see DECEIVE.
INVENT, TO, *V. T.*
ghaṛná; kaḍḍhná; banáuná; magazoṇ kaḍḍhná;
INVENTION, *N.*
banauṭ. *f;*
INVENTORY, *N.*
firist. *f;* bíjak. *m;*
INVERT, TO, *V. T.*
ulṭáuná; palṭáuná; ṭalaná paṭalná;
INVERTED, *A.*
múdha; puṭṭhá; úṇdhá; múṇdhá;
INVEST, TO, *V. T.*
gherná; gherá pá lainá; walná;
INVESTIGATE, TO, *V. T.*
dekh bhállná; puchchná; hál hawál puchchná; paṛtáuná; parchol karná; wichárná;
INVESTIGATION, *N.*
dhúṇd. *f;* parchol. *f;* paṛtál. *f;* partáwá. *m;* ṭol. *f;* peshí. *f;* bhál. *f;* puchchh páchchh. *m;*
INVESTIGATOR, *N.*
khojjí. *m;*
INVIGORATE, TO, *V. T.*
tagṛeáṇ karná; josh duáuná; jí kaḍḍháuná;
for oneself. ji kaḍḍhná;
INVINCIBLE. *A.*
ajít;
INVIOLATE, *A.*
pák; khális; khará;
INVISIBLE, *A.*
gupt; chhipiá hoyá; andekhiá; aṇdiṭṭh; lukhiá hoyá;
INVISIBLY, *Adv.*
parokhe; asujh; akkhíáṇ thoṇ parokhá; jehṛá ná disse;
INVITATION, *N.*
suddáwá. *m;* buláwá. *m;* dáut. *f;* sadd. *f;*
1. invitation to a wedding. gaṇdh *f;* káṇḍhá *m;*
2. proverb. The flour is not yet ground, and the invitations are already going about. áṭṭá píṭhá nahíṇ te káṇḍhe agge vade phirdín;
3. Proverb. First put the flour in the safe and then send out the invitations. pahle kúlhí áṭṭá páwan pichchhe káṇḍhe phiráwan;
INVITE, TO, *V. T.*
buláná; saddná; dáwat karní; to a wedding. gaṇḍh ghallní;
INVOCATION, *N.*
duá. *f;* bentí. *f;* duhái. *f;*
INVOICE, *N.*
hisáb. *m;* bil. *m;* bíjak. *m;* lekhá pattá. *m;* hisáb kitáb. *f;*
INVOKE, TO, *V. T.*
pukárná; duhái dení. see TO CALL.
INVOLUNTARILY, *Adv.*
badobadí; aiweṇ kíven;
INVOLVE, TO, *V. T.*
wal páuná; pech páuná; phasáuná; pher páuná;
INVOLVED, *A.*
pechwálá; pechdár; lapeṭwáṇ; waldár;
INWARD, *A.*
andarlá; vichlá;
IRASCIBILITY, N.
támsí. *f;* narázagí, *f;* waṭṭ. *m;* for a child. chhiṛham. *f;*
IRASCIBLE, *A.*
avaiṛá; chhitthá hoyá; for a child. chhiṛhamí;
IRON, *N.*
istrí. *f;*
IRON, *N.*
lohá. *m;*
IRON, TO, *V. T.*
istrí karní OR pher dená;
IRONMONGER, *N.*
lohá wechanwálá. *m;* lohṭiá. *m;*

IRONSMITH, *N.*
lohár. *m* ;
IRONWORK, *N.*
lohe dá kamm. *m* ;
IRONY, *N.*
jugat bází. *f*; makhaul. *m*; thaṭṭhá. *m* ;
IRRADIATE, TO, *V. T.*
lishkná ; chamakná ; damakná ;
IRRATIONAL, *A.*
bewaqúf ; múrakh ; besamajh ; wáhiyát ;
IRRATIONALITY, *N.*
besamajhgí. *f*; beaqlí. *f* ;
IRRECLAIMABLE, *A.*
1. lost. guáchiá hoyá ; jehṛá ná mil sake ;
2. incorrigible. ḍhíṭh ;
IRRECONCILABLE, *A.*
sakht ; karṛá ;
IRRECOVERABLE, *A.*
guáchiá hoyá ; gayá guátá ;
IRREGULAR, *A.*
ulṭ pulṭ ; beqaidá ; betaríqá ;
IRREGULARITY, *N.*
anrít. *f*; puṭhsidh. *m* ;
IRREGULARLY, *Adv.* ;
beqaidagí nál ; ulaṭ pulaṭ ;
IRRELAVANCY, *N.*
wakkhrí gal ; hor gal. *f* ;
IRRELAVANT. *A.*
wakkhrá ; hor ;
IRRELIGION, *N.*
bedíní. *f*; adharm. *m*; adharmtáí. *f*; beímángí. *f*; abhagtí. *f* ;
IRRELIGIOUS, *A.*
bedín ; kuráhá ; adharmí; bedharm; sharír ;
IRRELIGIOUSLY, *Adv.*
bedíní nál ;
IRRELIGIOUSNESS, *N.*
bedíní. *f*; bedharmí. *f* ;
IRREMEDIABLE, *A.*
beiláj ; ih dá iláj nahíṇ ;
IRREMISSIBLE, *A.*
ná bakhshan jog ;
IRREMOVABLE, *A.*
sábat ; paedár ; aṭall ;
IRREPARABLE, *A.*
ná gandhan jog ;
IRREPREHENSIBLE, *A.*
másúm ; bedosh ; bequsúr; bedosá;
IRREPRESSIBLE, *A.*
beqábú ; bewass ;
IRREPROACHABLE, *A.*
bedág ; bequsúr;
IRRESOLUTE, *A.*
do dilá ; dochittá ;
IRRESOLUTION, *N.*
dochitt. *m* ; dochittí. *f* ; kachch pakk. *m* ;
IRREVERENCE, *N.*
beadabí. *f*; bedíní. *f*; anádar. *m* ;
IRREVERENT, *A.*
dín walloṇ beparwáh ; bedín ;
IRREVERENTLY, *Adv.*
beadabí nál ;
IRREVOCABLE, *A.*
pakká ;
IRRIGATE, TO, *V. T.*
wattar wáste karná ; pání dená ; sinjná ; pailí bharná ; pání láuná ; pailí pichaná ;
IRRITABILITY, *N.*
narázagí. *f*; chhiṛham. *f*; rinjí, *f*; kiṛ. *f* ;
IRRITABLE, *A.*
naráz ; kauṛá ; saṛiá bhujiá ; chhiṛhmí ; rinj ;
IRRITANT, *N.*
dukh denwálí chíz. *f* ;
IRRITATE, TO, *V. T.*
dikk dená ; chheṛná ; jichch karná ; satáuná ; chipchaṛháuná ; rusáuná ; bhakháuná ; agg láuná ; gussá duáuná ; gussá chaṛháuná ; dil khaṭṭá karná ; luhná ; chaṭkáuná ; khijáuná ;
IRRITATED, TO BE, *V. I.*
dil khaṭṭá honá; ukkhaṛná; akkná ;
IRRITATION, *N.*
1. provocation. chheṛ. *f*; jichái. *f* ;
2. anger. gussá. *m*; waṭṭ. *m* ; támsí. *f*; hirkh. *m*; rinjí. *f* ;
IRRITATIVE, *A.*
dukkhdái ; dukhdenwálá ;
IRRUPTION, *N.*
hallá. *m*; chaṛhái. *f*; dháwá. *m* ;
IS, *V. I.*
hai ;
ISLAND, *N.*
tápú. *m* ;
ISOLATE, *TO*, *V. T.*
wakkho wakkh karná ; alag karná ;

ISOLATED, *A.*
wakkh; alag; wakkhrá;
ISSUE, *N.*
1. result. natíjá. *m;* naberá. *m;*
2. offspring. bachche. *m;* aulád. *f;* álaulád. *f;* putt pottare. *m;*
ISSUE, TO, *V. I.*
nikalná;
ISSUE, TO, *V. T.*
kaḍḍhná; dená;
IT, *Pro.*
ih; uh;
ITCH, *N.*
khurk. *f;* jhaur. *f;* kháj. *f;* jhauhar. *f;*
ITCH, TO, *V. I.*
jhaur auní; kháj honí OR áuní; to scratch. khurkná;
ITCHING, *N.*
khurk, *f;* jalun. *f;* jhaur. *f;* kháj. *f;*
ITEM, *N.*
gal. *f;*
ITERATE, TO, *V. T.*
dohráuná; dusráuná;
ITERATION, *N.*
dohar. *f;*
ITINERANT, *N.*
ráhí. *m;* paṇdhí. *m;*
ITINERARY, *N.*
daure dí farist. *f;*
ITINERATE, TO, *V. T.*
daurá karná;
ITINERATION, *N.*
daurá. *m;* safar. *m;*
ITSELF, *Pro.*
áp o áp;
IVORY, *N.*
hátthi daṇḍ. *m;* daṇḍ khaṇḍ. *f;* Proverb. elephant's teeth, some are for show and some are to eat with. háthí de daṇḍ, vikháun de hor, te khán de hor;

J.

JABBER, *N.*
luttar luttar. *f;* bak. *m;* bak jhak. *f;* gapp. *f;*
JABBER, TO, *V. T.*
bakbak karná; luttar luttar karní; magaz márná; ṭaiṇ ṭaiṇ karná; khapáná; sir khapáuná; bataule márná; see CHATTER.
JABBERER, *N.*
bakwásí. *m;* luttarí. *m;* luttará. *m;* gappí. *m;* palálí. *m;* baturá. *m;* batauliá. *m;* batuní. *m;*
JACKAL, *N.*
giddar. *m;* giddarí. *f;*
JACKET, *N.*
koṭ. *m;* jákat. *m;*
waist coat, used as a jacket. phatúhí. *f;*
JAIL, *N.*
jel ḳháná. *m;* bandí ḳháná. *m;* hawalát. *f;* kanjí haud. *m;*
JAILER, *N.*
darogá. *m;*
JALAP, *N.*
juláb. *m;*
JAM, *N.*
murabbá. *m;*
JANGLE, *N.*
jhagrá. *m;* laṛáí. *f;* aṇ baṇ. *f;*
JANGLING, *N.*
chaṇkár. *m;* jhaṇkár. *m;* ṭhaṇáká. *m;*
JAR, *N.*
matkí. *f;* martabáṇ. *m;*
JARGON, *N.*
luttar luttar. *f;*
JASMINE, *N.*
chambá. *m;*
JAUNDICE, *N.*
parneh. *m;* panrehe. *m;* yarkán. *m;*
JAUNT, *N.*
1. walk. sail. *m;*
2. itineration. daurá. *m;*
3. journey. safar. *m;* paṇdh. *m;*
JAVELIN, *N.*
kaṭár. *f;* ḳhanjar. *m;* see DAGGER.
JAW, *N.*
khakhwáṛá. *m;* jabáṛá. *m;*
one side of the jaw. harb. *f;*
JAY, *N.*
garar. *m;*
JEALOUS, *A.*
jaliá baliá; saṛiá baliá; riskí;
1. to be jealous. saṛná; khár karná;
2. why are you jealous? taiṇúṇ sáṛá kyun áundá hai?
JEALOUSLY, *Adv.*
khár nál; saṛáṇdh nál;

JEALOUSY, *N.*
khár. *f*; jalan. *f*; irkhá. *m*; sáṛá. *m*;
JEER. *N.*
ṭhaṭṭhá. *m*; makhaul. *m*; táná. *m*; mehná. *m*; hássá. *m*; bollí ṭhollí. *f*;
JEER, TO, *V. T.*
táná dená; makhaul karná; kachhán márná; mehná dená; ṭhaṭṭhá karná; bollí láuní OR mární;
JEERER, *N.*
makhauliá. *m*; ṭhaṭṭhebáz. *m*, maskará. *m*; khíllí báj. *m*;
JEERING, *N.*
ṭhaṭṭhá. *m*; táná. *m*; bollí ṭhollí. *f*; khíllí bájí. *f*;
JEERINGLY, *Adv.*
táne márke; makhaul nál;
JEHOVAH, *N.*
Yahováh. *m*;
JERK, *N.*
jhaṭká. *m*; hujká. *m*; jhaṭak. *f*;
JERK, TO, *V. T.*
jhaṭká láuná; jhaṭká márná;
JESSAMINE, *N.*
chambelí. *f*;
JEST, *N.*
ṭhaṭṭhá. *m*; maskarí. *f*; makhaul. *m*; ṭhiskarí. *f*; khíllí. *f*;
JEST, TO, *V. T.*
ṭhaṭṭhá márná OR karná;
JESTER, *N.*
maskará. *m*; ṭhaṭṭhebáz. *m*; makhauliá. *m*; bhanḍ. *m*; nakhrelo. *f*; ṭokí. *m*; nakhrelá. *m*;
JESTING, *N.*
ṭhaṭṭhá. *m*; majákh. *f*; maskarí. *f*; ṭhaṭholí. *f*;
JESTINGLY, *Adv.*
ṭhaṭṭhe nál; makhaul nál; hásse nál;
JESUS, *N.*
Yisú. *m*; Hazrat Isá. *m*;
JET, *N.*
of water or milk. dhár. *m*; phuárá. *m*;
JEW, *N.*
Yahudí. *m*; Ibrání. *m*;
JEWEL & JEWELERY. *N.*
tumb. *f*; gahiṇá. *m*; gánhán. *m*; see ORNAMENT.
1. setting or fastening in jewels. jaṛat. *f*;
2. studded with jewels. jaṛau;
3. to cause jewels to be set. jaṛáuná;
4. pay for setting up jewels. jaṛáí. *f*;
JEWELLER, *N.*
suniárá. *m*;
JEWESS, *N.*
Yahudaní. *f*;
JEWISH, *A.*
Yahudí;
JIG, TO, *V. T.*
nachná; see DANCE.
JINGLE, *N.*
jhaṇkár. *m*; raṇak. *f*;
JINGLE, TO, *V. I.*
chaṇ chaṇ karná; raṇakná; karakná; ṭhaṇakná;
JINGLING, *N.*
jhaṇkár. *m*; raṇak. *f*; ṭhaṇáká. *m*;
JOB, *N.*
1. contract. ṭheká. *m*;
2. work. kamm. *m*; kár. *m*; karní. *f*;
JOCKEY, *N.*
sawár. *m*;
JOCULAR, *A.*
ṭhaṭṭhebáz; maskará; hassanwálá; hass mukhá; makhauliá;
JOCULARITY, *N.*
hássí. *f*; maskarí. *f*; ṭhaṭṭhebází. *f*;
JOCUND, *A.*
maují; raṇggí; khush; anandí;
JOG, *N.*
dhakká. *m*; see JOLT.
JOGGLE, TO, *V. T.*
hiláuná; dhakká márná; dhakelná;
JOIN, *N.*
joṛ. *m*;
JOIN, TO, *V. T.*
joṛná; gaṭháuná; miláuná; láuná; ṭáṇkná; gaṇḍhná; gaṭṭhná;
1. to join threads. gaṭṭhní láuní;
2. to cause to be joined. ṭaṇkwáuná; gaṇḍhwáuná;
JOIN, TO, *V. I.*
juṛná; ralná; milná;
JOINER, *N.*
tarkhán. *m*;

JOINERY, *N.*
tarkháná kamm. *m ;*
JOINING, *N.*
gaṇḍh gaṭṭh. *m ;* gaṭṭhní. *f ;*
JOINT, *N.*
band. *m ;* joṛ. *m ;*
of the wrist. guṭṭ. *m ;*
JOINTLY, *Adv.*
ralke ; milke, ; kaṭṭhe ; ral milke ;
JOKE, *N.*
ṭhaṭṭhá. *m ;* maskarí. *f ;* hásse dí gal. *f ;* jugat. *f ;* maḳhaul. *m;*
JOKE, TO, *V. T.*
ṭhaṭṭhá karná ; maḳhaul karná ; hassná ;
JOKER, *N.*
ṭhaṭṭhebáz. *m ;* nakaliá. *m ;* maskará. *m ;* khilárí. *m ;* ṭhaṭṭhauliá; *m;*
JOKING, *N.*
ṭhaṭṭhá. *m ;* maḳhaul. *m ;* hássí *f ;* maskarí *f ;* ṭhaṭholí. *f ;*
JOKINGLY, *Adv.*
hásse nál ; maḳhaul nál ; hasske ;
JOLLITY, *N.*
ḳhushí. *f ;* hássí. *f ;* chohul mohul. *m ;*
JOLLY, *A.*
ḳhush ; rázi ; raṇggí ; raṇggílá ; hass mukhá ;
to have a jolly time. líllán luṭṭná ; bullehe luṭṭná ;
JOLT, *N.*
hujjká. *m ;* jhaṭká. *m ;* dhakká. *m ;* hajoká. *m ;*
JOSTLING, *N.*
dhakkam dhakká. *m*
JOSTLE, TO, *V. T.*
dhakká dená ; ṭakkar láuní ; dhus mární ;
JOT, *N.*
bindí. *f ;*
JOURNAL, *N.*
1. newspaper. aḳhbár. *f ;* kágat. *m ;*
2. diary. ḍairí. *f ;*
JOURNEY, *N.*
paiṇḍá. *m ;* sair. *m ;* sail. *m ;* paṇdh. *m ;*
JOURNEY, TO, *V. T.*
paiṇḍá karná ; safar karná ;

JOVIAL, *A.*
ḳhush ; maují ; raṇggí ; raṇggílá ; hassmukhá ;
a jovial person. chohulí. *m ;*
JOY, *N.*
ḳhushí. *f ;* anaṇd. *m ;* anaṇdtáí. *f ;* mauj. *f ;* sukh. *m ;*
JOY, TO, *V. T.*
ḳhushí karní OR manauní ; mauj karná ;
JOYFUL, *A.*
ḳhush ; magan; rází bází ; anaṇd ; bág bág ; nihál ; sulakkhná;
JOYFUL NEWS, *N.*
ḳhushí dí ḳhabar. *f ;* maṇgal samáchár. *m ;*
JOYFULLY, *Adv.*
ḳhushí nál ; cháín cháín ; ḳhush hoke ; jam jam ;
JOYFULNESS, *N.*
ḳhushí. *f ;* anaṇdtáí. *f ;* kallíáṇ. *f ;*
JOYLESS, *A.*
udás ; murjháyá hoyá ; nimújháṇ ; masosiá hoyá ;
JOYOUS, *A.*
ḳhush ; magan ; rází ; sulakkhná ; bág bág ; raṇggí ;
JUBILANT, *A.*
ḳhush ; magan ; rázíbází ;
JUBILATION, *N.*
ḳhushí. *f ;* mauj. *f :* anaṇdtáí. *f ;* maṇggal. *m ;*
JUDGE, *N.*
hákim. *m ;* munsif. *m ;* tahsíldár. *m ;* adálatí. *m ;* jaj. *m ;* majasṭreṭ. *m ;* niáuṇ karnwálá. *m ;*
JUDGE, TO, *V. T.*
adálat karní ; munsabí karní ; munsifı karní ; niáíṇ naberná ; faisalá karná ; najiṭṭhná ;
JUDGMENT, *N.*
1. act of judging. adálat. *f ;* niáuṇ. *m ;*
2. sentence. faisalá. *m ;* hukm. *m ;*
3. legal decree. digṛí. *f ;*
4. descernment. buddh. *f ;* chaukasi. *f ;* buddhmání. *f ;*
JUDGMENT DAY, *N.*
adálat dá din. *m ;* qiámat dá din. *m ;*
JUDGMENT SEAT, *N.*
adálat dá taḳht. *m ;*

JUDICIAL, *A.*
1. pertaining to justice. niáiṇ. adálatí;
2. wise. siáná; dáná; buddhmáṇ; aqliá; aqlwálá;
JUIDICIARY, *N.*
adálatí. *m*; munsif. *m*; majasṭret *m*;
JUDICIOUS, *A.*
siáná; suchet; chaukas; aqlwálá;
JUDICIOUSLY, *Adv.*
hoshiyárí nál; insáf nál; soch wichárke;
JUDICIOUSNESS, *N.*
insáfí. *f*; insáf; *m*; siánaf. *f*; niáiṇ. *f*; niáuṇ. *m*;
JUG, *N.*
gadwá. *m*; jag. *m*;
JUGGLE, TO, *V. T.*
tamáshá karná; bázígarí karní; kh ḍ wikháuní;
JUGGLER, *N.*
madárí. *m*; bázígar. *m*; jaṇtarí. *m*;
JUGGLING, *N.*
bází. *f*; madárí dí kheḍ. *f*;
JUICE, *N.*
ras. *m*; arak. *m*; rasá. *m*;
JUICELESS, *A.*
beras; phóklá;
JUIC NESS *A.*
rasdárí. *f*;
JUICY, *A.*
rasdár; raswálá; rasílá;
JUMBLE, *N.*
ghál mel. *m*; waní waní dí lakṛí. *f*;
JUMBLE UP, TO, *V. T.*
heṭh utáṇ karná;
JUMP, *N.*
ṭapp. *m*; chhál. *f*; phaláṇgh. *f*;
JUMP, TO, *V. T.*
ṭappná; chhál mární; kuddná; dhurlí mární; ṭapp márná; charappá márná;
Proverb. When you see the water is narrow don't make a great jump. chhoṭá pání wekh ke waḍḍá ṭapp ná már;
JUNCTION, *N.*
joṛ. *m*

JUNE, *N.*
háṛh. *m*; *i. e.*, June 13 to July 12;
JUNGLE, *N.*
jangal. *m*; juh. *f*;
JUNIOR, *A.*
chhoṭá; náib;
JURISDICTION, *N.*
kumán. *f*; ikhtiyár. *m*;
JUROR, *N.*
panchaití. *m*;
JURY, *N.*
panchait. *f*;
JUST, *A.*
niáiṇ; sachchá; ímándár; insáfwálá; niáikárí;
JUST, *Adv.*
zará; thoṛá jehá;
just now. huṇe;
JUSTICE, *N.*
1. rectitude. haqq. *m*; rástí. *f*; khariáí. *f*;
2. justice. sálasí. *f*; niáuṇ. *m*; insáf. *m*; niáiṇ. *f*;
JUSTIFICATION, *N.*
1. vindication. safáí. *f*;
2. remission. khalásí. *f*; chhuṭkárá. *m*; rihái. *f*;
JUSTIFIED, *A.*
barí;
JUSTIFY, TO, *V. T.*
barí ṭhahráuná OR karná; nirdos karná;
JUSTLY, *Adv.*
insáf nál; dharm nál; ímán nál; rástí nál;
JUVENILE, *A.*
nabálig;

K.

KEEN, *A.*
1. earnest. sargarm; shukín; joshwálá;
2. sharp. thikkhá; tez; kaṭílá;
3. shrewd. siáná; chalák; hoshiyár; buddhwáṇ;
KEENLY, *Adv.*
shauq nál; josh nál; ríjh nál;
KEENNESS, *N.*
ríjh. *f*; sargarmí. *f*; josh. *m*;
KEEP, TO, *V. T.*
pás rakkhná; sámbhná;
1. to keep one's promise. bachan pálná;

2. to keep a feast. íd karní;
3. to keep safe. richhiá karná;
4. that man always keeps his promise. uh bandá hamesh apní gall OR zabán OR qaul OR iqrár OR wáde utte pahrá dendá hai.
5. to keep bad company. kusaṇg karná;

KEEPER, *N.*
sambhálú. *m*; darogá. *m*;

KEEPING, *N.*
hawálá. *m*; rakhwáí. *f*; sipurdagí. *f*;

KEEPSAKE, *N.*
yádgár. *f*;

KEG, *N.*
pípá. *m*; ḍabbá. *m*;

KERNEL, *N.*
gulí. *f*; guddá. *m*;
of a cocoanut. garí. *f*; girí. *f*;

KEROSENE, *N.*
miṭṭí dá tel. *m*;

KESTREL, *N.*
chuhemár. *m*;

KETTLE, *N.*
ketalí. *f*;

KEY, *N.*
chábí. *f*; kunjí. *f*;

KICK, *N.*
chhaṛí. *f*;
1. with both feet. dulattá. *m*;
2. by cow or buffalo. chhaṛ. *f*;

KICKING, *N.*
of an animal. pachhaṇḍá. *m*;

KICK, TO, *V. T.*
thuḍḍá márná OR láná; latt mární; latiáuná; latt chaláuná; by a horse. pashaṇḍá márná; dulattá márná; pachhaṇḍá márná;

KID, *N.*
1. small. paṭhorá. *m*; lelá. *m*; memná. *m*; paṭṭhá. *m*; chhilá. *m*; jawák. *m*; chhilí. *f*;
2. large. bakroṭá. *m*; bagroṭá. *m*; bakrá. *m*;

KIDNAP, TO, *V. T.*
jorí karní; jorojorí le jáná; badobadí laí jáná; malomal le jáná;

KIDNEY, *N.*
gurdá. *m*; rukkrá. *m*;

KILL, TO, *V. T.*
már suṭṭná OR chhaḍḍná; nás karná; kohná; jánoṇ márná; sir kappná; waḍḍhná; tháṇ márná;
1. to kill animals for food, Sikhs. jhatká karná;
2. to kill animals for food, Muhammadans. halál karná;

KILLING, *N.*
khun, *m*; ghát. *f*;

KILN, *N.*
bhaṭṭhá. *m*;
1. small kiln which burns rubbish; áwí. *f*;
2. large kiln which burns rubbish &c. áwá. *m*;

KIN, *N.*
náttá. *m*; sák náttá. *m*; sák *m*; aṇgg sák. *m*; bháíband. *m*; rishtedár *m*; koṛmá. *m*; sákdárí. *f*;

KIND, *N.*
ját. *f*; parkár. *m*; qism. *m*;
1. all kinds of. bháṇt bháṇt de;
2. what kind? kiho jehá?

KIND, *A.*
mihrbán; narm; hitwálá; kirpáwán; kirpál;

KINDLE, TO, *V. T.*
bálná; magháuná; agg bální; dakháuná;
to kindle strife. agg lagáuná;

KINDLINESS, *N.*
mihrbání. *f*; mihr. *m*; dáyá. *f*; kirpá. *f*; parúpkár. *m*;

KINDLY, *Adv.*
mihrbání nál; dáyá karke; kirpá karke;

KINDNESS, *N.*
dáyá. *m*; kirpá *f*; mihrbání. *f*; upkár. *m*; mihrbángí. *f*; dayálgí. *f*;
Brother, it is your great kindness. bháí, sabh kirpá tuhaḍí hí hai;

KINDRED, *N.*
aṇgg sákk. *m*; kuram kutamb. *m*; koṛmá. *m*; see KIN.

KING, *N.*
bádsháh. *m*;
1. Muhammadan ruler. sultán. *m*;
2. Hindu or Sikh ruler. rájá *m*; mahárájá. *m*;

KINGCROW, *N.*
lát. *f*; kai krichchi. *f*;
KINGDOM, *N.*
ráj. *m*; bádsháhí. *f*;
KING FISHER, *N.*
machchí már. *m*;
KINGLY, *Adv.*
bádsháhí; sháhí;
KINSFOLK, *N.*
sák. *m*; angg sák. *m*; náttá. *m*;
sákdári *f*; see KIN.
KIRK, *N.*
girjá. *m*;
KISS, *N.*
chummá. *m*; chummí. *f*;
KISS, TO, *V. T.*
chummná; buggá lainá; chumm chattná; chattná chummná;
KIT, *N.*
asbáb. *m*; chíz wast. *f*; chíz wastá. *f*; wast walevân. *f*;
KITCHEN, *N.*
bawárchí khána. *m*; langar. *f*;
rasoí. *f*;
KITE, *N.*
1. bird. chíl. *f*; ill. *f*;
2. paper kite. A. square. guḍḍí. *f*; guḍḍá. *m*; patang. *f*;
B. pointed. tukull. *f*; kup. *m*;
3. to fly a kite. penchá laráuná;
KITTEN, *N.*
billí dá bachchá. *m*; bilungrá. *m*;
bilungá. *m*;
KNACK, *N.*
jách. *f*; thauh. *m*;
KNAPSACK, *N.*
1. large. jholà. *m*;
2. small. jholí. *f*;
KNAVE, *N.*
1. in cards. gulám. *m*;
2. a rogue. laphaṭiá. *m*; badmásh. *m*; see ROGUE.
KNAVERY, *N.*
sharárat. *f*; lapáṭṭ. *m*; see DECEIT.
KNAVISH, *A.*
makarhatthá;
KNEAD, TO, *V. T.*
1. to knead dough. gunnhná;
2. to rub. mallná;
3. to be kneaded. gujjhná;
4. to cause to be kneaded. gunnháuná; gujháuná;
5. a mass of kneaded flour. taun. *f*;
KNEADING, *N.*
gujhái. *f*;
KNEADING BOARD, *N.*
chakla. *m*;
1. brass kneading dish. parát. *f*;
2. earthenware kneading dish. kanálí. *f*;
KNEE, *N.*
goḍḍá. *m*;
Proverb. He cannot get up, and curses his knees. uṭṭh na sake áp, phiṭṭe múnh goḍḍán dá;
KNEECAP, *N.*
chhapní. *f*; chuní. *f*;
KNEEL, TO, *V. T.*
goḍḍe nawáuná OR ṭekkná;
to prostrate oneself. danḍaut karná;
KNICKNACKS, *N.*
maniárí. *f*; allar pallar. *m*;
nikk sukk. *m*; nikkar sukkar. *f*;
KNIFE, *N.*
churí. *f*;
1. with fixed blade, as butcher's knife. kard. *f*;
2. pen knife. chákkú. *m*; káchchú. *m*;
3. knife board. takhtí. *f*;
KNIGHT IN CHESS, *N.*
ghorá. *m*;
KNIT, TO, *V. T.*
unná;
KNITTING, *N.*
unái. *f*;
KNOB, *N.*
láṭṭú. *m*; see HANDLE.
KNOCK, *N.*
saṭṭ. *f*; ṭakkar. *f*;
KNOCK, TO, *V. T.*
kharkáuná;
to knock down. ḍháná; ḍegná;
ḍigáuná;
KNOT, *N.*
ganḍh. *f*; gaṭṭh. *f*; ghunḍí. *f*;
KNOT, TO, *V. T.*
gaṭṭh dení; ganḍh dená; gaṭṭháuná; ganḍh páuná;

KNOW, TO, *V. T.*
ján rakkhná ; pachhánná ; jánná ; malúm karná ; jánaná ;
1. I don't know. ḳhabare ; khaure ;
2. know thyself. apne dil dá patá kar ;
3. know well. ján rakkho ; pakk jáno ;

KNOWN, TO MAKE, *V. T.*
pargaṭ karná ; patá dená ; mashhúr karná ;
1. to make known by beat of drum. ḍhanḍhorá dená : hoká dená ;
2. to spread news abroad. dhumáuná ;
3. to become known. ugghar jáná ; nashar ho jáná ;
4. this thing became known in the whole town (especially of any bad thing). ih gal sáre shahr vichch nashar ho gayí ;

KNOWING, *A.*
chalák ; siáná ; hoshiyár ; giání ; sujan ;

KNOWINGLY, *Adv.*
ján bujh ke ; ján ke :
I did not do it knowingly. maíṇ jánke nahíṇ kítá ;

KNOWLEDGE, *N.*
ilm. *m ;* viddiá. *m ;* pachhán. *f ;* gián. *m ;* pachchhání. *f ;*
1. a little knowledge. chár harf. *m ;*
2. Proverb. A fool's knowledge is a danger to life. anján viddiá pránán dá kháú ;

KNOWN, *A.*
malúm ; nashar ;
the matter became known. ih gal ugghar gái ;

KNUCKLE, *N.*
ganḍh. *f ;*

L.

LABEL, *N.*
chiṭṭ. *f ;* sarnámá. *m ;*

LABEL, TO, *V. T.*
chiṭṭ láuná ; náwáṇ likhná ;

LABOUR, *N.*
mazdurí. *f ;* majurí. *f* ; mihnat. *f ;* kamm. *m*; mihnat mashaqqat. *f ;* kamm káj. *m ;* mihnat porhiá. *m ;*
1. field labour. sep. *f ;*
2. forced labour. wigár. *m ;* begár. *m ;*

LABOUR, TO, *V. T.*
kamm karná : mazduri karni ; mihnat karní ; majúrí karní ;
he began to work as a labourer. mihnat majúrí karan lag piá :

LABOURER, *N.*
mazdur. *m ;* majur. *m ;* diháṛedár. *m ;*
1. a field labourer paid in kind. sepí. *m ;*
2. a regular all time field labourer. áthṛí. *m ;*
3. a field labourer, occasional. kámá. *m ;*

LABOROUS, *A.*
1. hardworking. mihnatí ; kámá ; takaṛá : uddamí : kamáo ; himmatí ;
2. difficult. aukhá ; bikhṛá ; sauṛá ;

LABOURIOUSLY, *Adv.*
baṛí mihnat nál ; masíṇ masíṇ ; mushkil nál ; aukhá hoke ;

LABOURIOUSNESS, *N.*
mihnat mashaqqat. *f* ; kamm dhanḍá. *m ;*

LACE, *N.*
1. bootlace. waddhrí. *f ;* ḍorí. *f ;*
2. embroidery. kinárí. *f ;* kasídákárí. *f ;* phulkárí. *f ;* bág. *f ;* chop. *m ;*
3. gold or silver lace. goṭṭà. *m ;* kinárí. *f ;*
4. lace. les. *m ;* kingarí. *f ;*

LACERATE, TO, *V. T.*
páṛná ; chírná ; ghá páuná ;

LACERATION, *N.*
jakham. *m ;* ghá. *m ;* chír. *m ;*

LACK, *N.*
gháṭṭá. *m ;* thuṛh. *m ;* kamí. *f ;* kasar. *m ;* ghápá. *m ;* ṭoṭ. *f ;*
lack of knowledge. besamjhí. *f ;*

LACK, TO, *V. I.*
ghaṭṭ honá ; ghaṭṭná ; thuṛhná ;

LACKING, *A.*
ghaṭṭ ;

LACQUERED, *A.*
lákkhí ;

LAD, *N.*
muṇḍá. *m* ; laṛkà. *m* ; bachchá. *m* ; chhokrá. *m* ; chhohrá. *m* ;
LADDER, *N.*
pauṛí. *f* ; pauṛsáṇg. *f* ;
rope ladder. kamaṇd. *f* ;
LADE, TO, *V. T.*
laḍḍná ;
LADING, *N.*
bojhá. *m* ; lád. *f* ; asbáb. *m* ; bhár. *m* ;
a load for an animal. laddá. *m* ; ladd. *m* ;
LADLE, *N.*
dhoí. *f* ; kaṛchhí. *f* ; chimchá. *m* ;
for oil. pallá. *m* ; pallí. *f* ;
LADY, *N.*
begam. *f* ;
1. married European. memsáhib. *f* ; mem. *f* ;
2. unmarried European. Miss Sáhib. *f* ;
LAG, TO, *V. I.*
pichche OR magar rahná ; haulí haulí chalná ; saihe saihe turná ;
1. to lag behind and lose the way. pachchar jáná ;
2. to wander about. udále pudále phirná ;
LAGGARD, *N.*
kammchor. *m* ; kammkos. *m* ; kesal. *m* ; sust ádmí. *m* ; khiskú. *m* ;
LAIR, *N.*
ghurná. *m* ; khuṇdhar. *f* ; see DEN.
LAKE, *N.*
jhíl. *f* ; chhaṇbh. *m* ; ḍal. *m* ; sar. *m* ; see POND.
LAMB, *N.*
lelá ; *m* ; lelí. *f* ; memaní. *f* ; chhatará. *m* ; chhatarí. *f* ; jawák. *m* ;
LAME, *A.*
laṇgá ; laṇgṛá ; jaḍá ;
Proverb. The lame and the one-eyed have one vein more than other people. jaḍe te káne dí ikk rag wádhú hundí hai ;
LAME, TO, *V. T.*
laṇgṛá karná ;
LAME, TO, WALK, *V. I.*
laṇgáuná ;
LAMENESS, *N.*
laṇg. *m* ;
LAMENT, *N.*
síápá. *m* ; see LAMENTATION.
LAMENT, TO, *V. T.*
1. to weep. roná ;
2. to weep slightly. phus phus karná ; dhus dhus karná ; dhuskaná ; kurláuná ; bilápná ;
3. to sorrow. masosná ; hamsos karná ;
4. to weep over a death. piṭṭná ; birláp karná ;
LAMENTABLE, *A.*
afsos dí gal. *f* ;
LAMENTATION, *N.*
roná. *m* ; siápá. *m* ; kurláp. *m* ; wirláp. *m* ; chík chihárá. *m* ; dhạ́h. *f* ; dháṇh. *f* ; kurláṭ. *m* ; kurláhaṭ. *m* ;
LAMP, *N.*
battí. *f* ; dípak. *m* ;
earthen lamp. díwá. *m* ; dípak. *m* ;
lantern. laltain. *m* ; hatth battí. *f* ;
LAMP BLACK, *N.*
used to paint eyelids. kajjal. *m* ; kajlá. *m* ;
LAMP STAND, *N.*
diuṛí. *f* ; deoṛí. *f* ; diwákhṛí, *f* ;
recess in wall for lamp. álá. *m* ; diwákhá. *m* ; diwákhí. *f* ;
LANCE, *N.*
nejá. *m* ; barchhá. *m* ;
LANCE, TO, *V. T.*
nashtar mární ; chírná ; chirá dená ; pachchhná ; chír pháṛ karná ;
LANCET, *N.*
nashtar. *f* ; pachchhní. *f* ;
LAND, *N.*
1. world. dhartí. *f* ; dunyá. *f* ; jahán. *m* ;
2. ground. jamín. *f* ; bhon. *f* ; thal. *m* ; bhúm. *f* ;
Various kinds of land.
1. unirrigated land. baráni. *f* ; márú. *f* ;
2. land irrigated by canal. nahrí. *f* ;
3. land irrigated by well. cháhí. *f* ;
4. land of a village. chakk. *m* ;
5. uncultivated and useless land. banjar jamín. *f* ; karláthí jamín. *f* ;
6. high land. ṭibbá. *m* ;

7. level land. raṛa. *m* ; raṛí. *f* ;
8. low lying land. níwán. *f* ; nichán. *f* ;
9. low land near a river. beṭ. *m* ; mand. *m* ; mall. *m* ; khádar. *m* ; nawaḍḍá thán. *m* ;
10. bushy land. jangal. *m* ; bír. *f* ; jhangar. *m* ;
11. marshy land. khobhá. *m* ; tarái. *f* ;
12. fallow ground. parelí. *f* ; ráol pailí. *f* ;
13. loamy land, manured and irrigated. niáín. *f* ; mairá. *m* ;
14. land lying between two rivers. doábá. *m* ;
15. land between two mountain ridges. dúṇ. *f* ;
16. land on bank of river. ḍháhá. *m* ;
17. hard barren soil. bánggar. *m* ; rakkaṛ. *m* ; banjar jamín. *f* ; kallar. *m* ;
18. a bare plain. raṛ. *f* ; rauṛ. *f* ;
19. low ground near mountain. tallá. *m* ; pahár talí. *f* ; kandhí. *f* ;
20. land given as a reward, rent-free. jagír. *m* ; inámí. *f* ;
21. good damp soil. rohí. *f* ;
22. grazing ground. charáṇdh. *f* ; rakk. *m* ; chaugán. *m* ;
23. a plain. chaugán. *m* ;
24. good light sandy soil. ghas. *f* ; missí. *f* ;
25. manured land near village. niáíṇ. *f* ; madh. *f* ;
26. good alluvial land. chhal. *f* ;
27. unirrigated manured land. lipáṛá. *m* ;
28. a sandy region. thal. *m* ;
29. stiff clay land. dábar. *f* ;
30. newly ploughed land. wáhn. *m* ;
31. grazing ground. juh. *f* ;
32. land watered by floods. sailábá. *m* ;
33. a field of an acre. pailí. *f* ;
34. land from which the crop has been removed. waḍḍh. *m* ;
35. boundary pillar. thaḍḍá. *m* ; burjí. *f* ;

LAND, TO, *V. T.*
uttárná ;

LAND, TO, *V. I.*
uttarná ;

LANDHOLDER, *N.*
jamín dá málik. *m* ; murabbedár. *m* ; jamíndár. *m* ;

LANDING STAGE, *N.*
paṭṭan. *m* ;

LANDLORD, *N.*
ghar dá málik. *m* ; jamín dá málik. *m* ; málik makán. *m* ;

LANDMARK, *N.*
1. of earth. hadd. *f* ; banná. *m* ;
2. of masonry. thaḍḍá. *m* ; burji. *f* ;

LANE, *N.*
galí. *f* ;
1. lanes and allies. gáli kuche. *m* ;
2. in every lane. galí galí. *f* ;

LANGUAGE, *N.*
bolí. *f* ; jabán. *f* ; bhákhiá. *f* ; bháshá. *f* ;
1. bad language. gál. *m* ; gálí. *f* ; gálí galoch. *f* ; gál duppaṛ. *f* ;
2. literary language. kitábí bolí. *f* ;
3. colloquial language. bol chál díáṇ galláṇ. *f* ;

LANGUID, *A.*
sust ; ḍhillá ; ghaulí ; álasi ; álakí ;

LANGUIDLY, *Adv.*
aiweṇ ; eweṇ ; sustí nál ; dhíme nál ;

LANGUIDNESS, *N.*
sustí. *f* ; ghaul. *f* ;

LANGUISH, TO *V. I.*
kulmáuná ; murjháuná ; kumláuná ;

LANGOUR, *N.*
sustí. *f* ; ghaul. *f* ; álas. *m* ; ṭoṭṭá. *m* ;

LANK, *A.*
lammá ; patlá ;

LANTERN, *N.*
láltain. *m* ; hatth battí. *f* ;

LAP, *N.*
kuchchhaṛ. *m* ; bukkal. *f* ; god. *m* ; goddí. *f* ; jholí. *f* ; gadd. *f* ;
Proverb used when an evil return has been made under the guise of friendship. To pluck out one's beard when sitting in his lap. kuchchhaṛ baiṭhke dáhṛí khohná ;

LAP, TO, *V. T.*
1. to lick ; chattná ;
2. to lap up water as a dog. lakkṇá ; lakk lakk karná ;

3. Proverb. a river is not unclean because dogs lap its water. kutteáṇ de lakkián daryá palít nahíṇ hundá ;

LAPSE, *N.*
bhulekhá. *m* ; bhul chukk. *f* ; qusúr. *m* ; galatí. *f* ;

LAPWING, *N.*
ṭaṭaulí. *f* ;

LARCENY, *N.*
chorí. *f* ; chorí chakárí *f*;

LARDER. *N.*
botal ḳhána. *m* ;

LARGE. *A.*
waḍḍá ; baṛá ; moklá ;
1. very large. gaṇḍhál ;
2. rather large. waḍerá ;

LARGENESS, *N.*
waḍḍápaṇ. *m* ;

LARK, *N.*
1. bird. chanḍol. *m* ;
2. game. kalol. *f* ;

LARYNX, *N.*
saṇggh. *m* ;

LASCAR, *N.*
malláh. *m* ;

LASCIVIOUS. *A.*
guṇḍá ; luchchá ; kámí ; mastáṇá ; laṭpaṭá ; khíwá ; chhaṭṭiá hoyá ; mushṭaṇḍá ;

LASCIVIOUSLY, *Adv.*
mastevéṇ nál ; mastí nál ; to live lasciviously kheḍ tamáshe nále sharábáṇ maujáṇ karná ;

LASCIVIOUSNESS, *N.*
ḍhekkchál. *f* ; guṇḍpuṇá. *m* ; badfelí. *f* ; badí. *f* ; mastí. *f* ; mastevāṇ. *f* ; phateṇváṇ. *f* ; nikhiddh kamm. m ;

LASH. *N.*
chháṇṭ *f* ; chháṇṭá *m* ;

LASH, TO, *V. T.*
1. to whip. chábak márná ;
2. to kick. latt mární ; thuḍḍá márná OR láná ; latíauná ;
3. to bind. bannhná ;

LASHING, *N.*
baṇḍhaṇ. *m* ; waddhráṇ. *f* ;

LASS, *N.*
kúṛí. *f* ; see MAID.

LASSITUDE, *N.*
sustí *f* ; kamjorí. *f* ;

LASSO, *N.*
pháhí. *f* ;

LAST, *N.*
kalbút. *m* ;

LAST, TO, *V. I.*
hanḍhaná ;

LAST, *A.*
chhekaṛlá ; pichchlá ; áḳharí ;

LAST, *Adv.*
aṇt núṇ ; pichchlá ; oṛak núṇ ;
1. last time. pichchlí wárí ;
2. last night, rátíṇ ; ajj rát núṇ ajj dí rát ;
3. last year. paroṇ ; parru ; pichchle sál ; pichchle waṛhe ;

LASTING, *A.*
pakká ; hanḍhaṇ sár ; baṛá hanḍhanwálá ;

LASTLY, *Adv.*
chekaṛ núṇ ; chekaṛe ;

LATCH, *N.*
kuṇḍá. *m* ;

LATCH, TO, *V. T.*
kuṇḍá launá ;

LATCHET, *N.*
tasmá. *m* ;

LATE, *A.*
chirká ; chiráká ; kuvelá ; pachhet ; out of season. bemausam ; berutt ; avere ; pachhetá ;

LATE, *Adv.*
ḍer nál ; kuvele ; chiráká ; ḍhill karke ; chirká ; avere ; pachhetá ; abere ;
1. late in the morning. din chaṛhe ;
2. I was late. mainúṇ der ho gayí hai ;

LATELY, *Adv.*
ajj bhalak ; ajj kal ;

LATENESS, *N.*
ḍhill. *f* ; der. *f* ; derí. *f* ; aver. *f* ; averá. *m* ;

LATH, *N.*
karí. *f* ;

LATHE, *N.*
kharád. *m* ;

LATHER, *N.*
sában dí jhag. *f* ;

LATHER, TO, *V. T.*
sában láuná ;

LATHER, TO, *V. I.*
jhag áuná ;

LATIN, *N.*
látíní. *f* ;
LATISH, *A.*
pichchetará ;
LATRINE, *N.*
pae kháná. *m* ;
LATTER, *A.*
pichchlá ;
LATTERLY, *Adv.*
inhán dinán vichch ; ajj bhalak ;
LATTICE, *N.*
jhilmilí. *f* ; jálí. *f* ;
LAUD, TO, *V. T.*
waḍiáuná ; táríf karní ; saráhná ; guṇ gáuná ; saláhná ; kise dí waḍíáí karní ;
LAUDABLE, *A.*
táríf de laiq ; saláhan jog ; baṛá laiq ;
LAUDANUM, *N.*
behoshí dárú. *m* ;
LAUDATION, *N.*
waḍíáí. *f* ; táríf. *f* : sitáish. *f* ;
LAUGH, *N.*
hássí. *f* ; khillí. *f* ;
LAUGH, TO, *V. T.*
hassná ; híṇ híṇ karná ; chohul karná ; muskaráuná ; khilná ; hássá áuná ;
1. to laugh in the sleeve. dil vichch hassná ;
2. to laugh to scorn. hiṛhiṛáuná ; ṭhaṭṭhe vichch uḍáuná ;
3. to cause to laugh. hassáuná ; khilwáuná ;
4. he burst out laughing. uh hass piá ;
LAUGHABLE, *A.*
maskará ; hassan wálí gal ;
LAUGHINGLY, *Adv.*
hasske ;
LAUGHING STOCK, *N.*
makhaul dí gal. *f* ;
LAUGHTER, *N.*
hássí. *f* ; hássá. *m* ; halrá. *m* ; chohul. *m* ; khilná. *m* ;
Proverb. Excessive laughter, silence, clouds and sun are all injurious.
bahut bhalá ná halrá,
bahut bhalí ná chupp,
bahut bhalá ná meghlá,
bahut bhalí ná dhupp ;

LAUNDRESS, *N.*
dhoban. *f* ;
LAUNDRY, *N.*
dhobí kháná. *m* ;
LAVE, TO, *V. T.*
naháuná ; dhoná ;
LAVE, TO, *V. I.*
náhuná ; náhauná ; ashnán karná ;
LAVISH, TO, *V. T.*
1. to give freely. bakhshná ;
2. to squander. guá dená ; mál ujáṛná ; mál uḍáuná ;
LAVISHLY, *Adv.*
khullhe dil nál ; dil kholke ; behisábí nál ; waḍḍe dil nál ;
LAW, *N.*
qánún. *m* ;
1. Muhammadan law. sharíat. *f* ; shará. *f* ;
2. Mosaic Law. tauret. *f* ;
3. Law of the Lord. Prábhú dí nítí. *f* ; Khudáwand dí shará. *f* ;
LAWCOURT, *N.*
kacherí. *f* ;
LAWFUL, *A.*
jaiz ; halál ; rawá ;
LAWFULLY, *Adv.*
jaiz taur nál ;
LAWFULNESS, *N.*
haqq. *m* ;
LAWLESS, *A.*
beshará ;
LAWN, *N.*
khattá. *m* ; tottá. *m* ;
LAWSUIT, *N.*
maqaddamá. *m* ;
1. civil suit. diwání. *f* ;
2. criminal. faujdárí. *f* ;
3. date of suit. táríkh. *f* ; tarík. *f* ;
4. hearing. peshí. *f* ;
LAWYER, *N.*
wakíl. *m* ;
LAX, *A.*
sust ; ghauliá ; surliá hoyá ; see LAZY.
LAXATIVE, *N.*
juláb. *m* ;
LAXATIVENESS, *N.*
dast. *m* ; wáh. *f* ;
LAXITY, *N.*
sustí. *f* ; ghaul. *f* ; see LAZINESS.

LAXLY, *Adv.*
sustí nál ; aiweṇ ;
LAY, TO, *V. T.*
liṭáuná ; rakkhná ;
1. to lay an egg. áṇḍá dená ;
2. to lay down a thing. dharná ;
LAYER, *N.*
1. in a building. radá. *m* ;
2. fold. taih. *m* ;
LAYING BRICKS, *N.*
chinái. *f* ;
LAZILY, *Adv.*
sustí nál ; ghaul nál ; aiweṇ ; ḍhill nál ;
LAZINESS, *N.*
sustí. *f* ; álas. *m* ; álaspuṇá. *m* ; ḍhill. *f* ; ḍhill maṭṭh. *f* ; ghaul. *f* ; jillh. *f* ; áhlak. *f* ; álak. *f* ; daliddar. *m* ;
LAZY, *A.*
sust ; ḍhillá ; álsan ; álasí ; ghaulí ; jillhá ; kesal ; payzal ; surliá hoyá ; sullhá ; phúsí ; daliddarí ; kamm chor ; ḍhillaṛ ; ḍhillá maṭṭhá ; machall ; kammkos ; ghaulíá ; kuhaḍḍ ; áhlakí ; ḍhailá ; jiḍḍá ;
LEAD, TO, *V. T.*
laí jáná ; mohre chalná ; agge chalná ; agwáí karní; ráh malláuná; to lead astray. bhuláuná ; badráh kar dená ; badráh kar laíná ;
LEAD, *N.*
sikká. *m* ;
LEADER, *N.*
águ. *m* ; agwáhá. *m* ; sardár. *m* ; mohrí. *m* ; pardhán. *m* ;
1. religious leader. M. malwáná. *m*;
2. religious leader. H. parohat. *m* ;
3. Proverb. a thief and a pick-pocket are chaudharis, and a harlot a leader. chor uchakká chaudharí te gunḍí rann pardhán ;
LEADERSHIP, *N.*
hákamí. *f* ; sardárí. *f* ; pardhántái. *f* ;
LEADING STRING FOR CAMEL, *N.*
muhár. *f* ;
LEAD PENSIL, *N.*
pinsal. *f* ;
LEAF, *N.*
1. of a tree, etc.
pattá. *m* ; pattar. *m* ; patt. *m* ;
2. dry leaves of sugar cane. khorí. *f*;
3. of a book. pattar. *m* ; pattará. *m* ; warká. *m* ;
4. of an account book. panná. *m* ;
5. of a door. bhitt. *m* ; taḳhtá. *m* ; kawáṛ. *m* ;
LEAFAGE, *N.*
patte. *m* ;
LEAFLESS, *A.*
tund mund ;
LEAFLET, *N.*
parchí. *f* ;
LEAFY, *A.*
hariá bhariá ; pattedár ; ghaṇá ;
LEAK, *N.*
morí. *f* ; galí. *f* ; gharálá. *m*; muggh. *m* ;
LEAK, TO, *V. I.*
choná ; wagná ; simmná ; risná ;
LEAKAGE, *N.*
choá. *m* ;
LEAKY, *A.*
chonwálá;
LEAN, *A.*
lissá ; márá ; lissí ; akáhirá ; lín ; liserá; patlá ; sukkaṛ ; jhikh; sukṛú ; very lean márúá ;
LEAN, TO *V. I.*
1. to lean back, nál ḍhásná ; ḍholáná ; ḍhoh láni ;
2. to lean on. sahárá laíná ;
LEANNESS, *N.*
patlái. *f* ; maṛappaṇ. *m* ;
LEAP, *N.*
ṭapp. *m* ; phaláṇgh. *f* ; chhál. *f* ; for animals. chaukarí. *f* ;
LEAP, TO, *V. T.*
ṭappná ; ṭapp márná ; kuddná ; chhál márná ; chaukarí mární ; uchchalná ; bhurkaná ;
1. to cause to leap. ṭappáuná ;
2. to play leapfrog. ghoṛí ṭappná ;
LEAPER, *N.*
kudákal. *m* ; kudákú. *m* ;
LEAPING, *N.*
kudái. *f* ; ṭapái. *f* ; ṭappaṇ. *m* ; leaping and dancing. ṭappaṇ nachchaṇ. *m* ;
LEARN, TO, *V. T.*
sikkhná ; paṛhná ;
1. to learn a lesson. yád karná ; chette karná ;

2. to learn by heart. kaṇṭh karná ; muṇh zabání yád karní ; raṭ lená ; raṭṭná ;
LEARNED, *A*.
ilmdár ; ilamí ; ilmwálá ; álam ; viddiáwáṇ ; guṇwáṇ ;
LEARNEDLY, *Adv*.
viddiá nál ; ilm nál ;
LEARNER, *N*.
shagird. *m* ; sikkh. *m* ; chelá. *m* ; bálká. *m* ; chelará. *m* ;
LEARNING, *N*.
ilm. *m* ; viddiá. *f* ;
LEASE, *N*.
1. lease. ṭheká. *m* ;
2. lease agreement. patá. *m* ; kágat. *m* ; karáiá námá. *m* ;
LEASE, TO, *V. T*.
ṭheke te dená ;
LEASEHOLDER, *N*.
ṭhekedár. *m* ;
LEAST, *A*.
sáreáṇ náloṇ nikká ;
at least. ghaṭṭo ghaṭṭ ; ghaṭṭ thoṇ ghaṭṭ ;
LEATHER, *N*.
chamm. *m* ; chamṛá. *m* ;
untanned leather. khall. *f* ;
LEATHER WORKER, *N*.
chamiár. *m* ; khaṭík. *m* ;
boot maker. mochí. *m* ;
LEATHERN, *A*.
chamṛe dá ;
LEAVE, *N*.
chhuṭṭí. *f* ;
LEAVE, TO, *V. I*.
chaliá jáná ; turná ;
LEAVE, TO, *V. T*.
chhaḍḍ dená ; tajná ; tiágná ;
LEAVE OFF, TO, *V. I*.
báj áuná ;
LEAVEN, *N*.
khamír. *m* ;
LEAVEN, TO, *V. T*.
khamír karná OR uṭháuná ;
LEAVEN, TO, *V. I*.
khamír honá ;
LEAVENED, *A*.
khamírá khamír hoyá hoyá ;
LEAVINGS, *N*.
of a meal. júṭh. ; chagal. *f* ;
any food left over is júṭhá ;
LECTURE, TO, *V. T*.
likchar dená ;
1. to preach. wáz karná ; manádí karní ; updesh karná ;
2. to give instruction. nasíhat dení ; paṛháuná ;
LECTURE, *N*.
likchar. *m* ; wáz. *m* ;
LECTURER, *N*.
sikkhiá denwálá. *m* ;
LEDGE, *N*.
parchhattí. *f* ;
recess in wall. álá. *m* ;
LEDGER, *N*.
behí. *f* ; wehí. *f* ;
LEECH, *N*.
jok *f* ; jalam. *f* ;
LEER, *N*.
mailí akkh. *f* ;
LEET TO, *V. T*.
mailí akkh nál wekhná ;
LEFT, *A*.
khabbá ;
LEFT HANDED, *A*.
khabbá ; khabbí
LEG, *N*.
latt. *f* ; ṭang. *f* ;
1. lower part of leg. pinní. *f* ;
2. leg of table, &c. páwá. *m* ;
3. cover your legs. farz kajj ke baiṭho ;
LEGAL, *A*.
qánún walloṇ jaiz ; halál dá ;
LEGALIZE, TO, *V. T*.
jaiz ṭhahráuná ;
LEGALLY, *Adv*.
jaiz taur nál ;
LEGATEE, *N*.
wáris. *m* ;
LEGEND, *N*.
kaháṇí. *f* ; kathá. *m* ; see STORY.
LEGIBLE, *A*.
sáf ;
LEGIBLY, *Adv*.
safái nál ;
LEGION, *N*.
fauj. *f* ;
LEGISLATE, TO, *V. T*.
qánún banáuná OR ṭhahráuná ;
LEGISLATION, *N*.
waḍḍí kaunsal dá kamm. *m* ;

LEGISLATOR, *N.*
waḍḍí kaunsal dá mimbar. *m ;*
LEGISLATURE, *N.*
waḍḍí kaunsal. *f ;*
LEGITIMACY, *N.*
halál. *m ;*
LEGITIMATE, *A.*
halál dá ;
LEGITIMATELY, *Adv.*
jaiz taur nál ;
LEISURE, *N.*
vehl. *f ;* wándak. *f ;* vehlak. *m ;* wánd. *f ;*
1. at leisure. vehle ; wándá ; vehlá hoyá ;
2. I have no leisure now. huṇ vehlak nahíṇ ; mainúṇ vehl nahíṇ ;
LEISURELY, *Adv.*
1. slowly. haule haule ; saije saije ; tharáke ;
2. casually. aiweṇ ; eweṇ ;
LEMON, *N.*
nimbú. *m ;*
sweet lemon. miṭṭhá. *m ;*
LEMONADE, *N.*
miṭṭhá pání. *m ;* lamneṭ. *m ;*
LEND, TO, *V. T.*
udhár dená ; udháriáṇ dená ; mangwán dená ;
LENDER, *N.*
karár. *m ;* sháh. *m ;*
LENGTH, *N.*
lambáí. *f ;* lamáí. *f ;* lám. *m ;*
at length. oṛak núṇ ;
LENGTHEN, TO, *V. T.*
lammá karná ; lambáuná ; lambíáuná ; wadháuná;
LENGTHY, *A.*
lammá ;
LENIENCY, *N.*
narmí. *f ;* narmdilí. *f ;* mulaimí. *f ;*
LENIENT, *A.*
narmdil ; ráhmdil ; mihrbán ;
LENT, *N.*
rozeáṇ de din. *m ;*
LENTILS, *N.*
dál. *f ;* masar. *m ;*
LEOPARD, *N.*
chittrá. *m ;* chittará. *m ;* chítá. *m ;* chittá. *m ;*
LEPER, *N.*
koṛhá. *m ;* koṛhí. *f ;*
LEPROSY, *N.*
koṛh. *m ;*
LESS, *A.*
ghaṭṭ ; kassá ;
1. a little less. kaserá ; chhoṭerí
2. less or more. ghaṭṭ waddh ;
3. how are you now ? is the fever less ? huṇ kí hál hai ? tap laṭṭhá hai ?
LESSEN, TO, *V. T.*
ghaṭáuná; ghaṭṭ karná ; thoṛá karná ; halká karná ;
to lessen the price. mull kaṭáuná ; riayat karná ;
LESSER, *A.*
bahut thoṛá ;
LESSON, *N.*
sabaq. *m ;* santhá. *m ;*
LEST, *Conj.*
ajihá ná howe paí ; mate ; chetá ; jo kite ; matá ná ho ; mat kite ;
LET, TO, *V. T.*
1. to permit. karan dená ; hon dená ;
2. to give on hire. karáyá dená ;
3. to let down. lamká dená ; palmáuná ;
LETHARGIC, *A.*
sust ; ghaulí ; ḍhillá ; surliá hoyá ; postí ;
LETHARGY, *N.*
sustí. *f ;* ghaul. *f ;*
LETTER, *N.*
1. of the alphabet. akkhar. *m ;* harf. *m ;* labhaj. *m ;* painti. *f ;*
2. a note. rukká. *m ;* parchí. *f ;* pattar. *m ;*
3. a letter. ḳhatt. *m ;* ḳhatt pattar. *m ;* chiṭṭhí. *f ;* chiṭṭh pachattí. *f ;*
4. letters began to pass between them. ápe vichch chiṭṭhíáṇ áwan jáwán lagíáṇ ;
LETTUCE, *N.*
salád. *m ;*
LEVEL, *A.*
paddhrá ; suáhrá ; sáf ; raṛá ;
LEVEL, TO, *V. T.*
paddhrá karná ;
LEVELLER, *N.*
suhágá. *m ;*
LEVER, *N.*
tul. *f ;*

LEVERET, *N.*
sahá. *m* ; sehá. *m* ;
LEVITY, *N.*
hássí. *f* ; khushí. *f* ; kalol. *f* ;
LEVY, *N.*
1. tax. tikas. *f* ;
2. collection. chandá. *m* ;
3. forced levy. wásh. *m* ;
LEVY, TO, *V. T.*
ugráhuná ; tikas láuná; wásh lainá ;
LEWD, *A.*
guṇḍá ; luchchá ; kámí ; behayá ; besharm ;
LEWDLY, *Adv.*
mastevéṇ nál ; mastí nál ;
LEWDNESS, *N.*
guṇḍpúná. *m* ; luchchpúṇá. *m* ; luchaú *m* ;
LEXICON, *N.*
lugát. *f* ;
LIABILITY, *N.*
jummewárí. *f*; zimmewárí. *f* ; zimmá. *m* ; júlá. *m* ; pete. *m* ; bhárá. *m* ;
LIABLE, *A.*
jummewár ; zimmewár ;
LIAR, *N.*
jhuṭhá. *m* ; kurá. *m* ; lapáṛ. *m* ; lapáṛaṇ. *f*; jhuṭhiár. *m*; dojíbhá. *m* ;
LIBEL, *N.*
1. libel. niṇdiá. *m* ; badnámí. *f* ;
2. action for libel. izzat dá dává. *m*;
LIBEL, TO, *V. T.*
badnám karná ; niṇdiá karná ;
LIBELLER, *N.*
tohmatí. *m* ; niṇdak. *m* ;
LIBERAL, *A.*
dilwálá ; diler ; man chalá ; khullhe dilwála ; sakhí ; dáyáwán.
LIB R LITY, *N.*
sakhaut. *f* ; dát. *f* ; dilerí. *f* ;
LIBERALLY, *Adv.*
dil kholke ; khullhe dil nál ; waḍḍe dil nál ;
LIBERATE TO, *V. T.*
1. to release. chhaḍḍ dená ; azád karná ; rihái karní ;
2. to deliver. bacháuná ; chhuṭkárá dená ;
3. to release from handcuffs. beríáṇ kaṭṭṇíáṇ ;

LIBERATION, *N.*
khalásí. *f* ; chhuṭkárá. *m* ; azádí. *f* ; khullh. *f* ;
LIBERATOR, *N.*
chhaḍḍáunwálá. *m* ; bacháunwálá. *m* ;
LIBERTINE, *N.*
tamásbín. *m* ; luchch. *m* ; kharábatí. *m* ; chudwayyá. *m* ;
LIBERTINISM, *N.*
tamásbíní. *f* ; luchau. *m*; badkárí. *f* ; uchakkpúṇá. *m* ; badí. *f* ;
LIBERTY, *N.*
1. freedom. azádí. *f* ; azádagí. *f* ; khullh. *f* ; khalásí. *f* ; chhuṭṭí. *f* ;
2. lesiure. vehl. *f* ; wándak. *f* ; vehlak. *m* ;
3. permission. ijan. *f* ; ijázat. *f* ; manzúrí. *f* ; khullh. *f* ;
LIBRARY, *N.*
laibrarí. *f* ; kitáb ghar. *m* ;
room in a house. daftar. *m* ;
LICE, *N.*
jún. *f* ; júáṇ. *f*, plur ;
Proverb. A shaven head has neither lice nor nits. Roḍḍe sir jún ná líkh ;
LICENSE, TO, *V. T.*
laisans dená ;
LICENTIOUS, *A.*
badkár ; luchchá ; sharír ; ujáṛú ; guṇḍá ; luṇḍá ; bhaiṛá ; búrá ; belagám ; chauṛ chánaṇ ;
LICENTIOUSLY. *Adv.*
mastewéṇ nál ; mastí nál ;
LICENTIOUSNESS, *N.*
badmáshí. *f* ; luchchpuṇá. *m* ; badkárí ; *f* ; sharárat. *f* ; badpareji. *f* ;
LICK, *N.*
chaṭṭ. *m* ;
LICK, TO, *V. T.*
chaṭṭná ; chaṭṭ lainá ;
1. to lick, up. chaṭṭam karná ;
2. Proverb to show that a low person exalted still acts meanly. If a dog is set on a throne he goes off to lick the handmill ; kuttá ráj bahálie chakkí chaṭṭan já ;
LICORICE, *N.*
mulatthí. *f* ;

LID, *N.*
ḍhakná. *m* ; ḍhakní. *f* ; chappní. *f* ; chúṇí. *f* ;

LIE, *N.*
jhuṭh. *m* ; jhuṭh muṭh. *m* ; kúṛ. *m* ; kúṛá. *m* ; jhuṭhí muṭhí gal. *f* ; kusatt. *m* ;
lies. kúṛíáṇ galláṇ. *f* ;

LIE TO, *V. T.*
jhuṭh bolná OR márná OR kamáuná ; kúṛ bolná OR márná ; lapáṛ márná ; jhakk márná ; jakkaṛ márná ;
1. to keep on lying. jhuṭh bolná ;
2. don't tell such lies. gappáṇ ná máríá karo ;

LIE DOWN, TO, *V. I.*
lammá painá ;
1. to cause to lie down. liṭáuná ;
2. to lie in wait. ghát karná ; dáú láunná ; súh vichch honá ;
3. to lie in a pit fasting until some favour is obtained, practised by faqirs. páṛe painá ;

LIEUTENANT, *N.*
laftain. *m* ;
junior official. náib. *m* ;

LIFE, *N.*
zindagí. *f* ; jí. *m* ; jiṇd. *f* ; jíun. *f* ; ján. *f* ; jiṇḍrí. *f* ; jindagání. *f* ; jíuṛá. *m* ; paráṇ. *m* ;
1. eternal life. sadá dí zindagí. *f* ; hamesha dí zindagí. *f* ; sadípak jíwan. *f* ;
2. age. umr. *f* ;
3. Proverbs. while there is life there is hope. *viz* :—While the head exists the battle lasts. sir qaim, jang daim.
while life is yours the world is yours. ján nál jahán hai ;

LIFE INSURANCE, *N.*
bímá. *m* ;

LIFELESS, *A.*
1. dead. murdá ; beján ;
2. dull. súst ; postí ; surliá hoyá ; khuṇḍhá ;

LIFELONG, *A.*
zindagí bhar ; umr bhar ; sárí umr ;

LIFETIME. *N.*
1. Life. zindagí. *f* ;
2. In lifetime. jíuṇdiáṇ jí ;

LIFT, TO, *V. T.*
chukkná ; uṭháuná ;
to cause to be lifted. chukáuná ; chukwáuná ;

LIGAMENT, *N.*
paṭṭhá. *m* ;

LIGATURE, *N.*
paṭṭí. *f* ; chhubbá. *m* ; bannhan. *m* ;

LIGHT, *N.*
lo. *f* ; jot. *f* ; roshní. *f* ; roshnái. *f* ; chánan. *m* ; chánaná. *m* ; chánaní. *f* ;
light and shade. dhupp chhán. *f* ;

LIGHT, TO, *V. T.*
chánan karná ; roshní dení ;
1. to light a lamp. díwá bálná ;
2. to light a fire. agg láuná ; jaláuná ; magháuná ; agg bální ;

LIGHT, *A.*
1. not heavy. haulá ; halká ;
2. very light. haulá phull ; paṇjh phullá ;
3. bright. chamkílá ; ujalá ;

LIGHT, TO BE, *V. I.*
roshan OR chánan honá ;

LIGHTEN, TO, *V. T.*
1. to give light. chánan karná ; roshní dení ; lo karní ;
2. to ease a burden. haulíáṇ karní ; matthá karná ;
3. to flash. bijlí lishkdí hai ; gaṛbaṛná ;

LIGHT HEARTED, *A.*
khush ; magan ; raṇgí ; baṛá rází ;

LIGHTISH, *A.*
hulerá :

LIGHTNESS, *N.*
hauláрaṇ. *m* ;

LIGHTNING, *N.*
bijlí. *f* ;

LIGHTSOME, *A.*
khush ; rájí ; magan ; anaṇd ;

LIKE, *A.*
wargá ; wáṇgg ; wáṇjhu ; samán ;
1. he is like his father. uh de píu dí sárí shakal is de nál mildí hai ;
2. Proverb. Like begets like. one melon colours another. kharbuzá kharbuze thoṇ raṇg pakaṛdá ;

LIKE, *Prep.*
wáṇgúṇ ; wáṇgar ; wáṇgúr ; wáṇgaṇ ; wargá ; tull :

LIKE, TO, *V. T.*
bháunná ; pasiṇd karná ; chaṇgá lagná ; piyár karná ; hit rakkhná ;
1. I do not like that man. uh ádmí sánúṇ nahíṇ bháundá ;
2. I don't like your suggestion. tuháḍí ih gal sánúṇ nahíṇ bháundí ;
3. I do not like his talk. uh díáṇ gallán mainúṇ buríáṇ laggdíáṇ ne ;
4. I do not like to speak before you. mainúṇ tuháḍe sámne gal kardeáṇ sharm áundí hai ;

LIKELIHOOD, *N.*
ummed. *f* ;

LIKELY, *Adv.*
shayad ;

LIKENESS, *N.*
ḍaul. *f* ; shakal. *f* ; sáṇg. *m* ; mel. *m* ; wargá. *m* ;

LIKEWISE, *Conj.*
1. in like manner. usí taráh ;
2. also, too. bhí ; ví ;

LIKING, *N.*
cháh. *f* ; ichchhiá. *f* ; piyár. *m* ; bhauná. *m* ; ríjh. *f* ;

LILY, *N.*
sosan. *m* ;

LIMB, *N.*
aṇgg. *m* ; liṇg. *m* ;

LIME, *N.*
1. mortar. chuná. *m* ; kalí. *f* ;
2. lemon. nimbú. *m* ; kimb. *f* ; khaṭṭá. *m* ;
3. sweet lime. miṭṭhá. *m* ;

LIMEKILN, *N.*
bhaṭṭhá. *m* ;

LIMESTONE, *N.*
roṛ. *m* ;

LIMIT, *N.*
1. of time. miád. *f* ;
2. limitation. hadd. *f* ; ant. *m* ;
3. boundary of earth. banná. *m* ; waṭṭ. *f* ; banná channá. *m* ;

LIMIT, TO *V. T.*
hadd banáuná ; banná páuná ;

LIMITATION, *N.*
hadd. *f* ; ant. *m* ;

LIMITLESS, *A.*
behadd ; beant ; haddoṇ waddh ; hadd thoṇ báhar ; wadhík ;

LIMP, TO *V. T.*
laṇgáuná ;

LIMPID, *A.*
sáf ;

LINE, *N.*
1. a line drawn. lakír. *f* ; lík. *f* ; lí. *f* ; lakár. *f* ;
Proverb. my words are as a line upon a stone. merí gall patthar te lík hái ;
2. a cord. ḍorá. *m* ; ḍorí. *f* ; rassí. *f* ;
3. boundary. banná. *m* ; hadd. *f* ; waṭṭ. *m* ;
4. row. pál. *f* ; satar. *m* ;
5. line of print. satar. *m* ;
6. line of poetry. tuk. *f* ; dohá. *m* ;
7. line of birds in flight. ḍár. *f* ;
8. in lines. pálopál ;

LINEAGE *N.*
1. caste. got. *f* ; ját. *f* ; qáum. *f* ;
2. genealogy. nasabnámá. *m* ; kursí námá. *m* ; kullpattrí. *f* ;
3. family. ṭabbar. *m* ; ḳhándán. *m* ; ṭabbar kabílá. *m* ;
4. ancestral family. píṛí. *f* ; jad. *f* ; kul. *f* ;

LINEN DRAPER, *N.*
bajáj. *m* ;

LINGER, TO *V. I.*
ṭhahrná ; khaloná ; ráhná ; ṭikkná

LINGO, *N.*
bolí. *f* ;

LINIMENT, *N.*
málish karn dí dawá. *f* ;

LINING, *N.*
andras. *m* ; astar. *m* ;
lining of a shoe sole. patáwá. *m* ;

LINK *N.*
kuṇḍí. *f* ;

LINK, TO *V. T.*
gaṇḍhná ; joṛná ; miláuná ;

LINSEED, *N.*
alsí. *f* ;

LION, *N.*
sher. *m* ; shính. *m* ; babar sher. *m* ;

LIONESS, *N.*
sherní. *f* ; shíhní. *f* ;

LIP, *N.*
bull. *m* ;

LIQUEFY, TO *V. T.*
gálaná ; ghálaná ;

LIQUEFY, TO *V. I.*
galná ;
LIQUIDATE, TO *V. T.*
karj bhar dená ; udhár láhná ; udhár utárná ; tárná; bhugtáuná ;
LIQUOR, *N.*
sharáb. *m ;*
LIQUORICE, *N.*
mulatthí. *f ;*
LISPING, *N.*
thuthlá. *m ;*
LISP, TO *V. T.*
thuthláuná ; hakláuná ;
LIST, *N.*
firist. *f ;*
LISTEN, TO *V. T.*
sunná ; kann láuná ; dhián karná ;
LISTENER, *N.*
sunnanwáḷá. *m ;*
LISTLESS, *A.*
sust ; ḍhillá ; ghauliá ; postí ; surliá hoyá ;
LISTLESSLY, *Adv.*
ghaul nál ; sustí nál ;
LISTLESSNESS, *N.*
ghaul. *f ;* sustí. *f ;*
LITANY, *N.*
litániá. *m ;*
LITERAL, *A.*
lafzí ;
LITERARY, *A.*
paṛhiá hoyá ; kitábí ; likhiá paṛhiá ; viddiáwáṇ ;
literary language. kitábí bolí. *f ;*
LITERATE, *N.*
ilmdár. *m ;*
LITIGANT, *N.*
dávedár. *m ;* mudáí. *m ;* nálashí. *m;*
LITIGATE, TO *V. T.*
dává karná ; nálish karná ;
LITIGATION, *N.*
muqaddamabází. *f ;*
LITIGIOUS, *A.*
muqaddamabáj ;
LITTLE, *A.*
nikká ; nanná ; chhoṭá ;
LITTLE, *Adv.*
jará ; ratí ; ghaṭṭ waddh ; ratá ; kujh;
1. a little. ratákú ; thoṛá jehá ; jará ku ; thoṛá báhlá ;
2. very little. ruálak ;
3. too little. kassá ; thoṛá ;
LITTLENESS, *N.*
chhoṭíáí. *f ;*
LITURGY, *N.*
namàz. *f ;*
LIVE, TO *V. I.*
1. to exist. jíúná ; jíúndá ráhná ; jíún kaṭṭná ;
2. to live in a place. rahná ; wassná ; bás karná ; ṭikná ;
3. to make a living. gujrán OR guzárá karná ;
4. to make alive. jiwáuná ; juáuná ; jiláuná ; jiwálná ; juálná ;
5. to live at ease. raṇg rassná ;
6. since you have lived here ; jad dá terá wás is ghar hoyá hai ;
LIVELIHOOD, *N.*
guzárá. *m ;* gujárá. *m ;* rozí. *f ;* rozgár. *m ;* dáná pání. *m ;* jíuká. *f ;*
LIVELINESS, *N.*
khushí. *f ;*
LIVELY, *A.*
khush ; ráji ; parsinn ;
LIVER, *N.*
jigar. *m ;* kalejá. *m ;* káljá. *m ;*
LIVER COMPLAINT, *N.*
kaleje dí píṛ. *f ;*
LIVERY, *N.*
vardí. *f ;* bardí. *f ;*
LIVID, *A.*
jard ; píllá ;
LIVING, *N.*
guzárá. *m ;* gujárá. *m ;* gujrán. *f ;* see LIVELIHOOD.
LIVING, *A.*
jiṇdá ; jiuṇde jí ;
LIZARD, *N.*
1. small. kirlí. *f ;* kohaṛ kirlí *f ;*
2. large. kirlá. *m ;*
3. large jangal lizard. goh. *f ;*
4. Proverb used of the ambitious. A lizard by birth and swallowing a beam. zát dí kohaṛ kirlí shatíráṇ nál jhapphián ;
LOAD, *N.*
bhár. *m ;* bojh. *m ;* bojhá *m ;* lád. *f ;* ladd. *m ;* paṇḍ. *f ;* see BUNDLE.
1. one who carries a load. paṇḍí. *m ;*

2. load on one side of a camel. aṇḍḍá. *m* ;
A. the near load. orlá áṇḍḍá. *m* ;
B. the off load. parlá áṇḍḍá. *m* ;

LOAD, TO, *V. T.*
1. on an animal. laddná ;
2. on a cart, &c. chaṛháuná ;
3. to load a gun. bandúq bharná ;

LOAF, *N.*
1. Indian. roṭí. *f* ; chapátí. *f* ;
2. European. dabal roṭí. *f* ;

LOAFER, *N.*
nakhattú. *m* ;
Proverb. The bride died of hunger while the bridegroom was loafing. ṭabbar bhukk mare te baṇrá sailáṇ kare ;

LOAN, *N.*
udhár. *m* ; hudár. *m* ; qarz. *m*

LOAN, TO, *V. T.*
udhár dená OR chukáuná ; qarz dená ;

LOATHE, TO, *V. T.*
burá laggná ; sug karní ; ghináuná ; ghin áuní OR karní ; nafrat áuní ;

LOATHING, *N.*
sug. *f* ; karáhat. *f* ; ghiṇ. *f* ; nafrat. *f* ;

LOATHSOME, *A.*
bahut burá ; palít ; baṛá gaṇdá ; makrúh ; ghiṇáuná ; ghiṇáhdá ; máṛá ;

LOATHSOMENESS, *N.*
karáhat *f* ; ghiṇ. *f* ; sug. *f* ;

LOBBY, *N.*
deuhṛí. *f* ;

LOBE, *N.*
pápphrí. *f* ;

LOCALITY, *N.*
jagáh. *f* ; tháṇ. *f* ;

LOCALLY, *A.*
neṛe teṛe ;

LOCATE, TO, *V. T.*
rakkhná ; dharná ;

LOCAT. ON, *N.*
jagáh. *f* ; ṭhikáná. *m* ;

LOCK, *N.*
jaṇdrí. *f* ; jaṇdará. *m* ; tálá. *m* ;

LOCK, TO, *V. T.*
bheṛná ; jaṇdará de dená OR márná OR láuná ;
lock of hair, latt. *f* ;

LOCKER, *N.*
almárí. *f* ;

LOCKET, *N.*
1. small. námí. *f* ;
2. large. námá. *m* ;

LOCKUP, *N.*
havalát. *f* ; jel ḳháná. *m* ; bandí ḳháná. *m*; baurá. *m*; kaṇjí haud. *m* ;

LOCOMOTION, *N.*
chál. *f* ; chálá. *f* ; tor. *f* ;

LOCOMOTIVE, *N.*
anjan. *m* ;

LOCUST, *N.*
makrí. *f* ; airan. *f* ;

LODGE, TO, *V. T.*
rahná ; ṭikná ; wassná ;

LODGE, TO, *V. T.*
jagáh dení ; rakkhná

LODGING, *N.*
ṭhikáná. *m* ; jagáh. *f* ;

LOFTINESS, *N.*
uchchíái. *f* ;

LOFTY, *A.*
uchchá ;

LOG, *N.*
gelí. *f* ; mochchhá. *m* ; lakṛá. *m*
log tied round an animal's neck. kilá. *m* ; ḍáhá. *m* ;

LOGIC, *N.*
mantak. *f* ;

LOIN, *N.*
lakk. *f* ;

LOIN CLOTH, *N.*
kaháí. *f* ; lángar. *m* ; lúṇggí. *f* ; langottí. *f* ; kasotí. *f*; kasotá. *m* ; majlá. *m* ; langottá. *m* ; sudṇá. *m* ; chapárikkí. *f*; rumálí. *f* ; jáṇgiá. *m* ;

LOITER, TO, *V. I.*
1. to dawdle. ajj bhalak karná ; ghasar masar karní ;
2. to delay. chir láuná ;
3. to wander about. udále pudále phirná ; bhaṇbal bhuse kháná ; ḍáwáṇḍol phirná ;

LOITERING, *N.*
ghasar masar. *f* ;

LOLL, TO, *V. I.*
ḍhille ḍhálle baihná ;

LONE, *A.*
akallá ;
LONELINESS, *N.*
ikáṇt. *f* ; ikkalwáṇja. *m* ;
LONELY, *A.*
akallá ;
LONELY PLACE, *N.*
ikáṇt. *f* ; ikkalwáṇjá. *m* ;
LONG, *A.*
lammá ; lamochar ;
1. as long as. jinná chir ;
2. a long time. baṛá chir. *m* ; kei ḍher chir. *m* ; chokkhá chir. *m* ;
3. from a long time. kadokná ; chirokná ;
4. after a long time. chir pichchhe ; pichchhoṇ ;
LONG FOR, TO, *V. T.*
jí karná ; jí tarasná ; cháhuná ; tarafná ; dil baṛá karná ; táṇgh karní ; cháh karní ; lochná ; I long to see you. mainúṇ tuháḍe vekhan dá bahut hí shauq hai ;
LONGEVITY, *N.*
waḍḍí umr. *f* ; buḍhepá. *m* ;
LONGING, *N.*
cháh. *f* ; táṇgh. *f* ; chau. *m* ; ichchhiá. *f* ; bhauná. *m* ; shauq. *m* ; cháṭ. *f* ;
LONGINGLY, *Adv.*
baṛí cháh nál ; ríjh nál ;
LONGISH, *A.*
lamerá ;
LONGLIVED, *A.*
waḍḍí umr dá ;
LONGSUFFERANCE, *N.*
dhíraj. *m* ; sabr. *m* ; jigará. *m* ;
LONGSUFFERING, *N.*
dhírá ; gaurá ; dhímá ;
LONGWINDED, *A.*
gappí; gálarrí ; bakwási ; jatallí. *m* ;
LOOK, TO, *V. T.*
vekhná ; takkná ; johná ; nazr mární ;
1. to look up. nazr puṭṭná ;
2. to look out for. udíkná ; ráh vekhná ;
3. to look at with anger. akkh ghúrná ;
4. to look for. labbhná ; bhállná ; dekh bhál karná ; ḍhuṇḍhná ; ḍhuṇḍ ḍháṇḍ karná ;
5. to look steadfastly. akkh joṛná; táṛ láuná ; banáke vekhná ;
6. to look after. sámbhná ; sambhálná ;
7. to look stealthily. jhátí mární OR páuní ;
8. to look towards anyone. wall nigáh karní ;
9. to look after anything. dí takṛái rakkhní ;
10. to look at closely. níjh láuná ; najír láuná ;
11. to look ahead, to be careful. aggá pichchhá vekhná ; agge vekhná ;
LOOK, *N.*
nigáh. *f* ; jháká. *m* ; jhákk. *f* ; jhamáká. *m* ; takk. *m* ;
LOOK, *Interj.*
vekh ;
LOOKER, *N.*
vekhanwálá. *m* ;
LOOKING GLASS, *N.*
shíshá. *m* ;
LOOM, *N.*
khaḍḍí. *f* ;
LOOP, *N.*
ghuṇḍí. *f* ;
hole and button. ghuṇḍí bírá. *m* ;
LOOSE, *A.*
ḍhillá ; khullhá ; khulkhulá ;
LOOSEN, TO, *V. T.*
kholná ; moklá karná ; ḍhillá karná ;
to dig up and expose to view. ukherná ; puṭṭná ;
LOOSED, TO BE, *V. I.*
khullná ;
1. for running. chhuṭṭná ;
2. as machinery or roots. ukkhaṛná ;
LOOSENESS, *N.*
ḍhill. *f* ; khullh. *f* ; khullh ḍullh. *f* ;
LOOT, *N.*
lúṭ dá mál. *m* ;
LOP, TO, *V. T.*
chhángná ;
LOQUACIOUS, *A.*
gálaṛí ; gappí ; bakwásí ;
LOQUACITY, *N.*
bakwás. *m* ; chhúṭ. *f*; bahu bachan. *m* ;

LORD, *N.*
1. master. pattí. *m* ; málik. *m* ; hákim. *m* ;
2. GOD. Khudáwand. *m;* Rabb. *m;* Parmeshar. *m* ;

LORD, TO, *V. T.*
bádsháhí karní ; ráj karná ; hukúmat karní ; hukm chárhná ; jorá-warí karní ;

LORDLINESS, *N.*
hákamí. *f* ; majájí. *f* ; gamrúri. *f* ; damág. *m* ; see PRIDE.

LORDLY, *A.*
majájí ; hekar ; phiṭṭiá hoyá ;

LORDSHIP, *N.*
bádsháhí. *f* ; hákamí. *f* ;

LORE, *N.*
gián. *m* ; viddiá. *f* ; ilm. *m* ;

LOSE, TO, *V. T.*
guáuná ; guá dená ; kharáná ; khoná ; kharáchná ; guwáchná ;
1. to lose a game. bází charhná;
2. to lose a wager. bází hární.
3. to lose courage. hárná ; dhiggí dháuná ; himmat hární ; dil chhaḍḍná ;
4. to lose one's senses, to be confused; matt OR hosh OR aql OR vá márná.
5. to lose a law suit. muqadamá ḳhárij ho jáná ;
6. he has lost all his wealth, uh apná sárá mál guá baiṭhá hai ;

LOSE, TO, *V. I.*
ghus jáná ; wissar jáná ; guáchná ; gum honá ; kharáchná ; kho jáná ;

LOSER, *N.*
hárú. *m* ;

LOSS, *N.*
gháṭṭá. *m* ; kasar. *f* ; nuqsán *m* . harj. *m* ; hán. *f* ; bhánggá. *m* ;
1. financial loss. ṭoṭṭá. *m* ; mos. *f* ;
2. to suffer loss. kasar laggná ; gháṭṭá painá ; mos laggná ; ujjar pujjar ho jáná;
3. to make up a loss. gháṭṭá bharná ;
4. to pay for loss. nuqsán bharná ;
5. you will suffer loss. tainúṇ mos laggegí ;
6. he suffered serious loss. tagṛá ṭoṭṭá khádá ;

LOST, *A.*
guáchayá hoyá ;

LOSS AND GAIN, *N.*
wáddhá gháṭṭá. *m* ;

LOT, *N.*
1. part. hissá. *m* ; chháṇḍá. *m* ; bakhrá. *m* ;
2. lots. gune. *m* ;
3. to cast lots. gune páiná ; paríchhá páuná ;
4. a lot of work. chokhá kamm. *m* ;

LOTION, *N.*
ikk parkár dí dawái. *f* ;

LOTTERY, *N.*
látarí. *f* ;

LOTUS, *N.*
kammián. *f* ;

LOUD, *A.*
uchchá ; zor dá ; shorí ;
a loud voice. zorwálí awáz. *f* ;

LOUDLY, *Adv.*
zor nál ; uchchí karke ; uchchí uchchí ; uchchídiṇ ;
1 to cry out loudly. uchchí ḍanḍ painá ;
2. speak louder. zará dabbke ákho;

LOUDNESS, *N.*
raulá. *m* ; shor. *m* ; gaugá. *m* ;

LOUSE, *N.*
dhakkh. *f;* jún. *f;* júán. *f;* líkáṇ. *f* ;
1. to become lousy. júáṇ painián ;
2. to hunt louse. júáṇ vekhníán OR márnián ;

LOUSY, *A.*
líkhar ; júánwálí ; júán khádá ;

LOVABLE, *A.*
azíz ; piyárá ; dulárá ;

LOVE, *N.*
piyár. *m* ; muhabbat. *f* ; prem. *m* ; parít. *f* : cháh. *f* ; moh. *m* ; lagan. *f* ; hit. *m* ; sandeh. *m* ; dostí. *f* ; dulárá. *m* ; niuṇ. *m* ;
1. maternal love. mámtá. *f* ;
2. love for a man. ishk. *m* ;
3. love for a woman. mashúkí. *f* ;
4. intense love. gáhri parít. *f* ; saṇgní parít. *f* ;

LOVE, TO *V. T.*
piyár karná ; muhabbat karní ; moh karná ; prem piyár karná ; sandeh karná ; lagan laggní ; hit rakkhná ;
1. to love much. waddh piyár karná ;
2. to love coldly. kachchí parít karní ;
LOVELESS, *A.*
sakkchur ;
LOVELINESS, *N.*
ḳhubsuratí. *f ;* suthráí. *f ;* sohappan. *m ;* sohj *m ;* ḍuss. *f ;* sundarlá. *m ;*
LOVELY, *A.*
baṛá sohná ; ḳhubsurat ; sajílá ; suthrá ; sundar ; darshaní ;
LOVER, *N.*
dost. *m ;* premí. *m ;* hitkárí. *m ;* in a bad sense. ishkí tiḍḍá. *m;* yár. *m;* áshik. *m ;* mashúk. *f ;*
LOVING, *A.*
hitwálá ; premí ; muhabbatí ;
LOVING KINDNESS, *N.*
mihrbání. *f ;* mihr. *m ;* dáyá. *f ;* kirpá. *f ;*
LOVINGLY, *Adv.*
prem piyár nál ; baṛí muhabbat nál ;
LOW, TO *V. T.*
ringghná ; aringghná ; aráná ; ḍhikná ;
the cow is standing lowing. gáṇ ḍhikdí kharí hai ;
LOW, *A.*
1 low down. heṭh ; niwáṇ ;
2. abject. ájiz ; miskín ; nakárá ; nikammá ;
3. unworthy. chanḍál ; nalaiq ; kamíná ; máṛá ;
LOWBORN, *A.*
badját ; kamíná ; ních ;
LOWER, TO *V. I.*
1. to disgrace anyone. niwáuná ; níwán karná ; ḍegná ; múnh kálá karná ; pat láh suṭṭná ; bepat karná ;
2. to lower something. heṭháṇ karná ;
3. to lower with a rope. heṭháṇ palmáuná ; heṭháṇ lamkáuná ;

LOWLINESS, *N.*
ájizí. *f ;* garíbí. *f ;* dhíṇtái. *f ;* maskíní. *f ;*
LOWLY, *A.*
maskín ; ájiz ; garíb ; halím ;
LOW PRICED, *A.*
sastá ; sastmullá ; suwallá ; miṭṭí de mull ;
LOWRING, *A.*
gahrá ;
LOW SPIRITED, *A.*
udás ; bedil ; masosiá hoyá ; hamsosiá hoyá ; dil ḍhaṭṭhá ;
LOYAL, *A.*
sachchá ; lun halál ; khará ; suchiárá ; bol dá púrá ; gall dá pakká ;
LOYALIST, *N.*
sirkár dá ḳhairḳháh. *m ;*
LOYALLY, *Adv.*
dharmo dharmí ; rástí nál ; ḳhairḳháhí nál ;
LOYALTY, *N.*
nimak halálí. *f ;* ḳhairḳháhí. *f ;*
LUBRICATE, TO *V. T.*
tel páuná ;
to grease the wheels of a carṭ báṇggná ; wáṇggná ; chopaṛná ;
LUCERNE, *N.*
siṇjhí. *f ;*
LUCID, *A.*
1. clear. sáf ; suthrá ; nirmal ;
2. shining. chamkílá ; chamakdár; bhaṛakwálá ;
LUCIDLY, *Adv.*
safái nál ;
LUCIDNESS, *N.*
safái. *f ;*
LUCK, *N.*
qismat. *f ;* lekh. *f ;* sanjog. *m ;* bhágwání. *f ;*
Proverb. Your trowel is in the ghí to-day. *i.e.*, you are in luck. huṇ táṇ tuháḍá gheu vichch rambá hai ;
LUCKILY, *Adv.*
bhágán nál ; ḳhushnasíbí nál ; abiháre ;
LUCKINESS, *N.*
khushnasíbí. *f ;*
LUCKLESS, *A.*
badnasíb ; benasíb ; kambaḳht ; chaṇdará ; badqismat ; bekarmá ; abhágí ;

LUCKY, *A*.
bhágwán; nasíbánwálá; sulakkhaná; bhágánwálá; karmáwálá; partápwálá; sukhí;
If we are lucky we shall get what we desire. je ih sanjog ho jáwe, táṇ ichchhiá puran howegí;
LUCRATIVE, *A*.
faidedár; nafewand; baṛí khaṭṭíwálá; wáddhewálá;
LUCRE, *N*.
rupae paise. *m*;
LUDICROUS, *A*.
hassan jog;
LUG, TO, *V. T*.
ghasíṭná; khichchná; dhúná; dhiṛná;
LUGGAGE, *N*.
wast. *f*; chíjwast. *f*; nikksukk. *m*; bistrá boriá, *m*; wast walevá. *m*; bugchá. *m*;
Luggage receipt. biltí. *f*;
LUGUBRIOUS, *A*.
masosiá hoyá; udás; sogmáṇ; sasdil; dil ḍhaṭṭhá; nimújháṇ;
LUKEWARM, *A*.
kossá; guṇguṇá; sítgarm;
LULL, *N*.
1. calm. aman. *m*;
2. interval. tafrí. *f*;
LULL, TO, *V. T*.
1. to soothe a child. lorí dení; tháparná;
2. to quiet a horse. puchkárá dena;
3. to soothe a man. ṭhaṇḍá karná; dhímá karná:
LULLABY, *N*.
lorí. *f*; gít. *m*;
LUMBAGO, *N*.
kamar dí píṛ. *f*;
LUMBER, *N*.
1. goods. asbáb. *m*; wast. *f*; chízwast. *f*; nikk sukk. *m*;
2. old building material. malbá. *m*;
LUMINOUS, *A*.
1. shining. chamkílá; bhaṛakwálá;
2. clear. sáf; suthrá; nirmal;
LUMINOSITY, *N*.
chamak. *f*; lishk. *f*; parkásh. *m*;
LUMP, *N*.
1. of earth. ḍhemh. *f*; ḍhím. *f*; ḍhímá. *f*; roṛá. *m*; roṛí. *f*; chil. *f*;
2. of gur. gur dí roṛí. *f*;
3. of wet mud. thobá. *m*; maṭhunní. *f*;
4. of dough. maṭhunní. *f*; perá. *m*;
LUMPY, *A*.
gilhtewálá;
LUNACY, *N*.
shadá. *m*; jhall. *m*; págalpuṇá. *m*; kamal. *m*;
LUNATIC, *N*.
págal; kamlá; jhallá; sadáí; shadáí;
LUNG, *N*.
phephrá. *m*; phiphrá. *m*;
LURCH, *N*.
ḍigdá ḍhaindá. *m*;
LURCH, TO, *V. I*.
ḍigdaná ḍhainná;
LURE, *N*.
ulárá. *m*; tamá. *m*;
LURE, TO, *V. T*.
lalcháuná; lubháuná; tamá dená;
LURID, *A*.
1. yellow, píllá;
2. gloomy. udás; chitthá; chhinṭáwáṇ; sasdil; dil ḍhaṭṭhá,
LURK, TO. *V. I*.
dá láuná; ghát vichch baihná;
LURKING PLACE, *N*.
ghát. *f*; dáu. *m*;
LUSCIOUS, *A*.
sawádwálá; miṭṭhá; suádlá;
LUSCIOUSNESS, *N*.
1. sweetness. maṭhiás. *f*;
2. taste. suád. *m*;
LUST, *N*.
mastí. *f*; kam. *m*; kharmastí. *f*; masteváṇ. *m*; jom. *m*; lúchchpuṇá. *m*; bahir. *m*; phateṇváṇ. *f*;
1. of a mare. gurmáí. *f*;
2. evil lusts. búríáṇ wísíán. *f*;
LUST, TO, *V. T*.
mastí vichch áuná; mast ho jáná;
LUSTFUL, *A*.
mastáná; mast; kamí; luchchá; badját; jomí; khíwá; laṭpaṭá; chhaṭṭiá hoyá; mushṭaṇḍá;
lustful desire. kámṇá. *f*;
LUSTILY, *Adv*.
himmat nál; uddam nál; baṛe jor nál;

LUSTINESS, *N.*
mazbutí. *f;* táqat. *f;* wáh. *f;*
bal. *m;*
LUSTRATE, TO, *V. T.*
dhoná;
1. ceremonial, Muhammadan. wazú karná;
2. ceremonial, Hindu. ashnán karná;
LUSTRATION, *N.*
wazú. *m;* ashnán. *m;*
LUSTRE, *N.*
1. brightness. chamak. *f;* chilkárá. *m;* jot. *f;* jagmagát. *f;* parkásh. *m;*
2. renown. dhúm. *f;* jas. *m;* partáp. *m;* ghúkar. *f;*
LUSTROUS, *A.*
chamkílá.
LUSTY, *A.*
tagṛá; takṛá; táqatwálá; uddamí; mihnatí; himmatí; jorwálá;
LUTE, *N.*
1. small. báṇsarí. *f;*
2. large. waṇjhlí. *f;*
3. double. lagojá. *m;* mattíáṇ. *f;*
LUXURIANCE, *N.*
bhog. *m;*
LUXURIANT, *A.*
1. abundant. bahutá; wadherá;
2. green, rank. hariaulá; bhal bhaí;
LUXURIOUS, *A.*
bhogí; lahirí;
LUXURIOUSLY, *Adv.*
padárath de sababoṇ;
LUXURY, *N.*
padárath. *m;* bhog. *m;*
LYING, *A.*
jhuṭhá;
LYING, *N.*
jhuṭh. *m;* jhuṭh muṭh. *m;*
LYMPH, *N.*
chíp. *f;* muád. *m;*
LYNCH, TO, *V. T.*
már piṭ karná;

M.

MACADAMIZED ROAD, *N.*
pakkí saṛak. *f;*
MACARONI, *N.*
makrúní. *f:*
MACE, *N.*
chob. *f;*
MACEBEARER, *N.*
chobdár. *m;*
MACHINATION, *N.*
chálá. *m;* jugat. *f;* masaudá. *m;* juglá. *f;* jálsájí. *f;*
MACHINE, *N.*
kalá. *f;* mashín. *f;*
MACHINERY, *N.*
kalá. *f;*
MACKINTOSH, *N.*
barsátí. *f;*
MAD, *A.*
jhallá; saudáí; págal; kamlá ramlá; baurá; jhalliá hoyá;
MADAM, *N.*
mem sáhib. *f;* begam. *f;*
MADDEN, TO, *V. T.*
1. to make mad. págal karná;
2. to enrage. russáuná; agg láuná; luhná; khijáuná;
MADHOUSE, *N.*
págal khháná. *m;*
MADLY, *Adv.*
baṛe gusse nál; págal puṇe nál;
MADMAN, *N.*
págal. *m;* kamlá. *m;*
MADNESS, *N.*
saudá. *m;* jhall. *m;* kamal. *m;* págal puná. *m;*
MAGAZINE, *N.*
kitáb. *f;* pothí. *f;* pustak. *m;*
MAGGOT, *N.*
kíṛá. *m;* kirm. *m;*
MAGI, *N.*
najúmí. *m;*
MAGIC, *N.*
jádú. *m;* jádugarí. *f;* ṭuṇá. *m;* jháṛá phukkí. *f;* jháṛá. *m;*
MAGICAL, *A.*
jádú dá;
MAGICAL ARTS, *N.*
ṭúne ṭoṭke. *m;*
MAGICAL FORMULA, *N.*
jaṇtar maṇtar. *m;* shuṇshá. *m;*
MAGICALLY, *Adv.*
jádú nál; shuṇshá nál;
MAGICIAN, *N.*
jádugar. *m;* maṇtarí. *m;*
MAGISTERIAL, *A.*
hákamí; affsarí;

MAGISTRACY, *N*.
hákam. *m* ; affsar. *m* ;
MAGISTRATE, *N*.
majastreṭ. *m* ; hákam. *m* ; munsif. *m* ; jaj. *m* ; tahsíldár. *m* ;
MAGNANIMITY, *N*.
daryádilí. *f* ;
MAGNANIMOUS, *A*.
khullhá dil ; daryádil ;
MAGNANIMOUSLY, *Adv*.
khullhe dil nál ; daryádilí nál ; waḍḍe dil nál ;
MAGNATE, *N*.
ráís. *m* ; máldar. *m* ;
MAGNET, *N*.
chakmak. *m* ; maknátís. *m* ;
MAGNIFICENCE, *N*.
shán. *f* ; bharak. *f* ; partáp. *m* ; raunaq. *f* ; see SPLENDOUR.
MAGNIFICENTLY, *Adv*.
shán shauqat nál ; partáp nál ; raunaq nál ;
MAGNIFICENT, *A*.
shándár ; uttam ; tejwán ; jalálí ; partápí ; raunaqwálá ;
MAGNIFY, TO, *V*. *T*.
1. to enlarge. wadháuná ;
2. to praise. waḍíáuná ; máhimá karná ; saláhná ; guṇ gáuná ;
3. to exaggerate. gal wadháuná ; lúṇ mirch lagáuná ; masále láke dassná ; wáddhe láuná ;
MAGNIFYING GLASS, *N*.
jádú dá shíshá. *m* ;
MAGNILOQUENT, *A*.
ákkaṛ khán ;
MAGNITUDE, *N*.
lamataṇ chauṛataṇ. *f* ;
MAGPIE. *N*.
mahtáb. *m* ;
MAID, MAIDEN, *N*.
kúrí. *f*; kákí. *f*; laṛkí. *f*; kanníán. *f* ; bálṛí. *f* ; játakarí. *f* ;
MAIDENHOOD, *N*.
kuár. *f* ; kuárpuṇá. *m* ; kaṇwár-puṇá. *m* ;
MAIDSERVANT, *N*.
ṭahlan. *f* ; dássí, *f* ; naukaráṇí. *f* ; bándí. *f* ;
MAIL, *N*.
dák. *f* ;

MAIMED, *A*.
lúlá ; langáṇ ; see DEFORMED. ;
MAINLY, *Adv*.
asl vichch ;
MAINSTAY, *N*.
1. help. madat. *f* ; sahái. *f* sahaitá. *f* ; sahárá. *m* ;
2. support. thammí. *f* ; thamm. *m* ;
MAINTAIN, TO, *V*. *T*.
sambhálná ; pálná ; pálná posná ; sahárná ;
MAINTENANCE, *N*.
parwastí. *f* ; guzárá. *m* ; roṭí kapṛá. *m* ;
MAIZE, *N*.
júár. *m* ; makái. *f* ;
green maize. dodhá. *m* ;
MAJESTIC, *A*.
bádsháhí ; shándár ; partápí ; waḍḍá te sohṇá ;
MAJESTICALLY, *Adv*.
bádsháhí taur nál ; bádsháhí shán nál ;
MAJESTY, *N*.
bádsháhí. *f* ; partáp. *m* ; shán te bhaṛak. *f*; máhimá. *f*; upmán. *m*;
MAJOR, *A*.
waḍḍá ; baṛá ;
MAJOR, *N*.
mejar sáhib. *m* ;
MAKE, TO *V*. *T*.
banáuná ; ghaṛná ;
1. to make ready. taiyár karná ;
2. to make a face. burá múṇh banáuná ; matthe waṭṭ páuná ;
3. to make a living. gujárá karná ;
4. to make a noise. raulá páuná ; shor macháuná ;
5. to make away with. gapak lainá ;
6. to cause to be made. banwáuná ;
7. to make firm. diṛh karná ; dariṛh karná ;
MAKE, *N*.
banauṭ. *f* ;
MAKER, *N*.
1. Divine. kartá. *m* ; kartár. *m* ; sirjanhár. *m* ;
2. human. banáunwálá. *m* ; ghaṛú. *m* ; ghaṛanwálá. *m* ;
MAKESHIFT, *N*.
lag bhag. *m* ;

MAKEWEIGHT, *N.*
páskúṇ. *m*; pásaṇg. *m*;
MAKING, *N.*
banauṭ. *f*;
cost of making. banwái. *f*;
MALADMINISTRATION, *N.*
nádar sháhí. *f*; nádar gardí. *f*;
badintizámí. *f*; beḍhaṇgí. *f*;
andher nagarí. *f*;
MALADY, *N.*
bamárí. *f*; rog. *m*;
MALARIA, *N.*
táp. *m*; tap. *m*; kass. *f*;
MALCONTENT, *N.*
asantokhí. *m*; asantokhan. *f*;
MALE, *N.*
nar. *m*; mard. *m*; ádmí. *m*;
manukkh. *m*;
MALEDICTION, *N.*
lánat. *f*; bad duá. *f*; saráp. *m*;
durú. *m*; paletá. *m*; haṛdú
lánat. *f*; phiṭak. *f*; phiṭkar *f*;
MALEFACTOR, *N.*
hattiárá. *m*; buriár. *m*; dosí. *m*;
MALEVOLENCE, *N.*
adávat. *f*; see MALICE.
MALEVOLENT, *A.*
virodhí; darohí; gubrí; dokhí;
badnítá;
MALEVOLENTLY, *Adv.*
vair nál; adávat nál; khár nál;
MALFORMATION, *N.*
beḍhaṇg. *m*; kojhái. *f*; see
DEFORMED.
a man with six fingers. chháṇgá. *m*;
MALICE, MALICIOUSNESS, *N.*
adávat. *f*; dushmaní. *f*; vair. *m*;
kíná. *m*; kauṛ. *f*; badnítí. *f*;
rikhas. *f*; kiṛ. *f*; ḍáh. *f*; adáut. *f*;
MALICIOUS, *A.*
sharír; kuchal; kutab; badnítá;
MALIGN, TO *V. T.*
badnám karná; niṇdiá karná;
dosh láuná; náṇ wigáṛná; bhaṇḍná;
lutíáṇ láuná; jáṛ phuṭṭná;
MALIGNANCY, *N.*
dushmaní. *f*; badnítí. *f*; see
MALICE.
MALIGNANT, *A.*
dhokhí;

MALIGNANTLY, *Adv.*
vair nál; adávat nál; dushmaní
nál: khár nál;
MALINGNER, *N.*
kamm chor. *m*;
MALIGNITY, *N.*
kauṛ. *f*; dushmaní. *f*; see
HATE.
MALLET, *N.*
muṇglí. *f*; mohlí. *f*;
MALPRACTICE, *N.*
kukarm. *m*; bhaiṛ. *m*; badchalní. *f*;
bhaiṛá kamm. *m*; illat. *f*;
sharárat. *f*; paikaṛá. *m*;
MALTREAT, TO *V. T.*
ḳharáb karná; saḳhtí karní;
badsalukí karní;
MALTREATMENT, *N.*
badsalukí. *f*; saḳhtí. *f*; jástí. *f*;
MAMMA, *N.*
máṇ. *f*; mátá. *f*; ammán. *f*;
bebe. *f*;
MAMMON, *N.*
máyá. *m*; dhan. *m*; daulat. *f*;
mál. *m*;
MAN, *N.*
ádmí. *m*; manukh. *m*; purakh. *m*;
puras. *m*; bandá. *m*; insáṇ. *m*;
1. a small man. thingná. *m*;
wauná. *m*;
2. a young man. jawán. *m*;
gabhrú. *m*; gabhreṭá. *m*; gabh-
roṭá. *m*;
MANACLES, *N.*
beṛíáṇ. *f*; hatthkaríáṇ. *f*;
MANDATE, *N.*
hukm. *m*; ágiá. *m*;
MANACLE, TO *V. T.*
beṛíáṇ painí; júṛná;
MANAGE, TO *V. T.*
guzárá karná; chaláuná; intizám
karná; torná; oṛpoṛ karná;
he will manage somehow. uh
kujh upáu kareṇgá;
MANAGEMENT, *N.*
parbaṇdh *m*; sanjan. *m*;
intizám. *m*; oprá. *m*;
authority. iḳhtiyár. *m*; wass. *m*;
MANAGER, *N.*
sarbaráh. *m*; muḳhtiár. *m*;
intizámí. *m*;
for a moneylender. gumáshtá. *m*;

MANE, *N*.
ghoṛe dí dhaun OR gatthe de wál. *m* ;
MANFULLY, *Adv*.
dilerí nál ; sher hoke ; himmat nál ;
MANGE, *N*.
kuṭṭe khurk. *f* ;
MANGER, *N*.
khurlí. *f* ;
MANGLE, TO *V*. *T*.
ṭukṛe ṭukṛe karná ; pháṛná ;
MANGO *N*.
amb. *m* ;
1. mango blossom. amb dá búr. *m* ;
2. mango juice. amb ras. *m* ;
3. a ripe dropped mango. ṭapke dá amb. *m* ;
4. parings of mango dried in the sun. amb chúr. *m* ;
MANGY, *A*.
khurkwálá ;
MANHOOD, *N*.
jawání. *f* ;
MANIA, *N*.
págalpuṇá. *m* ; saudá. *m* ; jhall. *m* ; kamal. *m* ;
MANIAC, *A*.
págal ; sudáí ; diwáná ;
MANIFEST, *A*.
pargaṭ ; malúm ; záhir ; jáhir ;
MANIFEST, TO BE, *V*. *I*.
pargaṭ honá ; jápná ; záhir honá ; dissná ;
MANIFEST, TO *V*. *I*.
1. to show. dikháuná ; dikhlá dená ; záhir karná ; dikhálí dení ; pargaṭ karná ;
2. to prove. sábit karná ; nitárná ; sabútí dená ;
MANIFESTATION, *N*.
roshnáí. *f* ; pargaṭáí. *f* ;
MANIFESTLY, *Adv*.
sáf sáf ;
MANIFESTO, *N*.
hoká. *m* ; ishtihár. *m* ;
MANIFOLD, *A*.
saurangá ; kaí taráh dá ; bhúrangá ; bhánt bhánt dá ;
MANIPULATE, TO *V*. *T*.
hatth nál kamm karná ;
MANIPULATION, *N*.
hatth dá kamm. *m* ;

MANKIND, *N*.
insán. *m* ; manukkh. *m* ;
MANLINESS, *N*.
mardáú. *m* ; dilerí. *f* ; bahádurí. *f* ;
MANLY, *A*.
mardáná ; diler ; bahádur ; baṛá sher ;
MANNER, *N*.
1. method. taur. *m* ; ḍaul. *f* ; rauṇs. *f* ; súl. *m* ; bidhí. *f* ; ḍhaṇg. *m* ; jugat. *f* ; ḍhaṇg waṇg. *m* ; taur bhaur. *m* ;
2. deportment. chál ḍhál. *f* ; chál chalan. *m* ; subháo. *m* ; achár. *m* ;
3. kind. bháṇt. *m* ; qism. *m* ; parkár. *m* ;
4. good manners. sulakkhníáṇ wáddíáṇ. *f* ;
5. bad manners. buríáṇ ádatáṇ. *f* ;
6. his manner of life. uh dá subháo. *m* ;
7. his manner of life is abominable. uh dá achár bharisht ho gayá hai;
MANNERISM, *N*.
báṇkpuṇá. *m* ;
MANNERLINESS, *N*.
adab. *f* ; ádar. *m* ; ádar bháú. *m* ;
MANNERLY, *Adv*.
ádar mán nál ;
MANŒUVRE, *N*.
chalákí. *f* ; jugat. *f* ; chalittar. *m* ; lapeṭá. *m* ; wal pech. *m* ;
in a bad sense. chál. *f*; pakhaṇḍ. *m*;
MANŒUVRE, TO, *V*. *T*.
chalákí karní ; dáh launá ;
MANSION, *N*.
koṭhí. *f* ; waḍḍá makán. *m* ;
palace. mahal, *m* ;
MANSLAUGHTER, *N*.
khun. *m* ; qatal. *f* ;
MANSLAYER, *N*.
khuní. *m* ;
MANTEL, *N*.
parchhattí. *f* ;
MANUAL, *A*.
dastí ; hatth dá ;
MANUAL, *N*.
kitáb. *f* ; pothí. *f* ; kateb. *f* ;
of the Granth. gutká. *m* ;
MANUFACTORY, *N*.
kár khána. *m* ;

MANUFACTURE, TO, *V. T.*
banáuná; banwáuná; ghaṛná;
MANUFACTURE, *N.*
kárígarí. *f*; banauṭ. *f*;
MANURE, *N.*
rúṛí. *f*; mallaṛ. *f*; malhaṛ. *m*; rehí. *f*; rúṛí gatthá. *m*;
1. small cakes used for fuel. páttiáṇ. *f*; tháppíáṇ. *f*;
2. large cakes used for fuel. ḍhakille. *m*;
MANURE, TO, *V. T.*
reh páuná; rúṛí páuní; malerná; rúṛí gatthá páuná;
MANUSCRIPT, *N.*
kalamí kitáb. *f*;
MANY, *A.*
bathere; bahut; bahutá; anek; báhále; bahutere; bahu; ḍher sáre; wadhík; chokhe;
many times. lakkh wár;
MAP, *N.*
naqshá. *m*;
MAP, TO, *V. T.*
naqshá khichná OR banáuná;
MAR, TO, *V. T.*
wigáṛná; bagáṛná; ḳharáb karná; miṭṭí palít karní; chauṛ kar dená; nisṭ karná;
MARAUD, TO, *V. T.*
luṭṭná; ḍáká márná; már dhár karná; see ROB.
MARAUDER, *N.*
luṭerá. *m*; ḍákú. *m*; dháṛví. *m*;
MARBLE, *N.*
1. a little stone ball. golí. *f*;
2. a kind of stone. marmar. *m*;
MARBLE, *A.*
sangmarmar dá;
MARCH, *N.*
kúch. *m*; chalo chalí. *f*;
MARCH, TO, *V. T.*
kuch karná; tur painá; paiṇḍá márná;
MARE, *N.*
ghorí. *f*;
MARGIN, *N.*
1. bank or shore. kaṇḍhá. *m*; lámbh. *m*;
2. of cloth. kanní. *f*;
3. a ridge of earth. banná. *m*;

MARGINAL, *A.*
kaṇḍhe dá;
MARIGOLD, *N.*
gaiṇḍá. *m*; geṇḍà. *m*;
MARINE, *A.*
samundarí;
MARINER, *N.*
maláh. *m*; jahájí. *m*;
MARK, *N.*
nishán. *m*; dág. *m*; dáṇg. *m*, ládh. *f*; lík. *f*; nishání. *f*;
1. marks of animals' feet. khurá. *m*, khoj. *m*;
2. Híndu mark on forehead ṭikká. *m*; tilak. *m*;
MARK, TO, *V. T.*
nishán láuná; nishání karní; to mark timber by notching it ṭakkná; ṭakk láuná;
MARKET, *N.*
maṇḍí. *f*; bazár. *m*; bajár. *m*.
MARKET PRICE, *N.*
bhá. *m*; bháu. *m*; dar. *m*;
MARMALADE, *N.*
narange dá marabbá. *m*;
MARRIAGE, *N.*
nikáh. *m*; shádí. *f*; viáh. *m*; parnáṇ. *m*;
1. of a widow. karewá. *m*, dharewá. *m*;
2. infant marriage. guḍḍíáṇ dá viáh. *m*;
3. a marriage engagement. mangní. *f*; kurmái. *f*; rishtá náttá. *m*, maṇgewá. *m*;
4. a marriage party. janj. *f*;
5. marriage gathering. mel. *m*;
6. marriage gift. neuṇdrá. *m*; neuṇdá. *m*;
7. Proverb. Marriage depends on consent, if not it is death. parnáṇ ḳhúshí nál, ná táṇ marná;
MARRIAGEABLE, *A.*
viáhun jog;
MARRIED, *A.*
viáháyá hoyá; parnáhá hoyá; viáhtá;
1. for a woman only. nikáhı; viáhái hoí; parnáhí hoí;
2. a lawfully married woman. viáhtá. *f*;

MARROW, *N.*
bhejjá. *m* ;
MARRY, TO, *V. T.*
1. Christian and Muhammadan. viáh karná ; shádí karní; viáhuná; ghar karná ; ghar wassáuná ;
2. Hindu. láwáṇ lainá ; phere lainá ; maṇḍu paṛhná ;
3. Hindu widow remarriage. chádar páná ; chádrá páná ;
4. do you wish to get married or not ? terá viáh te dil kardá hai ki nahíṇ ?
5. so that they may marry. táṇ jo unháṇ dí joṛí ban jáwe ;
6. daughter, now you have to be married. Bíbí, tainúṇ huṇ garist vichch pair rakkhná hai ;
7. to marry an educated girl to an uneducated boy is like marrying a cow to an ass. paṛhí hoí dhí aṇpaṛh núṇ dení ih táṇ gáú khote núṇ ikaṭṭhá karná haí ;
MARSH, *N.*
jillan. *f* ; jhall. *m* ;
lake. jhíl. *f* ;
MARSHAL, TO, *V. T.*
kaṭṭhá karná ;
MARSHY GROUND, *N.*
khobhá. *m* ; jillan. *f* ;
MART, *N.*
maṇḍí. *f* ; bazár. *m* ;
MARTIAL, *A.*
jangí ; faují ;
MARTINGALE, *N.*
síne band. *m* ;
MARTYR, *N.*
shahíd. *m* ; sahíd. *m* ;
Proverb. A martyr if killed, a gází if he kills. mare táṇ sahíd, máre tá gájí ;
MARTYR, TO, *V. T.*
shahíd karná ; jánoṇ már suṭṭná ;
MARTYRDOM, *N.*
shahídí maut. *f* ;
MARVEL, *N.*
1. something strange. acharaj. *m* ; anokh. *m* ; achambhá. *m*
2. amazement. haráni. *f* ; haránagí. *f* ; habaṛ dabaṛ. *f* ; habṛá dabṛí. *f* ;
MARVEL, TO, *V. T.*
achambhá karná ; acharaj honá ; hairán honá ;
MARVELLOUS, *A.*
acharaj ; ajíb ; anokhá ;
MARVELLOUSLY, *Adv.*
ajab taur nál ; ajíb taur nál ;
MASCULINE, *A.*
1. male. nar ;
2. grammar. muzakkar ;
MASH, TO, *V. T.*
raláuná ;
MASH BRAN, *N.*
nihárí. *f* ;
MASHING, *N.*
ragṛá. *m* ;
MASK, TO, *V. T.*
chipáuná ; lukáuná ; ḍhakkná ; ḍhappná ;
to disguise. bhes waṭáuná OR badalná ;
MASON, *N.*
ráj. *m* ;
work of a mason. rájgírí. *f* ;
MASS, *N.*
kusk. *m* ; kunn. *m* ; kunnú. *m* ; ḍher. *m* ;
MASSACRE, *N.*
jí ghát. *m* ; qatal. *f* ; khun. *m* ;
MASSACRE, TO, *V. T.*
khun karná ;
MASSAGE, *N.*
muṭṭhí cháppí. *f* ;
MASSAGE, TO, *V. T.*
muṭṭhí cháppí karní ; muṭṭhíáṇ bharná ; ghuttná ;
1. to massage by treading. latáṛná ;
2. massage me. maiṇ núṇ muṭṭhíáṇ bharo.
MASSIVE, *A.*
waḍḍa sárá ; bahut bhárá ;
MAST, *N.*
mastúl. *m* ;
MASTER, *N.*
1. teacher. ustád. *m*; mudarras. *m* ;
2. ruler. hákam. *m* ; málik. *m* ; affsar. *m* ;
3. of the house. gharwálá. *m* ;
4. religious teacher. gurú. *m* ; gur. *m* ; murshid. *m* ;

5. Proverb. Earn as a servant and eat as a master. gollá hoke kamáwe, mián hoke kháwe;
6. Proverb. Without their master the cattle are miserable, no one rubs them down. sáin bájhoṇ mál ḍuhelá, hatth ná phere koí;

MASTER, TO, *V. T.*
1. to rule. hukúmat karní; ikhtiyár karná;
2. to subdue. dabáuná; hatth heṭh karná; qábú vichch leáuná; hall karná;
3. to subdue the passions. dil núṇ márná; jí núṇ márná; jí qábú vichch rakkhná;

MASTERFUL, *A.*
jabardast;

MASTERLESS, *A.*
bemálik; lawáris;

MASTERLY, *A.*
1. excellent. uttam; baṛá changá; suthrá; sohná;
2. skilful. guṇí; siáná;

MASTERSHIP, *N.*
1. office of a master. ustádagí. *f*;
2. mastery. málakí. *f*; hákamí. *f*;
3. authority. ikhtiyár. *m*; wass. *m*;

MASTERY, *N.*
1. authority. ikhtiyár. *m*; hákamí. *f*; wass. *m*;
2. victory. jit. *m*; fatáh. *f*;
3. skill. gúṇ. *m*; vithiá. *f*; ustádí. *f*; hujdá. *m*; ḍhab. *m*;

MASTICATE, TO, *V. T.*
chabná; chithná;

MASTICATION, *N.*
chabáí. *f*;

MASTIFF, *N.*
kuttá. *m*;

MASTURBATE, TO, *V. T.*
muṭṭh mární;

MASTURBATION, *N.*
muṭṭh mární. *f*; hatth rasí. *f*;

MAT, *N.*
saf. *f*; chaṭṭái. *f*; phúhṛí. *f*;
1. grass mat. muṛhá. *m*; tarúá. *m*; muṛhí *f*;
2. prayer mat. masallá. *m*. M;
3. Proverb. a brother-in-law for a neighbour is as bad as a grass mat for a pillow. sánḍhú guánḍhí te tarúá siránḍí;

MATCH, *N.*
1. a single one. tíllí. *f*;
2. a lot. díwá salái. *f*; tíllíáṇ. *f*;
3. match box. dabbí. *f*;
4. a game. mách. *m*;

MATCH, TO, *V. T.*
miláuná; melná; raláuná;

MATCHLESS, *A.*
sáreáṇ náloṇ changá; uttam;

MATE, *N.*
dost. *m*; yár. *m*; sáthí. *m*; mittar. *m*; hamjolí. *m*; nál dá sánjhí. *m*;
a fellow workman. joṭṭí. *m*;

MATERIAL, *N.*
samián. *m*; masálá. *m*;
old building materials. malbá. *m*;

MATERNAL LOVE, *N.*
mámtá, *f*;

MATHEMATICAL, *A.*
hisábí;

MATHEMATICIAN, *N.*
hisábí. *m*;

MATHEMATICS, *N.*
hisáb. *m*;

MATINS, *N.*
subah dí bandagí. *f*;

MATRIMONY, *N.*
shádí, *f*; viáh. *m*;

MATRON, *N.*
bíbí. *f*; bebe. *f*;

MATTER, *N.*
1. affair. bát. *f*; gal. *f*;
2. subject. mazmún. *m*;
3. pus. pák. *f*; rádh. *f*;
4. it doesn't matter. kí ḍar hai; uh jáṇe; kujh chiṇtá nahíṇ;
5. in the eye. giḍḍ. *f*; gidd. *f*; mail. *f*;
6. cause of trouble. wajáh. *f*; sabab. *m*;

MATTING, *N.*
1. reed matting. saf. *f*; phúhṛí. *f*; chaṭṭái. *f*;
2. fibre matting. múnj. *m*;
3. sacking. ṭáṭ. *m*; tarapaṛ. *m*;

MATTRESS, *N.*
gadelá. *m*; tulái. *f*; jullí. *f*; wichcháuní. *f*;

MATURE, *A.*
pakká; purí umr dá;

1. for girls only. mutiár;
2. for boys only. gabbhrú;

MATURE, TO, *V. T.*
pakkáuná;

MATURITY, *N.*
pakkiáí. *f;* pakk. *m;*

MAUND, *N.*
maṇ. *m;*

MAUSOLEUM, *N.*
1. Muhammadan. ḳhángáh. *f;* makbará. *m;*
2. Hindu. maṛhí. *f;* masáṇ. *m;*

MAXIM, *N.*
1. a saying. maslá. *m;* kaháut. *f;*
2. a rule. qánún. *m;* qaidá. *m;* bidhí. *f;*

MAXIMUM, *N.*
waddh thoṇ waddh;

MAY, *N.*
Jeṭh. *i.e.*, May 14 to June 13.

MAZE, *N.*
haráni. *f;* pareshání. *f;* see PERPLEXITY.

ME, *Pro.*
mainúṇ; menúṇ;

MEADOW, *N.*
ghá wálí pailí. *f;* júh. *m;*

MEAGRE, *A.*
1. scanty. ghaṭṭ; thoṛá; kassá;
2. thin. lissá; máṛá; jhíkh;

MEAGRELY, *Adv.*
ghaṭṭ;

MEAGRENESS, *N.*
thuṛ. *f;* gháṭṭá. *m;* kamí. *f;*

MEAL, *N.*
1. dinner,&c. roṭí. *f;* roṭí ṭukkar. *m;* an páni. *m;*
2. flour. áṭṭá. *m;*
3. pure white flour. maidá. *m;*

MEAN, *A.*
1. contemptible. máṛá; ních; nakárá; nachíz; chotná;
2. ignoble. badját; kamját; kamíná; hochchá; shodá;
3. illiberal. kanjús; taṇgdil; chíṛhá; shúm;

MEAN, *N.*
vichkár. *m;*
1. by all means. beshakk;
2. by means of. duáre;

MEAN, TO, *V. T.*
1. to think. ḳhayál karná; soch wichár karná;
2. to determine. irádá karná; ṭhánná; dhárná;
3. I mean. merá matlab ih hai;

MEANDER, TO, *V. I.*
phirná; bhondá phirná; bhulle phirná; bhauná; awárá phirná; ghummná; ḍáwáṇḍol phirná; udále pudále phirná;

MEANING, *N.*
matlab. *m;* arth. *m;*

MEANINGLESS, *A.*
bematlab; bearth; anarth;

MEANLY, *Adv.*
burí taráh nál; baṛe kamínpuṇe nál; bhaiṛtái nál;

MEANNESS, *N.*
kamínpuṇá. *m;* ních kamm. *m;* chandálpuṇá. *m;* kuttpuṇá. *m;* stinginess. shúmpuṇá. *m;*

MEANS, *N.*
khaṭṭí. *f;* parápat. *f;*
1. by any means. kíweṇ ná kíweṇ;
2. an exclamation, by all means. jam jam;
3. Proverb. Live according to your means. dál roṭí khá, te nakk dí siddhe já;

MEAN SPIRITED, *A.*
1. cowardly. ḍarákal; kamhimmatá;
2. low. kamíná; máṛá; chaṇḍál;

MEANTIME, *Adv.*
inne vichch; aine vichch; aine núṇ;

MEASLES, *N.*
khasrá. *m;*

MEASURE, *N.*
náp. *m;* máp. *m;* mep. *m;* mech. *m;* mechchá. *m;* pajmáná. *m;*
without measure. bahut sárá;

MEASURE, TO, *V. T.*
1. to measure out corn. &c. mechná; minná; michchná;
2. to measure with a yardstick. gaj pherná; mápná;
3. to measure land. kachchh lainá; kachchhná;
4. to be measured. miniá jáná;

MEASURELESS, *A.*
behisáb; beant.

MEASUREMENT, *N.*
mep. *m;* náp. *m;*
of a field. kachh. *m;*

MEASURER OF LAND, *N.*
kachhwáhá. *m;*

MEASURING, *N.*
minái. *f;* háṛá. *m;*

MEAT, *N.*
más. *m;* gosht. *m;* tarkárí. *f;* lauṇ. *m;*
1. meat and drink. ann jal. *m;* ann pání. *m;*
2. meat safe. ḍollí. *f;*

MECHANIC, *N.*
mistrí. *m;* kárígar. *m;*

MECHANICALLY, *Adv.*
aiweṇ; eweṇ;

MECHANISM, *N.*
kalá. *f;*

MEDAL, *N.*
takmá. *m;* tagmá. *m;*
medal clasp. kaṛí. *f;*

MEDDLE, TO, *V. T.*
chheṛná; ghusná; chhuhná; pair aṛáuná; hatth páuná; bhang páuná; ghusaṛná; bháṇjí mární;

MEDDLER, *N.*
dakhal denwálá. *m;* latt aṛáunwálá. *m;*

MEDDLESOME, *A.*
dhakkekhor.
Proverb said to a meddlesome woman. You are the barber's wife at the mourning. Túṇ táṇ siápe dí náín haiṇ;

MEDIAL, *A.*
vichlá; majholá; gabhlá;

MEDIATE, TO, *V. T.*
1. to arbitrate. sálasí karní; gaver kaḍḍhná;
2. to make peace. suláh karáuní; mel karáuná;

MEDIATION, *N.*
sálasí. *f;*

MEDIATOR, *N.*
wicholá. *m;* sálas. *m;*

MEDICAL, *A.*
hakímí; dáktarí;

MEDICAMENT, *N.*
dawáí. *f;* dawá. *f;*

MEDICINE, *N.*
dawáí. *f;* dawá. *f;* dárú. *m;* duá dárú. *m;* darmal. *m;*
the medical profession. hakímí. *f;*

MEDIOCRE, *A.*
ḳhásá;

MEDITATE, TO, *V. T.*
sochná; dhián karná; dhiáuná; soch wichár karná; chitáuná; gaur karná;

MEDITATION, *N.*
dhián. *m;* soch. *f;* soch wichár. *m;* chitwaní. *f;* gián dhián. *m;*

MEDITATIVE, *A.*
sochdár; dhiání; gaurá; sochmán; wichárak;

MEDIUM, *N.*
1. a go between. wicholá. *m;*
2. a means. wasílá. *m;*

MEED, *N.*
1. right. haqq. *m;*
2. reward. inám. *m;* inám shinám. *m;* ajr. *m;*

MEEK, *A.*
dil dá garíb; halím; ájiz; maskín; garíb dilwálá;

MEEKLY, *Adv.*
ájazí nál; garíbí nál;

MEEKNESS, *N.*
garíbí. *f;* ájazí. *f;* maskíní. *f;* adhiṇtái. *f;*

MEET, *A.*
jog; laiq; munásib;

MEET, TO, *V. T.*
milná; darshan karná; mulaqát karní; matthe laggná; ṭakkarná; mil painá;
1. to go to meet. aggalwáṇḍhí honá; aggoṇwálí milná; aggalwáṇḍhí milná;
2. he went out to meet him. uhnúṇ aggoṇwálí miliá;
3. he was frequently meeting him. uh de nál mel melává hundá rahndá;

MEETING, *N.*
darshan. *m;* mulaqát. *f;* milní. *f;* mel gel. *f;* ṭákrá. *m;* mel milává. *m;* milgil. *f;*

MEETING, N.
jalsá. m; sabhá. f; sangat. f; jhunḍí. f;
a Christian religious meeting. míṭin. f;

MELANCHOLY, N.
masosiá hoyá; udás;

MELEE, N.
laṛái. f; daṅggá fasád. m;

MELLOW, A.
pakká;

MELLOW, TO, V. T.
pakkáuná;

MELLOWNESS, N.
pakkiái. f;

MELODIOUS, A.
surílá; subák; miṭṭhí rágwálá;

MELODIOUSLY, Adv.
sur miláke; ṭhík sur nál; sur raláke;

MELODIOUSNESS, N.
sur. m; rág. m;

MELODY, N.
rág. m;

MELON, N.
1. water melons. kharbujá. m; matírá. m; tarbuj. m; hadwáná m;
2. Kabuli melon. sardá. m;
3. musk melon. khakkhrí. f;

MELT TO, V. T.
gálaná; khuráuná; paghráuná; khárná;
to cause to be melted. galwáuná;

MELT, TO, V. I.
1. as meat, rice. gallná;
2. as fat before a fire. paghar jáná;
3. to dissolve, as salt, sugar, in water. khurná; ghulná;

MELTING, N.
galái. f; paghrái. f;

MEMBER, N.
1. limb. aṅg. m; liṅg. m;
2. a person. sharík. m; mimbar. m;

MEMENTO, N.
yádgírí. f; yádgárí. f;

MEMORABLE, A.
1. worthy to be remembered. yád rakkhan de laiq;
2. famous. mashhúr;

MEMORIAL. N.
yádgírí, f; yádgárí. f;

MEMORIALIST, N.
sawálí. m;

MEMORIZE, TO, V. T.
yád rakkhná; kaṇth karná; múṇh zabání yád karná; simarná; saral karná;

MEMORY, N.
chetá. m; sudh. f; thauh. m;
1. bad memory. chetá kharáb;
2. in memory of. dí yádgírí vichch;
3. to commit to memory. kaṇṭh karná; saral karná;

MENACE, N.
dhauṇs. f; dhamkí. f; dábbá. m; jhiṛkí. f; ḍaráwá. m;

MENACE, TO. V. T.
dhauṇs dení; akkh wakháuní; dhamká dená; jháṛ páuná; dabkáuná; jhiṛkná; ḍaráuná; dhamkí dení; ghurakná;

MENACINGLY, Adv.
dhamkí deke; ḍaráke; jhiṛkí nál;

MEND. TO, V. T.
suwárná; sudhárná; ṭhík ṭhák karná; gaṇḍhaná; gaṇḍh túpp karná;
to darn. puṇná; túpp karná;

MENDACIOUS, A.
jhuṭhá; khoṭṭá;

MENDACITY, N.
jhuṭh. m; see DECEIT.

MENDICANT, N.
faqír. m; maṅggtá. m; see BEGGAR.
mendicant's cry. sadá. f;

MENDING, N.
gaṇḍh. m; gaṇḍh túpp. m; marammat. f;

MENIAL, N.
kamín. m; ních ját. m; chuhṛá. m;

MENIAL, A.
kamíná; ních;

MENSES, N.
pairá. m; kapṛe. m; nichare rít f; phull. m; naháuní. f; sir palít. m;

MENSTRUATE, TO, V. T.
kapṛe áuná; phull áune; lahú áuná: sír palít honá; naháuní auní;

MENTAL, *A*.
aqlí;
MENTAL ARITHMETIC, *N*.
zabání hisáb. *m*;
MENTION, *N*.
bayán. *m*; zikr. *m*; gal bát. *f*;
MENTION, TO, *V. T*.
bayán karná; zikr karná; jabán te liáuná; dassná;
do not mention it to anyone yet. kidhare báhar ná aje gal karíṇ;
MENTIONABLE, *A*.
dassaṇ jog;
MERCANTILE, *A*.
bapárí dá; wanjí dá; saudágarí dà;
MERCER, *N*.
bajáj. *m*;
MERCHANDISE, *N*.
saudá. *m*; vanj bapár. *m*; bapár. *m*; saudá súd. *m*; saudá pattá. *m*;
MERCHANT, *N*.
bapárí. *m*; saudágar. *m*; baniá. *m*;
MERCIFUL, *A*.
ráhm karnwálá; ráhmdil; dáyáwán; mihrbán; dáyáwaṇt;
for GOD only. rahím.
MERCIFULNESS, *N*.
ráhm. *m*; ráhmat. *f*; karm. *m*; dáyá. *m*;
MERCIFULLY, *Adv*.
ráhm karke; ráhm nál; kirpá karke;
MERCILESS, *A*.
beráhm; saḳht; betaras; bedard; patthar dil; haiṇsiárá; hattiárá; karṛá;
MERCILESSLY, *Adv*.
baṛí beráhmí nál; saḳhtí nál;
MERCILESSNESS, *N*.
beráhmí. *f*; saḳhtí. *f*; jástí. *f*; julm. *m*;
MERCURY, *N*.
párá. *m*;
MERCY, *N*.
dáyá. *m*; ráhm. *m*; tars. *m*; ráhmat. *f*; mihrbání. *f*; murabbat. *f*; kirpá. *f*; mehrbánagí. *f*; dayálgí *f*;
MERE, *A*.
nirá;
mere words. kahṇdíáṇ g ¹áṇ. *f*;
MERE, *N*.
chhaṇbh. *m*; ḍumbh. *m*; chhappar. *m*;
lake. jhíl. *f*;
MERELY, *Adv*.
nirá; sirf; kewál;
MERGE, TO, *V. T*.
miláuná; raláuná;
MERIT, *N*.
punn. *m*. H; guṇ. *m*, H; sawáb. *m*, M;
merits and demerits. guṇ auguṇ. *m*;
MERITORIOUS, *A*.
táríf de laiq; laiq;
MERITORIOUSLY, *Adv*.
laiq taur nál;
MERLIN, *N*.
turumtí. *f*; turmchí. *f*;
MERRILY, *Adv*.
hasske; baṛí ḳhushí nál; hásse nál; chaiṇ chaiṇ;
MERRIMENT, *N*.
ḳhushí. *f*; chohul. *m*; hássí. *f*; anaṇdtái. *f*; mauj. *f*; kallíáṇ. *f*; rangrallíáṇ. *f*;
MERRY, *A*.
ḳhush; rází; magan; anaṇd; raṇggí; raṇggílá;
MERRY, TO MAKE, *V. T*.
ḳhushí karní; maṇggalá chár karná;
MERRY MAKING, *N*.
hássí. *f*; chohul. *m*; ḳhushí karní. *f*;
MESMERIZE, TO, *V. T*.
ḍolí khiḍáuní;
MESS, *N*.
1. confusion. gabaṛ gaṇj. *f*; gaṛbaṛí. *f*; raulá. *m*;
2. army mess. miskoṭ. *f*;
MESSAGE, *N*.
sunehá. *m*; sannehá. *m*; sanehoṛá. *m*; sanáh. *m*; sandes. *m*; sanauhṛá. *m*; akhwá. *m*; sandesá. *m*;
to send a message. akhwá ghallná;
MESSENGER, *N*.
halkárá. *m*; sandesí. *m*; chaprásí. *m*;
the village chowkidar who takes messages. rabtí. *m*; rapṭiá. *m*;

MESSIAH, *N.*
Masíh. *m ;*
MET, TO BE, *V. I.*
milná ;
METAL, *N.*
dhát. *f ;*
METALLIC, *A.*
dhát dá ;
METAL WORKER, *N.*
ṭhaṭhiár. *m ;*
METE, TO, *V. T.*
nápná ; minná ; mechná ; michchná ;
METEOR, *N.*
ṭuṭdá tárá. *m ;*
METHOD, *N.*
taríqá. *m ;* taur. *m ;* ḍhaṇg. *m ;* qaídá. *m ;* ḍaul. *f ;* ḍhaṇg waṇg. *m ;* bidhí. *f ;* see MANNER.
METHODICAL, *A.*
báqaidá ; bátartíb ;
METHODIZE, TO, *V. T.*
tartíb dená ;
METROPOLIS, *N.*
waḍḍá shahr. *m ;*
METROPOLITAN, *N.*
waḍḍá lát Bishap Sáhib. *m ;*
METTLE, *N.*
dilerí. *f ;* hauṇsilá. *m ;* sargarmí. *f ;* josh. *m ;* himmat. *f ;*
METTLESOME, *A.*
diler ; uddamí ; phurtílá ; himmatí : sargarm ; joshwálá ;
MEW, TO, *V . T.*
míaukná ;
MEW, *N.*
míáun. *f ;*
MICROSCOPE, *N.*
khurd bín. *m ;*
MIDDAY, *N.*
dopaihar. *f ;*
at midday. dopaihariṇ ;
MIDDLE, *A.*
maṇjhlá ; majholá ; vichlá ; wishhkarlá ;
1. middle aged man. addh khaṛ ;
2. middle aged woman. addher ;
MIDDEN, *N.*
niáiṇ. *f ;*
MIDDLE, *N.*
vichkál. *m ;* máṇjhí. *f ;* maddh. *m ;* wichchkár. *m ;*

MIDDLEMAN, *N.*
dalál. *m ;*
MIDDLING, *A.*
ḳhásá ; maddham ;
middling in size. samaddhar ;
Proverb. Best is farming, middling trade, base is service, begging is worst. uttam khetí, maddham bapár, nikhiddh chákrí, bhíkh nadáṇ ;
MIDNIGHT, *N.*
addhí rát. *f ;*
MIDST. *Adv. & Prep.*
gabbhe ; vichkár ; vichkále ; vichkáhe ; vichch ; vichch vichále ; vichále ; vichghár ;
MIDWAY, *N.*
raste vichch ; wáṭe ;
MIDWIFE, *N.*
dáí. *f ;*
to act the part of a midwife. jaṇwáuná ; bachchá jaṇáuná ;
MIDWIFERY, *N.*
jaṇwáí. *f ;*
pay of a midwife. jaṇwáí. *f ;* jamáí. *f ;*
MIEN, *N.*
ro. *f ;*
MIGHT, *N.*
jor. *m ;* zor. *m ;* wáh. *f ;* bal. *m ;* majál. *f ;* táqat. *f ;* see POWER.
Proverbs. Might is right. Whoever has the club has the buffalo. jeh dí láṭhí use dí bhaiṇs ;
whoever has the sword has the cooking pot. jeh dí tegh use dí degh ;
MIGHTILY, *Adv.*
baṛe zor nál ; jor láke ;
MIGHTINESS, *N.*
táqat. *f ;* see MIGHT.
MIGHTY, *A.*
sabal ; balwálá ; táqatwálá ; mazbut ; jorwálá ; see POWERFUL AND STRONG.
MIGRATE, TO, *V. T.*
des chhaḍḍ jáná ; dujje des vichch já wassná ;
MILD, *A.*
nigghá ; asíl ; dhímá ; garíb ; ájiz ; dhírá ; narmdil ; mihrbán ; kúlá ;

MILDEW, *N.*
gam. *m ;*
MILDLY, *Adv.*
narmi nál;
MILDNESS, *N.*
mulaimí; narmí. *f;* narmdilí. *f;* halímí. *f;* ájizí. *f;* maskíní. *f;* komaltái. *f;*
MILE, *N.*
míl. *m ;*
MILEPOST, *N.*
míl dá patthar. *m ;* míl dá khambhá. *m ;* munárá. *m ;*
MILITANT, *A.*
laṛáká;
MILITARY, *A.*
faují; jaṇgí;
MILITARY, *N.*
sipáhí. *m ;*
MILK, *N.*
dudh. *m ;*
1. coagulated milk. dahín. *m ;*
2. butter milk. lassí. *f;*
3. milk of an animal which has just calved.
i. kil. *m ;*
ii. bauhlí. *f;*
iii. bauhlá. *m ;*
4. milk giving animal, cow, goat, &c. lawerí. *f;*
MILK, TO, *V. T.*
dhár kaḍḍhná; dudh cho leáná; choná; ḍohná;
1. to boil milk. dudh kárhná;
2. to permit to be milked. (cow) gáṇ milná; (buffalo) majjh milná;
3. Proverb. Do not milk a strange cow, lest she kick and break your arm. ná ḍoh begání gáṇ, máre latt te bhaṇne báṇh;
MILKING, *N.*
choáí. *f;*
MILK MAN, *N.*
ḍohjí. *m ;* ḍohyá. *m ;* gujjar. *m ;* gawálá; *m ;* dudhwálá. *m ;* dodhí. *m ;*
MILK PAIL, *N.*
bháṇḍá. *m ;* ḍohná. *m ;* ḍohní. *f;*
MILK SELLER, *N.*
gujjar. *m ;* gawálá. *m ;*
MILKY, *A.*
dudh jehá;
MILL, *N.*
1. small mill turned by hand. chakkí. *f;*
2. large mill turned by oxen. kharás. *m ;*
3. large mill turned by water. gharáṭ. *m ;*
MILL, TO, *V. T.*
chakkí píhná; see GRIND.
MILLENIUM, *N.*
uh zamáná jih de vichch Masíh hazár waṛheáṇ tíkar is dunyá utte ráj karegá;
MILLER, *N.*
gharáṭiá. *m ;* kharásí. *m ;* kharásiá. *m ;*
MILLET, *N.*
1. coarse. charí. *f;*
2. very fine. bájrá. *m ;*
3. Indian corn. juár. *f;*
MILLION, *A.*
das lakkh;
MILLIONAIRE, *N.*
karoṛáṇ patí. *m ;* karoṛí. *m ;* lakhpattí. *m ;* gaṇḍh dá púrá. *m ;*
Proverb. Not a mite in his pocket and called a millionaire. palle ná kaudí náṇ lakhpatí;
MILLSTONE, *N.*
puṛ. *m ;*
MIMIC, *N.*
bhanḍ. *m ;* naqliá. *m ;*
MIMIC, TO, *V. T.*
naql karná OR láuná; sáṇgg wikháuná;
MIMICRY, *N.*
sáṇgg. *m ;* bhanḍí. *f;*
MINARET, *N.*
mínár. *m ;*
MINCE, TO, *V. T.*
kímá karná;
MINCHEMEAT, *N.*
kímá. *m ;*
MIND, *N.*
1. memory. chettá. *m ;* thauh. *m ;*
2. understanding. aql. *f;* samajh. *f;* hosh. *m ;* buddh. *f;* bújh *f;* chitt. *m ;*
MIND, TO, *V. T.*
1. to obey. manná; ákkhe lagná;

2. to attend to. gaur karná; dhián karná; sochná; jí OR man lagáuná; kann láuná;
3. to take care. hosh karná; khabardárí karní;
4. never mind. kujh chintá nahíṇ; jáṇ do; uh jáne;
5. he does not mind what I say. uh merá kihá nahíṇ mandá;

MINDFUL, *A*.
suchet; siáná; hoshiyár; surt-ílá; surtá;

MINDFULLY, *Adv*.
diloṇ wajhoṇ hoke; gauh karke; dhián nal; soch wichárke;

MINDFULNESS, *N*.
dhián. *m*; chettá. *m*; yád. *f*; khabardárí. *f*; gauh. *m*; surt. *f*;

MINE, Pro.
merá; merí; apná; apní;

MINE, *N*.
suruṇg. *f*; kháṇ. *f*; kháṇḍ. *f*;

MINERAL, *N*.
dhánt. *f*;

MINGLE, TO, *V. T*.
miláuná; gholná; raláuná;
to become mingled. hil mil jáná;

MINIATURE, *N*.
chhoṭí taswír. *f*;

MINIMUM. *N*.
ghaṭ o ghaṭ;

MINISTER, *N*.
1. of Christian religion. pádrí sáhib. *m*; ḳhádim ud dín. *m*;
2. a servant. naukar. *m*; ṭah-liá; *m*;

MINISTER, TO, *V. T*.
ṭahl karná; ṭahl sewá karná; ḳhidmat karní;

MINISTRATION, *N*.
ṭahl. *f*; sewá. *f*; ṭahl sewá. *f*; ḳhidmat. *f*;

MINISTREL, *N*.
wajantrí. *m*; see MUSICIAN.

MINISTRY, *N*.
ḳhidmat. *f*; ṭahl sewá. *f*; see SERVICE.

MINOR, *N*.
1. a boy. munḍá. *m*;
2. under legal age. nabálig. *m*;

MINOR, *A*.
nikká; chhoṭá;

MINORITY, *N*.
nabáligí. *f*;

MINSTER, *N*.
waḍḍá girjá. *m*;

MINT, *N*.
1. for coin. ṭaksál. *f*; ṭaṇgsál. *f*;
2. herb. púdná. *m*;

MINUS, *A*.
ghaṭṭ;

MINUTE, *N*.
minaṭ. *m*; pal. *m*.

MINUTE, *A*.
1. small. nikká; chhoṭá;
2. fine. barík;

MINUTELY, *Adv*,
ṭhík ṭhák; ṭhíkam ṭhík; see EXACTLY.

MIRACLE, *N*.
karámát. *f*; mujizá. *m*;
Proverb. an acquaintance is better than a miracle. karámát koloṇ muláqát changí hai;

MIRACULOUS. *A*.
karámátí; ajíb;

MIRACULOUSLY, *Adv*.
mujize de taur nál;

MIRAGE, *N*.
mirg tarshaná dá jal. *m*.

MIRE, *N*.
chikkaṛ *m*; gár *f*: gárá. *m*; khubbhan. *f*;
in deep mire. ḍummh de chikkar vichch;

MIRROR, *N*.
shíshá. *m*;

MIRTH, *N*.
khushí. *f*; anaṇd maṇggal. *m*, hássí. *f*; chohul. *m*;

MIRTHFUL, *A*.
khush; magan; anaṇd; raṇggí; raṇggílá;

MIRTHFULLY. *Adv*.
hass ke; ḳhush hoke; ḳhushí nál;

MIRTHLESS. *A*.
udás; sogmáṇ; sasdil; dil dhaṭṭhá; santápí; dukhiá;

MIRY. *A*.
gaṇdhlá; baṛá chikkaṛ;

MISADVENTURE. *N*.
biptá. *m*; musíbat. *f*; see MISFORTUNE.

MISAPPLICATION, *N.*
galatí. *f* ;
MISAPPREHEND, TO, *V. T.*
bhulekhá laggná ; ulṭá samajhná ; galat samajhná ;
MISAPPREHENSION, *N.*
galatí. *f* ; bhulekhá. *m* ; see MISTAKE.
MISAPPROPRIATE, TO, *V. T.*
ḍakárná ; mál khání ; rupae khá lainá ; amánat gabban karná ; vichch khiánat karná ; mál márná ;
MISAPPROPRIATION, *N.*
chorí. *f* chorí chakárí. *f* ;
MISARRANGE, TO, *V. T.*
ulaṭ pulaṭ karná ; kharná ; betartíbí nál rakkhná ; sarkáuná ; ulad pulad karná ; tháṇ tháṇ karná ;
MISARRANGEMENT, *N.*
kusút. *m* ; betartíbí. *f* ;
MISBEHAVE, TO, *V. T.*
sharárat karní ; naṭ khaṭí karní ; kuchál chalná ; kárá karná ;
MISBEHAVIOUR, *N.*
kuchál. *f* ; sharárat. *f* ; badchalní. *f* ; bhaiṛá kamm. *m* ;
MISBELIEF, *N.*
1. heresy. bidat. *f* ; kufr. *m* ;
2. wrong thought. galat khayál. *m* ;
3. false teaching. jhuṭhí tálím. *f* ;
MISCALCULATE, TO, *V. T.*
bhulekhá laggná ;
MISCALCULATION, *N.*
hisáb vichch galatí. *f* ; hisáb vichch bhulekha. *m* ; bholá. *m* ; bholí *f* ;
MISCALL, TO, *V. T.*
badnám karná ; niṇdiá karná ; lutiáṇ láuná ;
MISCARRIAGE, *N.*
1. abortion. garbhpát. *m* ;
2. failure. nákámyábí. *f* ;
MISCARRY, TO, *V. T.*
1. to abort. gabb chhan jáná ; digg jáná ;
2. to abort. for animals. tu jáná ;
3. to fail. kujh ná banná ; ráh jáná ;
MISCELLANEOUS, *A.*
bhaṇt bhaṇt de ; har qism de ; har taráh de ; gaḍḍwaḍḍ ;

MISCHANCE, *N.*
shámat. *f* ; musíbat. *f* ; see MISFORTUNE.
MISCHIEF, *N.*
1. annoyance. naṭ khaṭí *f* ; sharárat. *f* ;
2. loss. harj. *m* ; kasar. *f* ; nuqsán. *m* ; bháṅggá. *m* ;
MISCHIEF MAKER, *N.*
bigáṛú. *m* ; naṭ khaṭ. *m* ; ghar phor. *m* ;
MISCHIEVIOUS, *A.*
naṭ khaṭ ; sharárati ; shokh ; fasádí ; kuját ; sharír ;
MISCHIEVOUSLY, *Adv.*
naṭ khaṭí nál ;
MISCHIEVOUSNESS, *N.*
naṭ khaṭí. *f* ; sharárat. *f* ;
MISCONCEIVE, TO, *V. T.*
ulṭá samajhná ; bhulekhá laggná ; puṭṭhá samajhná ;
MISCONCEPTION, *N.*
galat khayál. *m* ; bhulekhá. *m* ; galatí. *f* ;
MISCONDUCT, *N.*
sharárat. *f* ; badchalní. *f* ; kuchál. *f* ; páp. *m* ;
MISCONDUCT, TO, *V. T.*
páp OR gunáh karná ; kuchál chalná ;
MISCONJECTURE, *N.*
bhulekhá. *m* ; galatí. *f* ;
MISCONJECTURE, TO, *V. T.*
bhulekhá laggná ; see MISTAKE.
MISCONSTRUCTION, *N.*
galat fahmí. *f* ;
MISCONSTRUE, TO, *V. T.*
bhulekhá laggná ; puṭṭhá samajhná ;
MISCOUNT, TO, *V. T.*
hisáb vichch bhulekhá laggná ; bholá laggná ;
MISCREANT, *N.*
1. an unbeliever. munkar. *m* ; kufrí. *m* ;
2. a scoundrel. badmásh. *m* ; buriár. *m* ; guṇḍá. *m* ;
MISDEED, *N.*
qusúr. *m* ; sharárat. *f* ; aparádh. *m* ;
to reap the fruit of one's misdeeds. apná kítá pauná ; apní karní bhární ;

MISDEMEANOUR N.
qusur, *m* ; bhull chukk. *f* ;
MISDIRECT, TO, *V. T.*
ghusáuná ; see MISLEAD.
MISDOER, *N.*
taqsírí. *m* ; jurmí. *m* ;
MISDOING, *N.*
ḳharábí. *f* ; sharárat. *f* ; khoṭ. *f* ;
badí. *f* ; bhull chukk. *f* ;
MISER, *N.*
shúm. *m* ; kanjús. *m* ; joṛú. *m* ;
makkhí chús. *m* ; chaṇjús. *m* ;
nichoṛú. *m* ;
Proverb used concerning misers.
a quarter of a seer of atá and he is going to feast the neighbourhood ;
ḍiḍh pá áṭá, chubáre rasoí ;
MISERABLE, *A.*
1. Unfortunate. badnasíb ; kambaḳht ; bechárá ; karmá dá máriá ;
2. Sorrowful. udás ; masosiá hoyá ;
MISERABLY, *Adv.*
udás hoke ; gam nál ;
MISERLINESS, *N.*
shúmpuṇá. *m* ; kanjúsí. *f* ;
MISERLY, *Adv.*
chíṛhá ; lálchí ; marjiú ; jíṛá ;
MISERY, *N.*
kashṭ. *m* ; musíbat. *f* ; taklíf. *f* ;
jafar. *f* ; see DISTRESS.
MISFORTUNE, *N.*
1. trouble. biptá. *f* ; balá. *f* ; musíbat. *f* ;
2. bad fortune. benasíbí. *f* ; nakarmí. *f* ; kambaḳhtí. *f* ; kubhág. *m* ; shámat. *f* ; honí. *f* ;
3. harm. nuqsán. *m* ; harj. *m* ;
kasar. *m* ;
MISGIVING, *N.*
shakk. *m* ; shubhá. *m* ; jhakk. *m* ;
bharm. *m* ; khuṭká. *m* ; dubdhá. *m* ;
MISGOVERN, TO, *V. T.*
búrí taráh nál ráj karná ;
MISGOVERNMENT, *N.*
nádar sháhí. *f* ; nádar gardí. *f* ;
sikháṇ sháhí. *f* ; see MISRULE ;
MISGUIDANCE, *N.*
gumráhí. *f* ;
MISGUIDE, TO, *V. T.*
ghusáuná ; bhuláuná ; badráh kar dená ;

MISHAP, *N.*
dobbá sokká. *m* ; garauh. *m* ;
ḍho. *m* ; balá. *f* ; kambaḳhtí. *f* ;
musíbat. *f* ; haner. *m* ; hádsá. *m* ;
honí ; *f* ;
MISINFORM, TO, *V. T.*
jhuṭhí ḳhabar dení ; bhuláuná ;
MISINTERPRET, TO, *V. T.*
galatí nál matlab kaḍḍhná ;
MISJUDGE, TO, *V. T.*
faisalá karan vichch bhulekhá laggná ; galat ḳhayál karná ;
MISLAY, TO, *V. T.*
rakkh ke bhull jáná ;
Proverb used when one is looking for a thing, and all the time it is close at hand. The girl is sitting in his lap, and it is published in the city that she is lost. kuṛí kuchchhaṛ, te shahr ḍhaṇḍorá ;
MISLEAD, TO, *V. T.*
ghusáuná; bhuláuná ; kuráh páuná;
MISMANAGEMENT, *N.*
rám raulá ; *m* ; badintizámí. *f* ;
MISPLACE, TO, *V. T.*
wisar jáná ; rakkh ke bhull jáná ;
MISPRINT, *N.*
chhápe dí galatí. *f* ; akkhar dá mittná. *m* ;
MISPRINT, TO, *V. T.*
galat chhápná ;
MISPRONOUNCE, TO, *V. T.*
akkhar ṭhík ná bolná ;
MISREPRESENT, TO, *V. T.*
jhuṭh sachch kahná OR bolná ;
ṭálná ;
MISREPRESENTATION, *N.*
sachch jhuṭh. *m* ; ṭál maṭolá. *m* ;
dhokhá. *m* ; ṭál. *f* ; ṭálá. *m* ;
MISRULE, *N.*
nádar sháhí. *f* ; nádar gardí. *f* ;
sikháṇ sháhí. *f* ; aṇdhkár. *m* ;
anher kháttá. *m* ; anher. *m* ;
MISRULE TO, *V. T.*
nádar sháhí karní ; sikháṇ sháhí karní ;
MISS, *N.*
kuárí. *f* ;
MISS TO, *V. I.*
ghus jáná ; bhullná ;
to miss a train. gaḍḍioṇ khuṇjhná OR ráh jáná ;

MISSHAPEN, *A.*
badaul;
MISSING, *A.*
gumm; hájar nahíṇ;
MISSION, *N.*
mishan. *f*;
MISSIONARY, *N.*
mishaneri. *m*; pádrí sáhib. *m*;
MISSIVE, *N.*
rukká. *m*; chiṭṭhí. *f*; purjá. *m*;
MISSTATE, TO, *V. T.*
galat bayán karná; see MISREPRESENT.
MISSTATEMENT, *N.*
galat bayáṇ. *m*; banautí gall. *f*; banauṭ. *m*;
MIST, *N.*
dhuṇd. *f*; dhúr. *f*; gahir. *f*; dhundúkár. *m*; kuhar. *f*;
MISTAKE, *N.*
galatí. *f*; bhulekhá. *m*; chukk. *f*; bhull chukk. *f*; wissar bholá. *m*; bharm. *m*; bhull. *f*; bhulává. *m*; bholá. *m*; bholí. *f*;
MISTAKE, TO, *V. T.*
ghuss jáná; ghutt jáná; khunjhná; galatí karní; ulṭá samajhná; bhull jáná; ukk jáná; bhullná;
MISTAKEN, *A.*
bhulliá; ghutthá; ṭhík nahíṇ;
to be greatly mistaken. barí bhull vichch payá honá;
MISTAKINGLY, *Adv.*
bhull bhulekhé; galatí nál;
MISTINESS, *N.*
dhuṇd. *f*; jháulá. *m*; see MIST.
MISTRANSLATION, *N.*
galat tarjamá. *m*;
MISTRESS, *N.*
mem sáhib. *f*;
Proverb. She came for fire and became mistress of the house. agg láin áísí, ghar wálí ban baiṭhí;
MISTRUST, *N.*
shakk. *m*; shakk shubhá. *m*; khuṭká. *m*; bharm. *m*;
MISTRUST, TO, *V. T.*
bharm karná; shakk karná;
MISTRUSTFUL, *A.*
bharmí;
MISTRUSTFULNESS, *N.*
bharm. *m*; see MISTRUST.

MISTY, *A.*
dhuṇdlá; gahirá;
MISUNDERSTAND, TO, *V. T.*
ulṭá samajhná; bhulekhá laggná;
MISUNDERSTANDING, *N.*
galat fahmí. *f*; galatí. *f*; bhulekhá. *m*; ulṭí samajh. *f*;
between friends. wigáṛ. *f*;
MISUSE, TO, *V. T.*
bigáṛná; ḳharáb karná;
clothes, &c. madholná; middhná;
MITE, *N.*
ṭukṛá. *m*; see MORSEL.
MITIGATE, TO, *V. T.*
dhímá karná; matthá karná; ghaṭáuná;
MITIGATION, *N.*
kamí. *f*;
MITTEN, *N.*
dastáná. *m*;
MIX, TO, *V. T.*
gholná; miláuná; joṛná; maddhná;
MIXED, *A.*
ralá milá; raliá miliá; pachmel; gichch michch; gaḍḍ maḍḍ;
MIXTURE, *N.*
milau. *m*; ralá. *m*; ralau. *m*; ghál mel. *m*;
1. mixture of barley and corn. gojí. *f*;
2. mixture of corn and chunna. behṛá. *m*;
MOAN, *N.*
hauká. *m*; áh. *f*; huṇg. *f*; see GROAN.
MOAN, TO, *V. T.*
1. to cry. bhus bhus karná; kurláuná; roná;
2. to groan. huṇgná; aṛáná; hauke bharná OR lainá;
MOAT, *N.*
khál. *m*; morchá. *m*;
MOB, *N.*
ṭollá. *m*; jatthá. *m*; see HORDE.
1. an assembly. kaṭṭh. *m*; jamát. *f*; maṇḍlí. *f*; sabhá. *f*;
2. a crowd. bhíṛ. *f*; ṭollá. *m*;
MOCK, TO, *V. T.*
maḳhaul karná; ṭhaṭṭhe nál uḍáuná; ṭakor karná; jugat karná; khijáuná; ṭhaṭṭhá kar lainá;
to laugh at. khil khil karná; hirhiráuná; hássá karná;

MOCK, *A*.
jhuṭhá ; khoṭṭá ; naklí ; banáutí ; jáhlí ;

MOCKER, *N*.
maskará. *m* ; makhauliá. *m* ; ṭhaṭṭhebáj. *m* ;

MOCKERY, *N*.
makhaul. *m* ; ṭhaṭṭhá. *m* ; hássí. *f* ; hássá. *m* ; maskarí. *f* ; majákh. *m* ;

MODE, *N*.
ḍaul. *f* ; taríqá. *m* ; jugat. *f* ; ḍhaṇg. *m* ; dastúr. *m* ; ḍhaṇg waṇg. *m* ;
mode of dress. pahiráwá. *m* ;

MODEL, *N*.
namuná. *m* ; vaṇgí. *f* ; chuṇgg. *f* ;

MODEL, TO, *V. T.*
ghaṛná ; banáuná ;

MODERATE, *A*.
1. temperate. mulaim ; dhímá ; narm ;
2. middling. khássá ;
3. middling in size. samaddhar ;

MODERATE, TO, *V. T.*
1. to lessen. ghaṭṭ karná ; thoṛá karná ; ghaṭáuná ;
2. to quieten or appease. dhímá karná ; ṭhaṇḍá karná ; thammhná ; rází karná ;

MODERATE, TO, *V. I.*
ghaṭṭ honá ; ghaṭná ; nakhuṭṭná ; thuṛ jáná ; thammh jáná ;

MODERATION, *N*.
1. kindness. narmáí. *f* ; narmdilí. *f* ;
2. temperance. parejgárí. *f* ; rakkh shakkh. *f* ;

MODERN, *A*.
ajj bhalak dá ; inháṇ dináṇ dá ;

MODEST, *A*.
hayáwálá ; hayáwálí ; nek bakht ; lájwant ; sadháraṇ ; matthe kajjí ;

MODESTLY, *Adv*.
saṇg nál ; hayá nál ;

MODESTY, *N*.
hayá. *m* ; sharm. *f* ; láj. *f* ; saṇg. *f* ;

MODICUM, *N*.
ṭukṛá. *m* ; thoṛá jehá. *m* ; see MORSEL.

MODIFY, TO, *V. T.*
1. to reduce. ghaṭṭ karná ; ghaṭṭáuná ;
2. to change. badal karná ; waṭáuná ; waṭáṇḍrá karná ;
3. to correct. ṭhík ṭhák karná ; sodhná ; sudhráuná ;

MODULATE, TO, *V. T.*
1. to correct. ṭhík ṭhák karná sádhná ;
2. to try the pitch. alápná ;

MODULATION, *N*.
aláp. *f* ;

MOIETY, *N*.
1. portion. ṭukṛá. *m* ; ṭoṭṭá. *m* ;
2. share. hissá. *m* ; gapphá. *m* ; waṇḍá. *m* ; waṇḍ. *f* ;

MOIL, TO, *V. T.*
1. to dirty. mailá karná ; gaṇdá karná ; wigáṛná ;
2. to toil. mihnat karní ; kamm karná ;

MOIST, *A*.
gillá ; tar ; sillhá ; wattá ;
the air feels moist. wá vichch sejjal jápdí hai ;

MOISTEN, TO, *V. T.*
gillá OR tar karná ; bheonná ;
to moisten the surface only. ṭemná ;

MOISTNESS, *N*.
gill. *f* ; wattar. *m* ; watt. *f* ; silháb. *f* ; giláuṭ. *f* ;

MOISTURE, *N*.
gilaulá. *m* ; tarí. *f* ; see MOISTNESS.
A degree of moisture in the ground that renders it fit for ploughing. wattar. *m* ;

MOLAR, *N*.
ḍaṇḍ. *m* ; dáhar. *f* ;

MOLASSES, *N*.
ráb. *f* ;

MOLE, *N*.
1. animal. chhachhúndar. *f* ;
2. on the skin. til. *m* ; tilká. *m* ; lasan. *m* ; tuin. *m* ;

MOLEST, TO, *V. T.*
khijháuná ; satáuná ; chheṛná ; see ANNOY.

MOLESTATION, *N*.
jich. *m* ; dikk. *m* ; kashṭ. *m* ; taklíf. *f* ; khijh. *f* ;

MOLLIFY, TO, *V. T.*
dhímá karná ; ṭhaṇḍá karná ; rází karní ; narm karná ;

MOMENT, *N*.
pal. *m* ; dam. *m* ; palak. *f* ;
1. every moment. pal pal ;
2. in a moment. achának ; pal vichch ;

MOMENTARILY, *Adv*.
pal pal ; pal pal vichch ;

MOMENTARY, *A*.
ikk dam ; ikk pal vichch;

MOMENTOUS, *A*.
bhárí ; baṛí zarurí ;

MOMENTUM, *N*.
hill jull. *f* ; see MOVEMENT.

MONARCH, *N*.
1. king. bádsháh. *m* ;
2. Hindu or Sikh ruler. maharájáh. *m* ; rájá. *m* ;
3. Muhammadan ruler. sháh. *m* ; sultán. *m* ; amír. *m* ;

MONARCHIAL, *A*.
bádsháhí ; sháhí ;

MONARCHY, *N*.
ráj. *m* ; bádsháhí. *f* ;

MONASTERY, *N*.
maṭh. *m* ;

MONDAY, *N*.
Somwár. *m*. H. ; Pír. *m*.M.

MONETARY, *A*.
nakdí dá ;

MONEY, *N*.
rupae, *m* ; rupae paise. *m* ; rupae dhelá. *m* ; rokaṛ. *f* ; rok. *m* ; dhan. *m* ; máyá. *m* ; paisá. *m* ; paisá dhelá. *m* ;
1. money bag. thailí. *f* ;
2. corner or cloth used to keep money. pallá. *m* ;
3. money changer. sarráf. *m* ;
4. money lender. sáhukár. *m* ; sháh. *m* ; karáṛ. *m* ;
5. earnest money. sáhí. *f* ;
6. in money. naqd ;
7. ready money transaction. bikkarí. *f* ;
8. money making. sáhukárí. *f* ;
9. money given to dancing girls at a wedding. bel. *f* ;
10. money dealings. lainá dená. *m* ;
11. **Proverbs concerning the avariciousness of moneylenders.**
1. Those who fall into the clutches of the moneylender become homeless. sháh de qábú áe gharoṇ ghátoṇ jáe.
Do not have an account with the moneylender for fear you find yourself on the debit side. Lekhá ná kar sháháṇ de nál matáṇ kuchh dená áwe.
3. The moneylender is superior to the king. Pahle sháh, pichchhe bádsháh.
4. A hungry *karár* searches through his account books for old debts. Bhukkhá *karár* te behiyáṇ phole ;
5. The farmer's wife wets her thread, and the karár wets his weight (to make them more heavy). jaṭṭí phusái aṭṭí, karáṛ phusái waṭṭí ;

MONEYED, *A*.
máldár ; sáhukár ;

MONGOOSE, *N*.
neulá. *m* ; neul. *m* ; chaṇḍáúl. *m* ;

MONGREL, *A*.
dogalá ;

MONITION, *N*.
1. instruction. nasíhat. *f* ; matt. *f* ;
2. rebuke. jhiṛak. *f* ; malámat. *f* ; jhiṛkí. *f* ; dábbá. *m* ;

MONK, *N*.
mujáur. *m*. M ; muní. *m*. H ; wairágí. *m*. H ; sádh. *m*. H ;

MONKEY, *N*.
baṇdar. *m* ; báṇdar. *m* ; hanumán. *m* ; langúr. *m* ;
Proverb. To show that a mean person cannot appreciate a noble sentiment. What does the monkey know of the taste of ginger. báṇdar kí jáne adhrak dá sawád ;

MONOGRAM, *N*.
náṇ dá pahlá harf. *m* ;

MONOPOLY, *N*.
ṭheká. *m* ;

MONOTHEISM, *N*.
ikko Khudá núṇ manná. *m* ;

MONOTHEIST, *N*.
ikko Khudá núṇ mannanwálá. *m* ;

MONSOON, *N*.
barsát. *f* ;

MONSTER, *N.*
rákas. *m* ; deu. *m* ; jinn. *m* ;
MONSTROUS, *A.*
1. fearful. ḍaráuná ; ḍaráu ;
2. wonderful. aṇokhá ; acharaj ; virlá ;
MONSTROSITY, *N.*
aṇokh. *m* ;
MONTH, *N.*
mahíná. *m* ;
six months. chhimahí. *f* ;
MONTHLY, *A.*
máhwár ; har mahíne ;
MONUMENT, *N.*
yádgár. *m* ; nishání. *f* ;
in memory of deceased Hindu. maṛh. *m* ; maṛhí. *f* ; mat. *m* ; samádh. *f* ;
MONUMENTAL, *A.*
bahut waḍḍá ; waḍḍá sárá ;
MOODY, *A.*
naráz ; udás ; nimújhán ;
MOON, *N.*
chaṇd. *m* ; chaṇdarmáṇ. *m* ;
full moon. puranmásí. *f* ;
MOONBEAM, *N.*
chánaná. *m* ; chánaní. *f* ;
MOONLIGHT, *N.*
chánaní rát. *f* ;
MOONSTRUCK, *A.*
diwáná ;
MOOR, *N.*
jangal. *m* ;
MOOR, TO, *V. T.*
laṇgar láuná ;
MOOT, TO, *V. T.*
bahis karní ; bahisná ; hujjat karní ; dalíláṇ launí ;
MOP, *N.*
kúchchí. *f* ;
MOP, TO, *V. T.*
kúchchí pherní ; jháṛú dená ;
MOPE, TO, *V. T.*
udás honá ; masosná ; jhurná ; sog karná ;
MOPISH, *A.*
udás ; masosiá hoyá ; sasdil ; dil ḍhaṭṭhá ; santápí ;
MORAL, *A.*
1. holy. nek ; pák ;
2. righteous. rást ;
3. religious. díndár ; dharmí ;
4. pure. suddh ; pavittar ;
5. moral character. chál chalan. *m* ; lachchhan. *m* ;
6. moral precepts. nasíhat. *f* ;
MORALITY, *N.*
bhaliáí. *f* ; nekí. *f* ; rástí. *f* ;
MORALIZE, TO, *V. T.*
nasíhat dení ; updesh dená ;
MORALS, *N.*
chál chalan. *m* ; taur dauṛ. *m* ; lachchhan. *m* ; bol chál. *f* ; chál ḍhál. *f* ;
MORALLY, *Adv.*
rástí nál ; nekí nál ;
MORASS, *N.*
jhall. *m* ; jhaṇgaṛ. *m* ; jhillan. *m* ;
MORBID, *A.*
bimár ; roggí ; udás ; sasdil ; dil ḍhaṭṭhá ; sogmáṇ ;
MORBIDNESS, *N.*
bimárí. *f* ; rog. *m* ;
MORE, *A.*
jiádá ; ziyádá ; wadhere ; hor ;
MORE, *Adv.*
dher ; wadhík ; hor ; waddh ; adhak ;
1. more and more. hor ví ;
2. no more. hor nahíṇ ; bas ;
3. what more ? hor kí ?
4. more or less. ghaṭṭ wadh ;
5. how much more ? kinná wadh ;
6. to get more. ziástí milná ;
MOREOVER, *Adv.*
nále ; sagoṇ ; balak ;
MORNING, *N.*
fajar. *f* ; subah. *f* ;
MOROSE, *A.*
naráz ; khaṭṭá ; rukkhá ; muṇh ṭuṭá ; nakk chaṛhá ; sasdil ; badmaját ;
MOROSELY, *Adv.*
khafá hoke ; russ ke ;
MOROSENESS, *N.*
hirkh. *m* ; kauṛ. *m* ; rossá. *m* ;
MORPHIA, *N.*
afím. *f* ;
MORROW, TOMORROW, *Adv.*
bhálke ; kall ;
MORSEL, *N.*
bhorá. *m* ; ṭukṛá. *m* ; giráh. *m* ; ḍákkará. *m* ; gapphá. *m* ; burkí. *f* ;

MORTAL, *N*.
insán. *m*; ádmí. *m*; bandá. *m*; manukkh. *m*;
MORTAL, *A*.
maranhárá; ḳhákí; násmán; maranhár;
this mortal body. ih maranwálá jussá. *m*;
MORTAR, *N*.
ukhlí. *f*;
1. earthern mortar for spices. daurí. *f*;
2. stone mortar for spices. kúṇḍí. *f*;
3. mud mortar for building. gárá. *m*;
4. mortar for pointing. chuná. *m*;
5. a mortar bed. tagár. *m*;
MORTGAGE, TO, *V. T.*
gahne dhaṛná OR páuná;
MORTGAGE, *N*.
gahná. *m*;
MORTIFICATION, *N*.
khár. *f*; sáṛá. *m*; hasad. *m*;
MORTIFICATIONS, *N*.
tap. *m*;
MORTIFIED, *A*.
lajílá; lajjí; sharmíndá; sharmílá;
MORTIFY, TO, *V. T.*
bhukkh márná;
to mortify the deeds of the flesh. dehí de kárajáṇ núṇ márná;
MOSQUE, *N*.
masít. *f*;
MOSQUITO, *N*.
machchhar. *m*; guttí. *f*;
MOSQUITO NET, *N*.
jálí. *f*;
MOST, *A*.
sáreáṇ nálon waddh; sáreáṇ thoṇ waddh;
at most. waddh thoṇ waddh;
MOSTLY, *Adv*.
bahut karke; wadhík;
MOTE, *N*.
tiṇ. *m*; kaṇ. *m*;
MOTH, *N*.
pataṇgá. *m*; bhambaṭ. *m*; báhmaṇ bachchá. *m*; bhaṇbhaṭ. *m*;
moth in clothes. leh. *m*; lehá. *m*;
MOTHER, *N*.
máṇ. *f*; mátá. *f*; ammáṇ. *f*; máu. *f*; máuṇ. *f*; bebbe. *f*; maí. *f*;
1. mother-in-law. sass. *f*;
2. Proverb on putting the best face on a thing.
A. Nothing to eat in the house and mother has gone to grind the corn. ghar khán núṇ nahíṇ, máṇ chakkí píhan gaí.
B. No corn in the house, but mother has gone to grind it. ghar nahíṇ dáne, ammáṇ píhan gaí.
MOTHERLAND, *N*.
janam bhumí. *f*; watan. *m*;
MOTHERLESS, *A*.
mahittar;
MOTHER TONGUE, *N*.
mádarí bolí. *f*;
MOTION, *N*.
hill jull. *f*; chál. *f*; ṭor. *f*;
jolt. hohá. *f*;
MOTIONLESS, *A*.
mun sunn;
to be motionless. ṭhahrná;
MOTIVE, *N*.
matlab. *m*; murád. *f*; garz. *f*; káran. *m*; níat. *f*;
MOTLEY, *A*.
bahu raṇggí; dabbá;
MOTOR, *N*.
moṭar. *m*;
MOULD, TO, *V. T.*
ghaṛná; sáṇche vichch ḍhálná;
MOULD, *N*.
1. shape. sáṇchá. *m*; kalbút. *m*;
2. fungus. sawál. *m*; ullí. *f*; jálá. *m*;
MOULDY, *A*.
ullí lagí; behí;
to become mouldy. kujná; ullí lagní;
MOULT, TO, *V. I.*
par jháṛná;
MOULTING, *N*.
kuríj. *f*;
MOUND, *N*.
ṭibbá. *m*; ṭillá. *m*; ḍherí. *f*;
dhurobaṛá. *m*;
a mound of ruins. theh. *m*;

MOUNT, TO, *V. T.*
charháná ; chárhná ;

MOUNT, TO, *V. I.*
charhná ; charh jáná ;

MOUNTAIN, *N.*
pahár. *m ;* parbat. *m ;* gir. *m ;*
Idiom for when a man jibs at some
work. tainúṇ pahár nazr áundí
hai ?

MOUNTAINEER, *N.*
pahárí. *m ;*

MOUNTEBANK, *N.*
bájígar. *m ;* madárí. *m ;*

MOURN, TO, *V. T.*
roná ; piṭṭná ; hamsos karná ;
siápá karná ; mátam karná ; kurláuná ; bilápná ; bhus bhus karná ;
birláp karná ;

MOURNERS, *N.*
among the mourners. siápe vichch,
lit. in the mourning.

MOURNFUL, *A.*
udás ; sogmán ; masosiá hoyá ;

MOURNFULLY, *Adv.*
udás hoke ; gam nál ;

MOURNING, *N.*
siápá. *m ;* sog. *m ;* gamí. *f ;*
birláp. *m ;* see MOURNING.
1. united mourning. mukán. *f ;*
2. Proverb. When women go to
a mourning each weeps for her
own trouble. rann gaíṇ siápe,
dukh rowe ápo apne ;

MOUSE, *N.*
chúhí. *f ;* chúhá. *m ;*
Proverb. The mountain burst
and out came a mouse.
phuṭá pahár te nikhotthá
chuhá ;

HOUSE HOLE, *N.*
dudd. *f ;* rudd. *f ;*

MOUSETRAP, *N.*
chuhedán. *m ;*

MOUSTACHE, *N.*
muchchán. *f ;* muchch. *f ;* labbáṇ. *m ;*
side whiskers. kalam. *f ;* kala-
máṇ. *f ;*

MOUTH, *N.*
mukh. *m ;* munh. *m ;* mukhṛá. *m ;*
of horse, camel, &c. thothní. *f ;*
buttí. *f ;*

MOUTHFUL, *N.*
giráhí. *f ;* giráh. *m ;* burki. *f ;* gapphá. *m ;* phakká. *m ;*
a mouthful of liquid. ghuṭṭ. *m ;*

MOVABLES, *N.*
asbáb. *m ;* chíz wast. *m ;* laṭá
paṭá. *m ;* nikk sukk. *m ;*

MOVE, *N.*
hill jull. *f ;* see MOTION.

MOVE, TO, *V. T.*
chaláuná ; hiláuná ; khiskáuná ;
duláuná ;
1. to march. kuch karná ; sarkáná ;
2. to cause to move. reharná ;
chaláuná ;

MOVE, TO, *V. I.*
1. to shake. hillná ; hil jáná ;
dullná ; khiskná ; jhúlná ; ṭalná ;
2. to walk. challná ; ṭurná ; sarká
honá ; ṭharkná ;

MOVEMENT, *N.*
hill jull. *f ;* chál. *f ;* ṭor. *f ;* dol. *f ;*

MOW, TO, *V. T.*
gháh márná ; gháh waddhná ;

MUCH, *Adv.*
dher ; báhlá ; bahut ; ghanerá ;
wáfar ; ám ; bahterá ; bahu ; wadherá ; chokkhá ; bahutá ;
1. how much more. kinná waddh ;
kinná wadhík ;
2. much more then. táṇ is náloṇ
bahut wadh ke ;

MUCK, *N.*
gandagí. *f ;* gand. *m ;*

MUCUS, *N.*
balgam. *m ;* khaṇgár. *m ;*

MUD, *N.*
chikkaṛ. *m ;* gárá. *m ;* chikkaṛ
chambhaṛ. *m ;*
1. mud for building. gárá. *m ;*
gháni. *f ;*
2. mud left by a flood. rej. *f ;*

MUDDLE, *N.*
garbaṛí. *f ;* see CONFUSION.

MUDDLE, TO, *V. T.*
khallar páuná ; garbaṛí páuní ;

MUDDY, *A.*
gandhlá ;
1. muddy water. ganghlá ; gabirá ;
2. to muddy water. ganghálná ;
ghacholná ; gand láuná ;

MULBERRY, *N.*
shatút. *m* ; jalebá. *m* ;
MULBERRY TREE, *N.*
shatút. *m* ;
1. small mulberry tree. tutṛá. *m* ; tút. *m* ;
2. mulberry fruit. túti golá. *m* ; badáṇṇá. *m* ;
MULCT, TO, *V. T.*
1. to fine. jurmáná karná ; ḍann láná ; ḍanḍ lagáuná ; chaṭṭí láuní ;
2. to spoil. luṭṭná ;
MULE, *N.*
khachchar. *m* ;
MULISH, *A.*
khachchrá ;
MULISHNESS, *N.*
khachchrái. *f* ;
MULTIFARIOUS, *A.*
bhánt bhánt de ; taráh taráh de ; wakhowakh ;
MULTIFORM, *A.*
anek akár ; bahurúpí ;
MULTIPLICATE, TO, *V. T.*
wadháuná ;
MULTIPLICATION TABLE, *N.*
pahárá. *m* ;
MULTIPLY, TO, *V. T.*
wadháuná ; bahutá karná ;
MULTIPLY, TO, *V. I.*
wadhná ; bahut ho jáná ;
MULTITUDE, *N.*
dal. *m* ; bhíṛ. *f* ; ṭollí. *f* ; kaṭak. *m* ; mahaiṇ. *m* ; dháṛ. *f* ; ḍháṇí. *f* ;
MUM, *A.*
chup ; chup cháp; gumm summ ; chupp chapátá ;
MUMBLE, *N.*
guṇguṇ. *m* ;
MUMBLE, TO, *V. T.*
guṇ guṇ karná ; ghichch michch bolná ;
MUMPS, *N.*
bhaiṛe. *m* ; bhabbu. *m*;
MUNCH, TO, *V. T.*
chabbná ;
MUNDANE, *A.*
dunyáví ;
MUNIFICENCE, *N.*
punn. *m* ; dát. *f* ; sakhaut. *f* ; datárí. *f* ; dánn punn. *m* ;
MUNIFICENT, *A.*
mihrbán ; man chalá ; dilwálá ; saḳhí ;
MUNIFICENTLY, *Adv.*
dil kholke ; khullhe dil nál ; waḍḍe dil nál ;
MUNITION, *N.*
laṛái dá asbáb. *m* ;
MURDER, *N.*
ḳhun. *m* ; hattiá. *m* ; ghát. *f* ;
MURDER, TO, *V. T.*
jánoṇ waddhná ; ḳhún karná ; már dálná ; thánoṇ már suṭṭná ;
MURDERER, *N.*
ḳhuní. *m*; ádam már. *m* ; ghátak *m*; hattiárá. *m* ;
MURK, *N.*
andherá. *m* ;
MURKY, *A.*
dhunḍlá ;
MURMUR, *N.*
buṛ buṛ. *f* ; guṇ guṇ. *m*; ghur ghur. *f* ; kuṛ kuṛ. *f* ;
MURMUR, TO, *V. T.*
baṛbaṛáuná ; kuṛkuṛáuná ; kiṛkiṛáuná ; ghur ghur karná ; buṛ buṛ karná :
MURMURING, *N.*
ghur ghur. *f* ;
MUSCLE, *N.*
paṭṭhá. *m* ; chhalí. *f* ;
MUSCULAR, *A.*
sabal; moṭṭá tázá ; tagaṛá ; balwán;
MUSEUM, *N.*
ajaib ghar. *m* ;
MUSHROOM, *N.*
khumb. *f* ;
toad stool. padd bhaiṛá. *m* ; padd bheṛá. *m* ;
MUSIC, *N.*
gánná bájjá. *m* ; gájjá bájjá. *m* ;
music and dancing. rág nách. *m* ;
MUSICIAN, *N.*
gáyak. *m* ; kaláuṇt, *m* ; rabábí. *m* ; gawáiyá. *m* ; gawáiṇ. *f* ; wajantrí. *m* ; mirásí. *m* ; bajwáyyá. *m* ;
1. a caste of musicians. ḍúm. *m* ;
2. Proverb. Many female musicians cannot play on the tambourine at once, *i.e.*, too many cooks spoil the broth. bahutí ḍumní ḍhaḍḍ nahíṇ wajjdí ;

MUSK, *N.*
kasturí. *f ;*
MUSKET, *N.*
bandúq. *m ;*
MUSKRAT, *N.*
chakchúṇdhar. *f ;* chichúṇdar. *f ;*
MUSLIN, *N.*
malmal. *f ;*
figured muslin. naiṇú. *m ;*
MUSQUITO, *N.*
machchhar. *m ;*
MUSTACHE, *N.*
labbáṇ. *f ;* muchcháṇ. *f ;*
MUSTARD, *N.*
ráí. *f ;*
1. growing mustard. sarhoṇ. *f ;*
2. mustard poultice. ráí dá lep. *m ;*
MUSTER, TO, *V. T.*
1. to take the attendance. hájarí lainí ;
2. to count. giṇtí karní ;
3. to assemble together. kaṭṭhá karná ;
MUSTINESS, *N.*
ullí. *f ;*
MUSTY, *A.*
behí ; behí tabehí ;
MUTATION, *N.*
tabdílí. *f ;* badlí. *f ;*
MUTE, *A.*
chupp ; chupp cháp ; gupp chupp ;
MUTELY, *Adv.*
chupp cháp ; chupp chapátá ; chupp kíte ; chupp chupítá ;
MUTILATE, TO, *V. T.*
aṇg bhaṇg karná ; wigáṛná ;
MUTILATION, *N.*
wigáṛ. *m ;*
MUTINEER, *N.*
ákí. *m ;* bágí. *m ;* phatúrí. *m ;* phaturiá. *m ;*
MUTINOUS, *A.*
ákí ; bágí ; fasádí ; pasádiá ;
MUTINY, *N.*
daṇggá. *m ;* balwá. *m ;* bagáwat. *f ;* khurúd. *m ;* phatúr. *m ;*
MUTINY, TO, *V. T.*
kal jagáuná ; fasád karná ; daṇggá karná ; kharúd karná ; wichal jáná ;

MUTTER, TO, *V. T.*
buṛ buṛ karná ; muṇh vichch guṇ guṇ karná ; buṛbuṛáuná ;
to mutter incantations. jháṛá karná ; mantar paṛhná ;
MUTTERING, *N.*
buṛ buṛ. *f ;* baṛbaṛát. *m ;* buṛ baṛát. *m ;*
MUTTON, *N.*
bheḍ dá más. *m ;*
MUTTON BROTH, *N.*
shorbá. *m ;*
MUTUAL, *A.*
sáṇjhá ; duwallá ;
MUZZLE, *N.*
1. gag. chhabbú. *m ;*
2. of a gun. nálí. *f ;*
3. for cattle. chhabbú. *m ;* chhikká. *m ;* jhabbú. *m ;*
4. to muzzle cattle. chhikká chaṛhná ;
MY, *Pron.*
merá ;
MYRIAD, *A.*
aṇgint ; beshumár ; lakholakh ; behisáb ;
MYRRH, *N.*
mur. *m ;*
MYSELF, *Pron.*
maiṇ hí ; áp núṇ ;
MYSTERIOUS, *A.*
gaibí ;
MYSTERY, *N.*
ech pech. *m ;* híjpiáj, *m ;*
secret. bhet. *m ;*
MYSTIC, *N.*
yogí. *m ;* jogí. *m ;*
MYSTICAL, *A.*
samajh thoṇ báhar ;
MYSTIFY, TO, *V. T.*
ghabrá dená ;
MYTH, *N.*
kahání. *f ;*
MYTHICAL, *A.*
ḳhayálí ;
MYTHOLOGICAL, *A.*
ḳhayálí ;
MYTHOLOGY, *N.*
deotáṇ dá bayáṇ. *m*

N.

NAB, TO, *V. T.*
1. to seize. jhapaṭná ; phaṛ lainá ; jhapaṭ márná ;
2. to snatch away. khohná ; khohlená ; see SNATCH.

NAG, *N.*
ghoṛá. *m* ; ghoṛí. *f* ;
pony. ṭairá. *m* ;

NAIL, *N.*
1. small nail. brinjí. *f* ;
2. small nail. meḳh. *f* ; kil. *m* ;
3. finger nail. nauṇh *m* ;

NAIL, TO, *V. T.*
kil ṭhokná ;

NAKED, *A.*
naṇgá ; dhaṛall ; naṇgdhaṛaṇg ;

NAKEDNESS, *N.*
naṇg. *m* ;

NAME, *N.*
náṇ *m* ; náuṇ. *m* ; nám. *m* ;
name and address. pind pír. *m* ; náṇ patá. *m* ; náṇ nishán. *m* ;

NAME, TO, *V. T.*
náṇ rakkhná ;

NAMELESS, *A.*
gumnám ;

NAMELY, *Adv.*
yáne ; arthát ;

NAPE, *N.*
gichchí. *f* ; kiáṛí. *f* ; dhauṇ. *f* ;

NAPKIN, *N.*
dowattá. *m* ; parná. *m* ; tauliá. *m* ;

NARCOTIC, *N.*
uh dawá jis thoṇ níṇd áwe ;

NARRATE, TO, *V. T.*
bayán karná ; batláuná ; dassná ; kahná ; hakáyatáṇ karní ; kath karní ;

NARRATIVE, *N.*
bayán. *m* ; wártá. *f* ; kissá. *m* ; kathá. *f* ; kath. *f* ;

NARRATOR, *N.*
bayán karnwálá. *m* ;

NARROW, *A.*
bhíṛá ; sauṛá ; taṇg ;

NARROW, TO, *V. T.*
ghaṭáuná ; taṇg karná ;

NARROWLY, *Adv.*
mushkil nál ;

NARROWNESS, *N.*
taṇgí. *f* ;

NASAL, *A.*
nakk dá ;

NASAL DISCHARGE, *N.*
nalí. *f* ; sínd. *f* ;

NASTILY, *Adv.*
burí taráh nál ;

NASTINESS, *N.*
gaṇdagí. *f* ; gaṇd. *m* ;

NASTY. *A.*
gaṇdá ; mailá ; palíd ; búrá ;

NATION, *N.*
qaum. *f* ;

NATIONAL, *A.*
mulkí ; qaumí ;

NATIONALISM, *N.*
qaumí josh. *m* ;

NATIONALITY, *N.*
qaumiat. *f* ;

NATIVE, *N.*
desí ádmí. *m* ;

NATIVE, *A.*
desí ; mulkí ;
native language. mádrí bolí. *f* ;

NATIVITY, *N.*
janam. *m* ; paidaish. *f* ;
of a deity upon earth. autár. *m* ;

NATURAL, *A.*
zátí ; qudratí ; sabháuk ; subháwak ;

NATURALLY, *Adv.*
áp hí áp ; subháo thoṇ ; sabháukí ;

NATURE, *N.*
ját, *m* ; ḳhasíat. *f* ;
1. sort. qism. *m* ; ját. *m* ; bhaṇt. *m* ;
2. habit. subháo. *m* ; ádat. *f* ;
3. essence. asl. *m* ;
4. against nature. qudrat de ḳhiláf ;
5. by nature. subháo thoṇ ;
6. the creation. sarisht. *f* ; sarist. *f* ;

NAUGHT, *N.*
kujh nahíṇ ;

NAUGHT, *A.*
nikammá ; nachíz ; fajúl ;
to bring to naught. awirthá karná ;

NAUGHTINESS, *N.*
naṭkhaṭí. *f* ; sharárat. *f* ; aṛí. *f* ; zidd. *m* ;

NAUGHTY, *A.*
sharáratí ; sharír ;
to be naughty. machcharná ;

NAUSEA, *N*.
ghin. *f*; bakbakí; *f*; kirak. *f*; karáhat. *f*; bakbakáṭ. *m*;
NAUSEATING, *A*.
bakbaká;
NAVEL, *N*.
tunní. *f*; dhunní. *f*; náf. *f*;
an enlarged or protruded navel. dhunn. *m*;
NAVEL STRING, *N*.
ául. *m*;
NAVIGATE, TO, *V. T.*
jaház chaláuná;
NAY, *Adv*.
nahíṇ; náh;
NAY, *N*.
inkár. *m*;
NEAR, *Adv*.
pás; kol; neṛe;
NEAR, *A*.
kol; lágge; pás; neṛe; muḍḍh.
NEARLY, *Adv*.
lag bhag; andázan;
somewhat less. kujh ghaṭṭ;
NEARNESS, *N*.
neṛ. *f*; najíkí. *f*;
NEAT, *A*.
sáf; suthrá;
NEATLY, *Adv*.
ṭhík ṭhák; ṭhíkam ṭhík;
NEATNESS, *N*.
safái. *f*;
NECESSARIES, *N*.
jarúrí chízáṇ. *f*;
NECESSARY, *A*.
cháhidá: loṛídá; jarúrí;
NECESSITOUS, *A*.
garíb; garíb gurbá; kaṇgál; lachár;
NECESSITOUSNESS, *N*.
garíbí. *f*; thuṛ. *f*; taṇgí. *f*;
NECESSITY, *N*.
loṛ. *f*; see NEED.
NECK, *N*.
dhauṇ. *f*; ghiṭṭí. *f*; gichchí. *f*; galá. *m*; gaṭṭí. *f*; gal. *m*;
1. nape of the neck. gichchí. *f*; dhauṇ. *f*;
2. neck of a coat. galwíṇ. *f*; galwíná. *m*;
NECKLACE, *N*.
gal dá hár. *m*; hass. *m*; hár. *m*; málá. *f*; hasírá. *m*; hassí. *f*;
1. of gold or silver pieces. hambel. *f*; hamel. *f*;
2. of small bells for horses, &c. hamail. *f*;
3. of beads, &c., kaṇṭhá, *m*; kaṇṭhí. *f*; see ORNAMENT.
NECROMANCER, *N*.
maṇtarí. *m*; jádúgar. *m*; ṭunehár. *m*;
NECROMANCY, *N*.
jádúgarí. *f*; jádú. *m*; maṇta jaṇtar. *m*; ṭuná. *m*;
NECTAR, *N*.
amrit. *m*; lit. the nectar conferring immortality;
NEED, *N*.
loṛ. *f*; gauṇ. *m* & *f*; taṇgí. *f*; thuṛ. *f*;
1. to have need. loṛwand honá;
2. Proverb. Needs must when the devil drives. Necessity gets the barley parched, though it be wet. gauṇ bhunáve jaúṇ bháṇweṇ gille hoṇ;
NEEDFUL, *A*.
jarúrí;
NEEDINESS, *N*.
loṛ. *f*;
NEEDLE, *N*.
suí. *f*; tuppṇí. *f*;
1. large needle. ghaṇduí. *f*;
2. sacking needle. suá. *m*;
3. eye of a needle. suí dá nakká. *m*; suí dí duk. *f*;
NEEDLESS, *A*.
fajúl; khám; bearth;
NEEDLE WORK, *N*.
kasídá. *m*;
NEEDS, *N*.
loṛ. *f*;
NEEDY, *A*.
garíb; garíb gurbá; arthiá; hín; adíṇ; thuṛyal;
NEFARIOUS, *A*.
bahut burá; ghiṇáuná;
NEFARIOUSLY, *Adv*.
burí taráh nál;
NEGATION, *N*.
inkár. *m*;

NEGATIVE, TO, *V. T.*
nahíṇ karná ; náh karná ;
to refuse. inkár karná ; mukkarná ;
to reject. radd karná ;
NEGLECT, *N.*
gáfalí. *f* ; láparwáí. *f* ; see NEGLIGENCE.
NEGLECT, TO, *V. T.*
ghes mární ;
to be neglected. rulná ;
NEGLECTFUL, *A.*
bholú ; ghauliá ; gáfal ; ḍhillá ; bemukh ; sust ;
NEGLECTFULLY, *Adv.*
ghaul nál ; láparwáí nál ; biná soche samjhe ;
NEGLIGENCE, *N.*
ghassú. *m* ; ghaul. *f* ; ḍhill. *f* ; gáfalí. *f* ; beparwáí. *f* ; ghesal. *f* ;
NEGLIGENT, *A.*
ghassúmár ; ghaulí ; ḍhillá ; gáfal ; beparwáh ; surliá hoyá ; See CARELESS.
NEGLIGENTLY, *Adv.*
sustí nál ; láparwáhí nál ;
NEGOTIATION, *N.*
gall katth. *f* ; bandobast. *m* ;
NEGOTIATOR, *N.*
wicholá. *m* ; dalál. *m* ; árhatí. *m* ;
NEGRESS, *N.*
Habshan. *f* ;
NEGRO, *N.*
Habshí. *m* ;
NEIGH, TO, *V. T.*
hinakná ; hiṇkaná ;
NEIGHBOUR, *N.*
gawáṇḍhí. *m* ; guáṇḍhaṇ. *f* ; áhṇḍí gawáṇḍhí. *m* ; sawáṇḍrí. *m* ;
NEIGHBOURHOOD, *N.*
gawáṇḍh. *m* ; lámbh chhámbh. *f* ; áṇḍh guáṇḍh ;
NEIGHBOURING, *A.*
lágí ; pás ;
NEIGHBOURLY, *A.*
milansár ;
NEIGHBOURLY, *Adv.*
prem nál ;
NEIGHING, *N.*
hiṇkárá. *m* ; hiṇkát. *m* ;
NEITHER, *Adv.*
dohán vichchoṇ koí ná ;
NEPHEW, *N.*
1. brother's son. bhatíjá. *m* ; bhatríá. *m* ;
2. sister's son. bhanewáṇ. *m* ;
NERVE, *N.*
rag. *f* ; paṭṭhá. *m* ;
NERVE, TO, *V. T.*
dilerí dení ;
NERVOUS, *A.*
bháímán ; ḍarákal ;
NERVOUSNESS, *N.*
ḍar. *m* ; ḳhauf. *m* ;
NEST, *N.*
áhlaná. *m* ;
NET, *N.*
jál. *m* ; phaṇd. *m* ; kuṛikkí. *f* ; pháhí. *f* ;
1. net for chaff. traṇgar. *m* ; taṇggar. *m* ; taṇggarí. *f* ; palí. *f* ;
2. wire netting. jálí. *f* ;
NET, TO, *V. T.*
phaṇde vichch phasáuná ;
NETHER, *A.*
heṭhlá ;
NETHERMOST, *A.*
sabh thoṇ heṭháṇ ;
NETTING, *N.*
jálí. *f* ;
NETTLE, TO, *V. T.*
chheṛná ; khijháuná ; rusáuná naráj karná ;
NETWROK, *N.*
jálí. *f* ;
NEUTRALITY, *N.*
betarafdárí. *f* ; belággí. *f* ;
NEUTRALIZE, TO, *V. T.*
betásír karná ;
NEVER, *Adv.*
hargiz nahíṇ ; múl nahíṇ ; kadí nahíṇ ; nijj ;
NEVER, *Interj.*
tobbá tobbá ;
of incredulity. hekḳháṇ ;
NEVERTHELESS, *Adv.*
tad ví ;
NEW, *A.*
nawáṇ ; nawíṇ ; tázá ; lairá ;
1. fresh. sajjrá ; tázá ;
2. new unwashed cloth. korá kapṛá. *m* ;
NEWNESS, *N.*
tázagí. *f* ;

NEWS, *N*.
ḳhabar. *f*; sár. *f*; suh. *f*; patá. *m*; samáchár. *f*; suggh. *f*; uggh suggh. *f*;
1. incorrect news. gapp. *f*;
2. news of a death. sunauní. *f*;
3. news of a birth. jaṇáuní. *f*;

NEWSPAPER, *N*.
aḳhbár. *f*; samáchár patr. m; parchá. *m*;

NEXT, *A*.
parlá; nál dá; dujjá; aglá;

NEXT, *Adv*.
agge núṇ;

NIB, *N*.
chuṇjh. *f*;

NIBBLE, TO, *V. T*.
ghá charná;

NICE, *A*.
achchhá; chaṇgá;

NICELY, *Adv*.
chaṇgí taráh nál;
not nicely made, khossaṛ dubbaṛ;

NICETY, *N*.
durustí. *f*; suddh táí. *f*;

NICHE, *N*.
ták. *m*; álá. *m*; duákká. *m*;

NICK, *N*.
waḍḍhá. *m*;

NICK, TO, *V. T*.
pachchhaná;

NICKNAME, *N*.
cheṛh. *f*;

NIECE, *N*.
1. brother's daughter. bhatíjí. *f*;
2. sister's daughter. bhauejí. *f*; bhanewíṇ. *f*;

NIGGARD, *N*.
kanjús. *m*;

NIGGARDLINESS, *N*.
kanjúsí. *f*; sarfá. *m*; shúmpuṇá. *m*;

NIGGARDLY, *Adv*.
kanjúsí nál; sarfe nál;

NIGH, *A. Adv. Prep*.
neṛe; nazdík; lágge; muḍḍh;

NIGHT, *N*.
rát. *f*; rain. *f*;
1. night and day. rát din;
2. all night long. ráto rát; ráto rátíṇ;
3. moonlight night. chándní rát;
4. by night. rátí; rátíṇ; rátoṇ rát;
5. to night. ajj dí rát;
6. last night. kal dí rát;
7. nightfall. takáláṇ. *f*;

NIGHTINGALE, *N*.
bulbul. *m*;

NIGHTLY, *Adv*.
ráto rát; har rát;

NIGHTMARE, *N*.
ḍaráuní ḳháb. *f*;

NIGHTSOIL, *N*.
mailá. *m*; jháṛá. *m*;

NIL, *A*.
kujh nahíṇ;

NIMBLE, *A*.
tez; phurtílá; chalák; káhlá; turturá; tagṛá;

NIMBLENESS, *N*.
chálákí. *f*; shatábí. *f*; phurtí. *f*;

NIMBLY, *Adv*.
shatábí nál; see QUICKLY.

NINE, *A*.
nau;

NINETEEN, *A*.
unní;

NINETEENTH, *A*.
unníwáṇ;

NINETY, *A*.
nawe;

NINTH, *A*.
nauwáṇ;

NIP, *N*.
chúṇḍhí. *f*;

NIP, TO, *V. T*.
chúṇḍhí waḍḍhná;

NIPPER, *N*.
bachchá. *m*; ayáná. *m*;

NIPPERS, *N*.
mochná; *m*; jabúr. *m*;

NIPPLE, *N*.
chuchí. *f*;
india rubber nipple. chusní. *f*; chúpṇí. *f*;

NIT, *N*.
líkh. *f*;
Proverb. A shaven head has neither lice nor nits. Roḍḍe sir júṇ ná líkh;

NITRE, *N*.
shorá. *m*;

NO, *Adv*.
nahíṇ; ná;

NO, *A*.
nahíṇ ; ná ;
NOBILITY, *N*.
amírí. *f* ; umráí. *f* ; ambírí. *f* ; sajádṛí. *f* ;
NOBLE, *A*.
sharíf ; khará ; bhalámánas ;
NOBODY, *N*.
koí nahíṇ ;
NOCTURNAL, *A*.
rát dá ;
NOD, *N*.
sainat. *f* ; ishárá. *m* ;
NOD, TO, *V. T*.
sainat karní OR mární ;
NOD, TO, *V. I*.
jhukná ; jhokáṇ lainá ;
NOISE, *N*.
shor. *m* ; raulá. *m* ; hullar. *m* ; ḍaṇḍ. *f* ; chán bhán. *m* ; gharmass. *f* ; luḍí. *f* ; dhamúl. *m* ; tarthall. *m* ; khap. *m* ;
1. noise of footsteps, cart, &c. kaṛak. *m* ; kharká. *m* ;
2. why is there all this noise ? kí dhamúl chukkiá hoyá je ?
3. sound of voices. bulárá. *m* ;
NOISE, TO, *V. T*.
1. to make an uproar. shor macháuná ; raulá páuná ; tarthall macháuná ; khap páuná ;
2. to publish abroad. hoká dená ; parchár karná ; dhomáuná ; mashhúr karná ;
NOISY, *A*.
shorí ; khappí ;
NOMAD, *N*.
tapríwálá. *m* ; pakkhíwás. *m* ;
NOMENCLATURE, *N*.
nám. *m* ;
NOMINATE, TO, *V. T*.
nám lainá ; náṇ pesh karná ;
NON APPEARANCE, *N*.
gair házarí. *f* ;
NON ATTENDANCE, *N*.
gair házarí. *f* ;
NON COMPLIANCE, *N*.
náfarmání. *f* ; hukm udúlí. *f* ; ágiá bhaṇg. *f* ;
NONE, *A. & Pro*.
koí nahíṇ ;
NON EXISTENCE, *N*.
nestí. *f* ;
NONPLUS, TO, *V. T*.
ghabrá dená ;
NONSENSE, *N*.
wáhiyát galláṇ. *f* ; bakwás. *m* ; fijul gallán. *f* ; wáfrí. *f* ; jhak. *f* ; bhakkh. *m* ;
he talks all sorts of nonsense. uh piá bhakkháṇ chhaṇtdá haí ;
NONSENSICAL, *A*.
1. foolish. bewuqúf ; beaql ; nadán ;
2. without meaning. anarth ;
NOOK, *N*.
kuchchh. *f* ; nukkaṛ. *f* ; khúṇj. *f* ; guṭṭh. *f* ;
NOON, *N*.
dupaihar. *f* ;
at noon. dupaihrí ;
NOOSE, *N*.
1. a running knot. kamaṇḍ. *f* ;
2. a snare. phaṇdá. *m* ; jál. *m* ; kaṛikkí. *f* ;
3. a lasso. pháhí. *f* ; kamaṇḍ. *f* ;
NOOSE, TO, *V. T*.
phaṇde vichch páuná OR phasáuná ;
NOR, *Conj*.
ná ;
NORMAL, *A*.
ṭhík ;
NORTH, *N*.
paháṛ. *m* ; ubbhá. *m* ;
Proverb. The jackal died and the news spread North and South. Moyá táṇ giddaṛ ubbhe lamme pai huke ;
NORTH-EAST, *N*.
paháṛ te chaṛhde dí guṭṭh. *f* ;
NORTHERLY, *A*.
uttar púrab dá ;
NORTHWARD, *A*.
uttar wal ; paháṛ wal ;
NORTH-WEST, *N*.
paháṛ te laihnde dí guṭṭh. *f* ;
NOSE, *N*.
nakk. *m* ;
1. flat nosed. phíhná ;
2. blow the nose. nakk suṇkaná ;
NOSEBAG, *N*.
tobṛa. *m* ;
NOSE RING, *N*.
natth. *f* ;

NOSTRIL, *N.*
nás. *f* ; násáṇ. *f* ;
NOT, *Adv.*
nahín ; ná ; nijj ;
not at all. ukká ná ; atte ná ;
NOTABLE, *A.*
mashhúr ; námí ; bhall bhaí ;
manniá danniá ; parnámí ;
NOTABLY, *Adv.*
ḳháss karke ;
NOTCH, *N.*
waḍḍhá. *m* ; pachch. *m* ; ṭakk. *m* ;
NOTCH, TO, *V. T.*
pachchhná ; ṭakk láuná ;
NOTE, *N*,
rukká. *m* ; ḳhatt. *m* ; pattar. *m* ;
chiṭṭhí pachattí. *f* ;
NOTE, TO, *V. T.*
1. to notice. dhián karná ;
2. record. likhná ;
NOTEBOOK, *N.*
ḍairí. *f* ; kitáb. *f* ; kápí. *f* ;
NOTED, *A.*
waḍḍá námí ; manniá danniá ;
ghukiá hoyá ; minniá ginniá ;
NOTE PAPER, *N.*
chiṭṭhí dá kágaz. *m* ;
NOTEWORTHY, *A.*
gaur karan jog ; yád rakkhan de laiq ;
NOTHING, *Adv.*
kujh nahíṇ ;
1. nothing at all. kakkh ví nahíṇ ;
2. I got nothing out of it. maiṇ damaṛí pale nahíṇ baddhí ; mainúṇ kujh nahíṇ labbhá ;
3. He has nothing ; his dignity is all he sits on ! uh de kol huṇ kí rihá hai ? apní pat lai baiṭhá hai ;
NOTICE, *N.*
1. intimation. ishtihár. *m* ; ḳhabar. *f* ; patá. *m* ; suh. *f* ;
2. intelligence. suh. *f* ;
NOTICE, TO, *V. T.*
dhián karná ; sochná ; táṛ rakkhná ;
NOTIFICATION, *N.*
ḳhabar. *f* ; suh. *f* ; ishtihár. *m* ;
NOTIFY, TO, *V. T.*
ḳhabar dení ; sanehá ghallná ; dassná : taláh dení ;

NOTION, *N.*
ḳhayál. *m* ; soch. *m* ; raí. *f* ;
NOTORIOUS, *A.*
mashhúr ; nashar ;
NOTWITHSTANDING, *Prep.*
tad ví ; phir ví ; bháṇweṇ ;
NOUN, *N.*
ism. *m* ;
NOURISH, TO, *V. T.*
parwastí karní ; pálná posná ;
NOURISHER, *N.*
pálak ; *m* ;
NOURISHING, *A.*
táqat denwálá ;
NOURISHMENT, *N.*
ann páni. *m* ; ann jal. *m* ; roṭí. *f* ;
bhojan. *m* ; rozí. *f* ; kháná. *m* ;
parshád. *m* ;
NOVEL, *A.*
aṇokhá ; aṇokhí ; nawáṇ ;
NOVELTY, *N.*
aṇokh. *m* ;
NOVEMBER, *N.*
poh. *m* ;
NOVICE, *N.*
nawáṇ chelá OR shagird. *m* ;
NOW, *Adv.*
huṇ ; huṇe ; is vele ; hálí ; aitkíṇ ;
NOW-A-DAYS, *A.*
ajj kal ; inháṇ dináṇ vichch ;
NOWAYS, *Adv.*
kisí taráh nahíṇ ;
NOWHERE, *Adv.*
kisí jagáh nahíṇ ; kitale ná ;
nowhere else. kidhare ví nahíṇ ;
NOWISE, *Adv.*
kisí taráh nahíṇ ;
NOXIOUS, *A.*
burá ; gaṇdá ; máṛá ; ghiṇáuná ;
NOXIOUSNESS, *N.*
gaṇdagí. *f* ; palítí. *f* ; gaṇd. *m* ;
NOZZLE, *N.*
nakk. *m* ; thúthní. *f* ; thothní. *f* ;
NUDITY, *N.*
naṇgápuṇá. *m* ; naṇg. *m* ;
NUGATORY, *A.*
befaidá ; nikammá ;
NULL, *A.*
raddi ;
NULLIFY, TO, *V. T.*
radd kar dená ;

NUMB, *A*.
sunn ; ṭhareá hoyá ;
NUMB, TO BECOME, *V. I.*
pair sauná ;
NUMBER, *N*.
giṇtí *f* ; nambar. *m* ; gentrí. *f* ;
NUMBER, TO, *V. T.*
ginná ; gintí karní ;
NUMBERLESS, *A*.
aṇgint ; beshumár ; behisáb ;
NUMBNESS, *N*.
sunn. *m* ; ṭharan. *f* ; ṭhar. *f* ;
NUMERAL, *A*.
giṇtí dá ;
NUMERATE, TO, *V. T.*
ginná ; gintí karní ; hisáb karná ;
NUMERATION, *N*.
gintí. *f* ;
NUMERICALLY, *Adv*.
ginti vichch ;
NUMEROUS, *A*.
bahut ; dher sáre ; bahutere ;
NUPTIALS, *N*.
nikáh. *m* ; nikáh dí rít. *f* ;
NURSE, *N*.
dái. *f* ;
NURSE, TO, *V. T.*
1. to tend in sickness. bimárí dí ṭahl karní ;
2. to nurture. pálná posná ; parwastí karní;
NURSLING, *N*.
dudh chunganwálá bachchá. *m* ; niáná. *m* ;
NURTURE, *N*.
1. nourishment. ḳhurák. *f* ; kháná. *m* ;
2. education. tálím. *f* ; viddiá. *m* ;
NURTURE, TO, *V. T.*
1. to nourish. pálná posná ; khuáná ; parwastí karní ;
2. to educate. tálím dení ; paṛhàuná ;
NUT, *N*.
1. betel nut. supári. *f* ;
2. walnut. akhrot. *m* ;
3. pistachio. pistá. *m* ;
NUT BROWN, *A*.
bhúrá ; saulá ;
NUT CRACKERS, *N*.
sarautá. *m* ;
NUTMEG, *N*.
jáfal. *m* ;
NUTRIMENT, *N*.
roṭí. *f* ; ḳhurák. *f* ; bhojan. *m* ; kháná. *m* ;
NUX VOMICA, *N*.
kuchlá. *m* ;
NYMPH, *N*.
deví. *f* ; pari. *f* ; húr. *f* ;

O.

OAF, *N*.
dúss. *m* ;
an idiom, lit. a camel. uṭṭh. *m* ;
OAK, *N*.
balút. *m* ,
a boat) wanjh. *m* ;
OAR. *N*.
chappú. *m* ;
1. large. chappá. *m* ;
2. small. chappí. *f* ;
3. a bamboo pole for propelling a boat. waṇjh *m* ;
OAR, TO, *V. T.*
chappú chaláuná OR márná ; waṇjh láuná ;
OARSMAN, *N*.
malláh. *m* ; máṇjhí. *m* ; wáṇjhí. *m* ;
OAT, *N*.
gaṇdhel. *f* ;
OATH, *N*.
sauṇh. *f* ; saugaṇd. *f* ; qasm. *f* ;
to take an oath. sauṇh kháná ;
OATMEAL, *N*.
daliyá. *m* ;
OBDURACY, *N*.
haṭh. *f* ; patthar dilí. *f* ; sakhtí. *f* ;
see OBSTINANCY.
OBDURATE, *A*.
haṭhá ; ziddí ; magrá ; sakht dil ;
OBDURATELY, *Adv*.
haṭh nál ; sakht dilí nál ;
OBDURATENESS, *N*.
magrái. *f* ; magrúrí. *f* ; húṛh. *f* ;
see PERVERSENESS.
OBEDIENCE, *N*.
ágiákárí. *f* ; tábiádárí. *f* ; farmánbardárí. *f* ;
OBEDIENT, *A*.
tábiádár ; ágiákár ; ágiámán ;
obedient to one's guru. sugurú ;

OBEDIENTLY, *Adv.*
tábiádárí nál; ágiákárí nál;
OBEISANCE, *N.*
salám. *m;* namaskár. *m;* bandagí. *f;* ḍanḍaut. *f;* parnám. *m;*
I did obeisance. maiṇ matthá ṭekiá;
OBELISK, *N.*
burj. *m;*
OBESE, *A.*
ṭhullhá; ḍhiḍḍhu; subbhar; ḍhaṭṭá; ḍhiḍḍal; moṭṭá tázá; ghuchchmúchch; jhoṭaṛ;
OBEY, TO, *V. T.*
hukm manná; pichche ṭurná; kahine te jáná; bajá láuná; sir pur dharná; ákkhe laggná; kahiná mannà; sir matthe dharná; ágiákárí ho jáná; adhín honá; he does not obey any one. uh kise de kahe vichch nahíṇ;
OBFUSCATE, TO, *V. T.*
hanerá karná;
OBITUARY, *N.*
suwání umarí. *f;*
OBJECT, *N.*
1. a thing. chíz. *f;* shai. *f;*
2. purpose. matlab. *m;* gauṇ. *m;* muddá. *m;* káraj. *m;* manorath. *m;*
OBJECT, TO, *V. T.*
moṛ toṛ karná; uzr karná; hujjat kaḍḍhní OR karní OR launí; barjná; khundak kaḍḍhní;
OBJECTION, *N.*
khundak. *f;* manáhí. *f;* aṭak. *f;* rok ṭok. *f;* wigan. *m;*
1. an excuse. uzr. *f;*
2. I have no objection. koi sánúṇ ujr nahíṇ;
OBJECTIONABLE, *A.*
bhaiṛí; nikammí;
OBJECTOR, *N.*
itarází. *m;* manáhi karnwálá. *m;* hujjatí. *m;*
OBLATION, *N.*
chaṛháwá. *m;* niáz. *f;* najar niaj. *m;*
OBLIGATION, *N.*
1. kindness. nihcrá. *m;* asán. *m;* ihsán. *m;* mihrbání. *f;* kirpá. *f;* upkár. *m;*
2. duty. farz. *m;*

OBLIGATORY, *A.*
zarúrí; jarúrí;
OBLIGE, TO, *V. T.*
ihsán karná; mihrbání karní;
OBLIGED, *A.*
balihár;
OBLIGING, *A.*
mihrbán; kirpál;
OBLIGINGLY, *Adv.*
mihrbání nál; kirpá karke;
OBLIQUE, *A.*
salámí; kuásá; ḍhalwán;
OBLIQUELY, *Adv.*
moṛ toṛ karke;
OBLIQUENESS, *N.*
1. aslant. salámí. *f;*
2. wickedness. sharárat. *f;* badí. *f;* badráhí. *f;*
OBLITERATE, TO, *V. T.*
ghisáuná; mitáuná; meṭná; kalam pherní; miṭá dená;
OBLOQUY, *N.*
gál. *f;* mehná. *m;* bhaṇḍí. *f;* phakkaṛí. *f;*
OBNOXOUS, *A.*
bahut burá; bhaiṛá; máṛá; bharisht; múji;
OBSCENE, *A.*
luchchá; gaṇdá; ḳharáb;
OBSCENITY, *N.*
gálí galoch. *f;*
OBSCURE, TO, *V. T.*
dhuṇdlá karná; anherá karná;
OBSCURE, *A.*
1. meaning not clear. matlab sáf nahíṇ; ghusmusá;
2. misty. jhaulá; dhuṇdlá; gol mol;
OBSCURELY, *Adv.*
safái nál nahíṇ;
OBSCURITY, *N.*
dhuṇdh. *m;* dhuṇdhukár. *m;* gahir. *f;* anherá. *m;*
OBSECRATION, *N.*
duá. *f;* bentí. *f;* arz. *f;* minnat. *f;*
OBSEQUIES, *N.*
kafan dafan. *m,* **M**; kiryá karm. *m;* H;
OBSEQUIOUS, *A.*
1. fawning, cháplús; jholí chukk; adhíṇ;

2. obedient. tábedár; mannanwá'á;
OBSEQUIOUSLY, *Adv.*
adhíṇí nál; adhíṇ hoke;
OBSEQUIOUSNESS, *N.*
leṭ peṭ. *f;* leṭí peṭí. *f;* lallo patto. *f;* lollo poppo. *f;* choj. *m;* adhíṇṭáí. *f;*
OBSERVANCE, *N.*
1. attention. dhián. *m;* gaur. *m;*
2. custom. rít *f;* rawáj. *f;* dastur. *m;*
OBSERVANT, *A.*
hoshiyár; ḳhabardár;
obedient. tábíádár;
OBSERVATION, *N.*
dhián. *m;* wichár. *f;*
OBSERVE, TO, *V. T.*
dhiánaná; ákhe manná; tár rakkhná; see WATCH.
OBSERVER, *N.*
vekhanwálá. *m;* mannanwálá. *m;*
OBSERVINGLY, *Adv.*
dhián nál; soch wichár ke; soch samajh ke;
OBSOLETE, *A.*
puráne ḍhang dá;
OBSTACLE, *N.*
ṭhallh. *f;* aṭkáú. *f;* rok. *f;* aṛak. *f;* bháṇjí. *f;* ṭoká ṭáki. *f;*
OBSTINANCY, *N.*
ḍhíṭh. *f;* haṭh. *m;* ghes. *f;* ghesal. *f;* siḍḍá. *m;* siṛaṛ. *m;* machalpuná. *m;* khaih. *f;* ṭeḍh. *m;* kabb. *f;* jiraṛ. *f;* aṛi. *f;* húṛh. *f;* ghassú. *f;* zidd. *f;* machlai. *f;* taṛeḍh. *f;*
OBSTINATE, *A.*
ḍhíṭh; ḍhíṭhá; haṭhá haṭhílá; jiddí; kabbá; ṭeḍhá; aṛikhor; jiraṛí; tareḍhá; khachrá; aṛyal; machall;
OBSTINATELY, *Adv.*
haṭh nál; jidd nál; jiddo jiddí;
OBSTREPEROUS, *A.*
raulá paunwálá; fasádí; laṛáká;
OBSTREPEROUSNESS, *N.*
raulá gaulá. *m;* jidd. *f;*
OBSTRUCT, TO, *V. T.*
ḍakkná; ṭokná; haṭkaná; rokná; aṛikká pauná; ṭhillh páuná; see HINDER.
OBSTRUCTER, *N.*
rokanwálá. *m;* ṭokanwálá. *m;*
OBSTRUCTION, *N.*
aṛikkà. *m;* ḍakk. *m;* tok ṭák. *f;* ṭhillh. *f;* see OSBSTACLE.
OBSTRUCTIVE, *A.*
rokanwálá; ḍakkanwálá;
OBTAIN, TO, *V. T.*
labb lainá; milná; mallṛá; pauná; lainá; hatth áuná; parápat karná;
OBTRUDE, TO, *V. T.*
wáṛná; ghussná;
to force into; to stuff. ghuseṛná;
OBTRUSION, *N.*
ḍhíṭhái. *f;*
OBTRUSIVE, *A.*
dhíṭh;
OBTUSE, *A.*
beaql; kunḍ, see STUPID.
OBTUSENESS, *N.*
beaqlí. *f;* kúr magzí. *f;*
OBVERT, TO, *V. T.*
ulaṭ pulaṭ karná; ulṭá dená; pulṭá dená; múdhá kar dená;
OBVIATE, TO, *V. T.*
dur karná;
OBVIOUS, *N.*
jáhir; sáf; khullhá; malúm; partakkh;
it is obvious. ih táṇ partakkh hai;
OBVIOUSLY, *Adv.*
sáf sáf;
OCCASION, *N.*
1. opportunity. dá *m;* mauqá *m;* dáú. *m;* ṭáng. *m;*
2. cause. sabab. *m;* wajah. *f;*
3. need. loṛ. *f;*
OCCASIONAL, *A.*
kade kade; aiweṇ;
OCCASIONALLY, *Adv.*
kade kade; kade sabab nál;
OCCIDENT, *N.*
laiṇdhá. *m;*
OCCIDENTAL, *A.*
laiṇdher;
OCCIPUT, *N.*
sir dá pichhlá pásá. *m;*
OCCULT, *A.*
lukiá hoyá; gupt;
OCCUPANCY, *N.*
dakhal. *m;*

OCCUPANT, *N.*
rahnwálá. *m ;*
owner. málik. *m ;*
OCCUPATION, *N.*
kamm. *m ;* dhandà. *m* káj. *m ;* kamám. *m ;* wahár. *m ;* ahár kirat. *f ;* lánjhá. *m ;*
OCCUPIED, *A.*
ábád ;
OCCUPIED IN, TO BE, *V. I.*
runnhná ; ruddhná ;
OCCUPIER, *N.*
rahanwálá. *m ;* mallanwálá. *m .*
OCCUPY, TO, *V. T.*
1. to dwell. mallná ; ráhná ;
2. to seize. qabzá kar lainá ; khohná ; napp lainá ;
OCCUR, TO, *V. I.*
pesh áuná ; honá ; bítná :
OCCURRENCE, *N.*
gall. *f ;* wákiá. *m ;* wardát. *f ;*
OCEAN, *N.*
samundar. *m ;* ságar. *m ;*
OCEANIC, *A.*
samundarí ; samundar dá ;
OCHRE, *N.*
gerí. *f* pillí miṭṭí. *f ;*
OCTAVE, *N.*
sargam. *m ;* aṭh suráṇ. *m ;*
OCTOBER, *N.*
dasweṇ mahíne dá náṇ. *m ;*
OCTOGENERIAN, *N.*
assíáṇ waṛheáṇ dá. *m ;*
OCTROI, *N.*
chunggí. *f ;* mahsúl. *m ;*
OCULIST, *N.*
akkhíán dá láj karnwálá. *m ;*
ODD, *A.*
1. not even. ṭáṇk ;
2. unpaired. phuṭkal ;
3. odd and even. juft ṭáṇk ; ikkar dukkar ;
4. strange. anokhá ; ajíb ; acharaj ;
ODDITY, *N.*
aṇokh. *m ;*
ODDNESS, *N.*
aṇokhtái. *f ;*
ODDS, *N.*
farq. *m ;*
odds and ends. nikk sukk. *m ;*
ODE, N.
gít. *m ;* bhajan. *m ;*

ODIOUS, *A.*
bahut burá ; kamíná ; gaṇdá ; bhaiṛá ; ghiṇáuná ; palit ; máṛá ;
ODIOUSLY, *Adv*
vair nál ; baṛí nafrat nál ;
ODIOUSNESS, *N.*
karáhat. *f ;* nafrat. *f ;* gaṇd. *m ;*
ODIUM, *N.*
ghiṇ. *f ;* karáhat. *f ;*
ODOUR, *N.*
bás. *f ;* básná. *f ;* mahik. *f ;* bo. *f ;*
ODORIFEROUSNESS. *N.*
khushbo. *f ;* básná. *f ;* báshná. *f ;*
ODOROUS, *A.*
báshnáwálá ; khushbodár ;
OF *Prep.*
dá ; de ; dí ;
OFF, *Adv.*
dur ; pare ;
1. separate. vakhrá ;
2. begone. dúr ho :
OFFAL, *N.*
murdár. *m ;*
OFFENCE, *N.*
1. violation of the law. jurm. *m ;* qusur. *m ;*
2. displeasure. narázagí. *f ;* ris. *f ;* khapgí. *f ;* rossá. *m ;*
3. stumbling block. ṭheḍḍá. *m ;*
4. to take offence. burá manná ; burá manáuná ;
OFFENCELESS, *A.*
begunáh ; betaqsírá ; bholá ; bequsur ; bedosá ;
OFFEND, TO, *V. T.*
dil khaṭṭá karná ; chheṛná ; akáuná ; gussá diláuná ; naráj karná ;
If I have offended you, please forgive me. je maithoṇ koí tuháḍí ranjídagí dí gal yá ná ṭhík ṭhík satkár hoyá howe, táṇ mainúṇ bakhshná ;
OFFENDED, TO BE, *V. I.*
dil khaṭṭá honá ; dil chukkná ; muṇh moroṛná ; akkná ;
OFFENDER, *N'*
gunáhí. *m ;* gunáhgár. *m ;* taqsírí. *m ;* aparádhí. *m ;* jurmí. *m ;*
OFFENSIVE, *A.*
1. not pleasing. nápasind ;

2. dirty. mailá ; gaṇḍá ; palíd ;
3. loathsome. ghiṇáhdá ; ghiṇáuná ; makruh ;

OFFENSIVELY, *Adv.*
1. giving pain. dukh deke ;
2. in a nasty way. burí taráh nál ;
3. with enmity. adávat nál ;

OFFENSIVENESS, *N.*
palítí. *f* ; gaṇḍagí. *f* ; gaṇd. *m* ;

OFFER, *N.*
1. price. mul. *m* ;
2. bid. bolí. *f* ;

OFFER, TO, *V. T.*
agge rakkhná ; pesh karná ;
1. to offer up. bheṭ karná ; hom karná ; chaṛháuná ;
2. to offer a smaller sum of money. mull ghaṭṭáuná ;

OFFERING, *N.*
bhet. *f* ; nazar. *f* ; jhaṛáwá. *m* ; chaṛháwá. *m* ; baledán ; *m* ; pará-chitt. *m* ;

OFFERTORY, *N.*
chandá. *m* ;

OFFHAND, *A.*
aiweṇ ;

OFFICE, *N.*
1. rank. uhdá. *m* ; huddá. *m* ; darjá. *m* ;
2. public office. daftar. *m* ; sarkárí kacherí. *f* ;

OFFICE BEARER. *N.*
uhdedár. *m* ;

OFFICER, *N.*
affsar. *m* ; uhdedár. *m* ; hákim. *m* ;

OFFICIAL, *N.*
sarkárí ;

OFFICIALLY, *Adv.*
sarkár walloṇ ;

OFFICIATE, TO, *V. T.*
kise de thán kamm karná ;

OFFICIATING, *A.*
uh dí jagáh ; uh de thán ;

OFFICIOUS, *A.*
shokh ;

OFFICIOUSNESS, *N.*
shokhí. *f* ;

OFFSCOURING, *N.*
mail. *f* ; kúṛá. *m* ;

OFFSPRING, *N.*
bachchá. *m* ; nasal. *f* ; aulád. *f* ;

OFTEN, *Adv.*
ghaṛí muṛí ; ghaṛi ghaṛí ; kaí wár ; askar ; bahut dafá ; bahut wárí ; bhauṇ jhauṇ ; jhaṭe binde ; jhaṭe jhaṭe ;

OGLE, TO, *V. T.*
nigáh laṛáuná ; akkhíáṇ maṭkáuná ; burí nazar nál vekhná ; akkh mární ;

OGLING, *N.*
maṭkorá. *m* ; akkh maṭakká. *m* ; táṛ báji. *f* ;

OGRE, *N.*
deo. *m* ;

OGRESS, *N.*
deoṇí. *f* ; daiṇ. *f* ;

OH, *Interj.*
1. of surprise. halá ;
2. of sorrow. hai hai ;
3. of strong negation. tobbá tobbá ;laí ;

OIL, *N.*
chiknáí. *f* ; tel. *m* ;
1. paraffin oil. miṭṭí dá tel. *m* ;
2. oil to anoint bride. chikún. *m* ;

OIL, TO, *V. T.*
tel páuná ;
to oil the wheels of a bullock cart. báṇggná ; wáṇggná ;

OIL CAKE, *N.*
khal. *f* ; khalí. *f* ;

OILINESS, *N.*
chiknáí. *f* ; thiṇdíáí. *f* ;

OILMAN, *N.*
telí. *m* ;
wife of an oilman. telaṇ. *f* ;

OIL PRESS, *N.*
kohlu. *m* ; kolhu. *m* ; kohulu. *m* ;

OIL SEED, *N.*
sarhoṇ. *f* ;

OILY, *A.*
chikní ; chikná ; thiṇdá ;

OINTMENT, *N.*
malham. *m* ; lep. *m* ;

OLD, *A.*
birdh ; charoká ; kholá ;
1. an old woman. buḍḍhí. *f* ; baṛí umrwálí. *f* ;
2. an old man. khuḍhra. *m* ; khuṇḍh. *m* ; buḍḍhrá *m* ; sattriá bahattriá. *m* ;

3. very old persons. fach; bahut umrwálá; buḍḍhá;
4. old, of things. puráná;
5. he is ten years old. uhnúṇ daswáṇ waṛhá chaṛhiá hai;
6. he is fifteen years old. uh pandráh waṛheáṇ dá hai

OLD AGE, *N.*
buḍḍhepá. *m*; buḍḍhápá. *m*; baṛí umr. *f*; buḍḍhewáṛá. *m*;

OLDEST SON, *N.*
jeṭṭhá. *m*;

OLD FASHIONED, *A.*
puráne ḍhaṇg dá; puráne same dá;

OLD AND TORN, *A.*
phaṭá puráná;

OLDNESS, *N.*
purán. *m*;

OLEANDER, *N.*
kaner. *m*;

OLIVE, *N.*
zaitun. *m*; kaú. *m*;

OMEN, *N.*
1. sign. nishán. *m*; nisháni. *f*;
2. omen. sagan. *m*; fál. *m*;
3. ill omen. kulachhaṇ. *m*;
4. expounder of omens. phálú. *m*; sagnú. *m*;

OMINOUS, *A.*
asubh;

OMISSION, *N.*
bhull chukk. *f*; bharáṇtí. *f*; bhulekhá, *m*;

OMIT, TO, *V. T.*
1. not to include. shámil ná karná;
2. to leave. chhaḍḍ dená; tiágná; tajná;

OMNIPOTENCE, *N.*
Khudá dí qudrat. *f*;

OMNIPOTENT, *A.*
qádir-i-mutlaq; sarushakti-mán;

OMNIPRESENCE, *N.*
sarbaggi. *f*;

OMNIPRESENT, *A.*
hájar-o-nájar; sarbasti;

OMNISCIENT, *A.*
sabbho kujh jándá hai; sarabgiání; jáṇíjáṇ;

ON, *Prep.*
utte; te;

ON, *Adv.*
agge; pare;

ONCE, *Adv.*
ikk wárí; ikk wár; ikk ḍaṇg;
at once. turt; jhaṭ phaṭ; paund saṭṭe;

ONE, *A.*
ikk; hikk;
1. one after an other. agge pichchhe; aggar pichchhaṛ; uppar thalí;
2. one only. ikko;
3. one another. ikk dújjá;
4. one by one. ikk ikk karke;
5. some one. koí;
6. one and the same. ikk hí;
7. one's own. ghar dá;

ONE, *N.*
1. a man. ádmí. *m*; baṇdá. *m*; manukkh. *m*;
2. oneself. áp;

ONE EYED, *A.*
káná;

ONENESS, *N.*
ekká. *m*;

ONEROUS, *A.*
bhárá; bhárí;

ONION, *N.*
ganḍhá. *m*;

ONION LEAF, *N.*
bhuk. *f*;

ONLY, *Adv.*
nirá; kewal;

ONSET, *N.*
hallá. *m*; chaṛhái. *f*; jhaṛái. *f*;

ONUS, *N.*
1. burden. bojh. *m*; bhár. *m*;
2. responsibility. jummewárí. *f*; jummá. *m*;

ONWARD, *Adv.*
pare; agge núṇ;

OOZE, TO, *V. I.*
simmná; nikalná; choná;

OOZE, *N.*
gárá. *m*; chikkaṛ. *m*; chikkaṛ chambhar. *m*;

OOZING, *N.*
choá. *m*;

OPAQUE, *A.*
dhuṇdlá;

OPEN, *A.*
1. not closed. moklá; khokhlá; khullhá; khulkhulá;
2. an open door. latthá buhá;
3. public. ám;
4. libera. dilwálá; manchalá; sakhí;

OPEN, TO, . *T*.
kholná ; paṭṭná ; pholná ;
1. to open out machinery, &c. ugheṛná ; udheṛná ;
2. to open a door. buhá láhná OR kholná ;
open the door. buhá láh ;
3. to open the mouth. muṇh ṭaḍḍná ; muṇh ugháṛná ;
4. to open lock or window. láhná ;
5. to open shop, school, &c., kholná ;
6. to open a book. pholná ;

OPEN, TO, *V. I.*
khullná ; uggharṇà ;
1. as a flower. tahikná ; ṭaḍḍná ;
2. the door is open. buhá latthá hoyá hai ;

OPEN HANDED, *A.*
dilwálá ; manchalá ; sakhí ; khullhe dilwálá ;

OPENING, *N.*
chhed. *m* ; darár. *m* ; páṛ. *f* ; teṛ. *f* ; tareṛ. *f* ; khol. *m* ;
1. the mouth. múṇh. *m* ;
2. small opening. kholṛí. *f* ;

OPENLY, *Adv.*
khulham khullhá ; khullhá mukhullá ; dúhbadúh ; ghamágham ; khule khule ; dúbadú ; khullh ke ; dil kholke ; saríhan ;
to walk openly. khulliáṇ phirná ;

OPENNESS, *N.*
khullh. *f* ; khullh ḍullh. *f* ; safái. *f* ;

OPERATE, TO, *V. T.*
apreshaṇ karná ;

OPERATE, TO, *V. I.*
kamm vichch áuná ;

OPERATION, *N.*
apreshaṇ. *m* ; káṭkúṭ. *f* ;

OPERATIVE, *A.*
kamm dá ;

OPINE, TO, *V. T.*
sochná ; khayál karná ;

OPINION, *N.*
1. understanding. samajh. *f* ; tár. *f* ; buddh. *f* ; aql. *f* ;
2. thought. khayál. *m* ; wichár. *m* ; kiás. *m* ;
3. advice. rai. *f* ; saláh. *f* ;
4. in my opinion. mere bháṇe ;

OPINIONATED, *A.*
haṭṭhí ; ziddí ; magazí ; mazájí ;

OPIUM, *N.*
afím. *f* ;
opium plant, poppy. post. *m* ;

OPIUM EATER, *N.*
afimí. *m* ; postí. *m* ; amlí. *m* ;

OPPONENT, *N.*
dushman. *m* ; wairí. *m* ;

OPPORTUNE, *A.*
vele sir ; joggá ;

OPPORTUNELY, *Adv.*
vele sir ;

OPPORTUNITY, *N.*
dá. *m* ; ḍho. *m* ; mauqá. *m* ; gáshá. *m* ; dáú. *m* ; wíkhá. *m* ;
1. to get an opportunity. mauqá milná OR pauná ; dáú laggná ; kis taráh dáú chale ;
2. to lose an opportunity. mauqá chale jáná ;
3. to seek an opportunity. mauqá vekhná ;
4. if opportunity should occur. dá lage ;

OPPOSE, TO, *V. T.*
muqábalá karná ; sámhná karná ; khaihná ; múṇh barú honá ; bháṇjí mární ;
to stop. aṭkáuná ; rokná ; ḍakkná ; dabb rakkhná ;

OPPOSITE, *A.*
sámhne dá ; ámho sámhná ;
the opposite of. uh dá ulaṭ ;

OPPOSITION, *N.*
jidd. *f* ; wair. *m* ; ḍhuchchar. *m* ; sámhná. *m* ; jiraṛ *f* ; barkhaláfí. *f* ; virodh. *m* ; bháṇjí. *f* ; dushmaní. *f* ; khaih. *f* ; bhánní. *f* ;
out of opposition. jido jidí ;

OPPRESS, TO, *V. T.*
dukh dená ; satáuná ; zulm OR julm karná ; sakhtí karní ; aukhiáṇ karná ; taklíf dení ; anher karná OR macháuná ; dubáuná ;

OPPRESSED, *A.*
dukhí ; dukhiá ;

OPPRESSION, *N.*
zulm OR julm. *m* ; zabardastí. *f* ; sakhtí. *f* ; anher. *m* ; jabr. *m* ; beráhmí. *f* ; dabáo. *m* ; dhakká. *m* ; dhigáṇá. *m* ; bijj. *f* ; ziyádatí. *f* ; jástí. *f* ; hikk dá dhakká *m* ; jabarí. *f* ; jálamí. *f* ; loṛhá. *m* ; jor. *m* ; julmí. *f* ; jorí. *f* ; taddí. *f* ; luṭoluṭ. *f* ;

OPPRESSIVE, *A.*
jabardast ; sakht ; jálim ; ḍhaṭṭhá ; beráhm ; hattiárá ; karṛá ; betaras ; hainsiárá ;
OPPRESSIVELY, *Adv.*
badobadí ; baṛe julm nál ; baṛí sakhtí nál ; dhagáṇe ;
OPPREESSOR, *N.*
jálim. *m* ; jálam, *n* ; waḍḍá haner *m* ; dábbá denwálá. *m* ;
OPPROBRIOUS, *A.*
badjabán ; gaṇdá ; burá ;
OPPROBRIOUSLY, *Adv.*
gáli galauj nál ;
OPPROBRIOUSNESS, *N.*
gál. *f* ; gálí. *f* ; gálí galoch. *f* ; see ABUSE.
OPPROBRIUM, *N.*
badnámí. *f* ; gaṇd zabání. *f* ;
OPTIC, *N.*
akkh. *f* ; akkhí. *f* ; netar. *m* ; nain. *f* ;
OPTIMISM, *N.*
ummed. *f* ; ás. *f* ;
OPTION, *N.*
marzí. *f* ; bhauná. *m* ; ikhtiyár. *m* ;
OPULENCE, *N.*
máyá. *f* ; daulat. *f* ; mál. *m* ; dhan. *m* ; máldárí. *f* ; amírí. *f* ;
OPULENT, *A.*
máldár; daulatmand ; sháh ; dhaní; amír ; lakhpatí ;
OR, *Conj.*
yá ; jáṇ ; athwá ;
ORAL, *A.*
zabání ; múṇh zabání ;
ORALLY, *Adv.*
zabání ; múṇh jabání ;
ORANGE, *N.*
saṇtará. *m* ; sanggtará. *m* ; narangí. *f* ;
1. Maltá. máltá. *m* ;
2. to eat an orange. chúpná ;
ORANGE COLOURED, *A.*
gerví ; saṇtrá rang ;
ORATION, *N.*
wáz. *m* ; nasíhat. *f* ; wák. *m* ; kathá. *f* ; bání. *f* ;
ORATOR, *N.*
kathá wáchnewálá. *m* ;
ORB. *N.*
maṇḍal. *m* ; golá. *m* ;
ORBIT, *N.*
chakkar. *m* ;
ORCHARD, *N.*
wáṛí. *f* ; phulwáṛí. *f* ; bagíchá. *m* ;
ORDAIN, TO, *V. T.*
1. to appoint. muqarrar karná ; ṭhahráuná; thápná ; tháp rakkhná;
2. to order. hukm dená; ágiá karná;
ORDEAL, *N.*
1. a difficult thing. aukhí gal. *f* ;
2. a trial. ázmáish. *f* ;
ORDER, *N.*
1. command. hukm. m ; ágiá. *m* ;
2. a written order. parwánná *m* ;
3. method. ḍhang. *m* ; ḍaul. *f* ; dastur. *m* ; rahit bahit. *f* ;
4. class. darjá. *m* ;
5. in order to. es wáste paí ; táṇ jo ;
6. out of order. wigṛiá hoyá; kusúṭá;
ORDER, TO, *V. T.*
1. to command. hukm dená ; hukm karná ; ágiá dená ; kah dená ;
2. to arrange. ṭhík ṭhák karná ; sajáuná ; durust karná ;
ORDERING, *N.*
tartíb. *m* ;
ORDERLY, *N.*
ardarlí. *m* ; chaprásí. *m* ;
ORDERLY, *A.*
ṭhík ṭhák ; durust ;
ORDINANCE, *N.*
1. rule. qánún. *m* ; qaidá. *m* ; bidhí. *f* ;
2. custom. rít rasm. *f* ; dastur. *m* ; rawáj. *f* ; lokáṇ chárí. *f* ;
3. order. hukm. *m* ; ágiá. *m* ;
ORDINARILY, *Adv.*
bahut karke ; bahut wárí ; askar sadháraṇ ;
ORDINARY, *A.*
àm ; mámúlí ; khásá ; roz dí gal ;
ORDINATION, *N.*
pádrí banauṇ dí bandagí. *f* ;
ORDNANCE, *N.*
topkháná. *m* ;
ORDURE, *N.*
lid. *f* ; gohá. *m* ; guṇh. *m* ; see DUNG.
Proverb. To show that too much prudence is not always wise. A wise crow falls on ordure. siáná káṇ gúṇh te digdá hai ;

ORE, *N.*
kachchí dhát. *f*;
ORGAN, *N.*
bájá. *m*;
to play the organ. bájá wajáuná;
ORGANIST, *N.*
bájá wajáunwálá. *m*;
ORGANIZE, TO, *V. T.*
intizám karná;
ORIENTAL, *A.*
purabí;
ORIFICE, *N.*
1. mouth. múṇh. *m*;
2. perforation. chhed. *m*; chhek. *m*; see OPENING.
ORIGIN, *N.*
shurú. *m*; ád. *m*; araṇbh. *m*; muḍḍh. *m*; jaṛ. *f*; múl. *m*;
ORIGINAL, *A.*
aslí;
ORIGINAL, *N.*
asl. *m*;
ORIGINALLY, *Adv.*
shurú vichch;
ORIGINATE, TO, V. T.
1. to create. paidá karná; ráchná; utpat karná;
2. to begin. shurú karná; ád karná; ṭumbná;
ORIGINATION, *N.*
1. beginning. shurú. *m*; ád. *m*;
2. birth. paidaish. *f*; janam. *m*;
ORIGINATOR, *N.*
banáunwálá. *m*;
for GOD only. kartár. *m*;
ORISON, *N.*
duá. *f*; bentí. *f*; minnat. *f*; parárthná. *f*;
ORNAMENT, *N.*
ṭúmb. *f*; gahná. *m*;
Women's ornaments for the head.
1. large round ornament worn on top of head. chauṇk. *m*;
2. smaller ornaments, as chaunk, but worn on both sides of the head. phúl. *m*;
3. small ornament worn on forehead. biṇdí. *f*;
4. wafer, pasted by Hindus on the forehead. peurí. *f*;
5. two plates of silver worn on forehead. dauní. *f*; tikká. *m*;
6. worn on side of head, towards the front. tawittarí. *f*;
Women's ornaments for the ears.
1. small earrings. wálí. *f*; wáliáṇ. *f*, plur.; murkí. *f*;
2. large earrings. wále. *m*;
3. pendant for earring. morní. *f*;
4. pendant for ear worn by Hindus. karanphúl. *m*; ḍhedu. *m*;
Women's ornaments for the nose.
1. small nose ring. natth. *f*; natthlí. *f*;
2. medium sized nose ring. natth balák. *m*; murkí. *f*;
3. attached to central cartilage. machchlíánwálá balák. *m*;
4. small ornament worn on side of nose. tillí. *f*; tillá. *m*; laung. *m*;
5. heart shaped pendant to nose ring. morní. *f*; bohr. *m*;
Women's ornaments for the fingers.
1. signet ring. chháp. *f*; mundrá. *m*;
2, plain ring. chhallá. *m*;
3. mirror worn as a thunb ring. ársí *f*;
Women's ornaments for the neck.
1. gold or silver collar. hass. *m*; hár. *m*; hasírí. *f*;
2. necklace. máláṇ. *f*; kaṇḍhlí. *f*;
3. necklace of long pointed beads. chámkalí. *f*;
4, necklace of coins. bugtíáṇ. *f*;
5. chain for the neck. zanjírí. *f*;
Women's ornaments for the arms.
1. gold or silver bracelets, hollow. gokhru. *m*;
2. round. kangaṇ. *m*;
3. flat and engraved. churí. *f*;
4. armlet, worn on upper part of arm. bázúband. *f*; tadan. *f*; bahí. *f*; bahuṭṭá. *m*;
5. iron bracelet. churí. *f*; kaṇgganí. *f*;
6. bangles made of lac, round. waṇgg. *f*; waṇggáṇ. *f*; vaṇgg. *f*;
7. ornamented. gajará. *m*;
Women's ornaments for the ankles.
silver or gold anklets. toṛe. *m*; báṇká. *f*; pázeb. *f*; saṇglá. *m*;
Women's ornaments for the toes.
bichkanuá. *m*; pánjeb. *f*; panjáṇgalá. *m*; chhallá. *m*; chíchí. *f*;

Men's ornaments.
1. for the ears.
2. gold or silver earrings. murkíáṇ. *f*; nattíáṇ. *f*; birballíáṇ. *f*;
3. for the neck.
4. a medallion worn on a cord. inámá. *m*;
5. a necklace of coins. bugtíáṇ. *f*;
6. a rosary of beads. kaṇṭhá. *m*;
7. for the wrists.
8. bracelets. kaṛá. *m*; kangaṇ. *m*;
9. coloured cord, with cowries, tied on the wrist at marriage. gánáṇ. *m*;
10. for the fingers.
A. a plain ring. chhallá. *m*;
B. signet rings. chháp. *m*; mundrí *f*;
11. for the arms.
ṭolá. *m*; baṭṭú. *m*;
12. for the waist, a silver string worn by Hindus. taṛágí. *f*; tarágaṛí. *f*;

ORNAMENT, TO, *V. T.*
sajáuná; sudhárná; siṇgárná; see ADORN.

ORNAMENTAL, *A.*
sohná;

ORNAMENTATION, *N.*
sajauṭ. *f*;

ORNATE, *A.*
ḳhubsurat; sajílá; sohná; sundar; soháwará; phabiá;

ORPHAN, *N.*
yatím. *m*; láwáris bachchá. *m*;

ORPHANAGE, *N.*
yatím ḳháná. *m*;

ORPHANED, *A.*
yatím;

ORTHODOX, *A.*
pakká;
of Hindus. sanátani;

ORTHOGRAPHY, *N.*
likhat. *f*; likhái. *f*; lakhautí. *f*; ḳhatt. *m*;

OSCILLATE, TO, *V. I.*
hilná; jhulná; ulárá lainá;

OSCILLATION, *N.*
jhuláú. *m*;

OSCULATE, TO, V. *T.*
chumná; buggá lainá; chumm chaṭṭnà; chummí lainá;

OSCULATION, *N.*
chummá. *m*; chummí. *f*;

OSTENSIBLE, *A.*
1. apparent. záhirí;
2. pretended. jáhlí; banautí;

OSTENTATION, *N.*
dikhlává. *m*; wikhálá. *m*; dikhává. *m*; hú hawá. *f*; paṭaṇb. *m*;

OSTENTATIOUSLY, *Adv.*
dhúm dhám nál; baṛe shán nál; lokáṇchárí;

Proverbs concerning the ostentatious display of those who boast of having much while they really have nothing at all.
1. The mother died naked and the daughter's name is 'a bundle of clothes'. Máṇ mar gaí nangí, dhí dá náṇ buchkí.
2. He has a single spadeful of earth and calls himself a farmer or landowner. Ṭappá jamín dá, haqq te náṇ zamíndár.
3. His insides are hungry, but he has grains of rice on his moustaches. Áṇdráṇ bhukkhíán, te muchch te chaul.
4. Not a penny in his pocket and going to be married on Thursday. Palle nahíṇ paisá te Jumerát parhwaná.
5. Even one wife is not procurable, (yet he says) I will marry two. Ikk ḍhukdí nahíṇ, maiṇ do parnísáṇ.
6. Only a scrap of cloth on his head, and he calls himself Sarfaraz Khan. Taríj kapṛe dí sir te, te náṇ Sarfaráj Ḳhán.
7. She has the face of an owlet and she calls herself Nur Bibi. Chibrí dá chehrá te náṇ Nur Bíbí.
8. A hut of grass and water spouts of ivory. Kakkháṇ dí jhuggí, daṇḍ khaṇḍ dá parnálá.
9. It is only 'mohri' porridge, and gives itself the airs of 'palao'. Dál mohrí dí, dam pulá dá.
10. He has no water vessel and no loin cloth, yet he has gone to bathe. Ná gadvíá, ná dalá, te ashnán karan chalá;

11. A face like the bottom of a frying pan and her name is Lady of Light. Dáṇgi dá talá múṇh, te náṇ Roshan Khátún.
12. There is no grain in the house, and the mother has gone to grind. Ghar dáná ná phakká, ammáṇ pihaṇ gai.
13. The mother died eating dry bread, and the daughter's name is 'Curds.' Máṇ mare rukháni, dhí dá náṇ ḍahí.
14. A great name and a ruined village. Náṇ waḍḍá, deh sunj.
15. Not a mite in his pocket and calls himself a millionaire. Palle ná kaudí, náṇ lakhpatí.
16. She never saw a flower, and her name is Lady of Flowers. Akkhíáṇ nál phul ná ḍiṭṭhá te náṇ Gúl Bíbí.
17. He has two and a half sticks and is called Mr. Gardener. Ḍhái ḍhiṇggariáṇ te Mián Bágbán.
18. Two and a half ounces of rice and pulse, and a dinner on the housetop. Ḍhái páo khichchrí chubáre rasoí.

OSTLER, *N.*
saís. *m*; sahis. *m*;

OSTRACIZE, TO *V. T.*
chhek dená; kaḍḍhná; khárij karná; báhar kaḍḍhná; huqqá páni band karná;

OSTRICH, *N.*
shutar murg. *m*;

OTHER, *A.*
hor; dujjá;

OTHERWISE, *Adv.*
nahíṇ táṇ; hor;

OTTER, *N.*
luddhar. *m*;

OUGHT, *V.*
cháhidá;

OUNCE, *N.*
addh chitáṇk. *m*;

OUR, *Pro.*
sádá;

OURSELF, *Pro.*
apne ápnúṇ;

OURSELVES, *Pro.*
a íṇ áp;

OUST, TO, *V. T.*
chhekná; ḍhakkná; kaḍḍhná; nikálná; hatáuná;

OUT, *Adv.*
1. without. báhar;
2. in error. ṭhík nahíṇ;
3. Absent. hájar nahíṇ;

OUTBID, TO, *V. T.*
mull wadháuná; wadhke boli dení;

OUTBREAK, *N.*
daṇggá fasád. *m*; hagáma. *m*; hullaṛ. *m*; khalhbalí. *f*;

OUTCAST, *A.*
khárij;

OUTCASTE, *A.*
ních zát; kamína;

OUTCOME, *N.*
natíjá. *m*; gaveṛ. *m*; aṇt. *m*;

OUTCRY, *N.*
shor. *m*; raulá. *m*; awáz. *f*; gaugá. *m*; hugg. *f*; durohi. *f*; chík chihárá. *m*;

OUTDO, TO, *V. T.*
wadh jáná; pichchhe chhaḍḍná; uchchá hath ráhná;

OUTDOOR, *A.*
báhar dá;

OUTER, *Adv.*
báharlá;

OUTFIT, *N.*
safar dá asbáb. *m*;

OUTHOUSES, *N.*
naukaráṇ de ghar. *m*;

OUTLANDISH, *A.*
ajíb; aṇokhá;

OUTLAW, TO, *V. T.*
chhek dená; see OSTRACIZE.

OUTLAY, *N.*
lágat. *f*; lággá. *m*; kharach. *m*;

OUTLET, *N.*
guzar. *f*; ráh. *m*; rastá. *m*;

OUTLINE, *N.*
tál. *m*; naqshá. *m*; khaká. *m*;

OUTLINE, TO, *V. T.*
1. to sketch. taswír khichná;
2. to tell. batláuná; dassná; bayán karná;

OUTLOOK, *N.*
1. a vigilant watch. khabardárí. *f*; rákkhí. *f*;
2. prospect view. nazárá;

OUTLYING, *A.*
1. outside. báhar;
2. distant. dur; duráḍḍá; dureḍe; dúrwár;

OUTNUMBER, TO, *V. T.*
giṇtí vichch ziyádá honá;

OUT OF DOOR, *A.*
báhar;

OUT OF THE WAY, *A.*
aṇokhá; ajíb; awallá;

OUTPOST, *N.*
chaukí. *f;*

OUTRAGE, *N.*
1. rebellion. balwá. *m;* hagámá. *m;* gadr. *m;*
2. maltreatment. julm. *m;* saḳhtí. *f;* jástí. *f;* jálamí. *f;* lohṛá. *m;*
3. rape. zabr zanáhí. *f;* hatth gamaṇ. *m;*

OUTRAGE, TO, *V. T.*
1. to spoil. wigáṛ dená; chauṛ kar dená; pheṛná;
2. to rape. zabr zaná karná;

OUTRAGEOUS, *A.*
jhallá; see FRANTIC.

OUTRAGEOUSLY, *Adv.*
baṛe julm nál; gusse nál besudh hoke;

OUTRAGEOUSNESS, *N.*
jástí. *f;* julm. *m;* saḳhtí. *f;*

OUTRIGHT, *Adv.*
haddoṇ muḍḍhoṇ; ukká mukká; muloṇ muḍḍhoṇ; púrá;

OUTRUN, TO, *V. T.*
agge nikal jáná; wadh dauṛná;

OUTSET, *N.*
shurú. *m;* muḍḍh. *m;*

OUTSIDE, *Adv.*
báhar; banne; báharwár;
from outside. báharoṇ; banneoṇ;

OUTSIDER, *N.*
oprá bandá. *m;* paráyá. *m;*

OUTSKIRT, *N.*
hadd. *m;* kinárá. *m;* kanná. *m;* banná. *m;*

OUTSPOKEN, *A.*
aṇchakk; waddhiá hoyá;

OUTSTANDING, *A.*
1. remaining. baqí;
2. prominent. manniá danniá; mashhúr; manniá parwanniá; parnámí; ghukiá hoyá;

OUTSTRETCH, TO, *V. T.*
pasárná; phailáná;

OUTSTRIP, TO, *V. T.*
pichchhe chhaḍḍná;

OUTWALK, TO, *V. T.*
agge nikal jáná; pichchhe chhaḍḍná;

OUTWARD, *A.*
báhar dá; báharlá;

OUTWARDLY, *Adv.*
báhar; dekhaṇ vichch;

OUTWIT, TO, *V. T.*
chhalná; ṭhaggná; dhokhá dená;

OUTWORK, *N.*
morchá. *m;*

OVAL, *A.*
aṇḍá jehá;

OVATION, *N.*
táríf. *f;* mahimá. *f;* saláhat. *f;*

OVEN, N.
tanúrí. *f;* tandúrí. *f;* tandúr. *m;*
grain patcher's oven. bhaṭṭhí. *f;* bhaṭṭh. *m;*

OVER, *Adv.*
bahut; wadhík;
1. over against. sáhmne;
2. over and above. ih de siwá; ih de alává;
3. over and over again. muṛ muṛke; bár bár; muṛ ghiṛ;
4. to remain over. bach rahná;

OVER, *Prep.*
te upar;

OVERAWE, TO, *V. T.*
dabáuná; ḍaráuná; dabkáuná; datkaná; ḍar páuná; akkh wikháuná;
to be overawed. dabbná

OVERBEAR, TO, *V. T.*
dabáuná; rokná;

OVERBEARING, *A.*
1. proud. magrúr; gamrúr; ḍhaṭṭá; phiṭṭiá hoyá; majází
2. unmerciful. beráhm; saḳht; karṛá; hattiárá; bedard;

OVERBURDEN, TO, *V. T.*
waddh OR wadhík laḍḍná;

OVERCAST, *A.*
ḍhuṇdhlá; ghaṭṭá ṭiṭ; jhaṛ;

OVERCHARGE, TO, *V. T.*
hisáb víchch waddh lagáuná; waddh mul likhná;

OVERCOAT, N.
  bráṇḍí. f; waḍḍá koṭ. m;
OVERCOME, TO, V. T.
  haráuná ; jittná; hall karná ;
  gharkáuná; dabb láuná;
OVERCOME, TO BE, V. I.
  har jáná;
OVERDO, TO, V. T.
  bahut hí jatan karná;
OVEREAGER, A.
  bahut hí sargarm;
OVERFEED, TO, V. T.
  bahut ziyádá khuáná ; nakk takk
  khuáná;
OVERFLOW, N.
  káng. f; charháu. m ; umaḍ. f;
  chhall. f;
OVERLOW, TO, V. I.
  1. from a river, &c., jal thal
  honá; uchchhalná ; umaḍná ;
  2. from a vessel. chhalkná ;
  3. to boil over. ubbal jáná ;
  4. My cup runneth over. merá
  ṭhuṭhá ḍakáḍak chhalakdá
  hai;
OVERHAUL, TO, V. T.
  partál karná ; dekh bhál karná;
  see INSPECT.
OVERHEAD, A.
  utáṇ; uchchá; upar;
OVERHEAR, TO, V. T.
  1. deliberately. chorí OR malkrí
  sunná ; lukke sunná ;
  2. accidentally. sabab nál sunná ;
  eweṇ sunná ;
OVERJOYED, A.
  baṛá hí khush; anaṇdí; nihál ;
OVERLOAD, TO, V. T.
  wadh OR bahut laddná;
OVERLOOK, TO, V. T.
  1. to superintend. nigrání karní ;
  kamm vekhná ;
  2. to forgive. akkh pherní; ján
  dená ; muáf karná ; muáfí dení ;
  3. to mistake. bhullná; bhulekhá
  laggná ; ghuss jáná ; ukk jáná ;
OVERMASTER, TO, V. T.
  jittná ; dabáuná ; haráuná ; wass
  vichch leáuná ;
OVERMUCH, A.
  bahut ziyádá ; wadhík ;

OVERNIGHT, Adv.
  rátíṇ ; rátoṇ rát ; rátí ;
OVERPOWER, TO, V. T.
  hall karná ; dabb lainá ; jittná ;
  see OVERCOME.
OVERRULE, TO, V. T.
  1. to reject. radd karná ; tark
  karná ; tiágná ;
  2. not to accept. ná maṇzúr karná;
  3. not to allow. hon nahíṇ dená ;
  4. to correct. ṭhák dená ; sodhná ;
  ṭhík ṭháк karná ;
OVERSEE, TO, V. T.
  nigrání karní ;
OVERSEER, N.
  sarbaráh. m ; gardaur. m ;
OVERSHADOW, TO, V. T.
  sáyá dálná ; chháṇ karná ;
OVERSIGHT, N.
  1. superintendence. nigrání. f ;
  2. mistake. bhull chukk. f ;galatí. f.
  bhulekhá. m ; bhulává. m ;
OVERT, A.
  záhir ; malúm ;
OVERTAKE, TO, V. T.
  já ralná ; kol appaṛná ; á painá ;
OVERTASK, TO, V. T.
  taṇg karná ; sakhtí nál kamm lainá;
OVERTHROW, N.
  palṭá. m ;
OVERTHROW, TO V. T.
  ḍháhná ; ḍhaháur .. ; ḍháh dená ;
  degná ; palṭáuná ;
OVERTIRE, TO, V. T.
  bahut hí ṭhakáuná ;
OVERTLY, Adv.
  dúbadú ; see OPENLY.
OVERTURN, TO, V. T.
  ulṭáuná ; ḍigauná ; ulṭá suṭṭná ;
  mudhá karná ; palṭáuná ;
OVERTURNED, A.
  uṇdhá ;
OVERWEENING, A.
  mazájí ; magrúr ; see HAUGHTY.
OVERWHELM, TO, V. T.
  nighárná ;
OVERWHELMED, TO BE, V. I.
  nigghar jáná ;
OWE, TO, V. T.
  dharáuná ;
  1. what do I owe you. mair
  terá kí dharáundá háṇ ;

2. he owes. os dená hai;
3. he is owed. os lainá hai; uh núṇ áundá hai;

OWL, *N.*
1. large. ullú. *m;*
2. small. bilbathauri. *f;*

OWN, *A.*
apná;

OWN, TO, *V. T.*
rakkhná;

OWNER, *N.*
málik. *m;* haqqdár. *m;* patí. *m;* adhkárí. *m;*

OWNERSHIP, *N.*
málakí. *f;*

OX, *N.*
bald. *m;* dhaggá. *m;*
an ox with horns curved forward and downward. jhuṇgá. *m;*

OX WHIP. *N.*
puráṇí. *f;*

P.

PABULUM, *N.*
roṭí. *f;* ann pání. *m;* see VICTUALS.

PACE, *N.*
1. step. qadam. *f;*
2. two steps. karu. *m;* doláṇgh. *f;*
3. horse's pace. gám. *f;* karu. *m;* aláṇgh. *f;*
4. gait. chál. *f;* ṭor. *f;*

PACIFICATION, *N.*
sulah. *f;* sulah safáí. *f;* mel miláp. *m;* miláuní. *f;*

PACIFIER, *N.*
wicholá. *m;* sulah karaunwálá. *m;*

PACIFY, TO, *V. T.*
ṭhaṇḍá karná; rází karní; manauná; sulah karáuní; dhímá karná; patiáná;
1. to pacify a child. lorí dení;
2. to pacify a horse. puchkárná; buchkárná;

PACK, *N.*
1. a bundle. paṇḍ. *f;* gaṭṭhà. *m;* see LOAD and BUNDLE.
2. of cards. tásh. *m;*

PACK, TO, *V. T.*
asbáb tayár karná; asbáb band karná; asbáb bannhná;

PACKAGE, *N.*
gaṭṭhà. *m;* paṇḍokalí. *f;*
large. paṇḍ. *f;*

PACKET, *N.*
khalítá. *m;*
postal packet. pákat. *m;*

PACK HORSE, *N.*
láddú ghoṛá. *m;*

PACKING, *N.*
gaṭhṛí baṇḍí. *f;*

PACK SADDLE, *N.*
khurjí, *f;* súṇḍká. *m;*
of a mule. paláṇ. *m;* paláṇá. *m;*
see PANNIER.

PACT, *N.*
qaul qarár. *m;* nem. *m;* bachan. *m;*
a contract. ṭheká. *m;*

PAD, *N.*
gaddí. *f;*
for the head. binnú. *m;* innúṇ. *m;*

PADDLE *N.*
chappú. *m;*

PADDLE, TO, *V. T.*
chappú chaláuná;

PADDY, *N.*
jhonná. *m;* munji. *f;*

PADLOCK, *N.*
jaṇdará. *m;*

PADLOCK, TO, *V. T.*
jaṇdará márná OR dená OR láuná;

PAGAN, *N.*
butparast. *m;*

PAGANISH, *A.*
butparast;

PAGANISM, *N.*
butparastí. *f;*

PAGE, *N.*
patará. *m;* safáh. *m;*
one double page. warká. *m;*

PAGEANT, *N.*
tamáshá. *m;*

PAGEANTRY, *N.*
shúká shákí. *f;* bharak. *m;* dikhává. *m;* hú há. *f;* hú hawá. *f;* sajdhaj. *f;* sobhá. *f;*

PAIL, *N.*
bálṭí. *f;*

PAIN, *N.*
píṛ. *f;* dard. *f;* kashtaní. *f;* dukh. *m;* dukhṛá. *m;* chobh. *f;* kasṭ. *m;*

1. in horses and camels. súl. *m;*
2. griping pain. waṭṭ. *m;* maroṛ. *m;*
3. a sharp pain. chís. *f;*
4. pain in the side or head. hull. *f;*
5. shooting pain in head or eyes. tarát. *f;*
6. pain and pleasure. dukh sukh. *m;*

PAIN, TO, *V. T.*
dukh dená; dukháuná; aukhiáṇ karná;
1. to torment. satáuná; taṛpáuná; akáuná;
2. to endure pain. dukh saihná; dukh jhallná;
3. to feel pain. dukh laggná; chobh painí; chubhak painí; píṛ paini;
4. to be grieved. raṇj honá; jhurná; masosná;

PAINFUL, *A.*
aukhá; dukhdái; ḍákhṛá;

PAINFULLY, *Adv.*
dukhí hoke; aukhá hoke; baṛí taklíf nál; ḍáh de nál;

PAINFULNESS, *N.*
píṛ. *f;* see PAIN.

PAINSTAKING, *A.*
mihnatí; uddamí; jataní; suchet;

PAINT, *N.*
raṇg. *m;*

PAINT, TO, *V. T.*
raṇg bharná OR chaṛháuná OR láuná;

PAINTER, *N.*
1. artist. chaterá. *m;* nakásh. *m;*
2. working painter. raṇgsáz. *m;*

PAINTING, *N.*
murat. *f;* taswír. *f;*

PAIR, *N.*
joṛá. *m;* joṛ. *m;* joṛí. *f;*
1. one of a pair. joṭṭí. *m;* joṭṭídár. *m;*
2. of oxen. jog. *f;* hal. *m;*

PAIR, TO, *V. T.*
joṛná; raláuná; miláuná;

PALACE, *N.*
dhaular. *m;* mahal. *m;*

PALAQUIN, *N.*
ḍolí. *f;*

PALATABLE, *A.*
mazedár; saluná; suádí; see TASTY.
to be palatable. achchhá laggná;

PALATE, *N.*
tálú. *m;*

PALE, *A.*
pílá phatak; pílá; jard; zard; baggá;
to become pale. pílá painá;

PALENESS, *N.*
pílái. *f;*

PALFREY, *N.*
ṭaṭṭú. *m;* ṭaṭṭuá. *m;* ṭairá. *m;*

PALING, *N.*
jaṇgalá. *m;*

PALL, *N.*
kafan. *m. M.;*

PALLIATE, TO, *V. T.*
1. to extenuate. uzr karná; galloṇ láuná;
2. to mitigate. ghaṭáuná; matthá karná; dhímá karná;

PALLIATION, *N.*
uzr. *f;*

PALLID, *A.*
pílá; jard; baggá; phikká;

PALM, *N.*
1. tree. khajúr. *m;*
2. of the hand. talí. *f;*

PALMING, *N.*
wáchá. *m;*

PALPABILITY, *N.*
safái. *f;*

PALPABLE, *A.*
záhir; sáf; málúm; partakkh;

PALPITATE, TO, *V. I.*
taṛaphná; dhaṛakná; taṛpharáuná; kalejá kambná; talmaláuná; dhaṛkún dhaṛkún karná;

PALPITATION, *N.*
taṛpharát. *m;* taṛphát. *m;* taṛaph. *f;* dhaṛkí. *f;* hauldil. *m;*

PALSY, *N.*
jhollá. *m;* adhraṇgg. *m;*
one struck withpalsy. adhraṇggí. *m;*

PALTRY, *A.*
nikammá; nachíz; nakárá;

PAMPER, TO, *V. T.*
waḍḍe láḍ piyár nál pálná;

PAMPHLET, *N.*
rasálá. *m;* chhoṭí pothí. *f;*

PAN, *N.*
1. any kind of vessel. bhánḍá. *m;*
2. a brass pan. thálí. *f;*
3. a metal pan, large and deep. ḳaráhí. *f;* see VESSEL.

PANACEA, *N.*
iláj. *m;*

PANCAKE, *N.*
púrá. *m;* see FRITTER.

PANE, *N.*
shíshá. *m;*

PANG, *N.*
píṛ. *m;* chubhak. *f;* chubhká. *m;*

PANIC, *N.*
ḍar. *m;* ḳhauf. *m;* tharthalá. *m;* haul. *m;*

PANNIER, *N.*
1. for camels. kajáwá. *m;* kacháwá. *m;*
2. for donkeys. chaṭṭ. *f;* kháṇchá. *m;* see PACK SADDLE.

PANT, *N.*
hauṇkní. *f;* garkaní. *f;* gharkaní *f;* hatkorá. *m;* sukanná. *m;*

PANT, TO, *V. T.*
hauṇkná; chhetí chhetí sah lainá; háphná; garkná; gharakná; gharak jáná; dam chaṛhná; lamme lamme sáh lainá;

PANTALOONS, *N.*
1. English. patlúṇ. *m;*
2. native. men's. sutthan. *f;* salwár. *f;* paejámá. *m;*
3. women's. suthní. *f;* sutthan. *f;*

PANTHER, *N.*
chítá. *m;*

PANTING, *N.*
hauṇkní. *f;*

PANTOMINE, *N.*
tamáshá. *m;* rás. *f;*

PANTRY, *N.*
botal ḳháná. *m;*

PAPA, *N.*
báp. *m;* see FATHER.

PAPER, *N.*
kágaz. *m;*
1. newspaper. aḳhbár. *f;*
2. a small piece of paper. purjá. *m;*
3. waste paper. raddí kágaz. *m;*
4. a sheet of paper. tá. *m;*

PAPS, *N.*
mammá. *m;* bindu. *m;* chuchí. *f;*

PARABLE, *N.*
dristáṇt. *m;* misál. *f;* tamsíl. *f;*

PARABOLICAL, *A.*
tamsílí;

PARABOLICALLY, *Adv.*
misál de taur nál;

PARADE, *N.*
1. drill. paret. *f;* kawaid. *m;*
2. show. dhúm dhám. *f;* see PAGEANTRY

PARADISE, *N.*
1. Hindu. swarag. *m;*
2. Muhammadan. bihist. *m;*

PARAGON, *N.*
namúná. *m;*

PARAGRAPH, *N.*
pairá. *m;*

PARALLEL, *A.*
sáwáṇ; kol kol; barábar;

PARALYSIS, *N.*
luṇj. *m;* adhraṇg. *m;*

PARALYTIC, *N.*
adhraṇgí. *m;*

PARAMOUNT, *A.*
uttam; sáreáṇ náloṇ waḍḍá;

PARAMOUR, *N.*
dost. *m;* yár. *m;*

PARAPET, *N.*
banerá. *m;* kiṇggará. *m;* kaṇgurá. *m;*

PARAPHERNALIA, *N.*
chíz wast. *f;* asbáb. *m;* wast walevá. *f;* wast waleveáṇ. *f;*

PARAPHRASE, TO, *V. T.*
íbárat kholke kahná;

PARAQUET, *N.*
totá. *m;* túti. *f;*

PARASITE, *N.*
muḳht ḳhor. *m;* muḳht chaṭṭú. *m;* pacheu. *m;* kushámatí. *m;*

PARASOL, *N.*
chhatrí. *f;*

PARCEL, *N.*
paṇḍokalí. *f;*

PARCH, TO, *V. T.*
bhunná;
to be parched (as grain). bhujjná;

PARCHED, *A.*
1. cooked. bhujá hoyá;
2. dry. sukká;

PARDON, *N.*
muáfí. *f;* khimá. *f;* riháí. *f;*

PARDON, TO, *V. T.*
muáf karná; muáfí deni; khimá karná; bakhshná; riháí dení;

PARDONABLE, *A.*
muáfí de laiq;

PARDONER, *N.*
muáf karnwálá. *m*; muáfí denwálá. *m*;

PARE, TO, *V. T.*
chhillná;
pare the nails. nauṇh láhuná;

PARENT, *N.*
mán. *f*; báp. *m*; see FATHER.
parents. máṇ pitá. *m*; máṇ báp. *m*; mápe. *m*; wáldain. *m*;

PARENTLESS, *A.*
yatím; máṇ pio mahettaṛ;

PARING, *N.*
chhillaṛ. *m*; chhilká. *m*; katrá. *m*; chhillat. *f*;

PARISH, *N.*
aláqá. *m*; mahallá. *m*;

PARITY, *N.*
barábarí. *f*; barobari. *f*;

PARK, *N.*
maidán. *m*;

PARLANCE, *N.*
gal bát. *f*; bayán. *m*;

PARLEY, TO, *V. T.*
gal bát karní; saláh mashwará karná;

PARLEY, *N.*
mashwará. *m*;

PARLOUR, *N.*
gol kamrá. *m*;

PAROLE, *N.*
wádá. *m*;

PAROXYSM, *N.*
chakkar. *m*; lahir. *f*;

PARRICIDE, *N.*
ḳhuní. *m*; ghátak. *m*; hattiárá. *m*; ádam már. *m*;

PARROT, *N.*
totá. *m*;

PARRY, TO, *V. T.*
aí gaí karní; ṭál maṭolá karná; ṭalná;

PARSE, TO, *V. T.*
tarkib karná;

PARSIMONIOUS, *A.*
marjíuṛá; kanjús; chíṛhá; marjíṛá;

PARSOMONIOUSLY, *Adv.*
kanjúsí nál;

PARSIMONY, *N.*
sarfá. *m*; kanjúsí. *f*;

PARSING, *N.*
tarkíb. *m*;

PARSON, *N.*
pádrí. *m*; pástar. *m*;

PARSONAGE, *N.*
pádrí sáhib dá bangala. *m*;

PART, *N.*
1. portion. hissá. *m*; ṭukṛá. *m*; pattí. *f*; chhándá. *m*;
2. side. taraf. *f*; wal. *m*;
3. region. jagáh. *f*; aláqá. *m*;
4. for the most part. bahut karke;

PART, TO, *V. T.*
1. to divide. waṇḍná; waṇḍ dená; hissá karná;
2. to divide amongst two only. adho adh karná;
3. to separate. alag karná; aḍḍ karná; vakkh karná;

PART, TO, *V. I.*
vakkh honá; alag ho jáná;

PARTAKE, TO, *V. T.*
hissá lainá;

PARTAKE, TO, *V. I.*
sáṇhjí honá; ralná; shámil honá; sharík honá;

PARTAKER, *N.*
sáṇjhí. *m*; pattídár. *m*; hissedár *m*;

PARTIAL, *A.*
1. a little. ratá; kujh; ghaṭṭ; thoṛá;
2. biassed. uh de wal; tarafdár;

PARTIALITY, *N.*
1. bias. pakkh. *m*; pachch. *m*; pakkh pát. *m*; pachchhdárí. *f*; dhiṛ. *f*; tarafdárí. *f*; liház. *m*; múṇh rakkhní. *f*;
2. liking. shauq. *m*; ichchhiá. *f*; bhauná. *m*; cháh. *f*;
3. Proverb. The blind man distributes his sweets to his own relatives. annhá vaṇḍe shiṛíniṇ muṛ ghir apneáṇ núṇ de;

PARTIALLY, *Adv.*
ghaṭṭ waddh;

PARTICIPANT, *N.*
pattídár. *m*; hissedár. *m*; see PARTNER.

PARTICIPATE, TO, *V. T.*
sáṇjhí honá; bhai wal honá; shámil honá;
PARTICIPATION, *N.*
sáṇjhí, *f;*
PARTICLE, *N.*
ruál. *f;* kaṇi. *f;*
PARTI COLOURED, *A.*
dabb kaṛabbá;
PARTICULAR, *A.*
kháss;
full particulars. sárá hál. *m;*
PARTICULARIZE, TO, *V. T.*
wakkho wakkh kahná: púrá bayán karná;
PARTICULARLY, *Adv.*
1. specially. uchechá; khásskarke;
2. distinctly, ikk ikk karke:
PARTING, *N.*
1. separation. judái. *f;* vidiá. *m;* wichhoṛá. *m;*
2. parting of the hair. siṇdh. *f;*
3. Proverb. If you have an oilman for a lover your parting will be dirty. yár ví telí te siṇdh ví mailí;
PARTISAN, *N.*
1. follower. lágú. *m;* naukar. *m;* ṭahliá. *m;*
2. disciple. bálká. *m;* chelá. *m;* shágird. *m;*
3. friend. dost. *m;* yár. *m;* mittar. *m;* sajjan. *m;*
4. a party man. tarafdár. *m;*
PARTITION, *N.*
waṇḍ. *f;* paṭṭí. *f;*
PARTITION, TO, *V. T.*
waṇḍ dená; see PART.
PARTIZANSHIP, *N.*
tarafdárí. *f;* see PARTIALITY.
PARTLY, *Adv.*
kujh; thoṛá jehá;
PARTNER, *N.*
bhái wal. *m;* joṛídár. *m;* panjhál. *m;* sáthí. *m;* hissedár. *m;* sáṇjhí. *m;* saṇgatí. *m;* bhiál. *m;* paṭṭídár. *m;*
Proverb. He is not a good partner who steals and takes by force. sáṇjhí chaṇgá nahíṇ oh chorí chippí kháwe khoh;
PARTNERSHIP, *N.*
sáṇjh bhihálí. *f;* sáṇjh bhanjhálí. *f;* sáṇjh. *m;* bhiálí. *f;*
PARTRIDGE, *N.*
tittar. *m;*
Proverb. To fly roasted partridges, *i. e.*, to strive after impossibilities. bhunne tittar uḍáune;
PARTY, *N.*
ṭollí. *f;* dhir. *f;*
1. a man of the other party. dujjí dhir dá; dujje pásse dá;
2. a party of athletes. chungí. *f;*
3. a party of women and girls gathered to spin or sew. tiṇjaṇ. *f;* triṇjaṇ. *f;* bhohṛá. *m;*
PARTY SPIRIT, *N.*
tarafdárí. *f;* pachchhdárí. *f;*
PASS, TO, *V. I.*
laṇghná; tal jáná;
1. to pass away. mar ján;
2. to pass one. agge nikal jáná,
3. pass this way. aidharoṇ dí laṇgh áo;
4. to pass an exam. páss honá;
PASS, TO, *V. T.*
laṇgháná;
1. to pass blood. lahú áuná;
2. to pass the time. kaṭṭná;
PASS, *N.*
1. permission. ijázat. *f;* ijan. *f;* khullh. *f;*
2. a mountain pass. dará. *m;*
PASSABLE, *A.*
chaldá; khásá;
PASSAGE, *N.*
galá. *m;* rastá. *m;* gujar. *f;*
in a book. ibárat. *f;*
PASS BOOK, *N.*
hisáb dí kitáb. *f;*
PASSENGER, *N.*
sawár. *m;* suár. *m;* aswár. *m;*
PASSING, *A.*
chand rozá; thoṛeáṇ dináṇ dá;
PASSING ALONG, *P. P.*
laṇghdiáṇ hoíáṇ;
PASSION, *N.*
1. anger. pittá. *m;* gussá. *m;* roh. *m;* ris. *f;* karodh. *m;* jhak. *f;* jhall. *f;* kop. *m;*
2. suffering. jáṇkandaní. *f;* dukhṛá. *m;*

3. desire. kharmasti. *f*; jom. *m*; pápáṇ díáṇ kámanáṇ. *f*;
4. vile desires and passions.ních wásne. *m*; ních báshne. *m*;

PASSIONATE, *A*.
karopí; kopmáṇ; karodhí; gusail; jhallá; jomí;

PASSIONATELY, *Adv*.
baṛe josh nál; gusse nál; karodh nál; kop nál;

PASSIONLESS, *A*.
sunn; dhímá;

PASSIVE, *A*.
sunn;

PASSPORT, *N*.
ráhdárí. *f*;

PAST, *A*.
pichchhlá;

PAST, TO BE, *V. I*.
bít jáná;

PASTE, *N*.
lewí. *f*; leṭí. *f*;

PASTE, TO, *V. T*.
lewí lání; leṭí láuní;

PASTIME, *N*.
kheḍ. *m*;

PASTOR, *N*.
pádrí sáhib. *m*; pástar. *m*;

PASTRY, *N*.
kachaurí. *f*; púrí. *f*;

PASTURAGE, *N*.
júh. *m*; charáí. *f*; jangal. *m*; charáṇd. *m*;

PASTURE, TO, *V. T*.
chugáuná; charáuná; chárná;

PASTURE, *N*.
júh. *f*;

PAT, *N*.
dháppí. *f*; thapp. *m*; tháp. *m*; thaphokí. *f*; thápí. *f*; dháppá. *m*;

PAT, TO, *V. T*.
haulí jehí dháppá márná; thápí dení; tháparná; tháp márná; thápṛí mární;

PATCH, *N*.
gaṇḍh tupp. *m*; gaṭṭh. *m*; ṭákí. *f*; ṭallí. *f*; gaṇḍh. *m*;
1. of metal. taṇká. *m*;
2. he is not a patch on him. uh uhdá páskúṇ ví nahíṇ;

PATCH, TO, *V. T*.
gaṇḍh láuná; ṭákí láuní; gaṇḍh tupp karná; gaṭṭh láuná;

PATCHING, *N*.
gaṇḍh tupp. *m*; gaṭṭh. *m*;

PATCHWORK, *N*.
godrí. *f*;

PATE, *N*.
sir. *m*;

PATEN, *N*.
thálí. *f*; paleṭ. *m*;

PATENT, *A*.
záhir; malúm;

PATER NOSTER, *N*.
rabbání duá. *f*; Ḳhudáwand dí duá. *f*;

PATH, *N*.
ráh. *f*; rastá. *f*; pahiá. *m*; paihá. *m*; ráh páhrá. *m*; márg. *m*;
1. a ridge between two fields. banná. *m*;
2. a track. ghássí. *f*;

PATHWAY, *N*.
rastá. *m*; see PATH.

PATIENCE, *N*.
sabr. *m*; khiún. *m*; dhíraj. *f*; sahárá. *m*; dhír. *f*; hauṇslá. *m*; ghaliár. *f*; jigará. *m*;

PATIENT, *A*.
nigghá; dhímá; dhírajmáṇ; hauslewálá;
to be patient. nigghá ráhná; sabr karná; dhíraj karná;

PATIENT, *N*.
bamár. *m*; maríz. *m*;

PATIENTLY, *Adv*.
dhíre de nál; sabr nál; dhíraj nál;

PATRIARCH, *N*.
buzurg. *m*;

PATRIMONIAL, *A*.
gaddí; jaddí;

PATRIMONY, *N*.
málakí. *f*; milkh. *f*;

PATRIOTISM, *N*.
des OR vatan dí muhabbat. *f*;

PATROL, *N*.
1. the work of a patrol. gasht. *f*;
2. the guard. paihredár. *m*; chowkídár. *m*; pahrewálá. *m*;

PATROL, TO, *V. T*.
gasht phirná;

PATRON, *N.*
madadgár. *m*; pachchhí. *m*;
PATRONAGE, *N.*
sahaitá. *m*; madat. *f*;
PATRONIZE, TO, *V. T.*
1. to honour with one's presence. darshan dená; raunaq dená;
2. to place hand on head. sir te hatth rakkhná OR dharná;
PATRONYMIC, *N.*
nám. *m*; náṇ. *m*;
PATTERN, *N.*
namúná. *m*; váṇgí. *f*; bannagí. *f*; váṇg. *m*;
PAUCITY, *N.*
thuṛh. *f*; kamtí. *f*; gháṭṭá. *m*; kamí. *f*;
PAUNCH, *N.*
peṭ. *m*;
PAUPER, *N.*
shodá. *m*; garíb gurbá. *m*;
PAUPERISM, *N.*
garíbí. *f*; muhtájí. *f*; daliddar. *m*; daliddartáí. *f*;
PAUSE, *N.*
bhaṇg. *f*; rok. *f*;
in reading. rahá. *m*; ṭhahrá. *m*;
PAUSE, TO, *V. I.*
ṭhahrná; khalo jáná; astá jáná;
PAVEMENT, *N.*
faras. *m*; farash. *m*;
PAVILION, *N.*
1. tent. tambú. *m*; see TENT;
2. large awning. chánaní. *f*;
PAW, TO, *V. T.*
búrí taráh hatth páuná;
to paw the ground. khaurú kaḍḍhná; pauṛ márná;
PAW, *N.*
pahuṇchá. *m*; paṇjá. *m*;
PAWING OF A HORSE, *N.*
khaurú. *m*;
PAWN, *N.*
gahiṇá. *m*; girví. *f*; gáṇháṇ. *m*;
PAWN, TO, *V. T.*
girví páuní OR rakkhní; gahine páuná;
to be pawned. girví painá;
PAWNBROKER, *N.*
karáṛ. *m*; sháh. *m*;

PAY, *N.*
1. earnings. kamáí. *f*;
2. daily wages. diháṛí. *f*; mazdúrí. *f*;
3. monthly pay. tankháh. *f*; talab. *f*;
4. pay for rent. bháṛá. *m*; karáyá. *m*;
5. pay for grinding corn. &c., píswáí. *f*;
6. pay for carting. dhuáí. *f*;
7. pay for dyeing cloth. raṇgáí. *f*;
8. pay for washing clothes. dhuáí. *f*;
9. pay for planing wood. raṇdáí. *f*;
10. pay for keeping watch. rákkhí. *f*;
11. pay for collecting revenue. panjotrá. *m*;
12. pay to a midwife. jaṇwáí. *f*;
PAY, TO, *V. T.*
dená; tárná; chukáuná;
1. to pay a debt. udhár utárná; karj bhar dená; tárná; udhár láhná;
2. to pay taxes. tárná;
3. to pay in full. de dená; láhná;
4. to pay a fine. bharná; chaṭṭí dení OR bharní;
5. to pay attention. dhián karná; chitt láuná;
6. to pay reverence. hatth joṛná; matthe hatth láuná;
7. what did you pay for this bullock? ih bald tusáṇ kinne núṇ liá sí.
PAYABLE, *A.*
den jog;
PAYEE, *N.*
jis núṇ rupae ditte jáṇ
PAYER, *N.*
denwálá. *m*;
PEA, *N.*
maṭar. *m*;
PEACE, *N.*
sáṇt. *f*; sukh. *m*; salámatí. *f*; shántí. *f*; sáṇtagí. *f*;
1. between two parties. sulhá. *f*; suláh. *f*;
2. in a country. aman. *f*;
3. rest. arám. *m*; armán. *m*;

PEACEABLE, *A*.
milápaṛí; bholá; garíb; nischesṭ
PEACEABLY, *Adv*.
suláh safáí nál;
PEACEFUL, *A*.
milápaṛí;
PEACEFULNESS, *N*.
chain. *f*; aman. *m*;
PEACEMAKER, *N*.
suláh karáunwálá. *m*;
PEACH, *N*.
árú *m*;
PEACOCK, *N*.
mor. *m*;
PEAHEN, *N*.
morní. *f*;
PEAK, *N*.
choṭṭá. *m*; sirá. *m*; tísi. *f*; tishí. *f*; ṭillá. *m*; ṭillí. *f*;
PEAL, *N*.
kaṛak. *f*; garaj. *f*;
PEAL, TO, *V. I*.
kaṛakná;
PEAR, *N*.
náshpátí. *f*; nákh. *f*;
PEARL, *N*.
motí. *f*; jawáhar. *m*;
PEASANT, *N*.
piṇḍú. *m*; guár. *m*; gaṇwár. *m*; piṇḍ dá rahanwálá;
PEBBLE, *N*.
gíṭí. *f*; gáṭí. *f*; gíṭá. *m*; waṭṭí. *f*;
PECCABILITY, *N*.
gunáhgárí. *f*; buríáí. *f*;
PECCABLE, *A*.
1. sinful. gunáhgár; pápí; aprádhí; sharír;
2. weak. kamjor; ḍhillá; nirbal;
PECCANCY, *N*.
jurm. *m*; buríáí. *f*; dosh. *m*; bhull. *f*; qusúr. *m*;
PECCANT, *A*.
bhaiṛá; kharáb; máṛá;
PECK, *N*.
ṭhúṇggá. *m*;
PECK, TO, *V. T*.
ṭhúṇggá márná; chuggná; chunj mární;
PECKISH, *A*.
bhukkhá;
PECULATE, TO, *V. T*.
chorí karní; churáuná; rupae kháná; khaṛná; hatth márná;
PECULATION, *N*.
chorí. *f*; chorí chakárí. *f*;
Idiom. He used his opportunities for peculation. us ne naukarí vichch ḳhub hatth range haṇ. lit. he dyed his hands well in service.
PECULATOR, *N*.
chor. *m*; ṭhagg. *m*;
PECULIAR, *A*.
1. strange. aṇokhá; ajíb; wisekh;
2. special. ḳháss;
PECULIARITY, *N*.
1. strangeness. aṇokh. *m*;
2. quality. sift. *f*;
PECULIARLY, *Adv*.
ajíb taur nál; ḳháss karke;
PECUNIARY, *A*.
rupe dá;
PEDAGOGISM, *N*.
ustádagí. *f*;
PEDAGOGUE, *N*.
ustád. *m*; see TEACHER.
PEDDLE, TO, *V. T*.
chábṛí vechná; chápaṛí vechná;
PEDDLER, *N*.
basátí. *m*; chápṛíwálá. *m*; maniáríwálá. *m*;
PEDESTRIAN, *N*.
pándhí. *m*; ráhí. *m*; musáfir. *m*;
PEDIGREE, *N*.
1. tribe. got. *f*; kul. *f*; qaum. *f*;
2. paper of pedigree. kull pattrí. *f*; shajará gotar. *m*;
PEEL, *N*.
chill. *f*; chhillaṛ. *m*;
PEEL, TO, *V. T*.
chhillná;
PEEP, TO, *V. T*.
jhákná; jhát márná; jhátí mární; chhátíáṇ mární; jhamáká láuná;
PEEP, *N*.
1. a look. jhák. *f*; jhát. *f*; jhátí. *f*; jhamáká. *m*;
2. cry of a chicken; chíṇ chíṇ. *f*;
3. peep of day. sawerá. *m*; sawelá. *m*;
PEER, TO, *V. T*.
takkná; see PEEP.

PEERLESS, *A*.
uttam; sáreáṇ nálon changá;
PEEVISH, *A*.
kauṛá; náráz; vitriá hoyá; russiá hoyá; muṇh ṭuṭá; nakk charhá; khaṭṭá; rukkhá; chhiṛhmí; saṛiá bhujiá;
PEEVISH, TO BE, *V. I.*
jhunjláuná; chhiṛham chhiṛná;
PEEVISHLY, *Adv*.
náráz hoke; khafá hoke;
PEEVISHNESS, *N*.
waṭṭ. *m*; narázagí. *f*; chhiṛham. *f*;
PEG. *N*.
killí. *f*; khuṇḍá. *m*; khuṇḍ. *m*; kill. *m*; mekh. *f*;
PELF, *N*.
mál. *m*; daulat. *f*; see WEALTH.
PELLET, *N*.
golí. *f*; gulelá. *m*;
of earth. ḍhíṇḍá. *m*;
PELL MELL, *Adv*.
hallá karke nas jáná; ghál mel;
PELLUCID, *A*.
suthrá; sáf; nirmal;
PELLUCIDITY, *N*.
safáí. *f*;
PELT, TO, *V. T.*
suṭṭná; see THROW.
PEN, *N*.
kalam. *f*; likkhan. *f*;
1. pen holder. par. *m*;
2. pen and inkpot. kalam dawát. *f*;
PEN, TO, *V. T.*
likhná;
PENAL, *A*.
daṇḍ jog; sazá de laiq;
PENALTY, *N*.
1. fine. daṇḍ. *f*; ḍann. *f*; chaṭṭí. *f*; jurmáná. *m*; jarimáná. *m*;
2. punishment. sazá. *f*;
PENANCE, *N*.
1. religious austerity. tap. *m*; bairág. *m*;
2. punishment. sazá. *f*;
PENCE, *N*.
paise. *m*;
PENCIL, *N*.
pinsal. *m*; rúl. *m*;
PENDANT, *N*.
1. of a jewel. jhumká. *m*;
2. anything hanging. laṭkaṇ. *m*;
PENETRATE, TO, *V. I.*
khubbná; ghussná; waṛná; andar jáná; ghusáṛná; ghusaṛ jáná; dhasná;
PENETRATE, TO, *V. T.*
chhedná; dhasáuná;
PENETRATING, *A*.
tez; hoshiyár; siyáná; chalák;
PENETRATION, *N*.
aql. *f*; samajh. *f*; buddh. *f*; hosh. *m*;
PENHOLDER, *N*.
kalam. *f*; par. *m*;
PENIS, *N*.
ḍaṇḍá. *m*; faláṇ. *m*; indrí. *f*; lull. *m*; lullu. *m*;
1. small. lullí. *f*; ḍaṇḍí. *f*;
2. large. lann. *f*;
PENITENCE, *N*.
pachhtává. *m*; ranj. *m*; see REPENTANCE.
PENITENT, *A*.
pashemán; taubá karnwálá;
to be penitent. jhurná; taubá karná; pachotáuná;
PENITENTLY, *Adv*.
taubá karke; afsos nál;
PENKNIFE, *N*.
káchchú. *m*; chákkú. *m*;
PENMAN, *N*.
likhárí. *m*; likháú. *m*;
PENMANSHIP, *N*.
likháí. *f*; likháutí. *f*; likháut. *f*;
PENNANT, *N*.
jhaṇḍí. *f*;
PENNILESS, *A*.
miskín; kaṇggál; dámáṇḍol; muhtáj; garíb;
PENNY, *N*.
ikk anná. *m*;
Proverb. Penny wise and pound foolish. A jatt will give a ball of sugar away, but not a sugarcane. jaṭṭ gúṛ dí rorí dewe, par ganná náṇ dewe;
PENSION, *N*.
pinshan. *m*;
PENSION TO, *V. T.*
pinshan dená;
PENSIONER, *N*.
pinshan lainwálá. *m*;

PENSIVE, *A*.
udás; sasdil; dil dhaṭṭhá;
PENSIVENESS, *N*.
1. melancholy. gam. *m*; udásí. *f*; gamí. *f*; santáp. *m*;
2. thoughtfulness. dhián. *m*; chiṇtá. *f*;
PENTATEUCH, *N*.
Tauret. *f*;
PENTECOST, *N*.
Íd i Nuzúl. *f*;
PENURIOUS, *A*.
marjíuṛià; kanjús;
PENURIOUSLY, *Adv*.
kanjúsí nál;
PENURIOUSNESS, *N*.
kanjúsí. *f*; sarfá. *m*;
PENURY, *N*.
thuṛ. *f*; tangí. *f*; garíbí. *f*; kastaní. *f*; mandárá. *m*;
PEON, *N*.
chaprásí. *m*; naukar. *m*;
PEOPLE, *N*.
lok. *m*; lukái. *m*; bande. *m*; lokí. *m*; dunyá. *m*;
PEOPLE, TO, *V*. *T*.
wasáuná; abád karná;
PEOPLED, *A*.
abád;
PEPPER, *N*.
mirch. *f*;
1. black pepper. gol mirch. *f*; kálí mirch. *f*;
2. red pepper. lál mirch. *f*; piplán. *f*, plur;
3. green chillies. harí mirch. *f*;
4. Proverb. Pepper is in every relish. har masále piplán múl;
PEPPER BOX, *N*.
mirchdán. *m*;
PEPPER CORN, *N*.
mirch. *f*;
PEPPER MINT, *N*.
púdná, *m*;
PEPPER PLANT, *N*.
mirch. *f*;
PEPPERY, *A*.
mirch jehá; garm; tez;
PERADVENTURE, *Adv*.
ḳhabare; shayad;
PERAMBULATE, TO, *V*. *T*.
sair OR sail karná; phirná; ṭurná;
PERAMBULATION, *N*.
sail. *m*;
PERAMBULATOR, *N*.
bachcheáṇ dí gaḍḍí. *f*;
PERCEIVABLE, *A*.
záhir;
PERCEIVE. TO, *V*. *T*.
1. to see. vekhná;
2. to recognise. bujhná; pahchhánná; kalná; bhásná;
PERCEIVING, *P*. *P*.
bujhke;
PERCEPTIBLY, *Adv*.
vekhan vichch;
PERCEPTION, *N*.
sudh budh. *f*; chaukasí. *f*; pahchán. *f*; samajh. *f*; sujjh. *f*;
PERCH, *N*.
aḍḍá. *m*;
PERCH. TO, *V*. *I*.
aḍḍá jamáuná OR láuná;
PERCHANCE, *Adv*.
ḳhabare; sabab nál; shayad; kall kulotar;
PERCOLATE, TO, *V*. *T*.
chhánná; punná; nitárná; nichorná;
PERCOLATE, TO, *V*. *I*.
chhanná; choná;
PERCOLATION, *N*.
chhanái. *f*; choá. *m*;
PERDITION, *N*.
nás. *f*; khuárí. *f*; halákí. *f*; chauṛ. *m*; nisṭ. *f*; dobbá sokká. *m*;
PEREGRINATE, TO, *V*. *T*.
1. to wander about. awárá phirná; bhondá phirná; ḍawánḍol phirná; udále pudále phirná;
2. to tour. daurá karná;
PEREGRINATION, *N*.
daurá. *m*; safar. *m*;
PEREMPTORILY, *Adv*.
jorávarí nál; badobadí;
PEREMPTORY, *A*.
hákamáná; jorávar;
PERENNIAL, *A*.
sadá; hameshá;
PERFECT, *A*.
param; sunpuran; kamál; sapann;
PERFECT TO, *V*. *T*.
sidh karná;

PERFECTION, *N.*
kamál. *m*; kamáltái. *f*;
PERFECTLY, *Adv.*
ṭhík ṭhík; ṭhík ṭhák: hú ba hú; ṭhíkam ṭhík;
PERFECTNESS, *N.*
kamál, *m*;
PERFIDIOUS, *A.*
beímán; khoṭṭá; chalbáz; be-dharm; lunharám;
PERFIDIOUSLY, *Adv.*
beímání nál; beímán hoke;
PERFIDIOUSNES, *N.*
beímángí. *f*; beímání. *f*; pah-mánagí. *f*; lun harámí. *f*;
PERFORATE, TO, *V. T.*
chhekná; chhek páuná; chhedná; vinnhná; chubháuná; sallná;
PERFORATION, *N.*
chhek. *m*; chheh. *m*; chobh. *f*; gallí. *f*; chhed. *m*; saru. *m*; sall. *m*;
PERFORCE, *Adv.*
zor nál; jarúr;
PERFORM, TO, *V. T.*
1. to do. karná; kar lainá;
2. to finish. kar chhaḍḍná; nabá-huná; purá karná; naberṇá; nirbáhuná;
3. to perform a thing quickly. ghassá karná;
PERFORM, TO, *V. T.*
niberṇá; nibbaṛ jáná; nibhná;
PERFORMANCE, *N.*
naberá. *m*; nabáh. *m*;
1. acting. sáṇg. *m*;
2. work. kamm. *m*;
PERFORMER, *N.*
naṭ; *m*; bhaṇḍ. *m*; nakliá. *m*; sáṇgí. *m*;
PERFUME, *N.*
mahik. *f*; achchhí bo. *f*; lapat. *f*; máhimahát. *m*; atar. *m*;
PERFUME, TO, *V. T.*
mahikáuná;
to incense. dhup dená; dhupná;
PERFUMER, *N.*
gáṇdhí. *m*; atár. *m*;
PERFUMERY, *N.*
mahik. *f*; atar. *m*;
PERFUNCTORINESS, *N.*
láparwáí. *f*; gáfalí. *f*; ḍhill. *f*;
PERFUNCTORY, *A.*
gáfal; láparwá; ḍhillá; ḍhillá maṭṭhá; besurt;
PERHAPS, *Adv.*
khabre; said; shayad; kadá-chit; kite; kade; shait; shait khaure;
PERIL, *N.*
khatrá. *m*; dhuk dhuká. *m*;
PERILOUS, *A.*
ḍaráuná; khatrewálá; jokhoṇ dá;
PERIOD, *N.*
1. season. samá. *m*; arsá. *m*; zamáná. *m*;
2. fixed time. mohlat. *f*; miád. *f*;
3. long time. chir. *m*;
PERIODICALLY, *Adv.*
vele kuvele;
PERISH, TO, *V. I.*
mar jáná; nás honá; barbád honá; ujjaṛ pujjaṛ jáná; see DIE.
PERISHABLE, *A.*
fání; násmán;
PERISHABLENESS, *N.*
saṛan. *f*;
PERJURE, TO, *V. T.*
jhuṭhí sauṇh kháni;
PERJURER, *N.*
jhuṭhá. *m*; kúṛá. *m*; lapárí. *m*; lapáṭí. *m*; gappí. *m*;
PERJURY, *N.*
jhuṭhí sauṇh. *f*; banauṭ. *m*;
PERMANENCE, *N.*
diṛh. *m*; diṛhtá. *m*; ṭikáú. *m*; pakíáí. *f*;
PERMANENT, *A.*
qaim; mazbut; pakká;
of service, residence, &c. naṭháhú; naṭhehú;
PERMANENTLY, *Adv.*
sadá; nitt;
PERMEATE, TO, *V. T.*
ghussná; waṛná;
PERMEATION, *N.*
dakhal. *f*;
PERMISSIBLE, *A.*
jaiz;
PERMISSION, *N.*
ijan. *f*; ijázat. *f*; parwáṇagí. *f*; khullh. *f*; manzúrí. *f*;
PERMISSIVE, *A.*
jaiz;

PERMIT, TO, *V. T.*
hon dená; ijan OR ijázat dení;
PERMUTATION, *N.*
tabádalá. *m*; badalá. *m*; adal badal. *m*;
PERMUTE, TO, *V. T.*
tabádalá karná; badal dená;
PERNICIOUS, *A.*
bhaiṛá; máṛá; burá; gaṇḍá; ḳharáb; sharír; chaṇdrá; chaṇḍál;
PERPENDICULAR, *A.*
khaṛá; siddhá;
PERPETRATE, TO, *V. T.*
karná;
PERPETUAL, *A.*
sadá tík; hameshá;
perpetual motion. chaláchal. *f*; chaláchalí. *f*;
PERPETUALLY, *Adv.*
sadá; nitt; hameshá;
PERPETUATE, TO, *V. T.*
qaim rakkhná;
PERPETUITY, *N.*
hameshagí. *f*;
PERPLEX, TO, *V. T.*
dikk karná OR dená; ghabrá dená; raulá páuná; gallán nál phasáuná; bharmáuná;
PERPLEXED, *A.*
daṇg; harán; pareshán; dubdhe vichch; sasdil;
PERPLEXED, TO BE, *V. I.*
jaṇjál vichch phasná OR painá; hairán ho jáná; bakal jáná; chawakaṛí bhul jáná;
PERPLEXITY, *N.*
pareshání. *f*; ghabrát. *f*; pher. *m*; haránági. *f*; chakkar. *m*; dubhdhá. *f*; habaṛ dabaṛ. *f*; jaṇjál. *m*; habṛá dabṛí. *f*; sainsá; *m*;
PERQUISITE, *N.*
dastúrí. *f*; lág. *f*;
PERSECUTE, TO, *V. T.*
taṇg kar dená; chheṛná; aukhián karná; satáuná; see HARASS.
PERSECUTION, *N.*
julm. *m*; dukkh. *m*; kales. *m*;
PERSECUTOR, *N.*
jálim. *m*; dukhdenwálá. *m*; satáunwálá. *m*;
PERSEVERANCE, *N.*
khahṛá. *m*; dhíraj. *f*; siḍḍá. *m*;

PERSEVERE, TO, *V. T.*
khahiṛe páuná; tagná;
to cause to persevere. tagáuná;
PERSEVERING, *A.*
uddamí; sábat qadam;
PERSEVERINGLY, *Adv.*
gauh karke; dil lagá ke; dil nál;
PERSIA, *N.*
Fars dá des. *m*;
PERSIAN WHEEL, *N.*
halaṭ. *m*; haraṭ. *m*;
PERSIFAGE, *N.*
bakwás. *m*; maḳhaul. *m*; ṭhaṭṭhá. *m*; hujjat. *f*;
PERSIST, TO, *V. T.*
1. to persevere. khahiṛe páuná;
2. to annoy. jidd karná; kajá karní; haṭh karná; chheṛná;
3. to persist in a request. gal páiná;
PERSISTENCY, *N.*
siḍḍá. *m*; haṭh. *m*; haṭṭ. *m*; machlái. *f*; khichch. *m*;
with a bad meaning. kajá. *f*;
PERSISTENT, *A.*
ḍhíṭh; háṭṭhá; machall;
PERSON, *N.*
baṇdá. *m*; puras. *m*; ádmí. *m*; janá. *m*; manukkh. *m*; jan. *m*;
persons. jane. *m*; baṇde. *m*;
PERSONAL, *A.*
apná; zátí;
PERSONALITY, *N.*
zát. *f*; shaḳhshíat. *f*;
PERSONALLY, *Adv.*
áp hí; ḳhud;
PERSPICACITY, *N.*
hoshiyárí. *f*; dánái. *f*; buddh. *f*;
PERSPICIUTY, *N.*
safái. *f*;
PERSPICUOUS, *A.*
sáf;
PERSPIRATION, *N.*
muṛkhá. *m*; waṭṭ. *m*; trelí. *f*;
PERSPIRE, TO, *V. I.*
muṛkhá áuná; garmí áuní; paṛsijjná;
PERSUADE, TO, *V. T.*
manáuná; chukkná; samjháuná; maná láná; dhijáuná;
1. in a bad way. wargaláuná;
2. to egg on to fight. bhiṛáuná;

PERSUASION, *N.*
1. opinion. raí. *f;* khayál. *m;*
2. a creed. aqídá. *m;*
PERSUASIVENESS, *N.*
lárá. *m;* chukk. *f;*
PERT, *A.*
ḍhíṭh; ḍhíṭhá; shokh; tur turá; lutará; see IMPERTIN.
PERTAIN, TO, *V. I.*
laggná; wástá rakkhná;
PERTINACIOUS, *A.*
kabbá; jiddí;
PERTINACITY, *N.*
kabb. *f;* kháhṛá. *m;* himmat. *f;* hiṭh. *f;* see OBSTINANCY.
PERTINENT, *A.*
ṭhík; jog; munásib;
PERTLY, *Adv.*
gustákhí nál; shokhí nál;
PERTNESS, *N.*
machláí. *f;* machláhat. *f;* be-adabí. *f;* shokhí. *f;*
PERTURB, TO, *V. T.*
ghabráuná; hilkárná; gaṛbaṛí páuní; ghabrá dená;
PERTURBATION, *N.*
jichch. *f;* beqarárí. *f;* bearámí. *f;* dhuk dhuká. *m;* chaṭpaṭí. *f;*
PERTURBED, *A.*
jichch pichch; hairán;
1. to be perturbed. jichch honá;
2. I was greatly perturbed. mainúṇ cháín nahíṇ sí áundá;
PERTUSION, *N.*
chhed. *m;*
PERUSAL, *N.*
paṛtál. *f;*
PERUSE, TO, *V. T.*
paṛhná; vekhná; wáchná;
PERVADE, TO, *V. I.*
samáuná;
PERVERSE, *A.*
ḍhíṭhá; ghassu már; gheslá; machlá; khachrá; avaiṛá; replá; machall; mísná; jiddal; tattṛá; haṭhá; kabbá; nárá; aríkhor; magrá; jiraṛí; tareḍhá; aṛyal; aṛbangá; mínnhá;
a perverse nation. puṭhí qaum. *f;*
PERVERSELY, *Adv.*
jido jidí; zidd nál;
to act perversely. ghes mární;
PERVERSENESS, *N.*
kabb. *f;* huṛh; zidd. *f;* haṭh. *m;* aṛí. *f;* ghassu. *f;* jiraṛ. *f;* síṛaṛ. *m;* ghes. *f;* ghesal. *f;* machalpuṇá. *m;* machláí. *f;* ṭeḍh. *m;* tareḍh. *f;* khachráí. *f;* khacharpuṇá. *m;* khacharbází. *f;*
PERVERSION, *N.*
tabdílí. *f;*
PERVERSITY, *N.*
kuráh. *m;* ghassú. *f;* jidd. *f;* see PERVERSENESS.
PERVERT, TO, *V. T.*
1. to spoil. kharáb karná; wigáṛná; chauṛ kar dená; wichálná;
2. to foul. gaṇdá karná; palít karná;
3. to lead astray. wargaláuná; bhuláuná; badráh kar dená;
PESSIMISM, *N.*
náummedí. *f;* bedilí. *f;*
PEST, *N.*
balá. *f;* marí. *f;*
PESTER, TO, *V. T.*
aukhiáṇ karná; chheṛná; jich karná; akáuná; taṇg karná; taklíf dení; khijháuná; sir khapáuná;
PESTILENCE, *N.*
bamárí. *f;* marí. *f;*
PESTILENT, *A.*
burá; bhaiṛá;
PESTLE, *N.*
ghoṭná. *m;* moglá. *m;* mohlá. *m;* matkair. *m;*
1. pestle and mortar. daurí ḍaṇḍá. *m;* chattú waṭṭá. *m;*
2. in the ground. ukhlí múhlí. *f;*
PET, *N.*
láḍlá. *m;* pyárá. *m;*
an animal. páltú. *m;*
PET, TO, *V. T.*
pyár karná; láḍ laḍáuná; láḍ pyár karná;
PETAL, *N.*
pattí. *f;*
PETITION, *N.*
sawál *m;* ardás. *m;* arz. *f;* parárthṇá. *f;* darkhást. *f;*
legal. arzí. *f;*
PETITION, TO, *V. T.*
arz karní; sawál karná; minnat karní; bentí karní; tarle minnat karní; giṛgaṛáuná;

PETITIONER, *N.*
sawálí. *m*; dávedár. *m*; sawáliá. *m*;
PETROLEUM, *N.*
miṭṭí dá tel. *m*;
PETTICOAT, *N.*
ghaggarí. *f*; ghaggará. *m*; gardá. *m*; lahiṇgá. *m*; peṭíkoṭ. *m*;
Proverb. She wears a petticoat like the roof of a house. chhapar paindí ghaggará;
PETTISH, *A.*
kauṛá; nak chaṛhá; muṇh ṭuṭá; khaṭṭá;
PETTISHLY, *Adv.*
ḳhafá hoke;
PETTY, *A.*
1. small. chhoṭá; nikká;
2. useless. nakárá; nikammá; kise kamm dá nahíṇ;
PETULANCE, *N.*
ḍhíṭhái. *f*; waṭṭ. *m*; narázagí. *f*; chhiṛham. *f*;
PETULANT, *A.*
russiá hoyá; vitriá hoyá; kauṛá; ziddí; chhiṛhmí;
PETULANTLY, *Adv.*
1. peevishly. ḳhafá hoke; russ ke; naráz hoke;
2. pertly. beadabí nál; shoḳhí nál;
PEWTER, *N.*
jist. *m*;
PHAETON, *N.*
fiṭan gárí. *f*;
PHANTOM, *N.*
ḳháb ḳhayál. *m*; ḍutt. *m*;
PHARISEE, *N.*
farísí. *m*;
PHARMACIST, *N.*
hakím. *m*;
PHENOMENAL, *A.*
ajíb; aṇokhá; acharaj;
PHIAL, *N.*
shíshí. *f*; sísí. *f*;
PHILANTHROPIST, *N.*
upkárí. *m*;
PHILANTHROPY, *N.*
upkár. *m*; mihrbání. *f*;
PHILOSOPHER, *N.*
failsúf. *m*;
PHILOSOPHY, *N.*
failsúfí. *f*;
PHLEGM, *N.*
balgam. *f*; khaṇghár. *m*;
PHLEGMATIC, *A.*
sust; jillhá; álasí; postí;
PHOTOGRAPH, *N.*
taswír. *f*; foṭo. *m*;
PHRASE, *N.*
bachan. *m*; fikrá. *m*;
PHRASEOLOGY, *N.*
bolan dá taríqá. *m*;
PHRENZY, *N.*
sarsám. *m*;
PHTHISIS, *N.*
tapadikk. *m*; khái. *f*; ḳháirog. *m*;
PHYSIC, *N.*
dawái. *f*; dawá. *f*; dárú. *m*; duá dárú. *m*;
PHYSICAL, *A.*
jismání;
PHYSICALLY, *Adv.*
jismání taur nál;
PHYSICIAN, *N.*
hakím. *m*; dágtar. *m*; waid. *m*;
PIANO, *N.*
wájjá. *m*;
PICK, TO, *V. T.*
1. to choose. chuṇná; chugná; chháṇt kar lainá;
2. to pick flowers. khohná; toṛná;
3. to pick up a thing. chukkná;
4. to pick over. rolná;
PICK, *N.*
gaintí. *f*;
PICKING, *N.*
chháṇṭ. *f*;
PICKLES, *N.*
achár. *m*;
PICKPOCKET, *N.*
uchakká. *m*; gaṇḍ chor. *m*;
PICTURE, *N.*
murat. *f*; taswír. *f*;
PIEBALD, *A.*
chittará; ḍabbá; ḍabb kharabbá; garará;
PIECE, *N.*
ṭoṭá. *m*; ḍakkará. *m*; párchá. *m*;
1. of bread. ṭukkaṛ. *m*; ṭukṛá. *m*; ṭukk. *m*; khanní. *f*;
2. of cloth. tákí. *f*;
3. of meat. boṭí. *f*;
4. pieces. chúr bhúr. *m*; chúrá bhúrá. *m*;

PIECEWORK, *N.*
theká. *m;*
PIED, *A.*
dabb karabbá; chitkabrá;
PIERCE, TO, *V. T.*
vinnhná; dhasáuná; chhek suttná OR kaddhná; chobhná; khobhná; hujj mární OR láuní;
PIERCED, TO BE, *V. I.*
chubbhná; vijjhná; khubhná:
PIERCING, *A.*
tikkhá; tez;
piercing pain, chubhak. *f;* chubhká. *m;*
PIETY, *N.*
díndári. *f;* neki. *f;* rástí. *f;* satkár. *m;*
PIG, *N.*
súr. *m;* súrni. *f;* badd. *m;*
PIGEON, *N.*
kabútar. *m;*
1. green pigeon. haryál. *m;*
2. fantail pigeon. lakká. *m;*
3. tumbler pigeon. lotan. *m;*
PIGEON HOUSE, *N.*
1. in the ground, ukkal. *m;* gamhel. *m;*
2. on a pole. chhatri. *f;*
PIGMENT, *N.*
rang. *m;*
PILE, *N.*
dher. *m;* dherí. *f;* dandá. *m;* kunnú. *m;* kusak. *m;* thok. *m;*
1. very large. ganj. *m;*
2. a pile of grass or vegetables. thabbá. *m;* thabbí. *f;*
PILE, TO, *V. T.*
dherí láuní; kunnú láuná; dher láuná; kusak láuná;
PILES, *N.*
bawásír, *f;* mohká. *m;*
bleeding. khuní. *f;*
PILFER, TO, *V. T.*
hatth márná; chorí karní; churáuná;
PILFERER, *N.*
chor. *m;* chortá. *m;*
PILGRIM, *N.*
1. Muhammadan. to a tomb. jiáratí. *m;*
2. Muhammadan, to Mecca. hájjí. *m;*
3. Hindu. játrí. *m;* tírthí. *m;*
PILGRIMAGE, *N.*
1. to Mecca. hajj. *m;*
2. to a Muhammadan shrine. jiárat. *m;*
3. Hindu. játrá. *m;* tírath. *m;* tírath játrá. *m;*
4. to go on a pilgrimage. jiárat karná;
5. to the Ganges. ganggá játrá. *f;*
6. Proverb used of the conversion of old reprobates. The cat goes to Mecca after eating 700 mice. sát sau chuhe khá billí Hajj kún julí;
PILL, *N.*
1. round. golí. *f;* battí. *f;*
2. flat. tikkí. *f;*
PILLAGE, *N.*
lutt. *f;* see PLUNDER.
PILLAGE, TO, *V. T.*
luttná; dáká márná; see PLUNDER.
PILLAGING, *N.*
lutái. *f;* lotí *f;* lúto lút. *f;*
PILLAR, *N.*
1. small. thammbí. *f;* thuhní. *f;*
2. large. thammh. *m;* thamb. *m;*
3. of brick. kaulá. *m;*
PILLOW, *N.*
sarháná. *m;*
PILLOW CASE, *N.*
sarháne dá osháṛ. *m;* takiá dá uchár. *m;*
PIMP, *N.*
dallá. *m;*
PIMPLE, *N.*
phimhní. *f;* phimní. *f;* barúrí. *f;*
PIN, *N.*
pinn. *m;*
rolling pin. wellan. *m;*
PINCERS, *N.*
uchchá. *m;* sannhí. *f;* jabúr. *m;* jambúr. *m;*
PINCH *N.*
1. nip. chúndhí. *f;*
2. small quantity. chutkí. *f;* chúndhí dá;
PINCH, TO, *V. T.*
chúndhí waddhní;
PINE FOR, TO, *V. T.*
jí tarasná; chábná;

PINE, TO, *V. I.*
murjháuná; kuṛhná;
PINING, *N.*
jhorá. *m;*
PINION, *N.*
khambh. *m;*
PINION, TO, *V. T.*
mushkáṇ bannhníán;
with handcuffs. saṇgláṇ nál bannhná;
PINK, *A.*
piájí; gulábí;
PINNACLE, *N.*
manárá. *m;* kiṇggará. *m;*
PIOUS, *A.*
díndár; nek; dharmí; bhagat; saṇt; rást;
PIOUSLY, *Adv.*
díndárí nál;
PIP, *N.*
bí. *m;*
PIPE, *N.*
huqqá. *m;* hukṛí. *f;* hukṛá. *m;*
PIQUANCY, *N.*
mazá. *m;*
PIQUE, *N.*
waṭṭ. *f;* narázagi. *f;* hirkh. *m;*
PISTOL. *N.*
pistaul. *m;*
PIT, *N.*
ṭoá. *m;* khaḍolá. *m;* kháttá. *m;* khoh. *f;* kháḍḍá. *m;* bhorhá. *m;*
of small pox. dáná. *m;*
PITCH, *N.*
lukk. *m;*
Proverb. Play with pitch and you will soil your hands. In the brokerage of charcoal the face is blackened. koleáṇ dí dalálí dá múṇh kálá;
PITCH, TO, *V. T.*
1. to fix. gaḍḍná;
2. to throw. suṭṭná; vagháuná;
3. to pitch tents. láná;
PITCHER, *N.*
1. of brass. gágar. *f;*
2. of earthenware. ghaṛá. *m;*
PITCHFORK, *N.*
jaṇdrá. *m;* sángí. *f;* kuṇḍí. *f;*
see FORK.
PITEOUS, *A.*
1. miserable. udás; masosiá hoyá; sasdil; dil ḍhaṭṭhá;
2. compassionate. mihrbán; ráhmdil; kirpál;
PITEOUSLY, *Adv.*
gam nál; udás hoke; dáh de nál;
PITEOUSNESS, *N.*
ráhm. *m;* dayá. *m;* ráhmdilí. *f;* kirpá. *m;*
PITFALL, *N.*
khuttí. *f;* khuḍḍ. *f;*
PITH, *N.*
gobh. *m;* girí. *f;* guddá. *m;*
PITIABLE, *A.*
1. wretched. kambakht; khajjal kharáb; khuár; namáná;
2. deserving pity. ráhm jog;
PITIFUL, *A.*
narmdil; momdil; ráhmdil; dáyáwáṇ; dayál; kirpál;
PITIFULLY, *Adv.*
ráhm karke; ráhm nál;
PITIFULNESS, *N.*
ráhmdilí. *f;* narmí. *f;*
PITILESS, *A.*
sakht; karṛá; betaras; beráhm; bedard; jálim; patthar dil; hainsiárá; hattiárá; karárá;
PITILESSLY, *Adv.*
beráhmí nál; sakhtí nál;
PITILESSNESS, *N.*
beráhmí. *f;* sakhtí. *f;* loṛhá. *m;* rákhaspuṇá. *m;*
PITY, *N.*
ráhm. *m;* dáyá. *f;* tars. *m;*
PITY, TO, *V. T.*
ráhm karná; tars karná OR khánā;
PITINGLY, *Adv.*
ráhm karke; ráhm nál;
PIVOT, *N.*
1. for a door. chúthí. *f;*
2. for a bed. chúl. *f;*
PLACABILITY, *N.*
narmí. *f;* narmdilí. *f;*
PLACABLE, *A.*
narmdil; mulaim;
PLACARD, *N.*
ishtihár. *m;*
PLACE, *N.*
jagáh. *f;* tháṇ. *m;* thauṇ. *m;*
1. the place where cowdung is made ready for fuel. patheṛ. *m;*
2. out of place. kúthán;
3. in right place. tháṇ sir;

PLACE, TO, *V. T.*
dharná; ḍáhná; khaṛá karná; launá; rakkhná; ṭikáuná;
PLACED, TO BE, *V. I.*
ḍaihná;
PLACENTA, *N.*
1. of animals; jer. *f;* jhillí. *f;*
2. of women. aul. *m;*
PLACID, *A.*
dhímá; dhírá;
PLACIDLY, *Adv.*
dhíre dhíre; dhíme dhíme;
PLACIDITY, *N.*
dhíraj. *f;*
PLAGUE, *N.*
táún dí bamárí. *f;* manno. *f;*
PLAGUE, TO, *V. T.*
satáuná; sir khá jáná; taklíf dení; see TROUBLE.
PLAIN, *N.*
madán. *m;* raur. *f;* raṛá. *m;* raṛ. *f;* raṛí. *f;* piṛ. *m;* paddhar. *m;*
PLAIN, *A.*
1. simple. sádá; siddhá sádá; bholá;
2. clear. sáf; nirmal;
PLAINLY, *Adv.*
safáí nál; sáf sáf; dil kholke; see CANDIDLY.
PLAINNESS, *N.*
1. truthfulness. sachchíáí. *f;* rástí. *f;*
2. simplicity. sádagí. *f;* bholápaṇ. *m;*
PLAIN SPEAKING, *N.*
safáí nál bolná. *m;*
PLAINT, *N.*
duháí. *f;* dává. *f;* arz. *f;* sawál. *m;* arzú. *f;*
PLAINTIFF, *N.*
mudáí. *m;* nálashí. *m;* dávedár. *m;*
PLAINTIVE, *A.*
masosíá hoyá; udás; sasdil;
PLAIT, *N.*
míḍhí. *f;* meḍhí. *f;* meṇḍhí. *f;*
PLAIT, TO, *V. T.*
guṇdná;
1. to plait the hair. sir karná; wál guṇdná; wál suárná;
2. to plait a rope. waṭṭná;

PLAITED, *A.*
guthwáṇ;
PLAN, *N.*
1. scheme. saláh. *f;* upchár. *m;* upáo. *m;* tatbír. *f;* sahál. *f;* mith. *f;* tajwíz. *f;* ḍaul. *f;*
2. make some plan to obtain salvation, you will not live always in this world. kujh upáo mukt dá karo, jagg rahná nahíṇ.
3. sketch. kháká. *m;* naqshá. *m;*
PLAN, TO, *V. T.*
upchár karná; saláh karní; matá matáuná; matá pakáuná; ḍhaṇg sochná; upáo labbhná OR karná;
PLANE, *N.*
raṇdá. *m;*
PLANE, TO, *V. T.*
raṇdá pherná; raṇdná;
PLANK, *N.*
takhtá. *m;* phaṭṭá. *m;*
plank on which dhobi washes clothes. patṛá. *m;*
PLANT, *N.*
búṭá. *m;* búṭí. *f;* jháṛí. *f;*
1. young plants. paníṛí. *f;* bijárá. *m;*
2. Proverb. To show that poor people suffer when great men fall out. When buffaloes fight, small plants are torn up. bhiriṇ sáṇh paṭíjaṇ buṭe;
PLANT, TO, *V. T.*
1. to dig in. gaḍḍná;
2. to sow. bíjná;
3. to fix. láuná;
PLANTAIN, *N.*
kelá. *m;*
PLANTATION, *N.*
zakhírá. *m;*
PLASTER, *N.*
lipáí. *f;* lembí. *f;*
1. a new patch of plaster. le. *m;*
2. made of cowdung and earth. gobrí. *f;* see PLASTERING.
PLASTER, TO, *V. T.*
gachch karná OR láuná; lippná; limbná; limb dená; lep karná;
1. to plaster with cowdung. chaunká dená OR páuná; pochá dená
2. to cause to be plastered. lipwáuná;

PLASTERING, *N.*
lipáí. *f* ; limbáí. *f* ; leṇbí. *f* ;
1. pay for plastering. lipwáí. *f* ;
2. plastering tool. garmálá. *m* ;
PLAT. TO, *V. T.*
unná ;
PLATE, *N.*
pleṭ. *f* ; sáṇgkí. *f* ;
1. large brass plate. parát. *f* ; thál. *m* ;
2. of earthenware. tabákh. *m* ; tabákhará. *m* ;
PLATED, *A.*
mulammá ;
PLATFORM, *N.*
thaṛhá. *m* ;
erected in fields. manhá. *m* ;
PLATING, *N.*
ráj. *m* ;
PLATINUM, *N.*
sufed soná. *m* ;
PLAUDIT, *N.*
shábáshí. *f* ; jai jaikár. *m* ;
PLAY, *N.*
1. drama. rás. *f* ;
2. amusement. kheḍ. *f* ;
PLAY, TO, *V. T.*
1. to play a game. kheḍná ;
2. to play a musical instrument. bajáuná ; wajáuná ;
3. to play bat and ball. khiddo paṭṭí kheḍná ;
PLAYER, *N.*
khiḍárú. *m* ; khiḍárí. *m* ;
PLAYFUL, *A.*
khil khiláṛí ;
PLAYFULLY, *Adv.*
hássí nál ;
PLAYFULNESS, *N.*
chochláí. *f* ;
PLAYMATE. *N.*
laṇgoṭiá yár. *m* ; dost. *m* ;
PLAYTHING, *N.*
khiḍáuná. *m* ; bájí. *f* ;
PLEA, *N.*
arz. *f* ; bentí. *f* ; sawál. *m* ; árzú. *f* ; minnat. *f* ;
PLEAD, TO, *V. T.*
bentí karní ; arz karní ; minnat karní ;
PLEADER, *N.*
wakíl. *m* ;
PLEADING, *N.*
háhṛá. *m* ; hahre. *m* ; bentí. *f* ; minnat. *f* ;
PLEASANT, *A.*
dilpasind ; subh ; man bhauṇda ; Proverb used, when under most unpromising circumstances something pleasant turns up. Happiness in a wilderness. jangal vichch mangal honá ;
PLEASANTLY, *Adv.*
ḳhushí nál ; ḳhush hoke ;
PLEASANTRY, *N.*
hássí. *f* ; ḳhushí. *f* ;
PLEASE, TO, *V. T.*
rází OR ḳhush karná ; phuláuná ; magan karná ; rijháuná ; rangan rangná ; parsinn karná ;
PLEASED, TO BE, *V. I.*
ḳhush honá ; rijhná ; parsann honá ; phullná
1. I am very pleased with your matter. tuháḍí ih gall mainuṇ bhaundí hai ; maiṇ terí gall sunke baṛá parsann hoyá háṇ ;
2. all right, do as you please. achchhá, bháí, tusíṇ jánoṇ, jis taráh marjí je, karo ;
3. he does whatever he pleases. jo kujh uhnúṇ bhaundá hai, so uh kardá hai ;
4. are you pleased, then? pher tusáṇ núṇ parsíṇtá hundí hai?
5. I shall do as I please. jis taráh merí dalíl howegí, karángá ;
PLEASED, *A.*
ḳhush ; rází ; rájí ; magan ; gad gad ;
PLEASING, *A.*
manjúr ; dil pasiṇd ; pasiṇd ; dil chalá ; dil lagá ; man bhaundá ; sukhdáí ;
1. to be pleased. achchhá laggná ;
2. it pleased him. uhnúṇ chaṇgá lagá ;
PLEASURE, *N.*
ḳhushí. *f* ; cháh. *f* ; mauj. *f* ; anand. *m* ; bhauná. *m* ; bhauní. *f* ; parsintáí. *f* ; anandtáí. *f* ; lahir. *m* ; cháu. *m* ; rág raṇgg. *m* ;
1. to be given to pleasure. shuqín ban jáná ;

2. with pleasure. khushí nál; cháíṇ cháíṇ;

PLEAT, *N*.
bhann. *m*; waṭṭ. *m*;

PLEBIAN, *A*.
kamín;

PLEDGE, *N*.
gahiná *m*; gánháṇ. *m*;
earnest money. saí. *f*; biáná. *m*;

PLEDGE, TO, *V. T.*
girví páuná OR rakkhná; gahiṇe páuná; bandhe páuná OR rakkhná;

PLENTITUDE, *N*.
ḍher. *m*;

PLENTEOUS, *A*.
bahut; bahutá; bahterá; bahut sárá; ám; ḍher; wadhík; wáfar; ghanerá; sabargattá;

PLENTEOUSLY, *Adv.*
bahutait nál; kasrat nál;

PLENTIFUL, *A*.
ghanerá; see PLENTEOUS.

PLENTIFULLY, *Adv.*
wadhík; bahut karke;

PLENTIFULNESS, *N*.
ḍher. *m*,

PLENTY, *N*.
sukál. *m*;

PLENTY, *A*.
bahut; bahterá; bahut sárá; chokhí; ghattíṇmár; ghanerá; see ABUNDANT.

PLIABILITY, *N*.
lafau. *m*; lafá. *m*;

PLIABLE, *A*.
lifanwálá;

PLIGHT, *N*.
hál. *m*;

PLINTH, *N*.
kursí. *f*;

PLOT, *N*.
masandá. *m*; chálá. *m*; jálsájí. *f*; juglá. *f*;

PLOT, TO, *V. T.*
mansubá bannhná OR gharná; saláh pakáuní; gall pakáuní; sájish karná; uh de virodh matá karná; gundná; ḍhaṇg sochná; uh de khiláf saláháṇ karná; bar-khiláf saláh pakáuní; goreáṇ guṇdná; matá matáuná;

PLOUGH, *N*.
hal. *m*;
1. handle of plough. hatthá. *m*, hatthí. *f*;
2. body of plough. kuṛ. *m*
3. plough share. phálá. *m*

PLOUGH, TO, *V. T.*
hal joná OR wáhuná; wáhná;
Proverb. Labour spent in ploughing deep and in spinning is not wasted. ḍúṇghí wáhe gujjh chaláe birthá ná jae;

PLOUGHED LAND, *N*.
halohar. *f*; waríhál. *f*;
1. a ploughed field. wáhn. *m*;
2. Proverb. A ploughed field is nothing to a runaway. bhajdeáṇ núṇ wáhn ikko jehá;

PLOUGHING, *N*.
wahái. *f*;
1. a single ploughing. jotrá. *m*; jottá. *m*;
2. a second ploughing. dohaṛ *f*;
3. a third ploughing. tehaṛ. *f*;

PLOUGHMAN, *N*.
hálí. *m*; wáhak. *m*;

PLUCK, *N*.
dilerí. *f*; see BRAVERY.

PLUCK, TO, *V. T.*
kho lená;
1. pluck up. ukheṛná; puṭṭná;
2. pluck fruit. toṛná;

PLUCKILY, *Adv.*
dilerí nál; sher banke; himmat nál;

PLUCKY, *A*.
diler; bahádur; see BRAVE.

PLUG, *N*.
gaṭṭ. *m*; gaṭṭá. *m*; ḍakká. *m*,

PLUG, TO, *V. T.*
ḍakká dená;

PLUM, *N*.
alúchá. *m*; ber. *m*,
plum tree. berí. *f*;

PLUMAGE, *N*.
par. *f*;

PLUMBLINE, *N*.
sál *m*;

PLUME, *N*.
1. of a bird par. *f*;
2. on a helmet, & kalgí. *f*;

PLUMP, *A.*
ṭhullhá ; jabar katthá ; moṭá tázá ; see OBESE.
PLUNDER, *N.*
luṭṭ dá mál. *m* ; dháṛá. *m* ;
PLUNDER, TO, *V. T.*
luṭṭná ; dáká márná ; dháṛá márná ; már dháṛ karná ; muṭṭhná ;
PLUNDERED, TO BE, *V. I.*
luṭṭ már ho jáná ; ujjaṛ pujjaṛ jáná ; luṭṭiá jáná ; harná ;
PLUNDERER, *N.*
dháṛví. *m* ; ḍákú. *m* ; luṭerá. *m* ; luṭwayyá. *m* ; luṭerá. *m* ;
PLUNDERING, *N.*
loṭí. *f* ; luṭái. *f* ;
PLUNGE, *N.*
chubbhí. *f* ; see DIVE.
PLUNGE, TO, *V. T.*
1. to plunge anything into water. ḍob dená ; ḍobná ;
2. to dive. chubbhí láuní ; ṭubbí mární ;
PLURAL, *A.*
jamháṇ ;
PNEUMONIA, *N.*
númoniá. *m* ;
POACH, TO, *V. T.*
churáuná ; luṭṭná ;
POCKET, *N.*
gath. *f* ; khísá. *m* ; bojjhá. *m* ;
1. a knot in corner of sheet in which money is kept. gaṇḍh. *m* ;
2. in child's dress. gojhá. *m* ;
3. Proverb. Counting your chickens before they are hatched. He has nothing in his hand or purse, and shakes his pocket. hatth ná palle te khísá halle ;
4. Proverb used of the avarice of shrine keepers. Empty pockets and you come to petition God! gaṇḍhoṇ khálí Rabb de sawálí ;
POCKET BOOK, *N.*
chhoṭí kitáb. *f* ;
POCKET KNIFE, *N.*
káchchú. *m* ;
POCKET MONEY, *N.*
jeb kharach. *m* ;
POCK MARK, *N.*
mátá dá dág. *m* ;
POCKMARKED, *A.*
chutrambá ;
POD, *N.*
phalí. *f* ;
PODGY, *A.*
ḍhiḍḍal ; goggaṛ wálá ; moṭá ; see OBESE.
POEM, *N.*
nazm. *f* ; kabitt. *m* ;
line of poetry. tuk. *f* ;
POET, *N.*
sairí. *m* ; shairí. *m* ; sáir. *m* ;
POETRY, *N.*
kabísarí. *f* ; kabítá. *f* ; kabitá. *f* ; kabitt. *m* ; rágní. *f* ;
POIGNANCY, *N.*
sakhtí. *f* ;
POIGNANT, *A.*
1. bitter. kauṛá ; kusailá ;
2. severe. sakht ; haiṇsiárá ; hattiárá ; beráhm ;
POINT, *N.*
nok. *f* ;
1. point of a story. matlab. *m* ;
2. point of a goad. ár. *f* ;
POINT, TO, *V. T.*
ishárá karná ; unggal nál dikhláuná ; sainat mární ;
to point out. dassná ; dikhláuná ;
POINTED, *A.*
nokdár ; tikkhá ;
POISON, *N.*
wis. *f* ; zaihar. *m* ; mauhará. *m* ; weúh. *m* ; mahúrá. *m* ; bikh. *m* ;
Proverb. If you can gain your end by fair means, why use foul? If a man dies when you feed him with sugar, why give him poison? jekar koí guṛ khuáweṇ mare waíh dewan dí kí jarurat hai?
POISON, TO, *V. T.*
máuhará dená ; zaihár dená ;
POISONOUS, *A.*
zaiharí ;
POKE, TO, *V. T.*
hul mární ; hujj mární ; kurelná ; karolaná ;
POKER, *N.*
kurelní. *f* ;
wooden. kuḍḍhaṇ. *m* ; kuḍḍhaṇí. *f* ;
POLE, *N.*
ḍaṇḍá. *m* ; walí. *f* ; báṇs. *m* ; waṇjh. *m* ;
North Pole. kutab. *m* ;

POLEMICS, *N.*
bahis. *f* ;
POLICE, *N.*
polís. *m* ; sipáhí. *m* ;
POLISH, *N.*
1. a polishing fluid. rogan. *m* ;
2. a gloss. lishk. *f* ; chamak. *f* ; ghoṭ. *f* ; chilkárá. *m* ;
POLISH, TO, *V. T.*
jhalkáuná ; chamkáuná ; chilkáuná ; ghotná ;
POLISHED, *A.*
roganí ; chamakdár ;
POLITE, *A.*
milansár ; khulkí ; sharíf ;
POLITELY, *Adv.*
adab nál ;
POLITENESS, *N.*
adab. *f* ; ádar. *m* ; ádar bháú. *m* ; chál ḍhál. *f* ; chál wál. *f* ;
POLITICAL, *A.*
mulkí ;
POLITICS, *N.*
ráj nítí. *f* ;
POLL, TO, *V. T.*
voṭ dená ;
POLLUTE, TO, *V. T.*
gaṇdá karná ; wigáṛná ; kharáb karná ; palít karná ; labeṛná ; bhiṭṭ dená ; lithaṛná ;
to polute food by touching it. bhiṭáuná ;
POLLUTED, *A.*
gusaliá hoyá ; palít ; bharisht ; see IMPURE.
polluted (food). ; bharisht ;
POLLUTION, *N.*
napákí. *f* ; sug. *f* ; palítí. *f* ; gaṇdagí. *f* ; palidagí. *f* ;
by touching food. bhiṭṭ. *f* ;
POLTROON, *N.*
bhagaurá. *m* ; ḍaranwálá. *m* ; ḍárú. *m* ;
POLYTHEIST, *N.*
mushrik. *m* ;
POMADE, *N.*
phulel. *f* ; tel. *m* ;
ointment. malham. *f* ;
POMEGRANATE, *N.*
anár. *m* ;
POMELO, *N.*
chakodhrá. *m* ;
POMMEL, *N.*
hanná. *m* ;
POMP, *N.*
shán. *f* ; dhúm dhám. *f* ; shuká shákí. *f* ; saj dhaj. *f* ; hú há. *f* ; hú hawá. *f* ; chirhat. *f* ; jal jilau. *m* ; ṭháṭ. *f* ; see OSTENTATION.
POMPOSITY, *N.*
dikhává. *m* ;
POMPOUS, *A.*
1. displaying pomp. shándár ; raunaqí ;
2. showing self importance. phiṭṭiá hoyá ;
POMPOUSLY, *Adv.*
dhum dhám nál ;
POND, *N.*
1. very small. chhappṛí. *f* ;
2. small. chhappaṛ. *m* ;
3. large. ṭobhá. *m* ; ḍhab. *f* ;
4. large and deep. ḍummh. *m* ;
5. lake. kuṇḍ. *m* ; chhanbh. *m* ;
PONDER, TO, *V. T.*
dhián karná ; sochná ; gaur karná ; wichárná ; dhiánaná ; chitamná ;
PONDEROUS, *A.*
bhárá ; bhárí ; bojhal ; waḍḍá ;
PONY, *N.*
ṭairá. *m* ; ṭairí. *f* ; ṭaṭṭu. *m* ; ṭair. *f* ;
POOL, *N.*
chhappṛí. *f* ; see POND.
POOR, *A.*
garíb ; garíb gurbá ; kangál ; lachár ; shohdá : namáṇá ;
POORLY, *A.*
bamár ; kamjor ; ḍhillá maṭṭhá ;
POP, TO, *V. I.*
ṭhíṇ ṭhíṇ karná ;
POPE, *N.*
Roman Káthulikáṇ dá waḍḍá Bishap Sáhib. *m* ;
POPPY, *N.*
kaskhas. *f* ; post. *m* ;
POPPY HEAD, *N.*
ḍodá. *m* ; ḍoḍḍá. *m* ;
POPULACE, *N.*
lokí. *m* ; lok. *m* ; pablik. *m* ; ám lok. *m* ; mulkháiá. *m* ;
POPULAR, *A.*
manniá danniá ; manniá parwanniá ;
POPULATE, TO, *V. T.*
lok wasáuná ; wason karni ;

POPULATION, *N.*
wason. *f* ;
POPULOUS, *A.*
baṛí abádí ; saṅghní wason ;
PORCELAIN, *N.*
chiní. *f* ;
PORCH, *N.*
1. door. darwájá. *m* ; buhá. *m* ;
2. room at entrance. ḍeurhí. *f* ;
PORE, *N.*
masám. *m* ;
PORE, TO, *V. T.*
baṛe gaur nál paṛhná ;
PORK, *N.*
sur dá más. *m* ;
POROUS, *A.*
khokhlá ; pollá ; khokhrá ;
PORRIDGE, *N.*
daliyá. *m* ;
PORT, *N.*
1. harbour. bandargáh. tápú. *m* ;
2. wine. sharáb. *m* ;
PORTABLE, *A.*
safarí ;
light. haulá ;
PORTAL, *N.*
darwájá. *m* ; buhá. *m* ;
PORTEND, TO, *V. T.*
pahloṇ dassná ; jatáuná ;
PORTENT, *N.*
sagan. *m* ; fál. *m* ;
bad omen. bad sagan. *m* ;
PORTER, *N.*
kúlí. *m* ; mazdúr. *m* ;
PORTERAGE, *N.*
ḍhulwáí. *f* ; mazdúrí. *f* ;
PORTION, *N.*
hissá. *m* ; chháṇḍá. *m* ; dakkará. *m* ; pattí. *f* ; máwá. *m* ; waṇḍ. *f* ;
1. a small portion of anything. chuṇg. *f* ; chunggí, *f* ;
2. share. bakhrá. *m* ;
PORTION, TO, *V. T.*
waṇḍná ; waṇḍ dená ; hissá karná ; wartauná ;
between two. adho adh karná ;
PORTLY, *A.*
ḍhiḍḍal ; ghoggaṛ ; ḍhiḍḍhu ; see OBESE.
PORTMANTEAU, *N.*
thailá. *m* ;
PORTRAIT, *N.*
taswír. *f* ;
PORTRAY, TO, *V. T.*
taswír khichná ; chittarná ;
POSE, TO, *V. T.*
1. to perplex. ghabrá dená ; gallaṇ nál phasáuná ;
2. to place anyone. biṭhálná ;
POSITION, *N.*
1. rank. darjá. *m* ; ohdá. *m* ;
2. condition. hál. *m* ;
3. direction. rukkh. *m* ; walí. *f* ;
POSITIVE, *A.*
pakká ;
POSSESS, TO, *V. T.*
rakkhná ; de kol ; de pás ;
POSSESSION, *N.*
1. property. rás. *f* ; jaedád. *m* ; rás púnjí. *f* ;
2. ownership. málakí. *f* ;
3. to take possession. qabjá kar lainá ; mallná ;
POSSESSOR, *N.*
málik. *m* ;
POSSIBLE, *A.*
ho sake ; hon jog ;
as far as possible. wáh laggdiaṇ ;
POSSIBLY, *Adv.*
khabare ; shayad ;
POST, *N.*
1. service. naukarí. *f* ; asámí. *f* ; chákarí. *f* ;
2. lamp post. walá. *m* ; munná. *m* ;
3. telegraph post. walá. *m* ;
4. a support. mahál. *m* ; mohrí. *f* ;
5. door posts. muhaṭhín. *f* ;
POST, TO, *V. T.*
1. to station. dharná ; rakkhná ;
2. to post a letter. ḍák vichch páuná ;
POSTAGE, *N.*
ḍák mahsúl. *m* ;
POSTAGE STAMP, *N.*
tikaṭ. *f* ;
POST CARD, *N.*
post kád. *m* ;
POSTER, *N.*
ishtehár. *m* ;
POSTERIOR, *A.*
pichchlá ; pichche dá ;
POSTERITY, *N.*
puttar puttare. *m* ; aulád. *f* ;

POSTHASTE, *Adv.*
jhaṭ phaṭ; ikk dam; see IMMEDIATELY.

POSTMAN, *N.*
chiṭṭírisán. *m;* ḍákwálá. *m;* ḍákiyá. *m;* halkárá. *m;*

POSTMARK, *N.*
ḍák dí mohr. *f;*

POST OFFICE, *N.*
ḍák ḳháná. *m;*

POSTPONE, TO, *V. T.*
ṭálná; ajj bhalak karná; ṭál dená; pher te rakkhná; ṭálá bálá karná;
postpone a hearing in court. taríḳ pá dení;

POSTPONEMENT, *N.*
ṭál. *f;* see DELAY.

POSTURE, *N.*
ḍhang. *m;*

POT, *N.*
1. of all kinds. bhánḍá. *m;*
2. of earthnware for water. jhajjar. *m;* ghaṛá. *m;*
3. of brass for water. gagar. *f;*
4. large metal. deg. *m;* matt. *m;*
5. pots and pans. bhánḍe ṭinḍe. *m;* bhánḍá ṭinḍá. *m;*
6. potstand. ghaṛwanjí. *f;*

POTASH, *N.*
1. raw potash, sajjí. *f;*
2. prepared potash. khár. *m;*

POTATO, *N.*
álú. *m;*

POTBELLIED, *A.*
ḍhiḍḍal; ghoggaṛ;
a potbellied person. gugṛail. *m;* gugṛílá. *m;* peṭú. *m;*

POTENCY, *N.*
táqat. *f;* jor. *m;* shaktí. *f;*

POTENT, *A.*
mazbut; táqatwálá;

POTENTATE, *N.*
hákim. *m;*

POTENTIAL, *A.*
ho sakdá;

POTENTLY, *Adv.*
baṛe jor nál; táqat nál;

POTHER, *N.*
raulá. *m;* shor. *m;* see CONFUSION.

POTSHERD, *N.*
1. large piece, ṭhikṛá. *m;*
2. smallpiece. ṭhikṛí. *f;* babbari. *f;*

POTTER,
kumhár. *m;* ghamiár. *m;* parjápat. *m;*

POTTERY, *N.*
miṭṭí de bhánḍe. *m;*

POUCH, *N.*
1. small, khísí. *f;* thailí. *f;* potlí. *f;* guthlí. *f;*
2. large, khalítí. *f;* thailá. *m;* jholá. *m;* guthlá. *m;*

POULTICE, *N.*
lupparí. *f;* lep. *m;*

POULTRY, *N.*
kukṛí. *f;*

POUNCE, TO, *V. T.*
jhapaṭná; panjá márná;

POUNCING, *N.*
jhaṭṭ. *m;* jhapaṭ. *f;* jhapph. *f;*

POUND, *N.*
1. weight. addh ser. *m;*
2. money. paunḍ. *m;*
3. for cattle. phátak. *m.*

POUND, TO, *V. T.*
1. to pound by grinding. chúr chúr karná; ghoṭná;
2. to pound by beating. kuṭṭná;

POUR, TO, *V. T.*
ḍuhulná; ḍhilkáuná; roṛhná; roṛh dená; kerná; kiráuná; páuná; puáuná; witáuná; ḍuhlainá;
1. to pour out. lúd dená; ḍolná;
2. to cause to be poured out. ḍulhwáuná;
3. to be poured out. ḍhilakná; ḍulná; ḍhalná;

POUT, TO, *V. T.*
múnh sujáuná; ṭerná; ruṭṭhná; múnh bhaiṛá banáuná; bull kaḍḍhná;

POVERTY, *N.*
thuṛ. *f;* tangí. *f;* garíbí. *f;* muhtájí. *f;* tangsí. *f;* adhíní. *f;* daliddar. *m;* daliddartái. *f;*

POWDER, *N.*
1. gun powder. dárú. *m;*
2. medicine. phakkí. *f;*
3. powdered medicine wrapped in paper. puṛí. *f;*

POWDER, TO, *V. T.*
chúrá chúrá karná; zará zará karná; píhná; see POUND.

POWER, *N.*
táqat. *f*; jor. *m*; wáh. *f*; shaktí. *f*; majál. *f*; wass. *m*; samarthá. *f*; jorávari. *f*; tul. *f*; parákarm. *m*;
1. Divine power. qudrat. *f*;
2. to be in one's power. wass vichch áuná;
3. if you have the power. je wass lage;

POWERFUL, *A.*
tagaṛá; takaṛá; mazbut; táqatwálá; parbal; sabal; ḍáḍḍhá; jorwálá; balkárí; samarthí;
for GOD. qudratwálá;

POWERFULLY, *Adv.*
zor nál; jor láke;

POWERLESS, *A.*
kamjor; abass; natáná; nirbal; bewass;

POWERLESSLY, *Adv.*
kamjor hoke;

POWERLESSNESS, *N.*
kamjorí. *f*; natáqatí. *f*;

PRACTICABLE, *A.*
karne jog; honhár; jo ho sake;
easy. sukhálá; saukhá; ásán;

PRACTICAL, *A.*
amlí; kamm dá;

PRACTICALLY, *Adv.*
asl vichch;

PRACTICE, *N.*
jách. *f*; rauṇs. *f*; rawáj. *f*; rawaiyá. *m*; ḍaul chál. *f*; bheṛ chál. *f*; lí. *f*; bhus. *m*; dastúr. *m*;
habit. ádat. *f*; kho ḳhaslat. *f*; sabhá. *m*; gejh. *f*; ṭharak. *m*;

PRACTISE, TO, *V. T.*
wartná; sádhná; amal karná;

PRAISE, *N.*
saláhat. *f*; saráhat. *f*; táríf. *f*; ustut. *f*; guṇ. *m*; waḍiáí. *f*; mahimá. *f*; salauhat. *f*; sobhá. *f*;
Proverb. Sing his praise who feeds you. jih dá kháíe, uh dá gít gáie;

PRAISE, TO, *V. T.*
táríf karní; guṇ gáuná; waḍiáí karní; waḍiáuná; nám lainá; saráhná; mahimá karná; ustut karní; jas gáuná; shábásh dení; saláhná;
1. to sing one's own praises. apná rág gáuná;
2. Proverb. The potter's wife praises her own pots. ghumíárí apná hí bháṇḍá saláundí hai;

PRAISEWORTHY, *A.*
táríf de laiq; baṛá laiq; saláhán jog;

PRAISING, *N.*
kírtan. *f*;

PRANCE, TO, *V. T.*
sík páo honá; kuddná;

PRANK, *N.*
kheḍ. *f*; kalol. *f*;
mischievousness. sharárat. *f*;

PRATE, TO, *V. T.*
bak bak karná; chir chir karná; khaujhná; ṭarkná; magaz márná; chiṛchiṛáuná; ṭarṭráuná; see TATTLE.

PRATING, *N.*
jhakh. *f*; gapp. *f*; bak. *m*; bataulá. *m*; gapp chaṛapp. *f*;

PRATTLE, *N.*
bakwás. *m*; jhakk. *f*;

PRATTLE, TO, *V. T.*
jhakh mární; gapp márná; bataulá márná; chiṛchiṛáuná;

PRATTLER, *N.*
bakwásí. *m*; khappí. *m*; gapauṛí. *m*; gálaṛú. *m*; baṛbolá, *m*; gappí. *m*; padauṛá. *m*; jaṭallí. *m*;

PRAY, TO, *V. T.*
duá karní; bentí karní; maṇgná; parárthṇá karná; duá te minnat karní; path karná;

PRAYER, *N.*
duá. *f*; bentí. *f*; parárthṇá. *f*; minnat. *f*;
1. prayer connected with austeríties. tap. *m*;
2. to make long prayers. lammí chauṛí namáz paṛhná;

PRAYER BOOK, *N.*
namáz dí kitáb. *f*;

PRAYERFUL, *A.*
namájí;

PRAYER MEETING, *N.*
duá de wáste mitting. *m*;

PREACH, TO, *V. T.*
wáz karná; nasíhat dení; updesh karná; bachan karná; kalám karná; manádí karní;

PREACHER, *N.*
1. Christian. manád. *m;* waiz. *m;*
2. Hindu and Sikh. dharm updeshak. *m;* granthí. *m;* parchárak. *m;* pachárí. *m;*
PREACHING, *N.*
manádi. *f;*
PRECARIOUS, *A.*
pakkí nahíṇ ;
PRECAUTION, *N.*
ḳhabardárí. *f;* hosh. *f;*
to take precaution. uprálá karná ;
PRECEDE, TO, *V. T.*
agge chalná ; pahláṇ honá ;
PRECEDENCE, *N.*
buzurgi. *f;*
PRECEDENT, *N.*
1. custom. dastur. *m;* rawáj. *m;*
2. example. namúná. *m;*
3. there is no precedent for this. ih kadí nahíṇ hoyá ;
PRECEDING, *A.*
aglá ; pahláṇ ;
PRECEPT, *N.*
maslá. *m;* hukm. *m;*
religious precept or ordinance. bidhí. *f;*
PRECIOUS, *A.*
aṇmull ; amolak ; bahúmulle ; mahṇgá ; pyárá ; aṇmullá ; mahiṇg mullá ;
more precious. ziyádá mull de ;
PRECIPATELY, *Adv.*
1. without thinkng, biṇ soche ; biṇá soche samjhe ; jhapájhap ; biṇ soche ;
2. quickly. chhetí ; shatábí ; jhaṭ paṭ ; jaldí ; utaulá ;
PRECIPICE, *N.*
baṛi khaḍḍ. *f;* duṇgháí. *f;*
PRECIPITANCE, *N.*
tezí. *f;* josh. *m;* káhlí. *f;*
PRECIPITATE, TO, *V. T.*
chhetí turáuná ; dauṛáuná ;
PRECIPITATION, *N.*
josh. *m;* utaulá. *f;* káhlí. *f;*
PRECIPITOUS, *A.*
dhálú ;
PRECISE, *A.*
ṭhík ; durust ; sahí ; suddh ;
PRECISELY, *Adv.*
ṭhík ṭhák ; saṇwárke ; banáke ; hú ba hú ; see EXACTLY.

PRECISENESS, *N.*
durustí. *f;*
PRECISION, *N.*
durustí. *f;* suddhtái. *f;*
PRECLUDE, TO, *V. T.*
1. to hinder. rokná ; dakkná ; ḍáṭná ; aṭkáuná ;
2. to shut out. chhekná ;
PRECONCEIVE, TO, *V.T.*
pahle thoṇ sochná ;
PRECONCEPTION, *N.*
pahlá ḳhayál. *m;*
PREDECESSOR, *N.*
aglá. *m;*
PREDETERMINE, TO, *V. T.*
pahle thoṇ ṭhahráuná ;
PREDICAMENT, *N.*
hál. *m;*
PREDICATE, TO, *V. T.*
bayán karná ; dassná ; batláuná ;
PREDICT, TO, *V. T.*
pahle batláuná ; agamm báchchná ; pahle jatáuná ;
PREDICTION, *N.*
tewá. *m;*
PREDILICTION, *N.*
chatak. *f;* chaská. *m;* cháṭ. *f;*
PREDOMINANCE, *N.*
1. superiority. álá darjá. *m;* buzurgí. *f;*
2. authority. jor. *m;* iḳhtiyár. *m;* wass. *m;*
PREDOMINANT, *A.*
ḳháss ; uttam ; pardháná ;
PREDOMINATE, TO, *V. T.*
hukúmat karní ; iḳhtiyár karná ;
PREDOMINATE, TO, *V. I.*
gálib honá ; parbal honá ;
PREEMINENCE, *N.*
buzurgí. *f;* khubí. *f;*
PREEMINENT, *A.*
sáreáṇ nálon waḍḍá ; dáná ; pardháná ; waḍḍá buzurg ; bhalá chaṇgá ; álá ;
PREFACE, *N.*
dibáchá. *m;* bhúmaká. *m;*
PREFER, TO, *V. T.*
cháhuná ; bahut chaṇgá jánná ; pasiṇd karná ;
PREFERABLE, *A.*
chaṇgá ; achchhá ;
PREFERABLY, *Adv.*
ih chaṇgá jánke ;

PREFERENCE, *N.*
bhauná. *m*; ríjh. *f*; ichchhiá. *f*; cháh. *f*; bhauní, *f*;
PREFERMENT, *N.*
taraqqí. *f*;
PREGNANCY, *N.*
gábh. *m*; gabbh. *m*; garbh. *m*; hamal. *m*; umedwárí. *f*;
PREGNANT, *A.*
1. of women. pair bhárí; ḍhiḍḍ nál; garbhaní; garbhwálí;
2. of animals. gabhaní; gabbhan; súnwálí;
3. to be pregnant, of women. ḍhiḍḍ honá; uhnuṇ ummedwárí; aggá bhárí honá; pair bhárí honá; garbhaṇí honá; ásse honá;
4. to be pregnant, for animals. saurná; saur jáná; ásse laggná;
PREJUDGE, TO, *V. T.*
waqt thoṇ pahláṇ faisalá karná;
PREJUDICE, *N.*
liház. *m*; tarafdárí. *f*; pachchhdár. *f*; pachchh. *m*;
PREJUDICE, TO, *V. T.*
charáuná;
PREJUDICED, *A.*
pakkhí; tarafdár; uh de wal;
PRELATE, *N.*
bishap sáhib. *m*;
PRELIMINARY, *A.*
pahle;
PREMATURE, *A.*
agetá; agetare; waqt thoṇ pahláṇ; aggoṇ;
PREMATURELY, *Adv.*
waqt thoṇ pahle;
PREMEDITATE, TO, *V. T.*
pahle sochná;
PREMEDITATION, *N.*
pahle dí tajwíz. *f*;
PREMIER, *A.*
waḍḍá; pahláṇ;
PREMISE, TO, *V. T.*
pahle jatáuná;
PREMONISH, TO, *V. T.*
pahle jatáuná OR samjháuná; chitárná;
PREMONITION, *N.*
sagaṇ. *m*;
PREPARATION, *N.*
tiyárí. *f*; sajáut. *f*;

PREPARE, TO, *V. T.*
tíyár karná; sawárná; sájná; for burial. kafanáuná;
PREPARED, *A.*
tiyár;
PREPAY, TO, *V. T.*
pahle dená; peshgí dení;
PREPONDERANCE, *N.*
wadháu. *m*;
PREPONDERATE, TO, *V. T.*
waḍḍá honá; wadháuná;
PREPOSITION, *N.*
sambandak. *m*;
PREPOSSESSING, *A.*
baṛá chaṇgá;
PREPOSTEROUS, *A.*
ulṭá; ṭhík nahíṇ; beaqlí dí gal;
PREPOSTEROUSLY, *Adv.*
beaqlí nál;
PREROGATIVE, *N.*
haqq. *m*;
PRESAGE, *N.*
sagan. *m*;
PRESBYTER, *N.*
pádrí sáhib. *m*;
PRESCIENCE, *N.*
dúr dhián. *m*; dúr audeshá. *m*;
PRESCRIBE, TO, *V. T.*
dúá dárú dená; dawá dená;
PRESCRIPTION, *N.*
nuskhá. *m*; nukshá. *m*;
PRESENCE, *N.*
1. not absence. házarí. *f*;
2. of superior. hazúrí. *f*; hajúrí. *f*;
3. impressive mein. robkárí. *f*; rob. *f*; dabdabá. *m*;
PRESENT, *A.*
1. now existing. wartmán;
2. opposed to absent. hájar; házir.
PRESENT, *N.*
inám kinám. *m*; bakhshiá. *m*; ajr. *m*;
1. given to GOD. charává. *m*; nazar. *f*; hadyá. *m*;
2. given to a bride. khaṭṭ. *f*;
3. given with invitation to a wedding. bhájí. *f*;
4. given to girl at betrothal. sagaṇ. *m*;
5. the betrothal present had come. mangní dá sagaṇ á gayá sí;

5. given to bride by the bride-groom's people. jharáweṇ kapṛe. *m* ;
6. given to servants at a wedding. lág. *f* ;
7. for the present moment. aitkíṇ ;
8. of clothes given at a wedding. pahináuṇí. *f* ;

PRESENT, TO, *V. T.*
1. to give, dená ;
2. to put forward. pesh karná ; sáhmne karná ; agge karná ;

PRESENTATION, *N.*
inám. *m* ; ajr. *m* ;

PRESENTIMENT, *N.*
lakháu. *m* ; ḳhayál. *m* ;

PRESENTLY, *Adv.*
huṇe ; thoṛí der de bád ;

PRESERVATION, *N.*
bacháo. *m* ; richchhiá. *f* ; rákkhí. *f* ;

PRESERVE, TO, *V. T.*
bacháuná ; nistárná ; sámbh ke rakkhná ; sámbhná ; richchiá karní ; sambhálí rakkhná ; see PROTECT.
to preserve fruit. murabbá pauná ;

PRESERVER, *N.*
bacháunwálá. *m* ; rákkhá. *m* ; rachhpál. *m* ; rachhak. *m* ;

PRESERVES, *N.*
achár. *m* ;

PRESIDE, TO, *V. T.*
1. to sit as president. pardhán banná ; birájná ; mír majlis banná ;
2. to exercise oversight. nigrání karní ;

PRESIDENCY, *N.*
pardháṇtáí. *f* ; sardárí. *f* ;

PRESIDENT, *N.*
pardháṇ. *m* ; bhardán. *m* ;

PRESS, *N.*
1. printing. cháppá ḳháná. *m* ;
2. sugar. belná. *m* ;
3. book binder's. shakanjá. *m* ;

PRESS, TO, *V. T.*
ghuṭṭná ; dabbná ; nappná ;
1. to press oil, sugarcane. piṛná ;
2. to press down. dabáuná ;
3. to press together, to squeeze. pichkauná ; phíhná ;

PRESSING, *N.*
dabb. *f* ;

PRESSING, *A.*
zarúrí ;

PRESSINGLY, *Adv.*
zor nál ; dabb ke ;

PRESSURE, *N.*
dabb. *f* ; dabá. *m* ;

PRESTIGE, *N.*
mán. *m* ; ro. *f* ;

PRESUMABLY, *Adv.*
ḳhayál hai paí ;

PRESUME, TO, *V. T.*
gustáḳhí karní ;

PRESUMING, *A.*
gustáḳh ; see PRESUMPTIOUS.

PRESUMPTION, *N.*
1. arrogance. ḍhíṭhái. *f* ; haṇkár. *m* ; gustáḳhí. *f* ;
2. belief. yaqín. *m* ; partít. *m* ;

PRESUMPTIOUS, *A.*
ḍhíṭh ; ḍhíṭhá ; hekaṛ ; magrúr ; gamrúr ; ghamaṇḍí ; mazájí ; ḍakkará ;

PRETENCE, *N.*
pajj. *m* ; hil. *f* ; pher gher. *m* ; ánná baháná. *m* ; dhuchchar. *m* ; lichch gaṛichchiáṇ. *f* ; pakháṇḍ. *m* ; ḳhekhaṇ. *m* ; ghaí. *f* ; bejjá. *m* ; ṭhuṇá. *m* ;

PRETEND, TO, *V. T.*
bejjá márná ; dhokhá dená ; makr karná ; pakhaṇḍ karná ; bahána banáuná ; ṭhuṇá dená ; khekháṇ karná ;
1. to pretend not to know. machláuná.
2. he is only pretending to agree. aiweṇ uttoṇwálí háṇ kardá hai.

PRETENSION, *N.*
dává. *m* ; dalíl. *f* ;
false pretension. bejjá. *m* ;

PRETERMIT, TO, *V. T.*
ján dená ; muáf karná ;

PRETEXT, *N.*
pajj. *m* ; ánná bahána. *m* ; ṭhuná. *m* ; phauh. *m* ;
by some pretext or other. dáiṇ dáiṇ ; see PRETENCE.

PRETTINESS, *N.*
ḍuss. *f* ; see BEAUTY.

PRETTY, *A.*
sohná ; shakalwálá ; rupwálá ; mukhwálá ;

PREVAIL, TO, *V. T.*
1. to overcome, win. jittná; haráuná; dabb láuná; zor pá jáná;
2. to persuade manáuná; gharkáuná;
PREVALENCE, *N.*
dastúr. *m*; rawáj. *m*;
PREVALENT, *A.*
rawájí;
PREVARICATE, TO, *V. T.*
ṭálná; jabán badalní; jhuṭh bolná; jhuṭh sachch kahná; ghasal masal karná; ále ṭále karná; aí gaí karná; ṭál maṭolá karná; ṭhuṇá dená; bháṇt bháṇt dí bolí bolná;
PREVARICATION, *N.*
ṭál. *f*; ṭálá. *m*; álá ṭálá. *m*; ghasal masal. *m*; ghásal másal *m*; sachch jhuṭh. *m*; ṭhuṇá. *m*; her pher. *m*; ṭálmaṭolá *m*;
PREVARICATOR, *N.*
dhokhebáj. *m*; pakhaṇḍí. *m*;
PREVENT, TO, *V. T.*
ṭokná; ḍátná; aṭkáuná; ḍakkná; warajná; ṭhák dená; ṭhákná;
to be prevented. ḍakkiá rahná; rukiá rahná;
PREVENTION, *N.*
ṭhák. *f*;
PREVIOUS, *A.*
pahláṇ; aglá; agetará;
PREVIOSULY, *Adv.*
aggoṇ; pahláṇ; agetare;
PREY, *N.*
shikár. *m*;
PREY, TO, *V. T.*
luṭṭná; see ROB.
PRICE, *N.*
bhá. *m*; kharíd dá mull. *m*;
to fix a price. kharíd karná; uhdá mull ṭhahráuná OR pakáuná;
PRICELESS, *A.*
amolak; anmull; baṛe mull dá; baṛí piyárí; aṇmullá;
PRICK, *N.*
chobhá. *m*;
PRICK, TO, *V. T.*
chubháuná; chobhná; chobh dená;
to prick with a needle. suí mární;
PRICKED, TO BE, *V. I.*
kaṇḍḍá laggná; chubhná;
PRICKING, *N.*
chobhá. *m*;
PRICKLE, *N.*
kaṇḍḍá. *m*; paṇggá. *m*;
PRICKLY, *A.*
kaṇdiálá; kaṇḍeáṇwálá;
PRICKLY HEAT, *N.*
pitt. *f*; pittu. *f*;
PRIDE, *N.*
akkaṛ. *f*; magrurí. *f*; garab. *m*; henh. *f*; abhmán. *m*; damág. *m*; majáj. *f*; gubh gubháṭ. *m*; mikk. *f*; ghamaṇḍ. *m*; haṇkár. *m*; gumán. *m*; kibar. *m*; hakáṛ. *m*; hekaṛí. *f*; gamrúrí. *f*;
PRIEST, *N.*
1. Hindu. jájak. *m*; báhman. *m*; pujárí. *m*; parohat. *m*;
2. Muhammadan. maulví. *m*; majaur. *m*; malwáná. *m*; míáṇ. *m*;
3. Jewish. káhin. *m*;
4. Christian. pádrí. *m*; pír pádrí. *m*;
5. Sikh. granthí. *m*; gurú. *m*; gúr. *m*;
PRIG, *N.*
haṇkárí. *m*;
PRIGGISH, *A.*
haṇkárí;
PRIGGISHNESS, *N.*
haṇkár. *m*;
PRIMACY, *N.*
pardhántáí. *f*; sirdárí. *f*;
PRIMARILY, *A.*
kháss karke; asl vichch;
PRIMARY, *A.*
1. first. pahláṇ;
2. real. aslí;
PRIMATE, *N.*
Lát Bishap Sáhib. *m*;
PRIME, *A.*
baṛá chaṇgá; bhalá chaṇgá; suthrá; sohná; uttam;
PRIMER, *N.*
pahlí kitáb. *f*;
PRIMEVAL, *A.*
pahláṇ; aslí;
PRIMING, *A.*
dárú, *m*;
PRIMOGENITOR, *N.*
waḍerá. *m*; piudádá. *m*;
PRIMOGENITURE, *N.*
paleṭhí. *f*;

PRINCE, *N.*
sajádá. *m* ; kaur. *m* ; sháhzádá. *m* ;
PRINCELY, *A.*
sháhí ;
PRINCESS, *N.*
rájá dí dhí. *f* ; ráj kanniáṇ. *f* ; shájádí. *f* ; sajádí. *f* ; ráj putrí. *f* ;
PRINCIPAL, *N.*
prinsipal sáhib. *m* ;
PRINCIPAL, *A.*
sáreáṇ náloṇ waḍḍá ; mukh ; mukhí ; mukhiá ;
PRINCIPALITY, *N.*
rájwárá. *m* ;
PRINCIPALLY, *A.*
ḳháss karke ; bahut karke ;
PRINCIPLE, *N.*
1. a doctrine. maslá. *m* ;
2. the real thing. asal. *m* ;
PRINT, *N.*
chháp. *f* ;
PRINT, TO, *V. T.*
chhápná ;
to print cloth. thekarná ; ṭhappná ;
PRINTER, *N.*
chhápanwálá. *m* ;
PRINTING, *N.*
chhapáí. *f* ;
PRINTING PRESS, *N.*
chháppá ḳháná. *m* ;
PRIOR, *A.*
aglá ; pahláṇ ;
PRIORITY, *N.*
buzurgí. *f* ; pardhántáí. *f* ;
PRISON, *N.*
jel ḳhaná. *m* ; haválát. *f* ; kaṇjí haud. *m* ; baurá. *m* ; bande ḳháná. *m* ;
PRISONER, *N.*
qaidí. *m* ; bandhwá. *m* ; baṇdíwáṇ. *m* ;
PRIVACY, *N.*
ikkalwánjá. *m* ; ollhá. *m* ; ikáṇt. *f* ;
PRIVATE, *A.*
1. persona' nijj dá ; paṛde dí gal ; ollhe dí gal. *f* ;
2. secluded. alag ;
3. in private. pasitte hoke ; nawekle hoke ;
PRIVATELY, *Adv.*
gujjhe gujjhe ; paṛde nál ; pasitte hoke ; see SECRETLY.

PRIVATION, *N.*
taṇgí. *f* ; taṇgsí. *f* ; muhtájí. *f* ;
PRIVILEDGE, *N.*
ḳháss haqq. *m* ;
PRIVILY, *Adv.*
gujjhe gujjhe ; paṛde nál ;
PRIVY, *N.*
taṭṭí. *f* ; taraṭṭí. *f* ;
PRIZE, *N.*
inám. *m* ; ajr. *m* ;
PRIZE, TO, *V. T.*
qadr karná ; liház karná ; máṇ karná ;
PROBABILITY, *N.*
ummed. *f* ;
PROBABLE, *A.*
shayad ; sau wiswá ;
PROBABLY, *Adv.*
shayad ; wíh wiswe ; ummed hai paí
PROBATION, *N.*
ázmaish. *f* ; partává. *m* ;
PROBATIONER, *N.*
ummedwár. *m* ;
PROBE, *N.*
suá. *m* ;
lancet. nastar. *m* ;
PROBE, TO, *V. T.*
jakham ṭohná ; pholná ;
PROBITY, *N.*
ímándárí. *f* ; sachchiáí. *f* ; sídhíáí. *f* ;
PROBLEM, *N.*
suwál. *m* ;
PROBLEMATIC, *A.*
shakkí ;
PROBOSCIS, *N.*
búthá. *m* ;
PROCEDURE, *N.*
ḍhang. *m* ; dastur. *m* ;
PROCEED, TO, *V. I.*
agge jáná ; agge waddhná ;
PROCEEDINGS, *N.*
kárawáí. *f* ; kamm káj. *m* ;
PROCEEDS, *N.*
hásal. *m* ;
PROCESS, *N.*
ḍhang. *m* ;
PROCESSION, *N.*
jalús. *m* ; jatthá. *m* ;
PROCLAIM, TO, *V. T.*
ḍauṇḍí pherní ; ḍhaṇḍorá dená ; dhomáuná ; hoká dená ;
to preach. manádí karní ; parchár karná ;

PROCLAIMER, *N.*
ḍhanḍoriá. *m ;*
PROCLAMATION, *N.*
ḍhanḍorá. *m ;* hoká. *m ;* ḍauṇḍí. *f ;* parchár. *m ;*
PROCLIVITY, *N.*
chaunp. *f ;* cháh. *f ;* táṇgh. *f ;* laulá. *m ;* lilvilá. *m ;*
PROCRASTINATE, TO, *V. T.*
ajj kall karná OR dassná ; chir láuná ; siṭṭ siṭṭní ;
PROCRASTINATION, *N.*
ṭiraṛ phiss. *f ;* ḍhill. *f ;* ghaul. *f ;* sustí. *f ;* siṭṭ. *f ;*
1. Proverb. The house is burning and they are digging the well. agg laggíáṇ khúh khatáuná ;
2. The house is burning, where is the rain? agg laggíáṇ míṇh kitthe?
3. The marriage procession is at the door, and the bride's ears are not bored. búhe áí janj te vinhon kuṛí de kann ;
PROCREATE, TO, *V. T.*
paidá karná ; jamná ;
PROCREATION, *N.*
paidaish. *f ;*
PROCURABLE, *A.*
labháú ;
it is procurable. mildá hai ;
PROCURE, TO, *V. T.*
saheṛ lainá ; hásil karná ; lai lainá ; labbh lainá ; lená ; mallná ; mangáuná ;
PROCURER, *N.*
dallá. *m ;*
PROD, TO, *V. T.*
húl mární ; hujj mární ;
PRODIGALITY, *N.*
fuzúl kharach. *m ;*
PRODIGIOIUS, *A.*
bahut waḍḍá ; waḍḍá sárá ; baṛá bhárá ; moṭá tagaṛá ;
PRODIGY, *N.*
achambhá. *m ;* acharaj. *m ;* anokh. *m ;*
PRODUCE, *N.*
hásal. *m ;* háṇsal. *m ;* paidáwári. *f ;* utpatí. *f ;*
PRODUCE, TO, *V. T.*
paidá karná ; banáuná ; sirjná ;
PRODUCT, *N.*
hásal. *m ;* see PRODUCTION.
PRODUCTION, *N.*
paidáwárí. *f ;* háṇsal. *m ;*
PRODUCTIVE, *A.*
phaldenwálá ; phalwálá ;
PROFANE, *A.*
bedín ; adharm ;
PROFANE, TO, *V. T.*
palít karná ; napák karná ;
to speak profanely. kufr bakná ;
PROFANENESS, *N.*
kufr. *m ;*
PROFANITY, *N.*
kufr díáṇ galláṇ. *f ;*
PROFESS, TO, *V. T.*
1. to declare. bayán karná ; dassná ; iqrár karná ; dam bharná ;
2. to believe. manná ; yaqín karná ; partít karní ; patíjná ; ímán rakkhná ;
PROFESSION, *N.*
kamm. *m ;* kamám. *m ;* peshá. *m ;* báná. *m ;* kasab. *m ;*
PROFESSOR, *N.*
ustád. *m ;* professar sáhib. *m ;*
PROFFER, TO, *V. T.*
pesh karná ;
PROFICIENCY, *N.*
guṇ. *m ;* liyáqat. *f ;* ustádagí. *f ;* see ABILITY.
PROFICIENT, *A.*
guṇí ;
PROFICIENTLY, *Adv.*
baṛí liyáqat nál ; pure taur nál ;
PROFILE, *N.*
shakal. *f ;*
PROFIT, *N.*
faidá. *m ;* khaṭṭí. *f ;* lábh. *m ;* labhat. *f ;* láhá. *m ;* hásal. *m ;* lachchu. *m ;* gauṇ *m. & f ;* láh. *m ;* wáddhá. *m ;* gáilá. *m ;* bhadraká. *m ;*
profit and loss. nafá nuqsán. *m ;*
PROFIT, TO, *V. T.*
1. to derive profit. faidá uṭháuná ; nafá páuná ; lábh úṭháuná ;
2. to benefit another. faidá pahuncháuná ;
3. what good can be expected from him? is te kí bhadraká honá hai ;

PROFIT, TO, *V. I.*
saujalná; nafá milná; faidá ho jáná;
PROFITABLE, *A.*
faidemand;
to be profitable. saujalná;
PROFITABLY, *Adv.*
nafá kamáke;
PROFITLESS, *A.*
befaidá;
PROFLIGACY, *N.*
luchchpuṇá. *m;* badkárí. *f;* luchaú. *m;* badí. *f;*
PROFLIGATE, *A.*
luchchá; badmásh; badkár; ujárú; guṇḍá; bhaiṛá; gaṇdará;
PROFLIGATE, *N.*
luchch. *m;* luchchní. *f;*
PROFOUND, *A.*
gaihrá;
PROFOUNDITY, *N.*
gahráí. *f;*
PROFUSE, *A.*
bahut; bahterá; bahut sárá; ám; ḍher; wadhík; bahutá; wadeṛá;
PROFUSELY, *Adv.*
behisábí nál;
PROFUSENESS, *N.*
gháṇ. *m;* ḍher. *m;* butáit. *f;*
PROFUSION, *N.*
gháṇ. *m;* ḍher. *m;* butáit. *f;*
PROGENITOR, *N.*
waderá. *m;* waddh waderá. *m;*
PROGENY, *N.*
bachche. *m;* ans. *f;*
a man without progeny. auṇtará. *m;*
PROGNOSTICATE, TO, *V. T.*
pahle batláuná; agamm báchchná;
PROGRESS, *N.*
taraqqí. *f;*
Proverb. Re-making no progress. Brickbats before and waste behind. aggá raur, pichchhá chaur;
PROGRESS, TO, *V. T.*
agge jáná; waddhná;
PROGRESSION, *N.*
taraqqí. *f;*
PROGRESSIVE, *A.*
himmatí;
PROGRESSIVELY, *Adv.*
taraqqí karke;

PROHIBIT, TO, *V. T.*
warajná; rokná; ṭhák dená; ṭhákná; barajná;
PROHIBITED, *A.*
warjit;
PROHIBITION, *N.*
mamánat. *f;* ṭhák. *f;* nikhed. *m;*
PROJECT, *N.*
tajwíz. *f;* upáú. *m;*
PROJECTILE, *N.*
golá. *m;*
PROJENY, *N.*
auládd. *f;* bachche. *m;* ans. *f;*
PROLIFIC, *A.*
phaldár;
PROLOGUE, *N.*
dabáchá. *m;*
PROLONG, TO, *V. T.*
lammá karná; lambáuná; wadháuná; lambiáuná;
PROLONGATION, *N.*
lambáí. *f;* wadháú. *m;* phailáú. *m;*
PROMENADE, TO, *V. I.*
ṭahilná; sail karná;
PROMINENCE, *N.*
1. greatness. buzurgí. *f;* máhimá *f;*
2. a lump. gilhṭ. *m;* gilhṭí. *f;* roṛ. *m;* roṛká. *m;*
PROMINENT, *A.*
1. eminent. mashhúr; námí; manniá danniá;
2. clear. sáf; nirmal;
PROMISCUOUS, *A.*
gaḍḍ waḍḍ; gaḍḍ maḍḍ;
PROMISE, *N.*
wádá. *m;* bachan. *m;* nem. *m;* sukhan. *m;* qarár. *m;* partaggiá. *f;*
a false promise. lárá. *m;*
PROMISE, TO, *V. T.*
bachan dená; wádá dená OR karná; nem karná; qarár karná; qaul karná; qaul qarár karná; chuká lainá;
That man always keeps his promise. uh bandá hamesh apní gall OR zabán OR and qaul OR iqrár OR wáde utte pahrá dendá hai;
PROMOTE, TO, *V. T.*
taraqqí dení; dil wadháná;
PROMOTION, *N.*
taraqqí. *f;*

PROMPT, *A*.
taiyár ; chalák ; káhlá ;
PROMPT, TO, *V*. *T*.
ṭumbná ; sikhláuná ;
PROMPTITUDE, *N*.
chohulí. *f* ; uddam. *m* ; chustí. *f* ;
PROMPTLY, *Adv*.
chustí nál ; chetí ; jhaṭṭ paṭṭ ; see QUICKLY.
PROMPTNESS, *N*.
chustí. *f* ; káhlí. *f* ;
PROMULGATE, TO, *V*. *T*.
ḍaunḍí pherní ; ḍhanḍorá dená ; dhomáuná ; hoká dená ;
PROMULGATION, *N*.
hoká. *m* ; ḍhanḍorá. *m* ;
PRONENESS, *N*.
cháh. *f* ; shauq. *m* ;
PRONG, *N*.
kaṇḍḍá. *m* ;
PRONOUN, *N*.
parnám. *m* ;
PRONOUNCE, TO, *V*. *T*.
uchár karná ; bolná ; ucharná ;
PRONUNCIATION, *N*.
uchár. *m* ; bolí, *f* ; chaj. *m* ;
PROOF, *N*.
dalíl. *f* ; sabút. *m* ; parmáṇ. *m* ;
PROP, *N*.
thamb. *m*; thamm. *m*; thammhí. *f* ; sahárá. *m* ; ṭek. *f* ;
for trees. thúhṇí. *f* ;
PROP, TO, *V*. *T*.
ṭekná ; thammhná ; thammái dení ; sahárná ;
PROPAGANDA, *N*.
parchár. *m* ;
PROPAGATE, TO, *V*. *T*.
phailáuná ;
PROPAGATION, *N*.
1. spreading. phailáu. *m* ;
2. preaching. parchar. *m* ;
PROPEL, TO, *V*. *T*.
chaláuná ; dhakká dená ;
PROPENSITY, *N*.
tarafdárí. *f* ; laház. *m* ; pachchhdárí. *f* ; pachchh. *m* ;
PROPER, *A*.
jog ; durust ; cháhidá ; ṭhík ; súdh ; joggá ;
at their proper time. apne vele sir ;

PROPERLY, *Adv*.
ṭhíkam ṭhík ;
PROPERTY, *N*.
mál mátá. *m* ; mál. *m* ; rás. *f* ; milkh mulkh, *m* ; rás púṇjí. *f* ;
PROPHECY, *N*.
nabuvvat, *f* ; agamm wák. *m* ; peshingoí. *f* ;
PROPHESY, TO, *V*. *T*.
agamm wách karná ;
PROPHET, *N*.
nabí. *m* ; pakambar. *m* ;
PROPINQUITY, *N*.
ner. *f* ; lámbh chámbh. *f* ; ás pás. *m* ; gawáṇḍh. *m* ;
PROPITIATE, TO, *V*. *T*.
rází karní ; thaṇḍá karná ; mel miláp karná ; suláh karáuní ; dhímá karná ;
PROPITIATION, *N*.
1. reconciliation. suláh. *f* ; mel miláp. *m* ; suláh safáí. *f* ;
2. atonement. kafárá. *m* ; badlá. *m* ; chaṛhàvá. *m* ; baldán. *f* ; paráhchitt. *f* ;
PROPITIOUS, *A*.
dáyáwán ; mihrbán ; kirpál ;
a propitious day. shubh dihárá. *m* ;
PROPORTION, *N*.
hissá. *m* ; pattí. *f* ; gapphá. *m* ; waṇḍ. *f* ; see PORTION.
PROPOSAL, *N*.
tajwíz. *f* ; saláh. *f* ; upáú. *m* ; jugat. *f* ;
PROPOSE, TO, *V*. *T*.
1. to advise. saláh dení ; matt dení ;
2. to determine. irádá karná ; ṭháṭhná ; tháṇná ; dalíl karní ;
3. to make a proposal. gal pesh karní ;
PROPOSITION, *N*.
saláh. *f* ; see PROPOSAL.
PROPOUND, TO, *V*. *T*.
pesh karná ; saláh dení ;
PROPRIETOR, *N*.
málik. *m* ; haqqdár. *m* ; wálí. *m* ; patí. *m* ; adhkárí. *m* ;
PROPRIETY, *N*.
laiqí. *f* ;
PROPULSION, *N*.
dhakká. *m* ;

PROROGUE, TO, *V. T.*
ṭálná; multaví karní; see POSTPONE.

PROSCRIBE, TO, *V. T.*
1. to reject. radd karná; ṭiágná; tark karná;
2. to exclude. chhekná; ḳhárij karná;
3. to prohibit. maná karná; warajná; ṭhák dená;

PROSCRIPTION, *N.*
mamánat. *f;* ṭhák. *f;*

PROSECUTE, TO, *V. T.*
1. to persist in. kijá karná;
2. to take legal proceedings. nálish karná; dává karná; arjí de dení;

PROSECUTION, *N.*
nálish. *m;* muqadamá. *m;*
a criminal case sent up for trial. chaláṇ. *m;*

PROSECUTOR, *N.*
mudáí. *m;* nálashí. *m;* dávedár. *m;*

PROSELYTE. *N.*
muríd. *m;*

PROSPECT, *N.*
1. view. nazárá. *m;*
2. anticipation. ummed. *f;* uḍík. *f;*

PROSPECT, TO, *V. T.*
labbhná; ḍhuṇḍhná; see SEARCH.

PROSPECTUS, *N.*
ishtihár. *m;*

PROSPER, TO, *V. I.*
kámyáb ho jáná;

PROSPERITY, *N.*
bhágwání. *f;* ghukar. *f;* ḳhushhálí. *f;* sukh. *m;* ḳhairsallá. *f;* laihar baihar. *f;* chahil pahil. *f;* bol bállá. *m;*

PROSPEROUS, *A.*
ghukiá hoyá; bhágwán; bhágan; sulakkhná; nihál;

PROSPEROUSLY, *Adv.*
kámyábí nál;

PROSTITUTE, *N.*
kasbí. *f;* kanjarí. *f;* jární. *f;* bajárí aurat. *f;* chhenchal. *f;* beswá. *f;* luchchan. *f;*

PROSTITUTE, TO, *V. T.*
zinákárí karní; badkárí karní; yárí karní;

PROSTITUTION, *N.*
badkárí. *f;* zinákárí. *f;* yárí. *f;* zanáhí. *f;* chhinálá. *m;* see WHOREDOM.

PROSTRATE, TO, *V. T.*
ḍháh dená; ḍháhná; ḍegná; ḍigáuná;
to prostrate oneself. pairíṇ painá; daṇḍaut karná; neuṇná; sir jhukáuná

PROSTRATION, *N.*
1. weakness. kamjorí. *f;* nirbaltáí. *f;* thiṛ. *m;*
2. worship. sijdá. *m;* see WORSHIP.

PROTECT, TO, *V. T.*
sambhálná; rákkhí karní; sir te hatth dharná OR rakkhná; bacháuná;

PROTECTION, *N.*
dhir. *f;* parwastí. *f;* richchhiá. *f;* saran. *f;* rakhwálí. *f;* rákkhí. *f;* rakkhiá. *f;* rachchá. *m;*

PROTECTOR, *N.*
belí. *m;* rákkhá. *m;* madadgár. *m;* rakhwálá. rachpál. *m;* rachchak. *m;*

PROTEST, *N.*
moṛ gher. *m;* uzr. *f;* ujar. *f;*

PROTEST, TO, *V. T.*
moṛ gher karná; uzr karná; hujjat kaḍḍhní; galloṇ láuná;

PROTRACT, TO, *V. T.*
1. to lengthen. lammá karná; lambáuná; lambiáuná; lamkáuná; sar karná;
2. to postpone. ajj kal karná; multaví karní;

PROTRUDE, TO, *V. I.*
nikalná; waddhná;

PROTUBERANCE, *N.*
gilhṭ. *m;* gilhṭí. *f;*
a knob. láṭṭú. *m;*

PROUD, *A.*
phiṭṭiá hoyá; majájí; garbí; gamrúr; gabbar; nárá; majáj dá máriá hoyá; nakk chaṛhiá; ákaṛ báj; haṇkárí; hakárí;
That man is very proud. us ádmí dá magaz uchchá hai; us ádmí dá damák nahíṇ páyá jándá; uh thánedar banniá phirdá hai;

PROUDLY, *Adv.*
ákaṛke ; ákaṛ nál ; majáj nál ; haṇkár nál ; magrúrí nál ; kibr karke ;
PROVE, TO, *V. T.*
1. to prove true. sábit karná ; siddh karná ;
2. to test. nitárná ; parakhná ; paríkhiá láuná ;
3. to prove false. jhuṭhálná ; jhuṭhiáuná ; ímán guáuná ;
PROVEN, *A.*
sábit ;
PROVENDER, *N.*
chárá. *m ;* gháh pattá. *m ;* paṭṭhá daṭṭhá. *m ;* paṭṭhe. *m ;*
PROVERB, *N.*
misál. *f ;* tamsíl. *f ;*
a saying. kahaut. *f ;* akháṇ. *m ;* ákhiá. *m ;* ákhaṇ. *m ;*
PROVIDE, TO, *V. T.*
1. to make ready. tiyár karná ;
2. to put forward. pesh karná ;
3. to give. dená ;
PROVIDENCE, *N.*
Iláhí intizám. *m ;* Ḳhudá dí mihrbání. *f ;*
You must not think evil of Providence. Parmátmá dí kítí nún kadí bhí búrá nahíṇ manná cháhidá ;
PROVIDENT, *A.*
1. economical. sarfewálá ; wichár wálá ;
2. cautious. dáná bíná ; siáná ; dáná ; suchet ;
PROVIDER, *N.*
denwálá. *m ;* dátá. *m ;* parwardigár. *m ;* pálanhárá. *m ;*
PROVINCE, *N.*
subá. *m ;*
PROVINCIAL, *A.*
desí ;
PROVISIONAL, *A.*
árzí ; shartí ;
PROVISIONALLY, *Adv.*
árzí taur nál ;
PROVISIONS, *N.*
ann pání. *m ;* ann jal. *m ;* gijá. *f ;* rijak. *m ;* roṭí. *f ;* tossá. *m ;* ahár. *m ;*
PROVISO, *N.*
shart. *m ;*
PROVISORY, *A.*
árzí ; thoṛe dináṇ de wáste ;
PROVOCATION, *N.*
chheṛ. *f ;*
PROVOKE, TO, *V. T.*
chheṛná ; chiṛáuná ; russáuná ; luhná ; dil khaṭṭá karná ; raṛkáuná ; bhabkáuná ;
to stir up. jagáuná ; chukkná ;
PROVOKED, *A.*
lúh ; russiá hoyá ;
PROW, *N.*
muháná. *m ;*
PROWESS, *N.*
dilṛrí. *f ;* himmat. *f ;* surtái. *f ;* hauṇsilá. *m ;* bahádurí. *f ;* parákarm. *m ;*
PROWL, TO, *V. T.*
shikár laí phirná ;
PROXIMATE, *A.*
lag bhag ; nikaṭ ; ghaṭṭ waddh ;
PROXIMITY, *N.*
neṛ. *f ;* ás pás. *m ;* najíkí. *f ;*
PROXY, *N.*
sarbaráh. *m ;* muḳhtiár. *m ;* badlí. *m ;* wakíl. *m ;*
PRUDENCE, *N.*
hoshiyárí. *f ;* surt. *f ;* chaukasí. *f ;* hosh. *m ;* aql. *f ;* chatarí. *f ;* buddh. *f ;* dánái. *f ;* siánaí. *f ;* chárbáji. *f ;* chátarí. *f ;* sogghí. *f ;*
PRUDENT, *A.*
hoshyár ; suchet ; dáná ; chattur ; surtílá ; chaukas ; siáná ; aqlwálá ; buddhwán ; chárbáj ; sojhmán ; sogghá ;
PRUDENTLY, *Adv.*
hosh nál ; ḳhabardárí nál ; hoshiyárí nál ; aql nál ; jugtí nál ;
PRUNE, TO, *V. T.*
chhángná ; chhaṇgái karní ;
PRUNE, *N.*
álú bukhárá. *m ;*
PRY, TO, *V. T.*
jhákná ; jhát mární ; jháká láuná ; jhátí pauní ; jhamáká láuná ;
PRYING, *N.*
jhák. *f ;* jhát. *m ;* jhamáká. *m ;*
PSALM, *N.*
jabúr. *m ;* zabúr. *m ;*

PSALTER, *N.*
jabúr dí kitáb. *f ;*
PUBERTY, *N.*
jawání. *f ;* joban. *m ;*
1. of cattle. gaṛháp. *f ;*
2. a girl who has reached age of puberty. muṭiár. *f ;*
PUBLIC, *N.*
ám kháss lok. *m ;* pablik. *m ;* baṇde. *m ;* lokí. *m ;* lokáí. *m ;*
PUBLIC, *A.*
ám ;
PUBLICAN, *N.*
sharáb vechanwálá. *m ;*
PUBLICATION, *N.*
hoká. *m ;* parchár. *m ;*
PUBLIC HOUSE, *N.*
sharáb dá ṭheká. *m ;* sharáb dí dukán. *f ;*
PUBLICITY, *N.*
mashhúri. *f ;*
PUBLICLY, *Adv.*
khullhá mukhullhá ; khulham khullhá ; lokáṇ de sámhne ; khullhí taráh ;
PUBLISH, TO, *V. T.*
ḍhaṇḍorá dená ; hoká dená ; dhomáuná ; phailáuná ;
1. to publish by beat of drum. ḍauṇ ḍauṇ karná ;
2. to cause to be printed. chhapwáuná ;
3. newspaper to be published. akhbár nikalná ;
4. to pay others to praise you. jas khinḍáuná ;
5. to preach. parchár karná ; manádí karní ;
PUDDING, *N.*
puṭín. *m ;*
PUDENDUM, *N.*
falán. *m ;* lullú. *m ;* ḍaṇḍá. *m ;*
PUERILE, *A.*
chhachhohrá ;
PUFF, *N.*
faráṭá. *m ;* jhok. *f ;*
PUFF, TO, *V. T.*
1. to gasp. hauṇkná ; hatkore lainá ; lamme lamme sáh lainá ;
2. to swell. phul jáná ;
3. to blow. phúk márná ;
4. to puff up. phuláuná ;
PUFFED UP, TO BE, *V. I.*
phullná ; áphaṛná ; bhusarná ; phú phú karná ;
PUGNACIOUS, *A.*
fasádí ; daṇggáí ; laṛáká ; jhagṛálú ; ziddí ; fasádíá ;
PUGNACITY, *N.*
zidd. *m ;* bhiṛáí. *f ;* kabb. *f ;* hiṭh. *f ;*
PULL, *N.*
khichch. *m ;* khichch ghasíṭ. *f ;* dhu ghasíṭ. *f ;*
PULL, TO, *V. T.*
ghasíṭná ; dhuhná ; khichchná ; jhosá launá OR márná ; taṇná ; ghasírná ;
1. to pull down. ḍháhná ; ḍháh dená ; ḍegná ;
2. to pull a pankha. jhall márná ; pakkhá khichchná ;
3. to pull out ; nikálná ; puṭṭná ;
4. having pulled. khichch wichchke ;
PULLEY, *N.*
garárí. *f ;*
for a well. charakhṛí. *f ;* bhauní. *f ;*
PULLING AND PUSHING, *N.*
jhosá. *m ;*
PULP, *N.*
guddá. *m ;* gudd. *m ;*
PULPIT, *N.*
chabútrá. *m ;*
PULSATE, TO, *V. T.*
taṛaphná ; dhaṛakná ;
PULSATION, *N.*
taṛpharát. *m ;* taṛphát. *m ;*
PULSE, *N.*
1. grain. channá *m ;* dál. *f ;*
2. beating of artery nabaj. *f ;*
3. to feel the pulse. nabaj vekhná ;
PULVERIZE, TO, *V. T.*
píhná ; chúrá chúrá karná ; bhurbhuráuná ; bhorá bhorá karná ;
PUMICE STONE, *N.*
jháwáṇ. *m ;*
PUMP, *N.*
nalká. *m ;* pamp. *m ;*
squirt. pichkárí. *f ;*

PUMPKIN, *N*.
kaddú. *m*; kaṇdholá. *m*; ghiá. *m*;
PUNCH, *N*.
1. blow. ghasunn. *m*; húrá. *m*;
2. tool. chhainí. *f*;
PUNCH, *TO*, *V*. *T*.
húrá márná; ghasunn márná; hujj mární OR láuní;
PUNCTUAL, *A*.
vele sir;
PUNCTUALITY, *N*.
vele dá dhián. *m*;
PUNCTUALLY, *Adv*.
vele sir;
PUNCTURE, *N*.
chobh. *f*; chhek. *m*; sall. *m*;
PUNCTURE, TO, *V*. *T*.
chubháuná; see PERFORATE.
PUNCTURE, TO, *V*. *I*.
chobhná;
PUNGENCY, *N*.
tezí. *f*; khaṭṭái. *f*;
PUNGENT, *A*.
khaṭṭá; títh; kasailá;
PUNISH, TO, *V* *T*.
sazá dení; táṛná; ḍaṇḍ launá; ḍannaná;
Proverbs used when one is punished for another's fault.
The chief was fined and he made the town pay it. chaṭṭí paí mahar te, te mahar ghattí shahr te.
The grandmother marries a husband and the grandson is fined. nání khasam kítá, dohte nuṇ chaṭṭí paí.
PUNISHMENT, *N*.
sazá. *f*;
fine. ḍaṇḍ. *f*; ḍaṇ. *m*; chaṭṭí. *f*;
PUNY, *A*.
niáná; nikká;
PUP, *N*.
katúrá. *m*; gular. *m*; pillá. *m*;
Proverbs. The pup of a theivish bitch is a thief. chor kuttı dá gular chor;
PUPIL, *N*.
shagird. *m*; chelá. *m*; chelará. *m*; bálká. *m*;
of the eye. dhí. *f*; dhírí. *f*;
PUPPY, *N*.
katúrá. *m*; gullurá. *m*;
PURBLIND, *A*.
míkkhá; kujh annhá;
PURCHASE, *N*.
saudá. *m*; saudá súd. *m*; ḳharíd. *f*;
PURCHASE, TO, *V*. *T*.
mull lainá; ḳharídná;
PURCHASER, *N*.
ḳharídú. *m*; gáhk. *m*; mul lainwálá. *m*;
Proverb used when a purchaser expects something extra to be thrown in.
What! buy a goat and expect a camel to be thrown in. mull bakṛá, úṭṭh j huṇgá.
What! pick one seer (of cotton) and expect half as wages. ser chune te adh ser bháṇjíṇ?
PURE, *A*.
1. holy. pák; pák sáf; such pavittar; suddh; suchcham;
2. spotless. beaib; bedág; nirdos; nispáp;
3. clean; sutthrá; khará;
4. pure, *e. g.* language. ṭheṭh;
5. genuine. chokkhá;
6. unadulterated. nikhoṭ;
PURELY, *Adv*.
1. chastely. safái nál.
2. merely. aiweṇ; nirá; kewal;
PURENESS, *N*.
pákízagí. *f*; safái. *f*; suddhtái. *f*; khariái. *f*;
PURGATIVE, *N*.
jaláb. *m*;
PURGE, TO, *V*. *T*.
jaláb dená;
to take a purgative. jaláb lainá;
PURIFICATION, *N*.
1. Muhammadan. wazú. *m*;
2. Hindu. ashnán. *m*;
PURIFIED, *A*.
suddh; pák sáf; pavittar;
PURIFY, TO, *V*. *T*.
pák sàf karná; suddh karná; nirmal karná;
to wash. dhoná; ashnán karná;
PURITY, *N*.
safái. *f*; suddhtái. *f*; pákízagí. *f*; rástí. *f*; nekí. *f*; pavittartái. *f*; pavittartá. *f*; suchchamtái. *f*;
PURLOIN, TO, *V*. *T*.
churáke le jáná; chorí karní;

PURLOINER, *N.*
chor. *m*; chorṭá. *m*; choṭá. *m*; chorṭerá. *m*;
PURPLE, *A.*
lál; kirmchí; vaiṇganí;
PURPORT, *N.*
matlab. *m*; arth. *m*;
PURPORT, TO, *V. T.*
batláuná; bayán karná; dassná; jataúná;
PURPOSE, *N.*
irádá. *m*; gauṇ. *m*; garaz. *f*; matlab. *m*; dalíl. *f*; phurná. *m*; manshá. *m*; saláh. *f*; muddá. *m*; káraj. *m*; parojan. *m*;
1. to no purpose. dhigáṇe;
2. for what purpose did you go? kis káraj wáste gae sáo;
PURPOSE, TO, *V. T.*
irádá karná; jí karná; saláh karní; thánná;
PURPOSELESS, *A.*
bematlab; befaidá; dhigáṇe; ewen;
PURPOSELY, *Adv.*
ján bujh ke; ján ke; kise matlab nál;
I did not do it purposely. maiṇ jánke nahíṇ kítá;
PURSE, *N.*
guthlá. *m*; thailí. *f*; guthlí. *f*; guthí. *f*; baṭuá. *m*;
PURSUE, TO, *V. T.*
1. to chase. maggar bhajná; kháhṛá páuná; pichchhá karná; khaḍerná;
2. to continue. kardá rahná;
PURSUER, *N.*
pichchá karnwálá. *m*;
PURSUIT, *N.*
kháhṛá. *m*, pichchhá. *m*; khaḍeṛ. *m*;
PURULENT MATTER, *N.*
pák. *f*; mail. *f*;
PURVEYOR, *N.*
ṭhekedár. *m*;
PUS, *N.*
pák. *f*; mail. *f*;
PUSH, *N.*
dhakká. *m*; dhuss. *f*; ṭakkar. *f*;
PUSH, TO, *V. T.*
dhakká dená; dhikkná; ṭakkar láuní; dhuss mární; táh dená;
PUSHED, TO BE, *V I.*
dhakká kháná;
PUSHING, *N.*
dhakká. *m*; dhákká. *m*; dhuss. *f*;
PUT, TO, *V. T.*
dharná; láuná; rakkhná; páuná;
1. to put aside. ikk pásse rakkhná;
2. to put into. wáṛná;
3. to put out. chhekná; kaḍḍhná;
4. to extinguish. bujháuná;
5. to put off disrobe. láh suṭṭná; láh dená;
6. to put on. pahinná;
7. to put off fulfilling a promise. ṭál maṭolá karná; ṭálá bálá karná; ajj kal karná OR dassná;
PUTREFY, TO, *V. I.*
gallná; garná, saṛná; kujná; bus jáná;
PUTRESCENT, *A.*
gaṇḍá; saṛíháṇd;
PUTRID, *A.*
gaṇḍá;
PUTTY, *N.*
puḍḍing. *m*;
PUZZLE, *N.*
1. perplexity. haráni. *f*; garbarí. *f*;
2. a Chinese puzzle. gorakh dhaṇdá. *m*;
PUZZLE, TO, *V. T.*
ghabrá dená; galláṇ nál phasáuná;
PUZZLING, *A.*
aṇokhá; pechdár; pechwálá;
PYJAMAS, *N.*
1. men's. paijámá. *m*;
2. women's. sutthaṇ. *f*; see CLOTHES.
PYRAMID, *N.*
manár. *m*;
PYRE, *N.*
chikhá. *f*; chiká. *f*;
1. to light the pyre. dáh dená;
2. Proverb. Care and the pyre are equal. chiṇtá chikhá barábar; *i.e.*, the pyre burns the dead, and care kills the living.
PYTHON, *N.*
baṛá sapp. *m*;

Q.

QUACK, *A.*
jhuṭhá; jáhlí;
QUACKERY, *N.*
dhokhebází. *f;*
QUADRANGLE, *N.*
chauṇkuṭṭá. *m;*
QUADRANGULAR, *A.*
chauras; chaunukkar;
QUADRUPED, *N.*
chaupáyá. *m;*
QUADRUPLE, *A.*
chaukhúrá;
QUAFF, TO, *V. T.*
píná; pí lainá:
QUAGMIRE, *N.*
dhasan *f;* dhasán. *f;* jillhaṇ. *f;*
QUAIL, TO, *V. I.*
ḍarná; ḍar lagná: himmat hárná; sahimná:
QUAIL, *N.*
baṭer. *m;* baṭerá. *m;*
QUAINT, *A.*
ajíb; aṇokhá;
QUAINTNESS, *N.*
aṇokh. *m;*
QUAKE, TO, *V. I.*
1. to shake from cold. kambná; thar thar kambná;
2. to quake from fear. jhijakná;
QUAKINGLY, *Adv.*
ḍar ke; kamb ke;
QUALIFICATION, *N.*
guṇ. *m;* liyáqat. *f;*
QUALIFIED, *A.*
guṇí;
QUALIFY, TO, *V. T.*
guṇ dená OR rakkhná:
QUALITY, *N.*
guṇ. *m;* sift. *f;*
QUALM, *N.*
ḍar. *m;*
QUANTITY, *N.*
tol. *m;* jamá. *m;*
QUARREL, *N.*
jhagṛá. *m;* jhagṛá jhánjá. *m;* laṛái. *f;* khapp. *f;* bakheṛá. *m;* patháṛá. *m;* chesṭá. *m;* jherá. *m;* daṇggá. *m;* kaláṇ. *f;* kal. *f;* kalá *f;* puáṛá. *m;* ṭaṇṭá. *m;* khapárá. *m;* kapatt. *m;* reṛká. *m;* aṇbaṇ. *f;*

QUARREL, TO, *V. T.*
jhagṛá karná; bhiṛná; jhagaṛná; khapp karná; kijyá karná; laṛái karní; chhiṛná; kalá chheṛná; kalpauná;
1. to foment a quarrel clandestinely. agg bhakháuná;
2. to quarrel amongst your selves. áp vichch dí laṛná.
3. Proverbs. (*i*) It takes two to make a quarrel. Clapping is with two hands. dohatthar tárí wajjdí hai;
(*ii*) Quarrelling with circumstances. To live in the river and quarrel with the crocodiles! daryá vichch rahná te magar machch nál wair;
4. don't quarrel with him. uh de nál kauṛe bachan ná karná;
QUARRELING, *N.*
bakhí. *f;* bikhánd. *m;* laṛ bhiṛ. *m;* thuká thákí. *f;* bhiṛái. *f;* dab darerá. *m;* khaurú. *m;* khaṭápaṭí. *f;* khaṭṭ paṭṭ. *f;* chakarí. *f;* jhambel. *f;* see WRANGLING.
QUARRELSOME, *A.*
jhagṛálú; laṛáká; fasádí; kupattá; jhánjiá; daṇggái; khappí; ghaṇḍ;
1. a quarrelsome woman. ghaṇḍoní. *f;*
2. you are very quarrelsome. tainúṇ jhagṛeáṇ jheṛiáṇ dí ádat hai;
3, not quarrelsome. nischest;
4. Proverb to show that it is better to quarrel with relatives than with neighbours. kuram kupattá chaṇgá, guáṇḍh kupattá maṇdá;
QUARRELSOMENESS, *N.*
jhai. *f;*
QUARRY, *N.*
1. game. shikár. *m;*
2. excavation. patthar dí khán. *f;*
QUARTER, *N.*
1. one fourth. pá. *m;* chauthái. *f;*
2. section. khaṇḍ. *f;*
3. quarter of a seer. ikk pá. *m;*
4. direction. wall. *m;*

QUARTER MASTER, *N.*
koṭ mástar. *m ;*
QUASH, TO, *V. T.*
labáuná ;
QUAVER, TO, *V. I.*
kambná ; khijakná ;
QUAY, *N.*
pattan. *m ;* gháṭ. *m ;*
QUEEN, *N.*
rání. *f ;* malká. *f ;* begam. *f ;*
QUEER, *A.*
1. strange. aṇokhá ; ajíb ;
2. eccentric. págal jehá ; paglá ;
QUEERLY, *Adv.*
ajíb taráh nál ;
QUEERNESS, *N.*
aṇokh. *m ;*
QUELL, TO, *V. T.*
dabáuná ; hatth heṭh karná ; ghuṭṭná ;
QUENCH, TO, *V. T.*
bujháuná ; meṭná ; miṭáuná ;
to be quenched. miṭ jáná ; bujhná ;
QUERULOUS, *A.*
kauṛá ; saṛiá bhujiá ; vitriá hoyá ; chhirhmí ;
QUERULOUSLY, *Adv.*
naráz hoke ; ḳhafá hoke ;
QUERULOUSNESS, *N.*
ḳhafgí. *f ;*
QUERY, *N.*
sawál. *m ;*
QUERY, TO, *V. T.*
sawál karná ; puchchná ; patá puchchná ; parchol karná ;
QUEST, *N.*
partál. *f ;* ḍhúṇḍ. *f ;* ṭol. *f ;* ṭol bhál. *f ;*
QUESTION, *N.*
sawál. *m ;* prasan. *m ;*
QUESTION, TO, *V. T.*
sawál karná ; puchchná ;
to question among themselves. charchá karná ;
QUIBBLE, *N.*
hílá. *m ;* baháná. *m ;* jhuṭh. *m ;* huṭṭar. *m ;* ḍhuchchar. *m ;*
QUIBBLE, TO, *V. T.*
1. to excuse oneself. galloṇ láuná ; uzr karní ;
2. to lie. jhuṭh bolná OR márná OR kamáuná ; kúṛ bolná ;

QUICK, *A.*
jald ; káhlá ; phurt ; chalák ; tarikkhá ;
QUICKEN, TO, *V. T.*
tez karná ; chhetí turná ; pair uṭháke chalná ; káhlí chalná ;
QUICKLY, *Adv.*
shatábí ; jaldí ; chhetí ; jhabde ; jabde ; jhabde jhabde ; hill ke ; jhaṭṭ ; turt ; turt phurt ; jhab ; wagiá wagiá ; jhapájhap ; shapáshap ; káhlí nál ; paṭápaṭ ; wagde ; hall ke ; saṭṭ paṭṭ ;
QUICKNEESS, *N.*
jaldí. *f ;* tezí. *f ;* chustí. *f ;* káhlí. *f ;*
QUICKSAND, *N.*
jillhaṇ. *f ;* rubban. *f ;*
QUICKSILVER, *N.*
párá. *m ;*
QUICKWITTED, *A.*
siáná ; hoshiyár ; suchet ;
QUIESCENCE, *N.*
itminán. *m ;* aman. *m ;*
QUIET, *A.*
dhírá ; dhírají ; chupp ; chupp-chupátá ; maṭṭhá ;
QUIET, TO, *V. T.*
1. to appease. ṭhaṇḍá karná ; manáuná ; rází karní ;
2. to quiet a child. lorí dení ; thápaṛná ;
3. to quiet an animal. puchkárná ;
4. to silence. chupp karáuní ;
5. this child won't keep quiet. ih bachchá wirachdá nahíṇ ;
QUIETLY, *Adv.*
sahj nál ; sahje sahje ; sahe sahe ; malkaṛá ; chupp kíte ; haule haule ; chupp karke ;
QUIETNESS, *N.*
aman. *m ;* arám. *m ;* sáṇt. *f ;*
QUILL, *N.*
par. *f ;*
QUILT, *N.*
jullá. *m ;* lef. *m ;* rajái. *f ;*
1. old tattered quilt. gandolí. *f ;* lefṛá. *m ;* jull. *m ;*
2. a patched quilt worn by faqirs. gudṛí. *f ;* godṛí. *f ;*
3. cover of a quilt. uchháṛ. *m ;*

4. the underneath quilt. jullí. *f;*
    nihálí. *f;*
QUINCE, *N.*
    bíh. *m;* bahí. *f;*
QUIRE OF PAPER, *N.*
    dastá. *m;*
QUIT, TO, *V. I.*
    chhaḍḍná; chaliá jáná;
QUITE, *Adv.*
    muloṇ muḍḍhoṇ; ukká mukká ;
    haddoṇ muḍḍhoṇ;
QUITTANCE, *N.*
    rasíd. *m;*
QUIVER, *N.*
    targas. *m;* tarkash. *m;*
QUIVER, TO, *V. I.*
    thar thar kambná; thartharáuná ;
    dhuṛakná; ḍagmagáuná ;
QUIVERING, *N.*
    thartharí. *f;* t hartharáṭ. *f;*
QUOIT, *N.*
    chakkar. *m;*
QUOTE, TO, *V. T.*
    misál dení.

R.

RABBI, *N.*
    ustád. *m;*
RABBIT, *N.*
    saihá. *m;* sahá. *m;*
RABBLE, *N.*
    ṭollá. *m;* ṭollí. *f;* jatthá.   *m;*
    bhíṛ. *f;* mahain. *m;*
RABID, *A.*
    1. raving. jhallá; diwáná;
    2. enthusiastic. joshwálá; sar-
    garm; shukín;
    3. mad dog. halká;
RABIDNESS, *N.*
    1. anger. virodh. *m;* gussá. *m;*
    waṭṭ. *m;* rossá. *m;*
    2. enmity. adávat. *f;* khár. *f;*
    adaut. *f;* kiṛ. *f;* kíná. *m;*
RABIES, *N.*
    halak. *m;*
RACE, *N.*
    1. nation. qaum. *f;*
    2. lineage. nasl. *f;*
    3. mankind. insán. *m;* manuk-
    kh. *m;*
    4. running. dauṛ. *f;*
    5. current. wahn. *m;* dhár. *f;*

6. horse race. háṭh. *f;*
RACE, TO, *V. I.*
    dauṛnà;
RACE, TO, *V. T.*
    dauṛáná ;
RACE COURSE, *N.*
    ghoṛ dauṛ. *f;*
RACIAL, *A.*
    qaumí ;
RACK, *N.*
    1. shelf; phattá. *m;*
    2. in the corner. paṛchhattí. *f;*
    3. ruin. ujáṛ. *f;* ujáṛá. *m;* dobbá
    sokká. *m;*
RACK, TO, *V. T.*
    1. to torment. shikanje wichch
    khichná;
    2. to worry one. satáuná; dikk
    karná; sir khapáuná; chheṛná ;
    taṇg karná;
    3. to stretch. taṇggáuná; tánná;
    ṭáṇgná;
RACKET, *N.*
    raulá. *m;* ḍaṇḍ. *m;* shor. *m;*
RACKET, TO MAKE, *V. T.*
    ḍaṇḍ páuná; raulá páuná ;
    shor macháuná;
RACY, *A.*
    mazedár; suádí;
RADIANCE, *N.*
    jagmag. *f;* chamak. *f;* chil-
    kárá. *m;*
RADIANT, *A.*
    chamakdár; chamkanwálá;
RADIATE, TO, *V. T.*
    lishkná; jhalkná; chamakná;
    damakná; jagmagáuná;
RADICAL, *A.*
    aslí; asl; púrá;
RADICATE, TO, *V. T.*
    jaṛ pakaṛná;
RADISH, *N.*
    múlí. *f;*
RADIX, *N.*
    jaṛ. *f;*
RAFF, *N.*
    1. refuse. kúrá. *m;*
    2. mob. badmáshán dí ṭollí. *f;*
RAFFLE, TO, *V. T.*
    guṇe páuná; paríchhá páuná;
RAFT, *N.*
    beṛá. *m;*

RAFTER, *N*.
1. planed. bállá. *m* ;
2. unplaned and rough. kaṛí. *f* ;
RAG, *N*.
tákí. *f* ; chíthṛá. *m* ; lattá. *m* ; lír. *f* ; chiṭ. *f* ;
1. rags. líráṇ. *f* ;
2. a rag torn off by a faqir and given to a disciple as an amulet. búr. *f* ;
3. Proverb. The faqir's rag is as good as the rich man's pearl. faqír dí búr te amír dí dur barábbar ;
RAGE, *N*.
1. anger. gussá. *m* ; karodh. *m* ; narázagí. *f* ; roh. *m* ; rossá. *m* ; kop. *m* ; tamak. *f* ;
2. desire. táṇgh. *f* ; ichchhiá. *f* ; cháh. *f* ; ḳháhish. *f* ; shauq. *m* ;
RAGE, TO BE IN A, *V. I.*
russ painá ; gusse honá ; russ jáná ; jalná ; gussá chaṛhná ; gussá auná ; rat-o-rat ho jáná ; kichkicháuná ; agg laggní ; phiṇphaṇáuná ;
to be angry inwardly. lúsná ;
RAGGED, *A*.
páṭe hoe ; páṭe puráne ; pháṭṭá ;
RAGING, *A*.
janúní ; karodhí ;
RAID, *N*.
hallá. *m* ; dhává. *m* ;
RAID, TO, *V. T.*
luṭṭná ; see ROB.
RAIDER, *N*.
luṭerá. *m* ; see ROBBER.
RAIL, *N*.
1. railing. jangalá. *m* ; wáṛ. *f* ;
2. railway track. rel dí saṛak. *f* ;
RAIL, TO, *V. T.*
1. to scold. ghurakná ; jhiṛakná ; ghurná ; dhamkáuná ;
2. to use abusive language. gálí dení ; mehná dená ; gand bakná ; gál kaḍḍhní ;
RAILER, *N*.
maḳhauliá. *m* ; ṭhaṭṭhebáz. *m* ; hujjatí. *m* ;
RAILING, *N*.
1. scoffing. maḳhaul. *m* ; ṭhaṭṭhá. *m* ; hujjat. *f* ; táná. *m* ;
2. fencing. jangalá. *m* ;
RAILINGLY, *Adv*.
maḳhaul nál.
RAILLERY, *N*.
maḳhaul. *m* ; ṭhaṭṭhá. *m* ; háṇsí. *f* ; bollí ṭhollí. *f* ; hujjat. *f* ;
RAILWAY, *N*.
rel dí saṛak. *f* ; lain. *f* ;
RAIMENT, *N*.
líṛe. *m* ; bastar. *m* ; bhes. *m* ; kapṛe. *m* ;
RAIN, *N*.
warkhá. *m* ; mính. *m* ; máṇgalá. *m* ;
1. the rains. barsát. *f* ; warkhá dí rutt. *f* ;
2. long continued rain. jharí. *f* ;
3. small drops. puhár. *f* ; puhr. *f* ; khanníáṇ. *f* ; kiṇíáṇ. *f* ; bhur. *f* ; timak. *f* ;
4. early rain. pahlchhalle dí bárish. *f* ; pahil challá. *m* ;
RAIN, TO, *V. I.*
míṇh waṛhná ; míṇh wassná ; mính painná ; warkhá hunní ; páṇí painá ;
1. to rain in torrents. muhle dhár painá ;
2. to rain gently. phakk painí ;
3. to rain a sprinkle. kinná ; kinmanáuná ;
4. it began to rain. kaníáṇ laih paíáṇ ;
RAINBOW, *N*.
píṇgh. *f* ; guḍḍe guḍḍedí píṇgh. *f* ;
RAINFALL, *N*.
míṇh. *m* ; páṇí. *m* ;
RAIN GUAGE, *N*.
míṇh náp. *m* ;
RAINY, *A*.
barsátí ; ghaneyar ;
1. rainy season. warkhá dí rutt. *f* ; barsát dá mausim. *m* ;
2. Proverb. Whenever it is rainy then there is grass ; wherever there is a village, there is a path. ghaneyar tab gháh. jis wal piṇḍ us wal ráh ;
RAISE, TO, *V. T.*
1. to lift upwards. chukkná ; uchchá karná ; uṭháuná ; khará karná ; khalá karná ;

2. to elevate in rank. charháuná; taraqqí dení:
3. to excite. josh duáuná; halchal macháuná;
4. to awaken. jagáuná; ṭumbná; uskáuná;
5. to raise a disturbance. agg láuná;
6. to recall from death. jawálná;
7. to raise the voice in singing. awáj láuná; awáj lagáuná;

RAISIN, *N.*
1. small. saungí. *f;*
2. large. manakká. *m;*

RAJAH, *N.*
rájá. *m;*

RAKE, *N.*
1. an implement of two forks. sanggá. *m;*
of four or five forks. tanglí. *f;*
for making ridges of earth. jaṇdar. *m;* jaṇdará. *m;*
2. rope for the jaṇdará. chhik. *f;*
3. libertine. luchchá. *m;* badkár. *m;* ḳharábatí. *m;* luchch. *m;*

RAKISH, *A.*
báṇkí chál;

RALLY, TO, *V. T.*
1. to encourage. tagṛeáṇ karná; mazbut karná; sambhálná;
2. to banter. ṭhaṭṭhá karná; maḳhaul karná;

RALLY, TO, *V. I.*
wall ho jáná; changá ho jáná;

RAM, *N.*
1. goat. bakṛá. *m;*
2. sheep. chatrá. *m;* paháru. *m;* hundú. *m;* bheḍú. *m;*
3. fat tailed ram. dumbá. *m;* chakkí dumbá. *m;*

RAM, TO, *V. T.*
dhakká dená; ṭakkar láuní; dhusná;

RAMBLE, *N.*
sail. *m;*

RAMBLE, TO, *V. T.*
phirná; sail karná; ṭurná;

RAMMER, *N.*
1. ramrod. gaj. *m;*
2. heavy rammer for earth. durmat. *m;*

RAMP, TO, *V. T.*
1. to spring. kuḍḍná; ṭappná; purkaná; uchchalná;
2. to storm. bhamkaná;

RAMPAGE, *N.*
1. row. raulá. *m;* shor. *m;*
2. anger. gussá. *m;* waṭṭ. *m;* karodh. *m;* rossá. *m;*

RAMPAGE, TO, *V. T.*
raulá pauná; shor macháuná; laṛáí karní; jhagaṛná;

RAMPANT, *A.*
joshwálá;

RAMPART, *N.*
1. mound or wall. kaṇḍh. *f;* duár. *m;* duál *f;*
2. foṛt. burj. *m;* koṭ. *m;*

RAMROD, *N.*
banduq dá gaj. *m;*

RANCID, *A.*
bássí; behí tabehí;

RANCOROUS, *A.*
darohí; laṛáká; jhagṛálú;

RANCOROUSLY, *Adv.*
wair nál; dushmaní nál; khár nál;

RANCOUR, *N.*
adávat. *f;* wair. *m;* dushmaní. *f;* khár. *m;*

RANDOM, *N.*
ḍho. *m;*
at random. aiweṇ; eweṇ; aṭkal pachchu;

RANGE, *N.*
1. a row. pál. *m;* katár. *f;*
2. for soldiers. cháṇḍmárí. *f;*
3. a grate. chulhá. *m;* chulh. *m;*

RANGE, TO, *V. T.*
1. to classify. tartíb nál biṭhálná;
2. to wander about. bhoṇḍá phirná; awárá phirná; ḍáwánḍol phirná; udále pudále phirná;

RANK, *A.*
1. rancid. bássí;
2. luxuriant. hariaulá; sabaj;

RANK, *N.*
1. row. pál. *m;*
2. in ranks. pálopál;
3. position. uhdá. *m;* padwí. *f;*

RANKLE, TO, *V. T.*
khijná; saṛná; dil vichch khaṭakná; raṛakná;

RANKNESS, *N*.
1. luxurianca. hariául. *m* ;
2. smell. badbo. *f* ; bisáṇdh. *f* ; mushak. *m* ; sug. *f* ;
RANSACK, TO, *V. T*.
1. to search. labbhná ; bhálná ; ṭolná ; talásbí karní ;
2. to plunder. luṭṭná ; dáká márná ; már dháṛ karná ; muṭṭhná ;
RANSOM, *N*.
1. release. ḳhalásí. *f* ; chhuṭkárá. *m* ; rihá. *m* ;
2. price paid for release. utárá. *m* ;
RANSOM, TO, *V. T*.
1. to pay a ransom for. rupáe deke chhuḍáuná ;
2. to deliver. bacháuná ; chhuḍáuná ;
RANT, TO, *V. T*.
uchchí karke bolná ; bakná ; magaz márná ; sir khapáuná ;
RANTER, *N*.
bakwásí *m* ; palálí. *m* ; luttará. *m* ; bátuní. *m* ;
RAP, *N*.
dhappá. *m* ; thappaṛ. *m* ; dhaul. *m* ;
RAP, TO, *V. T*.
ṭakorná ; ṭhokná ; dhappá márná ;
RAPACIOUS, *A*.
1. greedy. lobhí ; lálachí ; labhí ; leṇjh ;
2. extortionate. saḳht ; jálim ; jabardast ;
RAPACIOUSLY, *Adv*.
1. avariciously. lálach karke ;
2. forcibly. badobadí ; jabaran ; malomalí ; zorázorí ; jorájorí ;
RAPACIOUSNESS, *N*.
saḳhtí ; ziyádatí. *f* ; jástí. *f* ;
RAPACITY, *N*.
julm. *m* ; beráhmí. *f* ; loṛhá. *m* ; jorávarí. *f* ;
RAPE, *N*.
zabr zanáhí. *f* ;
to commit rape. zabr zaná karná ; badobadí zináh karná ;
RAPE, *N*.
sarhoṇ. *m* ;

RAPID, *A*.
tez ; chhohlá ; káhlá ; trikkhá ; tikkhá ;
RAPIDITY, *N*.
jaldí. *f* ; tezí. *f* ; káhlí. *f* ;
RAPIDLY, *Adv*.
jaldí nál ; wagiá wagiá ; jhaṭá jhaṭ ; paṭápaṭ ; see QUICKLY.
RAPIER, *N*.
talwár. *m* ; see SWORD.
RAPINE, *N*.
luṭṭ. *f* ; luṭṭ dá mál. *m* ;
RAPT, *A*.
besudh ; magan ;
RAPTURE, *N*.
baṛí ḳhushí. *f* ; bhauná. *m* ; anaṇdtái. *f* ; magantái. *f* ; hulás. *f* ; hulásá. *m* ;
RAPTUROUS, *A*.
baṛá ḳhush ; anaṇd ; bág bág ;
RAPTUROUSLY, *Adv*.
baṛí ḳhushí nál ;
RARE, *A*.
1. unusual. anokhá ; virlá ; anúṭhá
2. excellent. uttam ; baṛá álá ;
RARELY, *Adv*.
bahut ghaṭṭ ; kadí kadí ;
RARENESS, *N*.
sugát. *f* ;
RARITY, *N*.
aṇokh. *m* ; sugát. *f* ; chiṛíáṇ dá dudh. lit. sparrow's milk, *i.e.*, rare things which are seldom met with.
RASCAL, *N*.
badmásh. *m* ; luteṛá. *m* ; dhokhebáz. *m* ; muṇhkálá te nílepair. *m* ; naṭ khaṭ. *m* ; aṛímár. *m* ;
RASCALITY, *N*.
badmáshí. *f* ; harámjádgí. *f* ;
RASE, TO, *V. T*.
ḍháh dená ; see RAZE.
RASH, *A*.
joshwálá ; utáulá ; káhlá ; jaldbáz ; aṇdhá dhuṇd ;
RASH, *N*.
pitt. *m* ;
RASHLY, *Adv*.
bin soche ; jhapájhap ; beaqlí nál ; biná soche samjhe ;
RASHNESS, *N*.
beaqlí. *f* ; nadání. *f* ; josh. *m* ; jaldbází. *f* ; utáulí. *f* ;

RASP, *N*.
ret. *m*; retí. *f*;
RASP, TO, *V. T.*
retná;
RASPBERRY, *N*.
ras bharí. *f*;
RASURE, *N*.
chhil chhal. *m*;
RAT, *N*.
chúhá. *m*;
1. a large rat. ghís. *m*;
2. musk rat. chichúṇdar. *f*;
3. rat trap. piṇjará. *m*;
RATE, *N*.
1. standard. bhá. *m*; bháu. *m*;
2. price. mull. *m*;
3. tax. takas. *m*;
RATE, TO, *V. T.*
1. to fix the value. bhá chukáná OR ṭhahráuná; mull karná;
2. to reprove. jhiṛakná; warajná; dhamkáuná
RATE COLLECTOR, *N*.
máhsuliá. *m*;
RATE PAYER, *N*.
máhsul denwálá. *m*;
RATHER, *Adv.*
sagoṇ;
RATIFICATION, *N*.
manzúrí. *f*; parmán. *m*;
RATIFY, TO, *V. T.*
pakkíáṇ karní; manzúr karná; háṇ karní; háṇ ṭhík ákhná; háṇ vichch háṇ miláuná;
RATIO, *N*.
andájá. *m*;
RATIOCINATE, TO, *V. T.*
bahs karná;
RATIONS, *N*.
rashan. *f*; rasat. *f*; bhojan. *m*; roṭí. *f*;
RATIONAL, *A*.
samajhdár; buddhwáṇ; dáná; aqlwálá;
RATIONALITY, *N*.
samajh. *f*; dhián. *m*; buddh. *f*; aql. *f*;
RATIONALLY, *Adv.*
soch samajhke; soch sách ke; aql nál; hoshiyárí nál;
RATTLE, *N*.
1. noise. khaṛak. *m*; khaṛká *m*;
2. toy. chankná. *m*; chhuṇchhuṇá. *m*;
RATTLE, TO, *V. I.*
khaṛakná;
RATTLE, TO, *V. T.*
khaṛakáuná;
RATTLESNAKE, *N*.
ikk parkár dá sapp. *m*;
RATTLING, *N*.
khaṛak. *m*; khaṛká. *m*;
RAUCOUS, *A*.
jeh dí awáz bhárí;
RAVAGE, TO, *V. T.*
luṭṭná; see ROB.
RAVAGER, *N*.
luteṛá. *m*; ḍákú. *m*;
RAVE, TO, *V. T.*
págal hoke bakná;
RAVEN, *N*.
pahárí OR páhṛí káṇ. *m*; ḍoḍarkáṇ. *m*;
RAVEN, TO, *V. T.*
1. to obtain by violence, khoh lená;
2. to devour. khá jáná; haṛap karná; khá lainá; leṛ márná;
RAVENOUS, *A*.
baṛá bhukkhá; hábaṛiá hoyá; bhukháulá;
RAVINE, *N*.
1. channel, nálá. *m*;
2. precipice. khaḍḍ. *f*; khuṇdhar. *f*;
RAVING, *A*.
besudh; janúní; págal; sudáí;
RAVING, *N*.
bakaṛwá. *f*; bakaṛwás. *f*;
RAVISH, TO, *V. T.*
1. to seize. khoh lená;
2. to commit rape. jabar janáhí karní; jabaran aurat nál badfelí karní;
3. to enrapture. bahut khush karná;
RAVISHMENT, *N*.
1. rapture. baṛí khushí. *f*; anandtaí. *f*;
2. rape. zabr zanáhí. *f*; jabar janáhí. *f*;
RAW, *A*.
1. not cooked. kachchá; dúdhyá; gijgijá;
2. green. hará;
3. unfinished. adhúrá;

RAWISH, *A.*
kachchá ;
RAWNESS, *N.*
1. state of being uncooked. kachchíái. *f;* gijgiját. *m;*
2. inexperience. khámí. *f;* kachch puṇá. *m;*
RAY, *N.*
chiṛing. *f;*
RAZE, *TO, V. T.*
1. to demolish. ḍháh dená; ḍháhná; ḍegná; ḍháuná; ḍháh chhaḍḍná;
2. to obliterate. meṭná; miṭáuná; ghisáuná; láhná; miṭá dená;
RAZOR, *N.*
pachchaná. *m;* ustará. *m;*
Proverb. A blind barberess and a razor of wood. annhá naiṇ te káṭhí dá ustará;
RAZOR STROP, *N.*
paṭási. *f;*
REACH, *N.*
pahuch. *f;* pahuṇch. *f;*
REACH, TO, *V. I.*
pujaná; appaṛná; pahuṇchná;
READ, TO, *V. T.*
paṛhná; paṛhke sunáuná; wáchná;
1. to read fluently. rawáṇ paṛhná;
2. to read a religious book as an act of devotion. páṭh karná;
3. can you read? tainúṇ paṛhná aundá hai?
READABLE, *A.*
paṛhan jog;
READER, *N.*
paṛhanwálá. *m;* paṛáhkú. *m;* wáchak. *m;*
READILY, *Adv.*
1. cheerfully. ḳhushí nál; dil nál; chaiṇ chaiṇ;
2. promptly. jhaṭṭ paṭṭ; cheṭí; jaldí;
READINESS, *N.*
1. preparedness. tiyárí. *f;*
2. alacrity. chustí. *f;* káhlí. *f;* uddam. *m;* chohulí. *f;*
3. willingness. ḳhushí. *f;*
READING, *N.*
paṛhná. *m;*

READJUST, TO, *V. T.*
phir ṭhík banáuná;
READMIT, TO, *V. T.*
dujjí wár dáḳhal karná;
READY, *A.*
taiyár;
READY MADE, *A.*
baní banáí;
ready made shoes. baníáṇ battríáṇ juttíáṇ. *f;*
READY WITTED, *A.*
hoshiyár; suchet; aqlwálá; hájar jawáb; siáná;
REAFFIRM, TO, *V. T.*
duhráuná; dusráke karná; dohr páuná;
REAL, *A.*
aslí; haqíqí; sachchá; haqqí; khará;
REALITY, *N.*
sachchíái. *f;* asl. *m;* muḍḍh. *m;* haqqí gal. *f;* purí gal. *f;* sachchí gal. *f;*
REALIZE, TO, *V. T.*
hásal karná; ugráhí karní;
REALISE, TO, *V. T.*
málúm karná;
REALLY, *Adv.*
sachche muche; asl vichch;
REALM, *N.*
bádsháhí. *f;* ráj. *m;*
REALNESS, *N.*
asl. *m;* haqíqat. *f;*
REANIMATE, TO, *V. T.*
jiwáuná;
REAP, TO, *V. T.*
1. to cut as grain. waḍḍhná;
2. to obtain. mallná; lainá; páuná; hatth lagná; milná;
3. to reap what one has sown. apná kítá pauná; apní karní bharní;
4. you reap as you have sown. terá phiria tere agge áyá; ak bíj ke amb kháná cháhunde ho?
5. for Proverbs see SOW.
REAPER, *N.*
wáḍḍhá. *m;* waḍhává. *m;* láwá. *m;*
pay of a reaper. láví. *f;*
REAPING, *N.*
wáḍḍhí. *f;*

REAPING, HOOK, *N.*
dátarí. *f ;*
REAPPOINT, TO, *V. T.*
dujjí wár muqarrar karná;
REAR, *N.*
pichchhá. *m ;* pichchárí. *f ;* pishlá pásá. *m ;* pacchwáṛá. *m ;* pachhwáṛí. *f ;* maggarlá. *m ;*
REAR, TO, *V. T.*
1. to bring up. pálná; parwastí karní;
2. to raise. chhukkná; uṭṭháuná;
3. to rise on hind legs. sikhpá honá; pichchlíṇ pairíṇ khalo jáná;
REARMOST, *A.*
pichchhá;
REASON, *N.*
1. ground of argument. sabab. *m ;* wáste. *m ;* matlab. *m ;* káran. *m ;* wajáh. *f ;*
2. intellect. samajh, *f ;* aql. *f ;* buddh. *f ;*
3. by reason of. uh de sababoṇ; uh de sabab karke; de máre;
4. by reason of anger. karodh de máre;
5. without reason. besabab; eweṇ;
6. with or without reason. ḳháh maḳháh;
7. for this reason. ise galle; ise sababoṇ; ise karke;
REASON, TO, *V. T.*
dalíl karní; aql duráuná;
to reason together. ápo vichch bahs karná;
REASONBBLE, *A.*
1. endowed with reason. chatann; samajhdár; aqlwálá; siáná;
2. right. munásib; ṭhík;
REASONABLY, *Adv.*
wájabí;
REASSURANCE, *N.*
tasallí. *f ;* tasallá. *m ;*
REASSURE, TO, *V. T.*
tasallí dení;
REBATE, TO, *V. T.*
1. to decrease. ghaṭáuná; ghaṭṭ karná;
2. to deduct. kaṭṭná; kujh chhaḍḍ dená;
REBEL, *N.*
ákí *m ;* bágí. *m ;* karodhí. *m ;* virodhí. *m ;*
REBEL, TO, *V. T.*
kal jagáuná; daṇgá karná; karodh karná; muṇh moṛnà; ákí honá; wichal jáná; wiṭṭarná;
REBELLION, *N.*
fasád. *m ;* daṇgá. *m ;*
to incite to rebellion. lutíáṇ láuná;
REBELLIOUS, *A.*
ákí; bágí; fasádí; nábar; pasádiá;
REBOUND, TO, *V. I.*
burkná;
REBUFF, *N.*
1. reproof. jhiṛak. *f ;*
2. refusal, inkár. *m ;* hatt. *f ;*
REBUFF, TO, *V. T.*
1. to reprove. jhiṛakná; dábá márná; see REPROVE.
2. to check. rokná;
3. to reject. radd kar dená;
BEBUILD, TO, *V. T.*
pher banáuná;
REBUKE, *N.*
jhiṛak. *f ;* guṛkí. *f ;* hiṛak jhiṛak. *f ;* dábbá. *m ;* waraj. *m ;* dutkárá. *f ;* see REPROOF.
REBUKE, TO, *V. T.*
dábá márná; jhár suṭṭná; dabká dená; jhiṛakná; warajná; jhiṛak jhamb kar dená; dudkárná; dabká dená; see REPROVE.
EEBUT, TO, *V. T.*
raddná; radd karná;
RECALCITRANT, *A.*
ákí; ziddí; jhakkí; ḍhíṭhá; háṭhá; aṛyal;
RECALL, TO, *V. T.*
pher buláuná;
RECANT, TO, *V. T.*
inkár karná; mukkarná;
RECNATATION, *N.*
inkár. *m ;* hutt. *f ;* náṇh mukkar. *m ;*
RECAPITULATE, TO. *V. T.*
duhráuná; dubárá dassná;
RECEIPT, *N.*
rasíd. *f ;*
railway receipt. biltí. *f ;*

RECEIPT, TO, *V. T.*
rasíd dení;
RECEIVE, TO, *V. T.*
qabul karná; qabulná; lená; páuná; milná; angíkár karná;
RECENT, *A.*
1. fresh. tájá; sajjrá
2. new. nawáṇ; nawíṇ;
RECENTLY, *Adv.*
jabde; jhabde; huṇe; ajj kal; ajj bhalak;
RECEPTACLE, *N.*
bháṇḍá. *m;* see VESSEL.
RECEPTION, *N.*
manzúrí. *f;*
reception room for men. baiṭhak. *f;*
RECESS, *N.*
1. interval. chhuṭṭí. *f;*
2. in the wall. álá. *f;*
RECEIPE, *N.*
nuskhá. *m;*
RECEIPT, *N.*
rasíd. *m;*
for cattle. ráhdárí. *f;*
RECEIPENT,
lainwálá. *m;*
one who receives a reward. inámí. *m;*
RECIPROCATE, TO, *V. T.*
badal dená; adal badal karná; waṭáuná; waṭá dená;
RECITAL, *N.*
bayán. *m;* kathá. *m;*
RECITATION, *N*
kath. *f;* kathà. *f;* páṭh. *m;*
recitation of religious poem or book. kathá wártá. *m;*
RECITE, TO, *V. T.*
1. to relate. bayán karná; sunáuná; kath karná; batláuná;
2. to recite from sacred books. páṭh karná;
RECKLESS, *A.*
1. excited. joshwálá; lohá lákkhá;
2. careless. láparwáh; gáfal; ghaulá; besurt; mastmalaṇg;
RECKLESSLY, *Adv.*
biṇ soche. beparwái nál; aiweṇ;
RECKON, TO, *V. T.*
hisáb karná; gin lainá; gintí karní; joṛná; lekhá karná;
to reckon the costs. lágat dá hísáb karná;
RECKONING, *N.*
hisáb *m;* gintí. *f;* lekhá. *m;* lekhá jokhá *m;* lekhá pattá. *m;*
RECLAIM, TO, *V. T.*
1. to reform. sawárná; durust karná; sudhárná;
2. to tame. gijháuná; hiláuná; cháṭ láuná;
RECLINE, TO, *V. I.*
leṭná; armán karná; lammá painá;
to lean back. dhásná karná;
RECLUSE, *N.*
sannyási. *m;* tiágí. *m;* baṇwási. *m;*
Hindu faqir. wairágí. *m;*
RECLUSION, *N.*
ikánt. *f;* aṭaṇk. *f;*
RECOGNITION, *N.*
pachhán. *f;* siháṇ. *f;*
RECOGNISE, TO, *V. T.*
siánná; pachhánná;
1. to be recognised. siátá jáná;
2. now I recognise you. huṇ maiṇ tuhánúṇ paihchán liyá hai.
3. I do not recognise you. maiṇnúṇ tuháḍí koí nasání chit nahíṇ aundá;
RECOIL, TO, *V. I.*
dur ráhná; pishán haṭná; pichháṇ palṭná; jhijakná; jhakkná;
RECOLLECT, TO, *V. T.*
yád áuná; yád karná; thauh karná; chetá karná; simarná; sudh rakkhní;
RECOLLECTION, *N.*
chettá. *m;* yád. *f;* thauh. *m;* simarná. *m;*
RECOMMENCE, TO, *V. T.*
pher shurú karná; muṛke arambh karná;
RECOMMEND, TO, *V. T.*
pakkh karná; safárish karná;
RECOMMENDATION, *N.*
safárish. *f;* pakkh. *f;* safáras. *f;*
RECOMPENSE, *N.*
harjánná. *m;*
RECOMPENSE, TO, *V. T.*
waṭṭá dená; badlá dená; ajr dená;

RECONCILE, TO, *V. T.*
  suláh karáná; rází karní; mí-
  láuná; mel miláp karná; manáuná;
RECONCILED, TO BE, *V. I.*
  ikk mikk honá; ikko mikko ho
  jáná;
RECONCILIATION, *N.*
  mel miláp. *m;* suláh safáí. *f;*
  sámtá. *f;*
RECONDITE, *A.*
  sáf nahíṇ; gaihrá;
RECONSIDER, TO, *V. T.*
  pher sochná;
RECORD, *N.*
  misal. *f;* lit. a file.
RECOUNT, TO, *V. T.*
  1. to count a second time. dujjí
    wár ginná;
  2. to relate. bayán karná; dassná;
RECOVER, TO, *V. T.*
  1. to get back. pher milná;
  2. to get better. achchhá ho
    jáná; arám páuná; wal ho
    jáná;
RECOVERY, *N.*
  wall. *f;*
RECREANT, *N.*
  bhagauṛá. *m;* see COWARD.
RECREATION, *N.*
  dil baihláwá. *m;*
RECRIMINATE, TO, *V. T.*
  ilzám láuná; káṇ káṇ karná;
  kalkal karná;
RECRUIT, *N.*
  rangrút. *m;*
RECRUIT, TO, *V. T.*
  bhartí karní; raṇgrutí karní;
RECTANGULAR, *A.*
  chaukúṇá;
RECTIFICATION, *N.*
  sudhár. *m;* sudháí. *f;* durustí. *f;*
RECTIFY, TO, *V. T.*
  sudhárná; suárná; durust karná;
  ṭhík ṭhák karná; sádhná; sar
  karná; sodhná; sudhráuná;
RECTITUDE, *N.*
  sudh. *f;* sachchíáí. *f;* ímándárí. *f;*
  siddhíáí. *f;*
RECTUM, *N.*
  buṇḍ. *m;* ḍhuí. *f;* gáṇḍ. *f;*

RECUMBENT, *A.*
  leṭiá hoyá; lammá piá hoyá;
RECUPERATE, TO, *V. I.*
  wall ho jáná;
RECUR, TO, *V. I.*
  pher honá;
RED, *A.*
  lál; gu ṛá lál; rattá; suhá; rattaṛá;
  to grow red, *i. e.*, angry or excited.
  lál suhá honá; lál honá; lákhí
  honá;
REDDISH, *A.*
  gerwí;
REDEEM, TO, *V. T.*
  bacháuná; chhuḍáuná; naját
  dení;
  to redeem one's pledge. sauṇh
  utární;
REDEEMER, *N.*
  muktídátá. *m;* naját denwálá. *m;*
  bacháunwálá. *m;*
REDEMPTION, *N.*
  muktí *f;* naját. *f;* chhuṭkárá. *m;*
  nistárá. *m;*
REDNESS, *N.*
  lálgí. *f;*
REDOLENCE, *N.*
  mahik. *f;*
REDOUBTABLE, *A.*
  diler; himmatí; bahádur;
REDRESS, *N.*
  1. relief. arám. *m;* armán. *m;*
  2. reparation. harjánná. *m;*
    badlá. *m;* see COMPENSATION.
REDRESS, TO, *V. T.*
  ṭhík ṭhák karná; see RECTIFY.
REDUCE, TO, *V. T.*
  ghaṭṭ karná; ghaṭáuná; thoṛá
  karná; taroṛná; see DEGRADE.
  to reduce to straits. padíṛná;
REDUCTION, *N.*
  gháṭṭá. *m;* ghaṭáú. *m;* mujráí. *f;*
  in price. riáit. *f;*
REDUNDANT, *A.*
  bahut wáddhú; fáltú;
REDUPLICATE, TO, *V. T.*
  dusráuná; duhráuná; duráuná;
  d sráke karná;
REDUPLICATION, *N.*
  duhrá. *m;* duháí tiháí. *f;* dugan. *f;*
RE-ECHO, TO, *V. I.*
  guṇjná;

REED *N.*
kánná. *m;* sirká. *m;* káhí. *f;* sarkará. *m;* sar. *m;*
REEL, *N.*
ríl. *m;*
REEL, TO, *V. T.*
1. to wind. walná; waleṭná; aṭerná;
2. to reel in drink. thib thib ke ṭurná; dig dig ke ṭurná; thibthibáuná; thiṛk thiṛk ṭurná; ḍol ḍol ṭurná; jhuldá phirná; ḍiggdá ḍhainná;
REFER, TO, *V. T.*
1. to enquire. puchchná; sawál karná; bhál karná; suh karná; patá puchchná;
2. to allude to. ishárá karná; nok láuní;
REFERENCE, *N.*
hawálá. *m;*
REFINE, TO, *V. T.*
nitárná; sáf karná;
1. to strain with sieve. chhánná;
2. to strain with cloth. punná;
REFIT, TO, *V. T.*
ganḍhaná;
REFLECT, TO, *V. T.*
chetná; soch wichárná; dhián karná; khavál karná; dhiánaná;
REFLECTION, *N.*
1. shadow. chháṇ. *f;* chháiá. *m;* parchává. *m;* parchháín. *f;*
2. thought. chiṇtá. *m;* soch. *m;* dhián. *m;* wichár. *m;* bichárak. *m;*
REFORM, TO, *V. T.*
sudhárná; see CORRECT.
how shall we reform ourselves? asíṇ kis taráh apná sudhár karíe?
REFRACTORY, *A.*
machall; ḍhíṭhá; jhakkí; ziddí; ákí; replá;
REFRAIN, TO, *V. T.*
1. to abstain from. parhez karná;
2. to leave. chhaḍḍná; tiágná; tajná;
3. to retire from. haṭ jáná; chaliá jáná;
REFRAIN IN MUSIC, *N.*
raháu. *m;*

REFRESH, TO, *V. T.*
1. to freshen. tázá karná;
2. to serve. ṭahl sevá karná;
REFRESHMENT, *N.*
ann pání. *m;*
sit down; will you have some refreshment? baiṭh jáo, thak gáe howoge, te pání dhání píná howe, táṇ dasso;
REFGUE, *N.*
panáh. *f;* ásrá. *m;* saran. *f;*
REFULGENCE, *N.*
jhalak. *f;* jhalká. *m;* see SPLENDOUR.
REFULGENT, *A.*
chamkílá; chamakdár; chamkanwálá;
REFUSAL, *N.*
inkár. *m;* hutt. *f;* námanzúrí. *f;* náh. *f;* náṇh. *f;* jabáb. *m;* sukká jawáb. *m;* nanná. *m;*
REFUSE, TO, *V. T.*
inkár karná; hutt karní; náh karní; inkárí karní; jabáb dená; mukkarná; adúl karná; ákhe ná manná;
REFUSE, *N.*
kúṛá. *m;* phog. *m;*
heap of refuse. rúṛí. *f;*
REFUTATION, *N.*
khanḍan. *m;* jawáb. *m;*
REFUTE, TO, *V. T.*
raddná; gall kaṭṭní; khanḍná; jhuṭhá sábaṭ karná; jhuṭheáṇ karná;
REGAL, *A.*
bádsháhí; sháhí;
REGALE, TO, *V. T.*
khush karná; see ENTERTAIN.
REGALLY, *Adv.*
baṛe jalál de nál; bádsháhí taur nál;
REGARD, TO, *V. T.*
akkh liház karná; kahine te jáná;
REGARD, *N.*
1. friendship. dostí. *f;* millat. *f;* mittartái. *f;*
2. love. muhabbat. *f;* prem. *m;* parít. *f;* moh. *m;*
3. consideration. liház. *m;*
REGARDING, *Prep.*
bábat;

REGARDLESS, *A.*
aṇchint; beparwáh; see HEEDLESS.
REGENERATION, *N.*
1. change of heart. dil dí tabdílí. *f;*
2. new conduct. nawáṇ chál chalan. *m;*
REGENT, *N.*
hákim. *m;*
REGIMENT, *N.*
1. foot. palṭaṇ. *f;*
2. cavalry. rasálá. *m;*
3. artillery. top ḳháná. *m;*
REGION, *N.*
iláqá. *m;* halká. *m;*
REGISTER, *N.*
bahí. *f;* daftar. *m;*
REGISTER, TO, *V. T.*
1. a letter. ṙajastrí karání;
2. to register, to put down. kitáb te cháṛhná;
REGRET, *N.*
hamsos. *f;* gam. *m;* gamí. *f;* hirkh. *m;* pachchotái. *f;* pastává. *m;* pachchtává. *m;* pachchotá. *m;*
REGRET, TO, *V. T.*
jhurná; pachtánná; afsos karná; hamsos karná; pastáuná;
Proverbs re useless regrets.
It is no good crying over spilt milk. The plate has fallen into the well what is the use of abuse. khúh piá thál, ná mehná ná gál.
It is of no use disputing about the price of a kid that has been taken by force. waṭh dí paṭh ná puchchh ná guchch.
REGULAR, *A.*
qaide nál; rawájí;
REGULARLY, *Adv.*
nitt; lagátár; barábar; barobar;
REGULATE, TO, *V. T.*
sádhná; sudhárná; ṭhík ṭhák karná;
regulate a watch. ghaṛí banáuní;
REGULATION, *N.*
qánun. *m;* hukm. *m;*
REHEARSE, TO, *V. T.*
dassná; bayán karná; sunáuná; kathná;
REIN, TO, *V. T.*
bág khichchná;
REINFORCE, TO, *V. T.*
jor dená; sahárná; mazbut karná;
REINFORCEMENT, *N.*
madat. *f;* sahárá. *m;*
REINS, *N.*
wág ḍor. *m;*
REINSTATE, TO, *V. T.*
pher rakkhná; bahál karná;
REITERATE, TO, *V. T*
riṛakná; dohr páuná; dusráke karná; duhráuná;
REITERATION, *N.*
duhráu. *m;*
REJECT, TO, *V. T.*
radd karná; raddná; tark karná; tiágná; adúl karná; námanzúr karná;
REJECTED, *A.*
raddí; ḳháraj;
to be rejected. raddiá jáná;
REJECTION, *N.*
námanzúrí. *f;* tark. *f;*
REJOICE, TO, *V. T.*
anaṇd karná; maujáṇ khaṛná; ḳhushí manáuní; nihál honá; jai jai karde jankáre bulauná; dhan dhan karná; maṇggalá chár karná;
REJOICING, *N.*
ḳhushí. *f;* jai jai kár. *f;*
REJOIN, TO, *V. T.*
jawáb dená;
RELATE, TO, *V. T.*
bayán karná; kathná; batláuná; dassná; kahná; sunáuná; dá withián karná;
RELATION, *N.*
1. relative. rishtedár. *m;* sák. *m;* sákdár. *m;* sák sáin *m;* sakká sák. *m;* sarbaṇdhí. *m;* sarbaṇdhaṇ. *f;* saṇbaṇdhí. *m;* sák náte. *m;* sák aṇg. *m;* aṇg sák. *m;*
2. affinity. sarbaṇdh. *m;* saṇbaṇdh. *m;*
3. relation by marriage. saggárittá. *m;*
4. intercourse. láká. *m;* wástá. *m;*

RELATIONSHIP, N.
náttá. m; sák náttá. m; kur-
matt. m; rishtedárí.f; sákádárí.f;
sarbandh. m; bháíchárá. m;
real brother. saká bhará. m;
sagá bhará. m;
RELATIVE, N.
sák. m; ang sák. m; najíkí. m;
najíkan. f; sákdár. m; see
RELATION.
RELAX, TO, V. T.
1. to loosen. dhillá karná; narm
karná; moklá karná;
2. to rest. sáh lainá; arám
lainá;
RELAXATION, N.
armán. m;
RELEASE, N.
chhutkárá. m; mukat. f;
muktí. f; riháí. f; nistárá. m;
RELEASE, TO, V. T.
chhaḍḍáuná; chhaḍḍ dená; riháí
karní;
RELENT, TO, V. T.
tars kháí; narm ho jáná; dhímá
honá;
RELENTLESS, A.
beráhm; betars; baŕá sakht;
RELIABLE, A.
atbárwálá; pakká; partítmán;
wihárí; hatth dá suchchá; dharmí;
RELIABILITY, N.
pukhtái. f;
RELIANCE, N.
atbár. m; ás. f; wisáh. m;
ásrá. m; bharosá. m; patíj. f;
takwá. m; partít. f;
RELIANT, A.
bekhauf; befikr; diler;
RELIEF, N.
1. alleviation. armán. m; arám. m;
2. deliverance. riháí. f; khalási. f;
3. assistance. madat. f; sahárá. m;
4. now I have some relief. huṇ
merí piŕ matthí hai;
RELIEVE, TO, V. T.
madat dení; sahaitá karná;
sahárá karná; báhurná; jhállú
banná; arám dená;
to relieve oneself. haggan jáná;
báhar jáná; mútarná;

RELIGION, N.
dín. m. M; paṇth. m. H; mazhab.
m, M; mat. m. H; dharm. m. H;
majab. m. M;
pertaining to religion. paṇthí. H;
mazhabí. M;
RELIGIOUS, A.
díndár; dharmí; mazhabí; namází; we Khattris have no time
for religious observances. sáḍí
Khattríaṇ dí gaṇgá jí táṇ haṭṭí
hai;
RELINQUISH, TO, V. T.
de chhaḍḍná; jáṇ dená; tiágṇá;
RELINQUISHMENT, N.
tark. f; chhaḍḍává. m;
RELISH, N.
suád. m; majá. m; bháuná. m;
lajjat. f;
RELISH, TO, V. T.
majá bhogná; majá karná;
majá luṭṭná; achchhá laggná;
RELUCTANCE, N.
bedih. f;
RELUCTANTLY, Adv.
dil nál nahíṇ;
RELY, TO, V. T.
patíjná; atbár karná; bharosá
rakkhná; tájá karná; wasáh karná;
REMAIN, TO, V. I.
ráhná; baiṭhná; ṭhahrná; ṭikná;
to remain over. bachná; báqí honá;
REMAINING, A.
rahiṇdá khúṇḍhá;
REMAINDER, N.
lagg laber. f; baqaiyá. m; jehŕá
báqí. m;
leavings of a meal. júṭh. f;
chagal. f;
REMAND, N.
taríkh. f;
REMAND, TO, V. T.
taríkh dení;
REMARK, N.
gal. f; bayán. m;
REMARK, TO, V. T.
bolná; ákhná; gal karní;
REMARKABLE, A.
ajíb; aṇokhá; awallá;
REMEDY, N.
1. medicine. dárú. m; dawá. f;
duá dárú. m;

2. that which cures. láj. *m* ; iláj. *m* ;
3. expedient. upáú. *m* ; chárá. *m* ;

REMEDY, TO, *V. T.*
iláj karná; upáú karná;

REMEMBER, TO, *V. T.*
yád karní; chettá karná; thauh karná; chetná; sudh rakkhní; gaṇḍh páná; saral karná; chatárná; simarná; chitt rakkhná; chettá á jáná;
1. I don't remember you. mainúṇ tuháḍí koí nasání chitt nahíṇ áundí;
2. to learn by heart. kaṇṭh karná; raṭ lená; raṭṭná;

REMEMBRANCE, *N.*
yád. *f* ; chettá. *m* ; thauh. *m* ;

REMIND, TO, *V. T.*
chitárná; jatáuná; yád diláuní; chitáuná; lakháuná; chukkiá karná;

REMINDER, *N.*
chettá. *m* ;

REMINISCENCE, *N.*
yád. *f* ; see REMEMBRANCE.

REMISS, *A.*
gáfal; ḍhillá; ḍhillá maṭṭhá; ghaulí; beparwáh;

REMISSION, *N.*
1. remission of revenue. ḳharábá. *m* ; chhod. *f* ;
2. remission of sins. muáfí. *f* ; chhuṭkárá. *m* ; riháí. *f* ; khalásí. *f* ;
3. discount. mujráí. *f* ;

REMISSNESS, *N.*
ḍhill. *f* ; gáfalí. *f* ; beparwáhí. *f* ;

REMIT, TO, *V. T.*
1. to send. ghallná; rupáe bhejná;
2. to relinquish. chhaḍḍ dená;
3. to forgive. muáf karná; muáfí dení;

REMITTANCE, *N.*
rupáe. *m* ;

REMNANT, *N.*
bachchat. *f* ; ráhiṇd khúṇḍh. *f* ;

REMONSTRANCE, *N.*
jhiṛak. *f* ; ghurkí. *f* ; dabb. *f* ;

REMONSTRATE, TO, *V. T.*
jhagaṛná; jhiṛakná;

REMORSE, *N.*
gam. *m* ; ranj. *m* ; hamsos. *f* ; hirkh, *m* ; pachtává. *m* ; afsos. *f* ;

REMORSEFUL, *A.*
ájiz; udás;

REMORSELESS, *A.*
beráhm; saḳht; kaṛṛá; betaras;

REMORSELESSLY, *Adv.*
beráhmí nál; saḳhtí nál;

REMOTE, *A.*
dúr; duráḍḍá; dureḍá;

REMOVAL, *N.*
badlí. *f* ; tabdílí. *f* ;

REMOVE, TO, *V. T.*
dhoná; khaṛná; laí jáná;

REMOVE, TO, *V. I.*
sarkná;

REMUNERATE, TO, *V. T.*
mazdúrí dení;

REMUNERATION, *N.*
1. pay. mazdúrí. *f* ; dihárí. *f* ; kamái. *f* ; talab. *m* ;
2. reward. inám. *m* ; inám kinám. *m* ; ajr. *m* ;

REMUNERATIVE, *A.*
faidedár;

REND, TO, *V. T.*
páṛná;
to rend asunder. toṛ suṭṭná;

REND, TO, *V. I.*
phaṭṭná;

RENDER AN ACCOUNT, *V. T.*
hisáb dená OR dassná;

RENEGADE, *N.*
bedín. *m* ; munkir. *m* ;

RENEW, TO, *V. T.*
nawáṇ karná; tájá karná; pher banáuná;

RENEWAL, *N.*
sarwái. *f* ; tázagí. *f* ;

RENNET, *N.*
jág. *f* ;

RENOUNCE, TO, *V. T.*
tark karná; chhaḍḍ dená; tiágná;

RENOVATE, TO, *V. T.*
1. to freshen up. tájá karná;
2. to restore to the first state. bahál karná;

RENOWN, *N.*
dhúm. *f* ; ghúkar. *f* ; partáp. *m* ;

RENOWNED, *A*.
manniá danniá; partápwálá; námí; jaswant; see FAMOUS.
RENT, *N*.
1. tear. langár. *m*; páṛ. *f*; tok. *f*; chírá. *m*;
2. hire. bháṛá. *m*; karáyá. *m*;
RENT, TO BE, *V*. *I*.
páṭ jáná; chirná;
RENUNCIATION, *N*.
inkár. *m*; tark. *f*; tiág. *m*;
REPAIR, *N*.
marammat. *f*;
REPAIR, TO, *V*. *T*.
gaṇḍh túp karná; gaṇḍhaná;
REPARATION, *N*.
badlá. *m*; see DAMAGES.
REPARTEE, *N*.
jawáb. *m*; uttar. *m*;
REPAY, TO, *V*. *T*.
qarz bhar dená; qarz láh chhaḍḍná; udhár utárná; kasar bharní; I can never repay you for your many kindnesses to me. jo jo dharm tusíṇ mere nál karde ho us dá badlá siwác Khudá de kaun de sakdá hai.
REPAYMENT, *N*.
badla. *m*;
REPEAL, TO, *V*. *T*.
khaṇḍan karná; radd kar dená; meṭná;
REPEAT, TO, *V*. *T*.
duráuná; pher ákhná; ghotná; dusráuná; riṛakná;
to repeat a lesson. paṭṭí paṛhná;
REPEATEDLY, *Adv*.
utto rittí; ghaṛí ghaṛí; ghaṛí muṛí; muṛ ghiṛ; jhaṭe binde; bhauṇ jhauṇ; jhaṭe jhaṭe; muṛ muṛ; bár bár; jhak jhaṭe; see FREQUENTLY.
REPEL, TO, *V*. *T*.
haṭáuná; rokná; ṭálná;
REPENT, TO, *V*. *T*.
taubá karná; pachchtáuná; jhurná; pastáuná; hatth malná;
REPENTANCE, *N*.
taubá. *m*; hamsos. *f*; gam. *m*; gamí. *f*; pachchotává. *m*; pastává. *m*; pachchtává. *m*; ranj; *m*;
REPENTANT, *A*.
pashemán;
REPETITION, *N*.
dohar. *f*;
of the names and attributes of God. jap. *m*; jáp. *m*;
REPINE, TO, *V*. *T*.
jhurná; kuṛhná; ghur ghur karná;
REPLACE, TO, *V*. *T*.
kasar bharní;
REPLENISH, TO, *V*. *T*.
purá karná; bhar dená;
REPLETE, *A*.
bharíá hoyá; rajiá hoyá; múṇhoṇ múṇh; dakk a dakk;
REPLY, *N*.
jawáb. *m*; uttar. *m*;
REPLY, TO, *V*. *T*.
jawáb dená; uttar dená;
REPORT, *N*.
sanáh. *m*; rabt. *f*; khabar. *f*; rapat. *f*; sár. *f*; uggh suggh. *f*; awái. *f*;
1. hearsay. suní sunáí gal. *f*; suníáṇ galíáṇ. *f*;
2. report of coming. awái. *f*;
REPORT, TO, *V*. *T*.
khabar dení; batláuná; dassná;
REPOSE, *N*.
arám. *m*; armán. *m*; ramán. *m*; wisrám. *m*;
REPOSE, TO, *V*. *T*.
arám OR armán karná; leṭ jáná; sáh lená;
REPREHEND, TO, *V*. *T*.
dhamkáuná; jhiṛakná; jhár karná; malámat karní; see REPROVE.
REPREHENSIBLE, *A*.
malámat de laiq;
REPRESENT, TO, *V*. *T*.
dikhláná; bakhánná;
REPRESENTATION, *N*.
1. that which represents. sáṇg. *m*;
2. request. ardás. *f*; bayán. *m*; arz. *f*; sawál. *m*;
REPRESENTATIVE, *N*.
gumáshtá. *m*; wakíl. *m*; mukhtiár. *m*;
REPRESS, TO, *V*. *T*.
dabáuná;
REPRESSION, *N*.
dabáu. *m*;

REPRIEVE, TO, *V. T.*
muáf karná; muáfí dení; ríá karná;

REPRIEVE, *N.*
muáfí. *f;*

REPRIMAND, *N.*
jhiṛak. *f;* ghurkí. *f;* jháṛ. *f;* ḍánṭ. *f;* uláhamá. *m;* habak dabak. *f;*

REPRIMAND, TO, *V. T.*
ghurakná; jhiṛakná; jháṛ karná; dabká dená; táṛná; nasíhat dení; habkaná dabkaná; uláhamá dená;

REPRISAL, *N.*
badlá. *m;* waṭṭá. *m;*

REPROACH, *N.*
ulámbhá. *m;* gilá. *m;* mehná. *m;* lán tán. *m;* táná. *m;* uláhná. *m;* lánat malámat. *f;*
shame. badnámí. *f;*

REPROACH, TO, *V. T.*
ghurakná; bollíáṇ mární; abe tabe bolná; táná márná; ulámbhá dená; ḍammh láuná; bolí ṭhaṭholí mární; taráṇ dená; dhikkárná;

REPROBATE, *N.*
rind. *m;*
a reprobate mind. maṇḍí buddh. *f;*

REPROBATION, *N.*
gilá gujárí. *f;* malámat. *f;*

REPROOF, *N.*
jhiṛak. *f;* ghurkí. *f;* uláhamá. *m;* dábbá. *m;* dábbá dhássá. *m;* jhiṛak jhamb. *f;* dhamkí. *f;* dabkí. *f;* habak dabak. *f;* dutkár. *m;*

REPROVE, TO, *V. T.*
jhiṛakná; samjháuná; ghurakná; dábá márná; dutkárná; nasíhat dení; tárná; jháṛ suṭṭná; thukkphiṭṭ karná; uláhamá dená; khijhná; habkaná dabkaná;

REPROVING, *N.*
jháṛ pachháṛ. *f;*

REPTILE, *N.*
jantú. *m;*

REPUDIATE, TO, *V. T.*
inkár karná; mukkar painá; mukkarná; hutt karní;

REPUDIATION, *N.*
inkár. *m;* mukkar. *m;* hutt. *f;*

REPUGNANCE, *N.*
1. dislike. karáhat. *f;* ghiṇ. *f;* nafrat. *f;*
2. reluctance. dil nahíṇ kardá;

REPUGNANT *N.*
bahut búrá; bharist; ghináhdá;

REPULSE, *N.*
1. refusal. inkár. *m;* námanzúrí. *f;*
2. defeat. hár. *f;*

REPULSE, TO, *V. T.*
haṭáuná; ṭálná; rokná;

REPULSION, *N.*
karáhat. *f;* nafrat. *f;* ghin. *f;*

REPULSIVE, *A.*
báhut búrá; see REPUGNANT.

REPUTABLE, *A.*
manníá danníá; jaswálá; surkhru;

REPUTATION, *N.*
páṇ patt. *f;* jas. *m;* náuṇ. *m;*

REQUEST, *N.*
arz. *f;* darkhást. *f;* arj. *f;* maṇg. *f;* ardás. *f;* sawál. *m;*

REQUEST, TO, *V. T.*
arz karní; ardás karní; sawál karná; minnat karní; maṇgná;

REQUIRE, TO, *V. T.*
1. to desire. cháhuná; jí karná; lochná; lalcháuná;
2. to request. maṇgná;

REQUIREMENT, *N.*
loṛ. *f;*

REQUISITE, *A.*
loṛídá; cháhídá; jarúrí;

REQUITAL, *N.*
1. recompense. badlá. *m;* harjánná. *m;*
2. reward. ajr. *m;* inám. *m;* inám shinám *m;*

REQUITE, TO, *V. T.*
1. to retaliate. badlá dená; pásoṇ badlá lainá; koloṇ waṭṭá lainá;
2. to reward. inám dená; haqq dená; ajr dená;

RESCIND, TO, *V. T.*
khaṇḍan karná; radd kar dená; maqúf karná;

RESCINDING, *N.*
khaṇḍan. *m;*

RESCUE, *N.*
rihái. *f;* bacháo. *m;* chhuṭkárá. *m;*

RESCUE, TO, *V. T.*
bacháuná; chhuḍáuná; ṭárná;

RESEMBLANCE, *N.*
mel. *m ;* sáṇg. *m ;* naql. *f ;* ḍaul. *f ;*
RESEMBLE, TO, *V. I.*
milná ; ralná ;
RESEMBLING, *A.*
wargá ; waṇgg ; ikk raṇg ; wáṇgar ; váṇgúṇ ; hu bu ; ikko jehá ;
RESENT, TO, *V. T.*
burá manná ;
RESENTMENT, *N.*
gussá. *m ;* wair. *m ;* qahr. *m ;* karodh. *m ;* ris. *f ;* kop. *m ;*
RESERVE, TO, *V. T.*
rakkh chhaḍḍná ; báj rakkhná ; dabb rakkhná ;
RESERVOIR, *N.*
chaubachchá. *m ;* hauj. *m ;* haud. *m ;*
with steps leading down. báṇ. *f ;*
RESIDE, TO, *V. T.*
ráhná ; wás karná ; wássná ; ṭikná ;
RESIDENCE, *N.*
wás. *m ;* ṭhikáná. *m ;* ghar. *m ;* makán. *m ;* thán. *m ;* waserá. *m ;* ghar ghát. *m ;* addá. *m ;* wásá. *m ;*
Proverb. Residence in the desert and the laughter of fools both are evil. burá jangal dá wásá, burá murakh dá hássá ;
RESIDENT, *N.*
ráhanwálá. *m ;* wassanwálá. *m ;* waskín. *m ;* wasník. *m ;* wássí. *m ;* wássú. *m ;*
RESIDUE, *N.*
baqaiyá. *m ;* bachchat. *f ;*
RESIGN, TO, *V. T.*
kamm chhaḍḍná ; istífá dená ; tajná ; likh ke dená ;
RESIGNATION, *N.*
istífá. *m ;*
RESIN, *N.*
gúnd. *f ;* ral. *f ;*
RESIST, TO, *V. T.*
khaihná ; sáhmná karná ; muqábalá karná ;
RESISTANCE, *N.*
sáhmná. *m ;* muqábalá. *m ;*
RESISTLESS, *A.*
1. irresistible. parbal ;
2. helpless. kamjor ; máṛá ; bechárá ; bewass ; besahárá ;

RESOLUTE, *A.*
pakká ; pakk paká ; mazbut ; ḍáḍhá ; himmatí ;
RESOLUTELY, *Adv.*
baṛí himmat nál ; baṛí dilerí nál ;
RESOLUTION, *N.*
siḍḍá. *m ;* himmat. *f ;* dilerí. *f ;* jigará. *m ;*
RESOLVE, TO, *V. T.*
dhárná ; irádá karná ; faisalá karná ; dalíl karní ; ṭhánná ;
RESORT, TO, *V. I.*
jáná ; jáyá karná ;
RESOUND, TO, *V. I.*
guṇjná ;
RESOURCE, *N.*
upáo. *m ;* kalá. *f ;*
RESOURCELESS, *A.*
bewasílá ; bewass ; besahárá ;
RESPECT, *N.*
adab. *m ;* ádar. *m ;* ádar bháú. *m ;* ádarí. *f ;* izzat. *f ;*
RESPECT, TO, *V. T.*
adab karná ; izzat karní OR dení ; manná ; ádar dená OR karná ; máṇ rakkhná ;
to pay respects to. pairíṇ painá ;
RESPECTED, *A.*
izzatwálá ; pánwálá ; ábrúdár ; supattá ; pardháná ; manniá danniá ;
RESPECTABLE, *A.*
patwálá ; ijjatdár ; bhalámánas ; supattá ; sáú ; paṭwaṇt ; paṭwaṇtá ;
RESPECTFUL, *A.*
adabwálá ;
RESPECTFULLY, *Adv.*
adab nál ; baṛí izzat nál ;
RESPECTER, OF PERSONS, *N.*
surat shakal dá liház karnwálà. *m ;*
RESPIRATION, *N.*
sáh. *m ;* dam. *m ;*
RESPIRE, TO, *V. T.*
sáh lainá ; dam lainá ;
RESPITE, *N.*
chir. *m ;* mohlat. *f ;*
1. to get respite for a year. waṛhá painá ;
2. I will give a respite of two months. maiṇ do mahíne páángá ;

RESPLENDENT, *A*.
chamkílá; chamakdár; tejwant; tejmán;
RESPOND, TO, *V. T*.
jawáb dená; uttar dená;
RESPONSE, *N*.
jawáb. *m*; uttar. *m*;
RESPONSIBILITY, *N*.
zimmá. *m*; jummá. *m*; peṭe. *m*; bhár. *m*; júlá. *m*;
at my responsibility. mere peṭe;
RESPONSIBLE, *A*.
jummewár;
to be responsible for. peṭe painá;
REST, *N*.
1. repose. arám. *m*; armán. *m*; ramán. *m*; wisrám. *m*; subehtá. *m*;
2. remainder. báqí. *f*; bachchat. *f*; baqaiyá. *m*;
REST, TO, *V. T*.
sáh lainá; arám OR armán karná; wisrám karná; dam lainá; ṭikná;
RESTFULLY, *Adv*.
arám nál;
RESTHOUSE, *N*.
1. for natives. dharmsálá. *m*; saráṇ. *m*;
2. for English. dák baṇgalá. *m*;
RESTITUTION, *N*.
badlá. *m*; see DAMAGES.
RESTIVE, *A*.
bearám; beqarár; nachallá; bechain; machall;
RESTLESS, TO BE, *V. I*.
jí ghabráuná; dhakke dhore kháná; chulbuláuná; chilam maláuná; hilná jullná; bilbiláuná; chulchuláuná;
RESTLESSNESS, *N*.
bearámí. *f*; bechainí. *f*; chiṇtá. *f*; achchawí. *f*; chulchulí. *f*, chanchaláí. *f*;
RESTORATION, *N*.
muáfí. *f*; bahálí. *f*;
RESTORE, TO, *V. T*.
nawáṇ karná; bahál karná; pher dená; wápis OR moṛ dená;
1. to restore to health. achchhá karná; naroíáṇ karná;
2. to restore to life. jiwálná;

RESTRAIN, TO, *V. T*.
aṭkáuná; rokná; báj rakkhná; see HINDER.
RESTRAINT, *N*.
1. abstinence. parej. *f*; rakkh. *f*; rakkh shakk. *f*;
2. hindrance. rok ṭok. *f*; rukávat. *f*; ṭok ṭák. *f*; ṭok. *f*;
RESTRICT, TO, *V. T*.
1. to lessen. ghaṭáuná; ghaṭṭ karná;
2. to restrain. rokná; ḍakkná;
RESTRICTION, *N*.
rukávat. *f*;
RESULT, *N*.
natíjá. *m*; asar. *m*; aṇt. *m*; gaver. *m*;
bad results. he sowed a flower, and thorns sprang up. bíjiá sí phul, par ug pae kaṇḍḍe;
RESUME, TO, *V. T*.
pher shuru karná;
RESURRECTION, *N*.
qiámat. *f*; hashar. *f*; hasar. *f*;
RESUSCITATE, TO, *V. T*.
jiwáuná;
RETAILING, *N*.
bikkarí. *f*;
RETAIN, TO, *V. T*.
pás rakkhná;
RETAINER, *N*.
laggá baddhá. *m*; naukar. *m*; ṭahliá. *m*;
RETALIATE, TO, *V. T*.
badlá lainá;
RETALIATION, *N*.
badlá. *m*;
RETARD, TO, *V. T*.
rokná; ḍakkná; see **HINDER.**
RETCH, TO, *V. T*.
kaí karná; **ulṭí karní; upal shál** karní;
RETINUE, *N*.
nál de bande. *m*; **thulá.** *m*; **jaleb.** *m*; bahute ádmí. *m*;
RETIRE, TO, *V. T*.
haṭṭ jáná; **phirná; phir jáná;** palaṭná;
RETIREMENT, *N*.
ikkalwáṇjá. *m*; **ollhá.** *m*; ikáṇt. *f*; aṭaṇk. *m*;

RETREAT, TO, *V. I.*
pichche haṭná; phirná; muṛná; palaṭná;

RETRENCH, TO, *V. T.*
ḳharach ghaṭáuná; ghaṭṭ karná; soch wichár ke ḳharach karná;

RETRIBUTION, *N.*
badlá. *m*;

RETRIEVE, TO, *V. T.*
wápis le áuná;

RETROCEDE, TO, *V. T.*
pichche haṭṭná; see RETIRE.

RETURN, *N.*
1. requital. badlá. *m*; waṭṭá. *m*; wáro sánwíṇ. *f*;
2. profit. faidá. *m*; láh. *m*; lábh. *m*; lachchú. *m*;

RETURN, TO, *V. I.*
pichcháṇ muṛná; haṭṭná; palaṭná; ṭal jáná; bahuṛná; phirná; phir áuná; parat jáná; muṛ auná; pichchlí pairíṇ muṛná; partná;
go and return quickly. jáo, par jhabde muṛ áná;

RETUN, TO, *V. T.*
wápis dená; moṛ dená;

REVEAL, TO, *V. T.*
záhir karná; dassná; bayán karná; khol dená; dikhálí dení; pholná; bhet dassná;
to publish abroad. hoká dená;

REVEL, TO, *V. T.*
bahár luṭṭná; bhogná; ḳhushí karní; mauj karná; majá luṭṭná;

REVELATION, *N.*
mukáshafá. *m*;

REVELRY, *N.*
anaṇd maṇgal. *m*; ḳhushí. *f*; chohul. *m*;

REVENGE, *N.*
badlá. *m*; waṭṭá. *m*; baṭṭá. *m*;

REVENGE, TO, *V. T.*
badlá lená; lahu dá ghuṭṭ píná; sijjhná; waṭṭá láuná;

REVENGEFUL, *A.*
badlá lainwálá;

REVENUE, *N.*
mámlá. *m*; lagán. *m*;
5% of revenue given to lambardars. paṇjotrá. *m*;

REVERE, TO, *V. T.*
ádar karná OR dená; see RESPECT.

REVERENCE, *N.*
ádar. *m*; ádar bháú. *m*; adab. *f*; mán. *m*; izzat. *f*; bháú bhagat *f*;

REVERENT, *A.*
ájiz;

REVERENTLY, *Adv.*
baṛí adab nál; baṛí ájizí nál;

REVERSE, TO, *V. T.*
1. to change. badal karná; waṭáuná;
2. to turn upside down. ulṭáuná; puṭṭhá karná;
3. to repeal. miṭáuná; khaṇḍan karná;

REVERSION, *N.*
ulṭ. *f*;

REVERT, TO, *V. I.*
haṭṭná; muṛná;

REVILE, TO, *V. T.*
bolí mární; bolliáṇ mární; burá ákhná; gál kaḍḍhní; taráṇ dená; nindiá karná;

REVILING, *N.*
láṇ táṇ. *f*; see ABUSE.

REVISE, TO, *V. T.*
durháná; dohráná;

REVISION, *N.*
najarsání. *f*;

REVIVAL, *N.*
1. freshness. tázagí. *f*;
2. new life. nawíṇ zindagí. *f*;

REVIVE, TO, *V. T.*
jiwáuná;
to revive a quarrel. qabráṇ de murde puṭṭná;

REVIVE, TO, *V. I.*
ṭahikná;

REVOKE, TO, *V. T.*
khaṇḍná; radd karná; see REFUTE and CANCEL.

REVOLT, *N.*
karúd. *m*; balwá. *m*; see REBELLION.

REVOLT, TO, *V. T.*
kal jagáuná; múṇh moṛná; bagávat karní; ákí honá; balwá karná; daṇgá karná;

REVOLTING, *A.*
ḍaráuná; bahut bhaiṛá;

REVOLUTION, *N.*
pherá. *m*; pher gher. *m*; ghumáí. *f*; ghummar. *m*;
rebellion. rájgardí. *f*; ráj raulá. *m*;
REVOLVE, TO, *V. I.*
chakkar kháná; phirná; bhaun láiná; ghumná;
REVOLVE, TO, *V. T.*
pher dená; gerná;
REVOLVER, *N.*
pistaul. *m*;
REWARD, *N.*
inám. *m*; ajr. *m*; inám shinám. *m*;
a return. badlá. *m*;
REWARD, TO, *V. T.*
inám dená; phal dená; ajr dená;
RHEUMATISM, *N.*
ganṭhiá. *m*; wáí. *f*; báddí. *f*; baí dí bímárí. *f*;
RHINOCERUS, *N.*
gaindá. *m*;
RHUBARB, *N.*
reuṇd. *f*;
RHYTHM, *N.*
bahar. *m*;
RIB, *N.*
paslí. *f*; passalí. *f*;
RIBBON, *N.*
fítá. *m*;
RICE, *N.*
1. for cooking. chául. *m*;
2. boiled rice. bhát. *m*; riddhe hoe chaul. *m*; rijjhe chaul. *m*;
3. growing rice. jhonná. *m*; munjí. *f*;
4. rice water. pichchh. *f*;
5. rice straw. parálí. *f*; parál. *m*;
RICH, *A.*
máldár; lakhpatí; daulatmand; dhaní; baḳhtáwar;
rich and poor. chhoṭá waḍḍá. *m*;
RICHES, *N.*
mál. *m*; daulat. *f*; dhaṇ. *m*; lachchho. *f*; máyá. *m*; see WEALTH.
RICKETS, *N.*
parchháwáṇ. *m*;
RIDDLE, *N.*
pahelí. *f*; parhelí. *f*; parelí. *f*;
RIDE, TO, *V. T.*
sawár honá;
RIDER, *N.*
sawár. *m*;
RIDGE, *N.*
banná. *m*; waṭṭ. *f*;
RIDICULE, *N.*
maḳhaul. *m*; hássí. *f*; hássá. *m*; bollí ṭhollí. *f*; ṭakauṇchí. *f*; ṭhaṭholí. *f*; majákh. *f*; ṭhiskarí. *f*; maskarí. *f*; khillí. *f*; ṭhaṭṭhá. *m*; hiṛhiṛát. *m*;
RIDICULE, TO, *V. T.*
maḳhaul karná; ṭhaṭṭhá karná OR márná; jugat karná; aṇggulí te nacháuná; hujjat karní; ṭhaṭṭhe vichch uḍáuná; ṭakor karná; ṭhíṭṭh karná;
the people ridiculed us. lokáṇ ṭhaṭṭhe nál sánúṇ ṭhíṭh kítá;
RIDING, *N.*
sawárí. *f*;
RIFLE, *N.*
rafal. *f*; banduq. *f*;
RIFLE, TO, *V. T.*
luṭṭná; ḍáká márná;
RIGHT, *N.*
1. a just claim. haqq. *m*;
2. justice. niáuṇ. *m*; niáíṇ. *f*; insáf. *m*;
RIGHT, *A.*
1. correct. sahí; ṭhík; ṭhík ṭhák; durust;
2. direction. sajjá; sajje pásse;
3. at the right time. ṭhík vele sir;
RIGHTEOUS, *A.*
bhagat; dharmí; sachchá; niáí; niáíṇ; nék; díndár;
RIGHTEOUSNESS, *N.*
rástí. *f*; rástbází. *f*; díndárí. *f*; nekí. *f*; sachchíái. *f*; dharm. *m*; sattiá. *m*; sáṇch. *m*;
RIGHT HAND, *A.*
sajjá hatth;
to the right. sajje pásse;
RIGHTLY, *Adv.*
ṭhíkam ṭhík; ṭhík ṭhák; durústí nál;
RIGID, *A.*
qaim; mazbút;
RIGOROUS, *A.*
saḳht; karṛá; kharhwá;
RIGOROUSLY, *Adv.*
saḳhtí nál; beráhmí nál;

RIGOUR, *N*.
sakhtí. *f*; karṛáí. *f*; jorávarí. *f*;
RIM, *N*.
1. of a vessel. kaṇḍhá. *m*;
2. of a wall. banerá. *m*;
RIND, *N*.
chhillaṛ. *m*; chhilk. *m*; chhil. *m*;
bark. sakk. *m*;
RING, *N*.
1. plain finger ring. challá. *m*;
2. signet ring. cháp. *m*; mundrá. *m*;
3. with a stone. mundrí. *f*;
4. thumb ring. ársí. *f*;
5. nose ring. natth. *f*;
6. ear ring. wálí. *f*; murkí. *f*;
7. toe ring. aṇgguṭhí. *f*;
RINGLEADER, *N*.
muhrlá. *m*;
RINGLET, *N*.
julf. *f*;
RINGWORM, *N*.
dadd. *f*; daddarí. *f*;
RINSE, TO, *V*. *T*.
haṇggháIná; khaṇggháIná; ghaṇgálná;
RIOT, *N*.
daṇggá. *m*; daṇggá fasád. *m*; hagámá. *m*; laṛáí. *f*; raṭṭá. *m*; balwá. *m*; már kuṭṭáí. *f*;
RIOTOUS, *A*.
fasádí; daṇggáí; laṛáká; pasádiá;
RIP, *N*.
chírá. *m*;
RIP, TO, *V*. *T*.
páṛná;
to open a seam. udheṛná;
RIP, TO, *V*. *I*.
uddhaṛná;
RIPE, *N*.
pakká;
half ripe. gaḍḍar; gaḍḍará; áhbú; ḍaḍḍará;
RIPENESS, *N*.
pakkíáí. *f*;
RIPPLE, *N*.
chhal. *m*;
RIPPLE, TO, *V*. *I*.
chhal chhaláuná;
RISE, TO, *V*. *I*.
1. to ascend. chaṛhná;
2. to stand up. uṭṭhná; khalo jáná;
RISING, *N*.
of a river. chaṛháu. *m*;
RISK, *N*.
1. chance. ḍho. *m*;
2. danger. khatrá. *m*; ján jokhoṇ. *m*;
RISK, TO, *V*. *T*.
himmat karní; dilerí karní;
RISKY, *A*.
khatrewálá;
RITE, *N*.
rít. *f*; rasm. *f*; dastúr. *m*; sagan bahar. *m*;
RIVAL, TO, *V*. *T*.
rís karná; khaihná; muqábalá karná; khaih karná; barábarí karní;
RIVALRY, *N*.
rís. *f*; khaih. *f*;
RIVER, *N*.
daryá. *m*; nai. *f*;
RIVET, *N*.
káblá. *m*;
RIVULET, *N*.
nálí. *f*; kúlh. *f*;
ROAD, *N*.
1. metalled road. saṛak. *f*; chhaṛak. *f*;
2. unmetalled road. paiyá. *m*; rastá. *m*;
3. Proverb. Three roads are bad roads, *viz*:—
the mill for a man, a road for a woman, the threshing floor for a buffalo. tinneṇ ráh kuráh, mard núṇ chakkí, rann núṇ ráh, saṇde núṇ gáh;
ROAM, TO, *V*. *I*.
ḍolná; ḍullná;
ROAN, *A*.
garrá;
ROAR, TO, *V*. *T*.
gajjná; bukkná; bhabakná; bhabbháṇ márná;
as a waterfall. jhir jhir karná;
ROARING, *N*.
gúṇj *f*; gaṛhak. *f*; gaṛhaká. *m*; gunjná *m*; bhabbháṇ. *m*;
ROAST, TO, *V*. *T*.
kabáb bhunná OR karná; bhunná;
ROASTED MEAT, *N*.
kabáb. *m*;

ROB, TO, *V. T.*
luṭṭná ; chhín lená ; ganḍh márná; chorí karní ; muṭṭhná ; kho lená ; ḍáká márná ; dháṛá márná ; már dháṛ karná ; churáuná ; khaṛná ; robbing, P. P., luṭ puṭ ke ;

ROBBER, *N.*
ḍákú. *m* ; luṭerá. *m* ; loṭú. *m* ; ṭhagg. *m* ; ḍháṛví. *m* ; luṭway-yá. *m* ; luṭerú. *m* ;

ROBBERY, *N.*
ḍáká. *m* ; chorí. *f* ; már dháṛ. *f* ; ṭhagg bájí. *f* ; ṭhagí. *f* ; ṭhagáí. *f* ; ḍháṛá. *m* ; loṭí. *f* ;

ROBE, *N.*
poshák. *f* ;
faqir's robe. kafní. *f* ;

ROBIN, *N.*
piddí. *f* ;

ROBUST, *A.*
sabal ; tagaṛá ; wall ; moṭá tázá ; haṭṭá kaṭṭá ;

ROCK, *N.*
ṭillá. *m* ; chatán. *m* ; ṭekrá. *m* ; ṭekrí. *f* ;

RACK, TO, *V. I.*
jhúllná ;

ROCKET, *N.*
hawái. *f* ;

ROCKY, *A.*
pathrelí ;

ROD, *N.*
gaj. *m* ;
1. iron rod. síkh. *f* ; kandlá. *m* ;
2. fishing rod. baṇsí. *f* ; charhí. *f* ;

ROGUE, *N.*
naktá. *m* ; badmásh. *m* ; naṭ khaṭ. *m* ; harám jádá. *m* ; lapáṭiá. *m* ; aṛíkhor. *m* ;
a rogue elephant. mast hátthí. *m* ;

ROGUERY, *N.*
harám jádgí. *f* ; naṭ khaṭí. *f* ; sharárat. *f* ;

ROLL OF CLOTH, *N.*
thán. *m* ;

ROLL, TO, *V. T.*
reṛhná ; lapeṭná ; rihaṛná ;
1. to roll in the dust. guthalná ; kukalná ;
2. to roll away, reṛhke lánbhe karná ;

ROLL, TO, *V. I.*
riṛhná ; loṭná ; loṭ poṭ honá ;
1. as a horse. leṭná ; liṭná ; leṭu peṭú honá ;
2. of a boat. beṛá ḍolná ;

ROLLER OF SUGAR MILL, *N.*
belaṇ. *f* ;

ROMP, TO, *V. T.*
kheḍná ; kalol karná ;

ROOF, TO, *V. T.*
chhattná ;

ROOF, *N.*
chhatt. *m* ;
1. a thatched roof. chhappar. *m* ;
2. roof of mouth. tálú. *m* ;

ROOK, *N.*
kán. *m* ; see CROW.

ROOM, *N.*
1. a room. koṭhrí. *f* ; kamrá. *m* ;
2. space. thán. *f* ; jagáh. *f* ; gunj-aish. *f* ; samaí. *f* ;
3. sitting room for men. baiṭhak. *f* ;

ROOMY, *A.*
moklá ;
rather roomy. moklerá ;

ROOST, TO, *V. T.*
waserá karná ; baserá lainá ;

ROOT, *N.*
jaṛ. *f* ; jaṛh. *f* ; muḍḍh. *m* ;

ROOT, TO, *V. T.*
ukháṛná ;

ROOT, TO, *V. I.*
uggná ; ugg painá ;

ROPE, *N.*
1. small rope. ḍorí. *f* ; ḍor. *f* ;
2. well rope. láṇ. *f* ; lajj. *f* ; rassá. *m* ; láuṇ. *m* ; lás. *m* ;
3. for horse's heels' pachhárí. *f* ;
4. for horse's forelegs. agárí. *f* ;
5. coarse rope made of straw. beṛ. *m* ;
6. rope halter. khabbhí. *f* ;
7. tent ropes. taṇáwáṇ. *f* ;
8. hopple. paikaṛ. *m* ;

ROSARY, *N.*
1. Muhammadan. tasbí. *f* ; tasbá. *m* ;
2. Hindu. kaṇṭhá. *m* ; japmálá. *f* ; simarní. *f* ; málá. *f* ;

ROSE, *N.*
guláb. *m* ;
a bed of roses. phulláṇ dí sej. *f* ;

ROSE COLOUR, *N.*
gulábí. *f ;*
ROT, *N.*
saṛaṇ. *f ;* sáṛá. *m ;* wisáṇdh. *f ;*
ROT, TO, *V. I..*
gallná ; tarakkná ; garná ; saṛná ; bus jáná ; bussná ;
1. as fruit. chalná ; saṛná ;
2. to cause to rot. tarkauná ;
ROTTEN, *A.*
gaṇdá ; wisáṇdhá ; boḍḍá ; boddá ; bhuggá ; chaliá hoyá ;
ROTTENNESS, *N.*
wisáṇdh, *f ;* gaṇdkí. *f ;*
ROUGH, *A.*
kharhwá ; khuráṇḍá ; karaṇḍ ; khohraṛí ; khaṛbaṛá ;
1. rough uneven ground. uchchí níwíṇ tháṇ. *f ;*
2. the river is very rough. lit. rolling in waves. daryá dharíáṇ piá marendá ;
ROUGHNESS, *N.*
khrappá. *m ;*
ROUND, *N.*
ger. *f ;* gerá. *m ;* pherá. *m ;* gird. *m ;*
ROUND, *A.*
gol mol ; gol ;
ROUND ABOUT, *Adv.*
ále duále ; irde girde ; chaugirde ; udále ; duále ; chauphere, lámbh chámbh ; chár chuphere ; chupher ; to take a roundabout way. chakkar kháná OR márná ;
ROUNDNESS, *N.*
golíáí. *f ;* goláí. *f ;* goltáí. *f ;*
ROUSE, TO, *V. T.*
jagáuná ; josh duáuná ; chukkná ;
ROUT, *N.*
jhissí. *f ;* jhijkí. *f ;* bhánj. *f ;* bhájaṛ. *f ;*
ROVE, TO, *V. I.*
landar phirná ; awárá phirná ; bhondá phirná ; galle galle phirná ; bhaṇbaí bhuse kháná ;
ROVING, *N.*
landar phirná. *m ;*
ROW, *N.*
1. line. pál. *m ;* katár. *f ;* lár. *f ;*
2. noise. raulá. *m ;*
3. what is all the row about ? kí raulá pán lag piá hai ;
ROW, TO, *V. T.*
beṛí chappú nál chaláuná ;
ROWDY, *A.*
shorí ; laṛáká ; phasádiá ; jhagṛálú ;
ROYAL, *A.*
bádsháhí ; sháhí ;
ROYALTY, *N.*
rájagí. *f ;*
RUB, TO, *V. T.*
ghasáuná ; khasar khasar karná ; malná ; ragaṛná ; ghasarná ; ragṛá dená ;
1. to rub the body with a cloth. khisarná ;
2. to cause to be rubbed. manjáuná ;
3. to massage. muṭhí chápí karní ; muṭhíáṇ bharná ; kuṭṭná ;
4. to stroke. palosná ;
5. Proverb. Without their master the cattle are miserable, no one rubs them down. sáín bájhoṇ mál duhelá, hatth ná phere koí.
RUB, TO, *V. I.*
ragaṛ laggní ; ghasná ; ghisar laggná ;
RUBBING, *N.*
ragṛá. *m ;* ragaṛ. *f ;* malwáí. *f ;* ghasar. *f ;* málish. *f ;* ghassá. *m ;* ghasáí. *f ;*
rubbing my eyes. akkhíáṇ mal mal ke ;
RUBBISH, *N.*
kúṛá. *m ;* guddar. *m ;* kheh. *f ;* kúṛá kaṭak. *m ;*
brick bats. iṭṭá waṭṭe. *m;*
RUBY, *N.*
lál. *m ;* mának. *m ;* yákút. *m ;*
RUDDER, *N.*
patwár. *m ;*
RUDE, *A.*
beadab ; jáhal ; kuḍhabá ; ḍhíṭh ; ḍhíṭhá ; magrá ; hochchá ; baṛbolá ; kuḍhang ; heṇkaṛ ; nakk chaṛhiá ; ḍakkará ;
RUDELY, *Adv.*
beadabí nál ; gustákhí nál ; akaṛ ke ; shokhí nál ;
RUDENESS, *N.*
beadabí. *f ;* shokhí. *f ;* chámalí. *f ;* haṇkár. *m ;* kharmastí. *f ;* besharmí. *f ;* ḍhíṭháí. *f ;*

RUFFIAN, *N.*
badmásh. *m* ; buriár. *m* ;
RUG, *N.*
galíchá. *m* ; namdá. *m* ; ásaṇ. *m* ;
RUIN, *N.*
ujáṛá. *m* ; chauṛ chapaṭ. *m* ; ḍobbá sokká. *m* ; tabáí. *f* ; binás. *m* ; ḍhá. *f* ; nuqsáṇ. *m* ; barbádí. *f* ; halákí. *f* ; kholá. *m* ; taraṭṭí chauṛ. *f.*
1. ruins. khole. *m* ;
2. a mound of ruins. theh. *m* ;
RUIN, TO, *V. T.*
nás karná ; jaṛ khohná ; ḳhajjal ḳharáb karná ; ujáṛná ; see DESTROY.
1. he is ruining himself. uh apne hí hatthíṇ apná nás kar laindá hai ;
2. to let go to ruin. rolná ; ruláuná ;
RUINED, TO BE, *V. I.*
rul jáná ; ḳhajjal ḳharáb ho jáná ; khel ral jáná ; ghar barbád honá ; ujjaṛ pujjaṛ janá ; ujjaṛná ; ḳhajjal ḳhwár honá ;
in a ruined state. ḍhaṭṭhiá hoyá ;
RULE, *N.*
1. reign. hukúmat. *f* ; hákamí. *f* ;
2. a rule. qaidá. *m* ; qánún. *m* ;
RULE, TO, *V. T.*
hukúmat karní ; ráj karná ; hukm karná ; hukúmat jatáuní ; wass rakhná ;
RULER, *N.*
hákim. *m* ; sardár. *m* ;
RUMBLE, TO, *V. I.*
ḍhiḍḍh bolná ; ḍhiḍḍh guṛáuná ; gaṛ gaṛ karná ;
RUMBLING, *N.*
guṇj. *f* ; gaṛhak. *f* ; gaṛhaká. *m* ;
of the bowels. gaṛhbaṛ. *f* ; gaṛhbaṛát. *m* ; gurguṛ. *f* ;
RUMINATE, TO, *V. T.*
dhián karná ;gaur karná ; dhíauná ;
RUMINATION, *N.*
dhián karná ; gaur karná ; dhíauná
RUMINATION, *N.*
dhián. *m* ; soch. *m* ; soch wichár. *m* ; chitwaní. *f* ;

RUMOUR, *N.*
uḍḍí ḳhabar. *f* ; suní sunáí gal. *f* ; suníáṇ galláṇ. *f* ; charchá. *m* ; awái. *f* ;
RUMP, *N.*
chunganá. *m* ; chúklá. *m* ;
1. rump of a horse. chutt. *f* :
2. Proverb. A horse's tail covers his own rump. ghoṛe dá puchchar apní chutt kajjdí ;
RUMPLE, TO, *V. T.*
middhná ; madhelná ; madholná ;
RUN, TO, *V. T.*
bhajjná ; dauṛná ; nass jáná ; naṭṭhná ; bhanná ;
1. to cause to run. dauráuná ; bhajjáuná ;
2. to run fast. khiṭṭ bhajjná ;
3. to run away. champat honá ;
4. he is running along. uh wagiá jándá hai.
5. to run away with a woman. udhálná ;
RUNG, *N.*
danḍá. *m* ;
RUNNER, *N.*
bhajjanwálá. *m* ;
RUNNING, *N.*
dauṛ. *f* ;
RUPEE, *N.*
rupiá. *m* ; rupá. *m* ;
slang term for a rupee. chillaṛ. *f* ;
RUPTURE, *N.*
phuṭṭ. *f* ;
RUSE, *N.*
chálá. *m* ; dá. *m* ;
RUSH, *N.*
jhapaṭ. *f* ;
the rushing of a tempest. anherí dí shúkar. *f* ;
RUSH, TO, *V. I.*
sir toṛ bhajjná ; bhajke jáná ;
the dog barked and rushed at me. uh kuttá mainúṇ bhabak ke piá ;
RUSH AT, TO, *V. T.*
dháwá karná ;
he rushed at me. uh mainúṇ ṭuṭṭke piá ;
RUST, *N.*
1. on iron, &c. jaṇgál. *m* ;
2. in wheat. kuṇggí. *f* ;

RUSTED, *A.*
jangálí;
RUSTIC, *N.*
pendú. *m;* jaṭṭ. *m;* guár. *m;* jaṭká. *m;* ganwár. *m;*
Proverbs describ ng sarcastically Panjab rustics and farmers.
1. Though the jatt becomes refined he will still use a grass mat for a handkerchief. jaṭṭ malúk, ṭalrúá rumál;
2. At the laugh of a jatt an ordinary man's rib breaks. jaṭṭ dá hássá te garíb dá bhanne pássá;
3. When the jatt's harvest is ripe he will beat even his mother, *i.e.*, to keep her from injuring his crop. jaṭṭe de jau pakke sitte, sakí máṇ núṇ máre dhakke.
4. A jatt is worse than a calamity. jaṭṭ báláioṇ pur;
5. Expect no favour from jatts, he will quarrel with his own priest. jaṭṭáṇ thoṇ nafá mul ná bhál, jaṭṭ guwáve murshad nál;
6. A jatt, raw silk, and a wound cannot be held without binding. jaṭṭ, pat, phat baddhe siwá qábú ná hundá;
7. A stupid jatt got a cup and swelled himself with drinking. hochche jaṭṭ katorí labbhí, pání pí pí áphriyá;
RUSTY, *A.*
jangálí;
RUT, *N.*
líh. *f;* lík. *f;*
RUTHLESS, *A.*
beráhm; patthardil;
RUTHLESSLY, *Adv.*
beráhmí nál; sakhtí nál;

S.

SABBATH, *N.*
sabt dá din. *m;* itwár dá din. *m;*
SABRE, *N.*
talwár. *f;* see SWORD.
SACK, *N.*
1. bag. boṛí. *f;* boṛá *m;* guní. *f;* guná. *m;*
2. plunder. lúṭṭ. *f;* ḍáká. *m;* dháṛá. *m;*
SACK, TO, *V. T.*
luṭṭná; már dháṛ karná; dháṛá márná; muṭṭhná;
to dismiss. jawáb dená; chhuṭṭí dení;
SACKCLOTH, *N.*
ṭáṭ. *m;* tappaṛ. *m;* tarappaṛ. *m;*
SACRAMENT, *N.*
sákrámint. *f;*
SACRED, *A.*
pák; pavittar;
SACREDNESS, *N.*
pákízagí, *f;* pákí. *f;* pavittartáí. *f;*
SACRIFICE, *N.*
qurbání. *f;* balí. *f;* balídán. *m;* balí bheṭ. *f;* bheṭ. *f;* sadká. *m;*
Hindu burnt sacrifice. hom dí balídán. *f;*
SACRIFICE, TO, *V. T.*
bheṭ chaṛhání OR dení; qurbání chaṛhání; balídán karná;
1. to sacrifice oneself. ghol ghumáuná;
2. to be sacrificed. bal bal jáná;
3. to become a sacrifice for the welfare of another. sadke honá OR jáná;
4. passing something round the head and giving it away. wárná; wár kar dená;
SACRILEGE, *N.*
kufr dá kamm. *m;* mazhabí beadabí. *f;* mazhabí hatak. *m;*
SACRILEGIOUS, *A.*
bedín; adharmí;
SAD, *A.*
masosiá hoyá; udás; dukhí; sogí; sogmáṇ; santápí;
SADDEN, TO, *V. T.*
dukháuná; dukh dená;
SADDLE, *N.*
káṭhí. *f;*
1. an old saddle. káṭhrí. *f;*
2. camel's saddle. kachává. *m;*
SADDLE, TO, *V. T.*
káṭhí páuní;
SADDLE BAGS, *N.*
khurjí. *f;*
1. for grain, for donkeys. chaṭṭ. *f;*
2. for bricks, for donkeys. boṛá. *m;*

SADDLE CLOTH, *N.*
táhrú. *m* ; káthí dá khes. *m* ; darí. *f* ; kambal. *m* ;
SADDLE GIRTH, *N.*
1. the girths proper. tang. *m* ;
2. a band to go over the saddle and under the belly. farákí. *f* ;
SADDLE MAKER, *N.*
saráj. *m* ; mochí. *m* ;
SADDLERY, *N.*
zínsází. *f* ;
SADDUCEE, *N.*
Sadúqí. *m* ;
SADLY, *Adv.*
gam nál ; udás hoke ; amsos karke ; dáh de nál ;
SADNESS, *N.*
udás. *f* ; gam. *f* ; hamsos. *f* ; ranj. *m* : sog. *m* ; udásí, *f* ;
SAFE, *A.*
sahí salámat. ; rází bází ;
SAFE, *N.*
1. large. petí. *f* ;
2. small. gallá. *m* ;
SAFEGUARD, *N.*
bacháo. *m* ;
SAFELY, *Adv.*
ḳhair nál ; salámatí nál ;
SAFETY, *N.*
salámatí. *f* ; sukh. *m* ;
SAFFRON, *N.*
kesar. *m* ;
SAG, TO, *V. I.*
lamakná ; palamná ;
SAGACIOUS, *A.*
hoshiyár ; buddhwán ; chaukas ; dáná ; siáná ; see PRUDENT.
SAGACIOUSLY, *Adv.*
hoshiyárí nál ; aql nál ; dánáí nál ; siyánaf nál ;
SAGACITY, *N.*
dánáí. *f* ; hoshiyárí. *f* ; buddh. *f* ; chatráí. *f* ;
SAGE, *A.*
siáná ; aqlwálá ; dáná ; see PRUDENT.
SAGELY, *Adv.*
aql nál ; hosh nál ; hoshiyárí nál.
SAGENESS, *N.*
dánáí. *f* ; aqlmandí. *f* ; hoshiyárí *f* ;
SAGO, *N.*
ságú dáná. *m* ;
SAIL, *N.*
pál. *m* ;
SAIL, TO, *V. T.*
pál nál berí chaláuná ;
SAILOR, *N.*
maláh. *m* ;
SAINT, *N.*
1. Muhammadan. pír. *m* ; walí. *m* ; rasúl. *m* ;
2. Hindu. sant. *m* ; rishí múní. *m* ; sádh. *m* ;
SAINTLY, *A.*
nek ; rást ; díndár ; dharmí ;
SAKE, *N.*
wástá. *m* ; ḳhátir. *f* ; ḳáran. *m* ; sadḳá. *m* ; nímatt. *m* ; nimitt. *m* ;
SALAD, *N.*
salád. *m* ;
SALARY, *N.*
1. monthly. talab. *f* ;
2. daily. mazdúrí. *f* ; diháṛí. *f* ;
3. yearly. kamáí. *f* ; See PAYMENT.
SALE, *N.*
vikkrí. *f* ; bikkarí. *f* ; táh. *m* ; gáhkí. *f* ;
auction. nilám. *m* ;
SALEABLE, *A.*
wikháú ;
SALINE, *A.*
salúná ; salúní ; nimkí ;
SALIVA, *N.*
thukk. *m* ; lál. *f* ; lálá. *f* ;
SALLOW, *A.*
píllá ; jard ; zard ;
unhealthy colour. sáulá ;
SALLOWNESS, *N.*
jardí. *f* ; jardáí. *f* ;
SALMON COLOURED, *A.*
bhagwá ; bhajwáṇ ;
SALOON, *N.*
baiṭhak. *f* ;
SALT, *N.*
lún. *m* ;
Proverb. To put salt on its tail. Why do you put salt on flying birds? udden paṇkkhíṇ kyún lún lende?
SALT, TO, *V. T.*
1. for meat. lúnwálá gosht karná ;
2. for vegetables. salúná karná ; lún páuná ;

SALT CELLAR, *N.*
lúndán. *m ;*
SALTISH, *A.*
salúná ; lúnwálá ;
SALTNESS, *N.*
salúní. *f ;*
SALTPETRE, *N.*
shorá. *m ;*
SALT WATER, *N.*
khárá pání. *m ;* lúnwálá pání. *m ;* salúná pání. *m ;*
SALUBRIOUS, *A.*
sihhat denwálá ;
SALUTARY, *A.*
wáddhewálá; nafewálá ;faidemand;
SALUTATION, *N.*
1. Muhammadan. salám. *m ;* salám-oalaiakam. *m ;*
2. Hindu. bandagí. *f ;* namaste. *m;* jaí Rám. *m ;* Rám Rám. *m ;* Sítá Rám ; jáí Sítá Rám. *m ;*
3. Sikh. wáh gurú jí ká khálsá ;
4. Akális. Sat Siri Akál ;
5. Jogis. ades. *m ;*
SALUTE, *N.*
salámí. *f ;*
SALUTE, TO, *V. T.*
matthá ṭekná ; salám karná ; parnám karná ;
1. to salute reverently. pairíṇ páuná OR painá ; godí hatth láuná ;
2. to fire a salute. salámí karní ;
SALVATION, *N.*
naját. *f;* bacháo. *m ;* ḳhalásí. *f ;* rihái. *f;* muktí. *f;* mukat. *f;* gatí. *f;* chhuṭkárá. *m ;* nistárá. *m ;*
SALVE, TO, *V. T.*
iláj karná ; malham pattí karní ;
SAME, *A.*
uhí ; uho ;
the same as this. eho jehá ;
SAMENESS, *N.*
barábarí. *f ;* ikko jehá ; barobarí. *f;*
SAMPLE, *N.*
namúná. *m ;* vaṇkí. *f ;* vaṇgí. *f ;* chuṇg. *f ;*
SANCTIFICATION, *N.*
pákízagí. *f ;* suddhtáí. *f ;* dil dí safáí. *f ;* pavittartáí. *f ;*
SANCTIFIER, *N.*
Pák Rúh. *m ;* Pavittar Átmá. *m ;*
SANCTIFY, TO, *V. T.*
pák karná ; pavittar karná ;
SANCTION, *N.*
manzúrí. *f ;* ijázat. *f ;* ijan. *f ;*
SANCTION, TO, *V. T.*
manzúr karná ; háṇ karná ;
SANCTIONED, *A.*
manjúr ;
SANCTITUDE, *N.*
pákízagí. *f ;* dil dí safáí. *f ;*
SANCTITY, *N.*
uttamtáí. *f ;* pákízagí. *f ;* suddhtáí. *f ;*
SANCTUARY, *N.*
1. church. girjá. *m ;*
2. refuge. saran. *f ;*
SAND, *N.*
ret. *f ;*
coarse sand. bálú. *f ;*
SANDBANK, *N.*
baretá. *m ;*
SANDAL, *N.*
chaplí. *f ;*
wooden sandals. ḳhaṛáwáṇ. *f ;* chapliáṇ. *f ;*
SANDALWOOD, *N.*
chandan. *m ;*
SAND HILL, *N.*
tibbá. *m ;*
SAND PAPER, *N.*
regmár. *m ;*
SAND PIPER, *N.*
kakúhá. *m ;*
SANDY, *A.*
retlá ; retlí ; retílá ;
SANE, *A.*
hoshwálá ; siáná ; dáná ;
SANGUINARY, *A.*
lahú luhár ; ḳhunokḳhun ; ratt o ratt ;
SANGUINE, *A.*
ummedwár ; ummed hai ;
SANGUINELY, *Adv.*
baṛí ummed nál ;
SANITARY, *A.*
sáf ; safá ;
SANITY, *N.*
suddh buddh. *m ;* hosh. *f ;* surt. *f ;*
SAP, *N.*
ras. *m ;*

SAPIENCE, *N.*
dánái. *f;* aql. *f;* buddh. *m;* samajh. *f;*
SAPIENT, *A.*
dáná; hoshiyár; siáná;
SAPLESS, *A.*
1. destitute of sap. beras;
2. dry. sukká pukká; sukká;
SAPLING, *N.*
rukkh. *m;* búṭá. *m;* búṭí. *f;*
SAPPHIRE, *N.*
nílam. *f;* líllá. *f;*
SARCASM, *N.*
ṭhaṭṭhá. *m;* bolí ṭholí. *f;* maḳhaul. *m;* hujjat bází. *f;* jugat bází. *f;*
SARCASTIC, *A.*
kuraṇggá; kauṛá;
SARSAPRILLA, *N.*
ushbá. *m;*
SASH, *N.*
paṭká. *m;* peṭí. *f;* lakk band. *m;*
SATAN, *N.*
Shaitán. *m;* Iblís. *m;*
SATANTIC, *A.*
shaitání;
SATCHEL, *N.*
ṭhailí. *f;* jholá. *m;*
for books only. bastá. *m;* see BAG.
SATIATE, TO, *V. T.*
1. to satiate oneself. leṛ márná;
2. to satiate another. rajáuná; rajwáuná; see GORGE.
SATIATED, TO BE, *V, I.*
1. with food. rajj jáná; appharná;
2. with food, spoken of cattle. lehná;
3. happy with something. man bharná; rází honá;
SATIETY, *N.*
rajj. *m;*
SATIN, *N.*
atlas. *f;*
SATIRE, *N.*
ṭhaṭṭhá. *m;* maḳhaul. *m;* hujjat. *f;*
SATIRICAL, *A.*
kuraṇggá; kauṛá; khaṭṭá;
SATIRICALLY, *Adv.*
ṭhaṭṭhe vichch; maḳhaul nál;

SATISFACTION, *N.*
tasallí. *f;* bhauná. *m;* dharwás. *m;* saṇtokh. *m;* nissá. *f;* nishá. *f;* parsiṇtáí. *f;* parsiṇtá. *m;* prasaṇtá. *m;* taript. *f;*
SATISFACTORILY, *Adv.*
changí taráh nál; ṭhík ṭhák; ḳhátir nál;
SATISFACTORY, *A.*
ṭhík;
SATISFIED, *A.*
rází; ḳhush; wall; taript;
SATISFY, TO, *V. T.*
ḳhush karná; nihál karná; rájí karná; tasallí dená; phuláuná; taráuná; nissá karná; taript karná;
to convince. manáuná; yaqín dawáuná;
SATISFIED, TO BE, *V. I.*
1. to be contented. ḳhush ho jáná; ríjhná; taript honá;
2. to be satisfied from hunger. rajj jáná;
3. spoken of cattle. lehná;
4. all right, do as you like, I am satisfied. hachchhá; rájí raho te sukkh bhogo, maiṇ baṛá parsann háṇ;
5. are you satisfied? phir tusáṇ núṇ parsintá hundí hai?
SATURATE, TO, *V. T.*
bheuná; tar karná; gillá karná; sinjarná;
SATURDAY, *N.*
Saníchar. *m.* M; Haftá. *m.* M; Sincharwár. *m.* M; Abbal haftá. *m.* M; bár. *m.* H;
SATYR, *N.*
jinn. *m;*
SAUCE, *N.*
1. relish. chaṭní. *f;*
2. insolence. gustáḳhí. *f;* shoḳhí. *f;* chauṛ. *f;*
SAUCE, TO, *V. T.*
gustáḳhí karní; ákaṛná; ṭhíṭṭh karná;
SAUCER, *N.*
pirich. *f;* rikábí. *f;* thálí. *f;*
SAUCILY, *Adv.*
gustáḳhí nál; shoḳhí nál;

SAUCINESS, *N*.
gustákhí. *f*; beadabí. *f*; see IMPERTINENCE.
SAUCY, *A*.
gustákh; shokh; ḍhíṭh; see IMPERTINENT.
SAUNTER, TO, *V. T*.
sail karná; phirná turná;
to saunter idly. ghaṭṭá uḍáuná;
SAVAGE, *N*.
vaishí. *m*; jangalí ádmí. *m*; ḍanggar ádmí. *m*;
SAVAGE, *A*.
1. wild. vaishí; jangalí; jáhil;
2. brutal. beráhm; sakht; karṛá; jálim; hainsiárá; hattiárá; patthar dil; betaras;
SAVAGELY, *Adv*.
beráhmí nál; baṛí sakhtí nál; betarsí nál;
SAVAGENESS, *N*.
julm. *m*; beráhmí. *f*; sakhtí. *f*; jástí. *f*;
SAVE, TO, *V. T*.
1. to make safe. bacháuná; naját dení; chhuḍáuná; nistárná; tárná, lit. to make swim across the river of death.
2. to lay up. jamá karná; kaṭṭhá karná;
3. to prevent. rokná; aṭkáuná; ḍakkná; thák dená;
SAVE, *Prep*.
bájhoṇ;
SAVINGS, *N*.
bachchat. *f*;
SAVIOUR, *N*.
bacháunwálá. *m*; naját denwálá. *m*; muktídátá. *m*; muktídenwálá. *m*; upkár karnwálá. *m*; tárú. *m*; munjí. *m*;
SAVOUR, *N*.
suád. *m*; majá. *m*;
SAVOURINESS, *N*.
suád. *m*; rasdárí. *f*;
SAVOURLESS, *A*.
besúád; bemazá;
without salt. alúná; see INSPID.
SAVOURY, *A*.
suádí; mazedár;
juicy. rasdár;
SAW, *N*.
1. small. árí. *f*;
2. large. árá. *m*;
3. for two men with frame. parnáhí. *f*;
4. for two men without frame. kalwattar. *m*;
SAW, TO, *V. T*.
árí nál chírná;
1. to saw a tree trunk. mochchhe páuná;
2. to cause to be sawn. chiráuná;
3. pay for sawing. chirái. *f*;
SAWCUT, *N*.
chír. *m*;
SAWDUST, *N*.
búrá. *m*; lakṛí dá búr. *m*;
SAWING, *N*.
chirái. *f*; chírái. *f*;
SAWYER, *N*.
lakṛí chíranwálá. *m*; árákash. *m*;
SAY, TO, *V. T*.
áhná; ákhná; kahná; dassná; bolná; gal karní;
SAYING, *N*.
ákhiá. *m*; kahaut. *f*; akhán. *m*; ákhat. *f*; ákhaṇ. *m*; akháut. *f*;
SCAB, *N*.
kharínḍh. *m*; papṛí. *f*;
scab from prickly heat. ghamrorí. *f*; thapphar. *m*;
SCABBARD, *N*.
mián. *m*; gátrá. *m*;
SCAFFOLD, *N*.
pháh. *m*; pháṇsí. *f*; sulí. *f*;
SCAFFOLDING, *N*.
1. round a building. go. *m*;
2. in field. manhá. *m*;
SCALD, TO, *V. T*.
sáṛná; lúhná;
SCALDED, *A*.
lúh;
SCALE OF A FISH, *N*.
chháná. *m*;
SCALES, *N*.
takkṛí. *f*; tarájú. *m*;
one side of the scales. chhábbá. *m*; palá. *m*;
SCALY, *A*.
kharínḍ;

SCAMP, *N.*
badmásh. *m* ; naṭkhaṭ. *m* ; luchchá. *m* ; laphaṭiá. *m* ;
SCAMPER, TO, *V. T.*
bhajjná ; nassná; naṭṭhná; dauṛná;
SCAN, TO, *V. T.*
takkná ; vekhná ; ṭol karná ; jhátí mární ;
SCANDAL, *N.*
gapp shapp ; *f* ; see TATTLE.
SCANDALIZE, TO, *V. T.*
1. to give offence. dil khaṭṭá karná ; chheṛná ;
2. to slander. badnám karná ; niṇdiá karná ; dág láuná ;
SCANDALOUS, *A.*
burá ;
SCANT, *A.*
ghaṭṭ ; thoṛá ; masákú ;
SCANTILY, *Adv.*
ghaṭṭ ;
SCANTINESS, *N.*
ghaṭṭá. *m* ; kamí. *f* ; thuṛ. *f* ;
SCANTY, *A.*
ghaṭṭ ; thoṛá ;
SCAPEGRACE, *N.*
badmásh. *m* ; naṭ khaṭ. *m* ;
SCAR, *N.*
zaḳhm dá nisháṇ. *m* ;
SCARCE, *A.*
wirlá ; maiṇghá ; aṇokhá ;
SCARCELY, *Adv.*
masáṇ ; masáṇ masáṇ ; aukh nál ; mushkil nál ;
SCARCENESS, *N.*
gháṭṭá. *m* ; kamí. *f* ; see SCARCITY.
SCARCITY, *N.*
gháṭṭá. *m* ; kahit. *m* ; garání. *f* ; thuṛ. *f* ; ṭoṭ. *f* ; maṇḍá. *m* ; maṇderá. *m* ; maiṇgh. *m* ; auṛ. *f* ; taṇgí. *f* ; kál. *m* ;
SCARE, TO, *V. T.*
ḍaráuná ; ḍar páuná ; ghabrá-dená ; kachráuná ;
SCARECROW, *N.*
ḍaráuná. *m* ; ḍarává. *m* ;
SCARF, *N.*
dupaṭṭá. *m* ;
SCARIFICATION, *N.*
pachchhná. *m* ;
SCARLET, *A.*
súhá ; kirmchí ; sokh lál ;
SCATHLESS, *A.*
benuqsán ; bedágá ;
SCATTER, TO, *V. T.*
1. strew about. khilárná ; chhitráuná ; chhaṭṭá dená ; kerná ; khiṇḍáuná ; khaṇḍáuná ; khiní khiní karní ;
2. disperse. phailauná ; khillár pullár dená ;
3. to sprinkle. chhinn bhinn karná ;
SCATTERED, TO BE, *V. I.*
khillar jáná ; khiṇḍná ; chhitarná ; ud pud jáná ; khillar pullaṛ jáná ; nikkhaṛ pukkhaṛ jáná ; khiṇḍ phuṭṭ jáná ;
SCATTERED, *A.*
khillare pullaṛe ; khiṇḍar ;
SCAVENGER, *N.*
chúhṛá. *m* ; mihtar. *m* ;
SCENE, *N.*
1. spectacle. tamáshá. *m* ;
2. panorama. najárá. *m* ;
SCENT, *N.*
1. track. khoj. *m* ;
2. scent of an animal. gaṇdh. *m* ; mushk. *m* ;
3. perfume. maihak. *f* ; hamkár. *m* ;
SCENTED, *A.*
maihakdár ; ḳhushbodár ; lapatdár ; báshnewálá ;
SCEPTIC, *N.*
kufrí. *m* ; munkir. *m* ; dahriá. *m* ; chárwákiá. *m* ;
SCEPTICISM, *N.*
kufr. *m* ; bharáṇtí. *f* ;
SCEPTRE, *N.*
assá. *m* ;
SCHEDULE, *N.*
fihrist. *f* ;
SCHEME, *N.*
1. plan. upáo. *m* ; tajwíz. *f* ;
2. purpose. irádá. *m* ; níyat. *f* ; dalíl. *f* ; gauṇ. *m* ;
SCHEME, TO, *V. T.*
gall ginná minná ; matá pakáuná ; ḍhaṇg sochná ; upáo labbhná ; gall pakání ; saláh pakáuní ;
SCHEMER, *N.*
ghátti. *m* ; darohí. *m* ;

SCHOLAR, *N*.
shagird. *m*; paṛhanwálá. *m*; vidiárthí. *m*; paṛhákú. *m*;
SCHOLARSHIP, *N*.
1. allowance. wazífá. *m*;
2. learning. ilm. *m*; viddiá. *f*;
SCHOOL, *N*.
madrasá. *m*; sakúl. *m*; páṭhsálá. *f*; chatsálá. *f*;
SCHOOL FELLOW, *N*.
jamáití. *m*; ikko sakul de. *m*;
SCHOOL MASTER, *N*.
ustád. *m*; munshí. *m*; páṇḍhá. *m*; paṛháunwálá. *m*;
SCHOOL MISTRESS, *N*.
ustádaní. *f*;
SCHOONER, *N*.
jaház. *m*; beṛá. *m*;
SCIENCE, *N*.
saians dá ilm. *m*; viddiá. *f*;
SCINTILLATE, TO, *V. T.*
látáṇ márná; chilakná; chamakná; jhalakná; lishkná;
SCINTILLATION, *N*.
jhalak. *f*; bhaṛak. *f*; chilkárá. *m*; jhamak. *f*;
SCISSORS, *N*.
kainchí. *f*; katarní. *f*;
SCOFF, TO, *V. T.*
ṭhaṭṭhá karná OR márná; makhaul karná; hujjat karní; táne dená; mehná dená;
SCOFFER, *N*.
makhauliá. *m*; ṭhaṭṭhebáj. *m*; maskará. *m*;
SCOFFING, *N*.
makhaul. *m*; ṭhaṭṭhá. *m*; táná. *m*;
SCOFFINGLY, *Adv.*
makhaul nál;
SCOLD, TO, *V. T.*
ghurakná; dhamkáuná; jhiṛkná; ghurná;
SCOLDING, *N*.
ghurkí. *f*; jhiṛak. *f*; malámat. *f*; jhiṛká jhiṛkí. *f*; jhahí. *f*;
SCOPE, *N*.
1. extent. samáí. *f*; gunjaish. *f*;
2. object. matlab. *m*; arth. *m*;
SCORCH, TO, *V. T.*
sáṛná; luhná; jhulsáuná;
SCORCH, TO, *V. I.*
saṛná; jhulas jáná; jhulliá jáná; bhulsiá jáná;
SCORCHING, *N*.
tattá; garm;
scorching heat. tapish. *f*;
SCORE, *N*.
1. reckoning. hisáb. *m*; lekhá. *m*; lekhá jokhá. *m*; lekhá pattá. *m*;
2. twenty. víh;
SCORN, *N*.
niṇdiá. *f*; ghin. *f*; hiqárat. *f*; see PRIDE.
SCORN, TO, *V. T.*
niṇdiá karná; haqír jáṇná; nachíz samajhná; haṇkár karná;
SCORNER, *N*.
niṇdak. *m*; makhauliá. *m*; niṇdiá karnwálá. *m*;
SCORNFUL, *A*.
mazájí; magrúr; gamrúr; phiṭṭiá hoyá; haṇkárí;
SCORNFULLY, *Adv.*
makhaul nál; magrúrí nál; akaṛ ke; kibr karke;
SCORPION, *N*.
ṭhúhán. *m*; waṭhúhán. *m*;
Proverb. The friendship of the base is like a scorpion's sting. kamíne dí yárí waṭhuheṇ dá ḍaṇg;
SCOUNDREL, *N*.
badmásh. *m*; sharír. *m*; riṇd. *m*; see RASCAL.
SCOUR, TO, *V. T.*
mánjná; malná; safá karná; kuchná;
SCOURGE, *N*.
koṛá. *m*; koṭrá. *m*;
SCOURGE, TO, *V. T.*
koṛá márná;
SCOWL, *N*.
ghúr. *m*; ghurkí. *f*; tiúṛí. *f*; ghurákiá. *f*; ghúrí. *f*;
SCOWL, TO, *V. T.*
ghúr dená; ghurákiáṇ kaḍḍhná; táṛná; ghúrí waṭṭní;
SCRAP, *N*.
khanní. *f*; chúr bhúr. *m*; párchá. *m*;
Proverb. A scrap at home is better than a whole loaf abroad. ghar dí khanní báhar dí sárí náloṇ chaṇgí hai;

SCRAPE, TO, *V. T.*
khotarná; ragaṛná; gharoṛná; kharochná; chhilná;
1. to scrape a pot. khurchná;
2. to scrape off plaster from a wall. khárná;

SCRAPER, *N.*
1. wooden. bhahauṛá. *m*; pahauṛá. *m*;
2. for a horse. kharkná. *m*;

SCRAPING, *N.*
ragaṛ. *f*;
pot scrapings. khurchan. *m*;

SCRATCH, *N.*
ragaṛ. *f*; jharíṭ. *f*; gharúṇḍ. *m*;

SCRATCH, TO, *V. T.*
khurkná; kháj karní; kharúṇḍ márná;

SCRAWL, TO, *V. T.*
ghasíṭná;

SCREAM, *N.*
chíkh. *f*; chikárá. *m*; cháng. *f*; kúk. *f*; cháṇggar. *f*;

SCREAM, TO, *V. T.*
chíkh mární; cháṇggar mární; chíkhná; chichláuná; kikiáuná; chiláuná;
to cause to scream. chikháuná;

SCREECH, TO, *V. T.*
chíkhná; chíṇ chíṇ karná;

SCREEN, *N.*
chík. *f*; paṛdá. *m*; luk. *m*; láwá. *m*;

SCREEN, TO, *V. T.*
1. to shade. paṛdà karná;
2. to hush up. paṛdá karná;
3. to hide. lukáuná; ohlá karná; chhipáuná; luká lainá;

SCREW, *N.*
pech. *m*;

SCREW, TO, *V. T.*
pech pherná OR kasná;

SCREWDRIVER, *N.*
pechkass. *m*;

SCRIBBLE, *N.*
badkhatt. *m*;

SCRIBBLE, TO, *V. T.*
jharítná; ghasíṭná; kágaz kálá karná;

SCRIMP, *N.*
shúm. *m*; kanjús. *m*; makkhí chús. *m*; joṛu. *m*; nichoṛú. *m*;

SCRIPTURE, *N.*
1. Christian scriptures. Pák Kalám. *m*; Injíl. *f*; Baibal Sharíf. *m*; dharm pustak. *m*;
2. Hindu scriptures. Dharm Sástar. *m*;
3. Muhammadan scriptures. Qurán. *m*;

SCROLL, *N.*
fihrist. *f*;

SCRUB, TO, *V. T.*
kuchná; máṇjná; ragaṛ ke dhoná; gharoṛná;

SCRUBBING BRUSH, *N.*
kuchchan. *f*;

SCRUPLE, *N.*
shakk. *m*; shubhá. *m*; bharm. *m*; shakk shubhá. *m*; jhakk. *m*; sainsá. *m*;

SCRUPLE, TO, *V. T.*
1. to doubt. shak karná; bharm karná; dhaṛakná; yaqín nahíṇ áuná;
2. to hesitate. jhakkná; jhakk paí jáná; jhullná; jhijhakná; jakko takk karná;

SCRUTINIZE, TO, *V. T.*
ṭol márná; vekhná; takkná; sodhná; jhátí mární;

SCRUTINY, *N.*
mulájá. *m*;

SCUFFLE, *N.*
jháṭam jháṭá. *m*; laṛáí. *f*; dhaul dhappá. *m*; puáṛá. *m*;

SCUFFLE, TO, *V. T.*
jháṭam jhuṭe karná;

SCULLERY, *N.*
bawárchi kháná. *m*;

SCULLION, *N.*
masálchí. *m*;

SCULPTOR, *N.*
chittarkar. *m*;

SCUM, *N.*
jhagg. *f*;
1. dregs. phog. *m*; lagg labeṛ. *f*;
2. green scum on ponds. búr. *m*; sáwil. *f*;

SCURF, *N.*
sikarí. *f*;

SCURRILITY, *N.*
gálí. *f*; gál. *f*; gaṇd zabání. *f*; gálí galoch. *f*;

SCURRILIOUS, *A.*
badzabán; gaṇḍá; see VILE.
SCURRILIOUSLY, *Adv.*
gálí galauj ná!;
SEA, *N.*
ságar. *m*; samundar. *m*;
SEACOAST, *N.*
samundar dá kanárá. *m*;
SEAGULL, *N.*
samundar dá baglá, *m*;
SEAL, *N.*
chháp. *f*;
SEAL, TO, *V. T.*
mohr láuná; chháp láuná;
SEALING WAX, *N.*
lákh. *f*;
SEAM, *N.*
darj. *f*; tunb. *m*; síun. *f*;
1. without seam. ansítá;
2. a join. joṛ. *m*;
SEAMAN, *N.*
maláh. *m*; ḳhalásí. *m*;
SEAPORT, *N.*
bandargáh. *f*;
SEARCH, *N.*
ḍhúṇḍ. *f*; ṭol. *f*; khoj. *m*; ḍhúṇḍ ḍháṇḍ. *f*; ṭol bhál. *m*; for stolen property. taláshí. *f*; gaver. *f*;
SEARCH, TO, *V. T.*
1. to enquire after. puchchná; patá lagáuná;
2. to look for. ḍhunḍhná; labbhná; bhálná; ṭolná; ḍhúṇḍh ḍháṇḍhná; khoj kaḍḍhná; ḍhúṇḍh ḍháṇḍh karná;
2. to search a house. talásḥí karní;
SEASON, *N.*
mausim. *m*; bahár. *f*; rut. *m*;
1. season of plenty. sukhál. *m*; sukál. *m*;
2. at the season. rut sir;
3. out of season. averá;
4. after the season. pichchetá;
5. Proverbs connected with the seasons.
A. When the grass flowers the rains are forgotten. gáh phulle, táṇ míṇh bhulle;
B. If it does not rain at Lohri the spring harvest will be a poor one. je míṇh ná páwe Lohṛí, hárí howegí thoṛí;
C. In the month of Sawan, *i.e.*, August, neither shade nor sunshine pleases. Saun máh dí rutt ná chháṇ bhánweṇ ná dhupp;
D. If frost has come in the winter then manure has come by the sackful. siál dá korá ruṛí dá borá;
SEASON, TO, *V. T.*
masálá páuná; baghárná;
SEASONED, *A.*
salúná; masáledár;
SEASONING, *N.*
masálá. *m*;
SEAT, *N.*
chauṇkí. *f*; kursí. *f*; see CHAIR.
1. place. tháṇ. *f*;
2. throne. gaddí. *f*;
3. seat of custom. chuṇgí dá chabutrá. *m*;
SEAT, TO, *V. T.*
biṭháuná; baháuná; bahálná; biṭhálná; biṭhláuná;
SEATED, TO BE, *V. I.*
baiṭhná; baiṭh jáná; baí jáná;
SECEDE, TO, *V. I.*
muṛnà; haṭ jáná;
SECESSION, *N.*
phuṭ. *f*; wichchoṛá. *m*;
SECLUDE, TO, *V. T.*
wakkhrá karná;
SECLUSION, *N.*
1. separation. wichchoṛá. *m*;
2. privacy. ikkalwánjá. *m*; ikáṇt. *f*;
SECOND, *N.*
pal. *m*; chhiṇ. *m*;
SECOND, *A.*
dujjá; dusrá;
1. in a second. dam vichch;
2. a second husband. duhájar. *m*; duhájú. *m*;
SECOND, TO, *V. T.*
1. to second a proposal. táíd karná;
2. to help. madat dení; sahárá dená; sahaitá karná; uprálá karná;

SECOND HAND, *A*.
puráná ;
SECRECY, *N*.
gujjh. *f*; ollhá. *m*; ollhá chollhá. *m* ;
SECRET, *N*.
bhet. *m* ; híjpiáj. *m* ; gupt gal. *f* ; ollhá chhappá. *m* ;
1. in secret. gupt vichch ; parde vichch
2. to betray a secret. bhet dená OR kholná ;
3. at last the secret was out. orak núṇ bháṇḍá phuṭṭ hí gayá ;
SECRET, *A*.
gujjhá ; gupt ; luká ;
SECRETARY, *N*.
sakattar. *m* ;
SECRETE, TO, *V. T*.
chhipáuná ; dil vichch rakkhná ; lukáuná ; uhlá OR ollhá karná ; ḍhappná ;
SECRETLY, *Adv*.
chhup cháp ; gujjhe gujjhe ; chorí chorí karke ; chorí ; andarkháne ; parokhe ; chup kíte ; parde nál ; akkh bachá ke ; chorí chhapí ; luk lukká ke ; chhipáke ; gujjhá gujjhá ; luk luk ; chupp kítiáṇ ; to come in secretly. akkh bachá-ke auná ;
SECT, *N*.
paṇth. *m* ; firqá. *m* ;
SECTARY, *N*.
paṇthí. *m* ;
SECTION, *N*.
1. part. hissá. *m* ; chháṇḍá. *m* ;
2. of a book. káṇḍ, *m* ; adhiyá. *m* ;
3. of fruit. pháṛí. *f* ;
SECULAR, *A*.
dunyáví ;
SECULARITY, *N*.
dunyádárí. *f* ;
SECURE, *A*.
pakká ; ṭhík ;
SECURE, TO, *V. T*.
1. to make safe. bacháuná ;
2. to confine. bannhná ; band karná ; kabjá karná ; ghere vichch lená ;
3. to get possession of, hásil karná ; qabzá kar lainá ; mallná ;
4. to secure one's end. matlab kaḍḍhná ;
5. to fasten. gaṇḍhná ; jorná ; bannhná ;
SECURITY, *N*.
1. safety. aman. *f* ; amán. *f* ;
2. deposit. zamánat. *f* ;
3. for a debt. manautí. *f* ;
SEDAN, *N*.
ḍolí. *f* ;
SEDATE, *A*.
dhírajmán ;
SEDATELY, *Adv*.
háyá nál ;
SEDATENESS, *N*.
dhiraj. *f* ; saṇjam. *m* ;
SEDIMENT, *N*.
rahindí khund. *m* ; phog phág. *m* ; nudgá. *m* ; phog. *m* ; lagg lagber. *f* ; gád. *f* ;
SEDITION, *N*.
daṇggá fasád. *f* ; bagávat. *f* ;
SEDITIOUS, *A*.
daṇggáí ; fásádí ; pasádiá ; nábar ;
SEDUCE, TO, *V. T*.
lubháuná ; baihkáná ; jháṇsná ; bharmáuná ;
to defile. ját bharist karná ;
SEDUCTION, *N*.
lubháo. *m* ; jháṇsá. *m* ; bahkád. *m* ;
SEDULOUS, *A*.
uddamí ; mihnatí ;
SEE, TO, *V. T*.
vekhná ; najar mární ; dhiánaná ; vehnná ;
1. to see a long way. dur dí sujjhní ;
2. we have come to see you. asíṇ tuháḍe darshan núṇ áe háṇ. ;
3. we shall see. wekhí jápegí ;
SEED, *N*.
bí. *m* ;
SEEDLING, *N*.
paníri. *f* ; bijárá. *m* ;
SEED POD, *N*.
phalí. *f* ;
SEEING, *Conj*.
kyuṇ jo ; is laí ;
SEEING, *N*.
díd. *m* ; tár. *m* ; daristi. *f* ;

SEEK, TO, *V. T.*
labbhná ; bhálná ; khoj kaḍḍhná ; ṭolná ; ḍhuṇḍhná ; bhál karná ;
SEEKER, *N.*
ḍhuṇḍhaulá. *m ;* ḍhuṇḍháú. *m ;*
SEEKING, *N.*
ḍhuṇḍ. *f ;* khoj. *m ;* see SEARCH.
SEEM, TO, *V. I.*
dissná ; jápná ;
SEEMLY, *Adv.*
munásib ; laiq ;
to be seemly. sajná ; phabná ;
SEEN, TO, BE, *V. I.*
dissná ; jápná ; sujjhná ;
SEETHE, TO *V. T.*
ubbálná ; kárhná ;
SEGMENT, *N.*
ṭukṛá. *m ;*
SEGREGATE, TO, *V. T.*
alag karná ; chhekná ;
SEIGE, *N.*
gherá. *m ;*
SEIZE, TO, *V. T.*
phaṛná ; phagaṛná ; phakaṛna ; hatth páuná ; napp lainá ; jhapphná ;
1. to seize one's opportunity. dá lainá ;
2. to snatch away. khoh lainá ;
SEIZED, TO BE, *V. I.*
phaṛiá jáná ; waliá jáná ;
SEIZURE, *N.*
phaṛwáí. *f ;*
SELDOM, *Adv.*
kade kade ; ghaṭṭ; ghaṭṭ waddh ;
SELECT, TO, *V. T.*
chunná ; pasiṇd karná ; ṭálná ; chugná ; chhaṇḍná ; chháṇná ; dhárná ;
SELECT, *A.*
kháss ; uttam ; choṇwáṇ. ;
SELECTED, *A.*
chuṇwáṇ ;
SELECTION, *N.*
chháṇṭ. *f ;* chuṇṭ. *f ;* chháṇṭ chuṇṭ. *f ;*
SELF, *Pro.*
áp ; khud ;
SELF ABASEMENT, *N.*
adhíṇagí. *f ;* adhíntái. *f ;* ájizí. *f ;* halímí. *f ;* maskíṇí. *f ;*
SELF CENTRED, *A.*
matlabí ; garjí ; khudí ; see SELFISH.
SELF CONCEIT, *N.*
haṇkáṛ. *f ;* hakáṛ. *m ;*
SELF CONTROL, *N.*
apne áp núṇ qábú vichch rakkhná ;
SELF CONSECRATION, *N.*
ghol ghumáí. *f ;* ghol ghattí. *f ;*
SELFISH, *A.*
garzí ; garjí ; matlabí ; matlab dá yár ; matlabiá ; matbalí ; matbaliá;
SELFISHLY, *Adv.*
khudí nál ;
SELFISHNESS, *N.*
gauṇ. *m ;* khudgarají. *f ;*
SELFSAME, *A.*
uhí ; uho hí ;
SELF SEEKER, *N.*
garjí. *m ;* matlab dá yár. *m ;* matlabiá. *m ;* see SELFISH.
SELF SUFFICIENT, *A.*
magrúr ; majájí ; kabbá ;
SELF WILLED, *A.*
jiddí ; ákí ; man mukh ; man dá maují ; kabbá ; ḍhíṭh ; khuráṇt ; aríkhor ;
SELL, TO, *V. T.*
vechná ; mull dená ;
to cause to be sold. wikáuná ;
SELL, TO, *V. I.*
bikná ;
SELLING, *N.*
bikkarí. *f ;* wikáú. *m ;*
SEMBLANCE, *N.*
ḍaul. *f ;* shakal. *f ;* sáṇg *m ;* mel. *m ;* wargá. *m ;*
SEMEN, *N.*
maní. *f ;* biṇd. *f ;* dháṇt. *f ;* tukham. *m ;*
SEMOLINA, *N.*
samlíná. *m ;*
SEND, TO, *V. T.*
ghallná ;
1. to send away. tor dená ; vidyá karná ;
2. to send a message. ákh ghallná ; sanehá ghallná ; akhwá ghallná ;
3. to send for. maṇgwáuná ; sadd ghallná ;

SENDER, *N.*
ghallanwálá. *m ;*
SENILE, *A.*
buḍhápe dá ; buḍḍhá ; fach ; jahíf ;
SENILITY, *N.*
buḍḍhápá. *m ;* buḍhepá. *m ;*
SENIOR, *A.*
waḍḍá ; buzurg ; waḍerá ;
SENIORITY, *N.*
buzurgí. *f ;*
SENNA, *N.*
saná. *m ;* sarná. *m ;*
SENSATION, *N.*
1. an impression. sudh. *f ;* ausáṇ. *m ;* sudh buddh. *f ;*
2. excitement. josh. *m ;*
SENSE, *N.*
1. understanding. aql. *f ;* hosh. *f ;* buddh. *m ;* sudh buddh. *f ;* chajj. *m ;*
2. meaning. matlab. *m ;* arth. *m ;*
3. five senses. panj tat. *m ;*
4. to come to your senses. surt vichch auná ;
SENSELESS, *A.*
1. foolish. beaql ; besudh ; bewaqúf ; behál ; buddhhíṇ ; hochchhá ; nadán ; murakh ; besamajh ; durbuddh ;
2. unconscious. behosh ;
SENSELESSLY, *Adv.*
bewaqúfí nál ; nadání nál ; beaqlí nál ;
SENSELESSNESS, *N.*
beaqlí. *f ;* bewaqúfí. *f ;* nadání. *f ;*
SENSIBILITY, *N.*
hosh. *m ;* hoshiyárí. *f ;* hoshmandí. *f ;* buddh. *m ;*
SENSIBLE, *A.*
hoshiyár ; buddhwán ; hoshwálá ; suchet ; chatann chatará ; chátar ;
SENSIBLENESS, *N.*
hoshiyárí. *f ;*
SENSIBLY, *Adv.*
hosh nál ; aql nál ; soch samajhke ;
SENSITIVE, *A.*
komal ;
SENSUAL, *A.*
luchchá ; guṇḍá ; mastáná ; laṭpaṭá ; khíwá ; ḍheká ; chhaṭṭiá hoyá ; mushṭaṇḍá ;
SENSUALIST, *N.*
luchch. *m ;* lahirí. *m ;*
SENSUALITY, *N.*
luchaú. *m ;* luchchpuṇá. *m ;* guṇḍpuṇá. *m ;* chaskebájí. *f ;* masteván. *f ;* phateṇváṇ. *f ;* mastí. *f ;* sensual desire. kámná. *f ;*
SENSUALLY, *Adv.*
masteván nal ; mastí nál ;
SENTENCE, *N.*
1. decision. faisalá. *m ;* hukm. *m ;*
2. legal. hukm. *m ;* digrí. *f ;*
3. grammar. wák. *m ;* fikrá. *m ;* jumlá. *m ;*
SENTENCE, TO, *V. T.*
sazá dá hukm dená ;
SENTIENT BEING, *N.*
jantu. *m ;*
SENTIMENT, *N.*
matá. *m ;* khavál. *m ;*
SENTIMENTAL, *A.*
narm ; komal ;
SENTIMENTALITY, *N.*
nikkíáṇ nikkíáṇ galláṇ dí soch. *f ;*
SENTINEL, *N.*
saṇtarí. *m ;*
SENTRY, *N.*
saṇtarí. *m ;*
SEPARATE, TO, *V. T.*
aḍḍ karná ; wakkh karná ; nakherná ; wichoṛ dená ;
1. to separate coarse from fine. rolná ;
2. to excommunicate. chhekná ;
3. to separate gold and silver from other things. niárá karná ;
4. to separate into two. aḍḍo aḍḍ karná ;
SEPARATE, TO, *V. I.*
wakkh ho jáná ; nikhaṛná ;
SEPARATE, *A.*
aḍḍo aḍḍ ; wakkhrá ; alag ; niárá ; wakkho-wakkh ; anjo anj ;
SEPARATELY, *Adv.*
wakkho wakkh ; alag alag ; bhinn bhinn ;
SEPARATION, *N.*
wichhoṛá. *m ;* duj. *f ;* durájí. *f ;* phúṭ. *f ;* nikheṛá. *m ;*
SEPULCHRE, *N.*
qabr. *f ;* see TOMB.
SEQUEL, *N.*
natíjá. *m ;* aṇjám. *m ;*

SEQUENCE, *N*.
tartíb. *m* ; lár. *f* ;
SEQUESTRATION, *N*.
kurkí. *f* ;
SERENE, *A*.
chuppchupátá ; sunnsán ; dhírá ;
SERENENESS, *N*.
suláh. *f* ; diljamáí. *f* ; dhíraj. *f* ;
see TRANQUILITY.
SERF, *N*.
gulám. *m* ; dáss. *m* ;
SERFDOM, *N*.
gulámí. *f* ;
SERGEANT, *N*.
havaldár. *m* ;
SERIES, *N*.
silsilá. *m* ; táṇtá. *m* ; lár. *f* ; pál. *f* ;
SERIOUS, *A*.
1. grave. gambhír ; gaurá ; dhíraj-máṇ ;
2. important. bhárá ; bhárí ; baṛí jarúrí ;
3. earnest. sargarm ; shukín ;
SERIOUSLY, *Adv*.
ríjh nál ; diloṇ wajoṇ ; jí ján nál ; manoṇ ;
SERIOUSNESS, *N*.
sanjídagí. *f* ; dhíraj. *f* ;
SERMON, *N*.
wáz. *m* ; nasíhat. *f* ; updesh. *m* ;
wák. *m* ;
Muhammadan sermon. ḳhutbá. *m*. M ;
SERMONIZE, TO, *V. T*.
wáz karná ; updesh karná :
SERPENT, *N*.
sapp. *m* ; nág. *m* ; sarp. *m* ;
SERVANT, *N*.
naukar. *m* ; ṭahliyá. *m* ; ṭahilaṇ. *f* ;
chákar. *m* ; bandá. *m* ; dás. *m* ;
gollá. *m* ;
1. farm servants. kámá. *m* ; sepí. *m* ; áthaṛí. *m* ;
2. servant who works for several houses as waterman, carpenter, &c. lággí. *m* ;
3. Government servant. mulá-zam. *m* ;
4. a devoted servant, hatthíṇ baddhíṇ gulám. *m* ;
5. servant girl. golí. *f* ; laundí. *f* ; tahilaṇ. *f* ;
6. Proverb. Earn as a servant and eat as a master. gollá hoke kamáve, mían hoke kháve ;
7. Proverb. If the servant works then the master eats. ráhak kamáe te sáín kháe ;
SERVE, TO, *V. T*.
ṭahl karná ; ṭahl sevá karná ;
ḳhidmat karní ; naukarí karní ;
1. to serve out food. rasoí paros-ná ; roṭí parihná ; roṭí wartauná ;
2. to serve one's own ends. gauṇ karná ; gauṇ kaḍḍháuná ; gauṇ láiná ;
SERVE, TO, *V. I*.
chalná ;
SERVICE, *N*.
1. act. naukarí. *f* ; ṭahl. *f* ; sevá. *f* ; chákarí. *f* ; ṭahl sevá *f* ; ḳhidmat. *f* ; ṭahl ṭakor. *f*,
2. religious. bandagí. *f* ; ibádat. *f* ; namáz. *f* ; duá bandagí. *f* ; girjá. *m* ; sevá *f* ; see WORSHIP;
3. benefit. faidá. *m* ; nafá. *m* ; láh. *m* ;
SERVICEABLE, *A*.
kamm dá ; kamm de laiq ;
SERVILE, *A*.
àjiz ; kamíná ; adhíṇ ; jholí chukk ;
SERVILITY, *N*.
leṭ peṭ. *f* ; adhíṇtáí. *f* ; leṭí peṭí. *f* ;
lollo poppo. *f* ; choj. *m* ; adhíṇagí. *f* ;
SERVITUDE, *N*.
gulámí. *f* ; dáspuṇá. *m* ; chákarí. *f* ;
SET, TO, *V. T*.
1. to place. láuná ; dharná ; rakkhná ; khaṛiá karná ;
2. to fix firmly. thápná ; gaḍḍná ;
3. to regulate. ṭhík ṭhák karná ; durust karná ;
4. to set a limb. joṛná ;
5. to set apart. wakkh kar rakkhná ;
SET, TO, *V. I*.
1. sun to set. ast hona ; astná ; lahiná ; dubb jáná ;
2. to set out. turná ;
3. to be set. gaḍḍ jáná ;
SETTLE TO, *V. T*.
1. a place. abád karná ; wa-sáuná ; pair jamáuná ;
2. to determine. faisalá karná ; pakkí karní ; chukáuná ; ṭhahrauná ;

3. a dispute. nibeṛná; doṭakk karná; agg bujháuná; mukáuná;
4. an account. hisáb bhugtáuna OR chukáuná; tárná; lekhá chukáuná;
5. to settle the price. ṭakk chhaḍḍná;

SETTLE, TO, *V. I.*
1. to become fixed. baiṭhná; gaḍḍ jáná;
2 to dwell. basná; wasná; ṭhahrná; pair laggná; rahná;
3. to sink in water. dubb jáná; baiṭhná;
4. to sink in mud. dhasná; dhas chalná;

SETTLED, *A.*
pakk paká;

SETTLEMENT, *N.*
1. colony. naví abádí. *f;*
2. act. nabeṛá. *m;* faisalá. *m;*
2. monetary. lekhá. *m;*
4. land settlement. bandobast. *m;*
5. settlement officer. muhtamím bandobast. *m;*
6. of the price of a thing. ṭakk. *m;*

SEVEN, *A.*
satt;

SEVENFOLD, *A.*
satauná; satguná;

SEVENTEEN, *A.*
satáráh;

SEVENTEENTH. *A.*
satáráhwán;

SEVENTH, *A.*
satwáṇ;

SEVENTIETH, *A.*
sattarwáṇ;

SEVENTY, *A.*
sattar;
seventy one. akhattar;
,, two. bahattar;
,, three. tihattar; taihattar;
,, four. chuhattar; churhattar;
,, five. panjhattar;
,, six. chehattar;
,, seven. satattar;
,, eight. aṭhattar;
,, nine. unássi;

SEVER, TO, *V. T.*
1. to cut. waddhná; kaṭṭná;
2. to separate. aḍḍ karná; wakkhrá karná;

SEVER TO, *V. I.*
judá honá; wakkhrá honá;

SEVERAL, *A.*
kaí; báje; chand;
several times. kaí wár;

SEVERALLY, *Adv.*
alag alag; wakkho wakkh;

SEVERANCE, *N.*
phaṭ. *f;* judáí. *f;*

SEVERE, *A.*
saḳht; rukkhá; karṛá; beráhm; hattiárá; hainsiárá;

SEVERELY, *Adv.*
beráhmí nál; saḳhtí nál; jástí nál;

SEVERITY, *N.*
saḳhtí. *f;* lohṛá. *m;* beráhmí. *f;* jorávarí. *f;* jástí. *f;* karṛái. *f;*

SEW, TO, *V. T.*
tarumbná; turpná; ṭaṇkná; tuppná; síuná; ṭáṇká láuná; trupná;

SEWAGE, *N.*
gaṇdagí. *f;*

SEWER, *N.*
bihíṇ. *m;* morí. *f;* khálí. *f;*

SEWING, *N.*
turpáí. *f;* saláí. *f;* saṇwáí. *f;*
pay for sewing. saṇwáí. *f;*

SEWING MACHINE, *N.*
síúnwálí mashín. *m;*

SEWING NEEDLE, *N.*
suí. *f;*

SEX, *N.*
jins. *f;*

SEXUAL, *A.*
nafsání;

SEX DESIRE, *N.*
lohṛá. *m;* bahir. *m;*
of a mare. weg. *f;* álaṇg. *f;* uthá. *m;*

SEXUAL INTERCOURSE, *N.*
junb. *m;* watí. *f;* gamaṇ. *m;* khuchwái. *f;*
to have s.i. khuchchná; laí painá; chodná;

SHABBINESS, *N.*
garíbí. *f;* muflisí. *f;*

SHACKLES, *N.*
beṛíáṇ. *f;*
handcuffs. hatthkaṛíáṇ. *f;*

SHACKLE, TO, *V. T.*
beṛíáṇ páuní;
SHADE, *N.*
chháṇ. *f;* sáyá. *m;* chháiá. *m;* parchháwáṇ. *m;* chhánu. *f;*
1. in the shade. chháweṇ;
2. over windows, &c. saíbán. *m;*
SHADE, TO, *V. T.*
sáyá karná;
SHADOW, *N.*
chháṇ. *f;* parchháiṇ. *f;* parchháṇ-weṇ. *f;* chháiá. *m;* chhánú. *f;*
to pass away as a shadow. parchháṇweṇ váṇgúṇ ḍhal jándí hai;
SHADY, *A.*
sáyádár; chháṇwálá;
SHAFT, *N.*
1. of a trap. bamb. *m;*
2. an arrow. tír. *m;*
SHAKE, TO, *V. T.*
1. to move. hiláuná; dhurlí mární; ḍolná; jhambhná; tharkáuná; ḍuláuná; jhaṭká láuná OR márná; chhaṇḍná;
2. to shake hands. hatth miláuná;
3. to shake a tree. jhunaná;
4. to shake off. pichchhá chhuḍáuná; chhaṇḍ dená;
5. to shake off the dust. chhaṇḍná;
SHAKE, TO, *V. I.*
hilná; ḍullná; khiskná; hallná; kambná; thatharáuná;
1. as flabby flesh. thalkaná;
2. to shake with cold. thurú thurú karná; síṇ síṇ karná;
SHAKE, *N.*
ḍol. *m;*
SHAKING, *N.*
of a conveyance. ḍakko ḍollá. *m;* hujká. *m;* haláwá. *m;* jhujká. *m;*
SHALLOW, *A.*
thoṛá; goḍe goḍe;
SHAM, *A.*
jáhlí; naqlí; banautí; jhuṭhá; sáng;
SHAME, *N.*
1. decency. sharm. *f;* saṇg. *f;*
2. dísgrace. hattak. *f;* laj. *f;* nomoshí. *f;* namosí. *f;* sharm. *f;* lajjiá. *m;* naṇg. *m;* beizzatí. *f;* sharmindagí. *f;* jhissí. *f;* lajjá. *f;* láj. *f;*
SHAME, TO, *V. T.*
beizzat karní; lajáuná; ṭhíṭṭh karná; sharmáuná; sharmindiá karná; nirádar karná;
the people shamed us. lokáṇ ṭhaṭṭhe nál sánún ṭhíṭṭh kítá;
SHAME, TO, *V. I.*
saṇggná;
SHAMEFACED, *A.*
besharm; beháyá; sharmau;
SHAMEFACEDNESS, *N.*
saṇg. *f;*
SHAMEFUL, *A.*
bhaiṛá; burá; máṛá; ghináuná; sharm dí gal;
SHAMEFULLY, *Adv.*
burí taráh nál;
SHAMELESS, *A.*
besharm; beháyá; belajj; ḍhíṭh; ḍhíṭhá; asaṇg; nisaṇg; nirlajj; kulajj; kulajjá; kusíl;
1. why are you so shameless? lajj sharm kyuṇ láhí;
2. Proverb. Sarcasm on the shameless, a moment's shame and a day's food. ikk pal dí sharmindagí sáre din dá adhár;
SHAMELESSLY, *Adv.*
besharmí nál; beháyái nál;
SHAMELESSNESS, *N.*
besharmí. *f;* beháyái. *f;* ḍhíṭhái. *f;* kusíltái. *f;* bhaṇḍí. *f;*
SHAMPOO, TO, *V. T.*
muṭṭhiáṇ bharní; muṭṭhí chápí karní;
SHANTY, *N.*
jhuggá. *m;* taprí. *f;* ḍhárá. *m;* jhuggí. *f;*
SHAPE, *N.*
ḍaul. *f;* ḍhangg. *m;* shakal. *f;* saj. *f;* sarúp. *m;* ḍhab. *m;*
SHAPE, TO, *V. T.*
ghaṛná; banauná; rachná;
SHAPELESS, *A.*
beḍaul; badshakal; arúp;
SHAPELY, *A.*
khubsurat; chhail; sohná; sundar; malúk;
SHARD, *N.*
ṭhíkrá. *m;*

SHARE, *N*.
hissá. *m*; pattí. *f*; gapphá. *m*; baḳhrá. *m*; chháṇḍá. *m*; bháṇgá. *m*; waṇḍárá. *m*; waṇḍ. *f*; waṇḍá. *m*;
share in a well. áddhí. *f*; pattí. *f*;
SHARE, TO, *V. T.*
hissá lainá; waṇḍ dená:
SHAREHOLDER, *N*.
pattidár. *m*;
SHARER, *N*.
hissedár. *m*; lawáhak. *m*;
SHARP, *A*.
1. not blunt. tikkhá; katílá; tez; tarikkhá; lagá hoyá;
2. bitter. kauṛá;
3. intelligent. siáná; chalák; hoshiyár;
4. quick. tez; chust; tikkhá;
5. very sharp. dudhár;
SHARPEN, TO, *V. T.*
tez karná; dhár láuní.
1. to sharpen a hoe; &c., by hammering. chaṇḍná;
2. to sharpen a pencil. ghaṛná;
SHARPER, *N*.
ṭhagg. *m*; dagebáj. *m*:
sharpers. chalák lok. *m*;
SHARPLY, *Adv*.
chalákí nál; ríjh nál; josh nál;
SHARPNESS, *N*.
1. alertness. tezí, *f*; chalákí. *f*; hoshiyárí. *f*;
2. tartness. khaṭṭá. *m*; khaṭṭíáí. *f*;
SHATTER, TO, *V. T.*
chúr chúr karná; bhanná; bhan suṭṭná; taroṛná;
SHAVED, *A*.
ghonmoṇ;
1. the whole head shaved. ghonná monná; roḍ roḍḍá; roḍḍá bhoḍḍá;
2. Proverb. A shaven head has neither lice nor nits. roḍḍe sir ná júṇ ná líkh; used when a man has no helper.
SHAVE, TO, *V. T.*
munná;
to cause the head to be shaved-sir munáuná; konní tind karáuná; konná sir karáuná; konní karáuná;
SHAVER, *N*.
nái. *m*; hajjám. *m*; rájá. *m*
SHAVING, *N*.
hajámat. *f*;
SHAVINGS, *N*.
sakk. *m*; sakkar. *m*; chhillaṛ. *m*;
SHAWL, *N*.
jhimmí. *f*; bhochhan. *m*; chunní. *f*; dopattá. *m*; dowattá. *m*; chadar. *f*;
1. made of light wool. loí. *f*;
2. made of coarse cotton. khes *m*;
SHEAF, *N*.
bharí. *f*; pulí. *f*; daggi. *f*;
SHEAR, TO, *V. T.*
katarná;
SHEARER, *N*.
kataranwalá. *m*;
SHEARS, *N*.
kátar. *f*; katarní. *f*; kaiṇchí. *f*;
SHEATH, *N*.
1. for a sword. gátrá. *m*;
2. a case. khol. *f*;
3. a covering. galáph. *m*;
SHEATHE, TO, *V. T.*
talwár gátre páuná;
SHED, *N*.
jhuggá. *m*; chhappar. *m*; taprí. *f*;
SHEEN, *N*.
chamkárá. *m*;
SHEEP *N*.
bheḍ. *f*; bheṛí. *f*;
fat tailed sheep. dumbá. *m*;
SHEEPFOLD, *N*.
wáṛá. *m*; báṛá. *m*; wáṛí. *f*;
SHEESHUM TREE, *N*.
táhlí. *f*;
SHEET, *N*.
1. of cloth. khes. *m*; chádar. *f*; ṭallá. *m*; thigaṛá. *m*;
2. of paper. tá. *m*;
SHELF, *N*.
takhtá. *m*; paṛchhattí. *f*; phattá. *m*;
a recess in a wall. álá. *m*;
SHELL, *N*.
1. of fruit. chhillaṛ. *m*; chhilk. *m*;
2. seashell. sippí. *f*; kaudí. *f*; ghogá. *m*; sipp. *m*;
3. explosive. golá. *m*;
4. of an egg. áṇḍḍe dá kholar. *m*;
SHELL, TO, *V. T.*
chhillar udheṛná OR láhuná;

SHELTER, *N*.
1. shade. sáyá. *m*; chháṇ. *f*; chháiá. *m*;
2. shelter or screen. lawá. *m*;
3. a roof. chhat. *m*;
4. a place of refuge. panáh. *f*; ṭhikáná. *m*; saran. *f*;

SHELTER, TO, *V. T.*
sáyá ḍálná; rákkhí karní; bacháuná;

SHELTERLESS, *A.*
bepanáh; natháwáṇ;

SHEPHERD, *N*.
ayálí. *m*; ájaṛí *m*; cheṛú. *m*; pálí. *m*;

SHERBET, *N*.
sharbat. *m*;

SHERD, *N*.
babbarí. *f*; ṭhikṛí. *f*;

SHIELD, *N*.
ḍhál. *f*;
a small shield used in fencing. pharí. *f*;

SHIELD, TO, *V. T.*
bacháuná; rákkhí karní;

SHIFT, TO, *V. T.*
badalná;

SHIFT, TO, *V. I.*
hilná; badal jáná;

SHIFT, *N*.
badlí. *f*; tabdílí. *f*;

SHIN, *N*.
sukṛaṇj. *f*; piní dí haḍḍí. *f*;

SHINE, TO, *V. T.*
1. to illuminate. raushní dení; lo karní;
2. to polish. chalkáuná; ghotná;

SHINE, TO, *V. I.*
jhalkná; lashkaná; lishkná; chilakná; chamakná; jhalak márná;
1. after rain. chilkorná; jhilmal jhilmal karná;
2. to begin to shine. jhalkan lagná;

SHINING, *A.*
chamakwálá; bhaṛakwálá; chamakdár; jal mal jal mal;

SHINING, *N*.
chilak. *f*; bhaṛak. *f*; lishak. *f*;

SHIP, *N*.
jaház. *m*; jaháj. *m*; beṛá. *m*;

SHIPWRECK, *N*.
jaház dí tabái. *f*; beṛá garq ho jáná. *m*;

SHIRK, TO, *V. T.*
khiskná; sustí karní; ḍhilláṇ rahná; rahe karná;

SHIRKER, *N*.
kamm chor. *m*;
Proverbs. Well enough to eat and drink, but deaf when it comes to work. khán 'pín nuṇ chaṇge bhalle, kamm káj núṇ ḍore.
What! unable to turn the hand-mill, and clever at putting in handfuls of grain! pheran dí árí, te chuṇg ghattan dí hoshiyárí.
She had not gone a mile when she said O grandfather, I am thirsty. koh ná challí, bábá tihái.

SHIRT, *N*.
1. native style. kuṛtá. *m*; jhaggá. *m*;
2. English style. qamís. *f*;

SHIVER, TO, *V. I.*
kambná; síṇ síṇ karná; thar thar karná; tharthharáuná; thur thur karná;

SHOAL, *N*.
baretá. *m*;

SHOCK, *N*.
ṭakkar. *f*; dhakká. *m*; saṭṭ. *f*; hujká. *m*;

SHOCK, TO, *V. T.*
dhakká dená; ṭakkar láuní OR mární;

SHOCKING, *A.*
ḍaráuná;

SHOCKINGLY, *Adv.*
búrí taráh nál;

SHOE, *N*.
juttí. *f*; paják. *m*; gauṇí. *f*; paulá. *m*;
1 child's shoe. maujjá. *m*;
2. old worn out shoe. chittar. *m*; littar. *m*; kosrá. *m*;
3. English boot. búṭ. *m*;
4. horse shoe. khurí. *f*; nál. *m*;
5. the upper part of a shoe. panná. *m*;

SHOE MAKER, *N*.
mochí. *m*;
wife of shoe maker. mochan. *f*;

SHOOT, TO, *V. T.*
banduq chaláuná ; fair karná ;
an arrow. káni mární ;
SHOOT OF A TREE, *N.*
gullá. *m ;* laggar. *f ;* kúmal. *f ;*
kúmali. *f ;* puṇgar. *m ;*
shoots round the root of a tree.
jhuṇḍí. *f ;*
SHOOTING, *N.*
shikár. *m ;*
SHOP, *N.*
haṭṭí. *f ;* dukán. *f ;* haṭ. *f ;*
to open or keep a shop. haṭṭí
karní OR lagáuní ;
SHOP, TO, *V. T.*
saudá lainá ;
SHOP BOOK, *N.*
behí. *f ;* wehí. *f ;* rokaṛ. *f ;*
SHOPKEEPER, *N.*
haṭṭíwálá. *m ;* baniyá. *m ;* karáṛ. *m ;* khattrí. *m ;* báṇiáṇ. *m ;*
haṭwániá. *m ;*
a caste of shopkeerps. bhabrá. *m ;*
SHOPKEEPING, *N.*
haṭṭí paṭṛí. *f ;* dukándárí. *f ;*
lekhá jokhá. *m ;*
SHORE, *N.*
kaṇdhá. *m ;* kanárá. *m ;*
of a river. káchhal. *f ;*
SHORT, *A.*
1. inadequate. ghaṭṭ ; kassá ; ajog ;
2. not long. ghaṭṭ ; nikká ;
3. near. neṛe ; kol ;
4. in stature. maḍhrá ; maṇḍhrá ; nikká ; wauhná ;
5. in short. pas ; gall kahdí ; gall kí ; tátpuraj ih hai ; mukddí gall ; garj kí ;
6. a short time afterwards. thoṛe jehe chir pichchoṇ ;
SHORTCOMING, *N.*
kán. *f ;* kamí. *f ;*
SHORTEN, TO, *V. T.*
1. to lessen. ghaṭáuná ; chhoṭá karná ;
2. to epitomise. nichoṛ kaḍḍhná ; arq kaḍḍhná ;
SHORTNESS,
gháṭṭà. *m ;* kamí. *f ;*
SHOT, *N.*
chharrá. *m ;*

SHOULDER, *N.*
kaṇdhá. *m ;* moḍhá. *m ;*
on theshoulder. kaṇdháré ; tangáre ;
SHOULDER, TO, *V. T.*
dhakká dená ; dhuss mární ;
ṭakkar mární ; moḍhá márná ;
pássá márná ;
SHOULDER BLADE, *N.*
phar. *m ;* pharh. *m ;*
SHOUT, *N.*
awáz. *f ;* kúk. *f ;* see SHRIEK.
SHOUT, TO, *V. T.*
awáz mární ; kúk mární ; chíkh
mární ;
to shout loudly. uchchí dittí
áwáz mární ;
SHOUTING, *N.*
hák pukár. *f ;* shor. *m ;* raulá. *m ;*
SHOVE, *N.*
dhakká. *m ;* dhakk. *m ;* ṭakkar. *f ;*
dhuss. *f ;*
SHOVE, TO, *V. T*
dhakká dená ; dhuss mární ;
ṭakkar láuní ; táh dená ;
SHOVEL, *N.*
belchá. *m ;* karch. *m ;*
SHOVING, *N.*
dhakká. *m ;* ṭakkar. *f ;*
shoving in between. ghasar massar. *f ;*
SHOW, *N.*
1. exhibition. tamáshá. *m ;*
2. display. dikhává. *m ;* wikhálá. *m ;* shúká shákí. *f ;* ṭháṭh. *m ;* sajdhaj. *f ;* sobhá. *f ;*
3. for show. wikhálán lai ; wikhále dá ; apní izzat wadháṇ waste ;
SHOW, TO, *V. T.*
1. to exhibit. dikhláuná ; wikhauná ; dikhá dená ; dikhálná ;
2. to inform. samjháuná ; dassná ; janáuná ;
3. to guide. le jáná ; ráh dassná ; agwái karní ; ráh malláuná ;
4. to show oneself. dídár dená ; muṇh dená ;
5. to show off. shán wikháuná ; daddh kaḍḍhní ; lamb kaḍḍhní ;
SHOW, TO, *V. I.*
dissná ; jáppná ; pargaṭ honá ;

SHOWER, *N.*
bhúr. *m;* phakk. *f;* phúhar. *f;*
SHOWER, TO, *V. I.*
kináuná; míṇh painá; phakk páiní;
SHOWY, *A.*
chhachhohrá;
SHRED, *N.*
ṭukṛá. *m;* lír. *f;*
SHRED, TO, *V. T.*
katarná; toṭe toṭe karná;
SHREWD, *A.*
hoshiyár; chalák; siáná; baṛá dáná; chátar; chatar;
SHREWDLY, *Adv.*
hoshiyárí nál;
SHREWDNESS, *N.*
hoshiyárí. *f;* chátarí. *f;* aqlmandí. *f;* ghágá. *m;* chatarái. *f;*
SHRIEK, *N.*
kúk. *f;* chíkh. *f;* kurlát. *m;* chikárá. *m;* cháṇg. *f;* cháṇggar. *f;*
SHRIEK, TO, *V. T.*
kúk mární; kikiáuná; chíkh mární; chichláuná; kurláuná; chíkh chihárá páuná; changhárná; changhár mární;
SHRILL, *A.*
chíkhá; tez;
SHRINE, *N.*
1. of Muhammadan Saint. ḳhángáh. *f;*
2. Hindu. maṛhí. *f;* samádh. *f;*
SHRINK, TO, *V. I.*
1. in fear. jhijakná; jhakkná; jakná; hichkaná; pishán haṭṭná;
2. to shrink from. dur rahná; jachná;
3. to shrink, as cloth. kuṇggaṛná; sangarná;
4. to cause cloth, &c., to shrink. kuṇggáṛná;
5. to shrink, through pain. sí karní;
SHRIVEL, TO, *V. I.*
jhauṇná; jhauṇ jáná;
of plants, &c. kamláuná;
SHROUD, *N.*
kafan. *m;*
SHRUB, *N.*
búṭá. *m;* búṭí. *f;* jháṛ. *m;* jháṛí. *f;* buchch. *m;*

SHRUNK, TO BE, *V. I.*
kuṇggaṛná; sukaṛjáná; sangaṛná;
SHUDDER, *N.*
kambní. *f;*
SHUDDER, TO, *V. T.*
kambná; jí dhaṛakná; jí kammná;
SHUFFLE, *N.*
1. act. ghasíṭ. *f;*
2. deceit. dhokhá. *m;* chálá. *m;* pakhand. *m;* echpech. *m;* herpher. *m;* farfej. *m;*
SHUFFLE, TO, *V. T.*
1. to drag one's feet. pair ghasíṭke chalná;
2. to deceive. ṭálá bálá karná; dhokhá dená; ṭhaggná; jabán badalní OR pherní; ghasal masal karná;
SHUFFLING, *N.*
ṭál. *f;* ṭálá bálá. *m;* ghasal masal. *m;* ghásal másal. *m;* ṭálmaṭolá. *m;*
SHUN, TO, *V. T.*
neṛe ná jáná; báj ráhná; dur ráhná; matthe ná laggná;
1. to be apart. wakkhrá honá;
2. to hide the face. múṇh lukáuná;
3. to go another way to avoid one. katráuná;
SHUT, TO, *V. T.*
1. to close the door. darwájá márná; buhá band karná; ḍhakkná; dhohná; dhoná; bheṛná; bhíṛná; pherná;
2. to shut a book. kitáb ṭhappná; kitáb band karná;
3. to prohibit. rokná; warajná; ṭhák dená;
4. to exclude. kaḍḍhná; chhekná; haṭá dená;
5. to close the eyes. akkhíáṇ mít láiná; akkhíáṇ mích lená; akkhíáṇ mít lená;
6. to shut up shops. hartál. *m;*
7. the door is shut. buhá wajjiá hoyá hai;
8. with close doors. wajjiṇ búhíṇ;
SHUTTER, *N.*
jharokhá. *m;* páṭ. *m;*
SHUTTLE, *N.*
nál. *f;* juláhe dí nál

SHY, *A*.
  saṇgdí;
  1. a shy man. hayáú. *m;* saṇgá-
    wálá. *m;*
  2. to be shy. saṇgná; jhakná;
SHYNESS, *N*.
  saṇg. *f;* jhákká. *m;* saṇgá. *f;*
  fear. ḍar. *m;* haul. *m;* bháí. *f;*
  saiṇsá. *m;*
SICK, *N*.
  bimár; maṇdá; rogí; kasrí;
  jáihmatí;
SICKEN, TO, *V. I.*
  bimár ho jáná;
SICKLE, *N*.
  dátrí. *f;*
SICKLY, *A*.
  bimár; sust; rogí; see SICK.
SICKNESS, *N*.
  bimárí. *f;* rog. *m;* máṇdagí. *f;*
    bhus. *m;*
  plague. manno. *f;* marí. *f;*
  tapáli. *f;* bímárí. *f;*
SIDE, *N*.
  1. border. pássá. *m;* wall. *f;*
    hatth. *m;* báhí. *f;* láhmb. *f;*
    pahilú. *m;*
  2. of the body. wakkhí. *f;* ḍhák. *f;*
  3. on all sides. chawhíṇ pássíṇ;
    chauphere; chaupheríoṇ;
    chawallí; sabhníṇ pássiṇ;
  4. on his side. uh de wall;
  5. on this side. urár; urlá;
  6. on the further side. pár;
  7. side by side. pás o pas;
  8. by way of the other side. ud-
    ḍhar dioṇ;
  9. he is on my side. uh mere wall
    hai ;
  10. outside. banne; báhar;
  11. on their side. unháṇ de wall
    hoke;
  12. on both sides (of a river, &c.)
    wár pár;
  13. get to one side. láhmbe OR
    ikk pásse ho já;
SIDE, TO, *V. T.*
  liház karná; tarafdárí karní;
SIDEWAYS, *Adv.*
  katráí;
SIEGE, *N*.
  g̱herá. *m;*

SIEVE, *N*.
  chháṇní. *f;* poná. *m;*
SIFT, TO, *V. T.*
  chháṇná; paṭakná; chhaṇḍná;
  to separate husk from the grain.
  chaṭṭná;
SIFTED, TO BE, *V. I.*
  waggná;
SIFTING, *N*.
  chhanáí. *f;*
SIGH, *N*.
  hauká. *m;* sáh. *m;* háe. *m;* áh. *f;*
  hatkorá. *m;*
SIGH, TO, *V. T.*
  áh márná; háhuke márná OR
  lainá OR bharna ; sáh lainá; hauká
  bharná ; hunganá;
  1. to sigh deeply. diloṇ hauká
    bharná ;
  2. remember God and leave off
    sighing. Allah nún yád kariá
    kar, te ḵhálí dam ná bhariá kar ;
SIGHT, *N*.
  1. seeing. nazar. *f;* dist. *f;* dis. *f;*
    táṛ. *m;* daristí. *f;*
  2. spectacle. tamáshá. *m;*
  3. of a gun. sist. *f;*
SIGHTLESS, *A*.
  annhá ; manákhá;
SIGHTLY, *A*.
  sohná ; sundar; joban;
SIGN, *N*.
  1. mark. nishání. *f;* nisání. *f;*
    náṇ nishán. *m;*
  2. signature. sahí. *f;* dastḵhat. *f;*
  3. gesture. sainat. *f;* ramaj. *f;*
  4. thumb mark. angguṭṭhá. *m;*
  5. there was not a sign of him.
    uh dá kakkh ná rihá;
SIGN, TO, *V. T.*
  sahí karní; akkhar kar dená ;
  to affix thumbmark. anguṭṭhá dená;
SIGNAL, *N*.
  sainat. *f;* sainak. *f;* nishán. *m*
  railway signal. saṇgal. *m;*
SIGNATURE, *N*.
  sahí. *f;* dastḵhat. *f;* nishán. *m;*
  thumb mark. angguṭṭhá. *m;*
SIGNET, *N*.
  chháp. *f;* mohr. *f;*
SIGNIFICANCE, *N*.
  matlab. *m;* arth. *m;*

SIGNIFICATION, *N.*
matlab. *m;* arth. *m;*
SIGNIFY, TO, *V. T.*
batláuná; dassná; bayán karná;
SILENCE, *N.*
chupp. *f;* ḳhámoshí. *f;* gumm summ. *m;*
Proverb. Excessive laughter, silence, clouds and sun are all injurious.
bahut bhalá ná halrá,
bahut bhalí ná chupp,
bahut bhalá ná meghlá,
bahut bhalí ná dhupp;
SILENCE, TO, *V. T.*
chupp kará dená; chupp karáuná; muṇh band karná;
to silence by argument. ṭhár dená;
SILENCE, *Inter.*
chupp.
SILENT, *A.*
chupp cháp; gupp chupp, gumm summ;
to sit silent. múṇh bannhke baiṭhná; chupp waṭṭ jáná; chupp kar jáná; daṛ waṭṭṇí;
SILENTLY, *Adv.*
chupp cháp; chupp chapátá; chupp chupítá; chupp kítá; malkṛí;
SILK, *N.*
paṭṭ. *f;*
SILKEN, *A.*
reshamí; paṭṭ dá;
SILKWORM, *N.*
resham dá kíṛá. *m;*
SILLILY, *Adv.*
bewaqúfí nál; nadání nál; biná soche samjhe;
SILLINESS, *N.*
nadání. *f;* bewaqúfí. *f;* beaqlí. *f;* anárviddiá. *f;*
SILLY, *A.*
bewaqúf; nadán; murakh; beaql; besamajh; lutrá; hochchhá; chabal;
a silly girl. chhohar chhiní. *f;*
SILT, *N.*
silháb. *f;* sill. *f;* bhal. *m;*
SILVER, *N.*
chándí. *f;* rupá. *m;*
SILVER, *A.*
chándí dá; rupe dá;
SILVERSMITH, *N.*
suniárá. *m;*
SIMILAR *A.*
wargá; wáṇgar; ikk raṇg; waṇgg; samán; wáṇjhú; wáṇgúṇ;
SIMILARLY, *Adv.*
usí taráh;
SIMILE, *N.*
dristánṭ. *m;*
SIMILITUDE, *N.*
1. simile. misál *f;* uḍíl. *m;* dristánṭ *m;*
2. similarity. mel. *m;* sáṇg. *m;* ḍhaṇg. *m;*
SIMMER TO, *V. I.*
haule haule khaulná; maṭṭhá tá pakkná;
SIMPLE, *A.*
1. silly. nadán; múrakh; chabal; besamajh;
2. easy. asán; saukhá; sawalaṛá; sukhálá;
3. simple hearted. siddhá; siddhá sádá; bholá bhálá; sádá; siddh paddhrá; sidmasídá,
4. you are very simple, (to a woman) túṇ baṛí bholí hai;
SIMPLENESS, *N.*
sádagí. *f;*
SIMPLETON, *N.*
bewaqúf. *m;* lullú. *m;* anárí, *m;* múrakh. *m;* aql dá annhá. *m;* dhuchchal. *m;* guárú. *m;*
SIMPLICITY, *N.*
sádagí. *f;* bholápan *m;*
SIMPLIFY, TO, *V. T.*
saukhá karná; asán karná;
SIMPLY, *Adv.*
nirá; sirf; sadháran;
SIMULATE, TO, *V. T.*
baháná karná; bejjá márná; see DECEIVE.
SIMULATION, *N.*
pajj, *m;* baháná. *m;* makr. *m;* fareb. *m;*
SIMULTANEOUS, *A.*
nál hí;
SIMULTANEOUSLY, *Adv.*
kaṭṭhe; nálonál; ikse wele;

SIN, *N.*
gunáh. *m*; páp. *m*; dosh. *m*; aparádh. *m*;
a great sin. mahápáp. *m*; parmpáp. *m*;
SIN, TO, *V. T.*
gunáh karná; páp karná; aparádh karná;
SINCE, *Conj.*
thoṇ; kyun jo; uh de bád;
SINCE, *Adv.*
jadoṇ; jis waqt thoṇ; jadoṇ dá; jad dá;
1. he has been gone since yesterday uh kal dá gayá hoyá hai;
2. since that day. us diṇ thoṇ;
3. since I came. jad da maiṇ áyá;
SINCERE, *A.*
sachchá; sáf; siddhá; sádá; sáf dil; hatth dá suchchá; siddh paddhrá; niskapaṭ;
SINCERELY. *Adv.*
dharm nál; dil nál; rásti nál; sáfdilí nál; diloṇ wajhoṇ hoke;
SINCERITY, *N.*
rástí. *f*; sachchiái. *f*; sáf dilí. *f*; sidhaut. *f*;
SINEW, *N.*
rag. *f*; paṭṭhá. *m*;
SINFUL *A.*
gunáhgár; pápí; aprádhí; gunáhí; bhaiṛá; chaṇḍál; chaṇdrá; sharír;
SINFULNESS, *N.*
sharárat. *f*; gunáhgárí. *f*;
SING, TO, *V. T.*
gáuná; sarod karná; rág gáuná;
1. to sing one's own praises. apná rág gáuná;
2. singing praises. shabadkírtan. *m*;
3. to sing in a high key. uchchí súr nál gáuná;
4. as a bird. cháhichaháuná;
SINGE, TO, *V. T.*
jhulsáuná; jhulas dená;
SINGE, TO, *V. I.*
jhulas janá; jhulasná;
SINGER, *N.*
gawaiyá. *m*; gáyak. *m*; kawál. *m*. gáyán. *f*; rággí. *m*; kaláunt. *m*; gaunwálá. *m*;
SINGING, *N.*
gáná. *m*; sarod. *m*;
SINGLE *A.*
1. one. akallá;
2. unmarried. kuárá;
3. one fold. akáhrá; kahirá; ighrá;
SINGLENESS, *N.*
yaktái. *f*;
SINGLY, *Adv.*
akallá; ikk ikk karke;
SINGULAR, *A.*
aṇokhá; ajíb; acharaj;
SINGULARITY, *N.*
aṇokh. *m*;
SINGULARLY, *Adv.*
ajíb taur nál;
SINISTER, *A.*
ḳharáb; burá; máṛá; bhaiṛá;
SINK, *N.*
chalhá. *m*;
SINK, TO, *V. T.*
ḍohná; ḍabáuná;
SINK, TO, *V. I.*
1. in water. ḍubbná;
2. in mud. khubbh jáná; dhas jáná; dhas chalná;
3. boat to sink. beṛá ḍob baiṭhná OR ḍubb jáná OR ḍubbná OR ruṛhná;
SINLESS *A.*
begunáh; pák; beáib; bequsúr; nirdosh; nispáp;
SINNER, *N.*
gunáhgár. *m*; pápí. *m*; badkár *m* pápan. *f*; gunáhí. *m*; auganhár. *m*; taqsírí. *m*; dokhí. *m*;
SIN OFFERING, *N.*
kafárá. *m*; See SACRIFICE.
SIP, *N.*
chuskarí. *f*;
SIP, TO, *V. T.*
chusná;
to take a gulp. ghuṭṭ lainá;
SIR, *N.*
sáhib. *m*; janáb. *m*; jí. *m*;
SIRE, *N.*
báp. *m*;
SIRUP, *N.*
patt. *f*; sharbat. *m*;
SISTER, *N.*
báhin. *f*;
1. wife's sister. sálí. *f*;
2. husband's sister. naṇáṇ. *f*;

SISTER'S SON, *N.*
bhanejá. *m;* bhanewáṇ. *m;* bhánjá. *m;*

SISTER'S DAUGHTER, *N.*
bhanejí. *f;* bhánjí. *f;* bhanewíṇ. *f;*

SISTER IN LAW, *N.*
1. brother's wife. bharjáí. *f;*
2. wife's sister. sálí. *f;*
3. husband's sister. nanáṇ. *f;*

SIT, TO, *V. T.*
baihna; baiṭhná;
1. to sit easy. lamme pair pasárná;
2. to sit cross legged. chauṇkṛí márke baihná; pair te pair rakkhna;
3. to cause to sit. bahálná;
4. to sit at stool. jháṛe baiṭhná;
5. to sit long in one place. naṭṭí. baihná;
6. to sit with legs stretched out. phasakkaṛ márná;
7. sitting. baiṭhiá hoyá;

SITE, *N.*
jagáh. *f;* ṭhikáná. *m;* tháṇ. *f;*

SITUATION, *N.*
1. state. hál. *m;* awastá. *f;*
2. service. naukarí. *f;* kamm. *m;* chákarí. *f;* asámí. *f;*
3. place. jagáh. *f;*

SIX, *A.*
chhe;

SIXFOLD, *A.*
chhiguná;

SIXTEEN, *A.*
soláh;

SIXTEENETH, *A.*
soláhwáṇ;

SIXTH, *A.*
chhewáṇ;

SIXTIETH, *A.*
saṭṭhwáṇ;

SIXTY, *A.*
saṭṭh;
sixty one. ikkáhaṭh; akáhṭh;
sixty two. báhṭh;
sixty three. trehṭh;
sixty four. chauhṭh; chauhaṭ;
sixty five. paiṇhṭh;
sixty six. cheáhṭh;
sixty seven. satáhṭh;
sixty eight. aṭháhṭh;
sixty nine. unhattar;

SIZE, *N.*
qadd. *m;*

SKEIN, *N.*
chírú. *m;* gunjí. *f;* aṭṭí. *f;* chhalli *f;*

SKELETON, *N.*
pinjará. *m;* pinjar. *m;* karang. *m;*

SKETCH, *N.*
taswír. *f;* murat. *f;*

SKETCH, TO, *V. T.*
taswír khichná;

SKEWER, *N.*
síkh. *f;*

SKIFF, *N.*
chhoṭí náu. *f;*

SKILFUL, *A.*
hoshiyár; guṇí; guṇwáṇ; ḍhaṇgí; kárígar; siáná; haṇḍhiá wartiá; to be very skilful. asmán de táre toṛná;

SKILFULLY, *Adv.*
hoshiyárí nál; ustádí nál;

SKILL, *N.*
vithiá. *f;* liyáqat. *f;* jách. *f;* viddiá. *f;* gúṇ. *m;* ustádí. *f;* hoshiyárí. *f;* vall. *m;* ballu. *m;* hujdá *m;* huṇdar. *m;* ḍhab. *m;* maṇd. *m;*
to have skill. ḍhab á jáná;

SKILLED, *A.*
hoshiyár;

SKILFULNESS, *N.*
guṇ. *m;* ustádí. *f;* liyáqat. *f;*

SKIM, TO, *V. T.*
malái láhní OR utární;

SKIMMER, *N.*
karchhí. *f;* poní. *f;*

SKIM MILK, *N.*
lassí, *f;*

SKIN, *N.*
1. leather. chamm. *m;* chamṛá. *m;* khall. *f;*
2. hide. khall. *f;* dhauṛi. *f;* chamm. *m;*
3. water skin. mashk. *f;*
4. a dry hide. khallaṛí. *f;* khallaṛ. *m;*
5. rind of fruit. chhilk. *m;* chhillaṛ. *m;*

SKIN, TO, *V. T.*
1. to flay. dhauṛí láh suṭṭní ; dhauṛí udheṛní ; chamm udheṛná OR láhuná ; khullná ; khalí láhuní ;
2. to peel fruit. chhillná ;
SKINFLINT, *N.*
kanjús. *m ;* joṛú. *m ;* makkhí chús. *m ;* nichoṛu. *m ;*
SKINNER, *N.*
chamár. *m ;*
SKINNY, *A.*
lissá ; patlá ; jhikh ; ákáhirá ;
SKIP, TO, *V. T.*
1. to jump. tappná ; chhál márná ; chhaláṇgh mární ; kuddná ;
2. to skip about. lah lah karná ;
3. to dance. nachná ; kalol karní ; lah lah karná ;
SKIPPING, *N.*
taposí. *f ;* luḍí. *f ;*
SKIRMISH, *N.*
jhagṛá ; *m ;* laṛáí. *f ;* laṛáí bhaṛáí. *f ;*
SKIRT, *N.*
ghágrá. *m ;* ghaggará. *m ;* korá. *m ;* sáyá, *m ;* laṛ *m ;* laihngá. *m ;*
1. worn by men, taihmat. *m ;* lunní. *f,*
2. skirt of a garment. pallaṛá. *m ;*
SKITTISH, *A.*
chaṇchal ;
SKITTISHNESS, *N.*
kalol. *f ;* chaṇchaltáí. *f ;*
SKULK, TO, *V. T.*
dabakná ; daṛakná ; khiskná ; kaniáuná ;
SKULKER, *N.*
kamm chor. *m ;*
SKULL, *N.*
khoprí. *f ;*
SKY, *N.*
asmán. *m ;* akál. *m ;* gagan. *m ;* ákás. *m ;*
SKYBLUE, *A.*
asmání ;
SKY ROCKET, *N.*
hawáí. *f ;*
SLABBER, TO, *V. T.*
muṇh vichchoṇ lár kaḍḍhná ;
SLACK. *A.*
1. lazy. sust ; ghaulí ; kammchor ; koss ; jillhá ; ḍhillá maṭṭhá ;
2. loose. ḍhillá ; khullhá ;
SLACKEN, TO, *V. T.*
1. to moderate. dhímá karná ; ghaṭṭáuná ;
2. to make loose. ḍhillá karná ;
SLACKLY, *Adv.*
sustí nál ; ghaul nál ;
SLACKNESS, *N.*
sustí. *f ;* ghaul. *f ;* jillh. *f ;* ḍhill maṭṭh. *f ;* ḍhill. *f ;* álas. *m ;*
SLAKE, TO, *V. T.*
tareh maṭṭhí karní ; pyás OR tareh bujháuná ;
SLAM, TO, *V. T.*
zor nál band karná ;
SLANDER, *N.*
chuglí. *f ;* badnámí. *f ;* lútí. *f ;* bhaṇḍí. *f ;* niṇdá. *m ;* totyá. *m ;*
SLANDER, TO, *V. T.*
chuglí karná ; baṇggoná ; badnám karná ; bhaṇḍná ; bhagí karní ; ujj láuní ; chuglí waṭṭní ; see BACKBITE AND CALUMINATE.
SLANDERER, *N.*
niṇdak. *m ;* tohmatí. *m ;* chugal-ḳhor. *m ;* ujj lánwálá. *m ;*
SLANDEROUS, *A.*
jhuṭhá ; bakhíl ;
SLANDEROUSLY, *Adv.*
chuglí karke ; jhuṭh bolke ;
SLANT, *N.*
nuáṇ. *m ;* ureb. *m ;* see SLOPE.
SLANTING, *A.*
salámí ; ḍhálwáṇ ; kuásá ;
SLAP. *N.*
dhappá. *m ;* chapeṛ. *f ;* thap-paṛ. *m ;* dohatthar. *f ;* chaṇḍ. *f ;* dhapphá. *m ;* thap. *m ;*
SLAP, TO, *V. T.*
dhappá OR thappaṛ OR dohat-thar OR dhaul OR chapeṛ márná ;
SLATE, *N.*
saleṭ. *f ;*
wooden. takhtí. *f ;*
SLATTERN, *N.*
kuchajjí. *f ;* geglí. *f ;* phúhaṛ. *f ;*
SLAUGHTER, *N.*
ḳhun. *m ;* waḍh katt. *f ;* qatal. *m ;* baḍháṇggá. *m ;*
great slaughter. gháṇ. *m ;*
SLAUGHTER, TO, *V. T.*
halál karná ; kaṭṭná ; waḍḍhná ; gattle karná ;

to slaughter an animal with one stroke. jhaṭakná;
SLAVE, *N.*
gulám. *m*; dás. *m*; gollá. *m*; bardá. *m*; bardí. *f*;
slave of habits. ṭharkí. *m*;
SLAVERY, *N.*
gulámí. *f*;
SLAVE TRADE, *N.*
bardá faroshí. *f*;
SLAY, TO, *V. T.*
kohná; halál karná; qatal karná; waḍḍhná;
SLEDGE HAMMER, *N.*
badán. *m*;
SLEEK, *A.*
ṭhullhá; moṭá tázá;
SLEEP, *N.*
nínd. *f*; níndar, *f*; níṇd sárkhí. *f*;
deep sleep. gárí nínd. *f*; ghúk níndar. *f*; ghúk sáuná. *f*;
SLEEP, TO, *V. I.*
so jáná; sáuná;
1. to sleep heavily. ghúk sáuná;
2. he is sleeping heavily. uh ghúk suttá hoyá hai;
SLEEPER, *N.*
sotaṛ. *m*;
a wooden sleeper. gellí. *f*;
SLEEPILY, *Adv.*
sustí ṅál;
SLEEPINESS, *N.*
khumár. *m*; khumárí. *f*;
SLEEPLESS, *A.*
uníndará;
SLEEPY, *A.*
uníṇdá; sotaṛ;
SLEET, *N.*
olá. *m*;
SLEEVE, *N.*
báhulí. *f*; báṇh. *f*;
SLEIGHT, *N.*
jugat. *f*; chalákí. *f*; hatt chalákí. *f*;
SLENDER, *A.*
patlá; sohal; see THIN.
SLENDERNESS, *N.*
patlái. *f*;
SLICE, *N.*
pháṇk. *f*;
of fruit. pháṛí. *f*;
SLICE, TO, *V. T.*
kaṭṭná; pháṛiáṇ karní; pháṇk karní;
SLIDE, TO, *V. I.*
tilakná; ghisarná;
SLIGHT, *N.*
beadabí. *f*; gustákhí. *f*;
SLIGHT, *A.*
1. light. haulá;
2. thin. patlá;
SLIGHTLY, *Adv.*
maṇd maṇd; thoṛá jehá;
SLILY, *Adv.*
chalákí nál; akkh bacháke;
SLIM, *A.*
patlá;
SLIME, *N.*
chikkaṛ. *m*; reg. *m*;
SLIMY, *A.*
chikkaṛdár;
SLING, *N.*
ghamání. *f*; kubháṇí. *f*; khan-bháṇí. *f*;
like a bow. gulel. *f*;
SLING, TO, *V. T.*
ghamání; chaláuná;
to throw. suṭṭná;
SLINK AWAY, TO, *V. I.*
kanícharáuná; khiskná; khikhi-áuná;
to slink in. akkh bacháke áuná;
SLIP, *N.*
1. the act. khisak. *f*;
2. mistake. bhúll. *f*; galatí. *f*; bhulekhá. *m*;
3. a piece. ṭukṛá. *m*;
SLIP, TO, *V. I.*
1. to slide. tilakná; ghisarná; tilak páiná; ṭir painá; ḍhalkná;
2. to run away. nikal jáná; bhajj jáná; natthná;
3. to err. bhulná; bhulekhá laggná;
4. to slip down. tilakke riṛhná;
5. to avoid anyone. ṭibh jáná; khikhiáuná; akkh bacháke jáná;
6. to slip from the mind. wissarná;
SLIP, TO, *V. T.*
khol dená;
SLIPPER, *N.*
juṭṭí. *f*; gurgábí. *f*;
SLIPPERY, *A.*
1. untrustworthy. be etibárí;
2. greasy. chíhkná, tilkaṇwálá;

SLIPPERY PLACE, *N.*
tilkan. *f;*
SLIT, *N.*
chír. *m;* tareṛ. *f;* chírá. *m;*
a slit in a garment. laṇgár. *m;*
chák. *m;*
SLIT, TO, *V. T.*
chírná; pháṛná;
to be slit. chírná;
SLOPE, *N.*
ḍhál. *f;* ureb. *m;* salámí. *f;*
nuáṇ. *m;* ḍháyá. *m;*
SLOPING, *A.*
salámí; ḍhálwáṇ;
SLOTH, *N.*
sustí. *f;* jillh. *f;* álas. *m;* machalpuṇá. *m;* ḍhill. *f;*
SLOTHFUL, *A.*
ghaulí; sust; ghísan; álasí; machall;
surliá hoyá; dhillaṛ; ḍhillá maṭṭhá;
SLOTHFULLY, *Adv.*
sustí nál; ghaul nál; láparwáhí
nál;
SLOUCH ABOUT, TO, *V. I.*
ḍáwáṇḍol phirná;
SLOUGH, *N.*
dhasaṇ. *f;* dhasáṇ. *m;* khubb-
haṇ. *f;*
SLOVEN, *N.*
geglá. *m;* gaṇdá. *m;*
SLOVENLINESS, *N.*
kuḍhaṇggí. *f;*
SLOVENLY, *Adv.*
kuchajjá; geglá; geglí; kuchajjí;
SLOW, *A.*
jillhá; ḍhillá; ḍhillá maṭṭhá;
maṭṭhá; sust; jiḍḍá;
deliberate. dhírajmáṇ;
SLOWLY, *Adv.*
áste áste; dhíre dhíre; haulíṇ
haulíṇ; tharákè; saihje; allak
nál; hundiáṇ hundiáṇ; haule
haule;
1. to walk slowly. ramak ramak
ṭurná; júṇ dí ṭor ṭurná;
2. this horse is slow. ih ghoṛá
maṭṭhá ṭurdá hai;
SLOWNESS, *N.*
ḍhill. *f;* sustí. *f;* jillhá. *f;* ḍhill
maṭṭh. *m;*
SLUGGARD, *N.*
sust ádmí. *f;* álasí. *m;* áhlakí. *m;*
SLUGGISH. *A.*
sust; álasí; jillhá; jiḍḍá;
SLUGGISHNESS, *N.*
sustí. *f;* jillh. *f;* álas. *m;* áhlak. *f;*
SLUICE, *N.*
morí. *f;*
SLUMBER, *N.*
nínd. *f;* níndar. *f;* see SLEEP.
SLUMBER, TO, *V. T.*
saúná; arám karná; hangláuná;
see SLEEP.
SLUR, *N.*
dhabbá. *m;* dág. *m;*
SLUR, TO, *V. T.*
badnám karná; see TRADUCE.
SLUSH, *N.*
chikkaṛ. *m;*
SLUT, *N.*
geglí. *f;* phúhaṛ. *f;* kuchajjí. *f;*
SLY, *A.*
chalák; makkár; see DECEIT-
FUL.
SLYLY, *Adv.*
chalákí nál; fareb nál;
SLYNESS, *N.*
chalákí. *f;* makkárí. *f;* see
DECEIT.
SMACK, *N.*
thappaṛ *m;* chapeṛ. *f;* dhappá. *m;*
SMACK, TO, *V. T.*
thappaṛ márná; márná; ṭakorná,
SMACK THE LIPS IN EATING,
V. T.
machkáuná; chatkáuná;
SMALL, *A.*
chhoṭá; nanná; nikká;
SMALLISH, *A.*
chhoṭá jehá; nikerá;
SMALLNESS, *N.*
chhoṭái. *f;* alpatá. *f;*
SMALL POX, *N.*
mátá. *m;* chíchak. *f;*
small pox to appear. mátá nikal-
ná;
SMART, TO, *V. I.*
chiṛmiṛáuná; dukhná;
SMARTING, *N.*
chiṛmaṛát. *m;* lúhaṇ. *f;* jalan. *f;*
SMARTLY, *Adv.*
chalákí nál; chustí nál;
SMARTNESS, *N.*
chalákí. *f;* phurtí. *f;*

SMASH, TO, *V. T.*
phití phití karná ; chúr chúr karná ; toṭe toṭe karná ; chaknáchúr karná ;

SMEAR, TO, *V. T.*
malná ; libeṛná ; libṛáuná ; libaṛná ; jhassná ; lippná ;
1. to smear with butter. makhná ; chopaṛná ;
2. to smear with ghi. chopaṛná ;
3. to smear the cooking place or floor. pochná ; pochá dená ;

SMEARED, *N.*
lethú pethú ; lathar pathar ; smeared with blood. lahú luhán ; lahú lauhák ; ratto ratt ;

SMEARING, *N.*
chupṛáí. *f ;*

SMELL, *N.*
1. a sweet smell. hamak *m ;* sugaṇdh. *m ;*
2. a sour smell. khaṭíáṇdh. *f ;* khaṭíáhṇ. *f ;* mushk. *m ;* básná. *f ;* gaṇdh. *m ;*

SMELL, TO, *V. T.*
súnghná ;

SMELL, TO, *V. I.*
1. nice. hamakná ;
2. unpleasant. bo áuní ; bobohhaḍḍní ; mushkná ;

SMELLING, *N.*
dhássá. *m ;*

SMILE, *N.*
guṭak. *m ;* muskaṛát. *f ;*

SMILE, TO, *V. T.*
muskaṛáná ; guṭakná ; guṛhkaná ; he broke out into a smile. guṭak piá ;

SMILINGLY, *Adv.*
hasske karná ;
lit. with blooming forehead. khiṛe matthe ;

SMIRCH, TO, *V. T.*
mailá karná ; gaṇdá karná ;

SMITE, TO, *V. T.*
márná ; chapeṛe márná ; duhatthaṛ márná ; dhraul mární ;

SMITH, *N.*
lohár. *m ;*

SMITHEREENS, *N.*
chakúr. *m ;* chakchúr. *m ;* chachkur. *m ;* chaknáchur. *m ;* chur. *m ;*

SMOKE, *N.*
dhúṇ. *m ;*

SMOKE, TO, *V. T.*
huqqá píná ; dam laggná ;
to smoke violently. suṭá márná ;

SMOKE, TO, *V. I.*
dhúṇ nikalná ; dhuáṇkhná ;

SMOKER, *N.*
huqqáí. *m ;*
a great smoker. piák. *m ;*

SMOKING, *P. P.*
dhukhdá hoyá ;

SMOKY, *A.*
dhuákhá ;

SMOOTH, *A.*
1. smooth ground. paddhrá ; suáhrá ; sáf ;
2. of a millstone. manráh ;
3. smooth to the touch. kulá ;

SMOOTH, TO, *V. T.*
lesná ; sútná ; ghoṭná ;
with a plane. randná ;

SMOOTHLY, *Adv.*
safáí nál ;

SMOOTHNESS, *N.*
paddhráí. *f ;*

SMOTHER, TO, *V. T.*
saṇggh ghuṭṭke márná ;

SMOULDER, TO, *V. I.*
dhukhná ;

SMUGGLE, TO, *V. T.*
chaukí mární OR bhanní ; máhsúl márná ;

SMUT, *N.*
kálak. *f ;*

SNAFFLE, *N.*
kajáí. *f ;*

SNAKE, *N.*
sapp. *m ;* nág. *m ;* sarp. *m ;*
1. a young snake. sapoliá. *m ;*
2. a cast off snake's skin. sappkunj. *f ;*
3. snake catcher. sapásá. *m ;*
4. snake charmer. madárí. *m ;* sappyádhá. *m ;*
5. proverb. Bitten by a snake it fears a cord, *i. e.*, a burnt child fears the fire. sapp dá khádá rasse te ḍardá ;

SNAP, TO, *V. I.*
ṭuṭná ;

SNAP, to. *V. T.*
tor dálná;
SNAP THE FINGERS, *V. T.*
chuṭkí bajáuní OR mární;
chaṭkáuná;
SNAP OF FINGERS, *N.*
chuṭkí. *f;*
SNAPPING, *N.*
jhaí. *f;*
SNAPPISH, *A.*
kauṛá; naráz; chitthá hoyá;
chhiṛhmí; avaiṛá;
SNAPPISHLY, *Adv.*
gusse nál;
SNAPPISHNESS, *N.*
jhiṛká jhiṛkí. *f;* narázagí. *f;*
SNARE, *N.*
phaṇḍhá. *m;* dáu. *m;*
net. jál. *m;*
SNARE, TO, *V. T.*
phandhe nál phaṛná; phasáuná;
SNARL, TO, *V. T.*
ghuṛ ghuṛ karná; ghuṛbuṛáuná;
kilkárí mární;
SNARLING, *N.*
bhabkí. *f;*
SNATCH, TO, *V. T.*
khoh lainá; khohná; jhuṭáh
márná; jharáṭ mární;
as a bird. panjá márná;
SNEAK, *N.*
chugallatá. *m;* chugalkhor, *m;*
SNEER, *N.*
bolí ṭhollí. *f;* táná. *m;* mehná. *m;*
SNEER, TO, *V. T.*
bolí dení; mehná márná OR dená;
táne márná; nakk chaṛháuná;
SNEEZE, *N.*
nichch. *f;*
SNEEZE, TO, *V. T.*
nichch márná; chhikk áuní;
chhikkná; nichcháuná; nichchná;
Proverb. Has the cat sneezed
lately? This is a bad omen.
Sarcasm for why don't you get
on with your work. hun kí billí
nichh gayí;
SNIFF, TO, *V. I.*
duskaná;
SNIP, *N.*
ṭukṛá. *m;*
SNIP, TO, *V. T.*
katarná;
SNIPE, *N.*
chàhá. *m;*
SNIVEL, TO, *V. T.*
bus bus karná;
SNORE, *N.*
ghurṛáṭà. *m;*
SNORE, TO, *V. I.*
ghurṛáṭe márná; ghuráṛe márná;
SNORING, *N.*
ghuráṛá. *m;*
SNORT, *N.*
phuràṭá. *m;*
SNORT, TO, *V. T.*
shúkaná;
SNOUT, *N.*
buthà. *m;* buthí. *f;*
pig's snout. sunní. *f;* thunní. *f;*
SNOW, *N.*
kakkar. *m;* korá. *m;* barf. *f;*
to snow. barf painí;
SNUB, *N.*
dudkárí. *f;* dabká. *m;*
SNUB, TO, *V. T.*
dabáuná; dabkáuná; dhamká
dená; dudkarná;
SNUBBING, *N.*
dábbá. *m;* dudkàr. *f;* abká
dabkà. *m;*
SNUFF, *N.*
naswár. *f;* nasuár. *f;* hulás. *f;*
SNUFF A CANDLE, *V. T.*
gul láhuná;
SNUFFLE, TO, *V. I.*
suṛkná;
SO, *Adv.*
ajehá; is taráh; upraṇd;
1. so great. aiḍá;
2. so large. aiḍá;
3. so much. ainá;
4. so spake. is ḍhang nál boliá;
SOAK, TO, *V. T.*
bheoná; bhagoná; see TO WET.
SOAK, TO, *V. I.*
bhijjná;
SOAKED, *A.*
bhinná hoyá;
SOAKING, *N.*
ḍobbá. *f;*
SOAP, *N.*
sabún. *m;*

1. soap nut. reṭhṛá. *m;* reṭhá. *m;*
2. soap seller. sábaniá. *m;*
SOAR, TO, *V. I.*
uḍḍná. chaṛh jáná;
SOB, TO, *V. I.*
duskaná; hauke lená; wilkná; ubbhe sáh lená; haṭghore lainá; riṇggná; ṭhinakná; bubháṇ mární;
SOBER, *A.*
1. temperate. parejgàr; jatí satí;
2. serious. soch karnwàlá; dhírajmáṇ;
3. not drunk. hosh vichch;
SOBERLY, *Adv,*
ján bujh ke;
SOBRIETY, *N.*
1. abstinence. parejgárí. *f;* saṇjam. *m;* rakkh shakkh. *f;*
2. seriousness. sanjídagí. *f;*
SOCIABILITY, *N.*
milansárí. *f;*
SOCIABLE, *A.*
milanwálá; maláṛṛá; miláuṛá;
SOCIETY, *N.*
1. association. mel jol. *f;* saṇgat. *f;*
2. brotherhood. barádarí. *f;* bhaíbandí. *f;* bháíchárá. *m;*
3. Muhammadan club. anjumán. *f;*
4. Hindu club. sabhá. *m;* samáj. *m;*
SOCK, *N.*
juráb. *m;* jareb. *f;*
for a child. massí. *f;*
SOCKET OF THE EYE, *N*
akkh dí koṭhí. *f;*
SODA, *N.*
khár. *f;* sodá. *m;*
SODOMITE, *N.*
muṇḍebáz. *m;* gáṇḍú. *m;* gáṇḍo. *f;*
SEDOMY, *N.*
muṇḍebází. *f;* buṇḍ bhiṛikká. *m;*
1. to commit sodomy. chuttaṛ kuṭṭná; gáṇḍ mární; buṇḍ mární;
2. to suffer sodomy. chuttaṛ kuṭáuná; buṇḍ maráuná;
SOFT, *A.*
narm; kúlá; kúlí kúlí;
1. of heart. narm; mulaim;
2. of meat. kulá;
3. of flesh. flabby; pilpilá;
4. of earth. pollá;
5. as a quilt. gudgudá;
SOFTEN, TO, *V. T.*
narm karná; políán karní; mulaim OR dhímá karná;
SOFT HEARTED, *A.*
narmdil; mihrbán;
SOFTLY, *Adv.*
haulí haulí; sahije; sahije sahije; dhíre dhíre;
SOFTNESS, *N.*
narmí; narmáí. *f;* gudgudáí. *f;*
SOIL, TO, *V. T.*
gothalná; gaṇdá karná; mailá karná; libeṛná; wigáṛná; miṭṭí karní;
SOIL, *N.*
1. earth. miṭṭí. *f;* jamín. *f;* bhon. *f;*
2. stain. dág. *m;* ḍabb. *m;*
3. dirt. mailá. *m;* gandagí. *f;*
4. manure. gobar. *m;* kúṛá. *m;* see LAND.
SOILED, *A.*
mailá kuchailá; ghasmailá;
SOILED, TO BE, *V. I.*
libaṛ jáná;
SOJOURN, *N.*
derá. *m;*
SOJOURN, TO, *V. I.*
rahná; wassná;
SOJOURNER, *N.*
wándhá. *m;* ráhí. *m;* musáfir. *m;*
SOLACE, *N.*
tasallí. *f;* dilásá. *m;* dilásaṛá. *m;* shántí. *f;*
SOLACE, TO, *V, T,*
tasallí dení; dilásá dená; khush karná;
SOLD, TO BE, *V. I.*
vikná;
SOLDER, *W.*
ṭáṇká. *m;*
SOLDER, TO, *V. T.*
ṭáṇkná; ṭáṇká lagáuná OR làuná; kalí karní;
SOLDIER, *N.*
1. Native. sipáhí. *m;* talaṇggá. *m;*
2. European. gorá. *m;*
SOLE, *N.*
1, of the foot. pair dí talí. *f;* talúá. *m;*
2. of a shoe. talá. *m;*

SOLE, TO, *V. T.*
talá láuná;
SOLE, *A.*
akallá;
SOLECISM, *N.*
bemuhávará. *m;*
SOLELY, *Adv.*
nirá; sirf;
SOLEMN, *A.*
gambhír; gaurá; bhárá gaurá; dhírajmáṇ;
SOLEMNITY, *N.*
1. gravity. dhíraj. *f;*
2. a rite. rít. *f;* rasm. *f;*
SOLEMNLY, *Adv.*
baṛí sanjídagí nál;
SOLICIT, TO, *V. T.*
maṇgná; tarle minnat karní; arz karní; bentí karní; ardás karní; sawál karná; uká karná; giṛgaṛáuná;
SOLICITATION, *N.*
arz. *f;* minnat. *f;* sawál *m;* tagádá. *m;*
SOLICITOR. *N.*
wakíl. *m;*
SOLICITOUS, *A.*
chiṇtáwáṇ;
SOLICITUDE, *N.*
chiṇtá. *m;* fikr. *m;*
SOLID, *A.*
piḍḍá; ṭhos; niggar;
1. hard. sakht;
2. strong. mazbut; pakká;
SOLIDITY, *N.*
mazbutí. *f;*
SOLIDLY, *Adv.*
mazbutí nál;
SOLILOQUIZE, TO, *V. T.*
dil vichch sochná;
SOLITARINESS, *N.*
ikkalwaṇjá. *m;*
SOLITARY, *A.*
akallá; alagg; ikláppá;
SOLITUDE, *N.*
1. loneliness. ikkalwaṇjá. *m;* ikánt *f;*
2. wilderness. jangal. *m;* ujáṛ, *f;* ban. *m;*
SOLUTION, *N.*
jawáb. *m;*

SOLVE, TO, *V. T.*
kaddhná; hall karná;
to solve a riddle. bujjhná;
SOMBRE, *N.*
udás; masosiá hoyá; sasdil;
SOME, *A.*
1. some persons. báje; kaí;
2. somewhat. kujh; ratí; thoṛe jehe;
SOMEBODY, *N.*
koí bandá. *m;*
SOMEHOW, *Adv.*
kisí taráh nál; kíweṇ; kisí surat nál;
1. somehow or other. kíweṇ ná kíweṇ;
2. with difficulty. masàṇ; masáṇ masáṇ; mase kíweṇ;
SOMEONE, *Pro.*
koí;
someone or other. koí ná koí;
SOMERSAULT, *N.*
kalá bází. *f;*
SOMETHING, *N.*
koí chíz. *f;*
something thrown in. jhuṇgá. *m;* rúnggá. *m;*
SOMETHING, *Adv.*
kujh; ratá;
something or other. kujh ná kujh;
SOMETIME, *Adv.*
kise vele;
SOMETIMES, *Adv.*
kade kade; kadí kadáíṇ;
SOMEWHAT, *Adv.*
kisí qadr; thoṛá jehá; rattákú; zarákú;
SOMEWHERE, *Adv.*
kidhre; kisí jagáh; kite; kitale;
SOMNOLENCE, *N.*
níṇd. *f;* níṇdar. *f;*
SON, *N.*
puttar. *m;* put. *m;* beṭá. *m;* jáyá. *m;* laṛká. *m;* janá. *m;* náṇgar. *m;*
1. legal term. wald. *m;*
2. he has a son. uh de ghar puttar hoiá hai;
SON-IN-LAW, *N.*
jawái. *m;* jawántrá, *m;* juátrá *m;* majmáṇ. *m;*
Proverb. In his father-in-laws house the son-in-law is like a dog. sauhre ghar jawáṇtrá kutte dí mánind;

SONG, *N.*
gít. *m;* gáun. *m;* bhajan. *m;* rág. *m;* raṇg rág. *m;*
1. song to Devi. chhand. *m;*
2. marriage song, ghoṛí. *f;*
3. obscene songs sung by women at weddings. siṭṭhní. *f;*

SONOROUS, *A.*
uchchí awáz;

SOON, *Adv.*
thoṛí der de bád; huṇ hí; jabde; jaldí;

SOOT, *N.*
kálakh. *f;* dhawáṇh. *m;* dhúáhán, *m;* dhúṇ. *m;*

SOOTHE, TO, *V. T.*
dalássá dená; ṭhaṇḍí karní; dhímá karná; patiáná; thamá dená; puchkárná;
1. to soothe a child. lorí dení; tháparná;
2. to soothe an animal. puchkárá dená; puchkárná;

SOOTHSAYER, *N.*
bheṭí. *m;* maṇtarí. *m;* raul. *m;* ramlí. *m;*

SOOTY, *A.*
dhúṇádár;

SOP, *N.*
garáhí. *f;*

SOP, TO, *V. T.*
tem tem ke láuná;

SOPRANO VOICE, *N.*
mahín awáz. *f;*

SORCERER, *N.*
jádúgar. *m;* ṭunehár. *m;* mantarí. *m;*

SORCERY, *N.*
jádúgarí. *f;* jádú. *m;* ṭúná. *m;*

SORDID, *A.*
1. dirty. mailá; ghísaṇ; gaṇdá; ghasmailá;
2. covetous. lálachí; pájí; lobhí;

SORDIDNESS, *N.*
1. filthiness. palítí. *f;* gaṇd. *m;* gaṇdagí. *f;*
2. avarice. lálach. *m;* lobh. *m;* hirs. *f;*

SORE, *A.*
chuchchá;
his eyes have become sore. uhdíáṇ akkhíáṇ áíáṇ hoíáṇ ne;

SORE, *N.*
1. wound. jakham. *m;* ghá. *m;* phaṭṭ. *m;*
2. afflicion. dukh. *m;* píṛ. *f;*
3. sore on back of horse, etc. lággá. *m;*
4. ulcer. phoṛá. *m;*

SORENESS, *N.*
dard. *f;* píṛ. *f;*
between the toes. khárwá. *m;*

SORROW, *N.*
ranj. *m;* gam. *m;* afsos. *m;* birláp. *m;* udásí. *f;* hirkh. *m;* pachhtává. *m;* pastává. *m;* gamí. *f;* hamsos. *f;* santáp. *m;* jhorá. *m;*

SORROW, TO, *V. T.*
jhurná; masosná; gam karná; sog karná; kabáb ho jáná;

SORROWFUL, *A.*
dukhí; dukhiá; udás; sogmáṇ; nimujhá; masosiá hoyá; hamsosiá hoyá; ranjúr; dil ḍhaṭṭá; sasdil; santápí;
very sorrowful. bahut [illegible] bahut udás;

SORROWFULLY, *Adv.*
ranj nál; pachhtà pachhtáke; dáh de nál;

SORRY, *A.*
udás; see SORROWFUL.

SORT, *N.*
ját. *f;* parkár. *m;* jiṇs, *f;* bháṇt. *m;*
what sort of a father have you? terà pità kis sabháu dà ádmí hai?

SORT, TO, *V. T.*
to sift. cháṇṭná; chháṇná;
2. to separate. wakhrá karná; wakkh karná; nakheṛná; aḍḍ karná;
3. to arrange. ṭhík ṭhák karná; durust karná;

SOUL, *N.*
1. spirit. ruh. *f;* átmá. *f;*
2. life. ján. *f;* jí. *m;* paráṇ. *m;* zindagí, *f;*

SOULLESS, *A.*
beján; murdá;

SOUND, *A.*
bhalá chaṇgá; tagaṛá; wall; naroá; achchhá; rází bází;

SOUND, *N.*
1. a voice. awáz. *f;* wáz. *f;*
2. a noise. shor. *m;* raulá. *m;* daṇḍ. *f;*
3. of footsteps and traffic. paich-haṛ. *f;* paichhal. *f*
4. sound of anything falling. khaṛák. *m;*
5. sound of quarrelling. bol bulárá. *m;* bolárá. *m;*

SOUND, TO, *V, T.*
1. to try. jáṇchná;
2. to measure the depth of water. pání dí tháh láná;

SOUNDLY, *Adv.*
dil te ján nál;

SOUNDNESS, *N.*
tandurustí. *f;* pakk. *m;*

SOUP, *N.*
shorbá. *m;* shorá. *m;* shurúá. *m;* tarí. *f;* kaṛhí, *f;*

SOUR, *A.*
khaṭṭá; kaṛvá; kauṛá; sour milk. dahíṇ. *f;*

SOUR, TO, *V. T.*
khaṭṭá karná;
milk to become sour. phiṭnà; saurná; kharáb ho jáná;

SOURCE, *N.*
muḍḍh. *m;* mul. *m;* muhíṇ. *f;* nikés. *m;*
origin or root. jáṛ. *f;*

SOURNESS, *N.*
khaṭṭáí. *f;* hirsáí. *f;*

SOUTH, *N.*
dakkhan. *m;* lammá. *m;*

SOUTH, *A.*
dakkhaní;

SOUTHEAST, *N.*
dakkhan te chaṛhde de wichlá pásá. *m;*

SOUTHWEST, *N.*
dakkhan te laihnde de wichlá pásá. *m;*

SOVEREIGN, *N.*
1. king. bádsháh. *m;*
2. Muhammadan ruler. sul- tán. *m.* M;
3. Hindu ruler. mahárájáh. *m* H;
4. a coin. pauṇḍ. *m.*

SOVEREIGNITY, *N.*
bádsháhí. *f;* ráj. *m;* hukúmat. *f;*

SOW, *N.*
bhuhn. *f;*

SOW, TO, *V, T.*
bí bíjná; bíjná ; biáí karní;
1. to sow broadcast. chhaṭṭá dená ;
2. to sow dissension. agg lagáuná ; chiṇggíáṛí láuní;
3. As you sow so you will reap. Good yields good. bhale dá bhalá.
4. The boat of a benevolent man crosses to the other side of the river. sakhí dá beṛá páṛ hai.
5. As you do so you will get. jaisí karní taisí bharní.
6. Do good, reap good, the end of good is good. kar bhalá, ho bhalá, aṇt bhale dábhalá.
7. The fruit of evil deeds is evil. bhaiṛe kammáṇ dá bhaiṛá phal.
8. As the soul is, so will the angel be. Jehí ruh tehá firishtá.
9. Plough and you will thresh, kar wáh, táṇ laiṇ gáh.

SOWING, *N.*
biáí. *f;* bíjáí. *f;*
1. sowing broadcast. chhaṭṭá. *m;*
2. P. P. bíjdeáṇ bíjdeáṇ;

SPACE, *N.*
witth. *m;* tháṇ. *m;* wát. *f;* bích. *m;* báṭ. *f;* chirkú, *m ;* khappá. *m;* bithak. *m;* bithák. *m;*
1. space of time. arsá. *m ;* chirk. *m;* chirká. *m ;* chirku. *m;*
2. a hand's space. giṭṭh bhar;

SPACIOUS, *A.*
khullhá; moklá; lammá chauṛá;

SPADE, *N.*
belchá. *m;*
native spade. kahí. *f;*

SPAN, *N.*
1. of oxen. jog. *f;*
2. space from thumb to little finger. giṭṭh. *f;*

SPANK, TO, *V. T.*
chapeṛná;

SPAR, TO, *V. T.*
jharafná;

SPARE, TO, *V. T.*
1. to grant. dená ;
2. to forgive. chhaḍ dená ; muáf karná ; bakhshnà ; muáfí dení; ján dená;
3. to be spared. bachná; bach jáná ;

SPARE, *A*.
1. scanty. ghaṭṭ; thoṛá;
2. thin. patlá; lissá; akáhirá;
3. extra. waddh; wádhú;

SPARING, *A*.
1. economical. sarfewálá; wichárwálá.
2. scanty. ghaṭṭ;

SPARINGLY, *Adv*.
sarfe nál; hoshiyárí nál;

SPARK, *N*.
chiṇggíáṛí. *f*; chiṛiṇgí. *f*; chiṛaṇg. *m*; chaṇgáṛá. *m*;

SPARKLE, TO, *V*. *T*.
chamakná; lashkaná; see GLITTER.

SPARKLING, *A*.
chamkílá; chamakdár; chamkanwálá;

SPARROW, *N*.
chiṛiyá. *m*; chiṛí. *f*;
young sparrow. boṭ. *m*;

SPARSE, *A*.
ghaṭṭ; virlá; thoṛá; ṭáwáṇ ṭáwáṇ;

SPARSELY, *Adv*.
virle;

SPARSENESS, *N*.
kamí. *f*;

SPASM, *N*.
maroṛ. *m*;

SPATTER, TO, *V*. *T*.
chikkaṛ nál mailá karná;
to get clothes covered with mud. kapṛe bharná;

SPATTERING, *N*.
chhiṭṭ, *f*;

SPAVIN, *N*.
haḍḍá. *m*; haḍḍemúte. *m*; haḍḍ mútrá. *m*;

SPEAK, TO, *V*. *T*.
bolná; gal bát karní; kúná; kahná; zikr karná;
1. to speak through the nose. guṇ guṇ karná; guṇguṇáuná;
2. to speak against. jhuṭh sachch kahná OR bolná; dí nindiá karná;
3. to speak slowly. miṇ miṇ karná;
4. to speak fast and indistinctly. ghachch ghachch karná OR márná; happ happ karnà; gichch michch bolná;
5. to speak rudely. túṇ táṇ karná;
6. to speak snappishly. ṭarṭráuná;
7. to speak out. bol uṭṭhná;
8. to speak indistinctly. ghapal ghapal karná;
9. to speak fluently. jabán taṛ taṛ challná;
10. speak louder. zará dabbke ákho;
11. to speak without restraint. chhúṭ karní;
12. to speak falsely. jhuṭh bolná; jakkaṛ márná;
13. to speak evil of another. chhaṭṭná;

SPEAKER, *N*.
bolanwálá. *m*;

SPEAKING, *N*.
gal bát. *f*; bát chít. *f*; bol. *m*;
much speaking. bahu bachan. *m*;

SPEAR, *N*.
barchhá. *m*; selá. *m*; nejá. *m*; bhálá. *m*; sel. *f*;

SPECIAL, *A*.
ḳháss; ḳhásí; nijdá; uchechá;

SPECIALLY, *Adv*.
ḳháss karke; uchechá;

SPECIALITY, *N*.
guṇ. *m*;

SPECIES, *N*.
jiṇs. *f*; qism. *m*; ját. *f*; parkár. *m*;

SPECIFIC, *A*.
ḳháss;

SPECIFICATION, *N*.
bayán. *m*;

SPECIFY, TO, *V*, *T*.
bayán karná; hisáb karná;

SPECIMEN, *N*.
vaṇagí. *f*; bannagí. *f*; namuná. *m*; wankí. *f*;

SPECK, *N*.
dág. *m*; chitkaná. *m*; chhit. *f*;
speck in the eye. phollá. *m*; tiṇ. *m*;

SPECKLED, *A*.
khilldár; ḍabbá; see SPCTTED.

SPECTACLE, *N*.
tamáshá. *m*;

SPECTACLES, *N*.
aiṇak. *f*;
1. to put on. aiṇak láṇí;
2. to take off. aiṇak láhní.

SPECTATOR, *N*.
vekhanwálá. *m*;
SPECTRE, *N*.
bhút. *m*; bhútná. *m*;
SPECULATE, TO, *V. T*.
wichárná; sochná;
SPECULATION, *N*.
ḳhayál. *m*; soch. *m*; soch wichár. *m*;
SPECULATIVE, *A*.
ḳhayálí; farzí;
SPEECH, *N*.
1. language. bolí, *f*; zabán. *f*; bain. *m*;
2. address. wáz. *m*; nasíhat. *f*; wák. *m*; bachaṇ. *m*; bák. *m*;
SPEECHLESS, *A*.
chupp; gungá;
SPEED, *N*.
shatábí. *f*; chhurak. *f*; káhlí. *f*; chhetí. *f*;
SPEED, TO, *V. T*.
chaláuná; shatábí karní; chhetí turáuná; dauṛáuná; bhajáuná;
SPEED, TO, *V. I*.
chhetí turná;
SPEEDILY, *Adv*.
jaldí nál; chhetí nál; jhabde jhabde; see QUICKLY.
SPEEDY, *A*.
káhlá; jhabde; utaulá; tez;
SPELL, *N*.
1. change. bárí. *f*; wárí. *f*;
2. charm. táwít. *f*; jádú. *m*;
3. short time. thoṛá chir. *m*;
SPELL, TO, *V. T*.
1. to read. paṛhná;
2. to spell a word. joṛ karná; hijá karná;
3. to charm. mantar paṛhná; jádugarí karní; jháṛá karná; dhúní dhukháuná;
SPELLING, *N*.
hijá. *m*; joṛ. *m*;
SPEND, TO, *V. T*.
1. to expend. ḳharch karná; wartná; ḳharch paṭṭná;
2. to pass the time. waqt kaṭṭná; luṭáuná; velá langháuná;
3. to spend one's life. jí khapáuná;
4. to waste the time. waqt záyá karná;
5. to spend a long time. chir láuná OR laggná;
SPENDTHRIFT, *N*.
chhijáú. *m*; gháú ghapp. *m*; uḍáú. *m*; lakkh luṭṭ. *m*; ujáṛú *m*; gawáú. *m*;
SPEW, TO, *V. I*.
kaí áuní; jí uchalná; see VOMIT.
SPHERE, *N*.
golá, *m*;
SPHERICAL, *A*.
gol mol;
SPICE, *N*.
ṃasálá, *m*;
SPICY, *A*.
mazedár; sawádí; suádlá; karará;
SPIDER, *N*.
makṛí. *f*; kaihná *m*; ḍáṇwar. *m* bambohí. *f*;
large spider. makkaṛ. *m*;
SPIKE, *N*.
kil. *f*; mekh. *f*; síkh. *m*;
SPIKE, TO, *V. T*.
kil ṭhokná;
SPIKENARD, *N*.
jatámásí, *f*;
SPILL, TO, *V. T*.
ḍhilkáuná; chhulkáuná; ḍulham dená;
SPILL, TO, *V. I*.
ḍhilakná; ḍulhná; ruṛhná; ḍhalná;
SPIN, TO, *V. T*.
kaṭṭná; tánná; gujjh chaláuní;
1. Proverb. Labour spent in ploughing deep and in spinning is not wasted. dúṇghí wáhe, gujjh chaláe birthá ná jáe;
2. to spin out. lambáuná; lamíàuná;
SPIN ROUND, TO, *V. I*.
ghumeṭá kháná;
SPINACH, *N*.
pálak. *m*; ság. *m*;
SPINDLE, *N*.
takklá. *m*; trakklá. *m*;
SPINE, *N*.
piṭṭh dí haḍḍí. *f*; ḍhuṇḍarí, *f*; kangroṛ. *f*;
SPINNER, *N*.
juláhá. *m*; juláh. *m*; katáí. *f*;

SPINNING, *N*.
juláhgarí, *f*; juláhpuṇ... *m*;
1. a party of wo... ...red for spinning. átan. ... ...ṇaṇ. *m*;
2. Proverb. Concerning ... way women waste their time gossiping at spinning parties. átan dí rann ná kár ná kamm;
3. Proverb. The wind blew away the charkhá and the woman is looking for her ball of cotton! charkhá wá udáriá rann gulendí púniáṇ;

SPINNING WHEEL, *N*.
charkhá. *m*;

SPINSTER, *N*.
kuárí. *f*; kanníyáṇ. *f*;

SPIRAL, *A*.
pechdár; waldár;

SPIRE, *N*.
kals. *m*; kalsí. *f*;

SPIRIT, *N*.
1. soul. ruh. *f*; átmá. *m*; prán. *m*;
2, courage. hauṇsilá. *m*; himmat. *f*; jigará. *m*; dilerí. *f*; have you so little spirit? terá dil aiḍá chhoṭá hai?
3. breath. sáh. *m*; sáṇs. *m*; dam. *m*;
4. life. jí. *m*; ján. *f*; zindagí. *f*; paráṇ. *m*; jiṇḍṛí. *f*; jún. *f*;
5. zeal. josh. *m*; sargarmí. *f*; ríjh. *f*;
6. desire. cháh. *f*; ḳháhish. *f*; árzú. *m*; táṇgh. *f*;
7. temper. mizáj. *m*; subháo. *m*; tabíat. *f*;
8. meaning. matlab. *m*;
9. Holy Spirit. pák ruh. *m*; pavittar átmá. *m*; Ruhul Quds. *m*;
10. an apparition. bhutná. *m*;
11. intoxicant. sharáb, *m*;

SPIRITED, *A*.
diler; sargarm; joshwálá; himmatí;

SPIRITEDNESS, *N*.
dilerí. *f*; sargarmí. *f*; josh. *m*; himmat. *f*; jurat. *f*;

SPIRITLESS, *A*.
dil chhoṭá; sust; udás; bedil; sasdil; dil ḍhaṭṭá;

SPIRITLESSNESS, *N*.
bedilí. *f*; sustí. *f*;

SPIRITUAL, *A*.
ruhání; átmak; átamík;

SPIRITUALITY, *N*.
ruhániyat, *f*;

SPIRITUALLY, *Adv*.
ruhání taur nál;

SPIT, *N*.
thúkk. *m*; thúkái. *f*; thú. *m*;

SPIT, TO, *V*. *T*.
thúkkná; thúkk siṭṭná;

SPITE, *N*.
hasad. *m*; kíná. *m*; wair. *m*; irakhá. *f*; ḍáh. *m*; dushmaní. *f*; kiṛ. *f*; adávat. *f*; gubar. *m*; khijh. *f*; virodh. *m*; rikhat. *f*; khár. *m*;

SPITE, TO, *V*. *T*.
dikk karná; gubar rakkhná;

SPITEFUL, *A*.
virodhí; gubrí; darohí; riskí; to be spiteful. khuṇsná;

SPITEFULLY, *Adv*.
wair nál; adávat nál; khár de máre;

SPITEFULNESS, *N*.
adávat. *f*; khár. *m*;

SPITTLE, *N*.
thúkk, *m*; profuse spittle. lál. *f*;

SPLASH, *N*.
chiṭṭ. *f*; chhiṭṭá. *m*; gharamm. *m*; chhalak. *m*; chhaláká. *m*; phaṭáká *m*;

SPLASH, TO, *V*. *T*.
chhiṭṭá márná OR dená OR páuná; chhalkaná; chhaṭṭe márne;

SPLEEN, *N*.
1. milt. tilí. *f*; lif. *f*;
2. anger. gussá, *m*; karodh. *m*; waṭṭ. *m*; rossá. *m*;

SPLENDID, *A*.
baṛá chaṇgá; tejwán; partápí; uttam; shándár;

SPLENDOUR, *N*.
raunaq. *f*; bhaṛak. *f*; sajdhaj. *m*; partáp. *m*; sobhá. *f*; tej. *m*; jhalká. *m*; táb. *f*; chamkárá. *m*; bháh. *f*; jhalkárá. *m*; chamak damak. *f*; chhab. *f*;

SPLICE, TO, *V*. *T*.
joṛná; goṭhná; gaṇḍhná; joṛ láuná, bannhná; bachchí láuní; gaṇḍh tupp kárná; gáṇḍhá láuná;

SPLICING, *N.*
gaṭṭh. *m*; gaṇḍh tupp. *m*;
SPLINTER, *N.*
chiltar. *f*; chobh. *f*; chhimbh, *f*;
SPLIT, TO, *V. T.*
chírná; pháṛná; chhekná; sallaná; ṭiráuná;
to cause to be split. chiráuná;
SPLIT, TO, *V. I.*
ṭarakná; ṭirná; ṭer painá; ṭirak jáná;
SPLIT, *N.*
1. in wood, chír, *m*;
2. in a garment. jharáṛ. *m*; laṇgár. *m*;
3. separation, phuṭṭ, *f*; phaṭ, *f*; wichhoṛá. *m*;
SPOIL, *N.*
luṭṭ. *f*; már dháṛ. *f*; dháṛá. *m*;
SPOIL, TO, *V. T.*
1. to plunder. luṭná; khoh lená; zabardastí nál chhínná; ghápá márná; ḍáká márná; dháṛá márná;
2. to corrupt. wigáṛná; bigáṛná; chauṛ kar dená; pheṛná; wichálná; ḳharáb kar dená; miṭṭí karní; khalal páuná;
SPOILED, TO BE, *V. I.*
wichalná; wiṭarná;
as fruit. chalná;
SPOILATION, *N.*
már dháṛ. *f*;
SPOILED, *A.*
wigaṛiá hoyá;
as fruit. chaliá hoyá;
SPOLED CHILD, *N.*
láḍlá. *m*; laḍikká. *m*;
SPOILER, *N.*
luṭerá. *m*; ḍákú. *m*; luṭwayyá *m*; luṭerú. *m*;
SPOKE, *N.*
ḍaṇḍá. *m*; ár. *m*; pinj dá árá. *m*;
SPONGE, *N.*
isfanj. *m*;
SPONGE ON, TO, *V. T.*
bhuṇggná;
he lives on what he can squeeze out of his friends. uh apneáṇ dostáṇ núṇ bhuṇg bhuṇg ke khándá hai.

SPONSOR, *N.*
1. godfather. dharm báp. *m*;
2. surety. jámin. *m*;
SPONTANEOUS, *A.*
áp hí;
SPONTANEOULSY, *Adv.*
ápe; áp hí áp; ichchhiá nál; marzí nál;
SPOOL, *N.*
guloṭá. *m*;
SPOON, *N.*
chamach. *m*; chimchá. *m*;
1. small wooden spoon. ḍoí. *f*; kaṛchí, *f*;
2. Proverb. He who holds the spoon dies of hunger. jeh de hath ḍoí, bukkh mare soí;
SPORT, *N.*
1. game. kheḍ. *f*;
2. mockery. maḳhaul. *m*; ṭhaṭṭhá. *m*; maskarí. *f*; majákh. *m*;
SPORT, TO, *V. T.*
kheḍná;
SPORTIVE, *A.*
chaṇchal;
SPORTSMAN, *N.*
1. hunter. shikárí. *m*;
2. player. khaḍárí. *m*;
SPOT, *N.*
ḍabb. *m*; dág. *m*; nishán. *m*; dáṇg. *m*; chitkaṇá. *m*; phuṭkaṛí. *f*; chhiṭṭ. *f*;
SPOTLESS, *A.*
bedág; beaib; pák; nirdos; niskalank;
SPOTTED, *A.*
dággí; kháldár; ḍabb kaṛabbá; ḍabbá; chitlá;
SPOUSE, *N.*
wahutí. *f*; bíwí. *f*; see WIFE.
SPOUSELESS, *A.*
kuárá;
SPOUT, *N.*
1. water spout. parnálá. *m*; parchchá. *m*;
2. spout of teapot. búkní. *f*; ṭúṭí. *f*;
SPRAIN, *N.*
maroṛ. *m*; maroṛá. *m*; machkor. *f*; moch. *f*;
to be sprained. moch nikalná; moh ghattná;

SPRAWL, TO, *V. I.*
lotná;
SPRAY, *N.*
ṭahní. *f;*
SPREAD, TO, *V. T.*
1. to spread tidings. phailáuná;
kerná; khabardení; dhumáuná;
2. to spread bedding. ḍáhná;
bichhá dená; wichháuná;
3. to spread out. táṇná; ṭaḍḍná;
4. to cause to be spread. bichh-
wáuná;
SPREAD, TO, *V. I.*
phailjáná; phailárná; phailarjáná;
SPRIG, *N.*
ṭahní. *f;*
SPRIGHTLINESS, *N.*
chustí. *f;* phurtí. *f;* hulás. *f;*
uddam. *m;*
SPRIGHTLY, *A.*
chust; chuhlá;
SPRING, *N.*
1. jump. chhál. *f;* jhapaṭṭá, *m;*
jhapaṭ. *f;* ṭapp. *m;* chhaláṇgh. *f;*
channkarí. *f;*
2. fountain. sotá. *m;* chashmá. *m;*
sumbh. *m;* choá. *m;*
3. season. pungáre dí bahár. *f;*
chetar wasákh. *m;* basant. *f;*
4. of a cart. kamání. *f;*
5. from the ground to horses
back. palákí. *f;*
6. origin. nikás. *m;*
7. when spring comes winter runs
away. áí basant te pálá udant;
SPRING, TO, *V. I.*
1. to jump. ṭappná;
2. to shoot up. phúṭná; uggná;
3. to spring up. uchchhalná;
4. as vegetation, &c. nissarná;
5. to spring on to horse's back.
palákí márni;
SPRINGINESS, *N.*
lachak. *f;*
SPRINGY, *A.*
lachlachá; lachakdár;
SPRINKLE, TO, *V. T.*
traukná; chhinkáuná; chhiṛkaná;
kinkináuná; chhiṭṭá dená OR
páuná;
to sprinkle salt, powder, &c.
barúrná;

SPRINKLING, *N.*
kiṇkiṇkát. *f;* kinmanát. *f;* chhiṭṭá.
m; chhaṭṭá. *m;* chhaṛkáu. *m;*
of water on the road. chhiṇká. *m;*
SPRITE, *N.*
bhút. *m;* bhutná. *m;*
SPROUT, TO, *V. I.*
uggná; phuṭṭná; puṇgarná;
uṇggarná;
SPRUCE, *A.*
sajáiá; chhabílá; sajá;
SPRY, *A.*
chalák; chust; uddamí;
SPUR, *N.*
kaṇḍḍá. *m;*
SPUR, TO, *V. T.*
1. to prick with spurs. ed láuní; táṛ
mární OR láuná; káṇtá márná;
2. to incite. lárá dená; uksáuná;
bhaṛkáuná; chukkná;
SPURIOUS, *A.*
khoṭṭá; jáhlí; naqlí; jhuṭhá;
banautí;
SPURN, TO, *V. T.*
1. to kick. latt márná; thuḍḍá
márná;
2. to despise. beqadrí karní;
niṇdiá karná; nakk chaṛháuná;
kise núṇ máṛeáṇ jánná;
3. to reject. radd kar dená;
táráṇ dená;
SPURT, TO, *V. I.*
uchchalná; nikalná;
SPUTUM, *N.*
thúkk. *f;* thú. *m;*
SPY, *N.*
suhá. *m;* bhetí. *m;* jásús. *m;*
bhediá. *m;*
informer. mukhbar. *m;*
SPY, TO, *V. T.*
soh lená; bhed lainá OR páuná;
dí chháí víchch honá;
to track. khoj kaḍḍhná OR láuná;
SPYGLASS, *N.*
dúr bín. *f;*
SPYING, *N.*
gháí. *f;* mukhbarí. *f;*
SQUABBLE, *N.*
jhagṛá. *m;* laṛáí. *f;* taṇtá. *m;*
See QUARREL.
SQUABBLE, TO, *V. T.*
jhagṛá OR laṛáí karní; jhagaṛná;

SQUABBLER, N.
jhagrálú. *m;* laŗáká. *m;*

SQUADRON, N.
jhuṇḍ. *m;*

SQUALID, A.
gaṇdá; mailá; mailá kuchailá;

SQUALL, N.
1. a cry. chíkh. *f;* kuk. *f;* hek. *f;*
2. a storm. jhakkaŗ. *m;* hanerí. *f;*

SQUALL, TO, V. T.
chíkh márni; roná;

SQUALOR, N.
gaṇdagí. *f;*

SQUANDER, TO, V. T.
guá dená; guáuná; uḍáuná;
ujáŗná; fazúl kharch karná;
phúk chhaḍḍná; aṇdhá dhuṇd
luṭáná;
Proverb. The father collects
cowdung aṇd the son gives away
dung heaps. báp phire phosí
phosí, pútt bakhshe goháre;

SQUANDERER, N.
gawáú. *m;* ujáŗú. *m;* lakkh
luṭṭ. *m;* chhijáú. *m;*

SQUARE, A.
murabbá; chauras; chaunkkará;

SQUARE, N.
1. in a city. chauṇk. *m;*
2. of land. murabbá. *m;*
3. carpenter's square. guṇiá. *m;*

SQUARE, TO, V. T.
chauras banáuná;

SQUASH, TO, V. T.
ghuṭṭná; mutíáṇ bharná; chitthná; napittná;

SQUAT, A.
madhrá;

SQUAT, TO, V. I.
pairáṇ bhár baihná; niṭṭhná;
okŗú baiṭhná;
to squat cross legged. chaukŗí
márke baihná;

SQUEAK, N.
chíkh. *f;* chíṇ chíṇ *f;* chíṇ
píṇ. *f;*

SQUEAK, TO, V. I.
chúṇ chúṇ karná; chíṇ chíṇ karná;

SQUEAL, TO, V. T.
chíṇ chíṇ karná; see SCREECH.

SQUEEZE, N.
dabáú. *m;*

SQUEEZE, TO, V. T.
dabáuná; ghuṭṭná; chhikkná;
pichkáuná; phehná;
1. to sponge on. bhuṇggná;
2. he lives on what he caṇ squeeze
out of his friends. uh apneáṇ
dostáṇ núṇ bhuṇg bhuṇg ke
khándá hai;
3. to be squeezed. phissná;
4. to wring out. nichoŗná; napíŗná;

SQUIB, N.
paṭáká. *m;*

SQUINT, TO, V. I.
tirchhá dekhná; ṭeḍhá wekhná;
bhaiṇgáná;

SQUINT EYED, A.
bhaiṇggá; jhítú; ṭírá;

SQUIRE, N.
lambardár. *m;*

SQUIRREL, N.
guláhiŗí. *f;* gáhlaŗ. *m;* galhaŗ. *m;*
káto. *f;*

SQUIRT, N.
pichkárí. *f;*

SQUIRT, TO, V. T.
pichkárí márni OR chaláuní;

STAB, N.
hujj. *f;* húl. *f;*

STAB, TO, V. T.
hujj márni; húl márni; katár
márná; chhurí márni;

STABILITY, N.
mazbútí. *f;* ghaliár. *f;* gharial. *m;*
kalihár. *m;*

STABLE, N.
taveláh. *m;* tabelá. *m;* astabal. *m;*
cow shed. kurh. *m;*

STABLE, A.
1. strong. pakká; mazbut; tikáú;
2. immovable. astbar; asthír;
astháwár;

STABLENESS, N.
mazbútí. *f;* sábtí. *f;* qaimí. *f;*
pakkíáí. *f;*

STACK, N.
nirá. *m;*
1. stack of wheat. chaff. músal. m;
kupp. *m;* kusak. *m;*
2. stack of grain after threshing.
bohal. *m;*
3. stack of dried cowdung cakes.
guhárá. *m;* guhárí. *f;*

STAFF, *N.*
soṭá. *m;* láṭhí. *f;* ḍáṇgá. *f;* ḍáṇḍá. *m;* ḍáṇg. *f;* ḍaṇgorí. *f;*
STAG, *N.*
haran. *m;* harní. *f;* bárán siṇgá. *m;* páhṛá. *m;*
STAGE, *N.*
1. platform. thaṛhá. *m;* sakkú. *m;*
2. halting place. manzil. *f;* paṛá. *m;*
3. in fields. manhá. *m;*
STAGGER, TO, *V. I.*
1. to fall down. ḍigg painá;
2. to stagger along. ḍolke ṭurná; ḍigḍeáṇ turná; jhuldá phirná; ḍiggdá ḍhaiṇṇá;
STAGNANT, *A.*
1. filthy. gaṇdá;
2. standing. khalotá hoyá;
STAID, *A.*
dhírajmáṇ;
STAIN, *N.*
dág. *m;* dáṇg. *m;* kalaṇk. *m;* phuṭkaṛí. *f;*
moral. dhabbá. *m;*
STAIN, TO, *V. T.*
1. to soil. gaṇdá karná;
2. to mark. dág láuṇá;
STAINED, *A.*
dággí; kalaṇkí;
STAINLESS, *A.*
1. ṣpotless. badág;
2. without fault. beaib;
STAIRS, *N.*
pauṛíáṇ. *f;* pauṛsáṇgg. *f;*
STAIRCASE, *N.*
pauṛí. *f;* pauṛsáṇgg. *f;*
STAKE, *N.*
1. a peg. meḳh. *f;* kil. *f;*
2. a stump or broken branch. khuṇgghá. *m;*
3. a gibbet. súlí. *f;*
STALE, *A.*
behá; behí;
1. bread cooked at night and eaten next day. behí roṭí;
2. bread cooked and eaten at once. sajarí roṭí. *f;*
3. cooked over night. parúthá;
4. Proverb. To eat last night's scraps produces forgetfulness. parúthá ṭukaṛ kháwán wisárá paidá karende;

STALK. *N.*
tukkhmá. *m;* kakkh. *m;* tílá. *m;* gandal. *m;*
1. of maize, sugar cane. ṭáuṇá. *m;*
2. of wheat, barley. nálí. *f;*
STALK, TO, *V. T.*
chhaihṇá;
STALL, *N.*
kurh. *m;*
STALLION, *N.*
sánh. *m;* sáṇḍh. *m;* sáhn. *m;*
STAMMER, *N.*
thuthlá. *m;*
STAMMER, TO, *V. T.*
thuthláuṇá;
STAMMERER, *N.*
haklá. *m;* hakṛá. *m;* thathlá. *m;*
STAMMERING, *N.*
thuthlá. *m;*
STAMP, *N.*
1. postage. ṭikaṭ. *m;* istámp. *m;*
2. seal. chháp. *f;* thappá. *m;* mohr. *f;*
3. thumb impression. aṇgguṭṭhá. *m;*
4. stamp of the foot, jarb, *f;*
5. stamped paper. istámp. *m;*
STAMP, TO, *V. T.*
1. to seal. mohr láuní; thappná; chhápná;
2. to stamp with the feet. pair márná.
STAMPEDE, *N.*
bhájaṛ. *f;* jhissí. *f;* jhijkí. *f;*
STAMPING, *N.*
ghamṃá ghamm. *m;*
STANCH, TO, *V. T.*
lahú band karná;
STAND, *N.*
1. a place. jagáh. *f;* ṭhikáná. *m;*
2. for carts. &c. aḍḍá. *m;*
3. resistance. sámhná. *m;* muqábalá. *m;*
4. for water vessels. ghaṛwanjí. *f;* ghaṛesaní, *f;*
STAND, TO, *V. I.*
1. to stand up. uṭṭh khalo jáná; khaṛá honá. khalotá ráhná;
2. to stop. ṭhahrná; thamm jáná; khaṛá rahná. ḍaṭná;
3. to stand by. báhurná;
4. to cause to stand. khaliárná;

STANDARD, *N.*
jhaṇḍá. *m*; dhajá. *f*;
STANDING, *N.*
darjá. *m*; uhdá. *m*;
STAPLE, *N.*
kuṇḍá. *m*;
STAR. *N.*
tárá. *m*;
STARCH, *N.*
máyá. *m*; kalaf. *m*; máwá. *m*;
STARCHING, *N.*
maṇḍáí. *f*; páṇ, *m*;
STARCH, TO, *V. T.*
maṇḍá;
1. to cause to be starched. maṇḍáuná;
2. put plenty of starch. chokkhí kalaf lání;
STARE, *N.*
takk. *m*; jhamáká, *m*; jháká. *m*;
STARE, TO, *V. T.*
táṛná; táṛí láuní; akkh laṛáuní; múṇh ṭakkná; ghurke vekhná; ṭakk láuní; ghúrná; najar bharke vekhná; ṭakar ṭakar vekhná; akkh bharke vekhná;
STARK NAKED, *A.*
naṇgg dhaṛaṇgg;
STARLING, *N.*
mainá. *m*; tilyar. *m*; guṭár. *f*;
START, *N.*
shurú. *m*; arambh. *m*;
START, TO, *V. T.*
1. to begin. shurú karná;
2. to cause to go. chaláuná;
3. to start off on a journey. tur painá;
4. to start a subject of conversation. gall chheṛná;
5. I will start this work to-morrow. bhalke hí is kamm núṇ karan lagg pawáṇgá;
STARTLE, TO, *V. T.*
ḍaráuná; taráhná; uchkáuná;
STARTLED, TO BE, *V. I.*
ḍarná; taraihná; chauṇkná;
STARVATION, *N.*
baṛí bhukkh. *f*;
STARVE, TO, *V. I.*
bhukkhá marná; bhukkh nál marná;

STATE, *N.*
1. condition. hál. *m*; hálat. *f*; hál hawál. *m*; hál chál. *m*;
2. rank. darjá. *m*; uhdá. *m*;
3. dignity. shán shaukat. *f*; ṭháṭh. *m*;
4. country. riyásat. *f*; mulk. *m*; ráje dá ràj. *m*;
5. affairs. ráj káj. *m*;
STATE, TO, *V. T.*
bayán karná; zikr karná; batláuná; dassná;
STATELINESS, *N.*
ṭhàṇs. *f*; buzurgí. *f*;
STATELY, *A.*
partápí; waḍḍá 'te sohná;
STATEMENT, *N.*
bayán. *m*; hál. *m*;
STATION, *N.*
1. railway. isteshan. *m*;
2. town. chhauṇí. *f*;
STATION, TO, *V. T.*
1. to place. rakkhná; dharná; ṭikáuná;
2. to stand. khaṛá karná;
3. to seat. bahàlná;
STATIONARY, *A.*
achar; aṭall;
STATUE, *N.*
murat. *f*; butt. *m*; parítmá. *m*; putlá. *m*;
STATURE, *N.*
qadd. *m*; díl. *m*;
a man of small stature. wauná; khaṇḍá;
STATUS, *N.*
darjá. *m*; uhdá. *m*;
STATUTE, *N.*
qánun. *m*;
religious. bidh. *f*; bidhí. *f*;
STAY, TO, *V. I.*
1. to remain. rahná; ṭikkná; ṭhahrná;
2. to take breath. dam lainá; sáh lainá;
3. I cannot stay here. merá itthe rahná bandá nahíṇ;
STAY, TO, *V. T.*
rokná; band karná; aṭkáuná;
STAY, *N.*
1. sojourn. raháish. *m*;
2. check. rok ṭok. *f*;

3. help. sahárá. *m;* sahaitá. *f;*
4. support. thamm. *m;* thammhí. *f;*

STEADFAST, TO BE, *V. I.*
tagná;

STEADFASTNESS, *N.*
mazbutí. *f;* táqat. *f;* see CONSTANCY.

STEADILY, *Adv.*
1. continuously. lagátár; barábar;
2. with strength. mazbutí nál;
3. to look steadily. banáke vekhná;

STEADY, *A.*
mazbut; kaṭṭhá; sábat; pakká; aḍol; qaim; isthar; asthír; asthäwar;

STEADY, TO, *V. T.*
mazbut karná; pakkeáṇ karná; sambhálná;

STEAL, TO, *V. T.*
chorí karní; churáuná; kharná; dakárná; gaban karná; see ROB.
1. to steal everything. chaunká pherná;
2. to steal away secretly. akkh bacháuná;

STEALING, *N.*
chorí. *f;* chorí chakárí. *f:*

STEALTHLY, *Adv.*
chorí; chupp cháp; akkh bacháke; chup chupátá; chorí chappí;

STEAM, *N.*
bháf. *f;*

STEAMER, *N.*
aganboṭ. *m;* jaház. *m;*

STEED, *N.*
ghoṛá. *m;* ghoṛí. *f;*

STEEL, *N.*
ispát. *m;*

STEEP, *A.*
uchchá; dhálú;

STEEP, TO, *V. T.*
bhigáuná; bhijá dená; bhigoná; see WET.

STEEPLE, *N.*
burjí. *f;* minár. *m;*

STEEPNESS, *N.*
uchchiáí. *f;* ucháhat. *f;*

STEER, *N.*
ḍhaggá. *m;* bald. *m;*

STEER, TO, *V. T.*
jaház chaláuná;

STEM, *N.*
1. branch. tahní. *f;*
2. of a pipe. naṛí. *f;* naichá. *m;*

STEM, TO, *V. T.*
rokná; aṭkáuná; ḍakkná;

STENCH, *N.*
badbo. *f;* see STINK.

STEP, *N.*
1. pace. dolángh. *f;* pauṇgkhá. *m;*
2. grade. darjá. *m;* ohdá. *m;*
3. step by step. pair o pair;

STEP, TO, *V. I.*
1. to move. chalná; turná; jáná;
2. to step back. haṭná;
3. to step aside. lámbhe ho jáná; alag ho jáná;

STEP, *Prefix.*
1. step son. matre puttar. *m;*
2. step daughter. matre beṭí OR dhí. *f;*
3. step mother. matreí máṇ. *f;* sutelí máṇ. *f;* masak máṇ. *f;*
4. step father. matre báp. *m;*
5. step brother. sutelá bhaí. *m;*
6. step sister. matreí bhaiṇ. *f;*

STERILE, *A.*
1. human. báṇjh;
2. land. banjaṛ; kallar;
3. animal. phanḍar;

STERLING, *A.*
aslí;

STERN, *A.*
sakht; karṛá;

STERN, *N.*
jaház dí pichhárí. *f;*

STERNNESS, *N.*
sakhtí. *f;*

STEW, TO, *V. T.*
rinnhná;

STEWARD, *N.*
mukhtiár. *m;* gumástá. *m;*

STEWARDSHIP, *N.*
mukhtiárí. *f;*

STEW PAN, *N.*
degchá. *m;*

STICK, *N.*
1. thin cane. soṭí. *f;*
2. strong stick. ḍanḍá. *m;* ḍáṇg. *f;* ḍangorí. *f;* guttká *m;* soṭá. *m;* láṭṭhí. *f;*
3. a stick with curved handle. khunḍá. *m;*

4. fuel. bálan. *m* ;
STICK, TO, *V. T.*
chipkáuná ;
STICK, TO, *V. I.*
jam jáná ; lag jáná ; chipakná ; lipaṭná ; chimbaṛ jáná ; chambaṛná ; chamaṛná ; chimmaṛná ; in mud. khubbhná ;
STICKY, *A.*
lággar ; chíplá ; laslasá ; lesalá ; libbá ;
STIFF, *A.*
sakht ; karárá ; káṭṭhá ; as paste, &c. ákrá ;
STIFFENING, *N.*
manḍáí. *f* ;
STIFFNESS, *N.*
karár puṇá. *m* ;
STIFLE, TO, *V. T.*
muṇh ghuṭṭná ; gal ghuṭṭke márná ; see STRANGLE.
STIFLE, TO, *V. I.*
baṛá waṭṭ lagná ;
STIFLING, *A.*
hussar ;
STIGMA, *N.*
dág. *m* ; dhabbá. *m* ; kalaṇk. *m* ;
STIGMATIZE, TO, *V. T.*
badnám karná ; daṇbh láuná ; kalaṇk dá ṭikká lagáuná ; dág láuná ;
STILE, *N.*
langháṇí. *f* ; charoliá. *m* ; lagání. *f* ;
STILL, TO, *V. T.*
chupp karáuná ; dabáuná ;
STILL, TO, BE, *V. I.*
chupp ráhná ;
STILL, *A.*
1. quiet. chupp ; chupp cháp ; chupp chapátá ;
2. motionless. nichall ; munn sunn ;
STILL, *Adv.*
tad ví ; phir ví ; aje ; táṇ ví ;
STILLNESS, *N.*
chupp. *f* ; khámoshí. *f* ;
STIMULANT, *N.*
garmáí. *f* ;
STIMULATE, TO, *V. T.*
agg bhaṛkáuná ; uskáuná ; lárá dená ; josh ḍuáuná ; see INCITE and STIR.
STIMULATION, *N.*
lárá. *m* ; dilerí. *f* ; chukk. *f* ; uchalá. *m* ;
STING, *N.*
ḍaṇg. *m* ;
STING, TO, *V. T.*
ḍaṇg márná ; ḍaṇggná ; ḍas jáná ;
STINGILY, *Adv.*
kanjúsí nál ;
STINGINESS, *N.*
kanjúsí. *f* ; shúmpuṇá. *m* ;
STINGY, *A.*
kanjus ; marjiú ; marjiúrán ; makkhí chús ;
STINK, TO, *V. I.*
hamakná ; mushkná ; bo mární ; bussṇá ; sariándháuní ;
STINK, *N.*
badbo. *f* ; gaṇd. *m* ; saṛiáṇdh. *f* ; dús. *f* ; bisúndh. *f* ; saṛián. *f* ; wisáṇdh. *f* ; saṛihán. *f* ; mushak. *m* ; básná. *f* ;
STINKING, *A.*
gaṇdá ; wisáṇdhá ; tarakkiá hoyá ; saṛiá galliá hoyá ;
STINT, TO. *V. T.*
ghaṭáuná ;
STIPEND, *N.*
talab. *f* ; tankháh. *f* ; mazdúrí. *f* ;
STIPULATE, TO, *V. T.*
shart karní OR láuní OR bannhní
STIPULATION, *N.*
1. condition. shart. *f* ;
2. promise. qaul qarár. *m* ; bachan. *m* ; iqrár. *m* ; wádá. *m* ;
STIR, *N.*
raulá. *m* ; shor. *m* ; gahimá gahun, *m* ; hill jull. *f* ; gahimá gahim. *m* ;
STIR, TO, *V. T.*
1. to move. hiláuná ; uṭháuná ;
2. to excite. chheṛná ; uskáuná ; bhakháná ; chukkiá karná ; chukkná ;
3. to stir liquid, &c. jhakolná ; gholná ; maddhná ;
STIR, TO, *V. I.*
hilná ; maskaná ;
STIRRUP, *N.*
rakáb. *f* ;
stirrup leather. rakáb duwál. *f* ;
STITCH, *N.*
ṭáṇká. *m* ; ṭoppá. *m* ; troppá. *m* ;

STITCH, TO, *V. T.*
síná ; turpná ; ṭuppná ; troppá láná ; toppá láuná ; trupná ; táṇká láuná ; bakhiá karná ; tarumbná ;
1. to join together. gaṇḍhná ;
2. to have stitch in the side. taṇe charh jáná ;
STITCHING, *N.*
bakhiá. *m* ;
STOCK, *N.*
sámán. *m* ; asbáb. *m* ; mál. *m* ; rás. *f* ;
of a gun. kuṇḍá. *m* ;
STOCK, TO, *V. T.*
rakkhná ;
STOCK BROKER, *N.*
dallál. *m* ;
STOCK IN TRADE, *N.*
rás. *f* ;
STOCKINGS, *N.*
moze. *m* ; jurábáṇ. *f* ;
STOCKS, *N.*
káṭh. *m* ;
STOLEN PROPERTY, *N.*
badí. *f* ;
STOMACH, *N.*
ḍhiḍḍ. *m* ; pet. *m* ; mehdá. *m* ; jhoj. *m* ;
Proverb. The stomach keeps a man and the stomach ruins a man. rakkhe ví ḍhiḍḍ te ujáṛe ví ḍhiḍḍ ;
STONE, *N.*
1. ordinary. patthar. *m* ; waṭṭá. *m* ;
2. mill stone. chakkí dá pur. *m* ;
3. fruit stone. gaṭak. *f* ; giṭṭak *f* ; hikkaṛ. *f* ; guṭhlí. *f* ; hirak *f* ;
4. in ring. thewá. *m* ;
5. in nose ornament. chúní. *f* ;
STONE, TO, *V. T.*
patthráṇ karná ; patthráuná ; pathráh dená ;
STONE BLIND, *A.*
annhá ;
STONY, *A.*
pathrílí ;
STONYHEARTED, *A.*
patthar dil ; sakht dil ; beráhm ;
STOOL, *N.*
murhá. *m* ; píṛhí. *f* ;
1. footstool. paundaṛ . *m* ;
2. to go to stool. jháṛe jáná ; jháṛe phirná ; hagg dená ;

STOOP, TO, *V. I.*
uṛná ; níwáṇ honá ; jhukná ;
1. to stoop down. hitháhán niuṇna ;
2. with age. kuṛh jáná ;
STOOPING, *N.*
jhuk. *m* ; jhukáú. *m* ;
STOP, TO, *V. T.*
band karná ; ḍakkná ; rokná ; dabb rakkhná ; aṭkáuná ; moṛná, ṭhillh páuní ; khaliárná ; see HINDER.
1. to stop a water channel. waṭṭ márná ;
2. stopping the road. rastá mallke ;
STOP, TO, *V. I.*
ṭhahrná ; ṭikná ; khalo jáná ; muṛná ; ṭhákná ; khuṭṭ jáná ; aṛná ; ḍaṭná ;
STOPPAGE, *N.*
rok. *f* ; aṭkáú. *m* ; ḍakká. *m* ; ṭhallh. *f* ;
STOPPER, *N.*
1. for a bottle, &c. kág. *m* ; ḍáṭ. *m* ; ḍáṭṭ. *m* ; gaṭṭ. *m* ; gaṭṭá. *m* ; ḍáṭṭá. *m* ; ḍakká. *m* ;
2. for a large hole. bujjá. *m* ; bujjí. *f* ;
STORE, *N.*
godám. *m* ; koṭhí. *f* ; modí kháná. *m* ; bhaṇḍár. *m* ; koṭhá. *m* ;
STORE, TO, *V. T.*
kaṭṭhá karná ; jamá karná ;
STOREKEEPER, *N.*
modí. *m* ;
STORES, *N.*
tossá. *m* ; saudá. *m* ;
STOREY, UPPER, *N.*
chubárá. *m* ;
STORK, *N.*
lamḍhíng. *f* ;
STORM, *N.*
hanerí. *f* ; anherí. *f* ; jhánjhá. *m* ; jhakkaṛ. *m* ; anratth. *m* ;
great storm. kálí bolí hanerí. *f* ; annhí hanerí. *f* ;
STORMY, *A.*
tufání ;
STORY, *N.*
1. tale. bát. *f* ; kahání. *f* ; kathá. *f* ; wartá. *f* ; kath. *f* ; hakáit. *f* ; bání. *f* ; kathá wártá. *f* ;
2. to tell a story. kathá páuná ;
3. lie. jhuṭh. *m* ; jhuṭh muṭh. *m* ; kúṛ. *m* ;

STOUT, *A.*
1. fat and lusty. tahiṛ ṭhuliá; moṭá tázá; haṭṭá kaṭṭá; see CORPULENT.
2. strong. mazbut; saṇḍhá; see STRONG.
3. bold. diler; takṛá; tagṛá;
STOUTLY, *Adv.*
dilerí nál; himmat nál; dabádab;
STOUTNESS, *N.*
1. strength. jor. *m*; zor. *m*; táqat. *f*;
2. boldness. dilerí. *f*; himmat. *f*;
STOVE, *N.*
aṇggíṭhí. *f*;
STOW, TO, *V. T.*
bhar dená; ḍhusná;
STRUGGLE, TO, *V. I.*
1. to lag behind. pichche rahná;
2. to wander about. awárá phirná; ḍáwáṇḍol phirná;
STRAIGHT, *A.*
1. straight ahead. siddhá; súl; suáhrá;
2. to go straight on. rawáṇ rawíṇ;
3. upright. suddh; khará;
STRAIGHTEN, TO, *V. T.*
sidh karná; siddhá karná OR banáuná;
STRAIGHTFORWARD, *A.*
siddhá; sachchá; siddhá; sádá; suddh; súdh;
STRAIGHTNESS, *N.*
1. uprightness. rástí. *f*; sachchíáí. *f*;
2. straight. siddh. *f*; sed. *f*;
STRAIGHTWAY, *Adv.*
jhaṭ phaṭ; ikk dam; oweṇ;
STRAIN, *N.*
1. effort. mihnat, *f*; jatan, *m*;
2. sprain. maroṛ. *m*; maroṛá. *m*;
STRAIN, TO, *V. T.*
1. to tighten, kassná;
2. to filter. punná; nachoṛná; nitárná;
3. to exert. baṛí mihnat karní; hílá karná; ján márná;
4. at stool. killhná;
5. to strain at lifting a burden. killhná;
STRAINER, *N.*
1. metal. chhánní. *f*;
2. cloth. poná. *m*;
STRAIT, *N.*
musíbat. *f*; taṇgí, *f*; lachárí. *f*; sauṛ. *f*;

STRAITENED, *A.*
láchár; taṇg; aukhá;
STRANGE, *A.*
1. wonderful. ajíb; aṇokhá; ajab;
2. foreign. ajnabí; oprá; wáṇḍhá; bagáná; paráyá;
STRANGELY, *Adv.*
ajíb taur nál;
STRANGER, *N.*
paráyá. *m*; pardesí. *m*; oprá bandá, *m*; wáṇḍhá. *m*;
STRANGLE, TO, *V. T.*
gal ghuṭṭná; khapná; jharáuná saṇgh ghuṭṭná; gal ghuṭṭke márná;
STRANGULATION, *N.*
saṇgghoṭ. *m*;
STRAP, *N.*
duwálí. *f*; tasmá. *m*; waddhrí. *f*;
STRAP, TO, *V. T.*
kassná; tasme nál bannhná;
STRATAGEM, *N.*
dá. *m*; chálá. *m*; chalákí. *f*; chhal chhiddar, *m*; bal chhal. *m*;
STRATEGY, *N.*
chalákí. *f*;
STRATUM, *N.*
part. *m*; tabká. *m*;
STRAW, *N.*
khar. *m*; nálí. *f*;
1. a bit of straw. kakkh. *m*; tílá. *m*; tukkhná, *m*;
2. the stalk of wheat or barley. náṛ. *f*; káh. *m*;
3. the straw of rice. parálí. *f*; parál. *m*;
STRAY, TO, *V. I.*
awárá phirná; chhuṭe phirná;
1. to err. ghussná; khuṇjhná;
2. to forget. bhullná; bhulí painá;
STRAY, *A.*
awárá;
STREAKED, *A.*
kháldár;
STREAM, *N.*
nadí, *f*; nálí. *f*;
1. river. daryá. *m*;
2. hill stream. naiṇ. *f*;
STREAM, TO, *V. I.*
wagná;
STREAMLET, *N.*
nadí. *f*;
fountain. sotá. *m*; sumb. *m*;

STREET, *N*.
1. narrow. galí. *f* ; kuchá. *m* ;
2. ordinary. bazár. *m* ;
3. wide road. saṛak. *f* ;
4. path. rastá. *m* ; ráh. *m* ; pahiá. *m* ; ghássí. *f* ;
5. square. chauṇk. *m* ;

STRENGTH, *N*.
zor. *m*; jor. *m* ; táqat. *f* ; ghariál. *m*; wáh. *f* ; samarth. *f* ; dariṛhtá. *f* ; asang. *m* ; samarthá, *f* ; tán. *m* ; bal. *m* ; tul. *f* ; pujj. *f* ; majbutí. *f* ;
1. used negatively. bhochhá. *m* ; *e.g.*, my strength is gone. merá bhochhá nikal gayá ;
2. of friendship. gúhaṛá. *m* ;
3. of mind. dariṛh. *f* ;

STRENGTHEN, TO, *V. T*.
mazbut karná ; jor dená ;

STRENGTHLESS, *A*.
kamjor ; nirbal ; lissá ; liserá ;

STRENUOUS, *A*.
sargarm ; joshwálá ; himmatí ;

STRENUOUSLY, *Adv*.
híle nál ; himmat nál ; jor láke ;

STRESS, *N*.
1. force. jor. *m* ; zor. *m* ; bal. *m* ; táqat. *f* ;
2. constraint. dabáo. *m* ;

STRESS, TO, *V. T*.
zor dená ;

STRETCH, TO, *V, T*.
tánná ; khichchná ; ṭaṇggáuná ; ṭaḍḍná ;
1. to stretch oneself. ákaṛná ; ákaṛ lená ; ákaṛ bhannhná ;
2. to stretch the legs. pasárná ;
3. to stretch out the warp. táná tánná ;
4. to stretch hither the hand. hatth ure karná ;
5. to stretch oneself before another, and so make him feel lazy. ákaṛáṇ páuná ;
6. Proverb. Cut your coat according to your cloth. Stretch your feet according to your sheet. jitní chadar ho utne hí páoṇ pasáro ; OR chadar vekh ke pair pasáro ;

STRETCH OUT, TO, *V. I*.
agere karná ; pasárná ;

STRETCHING, *N*.
machkoṛá. *m* ;

STREW, TO, *V. T*.
khilárná ; see SCATTER.

STRICKEN, *N*.
máriá hoyá ;
stricken with misfortune. biptá dá máriá hoyá ;

STRICT, *A*.
sakht ; karṛá ;
I told the strict truth. maiṇ sach sach boliá ;

STRICTNESS, *N*.
tagíd. *f* ;
severity. sakhtí. *f* ; jástí. *f* ; loṛhá. *m* ;

STRICTURE, *N*.
jhiṛkí. *f* ; jháṛ. *m* ; malámat. *f* ;

STRIDE, *N*.
qadam. *f* ;

STRIFE, *N*.
laṛáí. *f* ; jhagṛá. *m* ; kiṛ. *f* ; tánázá, *m* ; jhambel. *f* ; thuká tháki. *f* ;

STRIKE, TO, *V. T*.
márná ; piṭná ; ṭhokná ; dhappá márná ; dhappá láuná ;
1. to strike a bargain. saudá banáuná ; takk chhaḍḍná ;
2. to strike out something. harf kaṭṭná ; meṭná ; kalam pherní ; miṭáuná ;
3. to strike with the fist. hurá márná ; mukkí mární ;
4. to cause to be struck. marwáuná ;
5. he struck me four times with a shoe. us ne meriáṇ chár júttíáṇ máríáṇ.

STRIKE, TO, *V. I*.
lagná ;

STRIKING, *A*.
ajíb ; aṇokhá ;

STRIKINGLY, *Adv*.
ajíb taur nál ;

STRING, *N*.
ḍorí. *f* ; ḍor. *f* ; sutrí. *f* ; sutar. *f* ;
1. ball of string. pinná. *m* ;
2. of musical instrument. tánt. *f* ; taṇd. *f* ;
3. of a bow. chillá. *m* ;
4. string on beds. wán. *m* ;
5. strings of camels. uṭṭháṇ díáṇ katáráṇ. *f* ;

6. Proverb used of an impossibility. A string of camels is passing through the eye of a needle. súí dí duk vichchoṇ katár uṭṭháṇ dí laṇghí waiṇdhí ;

STRING, TO, *V. T.*
gaṇḍhná ;
1. to string beads. paroná ;
2. to string together papers. nattí karná ;

STRINGY, *A.*
reshá ;

STRIP, TO, *V. T.*
1. to pillage. luṭṭná ; kho lená ; ḍáká márná ;
2. to deprive of covering. naṇgá karná ;
3. to strip a tree. dharúhná ;

STRIP, *N.*
laṇgár. *m ;* líṛ. *f ;* chiṭ. *f ;* phaṭṭí. *f ;*

STRIPE, *N.*
1. a beating. már. *f ;*
2. a line drawn. lakír. *f ;* lík. *f ;* lakár. *f ;* lí. *f ;*
3. a weal. lás. *f ;*

STRIPED COTTON CLOTH, *N.*
ḍoriá. *m ;*

STRIPPED, *A.*
khutthá putthá ; buṭṭá ;

STRIVE, TO, *V. T.*
1. to labour. mihnat karní ; jatan karná ; uddam karná ; jor láuná OR márná ; diloṇ wajhoṇ koshish karná ;
2. to contend. laṛná ; jhagaṛná ;

STROKE, *N.*
1. blow. choṭ. *f ;* már. *f ;* saṭṭ. *f ;* dhappá. *m ;*
2. calamity. áfat. *f ;* musíbat. *f ;* biptá. *m ;*

STROKE, TO, *V. T.*
hatth pherná ; puchkárná ; thapparná ; puchkárí dení ; palosná ; to stroke the teats preparatory to milking. pasamná ;

STROKING, *N.*
puchkárí. *f ;* puchkárá. *m ;*

STROLL, TO, *V. I.*
tahilná ; sail karná ;

STRONG, *A.*
1. vigorous. tagaṛá ; takṛá ; ḍhaṭṭá ; laṭṭhá ; saṇḍhá ; kátthá ; balwáṇ ; akṛá takṛá ; balwaṇt ;
2. robust. moṭá tázá ; haṭṭá kaṭṭá ;
3. fortified. mazbut ;
4. powerful. sabal ; mushtaṇḍá ; táqatwálá ; balwáṇ ; saṇḍhá ;
5. rather strong. tagṛerá ;
6. of tea. sanhṇí ; gúṛhí ; gúhṛí ; tez ;
7. strong cloth. ḍáhḍá kapṛá. *m ;*

STRONGHOLD, *N.*
qilá. *m ;* gaṛhí. *f ;*

STRONGLY, *Adv.*
jor nál ; híle nál ; takaṛáí nál ; dabá ke ;

STROP, *N.*
patásí. *f ;*

STRUCTURE, *N.*
makán. *m ;*

STRUGGLE, TO, *V. T.*
hatth pair márná ; jhagaṛná ; khahibaṛná ;

STRUGGLE, *N.*
laṛáí *f ;* jhagṛá. *m ;*

STRUMPET, *N.*
kaṇjarí. *f ;* kaṇchaní. *f ;* chhinár. *f ;* jární. *f ;* bazárí aurat. *f ;* kasbí. *f ;*

STRUT, TO, *V. I.*
ákaṛná ; akaṛná ; aiṇṭh ke chalná ;

STRUTTING, *N.*
aiṇṭh. *f ;* ákaṛ. *f ;* bánkí chál. *f ;* the peacock is strutting. mor pail páundá piá ;

STUBBLE, *N.*
jiṇdh. *m ;* jindhá. *m ;* baḍḍh. *m ;*

STUBBORN, *A.*
magrá ; háṭhá ; jhakkí ; aṛyal ; ziddí ; see PERVERSE.

STUBBORNESS, *N.*
zidd. *f ;* húrh. *f ;* ghamaṇḍ. *m ;* síṛaṛ. *m ;* see PERVERSENESS;

STUD, *N.*
gudám. *m ;*

STUDENT, *N.*
chelá. *m ;* shagird. *m ;*

STUDIOUSLY, *Adv.*
dhián nál ; dil lagáke ;

STUDY, TO, *V. T.*
1. to consider. sochná ; khayál karná ;
2. to learn. sṭaḍí karní ; paṛhná ;

STUFF, TO, *V. T.*
bharná ; dhúhná ; ghuseṛná ; tunná ; dhúsná ; bhart bharná ;

1. overeating. múnhoṇ múṇh bharná; nakko nakk bharná;
2. to be stuffed. ṭhasná;

STUFF, *N*.
mál. *m;* nikk sukk. *m;* chízwast. *f;* nikkar sukkar. *f;* laṭá paṭá. *m;*

STUFFING, *N*.
bhartí. *f;*

STUMBLE, TO, *V. T*.
ṭhedá khána; ṭhuḍḍáṇ khána OR lagná; aukhaṛná; ṭhahikná; ṭhukráe jáná;

STUMBLE, *N*.
ṭhuḍḍá. *m;* ṭhedá. *m;*

STUMBLING BLOCK, *N*.
ṭhokar. *f;*

STUMP, *N*.
khunḍ. *m;* khunḍá. *m;* khuṇgghá. *m;*
of a tree. muḍḍh. *m;*

STUN, TO, *V. T*.
márke behosh karná;

STUPEFACTION, *N*.
behoshí. *f;*

STUPEFY, TO, *V. T*.
behosh karná;

STUPENDOUS, *A*.
waḍḍá;

STUPID, *A*.
bewaqúf; kaiṇdh; hochchhá; besamajh; kowallá; chabal; kulann; buddhú; kuṇḍh; muthum; allhaṛ; murakh; siddhá; paglá; ghísaṇ; khuṇḍhá; kuchahhá; aṇján; ṭhuṭh; ghuggú; kuchajjá; kuchajjí;
a fat stupid man. bainchhar. *m;*

STUPIDITY, *N*.
bewaqufí. *f;* beaqlí. *f;* nadání. *f;* hochchhápuṇá. *m;* besahúrí. *f;* aggián. *m;* besamjhí. *f;* hurh. *f;* murakhpuṇá. *m;*

STUPIDLY, *Adv*.
bewaqufí nál; beaqlí nál; nadání nál; biná soche samjhe;

STUPOR, *N*.
gash. *f;* behoshí. *f;*

STURDILY, *Adv*.
baṛí himmat nál; jor nál; sher banke;

STURDINESS, *N*.
dilerí. *f;*

STURDY, *A*.
takṛá; tagaṛá; diler; himtál; himmatí;

STUTTER, TO, *V. I*.
thathláuná; hakláuná;

STYE IN THE EYE, *N*.
guháṇdaní. *f;* guháṇjaní. *f;* phinsaní. *f;* phimmhaní. *f;*

STYLE, *N*.
ḍhaṇg. *m;* ḍhab. *m;*
do not affect such style. aiḍí shúká shákí ná kar;

SUAVE, *A*.
narm; mulaím;

SUBDUE, TO, *V. T*.
hall karná; sar karná; hatth heṭh karná; pitkáuná;
subdue the passions. dil núṇ márná;

SUBJECT, *N*.
1. people. parjá. *f;* raíyat. *f;*
2. theme. mazmún. *m;* parsaṇg. *m;*

SUBJECT, *A*.
adhíṇ; ágiákár;

SUBJECT, TO, *V. T*.
hatth heṭh karná;
to be subject. dabáú manná; adhíṇ honá;

SUBJECTION, *N*.
1. submissiveness. adhíngí. *f;*
2. obedience. tábedárí. *f;* ágiákárí. *f;*

SUBJUGATE, TO, *V. T*.
dabáuná; see SUBDUE.

SUBLIME, *A*,
uttam;

SUBMERGE, TO, *V. I*.
ḍubbná; nigghar jáná;

SUBMERGE, TO, *V. T*.
ḍobná; ḍubáuná;

SUBMERSION, *N*.
gottá. *m;*

SUBMISSION, *N*.
1. acceptance. manzúrí. *f;*
2. meekness. ájizí. *f;* adhíṇtáí. *f;* adhíṇgí. *f;*

SUBMISSIVE, *A*
adhíṇ; maskíṇ; gídí;
to be submissive. kann ná hiláuná;

SUBMISSIVENESS, *N*.
adhíṇtáí. *f;*

SUBMIT, TO, *V. I.*
manná ; dabáú manná ; gardan jhukáuná ; adhín honá ; hár manní ;
SUBORDINATE, *A.*
adhín ; heṭh ; matáihat ;
SUBORDINATION, *N.*
adhínṭáí. *f* ; adhíngí. *f* ;
SUBSCRIBE, TO, *V. T.*
dená ; chandá dená ;
SUBSCRIBER, *N.*
chandá denwálá. *m* ;
SUBSCRIPTION, *N.*
chandá. *m* ;
SUBSEQUENCE, *N.*
anjám. *m* ; natíjá. *m* ; gaveṛ. *m* ;
SUBSEQUENT, *A.*
pichchlá ;
SUBSEQUENTLY, *Adv.*
pichche ; pichchoṇ ; chhekaṛ ; magaroṇ ;
SUBSERVIENT, *N.*
gídí ; ájiz ; adhíṇ ;
SUBSIDE, TO, *V. I.*
1. to become less. ghaṭṭ jáná ; thuṛ jáná ; nakhuṭṭná ;
2. to sit down. baihná ;
3. to draw to a close. lahiná ;
SUBSIST, TO, *V. I.*
guzárá karná ;
SUBSISTENCE, *N.*
guzárá. *m* ; jiuká. *f* ;
SUBSTANCE, *N.*
1. essence. tatt, *m* ;
2. property. mál. *m* ;
SUBSTANTIAL, *A.*
bhárí ; sakíl ;
SUBSTANTIATE, TO, *V. T.*
sábit karna ;
SUBSTANTIALITY, *N.*
pakíáí. *f* ;
SUBSTITUTE, *N.*
badlí. *m* ; badlá. *m* ; iwazí. *m* ; ivají. *m* ;
SUBSTITUTE, TO, *V. T.*
badal dená ; waṭáuná ;
SUBSTRUCTURE, *N.*
níh. *f* ; bunyád. *f* ;
SUBTERFUGE, *N.*
makr. *m* ; fareb. *m* ; dhokhá *m* ; kapaṭ. *m* ; dhuchchar. *m* ; híl-hujjat. *f* ; dháṇḍal. *f* ; dháṇḍalí. *f* ; see TRICK.
to use subterfuge. suṭṭ suṭṭní ; dháṇḍal páuní ;
SUBTLE, *A.*
chalák ; makkar ; pechílá ;
SUBTLY, *Adv.*
fareb nál ; dhokhebází nál ; dáú nál ;
to deal subtily. chatarái karní ;
SUBTLENESS, *N.*
makr. *m* ; pech ghech. *m* ;
SUBTRACT, TO, *V. T.*
1. in arithmetic. minhá karná ; manfí karní ;
2. to take out. kaḍḍhná ;
SUBTRACTION, *N.*
minháí. *f* ;
SUBVERSION, *N.*
ulaṭ pulaṭ. *f* ; ulṭáú. *m* ;
SUBVERT, TO, *V. T.*
1. to spoil. kharáb karná ; wigáṛná ; ujáṛná ;
2. to throw down. ḍegná ; ḍháhná ; ḍháuná ;
3. to overturn. ulṭáuná ; mudhá karná ; palṭáuná ;
SUCCEED, TO, *V, I.*
1. to be successful. kámyáb honá ; kamm bannhná ; kamm toṛná ; chalná ;
2. to follow another. uh de tháṇ áuná ;
SUCCESS, *N.*
kámyábí. *f* ; jít. *f* ; fatáh. *f* ; ghukar. *f* ; bol bállá. *m* ;
SUCCESSFUL, *A.*
ghukiá hoyá ; kámyáb ;
SUCCESSFULLY, *Adv.*
kámyábí nál ;
SUCCESSION, *N.*
lár. *f* ; paṛín. *f* ;
1. in succession. agge pichchhe ;
2. in quick succession. hathohathí ;
SUCCESSIVELY, *Adv.*
lagátár ; har dam ; dam dam ; agge pichche ; upar thalí ;
SUCCOUR, *N.*
madat. *f* ; saháí. *f* ; sahárá. *m* ;
SUCCOUR, TO, *V. T.*
madat dení ; see HELP.
SUCCOURER, *N.*
sahái *m* ; sahaití. *m* ; bacháunwálá. *m* ; belí. *m* ;

SUCCULENT, *A.*
1. fresh. tázá;
2. juicy. rasdár; raswálá;
SUCH, *A.*
ajehá; jehá; eho jehá;
SUCK, TO, *V. T.*
chusná; chuṇgghná; chúpná;
1. to suck milk. dudh píná; chuṇgghná;
2. to absorb. chúpná; píná;
SUCKING, *N.*
chus. *m*; chusáí. *f*;
SICKLE, TO, *V. T.*
mammá dená; chuṇggháuná; piláuná; dudh piláuná;
SUCTION, *N.*
chusáo. *m*;
SUDDEN, *A.*
achának; jhaṭṭ; chánchuk;
SUDDENLY, *Adv.*
achának; achánchakk; chaupaṭṭ; jhaṭṭ phaṭṭ; malkaṛí; awághaṭṭ; cháṇchakke; achaṇchet;
SUE, TO, *V. T.*
arzí páuní; dáwá karní; nálish karná; muqaddamá karná OR banáuná;
SUET, *N.*
charbí. *f*;
SUFFER, TO, *V. I.*
sahárná; jhallná; dukh bhogná; sahiná; jarná; gakhná; bhugtaná; najiṭṭhná; dukh uṭháuná;
1. to suffer loss. dhakke laggná; waqt núṇ phaṛ baiṭhná; gháṭṭáauná; ujjaṛ pujjaṛ ho jáná;
2. to suffer neglect. rulná;
SUFFERANCE, *N.*
sabr. *m*;
SUFFERER, *N.*
dukhí. *m*; dukhiá. *m*; dukhiárá. *m*;
SUFFERING, *N.*
dukh. *m*; taklíf. *f*; dukhṛá. *m*;
SUFFICE, TO, *V. I.*
káfí honá;
SUFFICIENCY, *N.*
tipat. *f*; nabáh. *m*;
of food. rajj. *m*;
SUFFICIENT, *A.*
káfí; bas; bahut; jog; batherá; chokkhá;
SUFFICIENTLY, *Adv.*
mulloṇ;
SUFFOCATE, TO, *V. T.*
muṇh ghuṭṭná; dam rokná; dam ghuṭṭná; see STRANGLE.
SUFFOCATED, TO BE, *V. I.*
sáh ghuṭṭ jáná;
SUGAR, *N.*
miṭṭhá. *m*; chíní. *f*;
1. unrefined native sugar. khaṇḍ. *f*;
2. lumps of coarse native sugar. guṛ. *m*;
3. finer than gur. shakkar. *f*;
4. given to a new born child. guṛhtí, *f*;
5. Proverb. One who eats alone eats a bone; one who shares eats sugar. aḍḍ kháe so haḍḍ kháe, waṇḍ kháe so khaṇḍ kháe;
SUGAR CANE, *N.*
1. growing. kamád. *m*;
2. each cane. ganná. *m*;
3. thick kind for chewing. poná. *m*; ponná. *m*;
4. the juice. rauh. *f*; rahu. *f*;
5. dry leaves of cane. khorí. *f*;
6. small pieces cut for chewing. ganerí. *f*;
7. various kinds of cane. terú. *m*; tarerú. *m*; káṭṭhá. *m*; chiṇkhá. *m*; peṭkú. *m*; kánsá. *m*; metkú *m*; káú. *m*; shángá. *m*; sahární. *f*;
8. sugar cane slip for planting. bottá. *m*;
9. pile of sugar cane cuttings covered with earth, kept for seed. ṭig. *m*;
10. sugar cane after juice has been expressed. pachchhí. *f*;
11. sugar cane juice. rauh. *f*;
SUGARY, *A.*
miṭṭhá;
SUGGEST, TO *V. T.*
1. to put forward. pesh karná;
2. to advise. saláh dení;
3. to cause to be understood. samjháuná;
SUGGESTION, *N.*
saláh. *f*; mashvaráh. *m*;

SUICIDE, *N.*
ḳhudkushí. *f*; átam ghát. *m*;
SUIT, *N.*
1. a law case, maqadamà, *m*; nálish. *f*;
2. civil suit. díwání nálish. *f*;
3. criminal suit. faujdárí nálish. *f*;
4. of clothes. sút. *m*; jorá. *m*;
SUIT, TO, *V. T.*
ṭhík karná;
SUIT, TO, *V. I.*
phabbná; bháuṇá; bhalá laggná; changá laggná;
SUITABLE, *A.*
ṭhík; gattak; gattakdá; munásib; gochrá; karne jog; laiq;
you are not suitable. tuṇ sáḍe kamm dá nahíṇ;
SUITABLY, *Adv.*
láiq taur nàl;
SUITE, *N.*
jaleb. *m*;
SUITOR *N.*
mudáí. *m*; nálashí. *m*; dávedár. *m*;
SULK, TO, *V. I.*
russná; muṇh waṭṭná; hurakná; viṭṭar baiṭhná; ruṭṭhná; akkná;
SULKILY, *Adv.*
bhaiṛá muṇh banáke;
SULKINESS, *N.*
nárázagí. *f*; magrápuṇá. *m*; támsí. *f*;
SULKY, *A.*
naráz; udás; ḳhafá;
to be sulky. viṭṭar baiṭhná; ruṭṭhná;
SULLEN, *A.*
naráz; múṇh waṭṭiá hoyá; lusiá hoyá; chhitthá hoyá;
SULLENLY, *Adv.*
russke;
SULPHUR, *N.*
gaṇdhak. *f*;
SULTRINESS, *N.*
garmí. *f*; ghauṇ. *m*; hussaṛ. *m*; gummá. *m*; gommá. *m*; huṭṭ. *m*; waṭṭ. *m*; garmáí. *f*; waṭṭu. *m*;
SULTRY, *A*,
garm;
to be sultry. ghauṇ painá; gommá laggná;

SUM, *N*,
1. in arithmetic. hisáb. *m*; suwál. *m*;
2. of money. rakam. *f*; jamhá. *f*;
3. total. joṛ. *m*; mizán. *f*; jamhá. *f*;
SUM, TO, *V. T.*
joṛná; jamá karná;
SUMMARY, *N.*
ḳhulásá. *m*; nichoṛ. *m*; sár. *m*; arq. *m*;
SUMMER, *N.*
garmí. *f*; hárh. *m*; hunál. *m*; unhál *m*;
summer and winter. hárh te siál;
SUMMERSAULT, *N.*
kalábájí. *f*;
SUMMIT, *N.*
choṭṭá. *m*; choṭṭí. *f*; tísí. *f*; sirá *m*;
SUMMON, TO, *V. T.*
saddná; buláuná; see CALL.
SUMMONS, *N.*
1. call. sadd. *f*; buláwá. *m*;
2. legal. samman. *m*;
SUMPTUOUS, *A.*
shándár; uttam; see MAGNIFICENTS.
SUMPTUOUSLY, *Adv.*
aish ishrat nál;
SUMPTUOUSNESS, *N.*
shán, *f*; raunáq. *f*;
SUN, *N.*
suraj. *m*; rawí, *m*; sijh. *m*;
Proverb. The sun rose and darkness fled. sijh chaṛhià te gayá andherá;
SUNDAY, *N.*
Itwár. *m*; Sabt. *m*; Rawíwár. *m*;
SUN DIAL, *N.*
dhupp ghaṛí. *f*;
SUNDER, TO, *V. T.*
aḍḍ karná; vakkh karná; see SEPARATE.
SUNDRY, *A.*
bhánt bhánt de;
SUNLIGHT, *N.*
dhúpp. *f*; garmí. *f*; ṭáṭká. *m*;
SUNNY, *A.*
dhúpp;
1. to be sunny. dhupp painí;
2. don't stand in the sun. dhúppe ná khalo jáo;

SUNRISE, *N.*
sawerá *m ;* sawelá. *m ;*
1. at sunrise, jhaláṇghe; sáhjare;
2. time of morning twilight. muhánjalá ; jhusmusṛá;
SUNSET, *N.*
din chhipe. *m ;* shàm. *m ;*
half an hour after sunset. tarkálāṇ. *f ;*
SUNSHINE, *N,*
dhúpp. *f ;* parkásh. *m ;* ṭáṭká. *m ;*
SUNSTROKE, *N.*
sarsám. *m ;*
SUPERABUNDANCE, *N.*
ḍher sárá. *m ;*
SUPERANNUATE, TO, *V. T.*
buḍḍháppe de kàran piṇshan dená;
SUPERB, *A.*
uttam; see SUPERIOR.
SUPERCILIOUS, *A.*
magrúr; haṇkárá; majájí; gamrúr: ghumanḍí ; nakchaṛhiá;
SUPERCILIOUSLY, *Adv.*
magrúri nál;
SUPERCILIOUSNESS, *N.*
haṇkár. *m ;* gamrúrí. *f ;* heṇh. *f ;* damág. *m ;*
SUPERFICIAL, *A.*
kachchá;
SUPERFICIALLY, *Adv.*
aiweṇ;
SUPERFINE, *A.*
bahut mahíṇ ; bahut patlí;
SUPERFLUITY, *N.*
wadhíkí. *f ;* ḍher. *m ;* wáddhá. *f ;* bachat dá mál. *m ;*
SUPERFLUOUS, *A.*
wáddhú ; hadd thoṇ ziyádá; wáfar;
SUPERFLUOUSLY, *Adv.*
fazúl; aiwen ;
SUPERINTEND, TO, *V. T.*
mukhtárí karní; kamm vekhná; nigrání karní;
SUPERINTENDENCE, *N.*
nigrání. *f ;* ḳhabargírí. *f ;* muḳhtárí. *f ;*
SUPERINTENDENT, *N.*
kamm vekhanwálá. *m ;* darogá. *m ;* gardaur. *m ;* mainajar. *m ;*
of patwaris. kánúgo;

SUPERIOR, *A.*
uttam; jabar; suthrá; álá; ḳhásí; param; sarest;
SUPERIOR, *N.*
sardár. *m ;* afsar. *m ;*
superiors. achchhe achchhe. *m ;*
SUPERIORITY, *N.*
ḳhubí. *f ;* buzurgí. *f ;* bol bállá. *m ;*
SUPERLATIVE, *A.*
uttam:
SUPERNAL, *A.*
asmání;
SUPERNATURAL, *A.*
1 miraculous. karámatí;
2. wonderful. ajíb; acharaj;
SUPERSCRIPTION, *N.*
sarnámá. *m ;* paṭṭí. *f ;*
SUPERSEDE, TO, *V. T.*
dur OR wakkh OR alag karná; haṭáuná;
SUPERSTITION, *N.*
vahim. *m ;* waihm. *m ;*
SUPERSTITIOUS, *A.*
waihmí;
SUPERVENE, TO, *V. I.*
á painá; ghusarná;
SUPERVISE, TO, *V. T.*
dekh bhál karná; see SUPERINTEND.
SUPERVISION, *N.*
nigrání. *f ;* dekh bhál. *f ;* see SUPERINTENDENCE.
SUPINE, *A.*
sust; ḍhillá;
SUPINESS, *N.*
sustí. *f ;* àlas. *m ;*
SUPPLANT, TO, *V. T.*
ḍhakknà; haṭáuná; dhokhe nál tháṇ mallná; see SUPERSEDE.
SUPPLE, *A.*
1. soft. narm; kulá;
2. elastic. lifanwálá;
SUPPLEMENT, *N,*
zamímá. *m ;*
SUPPLEMENT, TO, *V. T.*
wadháuná; púrá karná;
SUPPLENESS, *N.*
lachak. *f ;*
SUPPLIANT, *N.*
sawáli. *m ;*
SUPPLICANT, *N.*
arthí. *m ;* arthiá. *m ;*

SUPPLICATE, TO, *V. T.*
duá OR minnat OR arz OR bentí OR parárthná karná; giṛgiṛáuṇá; mangná; tarle minnat karní; raiṇ raiṇ karná;
SUPPLICATION, *N.*
duá. *f;* minnat. *f;* bentí. *f;* tarlá, *m;* faryád. *f;* faríád. *f;* árjú. *f;* parárthná. *f;* háhrá. *m;* háhre. *m;*
SUPPLY, TO, *V. T.*
dená; samán dená;
SUPPLY, *N.*
samán. *m;*
SUPPORT, TO, *V. T,*
1. to uphold. jhallná; sambhálná; thamí dení; sahárná; thammhná; madat dení; sahaitá dená; pakkí karní; thamí lainá;
2. to encourage, dilásá dená; dilerí dení; jí kaḍḍhná;
3. to provide for. parwastí karní; sambhálná;
4. to nourish, pálná; pálná posná;
SUPPORT, *N.*
1. help. chárá. *m;* sahái. *f;* madat. *f;* ḍhásná. *m;* ṭek. *f;* sahárá. *m;*
2. a prop. tahmm. *m;* tahmmí. *f;* thammhí. *f;* thamb. *m;*
SUPPORTER, *N.*
bhartá. *m;* madatgár. *m;* belí. *m;* sambhálú. *m;*
SUPPOSE, TO, *V. T.*
ḳhayál karná; farz karná; sochná;
SUPPOSITION, *N.*
ḳhayál. *m;* soch. *m;* wichár. *m;*
SUPPOSITIOUS, *A.*
ḳhayálí; banautí;
SUPPRESS, TO, *V. T.*
1. conceal, lukáuná; chhipáuná;
2. to subdue. ghuṭṭná; hatth heṭh karná; dabáuná;
SUPPRESSION, *N.*
1. act of quelling. dabáú, *m;*
2. act of hiding. chhipáú, *m;*
SUPPURATE, TO, *V. I.*
pakkná; pák painí;
SUPPURATION, *N.*
pák, *f;* píp. *f;* pakáú. *m;*
SUPREMACY, *N.*
iḳhtiyár. *m;* sardárí. *f;*
SUPREME, *A.*
sáreáṇ de náloṇ waḍḍá; álá; param;
SURE, *A.*
1. true. sachchá. haqqí;
2. believable. yaqíní;
3. proved. sábit hoyá;
4. to make sure. pakkí karná;
SURELY, *Adv.*
sachch; sachch muchch; beshakk; sachche muchche; nisang;
SURETY, *N.*
1. one who gives surety, jámin. *m;* zámin. *m;* hájar jámin. *m;*
2. security. zamánat. *f;*
3. certainty. yaqín. *m;*
SURETY, TO GIVE, *V. T.*
jámin dená; zamánat dení;
SURFACE, *N.*
wistár, *f;*
SURFEIT, TO, *V. T.*
leṛ márná; bahut kháná; ḍapphná; gulak gulak kháná;
SURGEON, *N.*
dágtar. *m;*
SURLILY, *Adv.*
ḳhafá hoke;
SURLINESS, *N.*
ḳhafgí. *f;* támsí. *f;*
SURLY, *A.*
ḳhafá; naráz; khaṭṭá; rukkhá; kauṛá; múṇh ṭúṭá; minnhá; nak chaṛhá; badmajáj; mísná; ujad; beḍhangá; kaṭṭaṛ;
SURMISE, *N.*
1. thought. ḳhayál. *m;* soch wichhár. *m;*
2. doubt. shakk shubhá. *m;* see GUESS.
SURMISE, TO, *V. T.*
ḳhayál karná; soch wichár karnà;
SURMOUNT, TO, *V. T,*
hal karná; haráuná; see OVERCOME.
SURNAME, *N,*
nám. *m;* náṇ. *m;*
SURPASS, TO, *V, T.*
wadháuná; pichchhe páuná; uchchá hath ráhná; agge dhar lainá;
SURPASS, TO, *V. I.*
wadhná; de náloṇ chaṇgá honá; agge vadh jáná;

SURPASSING, *A.*
uttam ; see EXCELLENT.
SURPLUS, *N.*
bachchat. *f ;* wáddhà. *f ;*
SURPLUS, *A.*
fáltú ; wáddhú ;
SURPRISE, *N.*
haráni. *f ;* tajjab, *m ;*
SURPRISE, TO, *V. T.*
hairán karná ; hakká bakká karná ; ghabrá dená ;
SURPRISED, *A.*
hakká bakká ; hairán; harán; dang;
1. to be surprised. dang ho jáná ;
2. he was surprised. us ne acharaj manniá ;
SURPRISING, *A.*
acharaj ; ajíb ;
SURRENDER, *N.*
saunp. *m ;*
SURRENDER, TO, *V. T.*
1. to deliver up. hawále karná ; saunpná ;
2. to yield. hár manní ; hár jáná ; sir jhukáuná ;
3. relinquish. chhaḍḍ dená ; ján dená ; tiágná ;
SURREPTITIOUSLY, *Adv.*
chorí chorí ;
SURROGATE, *N.*
naib. *m ;* gumástá, *m ;*
SURROUND, TO, *V. T.*
gherná ; gherá pá lainá ; walná ;
SURROUNDING, *A.*
ále duále ;
SURVEILLANCE, *N.*
najarbandí, *f ;* see SUPERINTENDENCE.
SURVEY, *N.*
náp. *m ;*
SURVEY, TO, *V, T.*
1. to see. dekhná ; vekhná ;
2. to measure land. kachchhná,
SURVEYOR, *N.*
amín, *m ;*
SURVIVE, TO, *V. T.*
bach jáná ;
SUSPECT, TO, *V. T.*
shakk OR shubhá OR bharm OR gumán OR zan OR jann karná ; takkná ;
I suspect. I have a suspicion. mainúṇ bharm piá hoyá hai ;

SUSPEND, TO, *V. T.*
1. to hang. lamkáuná ; ṭang dená ; palmá dená ; laṭkáuná ; ṭanggná ; palmáuná ;
2. to cause to cease for a time, muattal karná ;
SUSPENSE, *N.*
dhuṛká. *m ;* dhuṛkí. *f ;* wiswás, *m ;* dubdhá, *f ;* duchittí. *f ;* jakk. *f ;* jakko takko. *f ;* shakk. *m ;* bhaṭká. *m ;* duṛakná. *m ;*
to be in suspense. jakko takk karná;
SUSPENSION, *N.*
1. hanging. laṭkáú. *m ;* lamkáú. *m ;*
2. dismissal. chhuṭṭhí. *f;* jawáb. *m;*
SUSPICION, *N.*
bharm. *m ;* jann. *m ;* sandeh. *m ;* shakk. *m ;* vahimá, *m ;* totyá, *m ;*
I have a suspecion. mainuṇ bharm piá hoyá hai ;
SUSPICIOUS, *A.*
bharmí ; riskí ; janní ;
SUSTAIN, TO, *V. T.*
jarná; jhallná ; dhárná ; sahná ; sahárná ; rakkhiá karná ; see UPHOLD.
SUSTAINER, *N.*
hámí. *m ;* sambhálú. *m ;*
SUSTENANCE, *N.*
roṭí. *f ;* bhojan. *m ;* ahár. *m ;* see FOOD.
SWAB, *N.*
subbar. *m ;* subb. *m ;*
SWADDLE, TO, *V. T.*
waleṭná ;
SWAGGER, TO, *V. T,*
ákaṛná ; ápharná ; ákaṛ ke chalná ;
SWAGGERER, *N.*
ákaṛbáj. *m ;*
SWALLOW, *N.*
1. gulp of drink. ghuṭṭ. *m ;*
2. gulp of food. garáhí, *f ;*
3. bird. abábíl, *m ;*
SWALLOW, TO, *V. T.*
ghuṭṭ bharná ; nigalná ; sanghoṇ utárná . jhapphná ;
1. to cause to swallow. nigláuná;
2. to swallow by gulps. suṛkhaná;
SWALLOWED UP, TO BE, *V. I.*
nigghar jáná ;
SWAMP, *N.*
jhall. *m ;* jhangar. *m ;* bellá. *m ;* khobhá. *m ;*

SWAN, *N.*
haṇs. *m ;*
Proverb. Used when a wise man has died and is succeeded by a foolish son. Swans have died and crows have become "diwans." haṇsá haṇsá chal gaí kágá bháí díwáṇ ;
SWARM, *N.*
1. of bees. ghaṇ. *m ;*
2. of flies. ḍár. *m ;* heṛháṇ de heṛh. *m ;*
3. a crowd. jhuṇḍ. *m ;* dal. *m ;*
SWARM, TO, *V. I.*
bhiṇakná ; bhiṇbhiṇáunà ;
SWATH, *N.*
paṭṭí. *f ;*
SWATHE, TO, *V. T.*
waleṭná ;
SWAY, *N.*
hákamí. *f ;* hukúmat. *f ;* sardárí. *f ;*
SWAY, TO, *V. T.*
jhutáuná ;
SWAY, TO, *V. I.*
hilná ;
SWEAR, TO, *V. T.*
sauṇh kháná ; qasm kháni ;
to swear by religion. dharm chukkná. *H ;* kalimá paṛhná. *M ;*
SWEAT, *N.*
muṛkhá. *m ;* paghar. *m ;* garmí. *f ;*
SWEAT, TO, *V. I.*
muṛkhá áuná ; parsijná ;
SWEEP, TO, *V. T.*
jháṛ poch karná ; jháṛú pherná ; húṇjná ; jháṛná ; sammarná ; sambarná ; jháṛú OR bahárí pherná OR denà ; buhárná ;
to sweep away. roṛhná ;
SWEEPER, *N.*
mehtar. *m ;* chuhṛá, *m ;* bhaṇjí. *m ;*
1. one who has become a Muhammadan. musallí. *m ;*
2, one who has become a Sikh. mazhabí, *m ;*
SWEEPINGS, *N.*
kúṛá. *m ;* guddar. *m ;*
SWEET, *A.*
miṭṭhá ;
SWEETNESS, *N.*
miṭṭhái. *f ;* miṭhás. *f ;*
SWEET POTATO, *N.*
shakar kandí. *f ;*
SWEETS, *N.*
miṭṭhái. *f;* murabbá. *m;* patáse. *m;* jalebí. *f ;*
Proverb. What ! a mad bitch to guard sweetmeats. chhítí kuttí jalebíáṇ dí rákkhí !
SWEETEN, TO, *V. T.*
miṭṭhá karná ; ras painá ;
SWEETHEART, *N.*
pyárá. *m ;* dildár, *m ;* dost. *m ;* mohan. *m ;* ján. *f ;* yár. *m ;*
SWEETLY, *Adv.*
pyár nál ;
SWEETMEATS, *N.*
barafí. *f ;* peṛá. *m ;* badáná. *m ;* laddú. *m ;* jalebí. *f ;* phallá. *m ;* patásá. *m ;* makháná. *m ;* raoṛí. *f ;* pakorí. *f ;* mígdí. *f ;* láchí dáná. *m ;* bhúndí. *f ;* kará. *m ;* luchí. *f ;* purí. *f ;* semí. *f ;* pápá halwá. *m ;*
SWEETMEAT SELLER, *N.*
halwái. *m ;*
SWEETNESS, *N.*
miṭhás. *f ;*
SWELL, TO, *V. I.*
phullná ;
1. as flesh. sujj jáná ;
2. as the stomach. áppharná ;
SWELLING, *N.*
soj. *f ;* súj. *f ;* lothtá. *m ;*
1. a glandular swelling. gadúd. *f ;*
2. swelling from a sting. dhappaṛ *m ;*
3. swelling behind the ears. kaneḍá. *m ;* kaneḍú. *m ;*
SWEPT AWAY, TO BE, *V. I.*
ruṛhná ; ruṛh jáná ;
SWEPT AND GARNISHED, *A.*
jháṛíáṇ saṇwáríáṇ hoyá ;
SWERVE, TO, *V. I.*
ghumná ; muṛná ; phir jáná ;
SWIFT, *A.*
tez ; káhlá ; phurtílá ; trikkhá ;
SWIFTLY, *Adv.*
jaldí ; shatábí ; see QUICKLY.
SWIFTNESS, *N.*
tezí. *f ;*
SWIM, TO, *V. T.*
tarná ;

SWIMMER, *N.*
táṛú. *m* ; táṛá, *m* ;
Parable. The swimmer always dies of drowning. táṛá hamesh daryá dí maut mardá hai;
SWIMMING, *N.*
táṛí. *f* ;
SWINDLE, *N.*
dhokhá, *m* ; see TRICK.
SWINDLE, TO, *V. T.*
dhokhá dená ; ṭhaggná ; muchchhná ; mál márná ;
SWINDLER, *N.*
dhokhebáj, *m*; chhaliá, *m*; ṭhagg. *m*; aṛí már. *m* ; see DECEIVER.
SWINE, *N.*
súr. *m* ;
SWING, *N.*
píṇgh. *f* ; jhúlá. *m* ;
of a pankah. jhall. *m* ;
SWING, TO, *V. T.*
jhuṭáuná ;
to pull a pankah. jhall márná ; pakkhá khichná ;
SWING, TO, *V. I.*
on a swing. jhullná ; píngh jhuṭná OR charháná; píngh de huṇṭe laine ;
SWINGING, *N.*
jhuláí. *f* ; ulárá. *m* ;
SWITCH, *N.*
baiṇt. *m* ; chharí. *f* ; chhamak. *f* ; chhujak. *f* ; shushak. *f* ;
SWIVEL, *N.*
kuṇḍá. *m* ;
SWOON, *N.*
murchhá. *f* ; daṇḍaṇ. *f* ; gash. *f* ; behoshí, *f* ; gashí. *f* ;
SWOON, TO, *V. T.*
daṇḍaṇ paí jáná ; gash kháná ; laṭpaṭáuná ; ḍob painá ; behosh honá ; murchhá á jáná ; gash á jáná ; khussná ;
SWOOP, *N.*
jhapp. *f* ; jhapaṭṭá. *m* ;
SWOOP, TO, *V. I.*
jhapp mární ; jhapphná ;
SWOP, *N*,
waṭándrá. *m*; badlá. *m*; vaṭṭá saṭṭá. *m* ; waṭṭo saṭṭá. *m* ; márchá *m* ;
SWOP, TO, *V. T.*
waṭáuná ; waṭṭo saṭṭá karná ; adal badal karná ; waṭá dená ;

SWORD, *N.*
talwár. *m* ; teg. *f* ; khanjar, *m* ; kaṭár. *m* ; kirpán. *f* ; sastar. *m* ; shastar. *m* ; khaṛg. *m* ;
1. to draw the sword. talwár dhú lainá ;
2. Proverb. Might is right. Whoever has the sword has the cooking pot. jeh dí teg use dí degh ;
SWORD BELT, *N.*
partalá. *m* ; peṭí. *f* ; tegbaṇd. *f* ;
SYCAMORE TREE, *N.*
gullar dá rukkh. *m* ;
SYCOPHANCY, *N.*
choj. *m* ; leṭí. peṭí. *f* ; lallo patto. *f* ;
SYCOPHANT, *N.*
jholí chuk. *m* ; jháṇsebáj. *m* ; cháplús. *m* ;
SYLVAN, *A.*
jangalí ;
SYMBOL, *N.*
nishán. *m* ; chihaṇ. *m* ;
SYMBOLIC, *A.*
misálí ;
SYMBOLICALLY, *Adv.*
tamsíl de taur nál ;
SYMPATHETIC, *A.*
dardmand ;
SYMPATHETICALLY, *Adv.*
hamdardí nál ;
SYMPATHISE, TO, *V. T.*
dukh waṇḍṇá ; khapná ; kise dá dard karná ; afsos karná ; dilásá dená ;
SYMPATHISER, *N*,
dardí. *m* ;
SYMPATHY, *N.*
dard. *m* ; dáyá. *f* ; santáp. *m* ;
SYMPTOM, *N.*
nishání. *f* ;
SYNOPSIS, *N.*
khulásá. *m* ; nichoṛ. *m* ;
SYPHILIS, *N.*
garmí. *f* ; bád. *m* ;
SYRINGE, *N.*
pichkárí. *f* ; phuhárá. *m* ;
SYRUP, *N.*
shírá. *m* ; chás. *f* ; chásní. *f* ;
SYSTEM, *N.*
bandobast. *m* ; intizám. *m* ;
1. rule, qaidá. *m* ;
2. custom. dastúr. *m* ;

T.

TABERNACLE, *N*.
tambu. *m* ; ḍerá. *m* ;
TABLE, *N*.
1. furniture. mez. *f* ;
2. list. gintí. *f* ;
TABLE CLOTH, *N*.
mez dí chádar. *f* ;
TABLET, *N*.
phaṭṭí. *f* ;
TACITURN, *A*.
gal nahíṇ kardá ; chuppú ; mínnhá ; mísná ; rukkhá ; múṇh ṭúṭá ;
TACK, *N*.
kil. *m* ; koká. *m* ;
TACK, TO, *V*. *T*.
kachchá kar lená ; kachchí suái karní ;
to patch. ṭáṇkná ; gaṇḍh láuná ; gaṇḍh tupp karná ; tákí launí ; gaṭṭh láuná.
TACKLE, *N*.
wast walevá. *m* ; samán. *m* ; samíán. *m* ;
TACT, *N*.
hoshiyárí. *f* ;
TADPOLE, *N*.
ḍaḍḍú dá bachchá. *m* ;
TAIL, *N*.
púshal. *m* ; puchh. *f* ;
1. of a bird or fish. búṇḍá. *m* ;
2. of a turban. laṛ. *m* ;
TAILLESS, *A*.
laṇḍá ;
TAILOR, *N*.
darjí. *m* ; darzí, *m* ;
TAINT, *N*.
1. a stain. chhiṭṭ. *f* ; dág. *m* ; kalaṇk. *m* ; phuṭkárí. *f* ;
2. a fault. dos. *m* ; kalaṇk. *m* ; dhabbá. *m* ;
3. foulness. gandagí. *f* ; gand, *m* ; palídagí. *f* ;
TAINT, TO, *V*. *T*.
1. to spoil. wigáṛná ; wichálná ; chauṛ kar dená ;
2. to polute. labeṛná ; palít karná ; gaṇdá karná ;
3. to make unclean as food. bhiṭṭáuná ;
TAINTED, TO BE, *V*. *I*.
unfit for food. chhúṭṭ lagnī ; bhiṭṭí jáná ;
of meat. humh jáná ;
TAINT FREE, *A*.
sáf ; nek kalaṇk ; nirdos ; beaib ;
TAKE, TO, *V*. *T*.
1. to grasp. phaṛná ; phagaṛná ; napp lainá ;
2. to take off clothes. lahuná ;
3. to accept. lainá ; manjúr kar lainá ;
4. to take possession. mál már lainá ; qabjá kar lainá ; sámbh lainá ;
5. to take down. láhná ; utárná ;
6. to take away. laí jáná ; khaṛná ;
7. to take heed. nijh launí ; dhián karná ;
8. to take by force. kho lainá ; phaṛná ;
9. to take charge of. jumá le lainá ; sámbh lainá ;
10. to lake in good part. bhalá manáunà ;
11. taking off your shoes, come in. jutíáṇ láh ke andar á já ;
12. I am not taken in by you. tuháḍe ṭhagíáṇ maiṇ ṭhagiá nahíṇ jándá.
TAKEN AWAY, TO BE, *V*. *I*.
nikheṛiá jáná ; khusná ;
TALC, *N*.
abrak. *m* ;
TALE, *N*.
bàt. *f* ; kathá. *f* ; wártá. *f* ; bártá. *f* ;
to tell a tale, bát páuní ;
TALE BEARER, *N*.
niṇdak. *m* ; see TATTLER.
TALENT, *N*.
guṇ. *m* ; shaktí. *f* ; pujj. *f* ;
TALENTED, *A*.
guṇí ; huṇdarí ; aqlwálá ;
TALK, *N*.
gal bát. *f* ; bátchít *f* ; bachan bilás. *m* ; charchá wártá. *m* ; gal katth. *f* ; galláṇ bátáṇ. *f* ; charchá. *m* ;
1. a talking about. charchá. *m* ;
2. foolish talk. gapp shapp. *f* ; wáhiyát galláṇ. *f* ; palál. *f* ;

TALK, TO, *V. T.*
1. to converse. gallán bátán karní; kahná; bolná;
2. to talk nonsense. wáhiyát gallán karní; aiven bolná;
3. to exaggerate. gapp márná; misále láke dassná; hadd karná;
4. to explain. samjháuná;
5. to tell. zikr karná; dassná; gal karní; batláuná;
6. to talk in one's sleep. barráuná;
7. to tlk about a thing. charchá karná;

TALKATIVE PERSON, *N.*
palálí. *m;* gálaṛí. *m;* gálaṛiá. *m;* khappí. *m;* gapaurí. *m;* baṛíán gallán karnwálá. *m;* lutrá. *m;* waḍboliá, *m;*

TALL, *A.*
lammá; uchchá;

TALLOW, *N.*
charbí. *f;*

TALLY, TO, *V. I.*
milná; ralná;

TALON, *N.*
náuh. *m;* pahunchá. *m;* naundhar. *f;*

TAMARIND, *N.*
imlí. *f;*

TAMBOURINE, *N.*
khanjrí. *f;* ḍhaḍḍ. *f;*

TAME, *A.*
páliá hoyá; rákhwá; rakhiá hoyá.
1. a tame pigeon. bíbá kabutar. *m;*
2. a wild pigeon. golá kabutar. *m;*

TAME, TO, *V. T.*
gijháuná;
to be tamed. gijh jáná;

TAMPER, TO, *V. T.*
hatth páuná; see MEDDLE.

TAN, TO, *V. T.*
chamṛá kamáuná;

TANGLE, *N.*
uljheṛá. *m;*

TANGLE, TO, *V. T.*
waṭṭ pá dená;
to be tangled. waṭṭ páyá jáná;

TANK, *N.*
1. a small pakká tank. chaubachchá. *m;*
2. a tank, kachchá or pakká talá. *m;* hauj. *m;* haud. *m;* ṭál. *m;*
3, a small pond dug to contain drinking water. ṭobhá. *m;* talṛí. *f;*
4. a pond for cattle. chhappaṛ. *m;*

TANNER. *N.*
chamiár. *m;* khaṭík. *m;* chamrang. *m;*

TANTALIZE, TO, *V. T.*
khajáuná; chheṛná; rusáuná; chhiṛauná; bhabkáuná;

TAP, *N.*
1. spigot. ṭuṭí. *f;*
2. pat. tháp. *m;* thápí. *f;*

TAP, TO, *V. T.*
1. to tap once. tháp márná; ṭakorná.
2. to pat a child to sleep. thápaṛná;
3. to tap on door. khaṛkáuná;

TAPE, *N.*
fítá, *m;*
1. of a garment. taṇí. *f;*
2. for beds. nuár. *f;*
3. for fastening pyjamas. nálá, *m;*

TAPESTRY, *N.*
galíchá, *m;*

TAR, *N.*
lukk, *m;*

TARDILY, *Adv.*
ḍhill nál; ghaul nál; ewen;

TARDINESS *N.*
1. dilatoriness. ḍhill maṭṭh, *f;* ghaul. *f;* sustí, *f;* álas. *m;*
2. lateness. chir. *m;* aver, *f;* averá. *m;*

TARDY, *A.*
ghaulí; ghauliá; sust; ḍhillá maṭṭhá; jillhá;

TARGET, *N.*
takhtá. *m;* chán. *m;*

TARIFF, *N.*
bhá. *m;*

TARNISH, TO, *V. T.*
mailá karná;

TARRY, TO, *V. I.*
1. to lag behind. pichche OR magar rah jáná;
2. to defer. chir láuná; ṭál shál kar chhaḍḍná;
3. to stay. rahná; ṭikkná; ṭhahrná;

TART, *A.*
khaṭṭá;
bitter. kauṛá;

TARTAR, *N.*
kareṛá. *m ;*
TARTNESS, *N.*
khaṭṭíáí. *f ;*
TASK, *N.*
kamm. *m ;* kár. *m ;*
TASSEL, *N.*
jhabbú, *m ;*
1. to a cap. phummaṇ. *f ;*
2. to the edge of cotton blanket.
bumbal. *m ;*
TASSELLED, *A.*
guchchedár ;
TASTE, *N.*
sawád. *m ;* bhauná. *m ;* majá. *m ;*
chakkhí, *f ;* chaská. *m ;*
inclination. jhass. *m ;* cháh. *f ;*
táṇgh. *f ;* chaská. *m ;*
TASTE, TO, *V. T.*
1. to taste food. sawád chhakkná ;
thoṛá jehá kháná ;
2. to experience. parakhná ; partáuná ;
3, to cause to taste. chakkháuná ;
chhakkáuná ;
TASTELESS, *A.*
besuád ; besuádá ; bemajá ; alúná ;
phoká ; phoklá ;
TASTY, *A.*
karará ; suádlá ; suádí ;
salty. salúná ;
TATTLE, *N.*
palál, *f ;* gapp. *f ;* gapp shapp. *f ;*
TATTLE, TO, *V. T.*
palál karná ; gapp mární ; aiweṇ
bolná ; bataule márná ;
TATTLER, *N.*
palálí. *m ;* lutrá. *m ;* batuṛá. *m ;*
batuní. *m ;* bataulá *m ;*
TATTOO, TO, *V. T.*
ukkhaṛná ; goddná ;
TAUNT, *N.*
mehná. *m ;* ṭhaṭṭhá. *m ;*
TAUNT, TO, *V. T.*
mehná dená OR márná ; nok láuní;
TAUNTINGLY, *Adv.*
ṭhaṭṭhe nál ; mehná márke ;
TAX, *N.*
máhsúl. *m ;* másúl. *m ;*
1. a compulsory contribution
levied on non-landowners in a
village. wásh. *m ;*

2. a tax on sales. dhaṛat. *m ;*
3. a tax levied by weighmen
being a portion of the goods
weighed. chuṇggí. *f ;*
4. Proverb. Whether he graze his
cattle or not, the grazing tax
must be paid. charánd chare
ná chare, tirní bhare ;
5. land tax. muámlá, *m ;*
TAX, TO, *V. T.*
máhsúl láuná ;
1. to pay taxes. máhsúl dená ;
mámlá tárná ;
2. to collect taxes. ugráhná ;
TAXATION, *N.*
on land. mámlá. *m ;* muámlá. *m ;*
TEA, *N.*
cháh. *m ;*
TEACH, TO, *V. T.*
sikhíá dení ; sikhláuná ; sikháuná ;
sikhálná ; sabaq dená ; paṛháuná ;
1. religious teaching. updesh dená
OR karná ;
2. he will have taught you everything. uh tainúṇ sárá hí kamm
sikhá dittá howegá ;
TEACHER, *N.*
ustád. *m ;* bhaí jí. *m ;*
1. Muhammadan religious teacher.
maulví. *m ;* murshad. *m ;*
2. Sikh religious teacher. mahant. *m ;* gur. *m ;* gurú. *m ;* updeshí. *m ;* giání. *m ;* updesak. *m ;*
3. Hindu religious teacher. Bráhman. *m ;* pandit. *m ;*
TEACHING, *N.*
sikkhiá. *f ;* tálím. *f ;* paṛhái. *f ;*
sikhautí. *f ;* sikhauṭí. *f ;* sikkh
matt. *f ;*
religious teaching. dharm updesh. *m ;* gián. *f ;*
TEACUP, *N.*
piyálá. *m ;*
TEAL, *N.*
murgábí. *f ;*
TEAPOT, *N.*
cháhpochí. *f ;*
TEAR, *N.*
1. weeping. atthar. *f ;* atthrúṇ. *f ;*
plur ; hanj. *f ;* hanjúṇ. *f,* plur ;
2. a rent. laṇgar. *m ;*

TEAR, TO, *V. T.*
páṛná;
1. to tear to pieces. bere bere kar dená; tukṛe tukṛe karná;
2. to be torn. laṇgár le jáná; páṭná; phaṭná;
TEASE, TO, *V. T.*
chheṛná; bhabkáuná; ḍhiṛáuná; khijháuná; satáuná; ruáuná; chip chaṛháuná; kalá jagáuní;
to be teazed. khijh jáná;
TEAT, *N.*
1. woman's. mammá. *m;*
2. animal's. thaṇ. *m;*
3. indiarubber. chusaní. *f;*
TEAZING, *N.*
chheṛ. *f;* khijh. *f;*
TEDIOUS, *A.*
1. dilatory. ḍhillá; sust; ḍhillá maṭṭhá; jillhá;
2. wearisome. dukhdáí; akáunwálá; thakaṇwálá;
TEETH, *N.*
dandáṇ. *f;*
double teeth. hannháṇ. *f;*
TELEGRAM, *N.*
tár. *m;* tár ḳhabar. *f;*
to telegraph. tár ghallní OR dení;
TELESCOPE, *N.*
dur vekhanwálí chíz. *f;* dur bíṇ. *f;*
TELL, TO, *V. T.*
1. to narrate. dassná; wárthá karná; bayán karná;
2. to make known. ḍhanḍorá dená; ḳhabar dení; samáchár dená; pargaṭ karná;
3. to count, ginná; gin lainá; gintí karní;
4. who told you this? tainúṇ kis ákhiá hai? tainúṇ ih gal kis dassí hai?
5. I told him everything. us núṇ sárá hál maiṇ dass chhaḍḍiá hai;
TELLING OF BEADS, *N.*
málá pherní. *f;*
TELLTALE, *N.*
bhaggí karnwálá. *m;*
TEMERITY, *N.*
dilerí. *f;*
enthusiasm. josh. *m;* ríjh. *f;*
TEMPER, *N.*
1. temperament, majáj. *f;* tabíat. *f;* subháo. *m;*
2. habit. ádat. *f;* ḳho. *f;* jhass. *m;* gejh. *f;* ḍhab. *m;*
3. irritation. karodh. *m;* gussá. *m;* waṭṭ. *m;* rossá. *m;*
TEMPERAMENT, *N.*
majáj. *f;* see TEMPER.
TEMPERANCE, *N.*
rakkh shakkh. *f;* parejgárí. *f;*
TEMPERATE, *A.*
parejgár; múṇh nahíṇ rakkhiá; jatí satí;
TEMPERATELY, *Adv.*
parejgárí nál; jat sat nál;
TEMPERATURE, *N.*
garmí. *f;*
TEMPEST, *N.*
1. wind and rain. jháṇjá. *m;*
2. of cold rain, jhakkaṛ. *m;*
3. of dust only. anherí. *f;*
TEMPLE, *N.*
1. Jewish. haikal. *m;*
2. Hindu. mandar. *m;* shawáiá. *m;* ṭhakar duárá. *m;* dharmsálá. *m;* síwálá. *m;*
3. Sikh. gurdwárá. *m;* dharmsálá. *m;*
4. of Shiv Ji. shawálá. *m;*
TEMPORARY, *A.*
thoṛeáṇ dináṇ wáste; thoṛe chir laí;
TEMPT, TO, *V. T.*
1. to seduce. bharmáuná; lubháuná;
2. to try. parakhná; partáuná;
TEMPTATION, *N.*
partává. *m;* parakh. *f;* ázmáish. *f;*
TEMPTER, *N.*
parkhanwálá. *m;* partáunwálá. *m;* ázmáunwálá. *m;*
TEMPTING, *A.*
dil núṇ khichanwálá;
TEN, *A.*
das;
TENACIOUS, *A.*
1. strong. karṛá; pakká; mazbut;
2. obstinate. ḍhíṭh; haṭṭí; haṭhílá; jhakkí; kabbá;
3. adhesive. laslasá; leslá; lesdár; cheplá;

TENACIOUSLY, *Adv.*
chambarke; mazbutí nál; phagṛáí nál;
TENANCY, *N.*
kabjá. *m*; qabzá. *m*;
TENANT, *N.*
1. of house. karáyádár. *m*;
2. of land. sámí. *m*; asámí, *m*; mujárá. *m*; ráhak. *m*;
TEND, TO, *V. T.*
1. to serve. ṭahl karní; ṭahl sevá karní; sevá karní; ḳhidmat karní;
2. to guard, rákkhí karní;
TENDENCY, *N.*
shauq. *m*; cháh. *f*; chaská. *m*;
TENDER, *N.*
bollí. *f*;
TENDER, *A.*
1. kindhearted. mulaim; muhabbatí; bholá bhálá;
2. for food. kulá; narm; malúk;
TENDER, TO, *V. T.*;
bollí dení;
TENDER HEARTED, *A.*
bholá bhálá; muhabbatí; narmdil; mihrbán; kúlá;
TENDER MOUTHED, *A.*
muṇh dá kachchá;
TENDERLY, *Adv.*
pyár nál; prem nál; narmí nál.
TENDERNESS, *N.*
pyár. *m*; narmí. *f*; mulaimí. *f*; komaltáí. *f*;
TENDON, *N.*
paṭṭhá. *m*;
TENDRIL, *N.*
wall. *f*; wel. *f*;
TENEMENT, *N.*
ghar. *m*; makán. *m*;
bangalow. koṭhí. *f*;
TENET, *N.*
1. point of doctrine. maslá. *m*;
2. creed. aqídá. *m*; asúl. *m*; kalamá. *m*;
3. faith. ímán. *m*; dharm. *m*;
TENFOLD, *A.*
dasguṇá;
TENNIS BALL, *N.*
khiddo. *m*; khenu. *m*;
TENOR, *N.*
matlab. *m*; arth. *m*;

TENT, *N.*
1. sahib's tent. ḍerá. *m*; tambu. *m*;
2. servant's tent. sholdárí. *f*;
3. cook's tent. rasoí. *f*;
4. small tent. tamboṭí. *f*; tammoṭí. *f*;
5. nomad's tent. pakkhí taprí. *f*; pakkhí. *f*;
6. to put up a tent. tambu láná;
7. to take down a tent. tambu puṭṭná;
8. tent maker. tambu síunwálá. *m*;
TENTATIVE, *A.*
kujh dináṇ de laí partáve wáste;
TENTH, *A.*
daswáṇ;
TENT PEGGING, *N.*
nejjábájí. *f*;
TENUOUS, *A.*
1. slender. patlá; sohal; see THIN.
2. fine. mahíṇ; barík;
TENURE, *N.*
kabjá. *m*; qabzá. *m*;
TEPID, *A.*
khuhnawáyá pání; kossá;
TERM, *N.*
1. a limit. miád. *f*;
2. a name. nám. *m*; náṇ. *m*;
TERMINAL, *A.*
miádí;
TERMINATE, TO, *V. T.*
mukáuná; nabheṛná; kar chhaḍḍná; kar haṭṭná;
TERMINATION, *N.*
1. of time. miád. *f*;
2. a border. hadd. *f*; banná. *m*;
3. a finish. nibeṛá. *m*; nibbaṛ tibbaṛ. *m*;
TERMINUS, *N.*
símá. *m*;
boundary. hadd. *f*; waṭṭ. *m*;
TERRIBLE, *A.*
ḍaráuná; ḍaráká; ḍaraú; jis thoṇ ḍar áwe;
very terrible. ḍáḍhá ḍaráuná;
TERRIBLENESS, *N.*
ḍaráwá. *m*;
harshness. saḳhtí. *f*; beráhmí. *f*; jástí. *f*;
TERRIBLY, *Adv.*
ḍaráke;

TERRIFY, TO, *V. T.*
ḍar páuná ; ḍaráuná ; akkh wikháuná ;
TERRIFYING, *A.*
ḍaráuná ; ḍaráú ; bháídáik ;
TERRITORY, *N.*
iláqá. *m ;*
1. country. des. *m ;*
2. territory of a raja. rajwáṛá. *m ;*
TERROR, *N.*
haul. *m ;* bhau. *m ;* ḍar. *m ;* bhái. *f ;* ḍaráví. *m ;* khaṭká. *m ;* dhuṛkí. *f ;* jhakk. *m ;* dhaṛak. *m ;*
terrors. ḍaráuníáṇ chízáṇ. *f ;*
TERSE, *A.*
mukhtasar ;
clear. sáf ;
TERSELY, TO SPEAK, *V. T.*
ghaṭṭ karke bolná ;
TEST, *N.*
parkhává. *m ;* partává. *m ;*
examination. imtehán. *m ;*
TEST, TO, *V. T.*
partáuná ; dá partává karná ; parkhná ; paríkhiá kar lainá ; paríkh lainá ; táná ; imtehán lainá ; tá sulák ke dekhná ;
to test a coin. tankánná ; wajáuná ;
TESTAMENT, *N.*
1. New Testament. Nayá Ahd Námá. *m ;*
2. Old Testament. Puráná Ahd Námá. *m ;*
3. Will. wasíat námá. *m ;* sikhshápattar. *m ;*
TESTICLES, *N.*
ṭaṭṭe. *m ;* nal. *m ;*
1. of goats. kipúre. *m ;*
2. of horses, dogs. aṇḍáṇ. *m ;*
TESTIFICATION, *N.*
guwáhí. *f ;* sákhí. *f ;*
proof. sabút. *m ;*
TESTIFY, TO, *V. T.*
1. to give evidence. gawáhí dení ; sákhí dení ;
2. to tell. bayán karná ; dassná ;
3. to prove. sábit karná ;
4. to testify in preaching. sákhí dení ;
TESTIMONIAL, *N.*
nek námí dí chiṭṭhí.
certificate. sáṭífikaṭ. *m ;*
TESTIMONY, *N.*
gawáhí. *f ;* ákhiá. *m ;*
1. as in preaching. sákhí. *f ;*
2. proof. sabút. *m ;* sabutí. *f ;*
TESTINESS, *N.*
gussá. *m ;* rossá. *m ;* hirkh. *m ;*
TESTY, *A.*
jaliá baliá ; kauṛá ; chirchará ; saṛiá bhujiá ; chhirhmí ; vitriá hoyá ; russiá hoyá ; khaṭṭá ;
TETHER, *N.*
rassá. *m ;*
1. for one foreleg. paiṇkhaṛ. *m ;*
2. for hindlegs. pacháṛí. *f ;*
3. for neck. agárí. *f ;*
TEXT, *N.*
1. of Bible. ayat. *f ;*
2. of Quran. ayat. *f ;*
3. of Granth. shalok. *m ;* tuk. *f ;*
4. of Veds. mantar. *m ;* samlás. *m ;*
THAN, *Conj.*
thoṇ ; náloṇ ; thíṇ ;
THANK, TO, *V. T.*
shukr karná ; guṇ gáuná ; dhannbád karná ; dhannwád karná ;
1. thank you. tuháḍí mihrbání hai ;
2. I have to thank you. tuháḍí dáyá hai. lit. it is your kindness.
THANKS, *N.*
shukrguzárí. *f ;* bandagí. *f ;* dhann. *m ;* dhannbád. *m ;*
thanks be to God. dhannbád hai Parmeshar dá ;
THANKFUL, *A.*
shukrguzár ; dhannwádí ;
THANKFULLY, *Adv.*
atí dhannwád karke ; shukrguzárí nál ;
THANKFULNESS, *N.*
shukrguzárí. *f ;* dáyáwángí. *f ;*
THANKLESS, *A.*
náshukrguzár ; náshukará ; akirgan ; baguṇá ;
THANKLESSLY, *Adv.*
náshukrguzárí nál ;
THANKLESSNESS, *N.*
náshukrguzárí. *f ;* náshukrí. *f ;* nádáyákí. *f ;* luṇharámí. *f ;*
THANKOFFERING, *N.*
shukráná. *m ;* bhet. *f ;*
THANKSGIVING, *N.*
dhannwáddí. *f ;*

THAT, *Conj.*
paí ; is wáste ; is laí ; jo ;
THAT, *Pro.*
uh ; jehṛá ; parlá ;
that is. arthát ;
THATCH, *N.*
chhappar. *m ;* tappará. *m ;* chhappará. *m ;*
THATCH, TO, *V. T.*
chhappar páuná ; chháuná ;
THE, *Art.*
ih ; uh ;
THEATRE, *N.*
kheḍán dá ghar. *m ;* tamásha ghar. *m ;*
THEE, *Pro.*
tainuṇ ;
THEFT, *N.*
chorí. *f ;* chorí chakárí. *f ;*
a theft took place there. us ghar vichch san lagg gayí ;
THEIR, *Pro.*
unháṇ dá ;
THEIST, *N.*
Ḳhudáwálá bandá. *m ;* Ḳhudá dá mannanwálá bandá. *m ;*
THEM, *Pro.*
unháṇ núṇ ;
THEME, *N.*
mazmún. *m ;* see TOPIC.
THEMSELVES, *Pro.*
apne ápnúṇ ;
THEN, *Adv.*
1. at that time. us vele ; tad hí ; udoṇ ; tadoṇ ;
2. afterwards. uh de pichche ; magaroṇ ; chhekaṛ ;
3. reasoning. táṇ ; phir ; upraṇd ;
THENCE, *Adv.*
utthoṇ ;
THENCEFORTH, *Adv.*
pichchoṇ ;
THEOCRACY, *N.*
Ḳhudá dí hukúmat. *f ;*
THEOLOGY, *N.*
dín dá ilm. *m ;* ilm Iláhí. *m ;*
THEORETIC, *A.*
ḳhayálí ;
THEORY, *N.*
ḳhayál. *m ;* dalíl. *f ;*
THERE, *Adv.*
utthe ; us jagah vichch ;

THEREAFTER, *Adv.*
uh de bád ; uh de pichche ; uh de magaroṇ ;
THEREFORE, *Adv.*
is laí ; is wáste ; is káran ; is karke ; tad ; is sabab karke ;
THEREUPON, *Adv.*
tad ; pichchoṇ ;
THESE, *Pro.*
ih ;
THESIS, *N.*
mazmún. *m ;* see TOPIC.
THEY, *Pro.*
uh ;
THICK, *A.*
moṭá ;
1. for cloth. gaf ; ṭhullhá ;
2. for liquid. saṇhṇá ; saṇghná ; gáhṛá ; gáṛhá ;
3. thick dirty water. gandhliá hoyá pání. *m ;* mailá kuchailá pání. *m ;*
4. Proverb. Thick clothes wear well. ṭhullhe kapṛe haṇdhe change ;
THICKEN, TO, *V. T.*
gáṛhá karná ; saṇghná karná ;
cloth to thicken in washing. gaf ho jáná ;
THICKET, *N.*
zaḳhírá. *m ;* jáṛ. *m ;* jhaṇgáṛ. *m ;*
1. large. jhaṇg. *m ;*
2. small. jhaṇgí. *f ;* jhoggí. *f ;*
THICKHEAD, *N.*
aql dá purá. *m ;* ullú. *m ;* útt. *m ;* bewaqúf. *m ;* beaql. *m ;*
THICKLY, *Adv.*
sown thickly. saṇghne ;
THICKNESS, *N.*
1. state of being thick, liquid. gáṛh. *m ;*
   state of being thick, material. muṭáí. *f ;*
2. of a wall. asár. *f ;*
THICKSET, *A.*
ṭhullhá ;
THIEF, *N.*
choṭá. *m ;* chorṭá. *m ;* chor. *m ;* chorṭerá. *m ;*
a thieving bitch. choṭí kuttí. *f ;*
THIEVE, TO, *V. T.*
chorí karní ; churáuná ;

THIGH, *N*.
jangh. *m* ; jángh. *m* ;
1. of a man. paṭṭ. *m* ;
2. of animals. ráṇ. *m* ;
THIMBLE, *N*.
aṇgúṭhí. *f* ;
THIN, *A*.
1. not fat. lissá ; máṛá ; jhikh ; ákáhirá ;
2. rather thin. patlerá ;
3. not coarse. mahín ; barík ;
THINE, *Pro*.
terá ;
THING, *N*.
chíz. *f* ; wast. *f* ; wastú. *f*. plur ; shaí. *m* ; chíz wast. *f* ;
THINK, TO, *V. T*.
ḳhayál karná ; sochná ; soch wichárná ; chetná ; bujjhná ; dhíán karná ;
1. I think. merí jach vichch ;
2. don't think that. ih khayál wisár chhaḍḍo ;
3. thinking over this. ih sabh soch sách ke ;
4. how does it appear to you? what do you think about it? tainúṇ kí bhásdá hai, te terá dil kí ákhdá hai?
5. Now they were thinking it over. uh huṇ wicháráṇ vichch páe hoe ne ;
6. I began to think much about this. maiṇ baṛí wichár karan lag gayá te dil vichch ih tháṇ lítí.
THINKING, *N*.
soch. *m* ; ḳhayál. *m* ; soch wichár. *m* ; chitmaní. *f* ;
THINLY, *Adv*.
sown thinly. wirle ;
THINNESS, *N*.
patlái. *f* ;
THIRD, *A*.
trijjá ; tijjá ; tiá ; tie ;
THIRD PART, *N*.
tihái. *f* ;
THIRST, *N*.
tareh. *f* ; pyás. *f* ; tihái. *f*; ḍinjh. *f*; teh. *f* ; tihá. *f* ;
intense thirst. bhaṛkí. *f* ;
THIRSTY, *A*.
tiháiá ; triháyá ; tarháyá ;
Proverb. The neighbour of a river is neither hungry nor thirsty. daryá dá hamsáyá ná bhukkhá ná tarháyá ;
THIRTEEN, *A*.
teráh ; teráṇ ;
THIRTEENETH, *A*.
teráhwáṇ ;
THIRTIETH, *A*.
tríhwáṇ ;
THIRTY, *A*.
tí ;
thirty one. ikattí ; akattrí ;
thirty two. battí ; battrí ;
thirty three. tetí ; tetrí ;
thirty four. chauntí ; chautrí ;
thirty five. paintí ; paiṇtrí ;
thirty six. chhattí ; chhattrí ;
thirty seven. saiṇtí ; saiṇtrí ;
thirty eight. aṭhattí ; aṭhattrí ;
thirty nine. untálí ; unthattrí ;
THIS, *Pro*.
eh ; urlá ;
THISTLE, *N*.
mamolí. *f* ;
THITHER, *Adv*.
utthe ; us taraf ;
THONG, *N*.
waddhrí. *f* ; chamm dí paṭṭí. *f* ;
THORAX, *N*.
hikk. *m* ;
THORN, *N*.
kaṇḍḍá. *m* ; súl. *m* ;
1. thorn hedge. jháṛ báṛ. *f* ;
2. thorn bush. jháṛí. *f* ;
3. thorn branch. ḍhíngar. *m* ; ḍhíngrí. *f* ; moṛhí. *f* ;
4. thorn apple. dhatúrá. *m* ;
THORNY, *A*.
kaṇḍeánwálá ; kaṇḍiálá ;
THOROUGH, *A*.
pakká ;
THOROUGHFARE, *N*.
1. in town. wide. bajár. *m* ; bázár. *m* ;
narrow. gallí. *f* ;
2. in village. bajár. *m* ; pihá. *m* ; líh. *f* ; páhiá. *m* ;
3. path. ráh. *m* ; rastá. *m* ;

THOROUGHLY, *Adv.*
pakkí taráh ; chaṇgí taráh ; ukká ; pakk ; purí taráh nál ;
THOSE, *Pro.*
uh ;
THOU, *Pro.*
túṇ ;
THOUGH, *Conj.*
bháṇweṇ ; bháṇweṇ jíkar ;
THOUGHT, *N.*
1. reflection. khayál. *m* ; chiṇtá. *f* ; chitamní. *f* ;
2. meditation. soch wichár. *m* ; soch. *m* ; dhián. *m* ;
3. intention. irádá. *m* ; dalíl. *f* ;
THOUGHTFUL, *A.*
suchet ; chiṇtáwattí ; gaurá ; wichárak ; sochmán ; sojhmán ; sochí ;
THOUGHTFULLY, *Adv.*
soch wichárke ;
THOUGHTFULNESS, *N.*
chiṇtá. *f* ; dhián. *m* ; thauh. *m* ;
THOUGHTLESS, *A.*
aṇchiṇt ; sochdá nahíṇ ; gáfal ;
THOUGHTLESSLY, *Adv.*
bin soche ; bin soche samjhe ;
THOUGHTLESSNESS, *N.*
aṇchiṇtá. *f* ;
THOUSAND, *A.*
hazár ;
THRALDOM, *N.*
gulámí. *f* ; kámgiṭṭí. *f* ;
THRASH, TO, *V. T.*
kúṭná ; már mukáuná ; see BEAT.
THREAD, TO, *V. T.*
paroná ;
to thread a needle. dhággá pauná ; paroná ;
THREAD, *N.*
dhággá. *m* ; sút. *m* ; tágá. *m* ; taṇd. *m* ; sutar. *m* ; ḍor. *f* ; ḍorá. *m* ;
sacred thread worn by Hindus. janeú. *m* ; tagg. *m* ;
THREAT, *N.*
dhamkí. *f* ; bhabkí. *f* ; dhauns. *f* ; ḍarává. *m* ; ghuṛkí. *f* ; hiṛak jhiṛak. *f* ; jhiṛak jhamb. *f* ;
THREATEN, TO, *V. T.*
dhamkáuná ; ḍaráuná ; dabkáuná ; ghurakná ; dabb dená ; dabbá dená ; dhamkí dení ; daṛakká márná ; dabká márná ; jháṛ pauní ; dhauṇs dení ;
THREATENING, *N.*
dhamkí. *f* ; ḍarává. *m* ; dhauṇs. *f* ; ghurkí. *f* ; dábbá. *m* ; dhássá. *m* ;
THREATENINGLY, *Adv.*
dhamká kar ; jhiṛkí nál ; ḍaráke ;
THREE, *A.*
tiṇ ; tíá ;
THREEFOLD, *A.*
tehará ; tigaṇá ;
THREE TIMES, *A.*
tiharam ; tehr ;
THRESH, TO, *V. T.*
gáh lainá ; gaháuná ; gáhná ; gáh páuná ;
THRESHING, *N.*
gahái. *f* ; gáh. *m* ;
THRESHING FLOOR, *N.*
piṛ. *m* ; khalwáṛá. *m* ; khalárá. *m* ; marálí. *f* ;
THRESHOLD, *N.*
dalíj. *f* ; sardal. *f* ; ḍeoḍhí. *f* ;
THRICE, *Adv.*
tín wárí ;
THRIFT, *N.*
mariádá. *f* ; sarfá. *m* ; siánaf. *f* ;
THRIFTINESS, *N.*
sarfá. *m*; see FRUGALITY.
THRIFTLESS, *A.*
mankhaṭṭu ; nikhaṭṭu ; ujáṛú ; gawáú ;
THRIFTY, *A.*
shum ; saṇguṛá ; saṇjuhṛá ;
THRILL, TO, *V. T.*
lauṇ lauṇ karná ; ghabráuná ; phurakná ;
THRIVE, TO, *V. I.*
phalná phulná ; waddhná ;
THRIVING, *A.*
nihál see PROSPEROUS.
THROAT, *N.*
1. outside. gal. *m* ; gáṭṭá. *m* ; gaṭṭí. *f* ;
2. inside. saṇggh. *m* ;
THROB, TO, *V. I.*
dukhná ; dhaṛakná ;
of the heart. dil dhaṛakná ;
dhaṛkúṇ dhaṛkún karná ;
THROBBING, *N.*
dhaṛkúṇ. *m* ; tís. *f* ; chís. *f* ;
THROES, *N.*
of death. phaṭká. *m* ;

THRONE, *N*,
gaddí. *f* ; singhásan. *m* ;
Proverb, to show that if a mean person is set on a throne he still acts meanly. If a dog is set on a throne he goes off to lick the hand-mill. kuttá ráj bahálie chakkí chaṭṭan já ;
THRONG, *N*.
bhíṛ. *f* ; kaṭṭh. *m* ;
THROTTLE, TO, *V. T.*
gal OR saṇggh OR saṇgghí ghuṭṭná; dam rokná ; pháhná ; gichchí ghuṭṭná ;
THROUGH, *Prep.*
duáre ; vichch ;
THROUGHOUT, *Adv.*
sárá ;
THROW, *N*.
jhaṭak. *f* ;
of a ball. tárá bochí. *f* ;
THROW, TO, *V. T.*
suṭṭná ; ghattná ; vagháuná ;
1. to throw in wrestling ḍháháuná; ḍháhná ; paṭká márná ;
2. to throw away liquid. roṛh chhaḍḍná ; ḍolh chaṛná ;
3. throw fuel into furnace. jhokná ;
4. to throw up a ball. tárá bochí dení ; ullo dení ; húll dení ;
5. to throw a thing down. paṭkáuná ;
6. to demolish. pachháṛná ;
7. to throw anything into the mouth from palm of hand. phakkná ;
8. to throw away. paráṇ suṭṭ dená ;
THROW DOWN, TO, *V. T.*
ḍegná ; ḍháhná ; ḍigáuná ; ḍháh suṭṭná ; ḍháuná ; paṭkáuná ; jhammná ;
THRUST IN, TO, *V. I.*
ghusaṛná ; badobadí waṛná ;
THRUST, TO, *V. T.*
dhakelná ; dhasáuná ;
1. to hit. húl mární ;
2. to push. dhakk dená ; dhakkná ;
THRUST, *N*.
dhakk. *m* ; húl. *f* ; dhakká. *m* ;

THUD, *N*.
ḍhamkká. *m* ; ḍhamákká. *m* ;
THUMB, *N*.
aṇgguṭhá. *m* ;
THUMB, TO, *V. T.*
aṇgguṭhe nál mailá karṇá ;
to affix thumb mark. aṇgguṭhá láná ;
THUMP, *N*.
mukká. *m* ; dhaul dhappá. *m* ; thápí. *f* ; dhaul mukká. *m* ;
THUMP, TO, *V. T.*
ṭakráuná ;
1. with the fist. mukká OR dhraul márná ;
2. on the door. khaṛkáuná ;
3. to thump slightly. paṭákná ; paṭokí mární ;
4. to pat on the back. thápí dení OR mární ;
THUNDER, *N*.
kaṛak. *m* ; gaṛak. *f* ; garaj. *f* ;
THUNDER, TO, *V. T.*
baddal gajjná OR garajná OR kaṛakná OR guṛhakná ;
1. it was thundering. badal gajjdá píá ;
2. Proverb. used of those who brag, but do nothing practical. Those clouds which thunder do not give rain. jehṛe gajjde haiṇ, uh warhde nahíṇ ;
THUNDER CLAP, *N*.
kaṛak. *f* ; garaj. *f* ;
THUNDERING, *N*.
garaj. *f* ; gunj. *f* ; gaṛhak. *f* ; gaṛhaká. *m* ;
THUNDERSTORM, *N*.
ṭháká. *m* ; jhaṛí. *f* ; jhaṛ. *m* ;
THURSDAY, *N*.
Jumerát. *f*. M ; Vírwár. *f*. H ; bírwár. *f*. H ;
THUS, *Adv.*
aṇjh ; uṇjh ; ajehá ;
THWACK, *N*.
már. *f* ; ḍhamákká. *m* ;
THWACK, TO, *V. T.*
márná kuṭṭná ;
THWART, TO, *V. T.*
chalittar kheḍná ; bhánní mární ; bhán márná ; dá márná ; aql már dení ;

THWARTING, *N.*
jidd. *f* ; zidd. *f* ;
THY, *Pro.*
terá ;
TIARA, *N.*
táj. *m* ;
TICK, IN DOGS, *N.*
chichchṛí. *f* ; chichchaṛ. *m* ;
TICKET, *N.*
ṭikaṭ. *m* ;
return ticket. wápsí ṭikaṭ. *m* ;
TICKLE, TO, *V. T.*
kutkutárí kaḍḍhní ; gutgutáuná ; gudgudáuná ;
TICKLING, *N.*
kutkutárí. *f* ; kutkutí. *f* ;
TIDE, *N.*
pání dá lahá chaṛhá. *m* ;
TIDILY, *Adv.*
ṭhík ṭhák ;
TIDINGS, *N.*
sanehá. *m* ; ḳhabar. *f* ; patá. *m* ; samáchár. *f* ;
TIDY, *A.*
ṭhík ṭhák ; sáf ; sutthrá ;
TIDY UP, TO, *V. T.*
ṭhík sáhmke rakkhná ;
TIE, *N.*
ganḍh. *f* ;
TIE, TO, *V. T.*
ganḍhná ; juṭṭná ; bannhná ; gaṭháuná ; juṛná ; juṭ karná ; kassná ; gaṭṭh dení ; gaṭṭhná ;
TIED, *P. P.*
baddhá hoyá ; kariá hoyá ;
TIFF, *N.*
kuhná. *m* ;
TIGER, *N.*
bágh. *m* ; sher. *m* ;
TIGHT, *A.*
bhíṛá ; sauṛá ; kassiá hoyá ;
1. of a knot. pích ;
2. this knot is very tight. ih ganḍh baṛí píchí OR ghuṭṭí hoí ;
TIGHTEN, TO, *V. T.*
kassná ; bajhná ; ghuṭṭná ; taṇná ; kichchná ;
TIGHTLY, *Adv.*
kasske ; ghuṭṭke ; taṇke ;
TIGHTNESS, *N.*
kass. *f* ; sauṛ. *f* ;
of a knot. pích. *f* ;

TIGRESS, *N.*
sherní. *f* ; bághní. *f* ;
TILE, *N.*
khapṛá. *m* ; tail. *m* ; khaprail. *f* ;
TILL, *N.*
gallá. *m* ; golak. *f* ;
TILL, *Prep.*
tíkar ; talak ; táṇí ; toṛí ;
TILL, *Conj.*
jichar núṇ ;
TILL, TO, *V. T.*
hal chaláuná ; hal wáhuná ; hal joná ;
TILLAGE, *N.*
khetí. *f* ; wáhí jotí. *f* ; wáhí. *f*. khetípatí. *f* ; jimídárí. *f* ;
TILLER, *N.*
jaṭ wáhí. *m* ; halwáh. *m* ; zamíndár. *m* ;
TIMBER, *N.*
lakkaṛ. *f* ; káṭh. *m* ; mochchhá. *m* ;
1. a thick piece of timber. gelí. *f* ; gelrí. *f* ; toṛá. *m* ;
2. a pile of timber. lakkaṛ káṭh. *m* ;
TIMBER MARKET, *N.*
lakkaṛ manḍí. *f* ;
TIMBREL, *N.*
khanjarí. *f* ; see TAMBOURINE.
TIME, *N.*
waqt. *m* ; velá. *m* ;
1. for a long time. charokná ;
2. time of the year. rut. *f* ; bahár. *f* ;
3. length of time. chir. *m* ;
4. at the right time. ṭhík vele sir ;
5. at the wrong time. kuvele ;
6. this time. aiṭkíṇ ; is phere ;
7. he struck me four times with a shoe. us ne meríáṇ chár júttíáṇ máriáṇ ;
8. age, past, present or future. samá. *m* ; jamáná. *m* ;
TIMELY, *Adv.*
vele sir ;
TIMESERVER, *N.*
khán dá yár. *m* ; matlabí. *m* ; lobhí. *m* ;
TIMIDITY, *N.*
ḍar. *m* ; ḳhauf. *m* ; kair. *m* ;
TIMID PERSON, *N.*
ḍarú. *m* ; ḍarákal. *m* ; thoṛ dil ádmí. *m* ;

TIMOROUS, *A.*
ḍarákal ; bujjhe dil wálá ;
TIMOROUSLY, *adv.*
ḍarke ; ḍar nál ;
TIMOROUSNESS, *N.*
ḍar. *m* ; kair. *m* ; ḳhauf. *m* ;
TIN, *N.*
kalí. *f* ;
tin canister. pípá. *m* ; kanastar. *m* ;
TIN, TO, *V. T.*
kalí karní ;
TINCTURE, *N.*
arkk. *m* ;
TINGE, *N.*
raṇggat. *f* ; raṇg. *m* ;
TINGLE, TO, *V. I.*
jhaṇjhaṇáuná ; jhaṇnáuná ;
TINGLING, *N.*
jhaṇjhuṇí. *f* ; jhaṇát. *f* ;
TINKLE, TO, *V. I.*
chhanakná ; wajjná ; ranakná ; chhan chhan karní ;
Proverb. Every woman wears anklets, but only some can make them tinkle. páwe har koí, ṭhankáwe koí ;
TINKLING, *N.*
ṭhanáká. *m* ;
TINT, *N.*
raṇggat. *f* ;
TINY, *A.*
nikká ; chhoṭá ; nanná ;
TIP, *N.*
chunj. *f* ;
of the finger. poṭṭá. *m* ;
TIPCAT, *N.*
gullí ḍaṇḍḍá. *m* ;
TIPPLER, *N.*
nasháí. *m* ; sharábí. *m* ;
TITOE ON, *Adv.*
pabbáṇ bhár ;
TIRE, *N.*
hál. *m* ; kaṛá. *m* ; muṭak. *m* ;
TIRE, TO, *V. T.*
thakáuná ; hapháuná ; hasráuná ; see HARASS.
TIRE, TO, *V. I.*
thak jáná ; hárná ; chúr ho jáná ;
TIRED, *A.*
thaká máṇḍá ; máṇḍá ; thakkiá hoyá ; chur hoyá hoyá ;
I am very tired. merá bochhá nikal gayá ; main thakke chúr ho gayá ;
TIREDNESS, *N.*
thakewáṇ. *m* ;
TITHE, *N.*
daswáṇ hissá. *m* ; daswandh. *m* ; dahyakkí. *f* ;
TITHE, TO, *V. T.*
daswáṇ hissá dená ; dahyakkí dená ;
TITLE, *N.*
1. rank. uhdá. *m* ; darjá. *m* ;
2. of a book. náṇ. *m* ;
3. of a heading. surḳhí. *f* ;
4. title, deed. paṭṭá. *m* ;
TITILLATION, *N.*
kutkutí. *f* ; kuṭkutáṛí. *f* ;
TITLE TATTLE, *N.*
gapp sharap. *f* ; gappáṇ. *f* ;
TO, *Prep.*
taraf ; wal ; tíkar ; táṇí ;
TOADY, TO, *V. T.*
muṇh chaṭṭná ; jholí chukkná ; see FLATTER.
TOAST, *N.*
tost. *m* ;
TOAST, TO, *V. T.*
sekná ;
TOBACCO, *N.*
tamákú. *m* ; tamákhú. *m* ;
TODAY, *Adv.*
ajj.
TODDY, *N.*
ṭárí. *f* ;
TOE, *N.*
1. large. angguṭhá. *m* ;
2. small. chíchí. *f* ;
TOGETHER, *Adv.*
nál ; nál nál ; kaṭṭhe ; milke ; ralke ; rale mile ;
TOGETHER, *Prep.*
sane ; saṇg ;
TOIL, *N.*
majúrí. *f* ; diháṛí dhappá. *m* ; mihnat mashaqqat. *f* ;
TOIL, TO, *V. T.*
mihnat karní ; kamm dhaṇdá karná ;
TOILSOME, *A.*
aukhá kamm ; mihnat dá ; taklífwálá ;
TOKEN, *N.*
nishán. *m* ; nashání. *f* ; lachchhaṇ. *m*; ládh. *f*; ramak. *f*; ramaj. *f* ;

TOLERABLE, *A*.
sahn jog ; sahinhár ;
TOLERANCE, *N*.
narmí. *f* ; saháu. *m* ;
TOLERANT, *A*.
1. soft hearted. narmdil ;
2. kind. mihrbán ;
3. forbearing. sahnwálá ;
TOLERATE, TO, *V. T*.
saihná ; sahárná ; jhallná ;
TOLERATION, *N*.
bardásht. *f* ; saháu. *m* ;
TOLL, *N*.
mahsúl. *m* ; lanḡhái. *f* ;
for merchandise. choṇggí. *f* ;
TOLL HOUSE, *N*.
choṇggí ḳháná. *m* ;
TOMB, *N*.
1. Muhammadan. qabr. *f* ;
2. Muhammadan saint's tomb. ḳhángáh. *f* ;
3. Hindu. samádh. *f* ; maṛí. *f* ; maṛhí ;
TOME, *N*.
pothí. *f* ; pustak. *f* ; kitáb. *f* ;
diary. pattrí. *f* ;
TOMORROW, *Adv*.
kall ; bhalke ; bhalak ;
TOMTIT, *N*.
pidrí. *f* ;
TONE, *N*.
sur. *f* ; bol. *m* ; rahá. *m* ; awáz. *f* ;
TONGS, *N*.
1. for fire. chimtá. *m* ;
2. for huqqa. uchchá. *m* ;
TONGUE, *N*.
1. organ of speech. jíbh. *f* ; jabán. *f* ; rasaná. *f* ;
2. language. bolí. *f* ;
3. of a bell. ruaṇá. *m* ; talí. *f* ; tuntuníáṇ. *f* ;
TONIC, *N*.
dawá. *f* ; dawái. *f* ; dárú. *m* ; dúá dárú. *m* ;
TONIGHT, *Adv*.
ajj rát núṇ ; ajj rátíṇ. ajj dí rát ;
TOO, *Adv*.
ví ;
TOOL, *N*.
sand. *m* ; aujár. *m* ; hathiyár. *m* ;
TOOTH, *N*.
daṇd. *m* ; daṇdí. *f* ;
1. double tooth. dáhaṛ. *f* ; hannho. *f* ;
2. canine tooth. súá. *m* ;
3. one whose teeth are broken. daṇd boṛá ;
TOOTHACHE, *N*.
dàṇd píṛ. *m* ; hannhoṇ dí píṛ. *f* ;
TOOTHLESS, *A*.
pappá ;
TOOTH BRUSH, *N*.
1. a stick used by Muhammadans. maswák. *m* ;
2. a stick used by Hindus. dátaṇ. *f* ;
TOOTHPICK, *N*.
chhiṇg. *f* ;
TOOTH POWDER, *N*.
daṇdáṇ dá maṇjan. *m* ;
TOOTHSOME, *A*.
suádlá ; suádí ; jaikedár ;
salty. saluná ;
TOP, *N*.
1. top. láṭṭú. *m* ;
2. summit. choṭṭá. *m* ; choṭṭí. *f* ; tísí. *f* ; sirá. *m* ;
3. from top to bottom. upparoṇ laike dhúr táiṇ ;
4. top of a page. sirá. *m* ;
5. top of bookcase, etc. chhatt. *m* ;
TOPER, *N*.
nashái. *m* ; sharábí. *m* ; sharábí kabábí. *m* ;
TOPIC, *N*.
bayán. *m* ; arthát. *m* ; áshá. *m* ; parjojan. *m* ; bháv. *m* ;
TOPKNOT, *N*.
1. Sikhs. júṛá. *m* ;
2. Hindus. boddí. *f* ;
TOPPING, *A*.
uttam ;
TOPSY TURVY, *A*.
ulṭ pulṭ ; heṭh upar ; heṭh utte ; úṇdhá ; agaṛ dugṛá ; ugṛá dugṛá ;
a vessel upside down. muddhá ; puthá ; ulṭá.
TORCH, *N*.
mashál. *f* ;
TORMENT, *N*.
ḍáḍhí píṛ. *m* ; sakht píṛ. *m* ; see TROUBLE.
TORMENT, TO, *V. T*.
bahut dukh dená ; taṛpáuná ; see TROUBLE.
TORMENTED, TO BE, *V. I*.
taṛaphná ; kalapná ;

TORMENTOR, *N*.
aukhíáṇ karnwálá. *m* ; pápí. *m* ; haṭṭiárá. *m* ;
TORN, TO BE, *V. I.*
páṭná ; chirná ;
TORNADO, *N*.
parlú. *m* ; parlo. *m* ;
1. of wind only. hanerí. *f* ;
2. of wind and rain. jhakkaṛ. *m* ; see TEMPEST.
TORPID, *A*.
sunn ;
lazy. sust ; postí ; surliá hoyá ;
TORRENT, *N*.
haṛh. *m* ; roṛh. *m* ;
TORRID, *A*.
1. dried. sukká ;
2. hot. garm ;
TORTOISE, *N*.
kachchhú kummáṇ. *m* ; kachchhú. *m* ;
TORTUOUS, *A*.
waldár ; pechdár ;
TORTURE, TO, *V. T*.
satáuná ; bahut dukh dená ; saḳhtí karní ; tarsáuná ;
to beat. márná ;
TOSS, *N*.
jhaṭká. *m* ; jhossá. *m* ;
TOSS, TO, *V. T*.
1. to throw. suṭṭná ;
2. to loss a ball. tárá bochí dení ; ullo dení ;
3. to throw fuel into furnace. jhokná ;
TOTAL, *A*.
kul ; sárá ; sabh ;
TOTAL, *N*.
kul jamhá. *m* ; joṛ. *m* ; jinná haigá ;
TOTALLY, *Adv*.
mulloṇ muddhoṇ ; ukká mukká ; haddoṇ muddhoṇ ;
TOTTER, TO, *V. I*.
hilná ; lahuná turná ; ḍagmagáuná ;
TOUCH, TO, *V. T*.
1. to feel. chhuhná ; chhohná ; chheṛná ; hatth lagáuná ; hatth láuná ; ṭohná ;
2. to interfere with. chheṛná ; akáuná ; pair aṛáuná ; dhasná ;
3. to impress. káṭ karná ;
TOUCH, *N*.
chhuáí. *f* ; chhuháí. *f* ; chhúhat. *f* ; chhút. *f* ; chhút chhát. *f* ; chhúh. *f* ;
TOUCHINESS, *N*.
karodh. *m* ;
TOUCHY, *A*.
chhirham ; chhirhmí ;
TOUGH, *N*.
karṛá ;
1. hard. saḳht ;
2. like leather. chamm wáṇgár ;
TOUGHNESS, *N*.
saḳhtíáí. *f* ;
TOUR, *N*.
daurá. *m* ; pherí. *f* ; pherá. *m* ;
TOUR, TO, *V. T*.
daurá karná ; phirná ;
TOWARDS, *Prep*.
wall ; walloṇ ; páse ; sehd ;
TOWEL, *N*.
parná. *m*; rauntá. *m* ; sáfá. *m*; sáfí. *f*;
TOWER, *N*.
1. fort. qilá. *m* ;
2. church tower, &c. burj. *m* ; burjí. *f* ; munárá. *m* ;
3. mud tower. maṭíálá. *m* ; maṭílá. *m* ;
TOWERING, *A*.
uchchá ;
TOWN, *N*.
shahr. *m* ; nagar. *m* ;
TOWNSMAN, *N*.
shahrí. *m* ; shahríá. *m* ;
TOY, *N*.
bájí. *f* ; khidáuná. *m* ;
TRACE, *N*.
1. footprint. khoj. *m* ; khuṛṛá. *m* ; pair. *m* ;
2. strap. jotar. *f* ; jot. *f* ;
3. sign. nishán. *m* ; patá. *m* ; khoj tevá. *m* ; nisháni. *f* ; ládh. *f* ;
TRACE, TO, *V. T*.
dí súh kaḍḍhní ; khoj kaḍḍhná ; patá lagáuná ; nishán labbhná ;
TRACK, *N*.
1. cart track. lík. *f* ; líh. *f* ; gail. *f* ;
2. path. ráh. *f* ; rastá. *m* ; pahiá. *m* ; paihá. *m* ;
TRACK, TO, *V. T*.
khoj láuná OR kaḍḍhná ;
TRACKER, *N*.
khojjí. *m* ;

TRACT, *N*.
gutká. *m* ; pothí. *f* ;
TRACTABILITY, *N*.
barkhudárí. *f* ; ágyákárí. *f* ;
TRACTABLE, *A*.
siddh paddhrá ; sulagg ; sáú ; baṛá gau ; ágyákár ;
TRADE, *N*.
1. commerce. wanj bapár. *m* ; shadágarí. *f* ; leṇ deṇ. *f* ; buhár. *m* ; leká deká. *m* ; leká dekí. *f* ;
2. trading one article for another. waṭṭo saṭṭá. *m* ;
3. occupation. guzárá. *m* ; peshá. *m* ; kamám. *m* ; kimám. *m* ; kamm káj. *m* ;
4. Proverb. Do not trade with friends. jitthe howe pyár utthe ná karie vihár ;
TRADE, TO, *V. T*.
leṇ deṇ karná ; waṭáuná ; bapár karná ;
TRADER, *N*.
bapárí. *m* ; shadágar. *m* ; bhanjárá. *m* ;
Hindu moneylending shopkeepers. karáṛ. *m* ;
TRADITION, *N*.
rít. *f* ; waḍḍeáṇ dí gal. *f* ; waḍḍeáṇ dá bol. *m* ;
TRADUCE, TO, *V. T*.
nindiá karná ; badnám karná ; nashar karná ; kalank launá ; kalank dá tikká láuná ; chhaṭṭná ;
TRAFFIC, *N*.
1. trade. wanj bapar. *m* ; see TRADE.
2. traffic. ráh dá waggná. *m* ;
3. there is much traffic on this road. is ráh auná jáná baṛá hundá hai ;
4. coming and going. awágauṇ. *m* ;
TRADEGY, *N*.
áfat. *f* ; gráh. *m* ;
TRAIL, *N*.
khoj. *m* ; lakír. *f* ; patá. *m* ;
TRAIL, TO, *V. T*.
1. to track. khoj kaḍḍhná OR láuná ;
2. to drag. dhuhná ; dhirná ; ghasíṭná ; kichch laí jáná ;
TRAIN, *N*.
rel gaḍḍí. *f* ;
TRAIN, TO, *V. T*.
gijháuná ; ádat páuní ; sikhláuná ;
to train oxen to the yoke. paṭáuná ;
TRAINED, *A*.
sikkhiá hoyá ;
TRAIT, *N*.
wasaf. *m* ; kho. *f* ; ádat. *f* ; guṇ. *m* ;
TRAITOR, *N*.
harám khor. *m* ; nimak harám. *m* ; adharmí. *m* ; ṭhagg. *m* ; kudharmí. *m* ;
TRAITOROUS, *A*.
beímán ; see TREACHEROUS.
TRAITOROUSLY, *Adv*.
beímání nál ;
TRAMMEL, TO, *V. T*.
rokná ; aṭkáuná ; see HINDER.
TRAMP, TO, *V. T*.
pairíṇ ṭurná ; ṭurke jáná ;
TRAMPLE TO, *V. T*.
latáṛná ;, mindhná ; chíthalná ; pair tale malná ; maddhná ; mindháṛná ;
TRAMPLING, *N*.
latáṛ. *f* ;
TRANCE, *N*.
puwár. *m* ;
1. a dream. sufná. *m* ;
2. to be in a trance. bekhud ho jáná ;
TRANQUIL, *A*.
magan ; dhírajmán ; anandí ;
tranquil and contented. sukhí ; sukhiá ;
TRANQUILIZE, TO, *V. T*.
dilásá dená ; ṭhandá karná ; see SOOTHE.
TRANQUILITY, *N*.
sukh. *m* ; sáṇt. *f* ; anand. *m* ; parsintái. *f* ; shántí. *f* ; asog. *m* ; sántagí. *f* ; arám. *m* ; salási. *f* ;
TRANSACT, TO, *V. T*.
1. to buy and sell. leṇ deṇ karná ;
2. to finish. naberná ; nabháuná ; mukáuná ;
3. to carry out. kamm chaláuná ;
TRANSACTION, *N*.
muámlá. *m* ; kár bár. *f* ; kamm. *m* ; kamm káj. *m* ;
TRANSCEND, TO, *V. T*.
wadháuná ; uchchá hatth ráhná ;

TRANSCENDENT, *A.*
uttam ; sohná ; baṛá chaṇgá ; álá ;
TRANSCRIBE, TO, *V. T.*
dobárá likhná ;
TRANSFER, *N.*
badlí. *f ;*
TRANSFER, TO, *V. T.*
badalná ; badalá karná ;
TRANSFERENCE, *N.*
badlí. *f ;* badalá. *m ;*
TRANSFIGURATION, *N.*
surat dí badalí. *f ;* káyá palaṭ. *m ;*
TRANSFIGURE, TO, *V. T.*
badal dená ;
TRANSFORM TO, *V. T.*
badalná ; bhes waṭáuná ;
TRANSFORMATION, *N.*
badalí. *f ;*
TRANSGRESS, TO, *V. T.*
gunáh OR páp karná ; ṭál dená ; hukm toṛná ; ulaṇgghaṇ karná ;
TRANSGRESSION, *N.*
gunáh. *m ;* páp. *m ;* aparádh. *m ;* khoṭ. *f ;* hukmudúlí. *f ;* jurm. *m ;* ulaṇgghaṇ. *m ;*
TRANSGRESSOR, *N.*
pápí. *m ;* gunáhí. *m ;* takhsírí. *m ;* apárádhí. *m ;* kudharmí. *m ;*
TRANSIT, *N.*
chaliá jáná. *m ;*
TRANSITION, *N.*
badalí. *f ;*
TRANSITORINESS, *N.*
nápaidárí. *f ;*
the transitoriness of life. ín dam dá paráhuná hai.
TRANSITORY, *A.*
anitt ; thoṛe chir laí ; jánhárá ;
TRANSLATE, TO, *V. T.*
tarjamá karná ;
TRANSLATION, *N.*
tarjamá. *m ;*
TRANSMIGRATE, TO, *V. T.*
juṇ bhogná ; juṇ paltaná ; churási bhogná ; juṇ badlaná ;
TRANSMIGRATION, *N.*
juṇ. *f ;* churási. *f ;* áwágauṇ. *m ;*
to exempt from transmigrations. nistárná ;
TRANSMIT, TO, *V. T.*
1. to sand. ghallná ;
2. to change. badalná ;

TRANSPARENCY, *N.*
nirmaltái. *f ;*
TRANSPARENT, *A.*
sáf ; nirmal ;
TRANSPORT, *N.*
1. conveying. bhár bardárí. *f ;*
2. exultation. baṛí ḳhushí. *f ;* harkh. *m ;*
TRANSPORT, TO, *V. T.*
dhoná ; laí jáná ;
TRANSPORTATION, *N.*
des nikálá. *m ;* des badává. *m ;*
TRANSPOSE, TO, *V. T.*
ulaṭ pulaṭ karná ; ikk dí jagáh dujje núṇ rakkhná ;
TRAP, *N.*
1. conveyance. gaḍḍí. *f ;* baggí. *f ;*
2. snare. pháí. *f ;* phaṇdá. *m ;* kuṛikkí. *f ;*
3. deceit. fareb. *m ;* chalákí. *f ;*
TRAP, TO, *V. T.*
1. to deceive. dhokhá deke phaṛná ; phasáuná ; bhan márná; chalittar kheḍná ; bhánní mární ;
2. to catch in a trap. phaṇde nál phasáuná ;
TRASH, *N.*
raddí chíz. *f ;*
TRAVAIL, *N.*
ján kandaní. *f ;* kashṭaní. *f ;*
TRAVEL, TO, *V. T.*
paiṇḍá karná ; paṇdh karná ; des pardes phirná ; chalná ;
to go a stage. paṛá jáná ;
TRAVELLER, *N.*
páṇdhí. *m ;* ráhí. *m ;* páṇdhaṇ. *f ;* paṇdheṛú. *m ;*
TRAVELLING, *N.*
sail. *m ;*
TRAVERSE, TO, *V. T.*
phirná ; see TRAVEL.
TRAY, *N.*
trel. *m ;*
TREACHEROUS, *A.*
kapṭí ; chálbáj ; khoṭṭá ; beímáṇ ; luṇharám ;
TREACHEROUSLY, *Adv.*
beímání nál ; kapaṭ nál ; chattrái nál ;
TREACHERY, *N.*
beímánagí, *f ;* dagá. *f ;* parfej. *m ;* parpanch. *m ;* luṇharámí. *f ;*

TREACLE, *N*.
ráb. *f* ; shírá. *m* ;
TREAD, *N*.
aláṇgh. *m* ; chaláṇgh. *m* ;
TREAD UNDER, TO, *V*. *T*.
latáṛná ; chittarná ; middhná ; ch thalná ; see TRAMPLE.
TREASON, *N*.
harámḳhorí. *f* ;
TREASURE, *N*.
ḳhazáná. *m* ;
property. mál. *m* ; mál mátá. *m* ; rás. *f* ;
TREASURE UP, TO, *V*. *T*.
kaṭṭhá karná ; baṭolná ;
TREASURER, *N*.
ḳhazánchí. *m* ; rokaṛiá. *m* ; bhaṇḍárí. *m* ;
TREASURY, *N*.
ḳhazáná. *m* ; ḳhajáná. *m* ; bhaṇḍár. *m* ;
TREAT, TO, *V*. *T*.
1. well. chaṇgá saluk karná ; achchhá wartáwá karná ;
2. badly. búrá saluk karná ;
3. to treat a patient. iláj karná ; duá dárú karná ;
TREATISE, *N*.
bakháṇ. *m* ;
TREATMENT, *N*.
wartáo. *m* ; salúk. *m* ; warat sarat. *m* ;
TREATY, *N*.
nem. *m* ;
peace. suláh. *f* ;
TREBLE, *A*.
tríná ; tehará ;
TREBLE TO, *V*. *T*.
tehr páuná ; tihráuná ;
TREE, *N*.
rukk. *m* ; buṭá. *m* ; birchh. *m* ; daraḳht. *m* ; peṛ. *m* ;
1. every thing connected with a tree. parwár. *m* ;
2. bark of a tree. chill. *f* ; chillaṛ. *f* ;
3. piece of bark. sakk. *m* ; sakkṛá. *m* ;
4. list of trees.
(For the Latin names I am indebted to the Panjabi Dictionary published by Gulab Singh & Sons.)

Acacia tree. (acacia arabica). kikkar. *f* ;
Acacia tree. (acacia speciosa). siríṇh. *m* ; siris. *m* ;
Acacia tree, the small twigs of which are used as tooth sticks. (acacia modesta). phuláh. *m* ; paláh. *m* ;
Almond tree. (amygdala dulcis.) badám. *m* ;
Apple tree. (pyrus malus.) seáṇ dá rukkh. *m* ;
Apricot tree. khurmání dá rukkh. *m* ;
Box tree. sanubar. *m* ;
Banyan tree. (ficus Indica.) boṛh. *m* ; bohṛ. *m* ; baṛh. *m* ; waṛ. *m* ;
Castor oil tree. (ricinus communis.) ariṇḍ. *f* ;
Citron tree. (citrus limonum.) khaṭṭá. *m* ;
Cypress tree. (sempervirens.) sarú. *m* ;
Date tree. khajúr. *f* ; chhuárá. *m*.)
Deodar tree. (cedrus deodara.) diár. *m* ;
Fig tree. (ficus carica.) phagwáṛá. *m* ;
Sacred fig tree, the pippal. (ficus religiosa.) pippal. *m* ;
Fir tree. pharwáṇh. *m* ;
Fir tree. chíhl. *f* ; chílh. *f* ; inferior wood to the díar ;
Guava tree. amrúd. *m* ;
Lime tree. (citrus acida.) nimbú. *m* ;
Lemon tree. (citrus limonum.) khaṭṭá. *m* ;
Mango tree. (magnifera Indica.) amb. *m* ;
Mulberry tree. (morus alba.) shatút. *m* ; tút. *m* ; tútṛá. *m* ;
Pomegranate tree. (punica granatum.) anár. *m* ;
Oak tree. bilut. *m* ;
Orange tree. (citrus aurantium.) naraṇggí. *f* ;
Pomello tree. (citrus decumaná.) chakodhrá. *m* ; chakotrá. *m* ;
Peach tree. (prunus domestica.) árú. *m* ;
Pine tree. (pinus excelsa) chíhl. *f* ; chíl. *f* ;

Pine tree. (cedrus deodara.) diár. *m* ;
Plane tree. (platanus orientalis). chanár. *f* ;
Plum tree. (jujuba.) ber. *m* ; berí. *f* ;
Plum tree. (cerasus cornuta.) jáman. *m* ;
Plum tree. (prunus onalifolia.) alúchá. *m* ;
Salvadora tree. waṇ. *m* ;
Sycamore tree. gullar. *m* ; gullnar. *m* ;
Shisham tree. (dalbergia sissoo.) shísham. *m* ;
Tamarind tree. (tamarindus Indica.) imlí. *f* ; amlí. *f* ;
A vine. bel. *f* ; dákh. *f* ;
(leguminosae.) ṭálhí. *f* ; ṭálí. *f* ;
(Bombax heptaphyllum) simbal. *m*; simmal. *m* ;
a large handsome tree, sometimes called the cotton tree.
(butea frondosa.) chhichhiá. *m* ; its large leaves are used by shopkeepers and hawkers for wrapping up goods.
(azadirachla Indica.) ním. *f* ;

TREFOIL, *N*.
siṇjhí. *f* ;

TRELLIS, *N*.
jaṇgalá. *m* ; jálí. *f* ;

TREMBLE, TO, *V. I*.
kambná ; kambní laggní ; thar thar kambná ; dil kamb uṭṭhná ; thartharauná ; chaṇchláuná ;
to cause to tremble. kambáuná ;

TREMBLING, *N*.
kambní. *f* ; thartharí. *f* ; thartharáṭ. *m* ; jhunjhúní. *f* ;

TREMBLINGLY, *Adv*.
kambke ; thar tharke ; tharu tharu karke ;

TREMENDOUS, *A*.
bahut waḍḍá ; moṭá bhárá ; baṛá bhárá ;

TREMOUR, *N*.
kambní. *f* ; thartharí. *f* ; thartharáṭ. *m* ;

TRENCH, *N*.
morchá. *m* ; kháí. *f* ; khál. *m* ;
trench for large cooking pots. chaṛh. *f* ;

TRENCH, TO, *V. T*.
morchá bannhná OR karná ; waṭṭ kaḍḍhní ;

TRESPASS, *N*.
páp. *m* ; gunáh. *m* ; aparádh. *m* ;

TRESPASS, TO, *V. T*.
páp OR gunáh OR qusúr karná ;

TRESPASSER, *N*.
taqsírí. *m*; pápí. *m* ; gunáhí. *m* ;

TRIAL, *N*.
1. legal. muqadamá. *m* ;
2. each appearance at trial. peshí. *f*; táríkh. *f* ;
3. to send up for trial. chalán karná ;
4. test. partává. *m* ; parakh *f* ; parkhiá. *f* ;
5. experience. tajrabá. *m* ; vekhiá chákhiá. *m* ;
6. trouble. taklíf. *f* ; kazálat. *f* ; kechal. *f* ; kechal kabal. *f* ;

TRIANGLE, *N*.
targuṭṭh. *m* ;

TRIANGULAR, *A*.
tarnukrá ; targuṭṭhá ;

TRIBE, *N*.
ját. *f* ; qaum. *f* ; jot. *m* ;

TRIBULATION, *N*.
musíbat. *f* ; taklíf. *f* ; biptá. *f* ;

TRIBUNAL, *N*.
kacherí. *f* ; adálat. *f* ;

TRIBUTARY, *N*.
shákk. *m* ; nadí. *f* ; báhá. *m* ;
of a canal. suá. *m* ;

TRIBUTE, *N*.
mahsúl. *m* ; jaziyá. *m* ; ṭaks. *m* ;

TRICK *N*.
fareb. *m* ; makr. *m* ; baháná. *m* ; chhal. *m* ; pakhaṇḍ. *m* ; kapaṭ. *m* ; chalittar. *m* ; lapeṭá. *m* ; wal pech. *m* ; khekhaṇ. *m* ; dhoppá. *m* ; hílá. *m* ; dá. *m* ; khuṭṭar. *m* ;
don't play such tricks. aiḍiáṇ chataráíáṇ ná kariá kar ;

TRICK, TO, *V. T*.
dhokhá dená ; fareb dená ; dá láná ; dagabází karní ; ḍhang karná ; khuṭṭar karná ;

TRICKERY, *N*.
shiltbiltí. *f* ; shalbází. *f* ; bhulává. *m*; chhalbal. *m*; hílá. *m*; chaláki. *f* ; dhoppá. *m* ; dagábází. *f* ·

TRICKLE, TO, *V. I.*
choná ;
TRICKLING, *N.*
choá. *m ;*
TRICKSTER, *N.*
ṭhagg. *m ;* dhoppebáz. *m ;*
TRICKY, *A.*
khuchí ; khochar ; chalák ; pakhanḍí ; khuṭṭarí; ḍhaṇgí ; farebí ;
TRIDENT, *N.*
tarsúl. *m ;*
TRIFLE, *N.*
kinká. *m ;* nikkí chíz. *f ;*
TRIFLING, *A.*
hochchhá ; lutrá ; chotná ; chhichhohrá ; chukkná ;
TRIGGER, *N.*
lablabí. *f ;* ghoṛá. *m ;*
TRIM, *A.*
ṭhík ṭhák ; sutthrá; típ táp ; sáj báj ;
TRIM TO, *V. T.*
1. prune. chháṇggná ; jháṛ suṭṭná ;
2. adjust. sajáuná ;suárná ; sohná banáuná ;
TRINITY, *N.*
Taslís. *m ;*
TRINKET, *N.*
wálí. *f ;*
TRIP, *N.*
daurá. *m ;* sail. *m ;* pherá. *m ;* panḍh. *m ;* painḍá. *m ;*
TRIP, TO, *V. T.*
ṭheḍá khánâ ; ṭhuḍḍaṇ laggná; aukhaṛná ;
for a horse. nauṇ lená ;
TRIPLE, *A.*
tehará ; tiharas ;
TRIPLICATION, *N.*
tehrau. *m ;*
TRIUMPH, *N.*
jít. *f ;* jit. *f ;* jet. *f ;*
TRIUMPH, TO, *V. T.*
1. to obtain the victory. jíttná ; jittná ; haráun á
2. rejoicing over success. jaí jaí karná ; jittke ḳhushí karní ; maṇggaláchár karná ; dandanáuná ; anand karná ;
TRIUMPHANT, *A.*
maṇggaláchár ; baṛá ḳhush ;
TRIUMPHANTLY, *Adv.*
fathe nál ;

TRIVIAL, *A.*
haulá ; nakárá ; nachíz ;
TRIVIALITY, *N.*
gapp shapp. *f ;*
TRODDEN UNDER, TO BE, *V. I.*
madheriá jáná ; middiá jáṇá ;
TROLLOP, *N.*
geglí. *f ;* besurí. *f ;* sarkhuttí, *f ;* kuchajjí. *f ;*
TROLLY, *N.*
ṭhella. *m ;*
TROOP, *N.*
ṭathá. *m ;* ṭollí. *f ;* ṭollá *m ;* kaṭṭh. *m ;*
1. an army. fauj. *f ;*
2. a troop. tarup. *m ;*
3. of animals. heṛh. *f ;* jhunḍ. *m ;*
TROOPER, *N.*
suár. *m ;*
TROT, *N.*
durkí. *f ;*
TROT, TO, *V. T.*
durkí OR poie painá ;
TROT, TO, *V. I.*
dulkí OR durkí chalná ;
TROTH, *N.*
1. truth. sachchiái. *f ;*
2. faithfulness. ímándárí. *f ;*
3. promise. qaul qarár. *m ;*
TROUBLE, *N.*
khechal. *f ;* janjal. *m ;* khachch gapp. *f ;* jichch. *f ;* khap. *m ;* wakht. *m ;* musíbat. *f ;* aukh. *f ;* khechal khabbhal. *f ;* jahímat. *f ;*
1. one who causes trouble. janjálí. *m ;* janjálan. *f ;*
2. what is the trouble ? tere sir kí baní hai ? tainúṇ kí aukaṛ baní hai ? tainúṇ kí wakht pai gayá hai ? tainúṇ kí bhárí baní hai ?
3. Proverb, to illustrate trouble upon trouble. Firstly, separation from my love, secondly, a dark night. ikk wichhoṛá yár dá dujjí rát kálí
TROUBLE, TO, *V. T.*
taklíf dení ; dukháuná ; akáuná ; dukh karná ; miṭṭí ḳharáb karná aukhíáṇ karní ; jichch karná ; khachch márná ; khechal dená ; dukh dená ;
1. to fall into trouble. siápá paí jáná;

2. to take trouble. taklíf karná;
3. he troubled me greatly, uh ne mainúṇ bahut akáiá hai; uh ne mainúṇ bahut taiá;

TROUBLED, TO BE, *V. I.*
ghábar jáná; ghábarná; jichch honá; behosh ho jáná; jaṇjál vichch phasná OR painá; ṭhaṭhanbarná;
if you get into trouble. je tainúṇ bhíṛ bannhe.

TROUBLESOME, *A.*
dukhdáí; kaṭhaṇ; jichchí;

TROUGH, *N.*
1. of earth. khurlí. *f;*
2. of wood. kaṭhṛá. *m;* for a well. káṭh dí nisár. *f;*
3. of brick or metal. chaubachchá. *m;* tagár. *m;*
4. a wooden kneading trough. parátṛá. *m;*
5. a brass kneading trough. parát. *f;*

TROUNCE, TO, *V. T.*
márná; már kuṭṭná; see BEAT.

TROUSERS, *N.*
1. English. patlún. *m;*
2. native. ghuṭanná. *m;*
3. women's. sutthan. *f;* see CLOTHES.

TROWEL, *N.*
rambá. *m;* khurpí. *f;*

TRUANT TO PLAY, *V. T.*
khunjháí márná; guchchí launí; khiskná; ghusáí márná; ghusár jáná; ghutthí láuná;

TRUCE, *N.*
thoṛe chir wáste suláh. *f;*

TRUCK, *N.*
ṭhellá. *m;* reṛhí. ; gaḍḍí. *f;*

TRUCULENCE, *N.*
1. rudeness. gustáḳhí. *f;* sáhmná bolná. *m;*
2. fierceness. jástí. *f;* saḳhtí. *f;*

TRUCULENT, *A.*
daṇggáí; fasádí; laṛáká; jhagṛálú; khappí; jháṇjiá;

TRUDGE, TO, *V. I.*
pairíṇ jáná; turíá jáná;

TRUE, *A.*
1. genuine. aslí; satt; sudh; khará; sachchá; haqqí;
2. faithful. bol dá púrá; gal l dá pakká; sachchá; dharmí; ímándár; suchiárá; suchárá;
3. exact. ṭhík; durust;

TRUEHEARTED, *A.*
sachchá;

TRULY, *Adv.*
sachí muchí; sachch; ṭhík ṭhák; dharmo dharmí;

TRUMPERY, *A.*
nikárá; raddí; see WORTHLESS.

TRUMPET, *N.*
dhútú, *m;* tuttí. *f;* turhí. *f;* turam. *m;* siṇggá. *m;*
1. to blow the trumpet. wajáuná;
2. to blow one's own trumpet. apná rág gáuná;

TRUMPETER, *N.*
turamchí. *m;* nagárchí. *m;* wajantrí. *m;*

TRUNK, *N.*
1. box. sanduq. *m;*
2. steel trunk. ṭarank. *m;*
3. of an elephant. sunn. *m;* suṇḍh. *m;*
4. of a tree. duṇḍ. *m;* porí. *f;* mochchhá. *m;*

TRUSS, *N.*
gattá. *m;* paṇḍ. *m;*

TRUST, *N.*
1. faith. bharosá. *m;* wisáh. *m;* ạsrá. *m;* ás. *f;* partít. *m;* patiárá. *m;* dhirvás. *m;* nischá. *m;* dhijá. *m;* patíj. *f;* ásá. *f;* yaqín. *m;* máṇ. *m;*
put not your trust in riches. apne mál dá máṇ ná karo.
2. deposit. amánat. *f;*
3. an advance. peshgí. *f;* sáí. *f;*
4. credit. udhár. *m;*

TRUST, TO, *V. T.*
1. to entrust. sauṇpná; hawále karná;
2. to believe. bharosá OR yaqín karná; patíjná; wasáh karná; patiánná;
3. to give credit. udhár dená;

TRUSTEE, *N.*
jámin. *m;* jummewár. *m;*

TRUSTFULLY, *Adv.*
yaqín nál; bharosá karke;

TRUSTINESS, *N.*
wafádárí. *f ;*
TRUSTLESS, *A.*
1. unbelieving. bepatíjá ; bewasáh ;
2. dishonest. beímán ; luṇ harám ;
TRUSTWORTHY, *A.*
dharmí ; hatth dá suchchá ; mutabar ;
atibárí, wihárí ; partítmáṇ ;
TRUTH, *N.*
1. veracity. sachchíái. *f ;* sachch *m ;* sattiá. *m ;* satt. *m ;*
2. honesty. ímándárí. *f ;* rástí. *f ;* dharm. *m ;* sáṇch. *m ;*
3. in truth. asl vichch ; sachch vichch ;
4. Proverb. Truth has nothing to fear. sáṇch núṇ koí áṇch nahíṇ ;
5. Tell me the truth about it. maiṇ núṇ sachchoṇ sachch hál sunáo ;
TRUTHFUL, *A.*
sachchá ;
TRUTHFULLY, *Adv.*
sachchoṇ sachch ; sachch sachch ; sachchí muchchí ;
TRUTHFULNESS, *N.*
sachchíái. *f ;*
TRY TO, *V. T.*
1. to test. azmáuná ; parakhná ; partáuná ; paríkhiá karná ; johná ; first try it then. pahláṇ paríkhiá karo, pher ;
2. to test a coin. táuná ; tankáuná ;
3. to attempt. jatan karná ; himmat karní ; pichchá karná ; pursharáth karná ;
4. to taste. chhakná ; suád vekhná ;
TRY, *N.*
jatan. *m ;*
TRYING, *A.*
aukhá ; sauṛá ; bikhṛá ;
TUB, *N.*
tap. *m ;* tagár. *m ;*
TUBE, *N.*
nalká. *m ;*
1. of a reed. naṛí. *f ;*
2. of huqqa on which the cup is placed. ábná. *m ;* ábnáe. *m ;*
3. of huqqa, for the mouthpiece. naṛí. *f ;*
4. of a blowpipe. phukní. *f ;*

TUCK, TO, *V. T.*
waleṭná ; lapeṭná ;
TUESDAY, *N.*
Mangal. *m. M ;* Mangalwár. *m. H ;*
TUFT, *N.*
laṭ. *f ;* jhhattá. *m ;* chhattá. *m ;*
of a Hindu's hair. boddí. *f ;* choṭṭí. *f ;*
TUG, *N.*
jhosá. *m ;* khichch. *m ;* khichch ghasíṭ. *f ;* jhaṭká. *m ;*
TUG, TO, *V. T.*
khichchná ; dhuhná ;
TUITION, *N.*
paṛhaí. *f ;*
TUMBLE, *N.*
ṭhedá. *m ;*
TUMBLE, TO, *V. I.*
ḍigg painá ; ṭhedá kháná ; ṭir painá ; see FALL.
Proverb. tumbling off makes a good rider. ḍig ḍig ke sawár hundá hai ;
TUMBLER, *N.*
gilás. *m ;*
TUMOR, *N.*
1. large. phoṛá. *m ;*
2. small. rasaulí. *f ;* gilṭí. *f ;*
3. hard. ghaṛ. *m ;*
TUMULT, *N.*
gaugá. *m ;* shor. *m ;* raulá. *m ;* hal chal. *f ;* hallaṛ. *m ;* balwá. *m ;* dhumm. *f ;* khalhbalí. *f ;*
quarrel. daṇggá fasád. *m ;* laṛái. *f ;* jhagṛá. *m ;*
TUMULTOUS, *A.*
shorí ;
TUNE, *N.*
1. air. rág. *m ;* sarod. *m ;* laí. *f ;* tál. *m ;*
2. pitch of tune. sur. *f ;*
3. in tune. ṭhík sur nál ; sur raláke;
4. out of tune. besur ; besurá ; sur nahíṇ raldí ;
5. Proverb. when the bow strikes the tune is recognised. kiṇg wajje te rág bujjhá ;
TUNE, TO, *V. T.*
sur miláuní ; sur ṭhík karní ;
TUNEFUL, *A.*
chaṇgí sur dá ;

TUNELESS, *A*.
besurá ;
out of tune. besurí ;
TUNIC, *N*.
kurtá. *m* ; jhaggá. *m* ;
small. jhaggí. *f* ;
TUNNEL, *N*.
surangh. *f* ; maghorá. *m* ;
TURBAN, *N*.
safá. *m* ; pagg. *f* ; paggṛí. *f* ;
1. small. faiṇtá. *f* ;
2. red or black. chírá. *m* ;
3. blue and white. lunní. *f* ;
4. large turban. paggaṛ. *m* ; pagṛá. *m* ;
5. to put on a pagg. pagg bannhná ;
6. to take off. pagg láhná ;
TURBID, *A*.
gahirá ; gandhlá ; mailá ;
TURBULENCE, *N*.
fasád. *f* ; shor. *m* ; raulá. *m* ; laṛáí. *f* ; jhagṛá. *m* ; see TUMULT.
TURBULENT, *A*.
fasádí ; danggáí ; laṛáká ; jhagṛálú ;
TURKEY, *N*.
perú. *m* ;
TURMERIC, *N*.
wasár. *f* ; hald. *f* ; haldí. *f* ; hardal. *f* ;
TURMOIL, *N*.
raulá. *m* ; gaṛbaṛí. *f* ; ghaugá. *m* ; see TUMULT.
TURN, TO, *V. T.*
moṛná ; pherná ; moroṛná ; bhuál dená ; partná ;
1. to turn a wheel. geṛná ;
2. to turn a mill. jhoná ;
3. to turn up one's nose. nakk chaṛháuná OR waṭṭná ;
4. to turn out. kaḍḍh dená ; báhar kaḍḍhná; hikkná; chhekná; nakheṛná ;
5. to turn over a page. uladdná ;
6. to turn over papers. pholná ;
7. to cause to turn. bhuáuná ;
TURN, TO, *V. I.*
muṛná ; bháuná ; muṛ áuná ; pichháṇ muṛná ; palaṭná ; part áuná ;
1. to retire from. haṭ jáná ;
2. to turn aside. ikk páse ho jáná; lámbhe ho jáná ; muṇh moṛná ; muṇh bhuá lainá ;
TURN, *N*.
1. a revolution. chakkar. *m* ;
2. rotation. bárí. *f* ; wárí. *f* ;
3. change. badlá. *m* ; badlí. *f* ;
4. by turns. wárí wárí ; wáro wárí ; wáro waṭṭí ;
5. in his turn . apní wárí sir ;
6. a turn in canal or road. moṛ. *m* ; gunjal. *m* ; goshá. *m* ; waráṇglá. *m* ;
TURNING, *A*.
bhauṇke ; pichchháṇ muṛke ;
TURNIP, *N*.
goṇglu. *m* ;
Proverb re eye service. To take the mud off turnips. goṇgluáṇ tho miṭṭí láhuní ;
TURNSCREW, *N*.
pechkass. *m* ;
TURPENTINE, *N*.
tárpín. *m* ;
TURPITUDE, *N*.
badzátí. *f* ; badkárí. *f* ; see DEPRAVITY.
TURRET, *N*.
kiṇggará. *m* ; kaṇgará. *m* ; burjí. *f* ;
TURTLE, *N*.
kachchhú. *m* ; kachchhú kumháṇ. *m* ; khachoprá. *m* ;
TURTLE-DOVE, *N*.
ghuggí. *f* ;
TUSK, *N*.
1. elephant's. ḍaṇd. *m* ;
2. boar's. huḍḍ. *m* ;
TUTELAGE, *N*.
nigahbání. *f* ;
TUTOR, *N*.
ustád. *m* ;
TUTORESS. *N*.
ustádní. *f* ;
TWADDLE, *N*.
gapp shapp. *f* ; gapp. *f* ; khapp. *f* ;
TWAIN, *A*.
do ;
TWEAK, TO, *V. T.*
waṭṭ dená ; maroṛná ;
TWEEZERS, *N*.
1. barber's. mochná. *m* ;
2. for huqqa. uchchá. *m* ;
3. for fire. chimtá. *m* ;

TWELFTH, *A*.
bárahwáṇ ;
TWELVE, *A*.
bárah ;
TWENTIETH, *A*.
víwáṇ ;
TWENTY, *A*.
ví ;
TWICE, *A*.
dubárá ;
TWIG, *N*.
ṭáhní. *f* ; dálí. *f* ; laggar. *f* ;
twigs cut off from a tree. cháppíán. *f* ; chháṇgg. *m* ;
TWILIGHT, *N*.
1. evening. tarkáláṇ. *f* ;
2. morning. muṇh anherá ; muhánjlá ; jhalángh ;
TWIN, *N*.
jauṛá. *m* ;
TWIN BROTHER, *N*.
jauṛeán dá bhará. *m* ;
TWINE, *N*.
sút. *m* ; sutar. *m* ;
TWINE, TO, *V. T*.
waṭṭná ;
TWINGE, *N*.
ṭís. *f* ;
TWINKLE, TO, *V. I*.
jhamakná ; jhalakná ; chamakná ;
TWINKLING OF AN EYE, *N*.
jhamak. *f* ; chhin. *f* ;
TWIRL, TO, *V. T*.
ghumáuná ; bhuáuná ;
TWIST, *N*.
wal. *m* ; maroṛ. *m* ; waṭṭ. *m* ;
TWIST, TO, *V. T*.
waṭṭná ; maroṛná ; guṭṭhná ; bal dená ;
1. to twist a rope. ban waṭṭná ;
2. to cause to be twisted. guṭṭháuná ; waṭṭáuná ;
3. to twist into a knot. gaṭṭhná ;
4. having thoroughly twisted. maroṛ maráṛke ;
TWIST, TO. *V. I*.
maroṛná ;
TWISTED, *A*.
churaṛ muraṛ ;
TWIT, TO, *V. T*.
táná márná ;
TWITCH, *N*.
kambní. *f* ; húk. *f* ;
TWITTER, TO, *V. I*.
bolná ; chuṇ chuṇ karná ; chíṇ chíṇ karná ;
TWO, *A*.
do ;
TWO AND A HALF, *A*.
dhái ;
TWO BY TWO, *Adv*.
do do karke ;
TWO FOLD, *A*.
do guná ; dúná ; dúní ; duganá ;
TWO STORIED, *A*.
dohásmá ; domaṇjalá ;
TYKE, *N*.
kuttá. *m* ;
TYPE, *N*.
1. stamp. chháp. *f* ;
2. shape. ḍaul. *f* ; shakal. *f* ; muháṇḍrá. *m* ;
3. symbol. nishán. *m* ;
TYPHOON, *N*.
tufán. *m* ; parlu. *m* ; parlo. *m* ;
TYPICALLY, *Adv*.
misál de taur nál ; namuná OR misál deke ;
TYPIFY, TO, *V. T*.
misál dení ;
TYRANNIC, *A*.
saḳht ; beráhm ; jabardast ; karṛá ;
TYRANNICALLY, *Adv*.
beráhmí nál ; baṛe julm nál ; badobadí ; baṛí saḳhtí nál ;
TYRANNIZE, TO, *V. T*.
julm karná ; saḳhtí karní ; jástí karní ; anher karná OR macháuná ; see OPPRESS.
TYRANNY, *N*.
jástí. *f* ; julm. *m* ; julmí *f* anher. *m* ; saḳhtí. *f* ; zálmí. *f* upádh. *f* ; see OPPRESSION.
TYRANT, *N*.
zálim. *m* ; waḍḍá haner. *m* ; upádhí. *m* ;
TYRE, *N*.
hál. *m* ;
bicycle tyre. ṭair. *m* ;

U.

UDDER, *N.*
hawánná. *m;*
flesh of the udder. khírí. *f;*
UGLINESS, *N.*
bedhangí. *f;* bedaulí. *f;* badsuratí. *f;*
UGLY, *A.*
kojhá; badshakal; kurúp; kojhrá; badaul; kushakal; kusohná; see UNGAINLY.
Proverb used of an ugly person who pretends to be handsome. No mouth or forehead and a fairy has come down from the hills. múṇh ná matthá te jinn paháṛoṇ latthá;
ULCER, *N.*
phorá. *m;* nasúr. *m;* nathúr. *m;*
ULTIMATE, *A.*
pichchlá; chekaṛ núṇ; chekaṛlá akhírí;
ULTIMATELY, *Adv.*
oṛak núṇ; ant núṇ; chekaṛ núṇ; chekeṛe;
ULTIMATUM, *N.*
1. order. hukm. *m;*
2. the last word. chekaṛlí gal. *f;*
UMBRAGE, *N.*
gussá. *m;* narájagí. *f;* rossá. *m;*
UMBRELLA, *N.*
1. large. chhatar. *m;* chháttá. *m;*
2. small. chhatarí. *f;*
3. umbrella cover. uchár. *m;*
UMPIRE, *N.*
tariákal. *m;* sálas. *m;* tarfain. *m;*
in a game. ampair. *m;*
UNABASHED, *A.*
beháyá; belajj;
UNABLE, *A.*
lachár;
he was unable. uh dí kujh pesh ná challí;
UNACCEPTABLE, *A.*
nápasiṇd; námanzúr;
UNACCOMPANIED, *A.*
akallá;
UNACCOMPLISHED, *A.*
1. ignorant. guṇwár; aṇpaṛh; kowallá; ṭhoṭh;
2. unfinished. adhúrá;
UNACCUSTOMED, *A.*
jách nahíṇ;
UNACQUAINTED, *A.*
nawáqif; bekhabará; obhaṛ;
to be unacquainted. bekhabar rahná;
UNADORNED, *A.*
sádá;
without earrings. bussá; buchá buchá; buṭṭá;
UNADULTERATED, *A.*
khará;
UNADVISABLE, *A.*
befaidá; nahíṇ cháhidá; nawájib;
UNADVISEDLY, *Adv.*
besoche samjhe; beaqlí nál;
UNAFFECTED, *A.*
1. real. aslí; haqqí; chokkhá;
2. simple. siddhá sádá; bholá bhálá; siddh paddhrá; sidmasídá;
UNALLOYED, *A.*
khális; khará;
for metals. chokkhá; kuṇdan;
UNAMIABLE, *A.*
rukkhá; saṛiá bujhiá; vitriá hoyá;
UNALTERABLE, *A.*
ná badlanwálá; sábat;
UNANIMITY, *N.*
sáreáṇ dí saláh. *f;* ikk dilí. *f;* sáreáṇ dá ekká. *m;*
UNANIMOUS, *A.*
ikk dil hoke; ikk jabán; sáreáṇ dí saláh;
UNANIMOUSLY, *Adv.*
ikk dil hoke; ikk man hoke; ittifáq katke;
UNANSWERABLE, *A.*
bejawáb;
UNAPPRECIATIVE, *A.*
niqadará;
UNARRANGED, *A.*
bedhangá; kusutá;
UNARMED, *A.*
khálí hatth; hathal; náhatthá;
UNASKED, *A.*
aṇpuchchá;
UNASPIRING, *A.*
thoṛdilá; chhoṭe dilwálá; behauṇsilá;
UNASSUMING, *A.*
siddhá sádá; bholá bhálá;

UNATTACHED, *A*.
akallá ; wakh ; wakhrá ; aḍḍrá ;
UNATTAINABLE, *A*.
aṇboní gall ;
UNATTENDED, *A*.
akallá ;
UNAUTHENTICATED, *A*.
kachchá ;
UNAUTHORISED, *A*.
najáiz ;
UNAVAILING, *A*.
akárath ; befaidá ;
UNAWARES, *Adv*.
achának ; ajáiṇ ; achánchak ;
achánchet ;
UNBECOMING, *A*.
náwájib ;
UNBELIEF, *N*.
bepartítí. *f* ; wiswás. *f* ; shakk. *m* ;
bharm. *m* ; shakk shubhá. *m* ;
UNBELIEVER, *N*.
káfar. *m* ; daihriá. *m* ; munkar. *m* ;
bedín. *m* ;
UNBELIEVING, *A*.
bepartítá ; bharmí ; beyaqín ;
bepartítí ;
1. to be unbelieving. beyaqín honá ;
2. concerning religion. káfar ;
UNBENDING, *A*.
sakht ;
UNBIASSED, *A*.
niáiṇ ; belag ;
UNBIND, TO, *V. T*.
1. to open. kholná ;
2. to loosen, ḍhillá karná ;
UNBLAMEABLE, *A*.
bevigan ;
UNBLEACHED, *A*.
korá ;
UNBLEMISHED, *A*.
bedág ; beaib ; bekhoṭ ; aṇkhoṭ ;
holy. pavittar ; pák ; suchcham ;
UNBLUSHING, *A*.
besharm ; beháyá ; belajá ;
UNBOLT, TO, *V. T*.
kuṇḍí kholní ; kuṇḍí láhoní ;
UNBOSOM, TO, *V. T*.
man OR dil kholná ; bhed dassná ;
batláuná ; dil kholke dassná ;
UNBOUND, *A*.
khullhá ;
UNBOUNDED, *A*.
behadd ;
UNBRIDLED, *A*.
bemuhár ;
1. for a horse. bewággá ;
2. for the tongue. baṛbolá ;
UNBROKEN, *A*.
sabutá ;
UNBURDEN, TO, *V. T*.
bhár láh lainá OR láh dená ;
UNBUTTON, TO, *V. T*.
bíṛe láhuná ;
native button. ghuṇḍí kholná ;
UNCASTRATED, *A*.
ánḍal ;
UNCEASING, *A*.
har dam ; har vele ; har ghaṛí ;
UNCEREMONIOUS, *A*.
beḍhangá ;
UNCERTAIN, *A*.
shakkí gal ; pakkí gal nahíṇ ;
shakk hai ;
UNCERTAINTY, *N*.
kachch pakk. *m* ; dubdhá. *f* ;
shakk. *m* ; shakkshubhá. *m* ;
1. in uncertainty. dubdhe vichch ;
2. Proverb on uncertainty of life. Life is but the guest of a moment. koí dam dá paráhuná hai ;
3. Proverb on uncertainty of riches. The man gathers oil in ladlefuls, God spills it by the jarful. Bandá joṛe palí palí ; Rabb ruṛháwe kuppá ;
UNCHANGEABLE, *A*.
aṭall ; sábat ;
UNCHARITABLE, *A*.
nirmoh ; rukkhá ; karṛá ; patthar-dil ;
UNCHARITABLY, *Adv*.
tangdilí nál ;
UNCHASTE, *A*.
nápák ; luchchá ; guṇḍá ;
for a woman. gashtí ;
UNCHASTITY, *N*.
nápákí. *f* ;
UNCHECKED, *A*.
bemuhár ; bewággá ; anmoṛ ;
behídayatá ;
UNCIRCUMSPECT, *A*.
beaql ; nadán ; bewaqúf ;

UNCIVIL, A.
guṇwár; ujaḍ; rukkhá; kuḍhanggá; see UNPOLITE.
UNCIVILISED, A.
jangalí; ḍhaggá jehá;
UNCIVILLY, Adv.
ujaḍpuṇe nál; beadabí nál;
UNCLAD, A.
nangá;
UNCLE, N.
1. father's younger brother.
cháchá. m;
2. father's elder brother. táyá. m;
bábbá. m;
3. mother's brother. mámmá. m;
4. father's sister's husband.
phupphar. m;
5. mother's sister's husband.
massar. m;
UNCLEAN, A.
1. dirty. gaṇdá; mailá; aṇdhottá;
2. sinful. nápák; palít; bharisht;
UNCLEANLINESS, N.
palítí. f; gaṇdpuṇá. f; gaṇd. f;
gaṇd maṇd. f;
UNCLOUDED, A.
asmán nitriá hoyá;
UNCOMELINESS, N.
beḍhangí. f;
UNCOMELY, A.
kojhá; beḍaul; see UGLY.
UNCOMFORTABLE, A.
aukhá;
UNCOMMON, A.
virlá; anokhá; táwáṇ táwáṇ;
anúthá;
UNCOMPLETED, A.
adhurá;
UNCONCERN, N.
beparwáí. f; befikrí. f; nachiṇt. m;
UNCONCERNED, A.
nachintá; beparwáh;
careless. daullá maullá;
UNCONCERNEDLY, Adv.
beparwáí nál;
UNCONDITIONALLY, Adv.
[muloṇ;
UNCONFIRMED, A.
pakká nahíṇ; sábit nahíṇ;
UNCONNECTED, A.
aḍḍ; alag; bejoṛ; wakh;
wakhrá;

UNCONQUERABLE, A.
ajít; jehṛá ná háre;
UNCONSCIOUS, A.
besudh; besurt;
UNCONSCIOUSLY, Adv.
biná soche;
UNCONTROLLABLE, A.
wágg chhut; bemuhár;
UNCOOKED, A.
kachchá;
half cooked. ḍaḍḍrá;
UNCORD, TO, V. T.
udheṛná; kholná;
to become uncorded. udhaṛná;
UNCORRUPT, A.
dharmí; rást; nek; see UN-
DEFILED.
UNCORRUPTEDNESS, N.
sachchíáí. f; rástí. f;
UNCOUPLE, TO, V. T.
1. to open. kholná;
2. to separate. aḍḍ karná; wakkh
karná;
UNCOUTH, A.
akkhar ḳhán; guṇwár;
UNCOVER, TO, V. T.
nangá karná; oghárná; uttoṇ
láhná;
UNCOVERED, A.
nangá; besatar;
UNCULTIVATED, A.
appaṛ; virán; paí hoí zamín;
banjar;
UNDAMAGED, A.
kujh nuqsán nahíṇ;
UNDAUNTED, A.
naḍar; diler; beḳhauf; nirbháo;
kaihaṇdh;
UNDAUNTEDLY, Adv.
baṛí dilerí nál; himmat nál;
UNDECEIVE, TO, V. T.
samjháuná; kann kholná;
UNDECIDED, A.
hálí faisalá nahíṇ;
UNDECORATED, A.
besaṇgár; see UNADORNED.
UNDEFILED, A.
pák; bedág; pavittar; suchíárá;
suchchá; narwair; suchcham;
UNDER, Prep.
heṭh; thalle;

UNDER, *Adv.*
heṭh ;
from under. heṭhoṇ ; thalleoṇ ;

UNDERFOOT, *A.*
pairán heṭh ;

UNDERGO, TO, *V. I.*
1. to endure. saihná ; sahárná ; jhallná ;
2. to experience. gákhná ; wartná ; bhogná ;

UNDERGROUND, *A.*
zamín de heṭháṇ ;

UNDERHAND, *A.*
farebí ; see DECEITFUL ;

UNDERLINE, TO, *V. T.*
akkaráṇ de heṭh lakír OR líkh khichná ;

UNDERMOST, *A.*
heṭhlá ;

UNDERNEATH, *A.*
thalle ; heṭháṇ ; heṭh ;

UNDERRATE, TO, *V. T.*
beqadrí karní ; naqadará jánná ;

UNDERSIZED, *A.*
madhrá ;

UNDERSTAND, TO, *V. T.*
samajhná ; bujjhná ; ján láuná ; kalná : samajh áuní ; jánaná ; tháh lainí ;
1. have you understood anything ? kujh piṛ palle piá hai ?
2. I have not understood a word. mere palle kakkh ví nahíṇ piá ;

UNDERSTANDING, *N.*
aql. *f* ; samajh. *f*; buddh. *f*; bodh. *f*; thauh. *m* ; chetá. *m* ; matt. *f* ; chajj. *m* ; súјh. *f* ; sohjí *f* ;

UNDERTAKE, TO, *V. T.*
bíṛá chukkná ; jumá chukkná ; hatth vichch le lainá ;

UNDERTAKING. *N.*
1. enterprise. kamm. *m* ;
2. promise. waidá. *m* ; bachan. *m* ; sukhan. *m* ; qaul qarár. *m* ;

UNDERWEIGHT, *A.*
kassá ;

UNDESERVED, *A.*
náhaqqá ;

UNDESERVING, *A.*
nálaiq ; nikammá ;

UNDESIGNEDLY, *Adv.*
beiráde ;

UNDESIGNING, *A.*
siddhá ; bholá bhálá ; siddhá sádá ; siddh paddhará ;

UNDESIRABLE, *A.*
achchhá nahíṇ ;

UNDESTRUCTIBLE, *A.*
anist ;

UNDETERMINED, *A.*
bharmí ; bharmílá ; see UNDECIDED.

UNDEVIATING, *A.*
sadá ikko jehá ;

UNDISCERNING, *A.*
nirbúјh ; kaiṇdh ;

UNDISCIPLINED, *A.*
1. disobedient. anmoṛ ; nábar ; bemukh ;
2. rude, senseless. guṇwár ; beaql ; besamajh ;

UNDISCRIMINATING, *A.*
nirbúјh ;

UNDISPUTED, *A.*
jih dí bábat koí hil hujjat ná ho sake ; pakkí ;

UNDISTURBED, *A.*
dhírá ; chupp chupátá ;

UNDIVIDED, *A.*
sábit ; sárá ; sabút ;

UNDO, TO, *V. T.*
kholná ;
1. to undo sewing. udheṛná ;
2. to undo a bed or machinery. ukheṛná ;

UNDONE, *A.*
kachchá ;
open. khuliá hoyá ;

UNDOUBTED, *A.*
biná shakk de ; haqqí ; ṭhík ; sachch ;

UNDOUBTEDLY, *Adv.*
nisang ; sachchí muchchí ;

UNDRESS, TO, *V. T.*
kapṛe lahná ; líṛe láhuná ;
to take off all your clothes. naṇgá karná ;

UNDUE, *A.*
nawájib ; náhaqq ;

UNDULY, *Adv.*
nahaqqí ;

UNDUTIFUL. *A.*
kuputt ; nábar ;
an undutiful son. kuputtar. *m* ;

UNDYED, *A.*
korá ;
UNEARTH, TO, *V T.*
puṭṭná ; kholná ;
UNEASILY, *Adv.*
bechainí nál ; khushí nál nahíṇ ;
UNEASINESS, *N.*
bechainí. *f ;*
UNEASY, *A.*
aukhá ; bearám ; ḍáwáṇḍol ; biákal ;
1. of a child. nachallá ;
2. to be uneasy. jí ghabráuná ; ghábarná ;
UNEDUCATED, *A.*
anpaṛh ; anpaṛhiá ; aggyání ;
UNEMPLOYED, *A.*
berozgár ; vehlá ; nakhṛammá ; nikammá ;
UNENDING, *A.*
amukk ; beaṇt ; behadd ; beoṛak ; atyant ;
UNEQUAL, *A.*
waddh ghaṭṭ ; bemel ; ikko jehá nahíṇ ;
Proverb used of two unequal things ; Heel ropes of silk and a bridle of munj. paṭṭ dí pichcháṛí te munj díáṇ wággáṇ ;
UNEQUALLED, *A.*
uttam ; ále darje dá ; sáreáṇ nálon changá ; wadhke ;
UNEQUITABLE, *A.*
anníáí ;
UNERRINGLY, *Adv.*
durustí nál ;
UNESSENTIAL, *A.*
fadúl ; jarúrí nahíṇ ;
UNEVEN, *A.*
kharbaṛá ; uchchá níwáṇ ; vinggá taṛinggá ;
rough uneven ground. uchchí níwíṇ tháṇ. *f ;*
UNEVENNESS, *N.*
aḍḍokhorá. *m ;*
UNEXAMPLED, *A.*
uttam ; is taráh dá hor koí nahíṇ ;
UNEXPECTED, *A.*
achának ; jhaṭṭ ;
UNEXPECTEDLY, *Adv.*
achának ; achanchet ; jhaṭṭ ; ajáín ; chánchak ;

UNFADING, *A.*
pakká raṇg ;
UNFAIR, *A.*
beímán ; ṭhagg ; see FRAUDULENT.
UNFAIRLY, *Adv.*
1. with injustice. beinsáfí nál ; beadalí nál ;
2. with deception. chhal nál ; dhokhebází nál ;
UNFAIRNESS, *N.*
beinsáfí. *f ;* pachchhdárí. *f ;* beadalí. *f ;*
UNFAITHFUL, *A.*
beímán ; khoṭṭá ; chálbáz ; jhuṭhá ;
1. of a subordinate. lúṇ harám ;
2. one unfaithful to his promise. sukhan OR qaul dá jhuṭhá. *m ;*
UNFAITHFULLY, *Adv.*
beímání nál ;
UNFAITHFULNESS, *N.*
beímání. *f ;* luṇharámí. *f ;*
UNFAMILIAR, *A.*
nawáqif ;
UNFASTEN, TO, *V. T.*
kholná ; ḍhillá karná ;
UNFATHOMABLE, *A.*
atháh ; agádh ; behátth ; asgáh ;
to be unfathomable. tháh ná áuní ; hátth ná áuní ;
UNFAVOURABLE, *A.*
1. against. uh de khiláf ;
2. unfortunate. benasíb ; see UNFORTUNATE.
3. not good, achchhá nahíṇ ; changá nahíṇ ;
UNFAVOURABLY, *Adv.*
1. against. ulṭá ;
2. unfortunately. benasíbí nál ;
UNFEELING, *N.*
bedard ; beráhm ; sakht ; karṛá ; betaras ; patthar dil ; hattiárá ; hainsiárá ; sakht dil ;
UNFEELINGLY, *Adv.*
beráhmí nál ;
UNFINISHED, *A.*
adhurá ;
UNFIT, *A.*
najog ; ṭhík nahíṇ ; laiq nahíṇ ;
UNFITNESS, *N.*
nalaiqí. *f ;*

UNFITTING, *A.*
nalaiq ; nawájab ; námunásib ;
UNFIX, TO, *V. T.*
kholná ; mokla karná ;
UNFLINCHING, *A.*
beḍar ; pakká ;
UNFOLD, TO, *V. T.*
1. to open out. kholná ;
2. to show. dikháuná ; dikhá dená ; dikhálná ;
UNFORESEEN, *A.*
achánchak ; itifáqí ; takdírí ;
UNFORGIVING, *A.*
sakht ; beráhm ; karṛá ; bedard ;
UNFORMED, *A.*
beḍaul ;
UNFORTUNATE, *A.*
abhágí ; wachárá ; kulaihná ; bebhág ; chaṇḍará ; bechárá ; bekarmá ; karamhíṇ ; nirbhágí ;
1. we are unfortunate. sáḍe lekh saṛ gaye ;
2. stricken with misfortune. biptá dá máriá hoyá ;
UNFORTUNATELY, *Adv.*
benasíbí nál ; badqismatí nál ;
UNFOUNDED, *A.*
uh dí bunyád koí nahíṇ ; be bunyád ; khashufá ; jhuṭhá ; bewajáh ;
UNFREQUENTLY, *Adv.*
bahut ghaṭṭ ; kadí kadí ; ghaṭṭ wadh hí ;
UNFRIENDLINESS, *N.*
dushmaní. *f ;* adávat. *f ;* wair. *m ;* khár. *m ;*
UNFRIENDLY, *A.*
rukkhá ; bedard ; virodhí ; saṛial ;
UNFRUITFUL, *A.*
bephal ; apphal ;
UNFULFILLED, *A.*
púrá nahíṇ hoyá ;
UNFURL, TO, *V. T.*
jhaṇḍá gaḍḍná ;
UNFURNISHED, *A.*
khálí ; samán kujh nahíṇ ; vehlá ;
1. ruined. kholá ;
2. unadorned, without jewellry. bussá ;
UNGAINLY, *A.*
beḍaul ; basúrá ; bhaddá ; kuḍhaṇggá ; kuḍhabá ; see UGLY.

UNGENEROUS, *A.*
haiṇsiárá ;
UNGENIAL, *A.*
rukkhá ; saṛial ;
UNGODLINESS, *N.*
bedíní. *f ;* adharmtái. *f ;* bedharmí. *f ;* narástí. *f ;*
UNGODLY, *A.*
bedín ; adharm ; kuráhá ; sharu ; kudharmí ;
UNGRACEFUL, *A.*
kuḍhabá ; anárí ; see UNGAINLY.
UNGRACEFULLY, *Adv.*
búrí taráh nál ;
UNGRACEFULNESS, *N.*
kuḍhaṇggí. *f ;* kuḍhabí, *f ;*
UNGRACIOUS, *A.*
rukkhá ; saṛial ;
UNGRATEFUL, *A.*
náshukrá ; náshukriá ; nirgúṇ ; kiratghaṇ ; baguṇá ;
1. of a subordinate. luṇharám ;
2. don't be so ungrateful. ṇále ghúrná te ṇále khánà !
UNGRATEFULLY, *Adv.*
náshukarguzárí nál ;
UNGRATEFULNESS, *N.*
náshukrí. *f ;* beguṇí. *f ;* náshukarguzárí. *f ;*
UNGRUDGINGLY, *Adv.*
dil kholke ; dil nál ; khushí nál ; khulhe dil nál ;
UNHAPPILY, *Adv.*
hamsos nál ; aukhíái nál ;
UNHAPPINESS, *N.*
gam. *m ;* udásí. *f ;*
UNHAPPY, *A.*
udás ; dukhí ; bedil ; sasdil ;
UNHARNESS, TO, *V. T.*
sáj láhuná OR kholná ;
UNHEALTHY, *A.*
bímár ;
UNHESITATINGLY, *Adv.*
nisaṇg ; hausile nál ;
UNHINGE, TO, *V. T.*
kholná ;
UNHOLINESS, *N.*
nápákí. *f ;* palítí. *f ;*
UNHOLY, *A.*
nápák ; palít ; bharist ;
UNHOOK, TO, *V. T.*
kholná ;

UNHOPEFUL, *A*.
beás; beummed;
UNIFORM, *N*.
vardí. *f*; bardí. *f*;
UNIFORM, *A*.
ikk ḍaul; ikko jehá; ikk taráh;
UNINFORMED, *A*.
beḳhabar;
UNIFORMLY, *Adv*.
hamesh; sadá; ghaṛí muṛí;
UNIMAGINEABLE, *A*.
samajh thoṇ pare; aql thoṇ pare;
UNIMPORTANT, *A*.
halkí gal; haulí gal; waḍḍí gal nahíṇ;
UNINHABITABLE, *A*.
ráhan jog nahíṇ; wasan de laiq nahíṇ;
UNINHABITED, *A*.
suṇjá; sunná; warán; beábád; ujáṛ; ujaṛíá hoyá;
UNINTELLIGIBLE, *A*.
samajh thoṇ pare;
UNINTENTIONAL, *A*.
aiweṇ; bemurád;
UNINTENTIONALLY, *Adv*.
wissar bholle;
UNINTERESTED, *A*.
khuṇḍhá;
UNINTERESTING, *A*.
suád koí nahíṇ; besuádá;
UNINTERRUPTED, *A*.
beṛok;
UNINTERRUPTEDLY, *Adv*.
ghaṛí muṛí; muṛ muṛ; niraṇtar;
UNINVITED, *A*.
ápe; saddeáṇ biná; aṇpuchchá;
UNION, *N*.
ekká. *m*; mel miláp. *m*; milává. *m* wástá. *m*; miláuní. *f*; saṇjog. *f*; juṛutt. *f*; láká. *m*;
UNIQUE, *A*.
ḳháss; awallá; aṇokhá;
UNIRRIGATED, *A*.
baráni;
UNISON, *N*.
mel. *m*; mel miláp. *m*; mel jol. *f*; ekká. *m*;
UNIT, *N*.
ekká. *m*;
UNITE, TO, *V. T*.
lagáuná; joṛná; miláuná; gaṭháuná; raláuná;
UNITE, TO, *V. I*.
ikk mikk honá; milná; ralná; ikko mikko honá; ghusar musar ho jáná;
UNITEDLY, *Adv*.
mil ke; mil kar; ikk dil hoke; kaṭṭhe;
UNITY, *N*.
ekká. *m*; ralmil. *f*; ghusar musar. *m*; see UNION.
UNIVERSAL, *A*.
álamgír;
UNIVERSALLY, *Adv*.
har jagáh; har tháṇ; sárí dunyá vichch;
UNIVERSE, *N*.
jagat. *m*; dunyá. *f*; jagg. *m*; jahán. *m*;
UNIVERSITY, *N*.
kálij. *m*;
UNJUST, *A*.
anníáí; anníáíṇ; beinsáf; kudharm;
UNJUSTIFIABLE, *A*.
najaiz; nawájabí;
UNJUSTIFIABLY, *Adv*.
nahaqq; beinsáfí nál;
UNJUSTLY, *Adv*.
ḍhigáṇe; jástí nál; julm nál; beinsáfí nál;
UNKIND, *A*.
betaras; saḳht; beráhm; riskí;
UNKINDLINESS, *N*.
saḳhtí. *f*; beráhmí. *f*;
UNKINDLY, *Adv*.
beráhmí nál; saḳhtí nál;
UNKINDNESS, *N*.
saḳhtí. *f*; apkár. *m*;
UNKNOWABLE, *A*.
samajh thoṇ pare;
UNKNOWINGLY, *Adv*.
beḳhabar hoke; aṇbhol hoke;
UNKNOWN, *A*.
jis dá patá nahíṇ;
UNLACE, TO, *V. T*.
ḍorí kholná;
UNLADE, TO, *V. T*.
bhár láhná OR utárná;
UNLAWFUL, *A*.
nájaiz; qánún de ḳhiláf; forbidden by religion. harám;
UNLAWFULLY, *Adv*.
nájaiz taur nál;

UNLEARNED, *A.*
aṇpaṛh ; aṇsikkhiá ; beilm ; jáhal ; kowallá ;
UNLEAVENED, *A.*
patírí ; fatírí ;
UNLESS, *Conj.*
je ;
UNLETTERED, *A.*
aṇpaṛh ; aṇpaṛhiá ; beilm ; kuḍhaṇggá ;
UNLIKE, *A.*
wakkhrá ;
UNLIKELY, *A.*
aṇhoní gal ; ummed nahíṇ ;
UNLIMITED, *A.*
aṇgint ; behadd ; haddoṇ waddh ; behisáb ; hadd thoṇ báhar ;
UNLOAD, TO, *V. T.*
bhár láhná OR utárná ;
UNLOADING, *N.*
laháí. *f* ;
UNLOCK, TO, *V. T.*
tálá OR jandará kholná; khol dená ;
UNLOVING, *A.*
rukkhá ; bedard ;
UNLUCKILY, *Adv.*
aṇbhágí nál ; badqismatí nál ;
UNLUCKINESS, *N.*
benasíbí. *f* ; badqismatí. *f* ;
UNLUCKY, *A.*
nahis ; benasíb ; nakarmá ; nirbhágí ; abhágí ; badnasíb ;
UNMANAGEABLE, *A.*
bemuhár ; qábú vichch nahíṇ ráhndá ;
UNMANLY, *A.*
daṛákal ;
UNMANNERED, *A.*
guṇwár ; jáhil ; kuḍhaṇggá ;
UNMANNERLINESS, *N.*
beadabí. *f* ; guṇwárí. *f* ;
UNMANNERLY, *A.*
uṛák ; kuḍhaṇgg ; kuḍhabá ;
UNMARRIED, *N.*
1. man. kuṇwárá. *m* ;
2. woman. kuṇwárí. *f* ;
UNMASK, TO, *V. T.*
múṇh naṇgá karná ; ghuṇḍ láhuná ; khol dená ;
UNMENTIONABLE, *A.*
jih dá zikr karná munásib nahíṇ ; dassaṇ de laiq nahíṇ ; burí gall ;
UNMERCIFUL, *A.*
haiṇsiárá ; hattiárá ; beráhm ; sakht ; bedard ;
UNMERCIFULLY, *Adv.*
betarsí nál ; beráhmí nál ;
UNMERITED, *A.*
nahaqq ; aiweṇ ;
UNMINDFUL, *A.*
gáfal ; besoch ; láparwáh ; achet ; nachint ; kuḍárí ;
UNMISTAKEABLE, *A.*
bilkul sáf ;
UNMIXED, *A.*
khális ; ṭheṭh ; suddhá ; nirol ;
UNMOORE, TO, *V. T.*
báhuná ; wáhuná ;
UNMOVED, *A.*
1. firm. qaim ; sábit ;
2. imperturable. dhírajmáṇ ; nigghá ;
UNNAMED, *A.*
gumnám ;
UNNECESSARILY, *Adv.*
kujh jarurat nahíṇ ; aiweṇ ;
UNNECESSARY, *A.*
ajáyá ; ajáí ; beloṛ ; loṛídá nahíṇ ; jarurí nahíṇ ;
UNNERVE, TO, *V. T.*
ḍaráuná ; ḍar páuná ; ghabrá dená ;
UNNOTICED, *A.*
aṇbhol ; bekhabar ;
UNNUMBERED, *A.*
aṇgint ; behisáb ;
UNOBSERVANT, *A.*
gáfal ; besoch ; kuḍárí ; see UNMINDFUL.
UNOBTAINABLE, *A.*
alabbh ;
UNOCCUPIED, *A.*
vehlá ; korá ;
UNOPENED, *A.*
baṇd ;
UNORNAMENTED, *A.*
sádá ; see UNADORNED.
UNOSTENTATIOUS, *A.*
sádá ; sádmurádá ;
UNPACK, TO, *V. T.*
asbáb kholná ;
UNPALATEABLE, *A.*
kauṛá ; khaṭṭá ; phoklá ; miṭhlúná ;
UNPARALLELED, *A.*
anokhá ; awallá ;

UNPLEASANT, *A.*
burá ; márá ; mandí gal ; luhnwálí ;
UNPOLISHED, *A.*
gunwár ;
UNPOLITE, *A.*
gunwár ; rukkhá ; urák ; arutt ; jáhal ; ujad ;
UNPOLLUTED, *A.*
khális ; suchchá ;
holy. pák sáf ; pavittar ;
UNPOPULAR, *A.*
is thon koí khush nahín ;
UNPOPULARITY, *N.*
badnámí. *f ;*
UNPRECEDENTED, *A.*
anokhá ;
UNPREJUDICED, *A.*
beriyá ; begaraj; ádal ; níáin; belág; khará ;
UNPREPARED, *A.*
taiyár nahín ;
UNPRETENDING, *A.*
siddhá sádá ; bholá bhálá ;
UNPRINCIPLED, *A.*
badját ; khottá ; aibí ;
to be unprincipled. thir jáná ;
UNPRODUCTIVE, *A.*
apphal ; bephal ;
UNPROFITABLE, *A.*
akárath ; befaidá ; apphal ; bearth ; nikammá ;
UNPROFITABLY, *Adv.*
befaidá ;
UNPROPITIOUS, *A.*
benasíb ;
these days are unpropitious for me. eh dín mere wáste bhárí hain ;
see INAUSPICIOUS.
UNPROTECTED, *A.*
anáth ; bepanáh ; beásrá ;
UNQUENCHABLE, *A.*
anbujh ; jehrí bujhanwálí nahín ;
UNQUESTIONABLE, *A.*
bewaswás ; beshubáh ; thík ;
UNQUESTIONABLY, *Adv.*
nisang ; aslon; biná shakk de; zarúr;
UNQUIETNESS, *N.*
bedilí. *f ;* beqarárí. *f ;* bechainí. *f ;*
UNRAVEL, TO, *V. T.*
suljháuná ; kholná ; see UNDO.
UNREADY, *A.*
taiyár nahín ;
UNREAL, *A.*
banautí ; jehrá aslí nahín ;
UNREASONABLE, *A.*
ziddí ; aryál ; kabbá ;
UNREASONABLENESS, *N.*
zidd. *m ;* kabb. *m ;*
UNREASONABLY, *Adv.*
zidd nál ; beaqlí nál ;
UNRECOGNISED, *A.*
bepatá ;
UNRELATED, *A.*
betaalluq ; belág ; láwasta
UNRELENTING, *A.*
beráhm ; karrá ; patthardil ; sakht ; mují ;
UNRELIABLE, *A.*
be etibárá ; lutrá ; nigallá
UNRESERVED, *A.*
1. full. purá ;
2. frank. sádá ;
UNRESERVEDLY, *Adv.*
dil kholke ; barí safái nál ; sáf dilí nál ; khullam khullhá ;
UNRESTRAINED, *A.*
1. free. nirbandh ; ázád ;
2. licentious. luchchá ; gundá ;
UNRESTRICTED, *A.*
nirbandh ; berok ;
UNREWARDED, *A.*
inám nahín miliá ; khálí rihá ;
UNRIGHTEOUS, *A.*
bhairá ; kudharm ; adharmí ; kusattí ;
UNRIGHTEOUSNESS, *N.*
adharm. *m ;* kudharm. *m ;* adharmtái. *f ;* kusatt. *m ;* bedíní. *f ;* asatt, *m ;*
UNRIP, TO, *V. T.*
udherná ;
UNRIPE, *A.*
1. immature. kachchá ;
2. green. hará ; sabaj ;
UNROBE, TO, *V. T.*
1. unrobe onself. kapre utárná ; kapre láhuná ;
2. to cause another to unrobe one. kapre laháuná ;
UNROLL, TO, *V. T.*
kholná ; pholná ;
UNRUFFLED, *A.*
dhírajmán ; sunnsán ; chupp chapátá ; see TRANQUIL.

UNRULINESS, *N.*
shor. *m;* raulá. *m;* gaṛbaṛí. *f;*
UNRULY, *A.*
daṇggái; laṛáká; fasádí; aryál;
UNSAFE, *A.*
ḳhatrewálá;
UNSANCTIFIED, *A.*
nápák; palít; bharisht;
UNSATIABLE, *A.*
baṛá petú; kháú;
UNSATISFACTORY, *A.*
ṭhík nahiṇ;
UNSATISFIED, *A.*
rází nahíṇ; ḳhush nahíṇ; náḳhush;
UNSAVOURY, *A.*
mithsalúná; besuádá; mithlúná; phoklá; see INSIPID.
UNSEAL, TO, *V. T.*
mohr toṛná OR kholná;
UNSEARCHABLE, *A.*
samajh thoṇ pare; aql thoṇ báhar;
UNSEASONABLE, *A.*
bemausim; bebahár; pichhetá; avere;
UNSEASONABLY, *Adv.*
kuvele; bewaqt;
UNSEEMLINESS, *N.*
behayáí. *f;* besharmí. *f;* múkálak de kamm. *m;* nikhiddh kamm. *m;*
UNSEEMLY, *Adv.*
laiq nahíṇ; nikhiddh;
UNSEEN, *A.*
aṇwekhiá; anḍiṭṭh; adisṭ;
UNSELFISH, *A.*
parshárathí;
UNSELFISHNESS, *N.*
parshárath. *m;*
UNSERVICEABLE, *A.*
jehṛá kise kamm dá nahíṇ; nikammá; nakárá;
for a man. nakhaṭṭo;
UNSETTLE, TO, *V. T.*
thiṛkáuná; thiṛáuná;
UNSETTLED, TO BE, *V. I.*
thiṛakná; thiṛk jáná; dhakke dhore kháná; ḍullná; bhaṇbal bhuse kháná; phirtú ghirtú honá;
UNSHAKEN, *A.*
aḍol; qáim; aṭall; sábat; achar;
UNSHAPED, *A.*
aṇghaṛiá; beḍául; beḍauliá hoyá;

UNSHAPELY, *A.*
beḍhaṇggá; beḍaul; see UGLY.
UNSHEATHE, TO, *V. T.*
dhu lainá; talwár khichná;
UNSHELTERED, *A.*
suṇján;
UNSHOD, *A.*
naṇge pair;
UNSIGHTLY, *A.*
kuḍaul; beḍhaṇggá; see UGLY.
UNSKILLED, *A.*
anárí; aṇján; aṇsikkh; allhar;
UNSKILFUL, *A.*
aṇján; aṇguṇá;
UNSOCIABLE, *A.*
kauṛá; kallḳhor;
UNSOLD, *A.*
vikkiá nahíṇ; nahíṇ bik gayá;
UNSOLICITED, *A.*
biṇmaṇge;
UNSOPHOSTICATED, *A.*
sádá; sádmurádá; siddh sabháu; sidmasídá; siddh paddhrá;
UNSOUGHT, *A.*
biṇmaṇge;
UNSOUND, *A.*
1. defective. ḳharáb; ṭhík nahíṇ;
2. sickly. mándá; rogí; bimár;
UNSPARING, *A.*
saḳht; see SEVERE.
UNSPARINGLY, *Adv.*
saḳhtí nál;
UNSPEAKABLE, *A.*
jeh dá bayán nahíṇ ho sakdá;
UNSPOTTED, *A.*
bedág; sáf; nirmal; nirwair;
UNSTABLE, *A.*
bezabáná; do dilá;
UNSTEADY, *A.*
1. shaky. hilanwálá; dagmag;
2. to be unsteady. chaṇchláuná; ḍullná;
3. fickle. do dilá; do chittá; phirtú ghirtú;
UNSTRING, TO, *V. T.*
udheṛná;
to become unstrung. udhaṛná;
UNSUBSTANTIAL, *A.*
kachchí píllí gal; ḳhayálí;
UNSUCCESSFUL, *A.*
apphal rah gáyá;
in an exam. fel ho gáyá;

UNSUITABLE, *A.*
ayog; ajog; ṭhík nahíṇ; matlab dí nahíṇ; sáḍe kamm dí nahíṇ; nikárí;
UNSULLIED, *A.*
bedág; sáf; sutthrá;
for food. suchchí;
UNSUPPORTED, *A.*
besahárá; anáth;
UNSURPASSED, *A.*
uttam;
UNSYMPATHETIC, *A.*
bedard; rukkhá; patthardil; khuṭaṛ;
UNTAINTED, *A.*
suchchá; ṭhík; sáf;
spotless. bedág; nirdos;
UNTAMED, *A.*
ujaḍ;
UNTAUGHT, *A.*
anpaṛh; anpaṛhíá; aṇsikkhhiá;
UNTENANTED, *A.*
vehlá; korá;
UNTHANKFUL, *A.*
nashukará; kirtghan; see UNGRATEFUL.
UNTHRIFTY, *A.*
ujáṛú;
UNTIDY, *A.*
ḍhillá ḍhállá; kuchajjí; kuchajjá;
dirty, mailá kuchailá; gaṇḍá; palít;
UNTIE, TO, *V. T.*
chhaḍḍná; khalás karná;
a knot. gaṇḍ kholná;
UNTIL, *Prep.*
tík; toṛí; talak;
UNTIL, *Adv.*
jad tík; tad tík; jichar toṛí;
UNTIMELY, *Adv.*
kuvelá; kuvele; bewaqt; ajáí; ajáyá;
UNTIRING, *A.*
aṇthakk;
UNTO, *Prep.*
tík; núṇ; de neṛe; talak;
UNTOUCHED, *A.*
achhúh; korá;
UNTOWARD, *A.*
ziddí; see PERVERSE.
UNTRIED, *A.*
aṇján; allhar;

UNTRUE, *A.*
jhuṭhá; asatt; see FALSE.
UNTRUSTWORTHY, *A.*
beatabár; beatbárá; nigallá;
UNTRUTH, *N.*
jhuṭh. *m;* jhuṭh. muṭh. *m;*
kúṛ. *m;* phauṛ gapp. *m;*
UNUSED, *A.*
korá; unlag;
UNUSUAL, *A.*
anokhá; ajíb; awallá;
UNUTTERABLE, *A.*
ná kahan jog;
UNVEIL, TO, *V. T.*
bepaṛdá karná; paṛdá uṭháuná; see UNMASK.
UNVENTILATED, *A.*
binájharná; bárí biná;
UNWARILY, *Adv.*
biná soche samjhe; bek͟habrí nál;
UNWARINESS, *N.*
bek͟habrí. *f;* see HEEDLESSNESS.
UNWARRANTABLE, *A.*
náwájab; nájaiz;
UNWARY, *A.*
bek͟habar; see HEEDLESS.
UNWASHED, *A.*
aṇdhotá;
new unwashed. korá;
UNWEARIED, *A.*
aṇthakk;
UNWELL, *A.*
bimár; sust; rogí; mándá; dukhíá;
UNWEILDINESS, *A.*
bojhalpaṇ. *m;*
UNWEILDY, *A.*
moṭá;
UNWILLING, *A.*
bedil; nák͟hush; badhá rudhá; rází nahíṇ;
UNWILLINGNESS, *N.*
bedilí. *f;*
UNWISE, *A.*
murakh; beaql; besamajh; nadán; buddhhíṇ;
UNWORTHILY, *Adv.*
nalaiqí nál;
UNWORTHINESS, *N.*
nalaiqí. *f;*
UNWORTHY, *A.*
nalaiq; chaṇḍál; bhaiṛá; nikammá;
unworthy son. kuputtar. *m;*

UNWRITTEN, *A*.
jabání ;
UNWROUGHT, *A*.
aṇghaṛiá ; aṇghaṛat ;
UNYIELDING, *A*.
khuráṇt ; haṭhílá ; kaṛrá ; háṭhá ;
UNYOKE, TO, *V. T*.
chhaḍḍná ;
UP, *Adv*.
utte ; uppar ; uttáṇ ;
UP, *Prep*.
utte ; ṭík ;
1. up to, till. táṇí ;
2. up and down. urháṇ parháṇ ;
UPBRAID, TO, *V. T*.
táṛná ; jhiṛakná ; uláhmáṇ dená ; tohmat láuná ;
UPBRAIDING, *N*.
mehná. *m* ; gilá. *m* ; nahorá. *m* ; naktoṛá. *m* ;
UPHOLD, TO, *V. T*.
sambhálná; sámbh lainá ; sámbhná; sahárí rakkhná ; bachái rakkhná ; thamm lainná ; see SUPPORT.
UPHOLDER, *N*.
sámbhú. *m* ; sambhálú. *m* ;
UPLIFT, TO, *V. T*.
utáṇ chukkná ; uṭháuná ; uchchá karná ;
UPON, *Prep*.
utte ; uppar ;
UPPER, *A*.
upparlá ; utlá ;
UPPERMOST, *A*.
upparlá ; utlá ;
UPPER ROOM, *N*.
chaubárá. *m* ;
UPRAISE, TO, *V. T*.
utáṇ chukkná ; uṭháuná ; uchchá karná ;
UPRIGHT, *A*.
siddh sabháu ; sachchá ; nek ; sáf dil ; suddh ; hatth dá suchchá ; ímánwálá ;
an uppright man. sachchiár. *m* ;
UPRIGHTLY, *Adv*.
dharm nál ; ímán nál ; rástí nál ;
UPRIGHTNESS, *N*.
siddhtái. *f* ; sidhaut. *f* ; ímándárí. *f*; sachchiái. *f* ;
UPRISE, TO *V. I*.
uṭṭhná ;
UPROAR, *N*.
chík chiháṛá. *m* ; raulá. *m* ; khapp. *f* ; tarthalí. *m* ; khalhbalí. *f* ; khalal. *m* ; hagámá. *m* ; see FRAY.
UPROOT, TO, *V. T*.
jaṛoṇ puṭṭná ; ukheṛná ; ukháṛná ; muddhoṇ puṭṭná ;
UPSET, TO, *V. T*.
ulṭáuná ; ḍohlná ; ulaṭ dená ; uladdná ; mudhá karná ;
to throw down. ḍegná ;
UPSET, *A*.
ghábar gayá ;
I was so upset at hearing this. merá dil ih sunke ajihá taṇg hoiá jo kujh ṭhík nahíṇ ;
UPSIDE DOWN, *Adv*.
úṇdhá ; mudhá ; puṭṭha ; heṭhlí utte ;
UPSTART, *N*.
nawán rajiá. *m* ;
UPWARD, *Adv*.
utáṇ ; utle pásse ;
URBANE, *A*.
melí ; miṭṭhá ; sharáf ;
URBANITY, *N*.
bhalmansái. *f* ; narmí. *f* ; ádar bhau. *m* ; ádar. *m* ;
URCHIN, *N*.
chhokrá. *m* ; muṇḍá. *m* ; káká. *m* ;
URGE, TO, *V. T*.
1. persuade. chukkná ; pakkí karní ; tágíd karná ; tapáuná ; ulárá dená ; gallíṇ láuná ; saláh dení ;
2. to hasten. chhetí turáuná ; dauṛáuná ; chaláuná ;
3. to importune. kajáuná ; pichche painá ; tarle minnat karní ; uke karní ; girgiráuná ;
4. to urge on an animal. ṭich ṭich karná ; ṭichkárná ;
with a goad. ár márná ;
URGENCY, *N*.
shatábí. *f* ; chetí. *f* ; káhlí. *f* ; jhab. *m* ; utaulí. *f* ;
URGENT, *A*.
jarúrí ; zarúrí ; jarúr ;
URGENTLY, *Adv*.
jaldí ; chhetí ; shatábí ; jarúr barjárúr ;
URGING, *N*.
tagádá. *f* ;

URINAL, *N*.
pasháb kháná. *m*; ṭaṭṭi. *f*;
URINE, *N*.
pasháb. *m*; karúrá. *m*; mútar. *m*; mút. *m*; chítá. *m*; baul. *m*;
URINATE, TO, *V. T.*
pasháb karná; dhár mární; mútarná; múťná;
US, *Pron.*
sánúṇ;
USAGE, *N*.
wartárá. *m*; mamúl. *m*; rauṇs. *f*; wartáo. *m*; rawáj. *m*; salúk. *m*; wartává. *m*; lokáṇ chárí. *f*;
USE, *N*.
1. benefit. faidá. *m*; nafá. *m*; láh. *m*;
2. usage. wartárá. *m*; rauṇs. *f*;
3. this is of no use to me. ih mere kamm dá nahíṇ;
USE, TO, *V. T.*
wartná; kamm vichch leáuná; kharchná; láuná;
to use up. chaṭṭ karná;
USED UP, TO BE, *V. I.*
ḍhalná; chaṭṭ honá;
USED TO, TO BECOME, *V. I.*
gákhná;
USEFUL, *A*.
kamm dá; kammwálá;
this is very useful. ih baṛá kamm aundá hai;
USEFULLY, *Adv.*
faide nál;
USEFULNESS, *N*.
faidá. *m*;
USELESS, *A*.
aphal; akárath; nikammá; fijúl; kise kamm dá nahíṇ; awirthá; chauṛ chappaṭṭ; khoṭṭá; bearth; befaidá; nakárá;
USELESSLY, *Adv.*
befaidá; eweṇ; dhigáṇe; awirthá;
USUAL, *A*.
mámulí; rawájí; wartmán;
USUALLY, *Adv.*
askar; bahut karke; hamesh; bahutá;
USURER, *N*.
biájariá. *m*; biájí. *m*; sháh. *m*; karáṛ. *m*;
USURP, TO, *V. T.*
haqq dabáuná; haqq márná; dabá lainá; jor nál lainá; náhaqq lainá;
USURPATION, *N*.
zabardastí. *f*; jástí. *f*; julm. *m*; wáddhá. *m*;
USURY, *N*.
biáj. *m*;
UTENSIL, *N*.
bháṇḍá. *m*;
UTILITY, *N*.
nafá. *m*; faidá. *m*;
UTILIZE, TO, *V. T.*
wartná; kamm vichch leáuná;
UTMOST, *A*.
wadhke; jinná ho sake;
UTTER, *A*.
sárá;
UTTER, TO, *V. T.*
bayán karná; dassná; bolná; ucharná;
UTTERANCE, *N*.
bayán. *m*; bachan. *m*; ucháraṇ. *f*; uchar. *m*;
UTTERLY, *Adv.*
att; sárá;
utterly useless. chauṛ chapaṭṭ;
UTTERMOST, *A*.
báhut;

V.

VACANCY, *N*.
kháli naukarí. *f*; khálí jagáh. *f*;
VACANT, *A*.
1. empty. sakkhná; khálí; phoká;
2. thoughtless. gáfal; besoch; beaql;
VACATE, TO, *V. T.*
vehlá OR khálí karní;
VACATION, *N*.
chhuṭṭí. *f*;
VACCINATE, TO, *V. T.*
lodá karná; ṭíká láuná OR lagáuná; mátá ṭhekná;
to cause to be vaccinated. ṭhikáná;
VACCINATION, *N*.
loda. *m*; ṭíká. *m*;
VACCINATOR, *N*.
lodá karnwálá. *m*; ṭíká lagáunwálá. *m*;

VACILLATE, TO, *V. T.*
hichkaná; gallé gallé phirná; bhanbal bhúse kháná; ḍáwáṇḍol OR ḍaṇwáḍol karná; see HESITATE.
VACILLATION, *N.*
kachch pakk. *m;* do chitt. *m;* dochittí. *f;*
VACUITY, *N.*
ḳhálí tháṇ. *m;* with. *m;*
VAGABOND, *N.*
awárá. *m;* raul. *m;* laphaṭiá. *m;* bhondú. *m;*
VAGRANT, *A.*
awárá;
VAGUE, *A.*
gol mol; gumgo; sáf nahíṇ;
VAIN, *A.*
1. conceited. phiṭṭiá hoyá; ghamaṇḍí; baṛe damágwálá; báṇká; ṭeḍhá; damákí;
2. in vain. aiweṇ; akárath; birthá; befaidá; virthá;
3. vain thoughts. phoke vichár. *m;* wáhiát sochál. *m;*
VAINGLORIOUS, *A.*
sheḳhíḳhorá;
VAINGLORY, *N.*
phauṛ. *m;* ghamaṇḍ. *m;*
VAINLY, *Adv.*
akárath; befaidá; aiweṇ; birthá;
VAIN THINGS, *N.*
phokíáṇ galláṇ. *f;*
to imagine vain things. kúṛe ḳhayál karná;
VALEDICTION, *N.*
vidiá. *m;*
VALET, *N.*
bahirá. *m;* naukar. *m;* ṭahliá. *m;*
VALIANT, *A.*
diler; dilaur; bahádur; ḥimmatí; see BRAVE.
VALIANTLY, *Adv.*
dilerí nál; himmat nál; bahádurí nál;
VALIANTNESS, *N.*
dilerí. *f;* bahádurí. *f;* mardau. *m;*
VALID, *A.*
ṭhík; jaiz; siddh;
VALIDITY, *N.*
pakkíái. *f;*
VALIDLY, *Adv.*
durustí nál; ṭhík ṭhák; ṭhíkam ṭhík;
VALLEY, *N.*
khaḍḍ. *m;* wádí, *f;* hiṭhár. *f;* dún. *m;* niwán. *m;*
1. the valley of the shadow of death. maut dí chháṇ dí khaḍḍ. *f;*
2. pass. dará. *m;*
VALOUR, *N.*
dilerí. *f;* jigará. *m;* surtáí. *f;* see VALIANTNESS.
VALUABLE, *A.*
waḍḍe mull dá; pyárá; máhngá; waḍḍ múllá;
VALUATION, *N.*
andájá. *m;* mull. *m;* tak. *m;*
VALUE, *N.*
1. profit. faidá. *m;* khaṭṭí. *f;* labhat. *f;*
2. price. mull. *m;* dám. *m;*
3. estimation. qadr. *m;*
VALUE, TO, *V. T.*
1. to esteem. qadr OR lihúz karná;
2. to estimate. háṛá lainá; andájá karná; háṛná;
VALUELESS, *A.*
nakárá; raddí. see WORTHLESS.
VANISH, TO, *V. I.*
uḍḍná; luk jáná; tal jáná; champat honá; alop ho jáná;
to vanish out of sight. cháíṇ máíṇ ho jáná;
VANITY, *N.*
1. affectation. ákaṛ. *f;* maṭak. *f;* báṇkpuná. *m;* heṇh. *f;* kibar. *m;*
2. worthlessness. augan. *m;* biarth. *m;*
3. vain things. phokíáṇ galláṇ. *f;* wáhiyát galláṇ. *f;*
4. a mere breath. sáh mátr. *f;* dam hí dam. *f;*
VANQUISH, TO, *V. T.*
1. to conquer. jitáuná; fatáh pauní; bhoh kar dená; hunjá pherná;
2. to refute. jhuṭhá karná; khaṇḍná; jhuṭheáṇ karná;
VAPOUR, *N.*
bháf. *f;*
1. steam from kettle or hot food. hawáṛ. *m;*

2. from the ground. bhaṛás. *f*;
VARIABLE, *A*.
dodilá; nigallá;
VARIABLENESS, *N*.
wádhá ghátá. *m*; beqarárí. *f*;
VARIANCE, *N*.
1. difference. farq. *m*;
2. disagreement. náittifáqí. *f*;
VARIATION, *N*.
farq. *m*; wádhá ghátá. *m*;
VARIEGATE, TO, *V. T.*
wagáṛná; farq páiná;
VARIEGATED, *V*.
chit kabrá; bahí raṇggí; ḍabbá; raṇg baraṇgí;
VARIETY, *N*.
1. difference. farq. *m*; bhinn. *m*;
2. kind. qism. *m*; jiṇs. *f*;
VARIOUS, *A*.
anek; wakkho wakkh; qism qism dá; bahut qism dá; bháṇt bháṇt dá;
VARIOUSLY, *Adv*.
bhinn bhinn; kaí ikk;
VARNISH, *N*.
raugan. *m*; raṇg. *m*;
VARNISH, TO, *V. T.*
raṇg karná; raugan karná; pálish karná;
VARY, TO, *V. T.*
badal dená; see CHANGE.
VARY, TO, *V. I.*
badal jáná;
VASSAL, *N*.
naukar. *m*; chákar. *m*; ṭahliá. *m*;
VASSALAGE, *N*.
chákarí. *f*; naukarí. *f*; gulámí. *f*;
VAST, *A*.
1. in numbers. aṇgint; beshumár;
2. in space. behadd;
VASTNESS, *N*.
waḍḍápaṇ. *m*;
VAT, *N*.
chaubachhá. *m*;
VAULT, *N*.
1. jump. chhál. *f*; haṛappá. *m*;
2. tomb. makbará. *m*; M; qabr. *f*; M., see TOMB.
VAUNT, *N*.
shekhí. *f*; gapp. *f*; gapp shapp. *f*; lafát. *f*;
VAUNT, TO, *V. T.*
shekhí mární; baṛíáṇ galláṇ karní; gapp mární; see BOAST.
VAUNTER, *N*.
gappí. *m*; ḍhakárí. *m*; lafatiá. *m*;
VAUNTINGLY, *Adv*.
shekhí nál;
VEGETABLE, *N*.
sabzí. *f*; ság. *m*; ság pattar. *m*; bhájí. *f*;
1. cooked vegetables. bhájí salúná. *m*;
2. caste of vegetable growers. ráín. *m*;
3. vegetable vendor. karúṇjṛá. *m*;
VEGETATION, *N*.
ság. *m*; sabzí. *f*;
VEHEMENCE, *N*.
josh. *m*; tezí. *f*; sargarmí. *f*; zor. *m*; lahir. *f*;
VEHEMENT, *A*.
joshwálá; tez;
VEHEMENTLY, *Adv*.
badobadí; zor nál; baṛe josh nál; dhakko dhakkí; zorí;
VEHICLE, *N*.
gaḍḍí. *f*;
VEIL, *N*.
ghuṇḍ. *m*; ghuṇggaṭ. *f*; chádar. *f*; dupaṭṭá. *m*;
1. child's veil. chuní. *f*;
2. Muhammadan veil, reaching to the ground. bhurká. *m*;
3. tinsel veil worn by bridegroom. sehrá. *m*;
4. Proverb, used of a person who does something secretly, which must come out. When she began to dance what was the use of a veil. nachchan laggí te ghuṇggaṭ kyá!
VEIL, TO, *V. T.*
1. to veil oneself. ghuṇḍ kaḍḍhná; pallá lainá;
2. to screen. paṛdá karná
VEIN, *N*.
náṛ. *f*;
1. varicose vein. phullí hoí náṛ. *f*;
2. Proverb, re the chalákí of blind beggars. annheáṇ dí ikk rag, wadhík hundí hai;

VELOCITY, *N.*
shatábí. *f;* chheti. *f;*
VELVET, *N.*
makhmal. *f;*
VEND, TO, *V. T.*
wechná ;
VENDEE, *N.*
kharídár. *m ;* gaihak. *m ;*
VENDER, *N.*
bapárí. *m ;*
vegetable vender. karúnjṛá. *m ;*
VENDIBLE, *A.*
wikáú ;
VENERABLE, *A.*
manniá daniá ; buzúrg ; waḍḍá ;
VENERATE, TO, *V. T.*
izzat OR adab karná ; manná ;
pujná ; see RESPECT.
VENERATION, *N.*
ádar. *m ;* izzat. *f;* waḍiáí, *f;* see
RESPECT.
VENGEANCE, *N.*
badlá. *m ;* waṭṭá. *m ;*
VENGEFUL, *A.*
minnhá ; badlá lainwálá ;
VENIAL, *A.*
muáf karan jog ;
VENSION, *N.*
haran dá más. *m ;*
VENOM, *N.*
1. enmity. kauṛ. *f;* wair. *f;*
dushmaní. *f;* adávat. *f;*
2. poison. wis. *f;*
VENOMOUS, *A.*
zaiharí ;
VENT, *N.*
gánḍ. *f;* chut. *m ;* bund. *m ;*
VENT, TO, *V. T.*
dassná ; mashhur karná ;
VENTILATOR, *N.*
roshandán. *m ;* bárí. *f;* jharokhá. *m;*
VENTURE, *N.*
1. danger. ján jokhoṇ. *m ;* khatrá. *m ;*
2. chance. dho. *m ;* sabab. *m ;*
mauqá. *m ;*
VENTURE, TO, *V. T.*
himmat OR dilerí OR hausilá
karná ;
VENTURESOME, *A.*
himmatí ; diler ; dilaur ; dilwálá ; bekhauf ; naḍar ;

VERACIOUS, *A.*
sachchá ;
VERACIOUSLY, *Adv.*
sachchíáí nál ;
VERACITY, *N.*
sachchíáí. *f;*
VERANDAH, *N.*
barándá. *m ;* ḍhárá. *m ;*
VERB, *N.*
fei. *m ;* kiriyá. *m ;*
VERBAL, *A.*
munh zabání ;
VERBALLY, *Adv.*
zabání ;
VERBATIM, *Adv.*
lafz balafz ; harf baharf ; ikk ikk
akkhar ;
VERDANT, *A.*
sáwá ; hariá ; sabz ; hariálá ;
see GREEN.
VERDICT, *N.*
faisalá. *m ;* hukm. *m ;*
1. decree. digarí. *f;*
2. opinion. raí. *f;*
2. advice. saláh. *f;*
VERDIGRIS, *N.*
janggál. *m ;*
VERDURE, *N.*
sabzí. *f* hariaul. *f;* sabjí. *f;*
sabjá. *m ;* hará. *m ;*
VERIABLE, *A.*
sábit ho sakdá ;
VERIFICATION, *N.*
partál. *f;* huliyá. *m ;* sabút. *m ;*
VERIFY, TO, *V. T.*
sábit karná ; sachchá ṭhahráuná ;
VERILY, *Adv.*
sachí muchí ; sachchíáí nál ;
VERITY, *N.*
sachchíáí. *f;* sachchí gal. *f;* purí
gal. *f;* haqqí gal. *f;*
VERMICELLI, *N.*
seviáṇ. *f;*
1. Indian. seviáṇ. *f;*
2. Italian. warmselí. *f;*
VERMILION, *N.*
shingraf. *m ;*
VERMIN, *N.*
chíchchaṛ. *m ;* pissú. *m ;*
VERMINOUS, *A.*
ganḍá ; mailá ; palít ;

VERNACULAR, *A*.
desí; mulkí; watani;
VERSATILE, *A*.
chapal; trikkhá; tez;
VERSATILITY, *N*.
chapaltái. *f*; tezí. *f*;
VERSE, *N*.
shabad. *m*; baiṇt. *f*;
1. of the Scriptures. ayat. *f*;
2. of poetry. tuk. *m*; wars. *m*; kawít. *f*; baiṇt. *f*;
2. of the Vedas. surtí. *f*;
VERSICLE, *N*.
ayat. *f*;
VERSIFIER, *N*.
sáir. *m*; shairí. *m*;
VERSIFY, TO, *V. T*.
kawít paṛhná OR kahná; baiṇt láuná;
VERSION, *N*.
1. translation. tarjamá. *m*;
2. account. bayán. *m*;
VERTEBRA, *N*.
lakk dí sanjlí. *f*; kaṇgroṛ. *f*;
VERTICAL, *A*.
siddhá; khaṛá;
VERTIGO, *N*.
chakkar. *m*; bhauṇ. *m*; naherní. *f*; girdaní. *f*;
VERY, *Adv*.
bahut; pujke; att; ḍáḍhí;
1. very much. bahutá; bahut sárá;
2. this boy is very foolish. eh muṇḍá pujke beaql hai.
VESPERS, *N*.
shám dí namáz. *f*;
VESSEL, *N*.
1. boat. A. small. beṛi. *f*; B. large. beṛá. *m*;
2. earthen vessel. bhánḍá. *m*; hánḍí. *f*;
3. earthen cooking pot. tauṛá. *m*; hánḍí. *f*; tauṛí. *f*;
4. large brass cooking vessel. walṭohí. *f*; deg. *m*;
5. large shallow dish. thál. *m*; tháli. *f*; parát. *f*;
6. large skin vessel for oil or ghi. kuppá. *m*;
7. oval shaped bowl used by faqirs. chippí. *f*; kapprí. *f*; kishtá. *m*;
8. shallow brass drinking vessel. chhanná. *m*;
9. brass glass. gilás. *m*;
10. earthen water pot with wide mouth. balhní. *f*;
11. bason of baked clay. dáurá. *m*; baṭhal. *m*;
12. a metallic water vessel. gágaṛ. *f*; gágaṛí. *f*;
13. Proverb. Empty vessels make the most noise. sakkhná te haulá bhánḍá bahut khaṛkdá hai!;
VEST, *N*.
banáiṇ. *f*; banyán. *f*;
VEST, TO, *V. T*.
1. dress. kapṛe páuná;
2. endow. ikhtiyár dená;
VESTIBULE, *N*.
deuṛhí. *f*; dálán. *m*; usárá. *m*;
VESTIGE, *N*.
patá. *m*; nám nishán. *m*; khoj. *m*;
VETERAN, *A*.
buzurg; buḍḍhá;
VETO, *N*.
námanzúrí. *f*;
VETO, TO, *V. T*.
maná karná; rokná; ṭhák dená;
VEX, TO, *V. T*.
chheṛná; satáuná; rusáuná; jich karná; taṇg karná; ruáuná; khechal karní; chiṛáuná; khijáuná; akáuná; aká dená; see ANNOY.
VEXATION, *N*.
1. trouble. dikkdái. *f*; taklíf. *f*; khechal. *f*; khachch. *f*;
2. grief. hamsos. *m*; afsos. *m*; kasálá. *m*;
VEXATIOUS, *A*.
dukhdái; mují; kaṭhan;
VEXED, *A*.
naráz; khafá; nimújháṇ;
to be vexed. russ jáná; sáṛáuná; khîjh jáná; akkná;
VEXING, *A*.
dukhdái;
VEXING, *N*.
khijh. *f*;
VIA, *Adv*.
dí ráhíṇ; de wasíle; de ráh; hoke

VIADUCT, N.
púl. m ;
VIAL, N.
shíshí. f ;
VIAND, N.
bhojan. m ; parshád. m ; ṭukk. m ;
see FOOD.
general name for food. roṭí. f ;
VIBRATE, TO, V. I.
hilná ; jhúlná ;
VIBRATION, N.
jhuláú. m ;
VICAR, N.
pádrí sáhib. m ;
VICARIOUSLY, Adv.
kise dujje dí ráhíṇ ;
VICE, N.
1. defect. aib. m ; nuqs. m ;
dos. m ; khoṭ. m ; dosh. m ;
2. wickedness. sharárat. f ; badkárí. f ; búrí ádat. f ;
3. blacksmith's vice. jamúr. m ;
sanní. f ;
VICINITY, N.
ásá pásá. m ; gawáṇḍh. m ; neṛ. f ;
álá dawálá. m ; verhṛá. m ;
see NEIGHBOURHOOD.
VICIOUS, A.
dosí ; aibí ; badját ; vailí ;
maṇḍá ; sharír ; chaṇḍál ; ját
bharisht ; chaṇdrá ; bhaiṛá ; máṛá ;
luṇḍá ; guṇḍá ; luchchá ; of a
horse. chak máranwálá ;
VICIOUSLY, Adv.
1. spitefully. wair nál ; adávat
nál ; khár nál ;
2. licentiously. badkárí nál ; masteweṇ nál ; mastí nál ;
VICIOUSNESS, N.
badzátí. f ; badkárí. f ; badí. f sharárat. f ; vail. m ; luchchpuṇá m ;
VICTIM, N.
bheṭ. f ; qurbání. f ; balídán. m ;
balí. f ;
VICTIMIZE, TO, V. T.
dhokhá dená ; see DECEIVE.
VICTOR, N.
jetú. m ; jittanwálá. m ; jítú. m ;
VICTORIOUS, A.
jittiá hoyá ; sarjít ;
VICTORIOUSLY, Adv.
baṛí fatáh nál ;

VICTORY, N.
fatáh. f ; jit . f ; jet. f ; sar. f ;
to gain a victory. fatáh páuní ;
jet milní ; haráuná ; jittná ;
sar karná ;
VICTUALS, N.
rasad. f ; dáná pání. m ; ann
pání. m ; parshád. m ; roṭí. f ;
rozí. f ; khádh khurák. f ; khájjá' m ;
VIE, TO, V. T.
rís OR jatan karná ;
VIEW, TO, V. T.
vekhná ; takkná ; dekhná ;
VIEW, N.
nazárá. m ;
VIGIL, N.
jagrátá. m ; jággá. m ;
VIGILANCE, N.
chatráí. f ; hoshiyárí, f ; khabardárí. f ;
VIGILANT, A.
chattar ; hoshiyar ;
VIGILANTLY, Adv.
chatráí nál ; hoshiyárí nál ;
ríjh nál ;
VIGOR, N.
1. bravery. himmat. f ;
2. alertness. chustí. f ;
3. strength. pursháráth. m ;
jor. m ;
4. zeal. josh. m ;
VIGOROUS, A.
himmatí ; uddamí ; tagṛá ; himmatwálá ; laṭṭhá ; chust ;
himtál ; haṭṭá kaṭṭá ;
VIGOROUSLY, Adv.
himmat nál ; zor nál ; uddam
nál ; dabb ke ; híle nál ;
VILE, A.
kamíná ; máṛá ; nikammá ;
bhaiṛá ; maháṇ pápí ;
VILELY, Adv.
bahut búrí taráh nál ;
VILENESS, N.
gaṇḍpuṇá. m ; luchchpuṇá. m ;
VILIFICATION, N.
badnámí. f ;
VILIFY, TO, V. T.
gál kaḍḍhní ; badnám karná ;
beizzátí karní ; niṇdiá karní ;
dé láuná ;

VILLAGE, *N.*
piṇḍ. *m ;* jhok. *f ;* garáṇ. *m ;* a small village. piṇḍorá. *m ;* paṇḍorá. *m ;*

VILLAGER, *N.*
gaṇwár. *m ;* jaṭṭ. *m ;* piṇḍ dá. *m ;* peṇḍú. *m ;* garáyáṇ. *m ;* jaṭṭ búṭ. *m ;* what do we villagers know about reading and writing? asíṇ piṇḍáṇ de rahnwále likhan paṛhan kí jánie?

VILLAIN, *N.*
badkár. *m ;* badmásh. *m ;* luchchá. *m ;* guṇḍá. *m ;*

VILLAINOUS, *A.*
badját; chaṇḍál; sharír; ḳharáb; guṇḍá;

VILLAINY, *N.*
sharárat. *f ;* badí, *f ;* badkárí. *f ;* ních kamm. *m ;*

VINDICATE, TO, *V. T.*
sachchá sábit karná;

VINDICATION, *N.*
parmán. *m ;* safáí. *f ;*

VINDICTIVE, *A.*
badlá lainwálá;

VINDICTIVELY, *Adv.*
adaut nál; dushmaní nál; wair nál; kiṛ nál; khár nál;

VINDICTIVENESS, *N.*
saḳhtí. *f ;* kíná. *m ;* jástí. *f ;* wair. *m ;* kiṛ. *f ;*

VINE, *N.*
dákh. *f ;* dákh bel. *f ;* fruitful vine. phullí hoí dákh. *f ;*

VINEGAR, *N.*
sirká. *m ;*

VINEYARD, *N.*
dákháṇ dá bág. *m ;*

VIOLATE, TO, *V. T.*
1. to do an injury. nuqsán karná; wigáṛná; ḳhajjal ḳharáb karná;
2. to desecrate. ḳharáb OR palít karná;
3. to rape. kuár bhannhná; zabr zanáh karná;

VIOLATION, *N.*
1. rape. hatth gamaṇ. *m ;* hatth bhog. *m ;* zabr zanáhí. *f ;*
2. transgression. gunáh. *m ;* qusúr. *m ;* páp. *m ;*

VIOLATOR, *N.*
taqsírí. *m ;* gunáhí. *m ;* pápí. *m ;* jurmí. *m ;*

VIOLENCE, *N.*
dhakká. *m ;* máromár. *f ;* saḳhtí. *f ;* dhakkebází. *f ;* wadhíkí. *f ;* jálamí. *f ;* zabardastí. *f ;* jor. *m ;* lohṛá. *m ;* jabarí. *f ;* dhakkesháhí. *f ;* jorí. *f ;* julm. *m;* haner. *m ;* jástí. *f ;* jarb. *f ;* taddí. *f ;* to use violence. jor márná OR launá;

VIOLENT, *A.*
zabardast; jorávar; joshwálá;

VIOLENTLY, *Adv.*
dhakko dhakkí; badobadí; dabbke; taṇo taṇí; dhiṇgadhaṇgí; chupaṭṭ; dhiṇgá mastí; see FORCIBLY.

VIOLIN, *N.*
sáraṇgí. *f ;* chakárá. *m ;*

VIOLINIST, *N.*
sáraṇggiá. *m ;* rabábiá. *m ;*

VIPER, *N.*
sapp. *m ;*

VIRGIN, *N.*
kuárí. *f ;* kanniyáṇ. *f ;* kaṇjak. *f ;*

VIRGINITY, *N.*
kuár. *f ;* kuárpuṇá. *m ;*

VIRILE, *A.*
tagṛá; mazbut; himmatí; jorwálá;

VIRILITY, *N.*
táqat. *f ;* himmat. *f ;* jor. *m ;*

VIRTUE, *N.*
gun. *m ;* chaṇgíáí. *f ;* nekí. *f ;*

VIRTUOUS, *A.*
dharmí; nek; díndár; pák; rást; gúní; satí; sádh; satwantí;

VIRULENCE, *N.*
dushmaní. *f ;* adávat. *f ;* kauṛ. *m ;* wair. *m ;*

VIRULENT, *A.*
khabís; saḳht;

VISAGE, *N.*
rupp. *m ;* muháṇḍrá. *m ;* muṇh. *m ;* muṛaṇggá. *m ;*

VISCOSITY, *N.*
les. *f ;*

VISCOUS, *A.*
lesalá; libbá; chíplá;

VISIBLE, *A.*
pargaṭ ;
VISIBLE, TO BE, *V. I.*
jápná ; sujjhná ;
VISIBILITY, *N.*
pargaṭái. *f* ;
VISION, *N.*
1. dream. sufná. *m* ; royá. *m* ;
2. eyesight. jotná. *f* ;
3. obscure vision. jháulá. *m* ;
VISIT, *N.*
darshan. *m* ; mel milává. *m* ; milní. *f* ; mel gel. *f* ;
VISIT, TO, *V. T.*
darshan karná ; milná ; matthe laggná ;
VISITOR, *N.*
wáhṇḍá. *m* ; parauhná. *m* ; melí. *m* ;
VITAL, *A.*
jání ;
essential. jarúri ;
VITALITY, *N.*
1. life. jí. *m* ; ján. *f* ;
2. strength. táqat. *f* ;
VITALIZE, TO, *V. T.*
ján páuní ;
VITIATE, TO, *V. T.*
ḳharáb karná ; wigáṛná ; chauṛ kar dená ;
VITIATED, *A.*
khoṭṭá ;
VITUPERATE, TO, *V. T.*
nindiá karná ; jháṛ karní ; gaṇḍ bakná ; gálí dení ;
VITUPERATION, *N.*
bhanḍí. *f* ; gál. *f* ; gálí. *f* ; phakkaṛ. *f* ; phiṭak. *f* ; gálí galoch, *f* ; see ABUSE.
VIVACIOUS, *A.*
chust ; chohulá ;
VIVACITY, *N.*
jí. *m* ; ján. *f* ; josh. *m* ; tezí. *f* ;
VIVID, *A.*
baṛá sáf ;
VIVIDLY, *Adv.*
baṛí safái nál ;
VIVIFY, TO, *V. T.*
jiwáuná ; jiwálná ;
VIXEN, *N.*
lomrí. *f* ;
VOCABULARY, *N.*
lafzán dí firist. *f* ;
VOCATION, *N.*
peshá. *m* ; kamm. *m* ; báná. *m* ;
VOCIFERATE, TO, *V. T.*
jor nál bolná ; uchchí uchchí karke bolná ; chíkná ;
VOCIFERATION, *N.*
shor. *m* ; raulá. *m* ;
VOCIFERIOUS, *A.*
shorí ;
VOGUE, IN, *Adv.*
wartmán ;
VOICE, *N.*
wáj. *f* ; wáz. *f* ;
VOID, *A.*
suṇn ; sunnsáṇ ; ḳhálí ; phoká ;
to make void, of no effect. akárath karná ;
VOLATILE, *A.*
phurtílá ; chalák ;
VOLCANO, *N.*
jowálá mukhí. *f* ; aggwálá paháṛ *m* ;
VOLITION, *N.*
marzí *f* ; cháh. *f* ;
VOLLEY, *N.*
wáṛ. *f* ;
VOLUBILITY, *N.*
tez zabání. *f* ; chattarái. *f* ;
VOLUME, *N.*
kitáb. *f* ; jild. *f* ; see BOOK.
VOLUNTARILY, *Adv.*
marzí nál ; apní marzí nál ; apne áp ;
happily. khushí nál ; chaiṇ chaiṇ ;
VOLUNTARY, *A.*
marzí dá ;
VOLUPTUOUS, *A.*
bhogí ; mastáná ; guṇḍá ; laṭpaṭá ; chaskebáj ;
VOLUPTUOUSNESS, *N.*
bhog. *m* ; guṇḍpuṇá. *m* ; luchcháú. *m* ; chaskebájí. *f* ;
VOMIT, *N.*
káí. *f* ; ulṭí. *f* ; upparchhal. *f* ; sutṇá. *n* ;
VOMIT, TO, *V. T.*
káí áuní ; káí honí ; ulṭí âuní ; jí uchalná ; jí kasiáuná ; ugláchh dená ;
VORACIOUS, *A.*
peṭú ; khaú ; leṇjh ; nadídá ;
VOTE, *N.*
voṭ. *m* ; raí. *f* ;

VOTE, TO, *V. T.*
vot dená ; raí dení ;
VOUCH, TO, V. T.
gawáhí dení ; ugáhí dení ;
VOUCHER, *N.*
rasíd. *f ;*
VOW, *N.*
mannat. *f ;* mannatá. *f ;* manaut. *f ;*
sukhan. *m ;* sukkhná . *f ;* qarár. *m ;*
VOW, TO, *V. T.*
mannat manná ; kalapná karní ;
wádá dená ; qaul qarár karná ;
sukkhná sukkhní ;
to pay vows. mannatán chaṛháuná ;
VOWEL, *N.*
laggá máttaran. *m* ;
VOYAGE, *N.*
samundrí safar. *m ;*
VULGAR, *A.*
gaṇwár ; bajárí ; jáhal ; ullú ;
VULGARITY, *N.*
beadabí. *f ;*
VULGARLY, *Adv.*
beadabí nál ;
VULTURE, *N.*
gidh. *f ;* girjh. *f ;* gilijh. *f ;*
VULVA, *N.*
chút. *f ;* kus. *f ;* phuddá. *m ;*

W.

WAD, *N.*
gaḍḍí. *f ;*
WADDING, *N.*
rúṇ. *m ;*
WADE, TO, *V. I.*
páṇí vichchoṇ laṇghná ;
WAG, *N.*
ṭhaṭṭhebáz. *m ;* makhauliá. *m ;*
WAG, TO, *V. I.*
hilná ; ḍullná ; lahilaháuná ;
WAG, TO, *V. T.*
hiláuná ; ḍuláuná ;
WAGE, *N.*
1. monthly pay. talab. *f ;*
2. daily wages. majdurí. *f ;* diháṛí. *f;*
3. earnings. kamáí. *f ;* lábh. *m ;*
WAGE, TO, *V. T.*
laṛáí karní ; jhagaṛná ;
WAGER, *N.*
bájí. *f ;* shart. *f ;*

WAGER, TO, *V. T.*
bájí láuní ; dá lagáuná ; vadná ;
WAGGERY, *N.*
nakhrá. *m ;* hássí. *f ;* maskarí. *f ;*
makhaul. *m ;*
WAGGISH, *A.*
maskará ; ṭhaṭṭhebáz ; makhauliá ;
WAGGISHLY, *Adv.*
hásse nál ; makhaul nál ; hasske;
WAGON, *N.*
gaḍḍá. *m ;*
WAGTAIL, *N.*
mamolá. *m ;*
WAIF, *N.*
yatím. *m ;*
WAIL, *N.*
roná. *m ;* see WAILING.
WAIL, TO, *V. T.*
bilápná ; chíkná ; roná ; wilkná ;
kurláuná ;
WAILING, *N.*
durohí. *f ;* roná. *m ;* siápá. *m ;*
WAIST, *N.*
kamar. *f ;* lakk. *m ;* tikk. *m ;*
the body from waist downwards.
teṛ. *m ;*
WAISTBAND, *N.*
paṭká . *m ;* peṭí. *f ;*
WAISTCOAT, *N.*
waskaṭ. *f ;* phatúhí. *f ;* salúká. *m ;*
kuṛtí. *f ;*
WAIT, TO, *V. I.*
ḍhil karná ; uḍíkná ; ṭhahrná ;
rastá vekhná ; khaṛá ráhná ; ráh
vekhná ;
1. to wait for one. uh dá ráh
uḍíkná ;
2. to lie in wait. dá vichch ráhná ;
súh vichch honá ; chhái márná
OR láuná ;
WAITER, *N.*
chákar. *m ;* naukar. *m ;* ṭahliá. *m ;*
WAITING, *N.*
uḍík. *f ;* jhák. *f ;*
WAIVE, TO, *V. T.*
chhaḍḍná ; ján dená ;
WAKE, TO, *V. T.*
jagáuná ; uskáuná ; uṭháuná ;
WAKE, TO, *V. I.*
jág painá ; jáganá ; akkh kholná ;
nindar uggháṛná ;

WAKEFUL, *A.*
jágdá ; chaukas.
Proverb. The wakeful have female buffaloes born, the sleepy have (only) male ones. jágdeáṇ díáṇ kaṭṭíáṇ te sutteáṇ de kaṭṭe

WAKEFULNESS, *N.*
jág. *m ;*

WALE, *N.*
már. *f ;* chábak dá nishán. *m ;* lás. *f ;*

WALK, *N.*
sail. *m ;* sail sappattá. *m ;*

WALK, TO, *V. I.*
ṭurná ; chalná ; phirná ; sail OR sair karná ; ṭuriá jáná ;
1. to walk fast. pair chukke ṭurná ;
2. to walk lame. langáuná ;
3. to walk honestly. siddhe chál OR ráh chalná ;
4. to walk openly. khulliáṇ phirná ;

WALKING STICK, *N.*
1. straight. soṭí. *f ;*
2. with crooked handle. khunḍí. *f ;*
3. cane. beṇt. *m ;*

WALL, *N.*
kaṇḍh. *f ;* dawál. *f ;*

WALLET, *N.*
jholí. *f ;* jholá. *m ;* khurjí. *f ;* baṭúá. *m ;*

WALLOW, TO, *V. I.*
loṭná ;

WALNUT, *N.*
akhroṭ. *m ;*

WALTZ, *N.*
nách. *m ;*

WAN, *A.*
pílá ; jard ;

WAND, *N.*
láṭhí. *f ;* ḍaṇḍá. *m ;* soṭá. *m ;*

WANDER, TO, *V. I.*
awárá phirná ; ghummná ; bhulle phirná ; beráh bhoṇḍá phirná ; bhaṇbal bhúse khánná ; udále pudále phirná ; ḍawáṇḍol phirná ;
as a faqir. ramtá honá ;

WANDERER, *N.*
awárá. *m ;* bhondú. *m ;* saláлі. *m ;*

WANDERING, *A.*
ghumde ghumde ;

WANDERING, *N.*
kuráhí. *f ;* bhaṇbal bhúse. *m ;*
of a faqir. ramtá. *m ;*

WANE, *N.*
kamí. *f ;* kasar. *m ;* thuṛ. *f ;* see DECREASE.

WANE, TO, *V .I.*
ghaṭṭ honá ; thuṛ jáná ; ghaṭṭ-ná ; nakhuṭṭ jáná ;

WANNESS, *N.*
pílái. *f ;* jardí. *f ;*

WANT, *N.*
garíbí. *f ;* thuṛ. *f ;* loṛ. *f ;* ṭoṭ. *f ;* kasar. *f ;* ghápá. *m ;*
in want. thuṛyal ;

WANT, TO, *V. T.*
cháhuná ; jí karná ; see DESIRE.

WANTING, *A.*
1. necessary. loṛídá ; jarúrí ;
2. short, missing. ghaṭṭ ;

WANTON, *A.*
khíwá ; mastáná ; mast ; luchchá ; badját ; laṭpaṭá ;
1. a man of wanton habits. ṭapká. *m ;*
2. a woman of wanton habits ṭapkí. *f ;*

WANTONLY, *Adv.*
mastí nál ; masteweṇ nál ;

WANTONNESS, *N.*
chanchalái. *f ;* kharmastí. *f ;* mastí. *f ;* ḍhekchál. *f ;*

WAR, *N.*
jaṇg. *m ;* laṛái. *f ;* lám. *f ;*
1. Hindu holy war. juddh. *m ;*
2. Muhammadan holy war. jihád. *m ;*

WAR, TO, *V. T.*
laṛái OR jaṇg OR juddh karná ;

WARBLE, *N.*
wáj. *f ;* wáz. *f ;*

WARBLE, TO, *V. T.*
1. to voice. wáz dení ;
2. to tune the voice. alápná ;
3. to sing. gáuná ;
4. as a bird. chuṇ chuṇ karná ;

WARD, *N.*
nábálig. *m ;*

WARDER, *N.*
darogá. *m ;*

WARDROBE, *N.*
almárí. *f ;*
WARES, *N.*
saudá. *m ;* saudágarí dá mál. *m ;* mál matáh. *m ;*
WAREHOUSE, *N.*
gudám. *m ;* kothí. *f ;* dukáṇ. *f ;* málkháná. *m ;* mál gudám. *m ;* bhaṇḍár. *m ;*
WARFARE, *N.*
laṛáí. *f ;*
WARILY, *Adv.*
chaukasí nál ; hoshiyárí nál ;
WARINESS, *N.*
chaukasí. *f ;* chalákí. *f ;* khabardárí. *f ;* hoshiyárí, *f ;* sojh. *f ;*
WARLIKE, *A.*
laṛáká ; talangá ;
WARM, *A.*
garm ; tattá ; tapiá hoyá ;
luke warm. kosá ;
WARM, TO, *V. T.*
1. at fire. agg sekná ; tauná ; tattá karná ; tapáuná ; nighá karná ; garm karná ;
2. in sun. dhuppe sekná ; siyyá sekná ;
WARMHEARTED, *A.*
dilwálá ;
WARMLY, *Adv.*
jor nál ; dil nál ; diloṇ wajhoṇ ; see HEARTILY.
WARMTH, *N.*
garmáí. *f ;* garmí. *f ;* tezí. *f ;* niggh. *m ;* waṭṭ. *m ;* tá. *m ;*
enthusiasm. josh. *m ;*
WARN, TO, *V. T.*
samjháuná ; jatáuná ; chitárná ; nasíhat dení ; tágíd karná ; janáuná ;
WARNED, TO BE, *V. I.*
chitáriá jáná ; chitáyá jáná ; pattá lagná ;
WARNING, *N.*
1. admonition. jhiṛak. *f ;* nasíhat. *f ;* tágid. *f ;*
2. notice. khabar. *f ;* suh. *f ;*
WARP, *N.*
1. of cloth. táni. *f ;*
2. in wood. ḍingg. *m ;* wiṇg. *m ;* tedh. *m ;*
3. warp and woof. táná báná. *m ;*
WARP, TO, *V. I.*
moṛná ; wiṇgá karná ; ḍiṇgá karná ; suṇggaṛná ;
to stretch out the warp. táni tanní ;
WARPED, *A.*
diṇggá ; wiṇggá ; tedhá ;
WARRANT, *N.*
parmán. *m ;* hukm námá. *m ;* parwáná. *m ;*
1. of arrest. baranṭ. *m ;*
2. of attachment. kurkí dá parwáná. *m ;*
WARRANT, TO, *V. T.*
jumme lainá ; jámin honá ;
WARRANTEE, *N.*
jámín. *m ;*
WARRANTY, *N.*
jámaní. *f ;* jamánat. *f ;*
WARRIOR, *N.*
surmá. *m ;* jangí sipáhí. *m ;* faují. *m ;* jodhá. *m ;*
WART, *N.*
mahuká. *m ;* mohká. *m ;*
WARY, *A.*
suchet ; hoshiyár ; chaukas ; chalák ; siáná ; samajhdár ; daná ; sochmán ; sojhmán ;
WASH, *N.*
ashnán. *m ;*
WASH, TO, *V. T.*
dhoná ; ashnán karná ; naháuná ; suddh karná ;
1. ceremonially. wazu karná, M ;
2. to cause to be washed. dhuláuná ; dhulwáuná ;
3. to be washed. dhotá jáná ; dhuppná ; dhuchchná ;
WASHERMAN, *N.*
dhobí. *m,* M ; chhinbá. *m,* H ;
WASHERWOMAN, *N.*
dhobaṇ. *f,* M ; chhiṇbaṇ. *f,* H ;
WASHING, *N.*
dho. *m ;* dhuláí. *f ;* dhopat. *f ;*
1. pay for washing. dhulwáí. *f ;*
2. clothes for one washing. jugán. *f ;*
WASP, *N.*
bhúṇḍ. *m ;* demí. *f ;* dhamúṛí. *f ;* dhamoṛí. *f ;*
1. long thin species. ghuraiṇ. *f ;*
2. wasps' nest. bhuṇḍáṇ dí khakkhar. *f ;*

WASTE, *N.*
ujáṛ. *f*; nuqsán. *m*; barbádí. *f*;
WASTE, TO, *V. T.*
guáuná; gawáuná; mál uḍáuná; wigáṛná; gumáuṇá;
WASTE, TO, *V. I.*
uḍ puḍ jáná; ḳharáb honá; ujáṛná; gal jáná; akárath jáná;
WASTED, *A.*
súṇj. sunnsáṇ; barbád;
WATCH, *N.*
ghaṛí. *f*;
guard. pahirá. *m*; pahrewálá. *m*; paiharà chaungkí. *f*;
WATCH, TO, *V. T.*
táṛná; táṛ rakkhná; ráh takkná; jagáná; paihará dená; ḳhabar lainí;
WATCHFUL, *A.*
jágdá; chaukas; suchet;
WATCHFULLY, *Adv.*
dhíán nál; soch wichárke; hoshiyárí nál;
WATCHFULNESS, *N.*
chitt. *m*; chettá. *m*; dhíán. *m*; chuksái. *f*;
WATCHING, *N.*
jággá. *m*; chaukídárí. *f*;
WATCHMAKER, *N.*
ghaṛísáz. *m*;
WATCHMAN, *N.*
chaukídár *m*; bárwálá. *m*; pahirá. *m*; rabtí. *m*; rabtiá. *m*; pahrewálá. *m*; rákkhá. *m*;
WATER, *N.*
páṇí. *m*; jal. *m*; nír. *m*;
1. water of life. amrít. *m*;
2. water flag. dabbh. *m*;
3. water creatures. tarwar. *m*;
WATER, TO, *V. T.*
1. to irrigate land. sinjhná; pailí bharná; pailí píchaná; rauní karná; páṇí dená OR láuná; tar karná;
2. to water cattle. páṇí ḍáhunná OR ḍaháuná; ḍáhná;
WATERBEARER, *N.*
bihistí. *m*, M; jhiúr. *m*, H; máshkí. *m*, M; kahár. *m*, H; sakká. *m*, M; panihár. *m*, H; panihárá. *m*, H; mahírá. *m*, H;
WATERCOURSE, *N.*
khál. *m*; kassí. *f*; áḍ. *f*; nálá. *m*; see CANAL.
WATERDRAIN, *N.*
nálá. *m*;
WATERFOWL, *N.*
murgábí. *f*;
WATERING CAN, *N.*
phuárá. *m*;
WATER MELON, *N.*
haduáná. *m*; tarbúj. *m*; matirá. *m*;
WATERMILL, *N.*
gharáṭ. *m*; panchakkí. *f*;
WATERPITCHER, *N.*
suráhí. *f*; ghaṛá. *m*;
WATERPOT, *N.*
ghaṛá. *m*; jhajjar. *f*; gaḍwá. *m*; see VESSEL.
WATERPROOF, *N.*
barsátí. *f*;
WATER REVENUE, *N.*
ábyánná. *m*;
WATER SPOUT, *N.*
parnálá. *m*;
WATER TROUGH, *N.*
áḍ. *f*; chaubachchá. *m*; hauj. *m*; haud. *m*;
WATERY, *A.*
ábí;
WAVE, *N.*
káṇgg. *f*; ṭháṭh. *f*; ṭhall. *f*; chhal. *f*;
ripple. laihr. *f*;
WAVE, TO, *V. T.*
1. to shake. hiláuná;
2. to wave the head up and down. jhumná; jhulná;
WAVE, TO, *V. I.*
lahilaháuná; lahí lahí karná;
WAVER, TO, *V. I.*
jhakkná; shakk vichch ráhná; sauṇká karná; ḍolná;
WAVERING, *A.*
duchitt; duchittá; dodilá; benítá;
WAVING, *N.*
lahik. *f*; lahilaháṭ. *f*;
WAX, *N.*
mom. *f*;
sealing wax. lákh. *f*;
WAX CANDLE, *N.*
mom baṭṭí. *f*;
WAXEN, *A.*
momí;

WAY, *N.*
1. path. ráh. *m ;* rastá. *m ;* pahiá. *m ;* márg. *m ;*
2. journey. paṇdh. *m ;* waṭ. *m ;* paiṇdá. *m ;*
3. on the way. wáṭe ; ráh vichch ;
4. method. ḍhang. *m ;* rauṇs. *f ;*
5. the way of the world. lokáṇ chárí. *f ;*

WAYFAIRER, *N.*
ráhí. *m ;* páṇdhí. *m ;*

WAYLAY, TO, *V. T.*
ghát láuní ; ghát vichch baiṭhná ; ḍáká márná ; taṛde ráhná ; dí chháhí vichch laggná ;

WAYWARD, *A.*
ziddí ; ḍhíṭhá ; ákí ; haṭhí ;

WAYWARDLY, *Adv.*
gustákhí nál ;

WAYWARDNESS, *N.*
ghamaṇḍ. *m ;* zidd. *m ;* kabb. *f ;*

WAYWORN, *A.*
thakká máṇdá ;

WE, *Pro.*
asíṇ ; ápáṇ ;

WEAK, *A.*
lissá ; nirbal ; nadhál ; kamjor ; hína ; máṛá ; natáná ; huttiá ; ḍhillá ; balhín ; durbal ;
1. weaker. liserá ;
2. very weak. máṛúá ; huttiá hoyá ;
3. weak (tea). patlí ;
4. weak (in character) kachchá ;

WEAKEN, TO, *V. T.*
kamjor OR lissá karná ; zor ghaṭṭáuná ; nirbal karná ;

WEAKLING, *N.*
poh dá jammiá hoyá. *m ;* dil dá kachchá. *m ;*

WEAKLY, *Adv.*
kamjor hoke ; thiṛke ;

WEAKNESS, *N.*
nirbaltáí. *f ;* kamjorí. *f ;* nátáqatí. *f ;* thiṛ. *m ;* bhus. *m ;*

WEAL, *N.*
1. happiness. ḳhushi. *f ;* anaṇd. *m ;* mauj. *f ;*
2. weal or woe. nekí badí. *f ;*
3. mark of a stroke. lás. *f ;*

WEALTH, *N.*
daulat. *f ;* máyá. *f ;* dhan. *m ;* ḳhajáná. *m ;* daulat máyá. *f ;* padárath. *f ;* púnjí. *f ;*
wealth and riches. mál dhan. *m ;*

WEALTHY, *A.*
máldar ; dhanwáṇ ; dhaní ; amír ; ambír ; baḳhtáwar ; dhanmáṇ ;
a wealthy man. dudh putt wálá. *m ;* lakhpatí. *m ;*

WEAN, TO, *V. T.*
dudh chhuḍḍáuná ;

WEAPON, *N.*
hathiyár. *m ;* shastar. *m ;*
weapons and accoutrements. shastar bastar. *m ;*

WEAPONLESS, *A.*
behathiyárá ; náhatthá ;

WEAR, TO, *V. T.*
1. to wear out. haṇḍháuná ;
2. to put on. pahinná ; páná ;
3. to wear one out. sir khá jáná ;

WEAR, TO, *V. I.*
haṇḍhná ; haṇḍh jáná ;
to wear away. ghasná ;

WEARIED, *A.*
máṇdá ; thakká máṇdá ; thakiá ṭuṭiá hoyá ; hariá hoyá ;
wearied with the journey. paindá kardeáṇ kardeáṇ thakkiá hoyá ;

WEARINESS, *N.*
máṇdagí. *f ;* thakewáṇ. *m ;* khechal. *f ;*

WEARISOME, *A.*
thakáṇwálä ; akáuṇwálá ;

WEARY, *A.*
thakká máṇdá ; thakkiá tutiá hoyá ;

WEARY, TO, *V. T.*
hapháuná ; thakáuná ; taṇg karná ; chheṛná ; taklíf dení ; dukháuná ; aukhíáṇ karní ; sir khapáuná ; khechal karná ; dukh dená ; satáuná ;

WEASEL, *N.*
niaulá ; *m ;*

WEATHER, *N.*
rut. *f ;* bahár. *f ;* lit. season.
to be fair weather. khará ho jáná ;

WEATHER, TO, *V. T.*
sahárná ; saihná ;

WEAVE, TO, *V. T.*
uṇná ; uṇ lainá ; bunná ;

WEAVER, *N.*
  juláhá. *m ;* juláh. *m ;* paulí. *m ;*
  1. a caste of weavers. káshbí. *m ;*
  2. Proverb. What! a Pathan
  the forced labourer of weavers.
  paulíáṇ de Pathán wagárí ;
  Himself a weaver and his servant
  a Sayyid ! áp paulí te Sayyad
  naukar !
WEAVER'S PIT. *N.*
  khaḍḍí, *f ;*
WEAVING, *N.*
  juláhgarí. *f ;* juláhpuṇá. *m ;*
  unat. *f ;*
  price of weaving. bunáí. *f ;*
WEB, *N.*
  jálá. *m ;*
WEBBING, *N.*
  nawár. *f ;*
WED, TO, *V. T.*
  shádí karní ; wiáhuná ; wiáh karná ;
WEDDING, *N.*
  viáh. *f ;* káj. *m ;* shádí. *f ;*
  suhág. *m ;*
  1. wedding guest. melí. *m ;*
  melán. *f ;*
  3. wedding procession. janj. *f ;*
  janet. *m ;*
  3. one of a wedding party. jane-
  tí. *m ;* janetiá. *m ;* janjí. *m ;*
  4. to appoint a day for a wedding.
  gaṇdh páuní ;
WEDGE, *N.*
  pachchar. *f ;* phánná. *m ;* chappar. *f ;* phál. *f ;*
WEDLOCK, *N.*
  viáh. *m ;* nikáh. *m ;*
WEDNESDAY, *N.*
  buddhwár. *m,* H ; buddh. *m,* M ;
WEE, *A.*
  nikká ; chhoṭṭá ;
WEED, *N.*
  kádhá. *m ;* bútí. *f ;* maríṛí. *f ;*
  1. a weed which grows among
  wheat. piájí. *f ;*
  2. Proverb. Money borrowed on
  interest is as bad as piájí in a
  wheat field. dám biájí, khet
  piájí ;
WEED, TO, *V. T.*
  kádhá kaḍḍhná ; guḍḍná ; goḍḍí
  karní ; godná ;

WEEDING, *N.*
  kádháí. *f ;* guḍáí. *f ;*
WEEK, *N.*
  haftá. *m ;* aṭṭh din. *m ;* aṭh-
  wárá. *m ;*
WEEKLY, *Adv.*
  har hafte ; aṭṭhíṇ diníṇ ;
WEEP, TO, *V. T.*
  kurláuná ; roná ; hanjú waháuná ;
  chíkchiháṛá páuná ; athru
  waháuná ; athru wagg painá ;
  akkhíáṇ dá nír chal jáná.
  1. to weep bitterly. wilkná ;
  2. to weep quietly. dhuskná ;
  3. to weep continually. julhakná ;
WEEPER, *N.*
  roṇwálá. *m ;*
WEEPING, *N.*
  werág. *m ;* roná. *m ;* roná piṭṭná. *m ;* chík chiháṛá. *m ;* war-
  láp. *m ;* rudan. *m ;*
  why are you weeping so ? túṇ
  sabhnáṇ dí tarfon ron dá ṭheká
  liyá hai ?
WEEPINGLY, *Adv.*
  ro roke ; roṇde hoe ;
WEEVIL, *N.*
  sussarí. *f ;* kíṛá. *m ;* dhorá. *m ;*
  dhorí. *f ;*
WEIGH, TO, *V. T.*
  tolná ; háṛá lainá ; háṛná ; háṛ
  lainá ; jokhná ;
  to cause to be weighed. tulwáuná ;
  jokháuná ; haṛáuná ;
WEIGH, TO, *V. I.*
  tulná ;
WEIGHER, *N.*
  dhaṛwáí. *m ;* háṛú. *m ;* jokhá. *m ;*
  tolá. *m ;*
WEIGHING, *N.*
  tulwáí. *f ;* tuláí. *f ;* háṛáí. *f ;*
  jokháí. *f ;*
  1. the business of weighing.
  dhaṛwáí garí. *f ;*
  2. deception in weighing. ṭhúṇgá.
  m ;
  3. money paid for weighing.
  tuláí. *f ;*
  4. one who gives light weight.
  ṭhúṇge már. *m ;*
WEIGHING MACHINE, *N.*
  kaṇḍá. *m ;* takrí. *f ;*

WEIGHT, *N*.
tol. *m*; wazan. *m*; bhár. *m*;
1. good weight. achchhá tol. *m*;
2. weight in a cart too much forward. dábú. *m*;
3. weight in a cart at the back. ulár. *m*;
4. weight for scales. waṭṭá. *m*;

WEIGHTY, *A*.
bhárá; bojhal; ḍhaṭṭá; vajandár;

WEIRD, *A*.
anokhá; jádú dá; achanbá;

WELCOME, *N*.
aubhagat. *m*; jí áiáṇ núṇ; ágat. *m*;

WELCOME, TO, *V. T*.
aubhagat karná; ádar karná;

WELD, TO, *V. T*.
joṛná; ghar ke miláuná; táṇkná;

WELFARE, *N*.
ḳhair. *f*; ḳhair ḳharíyat. *f*; ḳhair sullá. *f*; sukkh sáṇḍ. *m*; kallíáṇ. *f*; bhagat. *f*;

WELL, *N*.
khúh. *m*;
1. deserted well. ḍall. *f*;
2. well with steps down to it. baolí. *f*;
3. masonry on top of the well. maṇ. *m*;
4. this well is almost dry .is khúh vichchoṇ pání nakhuṭṭ gayá;
5. a well which gives little water. choṛhá. *m*;
6. Proverb. Good to look at, but for nothing else. dissaṇ dá chaṇgá te pání dá choṛhá;
7. Proverb. Without wisdom the well is empty. aql bájhoṇ khúh ḳhálí;

WELL, *A*.
achchhá; naroá; wall; chaṇgá; bhalá; rází; see HEALTH.

WELL, *Adv*.
banáke; changí taráh nál; rás karke; bhalí taráh nál;

WELL, *Exclam*.
ḳhair; achchhá; halá; ḳhair sallá;

WELL BEHAVED, *A*.
bhalá; khulkí; nek chalan; suchál; suchálá;

WELL BEING, *N*.
ḳhair. *f*; ḳhair ḳharíyat. *f*;

WELL BORN, *A*.
sharíf; ḳhándání;

WELL BRED, *A*.
bhalamánas;

WELL DOING, *N*.
nekí. *f*; bhalíáí. *f*; subh karm. *m*;

WELL DINE, *Interj*.
shábásh; wáh wáh; sohná;

WELL EDUCATED, *A*.
chaṇgá paṛhiá hoyá;

WELL INFORMED, *A*.
ilmwálá; samajhwálá;

WELL KNOWN, *A*.
mashhúr; manniá danniá; námí;
Proverb. The well known money-lender thrives, but the well known thief is hung. námí sháh khaṭṭ khaí, námí chor máriá jáe;

WELL MADE, *A*.
pakká; suthrá baniá hoyá;

WELL MEANING, *A*.
nek níyat;

WELL NIGH, *Adv*.
lag bhag; neṛe;

WELL READ, *A*.
chaṇgá paṛhiá hoyá;

WELL SHAPED, *A*.
sajílá; suḍaul; sajdár;

WELL TO DO, *A*.
rizakwálá;

WELL WISHER, *N*.
hittú. *m*; hamaití. *m*;

WELT, *N*.
magzí. *f*;

WEST, *N*.
laiṇḍhá pásá. *m*; lahiṇḍá. *m*;

WEST, *A*.
laiṇḍhá;

WESTERLY, *A*.
pachhwá;

WET, *A*.
tar; gillá; bhijiá hoyá; silá; wattreá hoyá;

WET, TO, *V. T*.
gillá OR tar karná; bheuṇ dená; bheuná; pání páuná; sijáuná; bhigáuná; nam dená; bhigoná; bhijáuná;

WETTING, *PP*.
bheuṇke;

WETNESS, *N*.
gill. *f* ;
WHACK, TO, *V. T.*
márná ; kuṭṭná ;
WHARF, *N*.
ghát. *m* ; pattan. *m* ;
WHAT, *Pro.*
kis ; kaun ; kehṛá ;
WHAT, *Inter.*
kí ;
WHAT ELSE, *Ques.*
hor kí !
WHATEVER, *Pro.*
jo kujh ; jinná ;
WHEAT, *N*.
kaṇak. *f* ; baḍáṇak. *f* ; waḍának. *f* ;
1. bearded wheat. kasírí. *f* ;
2. white wheat. chitthí kaṇak. *f* ;
WHEATEN, *A*.
kaṇak dá ;
WHEEDLE, TO, *V. T.*
bhuchláuná ; jháṇsá dená ; dhokhá deke manáuná ; bhochalná ; see CAJOLE.
WHEEDLING, *N*.
jháṇsá. *m* ; lallá pallá. *m* ; dambájí. *f* ;
WHEEL, *N*.
pahiá. *m* ; piṇj. *m* ; chakká. *m* ;
1. Persian wheel. hort. *m* ; halṭ. *m* ; ḍhol. *m* ;
2. spinning wheel. charkhá. *m* ;
WHEEZE, TO, *V. T.*
saskaná ;
WHELP, *N*.
kuṭṭe dá bachchá. *m* ; katurá. *m* ; kur. *m* ; gullurá. *m* ;
WHEN, *Adv.*
1. Interrog. kad ; kis vele ;
2. Relative. jad ; jis vele ;
WHENCE, *Adv.*
1. Relative. jitthon ;
2. Interrog. kitthoṇ ;
WHENEVER, *Adv.*
jad kadí ; jad kad ;
WHERE, *Adv.*
1. Relative. jitthe ;
2. Interrog. kitthe ;
where do you live ? tusíṇ kehṛá tháon de ho ?
WHEREABOUTS, *Adv.*
1. Relative. jitthe ;
2. Interrog. kitthe ;
WHEREAS, *Conj.*
kyuṇ jo ;
WHEREAT, *Adv.*
jis te ;
WHEREBY, *Adv.*
jis thoṇ ; jis de káran ;
WHEREFORE, *Adv.*
is laí ;
as a question. kis karke ; kis laí ;
WHEREIN, *Adv.*
jih de vichch ;
WHEREOF, *Adv.*
jih dá ;
WHEREON, *Adv.*
jih de sababoṇ ; jis te ;
WHERESOEVER, *Adv.*
jitthe kitthe ;
WHERETO, *Adv.*
kis wáste ; kitthoṇ tík ;
WHEREUPON, *Adv.*
tad ;
WHEREVER, *Adv.*
jitthe kitthe ;
WHEREWITH, *Adv.*
kis de nál ; jis de nál ; kis thoṇ ; jis thoṇ ;
WHET, TO, *V. T.*
sáṇ te chaṛháuná ;
WHETHER, *Conj.*
jáṇ ; paí ; je ;
WHETSTONE, *N*.
sáṇ. *f* ; pathrí. *f* ;
WHICH, *Pro.*
jehṛá ; jo ; kehṛá ;
WHICHEVER, *Pro.*
jo koí ; jo kujh ;
WHIFF, *N*.
phúk. *f* ;
of a huqqa. dam. *m* ; suṭá. *m* ; ghutt. *m* ;
WHILE, *Adv.*
jad ; jis vele ;
WHILE, *N*.
waqt. *m* ;
WHILST, *Adv.*
jad ; jis vele ;
WHIM, *N*.
gumáṇ. *m* ; lahír. *f* ; lallhu. *m* ; man dí mauj. *f* ; waiham. *m* ;
WHIMPER, *N*.
chíṇ píṇ. *f* ;

WRONGDOING, *N.*
sharárat. *f ;*
WRONGFULLY, *Adv.*
1. unjustly beinsáfí nál ;
2. mistakenly. galatí nál ; bhulekhe nál ;
WRONGLY, *Adv.*
galatí nál ;
WROTH, *A.*
karodhí ; karoṇí ;
WRY, *A.*
wiṇggá ; teḍhá ;

Y.

YARD, *N.*
1. measure. gaj. *m ;*
2. courtyard. wehṛá. *m ;* weṛhá. *m ;* behṛá. *m ;* sahin. *m ;*
3. compound. ahátá. *m ;*
YARN, *N.*
1. thread. sútar. *m ;* sút. *m ;*
2. story. ḳahání. *f ;* bát. *f ;*
YAWN, *N.*
ubásí. *f ;* jamhái. *f ;*
YAWN, TO, *V. I.*
jamhái áuní ; muṇh ṭaḍḍná ; ubásí lainí OR áuní ;
YEA, *A.*
háṇ. ; jí ;
YEAR, *N.*
waṛhá. *m ;* sál. *m ;*
1. this year. aitkáṇ ; is sál ; aitkíṇ ;
2. last year. parúṇ ; par ;
3. year before last. parár ;
4. next year. aunde sál ;
5. a year passed by. koí waṛhá din ho gayá hai ;
YEARLY, *Adv.*
saláná ; waṛhe dá ;
YEARLY, *A.*
waṛhe de waṛhe ;
YEARN, TO, *V. T.*
cháh nál cháhná ; jí tarasná ;
YEARNING, *N.*
cháh. *f ;*
YEAST, *N.*
ḳhamír. *m ;*
YELL, *N.*
chíkh. *f ;* kúk. *f ;* hák. *m ;*
YELL, TO, *V. T.*
chíkh mární ; pukárná ; chilláuná ; hák márná ;
YELLOW, *A.*
pítal ; pilíá ; khaṭṭá ; basantí ; bhagwá ; kapurí ; khaṭṭí ; zard ;
YELLOWNESS, *N.*
pílái. *f ;*
YELP, TO, *V. I.*
bhauṇkná ;
YES, *Adv.*
háṇ ; áho ;
YESTERDAY, *Adv.*
kall ;
YESTERDAY EVENING, *N.*
kall dí rát. *f ;*
YET, *Adv.*
ajje ; phir ví ; tad ví ;
YET, *Conj.*
lekin ; par ;
YIELD, *N.*
hással. *m ;*
YIELD UP, TO, *V. T.*
ján dená ; chhaḍḍná ;
YEILD, TO, *V. I.*
gardan jhukáuná ; miṭná ; tábe honá ; dabb jáná ; níwíáṇ honá ; leṭná ; liṭná ;
YIELDINGNESS, *N.*
narmí. *f ;*
springiness. lafáu. *m ;*
YOKE, *N.*
panjálí. *f ;* panjálá. *m ;* julá *m ;*
YOKE, TO, *V. T.*
jotná ; joná ;
for ploughing. hal joná ;
YOKE, *N.*
ánḍe dí jardí. *f ;*
YONDER, *Adv.*
utthe ; parlá ;
YONDER, *Adv.*
pare ; thoṛí dúr ; pareḍe ;
YOU, *Pro.*
tusíṇ ;
YOUNG, *A.*
nanná ; chhoṭá ; nábálig ; nikká ; níáná ; láirá ; lauḍhá ; thoṛí umr dá ;
1. you are very young. tuṇ aje umr vichch chhoṭá hai ;
2. he is still young. aje umr dá ví koí waḍḍá nahíṇ ;

YOUNG, *N.*
bachche. *m ;*
YOUNSTER, *N.*
gabhrú. *m ;* jawán. *m ;* gabhretá. *m;* gabhrotá. *m ;*
YOUR, *Pro.*
tuháḍá ; tuháḍí ;
YOUTH, *N.*
1. young man. jawán. *m ;*
2. young manhood. jawání. *f ;*
YOUTHFUL, *A.*
jawán ;
YOUTHFULNESS, *N.*
jawání. *f ;* joban. *m ;*

Z.

ZEAL, *N.*
shauq. *m ;* sargarmí. *f ;* josh. *m ;*
ZEALOUS, *N.*
gairatí ; joshwálá ; sargarm ; tez ; shukín ;
ZEALOUSLY, *Adv.*
josh nál ; uddam nál ; dil nál ; jí ján nál ; dil lagáke ; manoṇ ; man nál ; diloṇ wajhoṇ ; dil kholke ; manoṇ tanoṇ hoke ; chitt nál ;
ZEST, *N.*
shauq. *m ;* josh. *m ;* sawád. *m ;*
ZIGZAG, *A.*
pechdár ;